HORTICU

Principles and Practices

HORTICULTURE

Principles and Practices

Fourth Edition

George Acquaah

BOWIE STATE UNIVERSITY, MARYLAND

PHI Learning Private Limited

New Delhi-110001

2009

This Indian Reprint—Rs. 695.00
(Original U.S. Edition—Rs. 5791.00)

HORTICULTURE—Principles and Practices, 4th ed.
by George Acquaah

Original edition, entitled *Horticulture—Principles and Practices*, 4th ed. by George Acquaah, published by Pearson Education, Inc., publishing as Pearson Prentice Hall.

Copyright © 2009 Pearson Education Inc., Upper Saddle River, New Jersey 07458, U.S.A.

ISBN-978-81-203-3820-3

Indian edition published by PHI Learning Private Limited.

This edition is manufactured in India, and is authorized for sale in India, Pakistan, Sri Lanka, Bhutan, Bangladesh, Nepal and the Maldives only.

Published by Asoke K. Ghosh, PHI Learning Private Limited, M-97, Connaught Circus, New Delhi-110001 and Printed by Mohan Makhijani at Rekha Printers Private Limited, New Delhi-110020.

With love to Theresa, quarterback; Parry, wide receiver; Kwasi, running back; Bozuma, homecoming queen; and Tina, cheerleader extraordinaire. In my book you will always be winners!

Brief Contents

Contents

PART 4   **GROWING PLANTS INDOORS 343**

Preface

Horticulture is the area of plant science that caters to the needs of a broad range of people, from the small backyard farmer in the urban area to the large-scale producer. Horticulture's adaptability to the home situation makes it attractive to people from all walks of life, including those who may not wish to study agriculture or be identified as farmers in the way society defines them, but are willing to grow and care for plants. Thus, horticulture is a popular instructional program and part-time activity indulged in by many people. The horticulture industry is making it increasingly easier and more attractive for nonprofessional plant growers to participate in plant culture at various levels and for various needs.

This text is an instructional resource in the fundamentals of horticulture and a reference for hobbyists and professionals. As an instructional text, *Horticulture: Principles and Practices* is designed for use at the undergraduate level. Emphasis is placed on instruction in the basic principles and practices of horticulture, thereby minimizing regional and national biases.

Horticulture is presented as a science, an art, and a business. The principles discussed are applicable to both small- and large-scale production. A format with unique features is adopted throughout the text. First, the text is divided into parts, within which related topics are treated as chapters. Chapters on broad topics are subdivided into appropriate modules. Each chapter opens with a stated purpose or objective, followed by a list of expected outcomes upon completion of the chapter. The overview introduces the subjects to be discussed and defines the scope of presentation. Each subject is discussed under clearly defined headings and subheadings. *Key terms* are highlighted and defined or explained. A brief summary at the end of each chapter reviews the main message for emphasis. References are presented at the end of each chapter to acknowledge the sources consulted by the author in preparing the text and to suggest sources for further information on the topics discussed. If the reader has difficulty in defining or explaining any term or key word, the Glossary at the end of the text may be used as a quick reference. Practical activities to enhance the understanding of the material discussed are suggested at the end of the chapters. Finally, the student is provided an opportunity to assess whether the material in the chapter was really understood.

A unique feature of this book is the inclusion of industry highlights. University professors and other industry professionals with expertise in specific aspects of horticulture were invited to contribute papers or photos to enhance topics in selected chapters.

The text includes many photographs, line drawings, and tables to facilitate the comprehension of the material and can be used for a quick reference. The materials included were chosen to provide a complete introduction to the four general areas of horticulture: ornamental horticulture, fruit culture, vegetable culture, and landscape architecture. Part 1 describes the underlying science. The amount of time spent on these chapters depends on the background of the student. Topics are presented from the point of view of the horticulturist. The reader clearly sees the relevance of the science in horticulture. The chapters take the reader through a review of pertinent topics in plant taxonomy, plant anatomy, plant growth environment, plant physiology, and plant improvement. The role of these disciplines of science in the horticultural industry and how they are applied or manipulated to increase the performance of plants are also discussed.

Part 2 discusses how horticultural plants are protected. The student learns about biological enemies of horticultural plants, and the principles and methods of disease and pest control. Part 3 presents plant propagation and discusses the characteristics of sexual and asexual methods of propagating plants.

Growing plants indoors forms the theme for Part 4. Horticulture can be conducted in an open area or under a controlled environment where growth factors are manipulated for the optimal performance of plants. The student learns how the greenhouse is designed and used in the production of plants. Hydroponics is discussed in detail. In this section, the student is instructed in the science and art of growing plants in containers in the home and office.

Part 5 discusses growing plants outdoors, including detailed coverage of the installation, use, and maintenance of plants in the landscape. A discussion on the establishment and maintenance of a lawn, as well as pruning and landscape maintenance tools, is also presented.

Part 6 focuses on the culture of plants for food. Selected crops and herbs are also discussed, as well as the establishment and maintenance of an orchard.

Part 7 discusses special horticultural techniques, specifically floral design, terrarium culture, and bonsai. Flower arranging is a major activity in the horticultural industry that can be engaged in by both professionals and hobbyists. The postharvest handling of horticultural products is also discussed.

Instructor Resource Center

Register today at www.prenhall.com to access instructor resources digitally.

ONLINE RESOURCES

To access supplementary materials online, instructors need to request an instructor access code. Go to **www.pearsonhighered.com/irc**, where you can register for an instructor access code. Within 48 hours after registering, you will receive a confirming e-mail, including an instructor access code. Once you have received your code, go to the site and log on for full instructions on downloading the materials you wish to use.

ACKNOWLEDGMENTS

I am very grateful to Jeanne Bronson, whose persistence inspired me to undertake the first edition of this project. I extend sincere thanks to the management of TLC Greenhouse of Edmond, Oklahoma, for allowing me free access to its facilities for many of the photos. I also want to acknowledge and thank reviewers of the text, who provided valuable feedback that was extremely helpful in shaping the outcome of this fourth edition. They are Gary Bachman, Illinois State University; David Berle, University of Georgia; Cindy Burgess, Dickinson State University; Charles Drake, Ferris State University; Philip Gibson, Gwinnett Tech College; John Kahre, Oklahoma State University; Mel Knapton, Century College—White Bear Lake; Donna Rankin, Metropolitan Community College; George Rogers, Palm Beach Community College; Jerry Sites, Arkansas State University; Charles Tarrants, SUNY A&T College, Delhi; and Michael Toscano, San Joaquin Delta College. The highlights contributed by professionals add a unique perspective to selected topics in the book for which I am very grateful. They have been identified and acknowledged in the list of contributors. Finally, I thank Nana Nyame for his guidance, support, and help throughout the entire project.

INDUSTRY HIGHLIGHTS CONTRIBUTORS

Louis D. Albright
Professor of Biological and Environmental Engineering and
Stephen H. Weiss Presidential Fellow
304 Riley-Rob Hall
Cornell University
Ithaca, NY 14853-5701

Paul Fanz
North Carolina State University
Department of Horticultural Science
Box 760g
Raleigh, NC 27695-7609

Ethan Waltermire
Colorado Seed Laboratory
Campus Delivery 1170
Fort Collins, CO 80523-1170

Michael L. Parker
Associate Professor
North Carolina State University
Department of Horticultural Science
Box 7609
Raleigh, NC 27695-7609

A. J. Both
Associate Extension Specialist
Rutgers, State University of New Jersey
Bioresource Engineering
Department of Plant Biology and Pathology
20 Ag Extension Way
New Brunswick, NJ 08901-8500

Michael Orzolek
Pennsylvania State University
203 Tyson Building
University Park, PA 16802

Allan Storjohann
Myriad Botanical Gardens
100 Myriad Gardens
Oklahoma City, OK 73102

Terri W. Starman
Department of Horticultural Sciences
Room 202 Horticultural/Forest Science Bldg.
2133 TAMU
College Station, TX 77843-2133

Bill McKinley
Associate Dean, Career Technologies
Kishwaukee College
21193 Malta Rd.
Malta, IL 60150

Clark Williams
Department of Agriculture and Natural Resources
Langston University
P. O. 1500
Langston, OK 73050

Raymond Faucette
Department of Agriculture and Natural Resources
Langston University
P. O. 1500
Langston, OK 73050

Kanyand Matand
Center for Biotechnology Research and Education
Langston University
P. O. 1500
Langston, OK 73050

David Berle
Department of Horticulture
University of Georgia
1111 Plant Science Bldg.
Athens, GA 30602-7273

PART 1

THE UNDERLYING SCIENCE

What Is Horticulture?

PURPOSE AND EXPECTED OUTCOMES

This chapter is devoted to discussing the operational and scientific boundaries and the importance of horticulture to society. Horticulture is presented as a science, art, and business. This discussion is preceded by a brief history of horticulture. The role of computers and the Internet in horticulture is also highlighted.

After studying this chapter, the student should be able to

1. Define the term *horticulture*.
2. Briefly discuss the history of horticulture.
3. Describe the boundaries of horticulture in relation to other applied sciences.
4. Discuss the importance of horticulture in society.
5. List ten jobs that require training *in* horticulture.
6. List and describe four horticulture-related industries (service industries).

[COLOR PLATES—*see color plate 1* for additional chapter photos]

OVERVIEW

Horticulture is a very important branch of plant science. It accounts for food from three major sources: vegetables, fruits, and nuts. Apart from food, it plays a significant role in other aspects of society. It provides employment and also beautifies the environment. In this introduction, the divisions of professional horticulture are discussed, along with the field's importance to society. Horticulture is presented as an art, a science, and a business. Scientists use knowledge from genetics, physiology, botany, chemistry, and other disciplines to produce elite cultivars of plants and prescribe the best cultural practices to use for success in their production. Horticulture is supported by a variety of service industries that develop and provide chemicals, machinery, and implements for its numerous activities. Many people who do not care to grow food crops often enjoy growing flowers outdoors or indoors for aesthetic purposes.

1.1 WHAT IS HORTICULTURE?

Horticulture
Science and art of cultivating, processing, and marketing of fruits, vegetables, nuts, and ornamental plants.

The term **horticulture** is derived from the Latin *hortus* (garden) and *cultura* (cultivation), which means garden cultivation. Modern horticulture is the science and art of cultivating fruits, vegetables, and ornamental plants (Figure 1–1). Certain institutions of higher learning such as colleges and universities have educational programs in horticulture for training as well as conducting research to advance the area of study. Some of these academic programs are general in their scope of coverage, whereas others are devoted to in-depth research and training in a specific aspect of horticulture. Modern horticulture is also big business. It provides employment for people with a wide variety of skills and is supported by an equally large number of service industries. When considered from both the science and business perspectives, horticulture can be more broadly defined as the "science and art of cultivating, processing, and marketing of fruits, vegetables, nuts, and ornamental plants."

Horticulture is related to other plant sciences (Figure 1–2). From the four divisions of the horticulture industry shown in Figure 1–3, it is clear that horticulture has two main goals—to provide food and to impact the environment. The relationship between horticulture and other plant sciences is evidenced by the fact that plants cannot be confined strictly to one category distinguished from others by features such as use and cultural practices. For example, an oak tree has great ornamental value in the landscape, but as a forest tree, oaks are excellent sources of lumber for high-quality furniture. Similarly, Bermuda grass may be cultivated as an agronomic crop for feeding livestock and also makes an excellent turfgrass in the landscape.

Generally, growing horticultural plants is more production intensive than growing agronomic and forest plants. The returns on investment per unit area of production are also generally higher for horticultural plants. Further, horticultural plants are largely utilized fresh or as living materials (as ornamentals in the landscape), whereas agronomic and forestry products are generally utilized in the nonliving state (e.g., as grain, fiber, and timber).

1.2 A BRIEF HISTORY OF HORTICULTURE

The deliberate use of plants by humans for aesthetic and functional purposes has its origin in antiquity. The Hanging Gardens of Babylon were hailed as one of the seven wonders of the ancient world. As society evolved, deliberate cultivation and domestication of edible plants replaced the less efficient food-gathering habits of primitive societies. Agriculture, and for that matter horticulture, is therefore not a modern-day invention but one that continues to be transformed as society advances technologically.

In terms of food production, ancient civilizations, notably that of Egypt, pioneered the basic crop production methods still in use today with modification and modernization. Land was set aside and prepared by plowing; crops were provided with supplemental irrigation for increased productivity in cultivation; crops received appropriate plant husbandry for the best results. Postharvest storage and processing (e.g., drying, fermenting, and milling) were employed to increase the shelf life of the otherwise highly perishable horticultural products. Most of the valued ancient crops are still of interest today. They include fruits (e.g., dates, figs, grapes, pomegranates, and olives), vegetables (e.g., garlic, melons, radishes, lentils, artichokes, and chicory), oil and fiber crops, and medicinal herbs. For aesthetic uses, gardeners were employed to manicure the formal gardens of ancient royalty. As already mentioned, the gardens and landscape designs of the Babylonians were proverbial.

(a)

(b)

(c)

(d)

(e)

(f)

(g)

(h)

(i)

FIGURE 1–1 The many faces of horticulture. Horticulture's role in society is diverse: (a) horticultural produce is found in the grocery store; (b) greenhouses provide employment and plants for various uses; (c) landscaping enhances urban centers; (d) landscaping residential areas; (e) potted plants are used to enhance the interior and exterior decor of homes; (f) researchers and teachers of horticulture train students and develop improved cultivars of plants; (g) florists cater to a variety of needs in the community where flowers play a role and provide jobs; (h) botanical gardens provide recreational and educational opportunities to visitors; and (i) commercial producers of horticulture crops contribute to the local and national economies.

(Source: For (a), (b), (e–h): George Acquaah, (c) Kim Sayer © Dorling Kindersley, (d) Alan Keohane © Dorling Kindersley (i) USDA),

Myriad Botanical Gardens
100 Myriad Gardens
Oklahoma City, OK 73102

Dr. Allan Storjohann, Manager

History of the Gardens

The idea of cultivating a garden in downtown Oklahoma City began when world-renowned architect I. M. Pei was commissioned by city leaders, led by oil and gas pioneer Dean A. McGee (CEO of Kerr-McGee Corporation), in 1964 to create a revitalization plan for downtown Oklahoma City. The resulting Pei Plan incorporated parkland for the development of a cultural, recreational, and commercial complex. The area that is now the Myriad Botanical Gardens was originally designed by I.M. Pei to model the Tivoli Gardens in Copenhagen, Denmark.

The development of the Pei Plan, and the gardens in particular, became the lifelong project of McGee. He even motivated a core group of civic leaders to travel to Tivoli Gardens and learn more about the success of the celebrated attraction.

On May 5, 1970, the name Myriad Gardens was officially adopted. Three months later, on August 11, 1970, the Oklahoma City Council established a 19-member Myriad Development Task Force. The principal responsibility of the task force was to assist the City in the successful planning, programming and implementation of the Myriad Gardens. After a national competition in 1971, the task force chose an architect for the Gardens, the New York firm of Conklin & Rossant.

The City of Oklahoma City purchased the site for the Myriad Gardens in 1975 for $900,000. Investment in the development phase, including initial site clearing and utility relocation, was approximately $1.2 million. Buildings that originally stood on the Myriad Gardens site included the Biltmore Hotel, City National Bank Building, and the Oklahoma Club.

On September 16, 1975, the Myriad Gardens Authority, a public trust, was created and charged with developing the 17-acre property. McGee continued his leadership role at the Gardens and was appointed as the Trust Chairman. Work began on the Gardens on November 17, 1977, with a ceremonial groundbreaking.

Construction of the garden's infrastructure, including the base of the conservatory, tunnel, water stage, and other core facilities continued over the next four years as funding became available. Oklahoma City–based RGDC was the structural engineering firm heading the project.

In 1981, the Myriad Gardens Foundation was formed to raise private funds for the construction of the conservatory designed by Conklin & Rossant. It was also at this time that Oklahoma City–based architectural firm HTB was hired to design and landscape the west perimeter of the outdoor gardens.

Lippert Brothers Construction began work on the Conservatory in September 1983. Edmond, Oklahoma–based Trafco Constructors Inc. accomplished the difficult task of designing and building the 17 tricord trusses that make up the framework of the unique conservatory.

The structure was completed in 1985. The interior design of the Crystal Bridge was done by Loftis Bell Downing and Partners, Architects and Planners with the exotic plants being acquired and installed from 1987 to 1988 by Director Mike Bush (Figure 1).

In the summer of 1987, the Oklahoma City Parks and Recreation Department took over the operation and maintenance of the Gardens. The Crystal Bridge opened its doors to the public on March 25, 1988.

The outdoor grounds continued to grow as funding became available. The Herman and LaDonna Meinders Foundation donated two outdoor specialty gardens to the Myriad

FIGURE 1 The plaza view of the Crystal Bridge. *(Source: Dr. Allan Storjohann)*

Gardens Foundation. The first, located north of the Crystal Bridge, was completed in 1996. The second, representing the largest single donation for the beautification of Oklahoma City, is located on the northeast corner of the Gardens and was completed in 1998.

On June 28, 2001, the Dean A. McGee Center, a 5,000-square-foot, multiuse and meeting facility funded by the Myriad Gardens Foundation, was opened for public use. The facility was named in honor of early Gardens' visionary and benefactor Dean A. McGee.

CRYSTAL BRIDGE FACTS

The Crystal Bridge's unique design has earned attention and praise in the architectural community.

- The Crystal Bridge is 224 feet long and 70 feet in diameter. It is covered by 3,028 sections of translucent, double-layered Exolite acrylic panels.
- It took the largest crane in a five-state region to install the 17 tricord trusses that form the framework of the Bridge, which resembles a massive steel rib cage.
- The Conservatory includes 13,000 square feet of plant display area.
- April of 1987 marked the beginning of planting inside the Crystal Bridge, with most items purchased from specialty nurseries in Florida and California. Generous donations of plants from local collectors also helped beautify the Conservatory.
- Plants thrive in two distinct climates inside the Crystal Bridge: the Tropical Wet Zone, which is at the south end and is watered daily, and the Tropical Dry Zone at the north end which receives water from April through September, followed by drought from November through March.
- The wide variety of plants requires daily hand watering using purified and pH-adjusted water, which is treated by a specialized reverse osmosis system. The R.O. system removes minerals, such as salt, from the water preventing a buildup that can harm and even kill the plants. The water is just like the tropical rain that the plants would experience in their native habitat.
- Crashing down from a height of 35 feet, the tropical waterfall on the Wet Mountain pushes 60-80 gallons of water over its edge per minute. This is accomplished using two pumps, one 10 horsepower and the other seven.
- Twenty evaporative coolers cool the air inside the Crystal Bridge, each supplying 16,000 cubic feet of air per minute. This keeps the air at a constant temperature for the plants to thrive. Indoor temperatures range from 62–87 degrees Fahrenheit in the south end and 60–95 degrees Fahrenheit in the north end in the summer. In the winter, temperature ranges from 62–78 degrees Fahrenheit, depending on cloud cover outside.

- Applying silicone latex onto actual rock outcroppings created the realistic appearance of the rock walls in the Crystal Bridge. The latex was used to fabricate molds, which were installed onto reinforced steel angle iron.

OUTDOOR GARDENS FACTS

The Myriad Botanical Gardens' outdoor grounds include 17 acres of gently rolling hills.

- Hundreds of trees, including both native and non-native species, are planted throughout the grounds.
- Unique and popular specialty gardens dot the outdoor landscape displaying ornamental plants. The Meinders Gardens, at the northeast corner of the outdoor grounds, includes two extensive water gardens, shaded seating, and a wooden footbridge.
- The Myriad Botanical Gardens' lake covers two acres and is fed by the existing water table 22 feet below street level. The lake is home to several varieties of fish including goldfish and Japanese Koi, some of which reach as large as 20 pounds!
- Situated on the lake next to the Crystal Bridge, the Water Stage provides enough seating for several hundred people. It has become a popular spot for concerts, theatrical productions, weddings, and other special events.
- Paths wind their way around the lake and outdoor grounds leading guests through shaded, tree-lined walks, lively fountains, and beds of vibrant flowers ranging from the expertly manicured to the serenely natural. The majority of these paths run throughout the north and west side of the outdoor grounds.
- Dotting the outdoor grounds, amid the lake and gardens, stand several large sculptures. Some were purchased by the City of Oklahoma City and some were donated; all are unique and beautiful.

PLANTS IN THE CRYSTAL BRIDGE

There are more than 1,000 species of plants in the Crystal Bridge, representing plants from every continent except Antarctica. They are located in two habitat regions in the conservatory.

The Tropical Rain Forest Zone, called the Wet Mountain, is located on the south end of the Conservatory. Plants here come from Amazonia, Central Africa, Southeast Asia and the South Pacific Islands where rain falls year-round. These plants are watered every day.

The Dry Tropical Zone, called the Dry Mountain, is on the north end of the Conservatory. These plants are put through a drought from November to March, followed by regular watering during the summer months to simulate the weather patterns in their native areas. Most of these specimens come from South Africa, Madagascar, and Mexico.

While the plant collection in the Crystal Bridge rivals most botanical gardens across the country, several elements are outstanding:

PALMS

There are over 100 species of palms represented in the Crystal Bridge. Palms are the epitome of tropical trees. Found throughout the southern United States, palms only grow in tropical and sub-tropical climates and are often found close to water. There are many unique species growing in the Crystal Bridge. The Old Man's Palm, *Washingtonia filifera*, is a slow-growing palm that has long, pale brown "hair" covering the trunk. The Foxtail Palm, *Wodyetia bifurcata*, has unique leaflets radiating from the stalk giving it a foxtail appearance. On the northeast corner, the young *Bismarckia nobilis* palm, with perhaps the world's largest palm leaves, at a spectacular 10 feet wide, can be viewed.

CYCADS

Many people mistake these prehistoric plants for palms. But these "living fossils" have their own unique identity. Cycads flourished in primeval forests during the time of the dinosaurs. In fact, the Jurassic Period is often dubbed the "Age of the Cycads." At that time, cycads made up 20 percent of the world's flora. They still exist today, in much the same form as their ancestors have existed for the past 300 million years, although only about 200 species remain. Many species can be found in Mexico, the Caribbean, and South Africa. Genera to look for in the Crystal Bridge collection include Cycas, Dioon, Zamia, Bowenia, Stangeria, and Encephalartos.

GINGERS

Most people are familiar with the culinary variety of ginger. However, many members of this "spicy" plant family are also quite beautiful and are normally seen only in expensive floral bouquets. The stepladder ginger (*Costus malortieanus*) next to the wooden bridge has furry leaves arranged spirally along the stem. Many of the Conservatory's *Alpinias* have flower bracts resembling bright red plastic pinecones, which last for months.

BROMELIADS

Bromeliads are typically brightly colored, funnel-shaped plants that hold a surprise for curious guests—in the center of the funnel is a pool of water! This is because most bromeliads are epiphytes, meaning that they attach themselves to trees instead of rooting in soil, so this is how they get their moisture. Of course, not all bromeliads are epiphytes, some are terrestrial like our *Cryptanthus* species (Earth stars), or the most familiar of the family, the Pineapple (*Ananas comosus*). On both mountains, guests can see bromeliads "planted" on the rock slopes; these are clusters of small, green or grey-leafed "air plants," or *Tillandsias*.

ORCHIDS

Orchids adorn nearly every corner of the Wet Mountain and are easily the most popular plants in our collection. At any time of the year, dozens of varieties of orchids can be seen blooming. With their delicate petal and distinctive look, most orchids are grown for their beauty alone, however, the agriculturally important vanilla orchid, from which vanilla can be extracted, is also featured in the Crystal Bridge. One of the highlights of the orchid collection is the *Dendrobium superbum* var. *alba* which explodes with over 300 blooms each February. So impressive is its show of color that the Orchid Society of America awarded this plant the "Culture of Merit" award and named the variety in honor of the Crystal Bridge.

In February 2002, the Myriad Botanical Gardens received more than 1,200 orchids bequeathed to the Gardens by long-time orchid collector Mr. Fred Strothmann. From his Edmond, Oklahoma, greenhouses, Mr. Strothmann cultivated some of the most exotic orchids in the world. He traveled around the world, collecting orchids in such exotic places as Kenya, Uganda, Burma, Indonesia, the Philippines, Australia, Mexico, and parts of South America. The Strothmann collection is an important part of the Crystal Bridge's year-round orchid display.

EUPHORBIAS

Visitors to the Crystal Bridge are always surprised to hear that a majority of the spiny plants growing on the Dry Mountain are not cacti, but euphorbias. These varied plants can range in size from mini grass like plants to huge trees. The difference between the cactus and a euphorbia species is slight, the major difference being that cacti only grow in the New World (Western Hemisphere) while euphorbias are native to the Old World (Eastern Hemisphere). Many euphorbias found in Africa and Madagascar survive in much the same way cacti do in the deserts of Central and North America. Thick, succulent stems filled with milky sap and protected by pairs of sharp spines characterize this bizarre group of plants. There are over 40 species of euphorbias in the plant collection.

BEGONIAS

While most gardeners are familiar with begonias as one of the more attractive annuals for a summer garden, few realize there are over 900 different species found throughout the world. Begonias are a plant of the tropics; there are no indigenous species in the United States. These plants come in a variety of succulent herbs, shrubs, and vines, all of which bloom. However, it's the color and texture, not the flower that makes begonias so popular. With over 100 varieties of begonias, the Crystal Bridge provides the best opportunity for our visitors to experience the tremendous beauty of this group of plants.

TITAN ARUM

The world's largest unbranched inflorescence, *Amorphophallus titanum*, also known as Titan arum or corpse flower, bloomed in the Crystal Bridge Tropical Conservatory on June 29, 2005 (Figure 2). The 42-inch tall corpse flower lasted through Tuesday, July 5, before it collapsed. Staff brushed pollen donated by Fairchild Tropical Botanic Garden in Miami onto the female flowers on Thursday, June 30 in hopes the plant will produce seed. With any luck the Crystal Bridge will be home to more corpse flowers in the future. Pollen samples were taken from the plant on July 2.

The Titan arum bulb was donated to the Myriad Botanical Gardens on July 13, 2000, by Baltimore physician Clark T. Riley after visiting the Crystal Bridge. The flowering of a titan arum is a rare and significant horticultural event that has occurred less than 10 times worldwide in 2005.

ANIMAL LIFE IN THE CRYSTAL BRIDGE

Plants aren't the only things to call the Crystal Bridge home. Lizards, fish, and butterflies are among the creatures that dart, swim, and flit throughout the Crystal Bridge's tropical environment. Their free reign means guests never know when a lizard might peek out from a rock or a butterfly might land gracefully on a petal.

REPTILES AND AMPHIBIANS

Reptiles and amphibians in the Crystal Bridge include the American anole, Cuban anole, day geckos, house gecko, tokay gecko, leopard gecko, bronze frog, green tree frog, and greenhouse frog. The lizards have been extremely successful in adapting to the environment

FIGURE 2 The world's largest unbranched inflorescence, *Amorphophallus titanum*, also known as Titan arum or corpse flower. *(Source: Dr. Allan Storjohann)*

of the Crystal Bridge—the anole in particular. Two species of anoles, *Anolis carolinensis*, originating in the southeast United States, and *Anolis sagrei*, native to islands of the Caribbean Sea, have established thriving populations in the Crystal Bridge.

BIRDS

Muffin and Bo jangles are the rulers of the roost in the Crystal Bridge. The pair are double yellow-headed Amazon parrots that were donated to the gardens in 1993. The parrots reside in the lobby of the conservatory and entertain guests with their antics and loud talking.

BUTTERFLIES

The zebra longwing (*Heliconius charitonius*), a tallow and black tropical butterfly native to the southern United States, was introduced to the Crystal Bridge in 1993. This species was selected because the caterpillar feeds only on passion vine and does not damage any of the other plants in the Crystal Bridge. After the caterpillars spin themselves into their chrysalises, they are gathered up and kept in a special chrysalis case until they are ready to emerge as winged adults. These butterflies are then released into the Crystal Bridge. The adult butterflies are happy to stay right in the conservatory to remain close to their food supply.

FISH

Fish were among the first animals introduced at the gardens. There are a variety of small fish swimming throughout the pond and stream system that are native to the tropical aquaria. Tropical fish in the Crystal Bridge include Pacu, Jack Dempsey Cichlid, Oscar, Albino Oscar, and Plecostomus.

AALSMEER FLOWER AUCTION – A WORLD LEADER

Department of Agriculture and Natural Resources
Langston University, Oklahoma

CLARK WILLIAMS

Almost every country in the world produces flowers for domestic consumption. But only a few countries produce enough for export. Of these exporting countries, the world leader is Holland. Historically, Holland is responsible for the export of over half of the world's floral products including cut flowers, foliages, and pot plants.

One of the reasons for Holland's position as the world leader is due to their flower auctions. This includes Bloemenveiling Aalsmeer which is the worlds largest flower auction. The Aalsmeer Flower Auction, located outside of Amsterdam, is considered to be the largest commercial facility in the world. Collectively, the buildings used by the Aalsmeer Flower Auction cover over one million square meters which is the equivalent of over 200 football fields. In 2006 the facility utilized 979 full-time employees and 853 part-time employees.

The quantity of flowers and plants sold on a daily basis are staggering. Each day approximately 19 million flowers and 2 million plants are auctioned and sold to buyers worldwide. In 2006, the Aalsmeer Flower Auction sold 4.784 billion cut flowers, 407 million plants, and 157 million garden plants. These numbers gave Bloemenveiling Aalsmeer a 44.7 percent share of the Dutch export market and accounted for 1.756 billion euros (approximately 2.35 billion U.S. dollars) of total sales.

Even though Holland is a world leader in flower production, a large amount of flowers that are sold in the auctions are imported. A very large percentage of these imports came from Africa with Kenya, Ethiopia, Uganda, and Zimbabwe being 4 of the top 5 importing countries. Israel was the only non-African country in the top 5.

The top five cut flowers sold through the Aalsmeer Flower Auction in 2006 were as follows: Roses – 1.762 billion, Tulips – 676 million, Chrysanthemums – 526 million, Transvaal Daisies – 269 million, and Lilies – 131 million. The majority of these flowers were purchased and sent to other European Union countries with Germany, the United Kingdom, and France being the largest customers.

The reason that Bloemenveiling Aalsmeer can sell and export such a large quantity of flowers each day is by using the Dutch auction method and the use of 13 auction clocks. The Dutch auction process involves starting at a high asking price and having the price continually drop until a buyer bids and gets the item at that price. If you wait too long in hopes of a lower price, you get shut out by the other buyers. Trains of carts loaded with flowers continually flow through each of the 13 auction houses (Figure 1). Individual auctions for each cart take a matter of seconds utilizing the 13 large auction clocks. In 2006,

FIGURE 1 Flower auction in progress at Aalsmeer.
(Source: Clark Williams)

FIGURE 2 Sold flowers are loaded on carts for shipping to destinations. *(Source: Clark Williams)*

the Aalsmeer Flower Auction averaged 43,860 transactions per day which works out to an average of 1,076 transactions per clock per hour. The sold flowers are then reorganized on new carts according to who made the purchase (Figure 2). At the end of the auction day, these carts are taken to the nearby airport and shipped worldwide.

Additional information about Bloemenveiling Aalsmeer, the world's largest flower auction, can be found by visiting their website at www.vba.nl/.

The foundation of agriculture was built upon by civilizations that followed the Egyptians. The Greeks and Romans were next to impact practical agriculture, with the Greeks being noted for their contributions to early botany, as chronicled in some ancient writings—notably those of Theophrastus of Eresos (372–287 B.C.), especially in *Historia Plantarium* (*History of Plants*). However, the Romans were more agriculturally oriented than the Greeks. They refined some of the technologies of their Egyptian predecessors. Records show that the Romans used horticultural practices such as grafting, budding, fertilization, and crop rotation, which are still in use today. In fact, their use of structures that functioned like greenhouses for forcing vegetables to grow indicates that they understood the principles of controlled-environment agriculture. With the advent of the slave trade, commercial production on plantations or large tracts of land was introduced. During this era, ornamental horticulture received great attention; the wealthy and nobility maintained elaborate gardens on their lavish estates. Growing plants in containers and

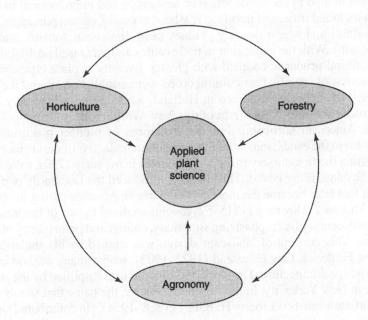

FIGURE 1–2 Horticulture is interrelated with other disciplines of applied sciences.

FIGURE 1–3 The four divisions of professional horticulture. The role of fruit and vegetable culture is to provide food; ornamental horticulture and landscape architecture impact the environment aesthetically or functionally, depending on the goal of the designer.

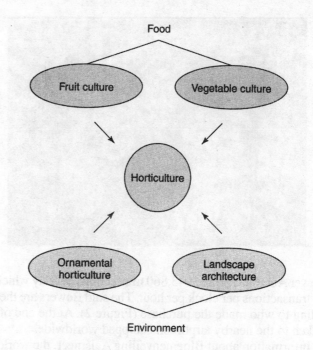

topiary (plant sculpting) became part of the landscape of these estates, some of which included swimming pools (Figure 1–4a–i).

During the Middle Ages, monasteries became a significant factor in the preservation and advancement of horticulture. Fruit and vegetable gardens became an integral part of monastic life. One of the most significant contributions to science was made by Gregor Mendel (1822–84), an Augustinian monk, while working with plants in a garden monastery. Mendel's laws provide us with an understanding of how traits are transmitted from one generation to another. With the Renaissance came a resurgence in the interest in horticulture. Gardening not only became popular but also formalized. Landscaping was pursued with great creativity and diligence, resulting in some of the most magnificent designs ever produced, as exemplified by the gardens of the Palace of Versailles in France, designed by André Le Nôtre (Figure 1–5).

Horticulture was further advanced with the discovery of the New World. This advancement came not only in the areas of new and improved technology and an increase in knowledge but also in the introduction of new crops and improvement in trade. New World crops included fruits and nuts (e.g., cashew, avocado, pecan, pineapple, cranberry, and black walnut) and vegetables (e.g., kidney bean, lima bean, tomato, maize, potato, and sweet potato). With the expansion in trade routes and increased profitability of trading in horticultural products, coupled with greater diversity in plant types, various centers of production of specific horticultural crops were established around the globe. For example, the bulb industry flourished in Holland, while the cacao industry blossomed from the introduction into West Africa of this New World crop.

On the American horticultural scene, a number of pioneer practitioners played significant roles in the establishment of the horticulture industry. Robert Prince is credited with establishing the first nursery in the United States in the early 1730s, called the Prince Nursery at Flushing, Long Island. This nursery introduced the Lombardy poplar plant in 1784, a plant that later became the most common tree in America during the post revolutionary era. Andrew J. Downing (1815–52) revolutionized the art of landscaping in the early eighteenth century by emphasizing simplicity, nature, and permanency of exhibits in the landscape. This concept of landscape design was studied by his students, the most famous being Frederick Law Olmstead (1822–1903), whom many acknowledge as the father of landscape architecture. The work of Olmstead is exemplified by the still-popular Central Park in New York City. In the twentieth century, the name that stands out among American horticulturalists is Liberty H. Bailey (1858–1954). He contributed significantly

FIGURE 1–4 Formal landscaping featuring topiary. *(Source: Steven Wooster © Dorling Kindersley)*

FIGURE 1–5 Landscaped European palace. *(Source: Demetrio Carrasco © Dorling Kindersley)*

to horticulture in the areas of nomenclature and taxonomy, among others. His outstanding publications include *The Manual of Cultivated Plants* and *How Plants Get Their Names.*

Up until this period in history, horticultural production benefited primarily from improvements and changes in the production environment. Evidence suggests that genetic improvement (breeding) was conducted in the Middle Ages. The simplest method of breeding entails visual selection and saving seeds from a plant with desirable characteristics for planting in the next planting cycle. Knowledge of categorization or classification of plants according to use and other characteristics existed. With time, additional discoveries were made about the nature of things. Curiosity about the nature and response of plants to their environment led to an interest in the practical application of the existing knowledge through formal experimentation such as hybridization. Plant classification was improved with the systematic method developed by Carolus Linnaeus (1707–1978) described in his 1753 landmark publication *Species Plantarium*. One way of displaying the tremendous variability in plants for public enjoyment is through the establishment of botanical gardens. Advances, including modern machinery and equipment for planting and harvesting crops and chemicals to protect crops from harmful pests and to provide supplemental nutrition, have been made through the accumulation of knowledge in a diversity of disciplines.

Modern horticulture continues to see advances in the way crops and other plants are produced. Productivity per unit area has increased, and mechanization makes it possible to grow large acreages of plants. Plant diversity has increased through advanced breeding practices. Modern horticulture also enjoys tremendous support from academic programs in institutions of higher learning, research in public and private sectors, and industry. Advanced processing and storage techniques have extended the shelf life of products.

However, with advances in development and application of technology have come a variety of issues of great social concern. For example, increased use of agricultural chemicals has produced serious environmental consequences such as groundwater pollution. Production of crops under controlled environments (greenhouses) has expanded production of plants, making it possible to produce plants in and out of season. New production techniques such as hydroponics, tissue culture, and other biotechnological advances promise to take horticulture to a new height. However, biotechnology is embroiled in a variety of safety and ethical debates.

1.3 DIVISIONS OF HORTICULTURE

Horticultural activities may be divided into several broad categories based mainly on the kinds of plants involved. These divisions form the basis of certain academic programs in horticulture:

Pomology
The science and practice of fruit culture.

Olericulture
The science and practice of growing vegetables.

Ornamental Horticulture
The branch of horticulture that deals with the cultivation and use of plants for their aesthetic value.

Floriculture
The science and practice of cultivating and arranging ornamental flowering plants.

Arboriculture
The science of growing and caring for ornamental trees.

Landscape Architect
A professional who designs landscape plans.

1. *Fruit culture.* Fruits vary in numerous ways. Some are borne on trees, others on bushes. Some fruits are succulent and juicy, whereas others are dry. Growing fruits is a long-term operation. *Fruit trees* take a long time (several years) to come into bearing. They also require more growth space per plant than vegetables. An area of land on which fruit trees are grown in a significant concentration is called an *orchard.* The branch of horticulture involved with the production (including growing, harvesting, processing, and marketing) of fruit trees (including nuts) is called **pomology.** Fruit trees such as apple, orange, and pear are operationally distinguished from *small fruits* such as grapes, blueberries, and strawberries.

2. *Vegetable culture.* Vegetable production is one of the most popular horticultural activities indulged in by homeowners, often in the backyard or private section of the property. The branch of horticulture involved with the production of vegetables is called **olericulture.** Some vegetable plants are grown for their fruits (e.g., tomato), leaves (e.g., spinach), roots (e.g., carrot), or pods (e.g., bean). Unlike fruits, vegetables are generally short-duration plants that need to be restarted each growing season. Vegetables may be harvested and used fresh. However, they are also processed in a variety of ways.

3. *Ornamental horticulture.* The production and use of ornamentals is the branch of horticulture generally called **ornamental horticulture.** The term *use* is included in the definition because it is an integral part of this branch of horticulture. Ornamentals may be cultivated in open space (or landscape) or in indoor containers. They may also be grown, arranged, and displayed in a variety of ways. Subdivisions of this branch of horticulture involve distinct activities. **Floriculture** is the production and use of flowering plants and one of the areas most readily identified with when horticulture is mentioned. An important aspect of the landscape is the ground covering, which is usually grass. *Turfgrass science* has developed into a full-fledged program at many colleges. A lawn is the basic landscape element in most cases. Other plants are then added to this ground cover. Turfgrasses can be found on football fields, golf courses, playgrounds, and home grounds. Flowers in the landscape may be herbaceous or woody. The branch of horticulture involved with the production of trees is called **arboriculture.** Trees are perennial elements in a landscape design. They usually are large in size and hence require more space than annual plants.

4. *Landscape architecture. Landscaping* is the use of ornamental plants in conjunction with other elements to beautify a given area. The professionals who design such plans are called **landscape architects.** Since landscaping can enhance a property, it has become an integral part of home construction. Commercial facilities and other public areas are also appropriately landscaped. Malls, playgrounds, boulevards, and parks are examples of public places where ornamental plants are used to enhance the environment aesthetically and make it more functional. The use of plants indoors is called *interiorscaping* (as opposed to landscaping).

1.4 ROLE OF THE NURSERY AND SEED INDUSTRIES IN HORTICULTURE

Horticulture as a modern industry is heavily dependent on the *nursery industry* and *seed industry.*

1.4.1 THE NURSERY INDUSTRY

The growth in the horticultural industry today is attributable in part to the growth in the nursery industry. Nurseries provide seedlings for growers who do not want to raise plants from seed and prefer to take advantage of their convenience (Chapter 16). In fact, certain plants are difficult to propagate without special conditions that the homeowner ordinarily cannot provide. Nurseries also grow and sell mature plants in containers for use indoors and outdoors (Figure 1–6). Nurseries facilitate the work of landscape architects and contractors by providing materials that are ready to be installed on-site, enabling a bare ground to be instantly transformed into a lawn with trees and other ornamental plants. Commercial nurseries are equipped to provide ideal conditions for plant growth. By growing plants under a controlled environment, nurseries provide growers a head start on plant production for the season. They start the plants in the greenhouse in winter when growing them outside is impossible. These plants are timed to be ready for transplanting into the field when spring conditions arrive. Nurseries produce a variety of plants—bushes, trees, tubers, roots, and other succulent and woody plants. They can handle tropical and temperate (warm- and cool-season) plants because they are equipped to control the plant growth environment. The small-scale home grower can purchase portable plant growth chambers for use at home.

1.4.2 THE SEED INDUSTRY

Researchers (geneticists and breeders) are continually developing new plant cultivars. These new types may be higher yielding, more resistant to environmental stresses (such as moisture, temperature, and light) and diseases, higher in nutritional value, or aesthetically more pleasing, among other qualities. Seeds from the research domain reach the consumer after going through several steps in the seed release process. Once the seed is certified and released as a cultivar, seed growers in the seed industry become responsible for multiplying the seed of the new cultivar, processing it, and packaging it for sale. The role of the seed industry is crucial to the success that the horticultural industry currently enjoys (Figure 1–7). Seed packets come with instructions about how the plant should be raised to maturity. These instructions are of tremendous help,

(a)   (b)

FIGURE 1–6 Nurseries grow trees, shrubs, and various plant types in a variety of containers for sale to the general public.
(Source: George Acquaah)

FIGURE 1–7 Seed packets.
(Source: George Acquaah)

TABLE 1–1 Sample of Seed Companies

Abbott & Cobb, Inc., PO Box 307, Trevose, PA 19053, Phone: 215-245-6666, Fax: 215-245-9043,
 Specialty: Sweet corn, watermelon, pepper, cantaloupe, squash

American Takii, Inc., Contact: Rick Falconer, 301 Natividad Rd, Salinas, CA 93906,
 Phone: 831-443-4901, Fax: 831-443-3976, Specialty: Vegetable seed

Arteco-USA, Contact: Shamim Zaidi, 3150 Hilltop Mall Road, Richmond, CA 94806,
 Phone: 510-970-7676, Fax: 510-758-7001, E-Mail: arteco@pacbell.net, Specialty: All vegetables,
 field planting seeds

Asgrow Seed Co., 1081A Harkins Rd, Salinas, CA 93901, Phone: 408-424-6905, Fax: 831-422-1417,
 Specialty: Full line

Asgrow Vegetable Seeds, Contact: Robert Zagajeski, 1905 Lirio Avenue, Saticoy, CA 93007-4206,
 Phone: 805-647-5912, Fax: 805-672-1939, Specialty: fresh market tomato, carrot, snapbean,
 cantaloupe; full product line

Atlee Burpee Co., W, Contact: George C. Ball, Jr., 300 Park Avenue, Warmster, PA 18974,
 Phone: 215-674-4900, Fax: 215-674-7170, Specialty: All varieties

Ball Seed, 622 Town Road, West Chicago, IL 60185-2698, Phone: 317-577-9917, Fax: 317-577-9918,
 Email: dross@ballseed.com , http://www.ballseed.com

Burrell Seed Growers Co., D. V., Contact: Richard Burrell, PO Box 150, Rocky Ford, CO 81067-0150,
 Phone: 719-254-3318, Fax: 719-254-3319, Specialty: watermelon, cantaloupe, squash, pumpkin

Crop King, Inc., 5050 Greenwich Rd, Seville, OH 44273-9413, Phone: 330-769-2002,
 Fax: 330-769-2616, E-Mail: cropking@cropking.com, Specialty: Tomato, lettuce, cucumber, pepper

Global Seeds, Inc., Contact: Richard Gomer, PO Box 207, Hollister, CA 95024-1207,
 Phone: 408-637-8251, Fax: 408-637-8254, Specialty: Vegetable crops

Johnny's Selected Seeds, 955 Benton Avenue, Winslow, Maine 04901-2601, Commercial
 Phone: 207-861-3902, Fax: 800-437-4290, Web: www.johnnyseeds.com Specialty: Fresh market
 varieties for direct marketers

Harris Seeds, Contact: Mark Willis, 60 Saginaw Drive, PO Box 22960, Rochester, NY 14692-2960,
 Phone: 800-544-7938, Fax: 716-442-9387

Novartis Seeds, Inc., Contact: John Sorenson, PO Box 4188, Boise, ID 83711-4188,
 Phone: 208-322-7272, Fax: 208-322-1436, Specialty: Large and small seeded vegetables

Rupp Seeds, Inc., 5-17919 Co Rd B, Wauseon, OH 43567, Phone: 419-337-1841, Specialty:
 All vegetables, herbs

Seminis Vegetable Seeds, PO Box 4206, Saticoy, CA 93007-4206, Phone: 805-647-1188,
 Fax: 805-656-4818, Specialty: All varieties

Syngenta Seeds, Inc. Rogers brand, P.O. Box 4188, Boise, ID 83711

---

especially to novice growers. The seed industry has eliminated the need for growers to produce their own seed for planting, unless they so desire. The price of commercial seed is reasonable, and mail-order purchases are possible in many cases. Seed production is usually concentrated in areas where the growing season is most favorable for cropping. A list of some of the major companies is presented in Table 1–1.

Horticulture is important to society in a variety of ways, including as a source of food, ornamentals, and jobs.

1.5.1 SOURCE OF FOOD

Society depends on horticulture for a substantial portion of its food needs in the form of vegetables, fruits, and nuts. These types of food sources are high in complex carbohydrates and rich in vitamins and minerals. Leguminous vegetable plants are high in both carbohydrates and protein. Horticultural products are hence part of a balanced diet for humans.

Commercial producers account for most of the horticultural products in the nation. However, numerous homeowners are engaged in gardening on their property as a source of fresh produce for the table and as a hobby for recreation and exercise. Horticultural products may be purchased fresh or processed. For example, certain vegetables (such as carrots, lettuce, tomatoes, and peppers) may be eaten fresh and raw in salads, and fruits (such as apples, oranges, and grapes) may be eaten fresh or processed into beverages.

1.5.2 ECONOMIC IMPORTANCE OF HORTICULTURE

The United States imports significant amounts of fruits and vegetables from all over the world (Table 1–2). This indicates the potential for growth in the horticultural industry. In 2007, an estimated 25.5 percent of U.S. agricultural exports comprised fruits and vegetables (Table 1–3). On the local scene, horticultural products, both food and ornamentals, are widely consumed by the public, on regular as well as festive occasions. The top five producers of horticultural products in 2006 were California, Florida, Michigan, Texas, and New York (Table 1–4). Most vegetables and fruits are produced in the West, Northwest, Midwest, Northeast, and Southwest United States (Figure 1–8).

1.5.3 ORNAMENTALS

As previously indicated, landscaping has become an integral part of home construction. Ornamentals are found both indoors and outdoors. Plants in the landscape include trees, shrubs, bedding plants, and grasses. Ornamentals are formally displayed for public enjoyment in places such as arboretums, parks, and botanical gardens. Botanical gardens are designed to exhibit a large variety of plant types for the pleasure and education of visitors. Public areas such as malls, playgrounds, and cemeteries are places where plants are displayed for specific purposes. In many societies, certain flowers are associated with specific social events. For example, roses are associated with Valentine's Day, carnations with graduation and Mother's Day, poinsettias with Christmas, and lilies with Easter, which is not to say that these flowers cannot be used for other purposes. Flowers feature very prominently at funerals and weddings. The golf course industry is a major horticultural enterprise that involves not only turfgrasses but also a wide variety of trees, shrubs, bedding plants, and other ornamentals.

1.5.4 JOBS

The ornamental industry provides a wide variety of jobs for many categories of people, directly or indirectly. Conducting a computer search via the Internet reveals a wide variety of advertised jobs.

TABLE 1–2 U.S. Fruit and Vegetable Imports, 2007

Fruits – fresh or frozen

Country of origin	Value (Million $)
Chile	759
Mexico	435
Costa Rica	273
Guatemala	160
Canada	141
Ecuador	141
European Union	133
Colombia	71
Honduras	68
Argentina	56
World total	**2,440**

Fruits – prepared or preserved

Country of origin	Value (Million $)
China	135
Thailand	90
Mexico	69
Philippines	55
European Union	51
Canada	46
Turkey	22
Indonesia	13
Chile	13
Brazil	11
World total	**589**

Vegetables – fresh or frozen

Country of origin	Value (Million $)
Mexico	1,463
Canada	549
Peru	03
China (Mainland)	64
European Union	55
Guatemala	29
Costa Rica	27
Ecuador	15
Dominican Republic	12
Honduras	11
World total	**2,390**

Vegetables – prepared or preserved

Country of origin	Value (Million $)
European Union	241
China (Mainland)	130
Mexico	108
Canada	91
Peru	61
Turkey	32
India	27
Chile	19
Thailand	16
Morocco	13
World total	**842**

TABLE 1–3 U.S. Horticultural Exports, 2007

Commodity	Value (Million $)
Total agricultural export value	33,515
Fruits and products	1,580
Fruits, fresh	1,182
Fruits, prepared or preserved	398
Fruits, juices	385
Vegetables and products	1,709
Vegetables, fresh	740
Vegetables, processed or preserved	969
Tree nuts and preparations	1,587

TABLE 1–4 Top Five Producers of Horticultural Products, 2006

Commodity	Rank	Value ($)		Percent of U.S. total				
Total whole sale		5,08,421		19.4	18.9	7.2	5.4	3.6
			State	CA	FL	MI	TX	NY
Annual bedding plants	1	1,904,921		12.6	9.6	9.4	7.6	4.9
			State	CA	MI	TX	FL	MO
Potted houseplants	2	808,941		24.6	11.7	6.1	5.8	4.9
			State	CA	FL	NY	TX	MO
Foliage indoor plants	3	721,049		69.8	16.2	2.8	2.4	1.0
			State	FL	CA	TX	HI	MO
Herbaceous perennials	4	708,865		11.2	8.9	7.6	6.7	6.6
			State	CA	SC	MI	IL	NJ
Cut flowers, greens	5	601,860		67.6	18.6	8.7	8.4	2.0
			State	CA	FL	WA	HI	OR

Direct Jobs

A large number of jobs require knowledge and training in horticulture. The level of training could be vocational or at the college level. The work may be indoors or outdoors. Intense manual labor or paperwork in the office may be involved. Many jobs in horticulture require a high school diploma and a short course in horticulture or agriculture. A college education provides more in-depth knowledge of the field and offers job opportunities at supervisory or managerial levels and to conduct research. The following are selected categories of jobs that require varying degrees of familiarity with horticulture:

Nursery Operation

1. Nursery manager—responsible for coordinating the whole nursery operation; oversees personnel; develops operational budget; develops production and marketing plans
2. Propagator—responsible for raising planting materials using various methods of propagation (e.g., cutting, grafting)
3. Field supervisor—oversees fieldworkers; making work schedules; and ensuring that fieldwork is done properly and on time
4. Salesperson—promotes nursery operation; sells plant materials to customers
5. Garden center manager—handles the retail section of the nursery (inventory, sales, advertising, etc.)
6. Plant technician—knowledgeable in plant problems and advises on proper plant care for highest-quality products

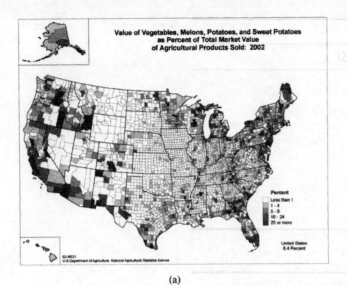

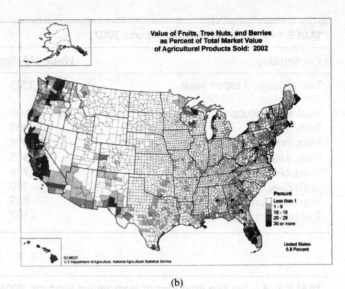

(a)   (b)

FIGURE 1–8 Geographic distribution of
horticultural production in the U.S.:
a) Vegetables, b) Fruits and nuts,
c) Nursery and greenhouse production.
(Source: USDA)

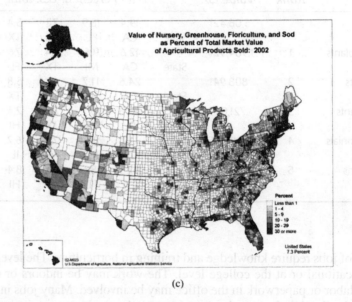

(c)

Greenhouse Operation

1. Greenhouse manager—similar duties as those of nursery manager
2. Sales manager—coordinates product sales and inventory
3. Nursery manager—(see nursery operation)
4. Technician—provides technical support to greenhouse operations, including equipment operation and maintenance
5. Sales assistant—provides assistance to customers to help in choices

Landscape Operation

1. Architect/designer—develops landscape designs for customers
2. Construction supervisor—oversees the installation of a landscape according to landscape drawings
3. Groundskeeper/landscape maintenance technician—responsible for maintenance of a landscape
4. Tree surgeon—responsible for tree management (pruning, etc.)

Turfgrass Operation

1. Landscape technician—oversees installation and maintenance of landscape
2. Golf course architect—designs golf course
3. Golf course superintendent—supervises construction and maintenance of golf course

Crop Production

1. Farm manager—oversees production of vegetable or fruit production operation
2. Vegetable/fruit grower—owns vegetable/fruit production operation

Florist Operation

1. Floral designer—creatively arranges flowers for various occasions
2. Store manager—in charge of business operation, makes arrangements for special events (e.g., weddings)

Education

1. Teacher—teaches horticulture in formal or informal settings
2. Researcher—conducts research to develop new products (e.g., plant varieties) and to provide solution to agronomic problems
3. Extension person—provides information to general public to promote horticultural industry

As mentioned earlier, certain jobs do not require any familiarity with horticulture by way of formal training. For example, one can find numerous jobs in the greenhouse that require only an ability to follow directions and instructions and a sense of responsibility. Many workers in the greenhouse perform jobs such as watering, transplanting, filling pots with media, harvesting produce, and so on. Job prospects for those who pursue formal training in agriculture or horticulture are very bright.

Indirect Jobs

The ornamental industry has spawned a number of supporting or service industries, including the following:

1. *Research.* Many scientists are engaged in developing new and improved types of vegetables, fruits, and ornamentals. These new cultivars may have wider and better adaptation, be higher yielding and of higher nutritional quality, and have other qualities depending on breeding objectives. Research is conducted in both private and public sectors (at universities, research institutes, and research companies) to find solutions to problems in the horticultural industry. College-level training (often graduate level) is required to adequately prepare for a career in research. Research institutes invest a great amount of human and financial resources in developing new cultivars, which is why commercial seed companies sell their improved seed (such as *hybrid* seed) at premium prices. Apart from improving the agronomic and nutritional qualities of plants, horticultural scientists also devote considerable time to improving the aesthetics of ornamentals and the quality of products.
2. *Chemical industry.* The horticulture industry depends on large amounts and varieties of chemicals, including fertilizers, pesticides, and growth hormones. Many companies are involved in producing chemicals that are used to enhance plant production and the quality of produce. Chemicals (called agrochemicals) are an integral part of modern high-input production practices. The increasing

trend toward ensuring a safer environment has been the impetus for the creation and enforcement of laws and guidelines for the judicious and safe use of chemicals. Crop production using little or no chemicals, called *organic farming,* is gradually gaining popularity.

3. *Machinery.* Engineers design and produce tools and machinery for use in the production of horticultural plants. Machinery and implements are available for preparing land, planting, cultivating, spraying, harvesting, storing, and packaging. These aids enable large-scale production of horticultural plants to be undertaken. Home garden versions of some of this machinery and equipment are available.

4. *Distribution.* Horticultural products are transported from the areas of production to marketing outlets. Because of their largely perishable nature, horticultural produce and products require special handling in transportation to retain their quality for a long time. Certain items require refrigeration during storage. Horticulture has spawned an elaborate transportation and distribution network. Because most horticultural products are harvested and used fresh, the ability to preserve quality in transit is critical to the industry. In certain cases, the produce is harvested before it ripens in order to increase its shelf life. Home gardeners have the advantage of ready access to vine-ripened and fresh produce.

Numerous jobs are available in these four general areas at various levels. These jobs can be obtained by persons trained in fields other than horticulture, such as basic science, engineering, economics, marketing, agribusiness, genetics, and postharvest physiology.

1.6 THERAPEUTIC USE OF HORTICULTURE

Horticulture is known to have therapeutic value that can be derived by participating in it or simply enjoying what has been created by others. Walking through a botanical garden can be very relaxing and healthy.

Also called therapeutic horticulture, horticultural therapy uses plants and horticultural activities to improve the well-being of people of all ages. It is used especially to improve the psychological and physical adjustment of persons with physical disabilities, mental illness, developmental disabilities, and the elderly.

People with emotional and mental problems have been helped when they were deliberately exposed to ornamental plants. For the visually impaired, horticulture can be enjoyed by touching the plant parts and enjoying the sweet scents.

Gardening can be undertaken by people to keep fit or to relieve boredom and other negative emotions. People who are incarcerated or severely limited in their movement are prone to frustration. For such individuals, horticultural activities can be helpful in better managing their emotions.

Throughout horticultural therapy, people recovering from long-term illness and who have been at the receiving end of care can be assigned the care of a plant in a role reversal to boost their confidence and to give them a renewed sense of purpose.

1.7 HORTICULTURE ON THE INTERNET

This section is designed to provide the reader a quick overview of horticulture as an industry and academic discipline. The sites featured were selected for their content as well as the effective use of visuals to enhance the presentation. These sites also show how faculty, students, and all who are interested in horticulture may search the Internet to find information to supplement what has been presented in this book. Selected sites are as follows:

What Is Horticulture?

This site provides a detailed account of the history of horticulture by Professor Jules Janick of Purdue University. It presents an account of how the industry has evolved over the ages, and discusses the contributions of key horticulturalists in the development of horticulture as a science and a business.

http://www.hort.purdue.edu/newcrop/history/default.html

Botanical Gardens

Botanical gardens are places where the general public may go to view a variety of horticultural displays. While some displays involved common plant species, these facilities often have unique exhibits such as tropical gardens and rare specimens.

Myriad Botanical Gardens, Oklahoma City, http://www.myriadgardens.com/index.html
Missouri Botanical Gardens, http://www.mobot.org/
Kew Botanical Gardens, http://www.rbgkew.org.uk/

Horticultural Societies

There are professional societies devoted to promoting a forum for professionals in academia for exchange of ideas in a formal setting. There are other societies whose membership is more open to the general public, and that focus on specific species (e.g., the Rose or Orchid Societies), among other purposes.

American Horticultural Society, http://www.ahs.org/

Overview of Horticulture

This site is an excellent source of information on various aspects of horticulture. Such information is presented in visual forms through photos and videos.

http://webgarden.osu.edu/

Growing Houseplants

Growing houseplants is one of the most common ways in which the public participates in horticulture. Many sites provide excellent information on selecting and growing houseplants.

http://www.urbanext.uiuc.edu/houseplants/

Landscape Plants

The use of ornamentals in landscaping is another popular and visible application of horticulture in society. Many sites provide guidelines to selecting and using landscape plants.

http://oregonstate.edu/dept/ldplants/gardem-p.htm

The Science of Horticulture

Horticulture is a science, an art, and a business. The Internet is an integral part of modern classroom instructional delivery system. Many instructors post excellent teaching materials on the Web that can be accessed to supplement teaching by others. Here is a sample of such materials:

Classifying and naming plants

Very good and well-illustrated discussion of plant classification
http://www.dmturner.org/Teacher/Library/4thText/PlantsPart1.html#classification

Inflorescence types

A well-illustrated discussion of the floral structure
http://www.pssc.ttu.edu/pss1411cd/STRUCTUR/inflores/inflores.htm

Plant anatomy

Excellent and comprehensive collection of slides on plant anatomy; electron
microscopy
http://botweb.uwsp.edu/anatomy/
Excellent photos of plant structures
http://www.pssc.ttu.edu/pss1411cd/CDROM/DEFAULT.HTM

Hydroponics system

Excellent discussion on types; line diagrams to show differences
http://www.simplyhydro.com/system.htm

Flower arranging

The site presents a good introduction to the art of floral arranging
http://interiordec.about.com/od/arrangingflowers/How_To_Arrange_Flowers.htm

SUMMARY

Horticulture (garden cultivation) is the branch of agricultural plant sciences that deals with the production of fruits, vegetables, nuts, and ornamentals. It is a major source of food and employment in society. Operationally, there are several divisions of horticulture: pomology (tree fruit production), olericulture (vegetable production), ornamental horticulture, floriculture (flower production), turfgrass science (turf production), arboriculture (tree production), and landscape architecture (design and use of plants in the landscape). Horticultural foods are rich in minerals and vitamins. Horticulture can be undertaken on a small scale by homeowners on their property, producing flowers and food plants. As an industry, horticulture is supported by a large number of service providers that supply equipment, chemicals, and implements. Nurseries provide plant materials for growers. Numerous jobs are available to persons with formal training in horticulture, but an equally large number of jobs in this branch of agriculture requires little or no formal training.

REFERENCES AND SUGGESTED READING

Janick, J. 1986. *Horticultural science*, 4th ed. San Francisco: W. H. Freeman.

American Horticultural Societies
http://www.ahs.org/

American Horticultural Therapy Association
http://www.ahta.org/

Examples of botanical gardens
http://www.myriadgardens.com/index.html
http://www.mobot.org/
http://www.rbgkew.org.uk/

Excellent overview of the history of horticulture.
http://www.hort.purdue.edu/newcrop/history/default.html

General information on various aspects of horticulture.
http://webgarden.osu.edu/

Jobs in horticulture as advertised by the American Society of Horticulture Science
http://www.ashs.org/hortopport/index.html

US Horticultural trade reports
http://www.fas.usda.gov/htp_arc.asp

PRACTICAL EXPERIENCE

1. Consult the commercial edition of your local telephone book (the yellow pages) and list up to ten businesses each in the following categories:
   a. Florists
   b. Nurseries or greenhouses

2. Visit a local business in each of the following categories. During the visit, obtain information about the following: plants cultivated (or plants and flowers used), educational level or training of the owner or manager, size of the operation, and profitability.
   a. Florist shop
   b. Greenhouse
   c. Vegetable farm
   d. Fruit farm

3. Visit the library for the following exercise.
   a. Select a local periodic publication. For a period (e.g., three months), count the number of advertised horticultural and allied jobs.
   b. Find the job description of each of the following jobs from, for example, the *Occupational Outlook* publication.
      1. Golf course manager
      2. Greenhouse manager
      3. Three other horticultural jobs

4. Internet search. Search the Internet to find out the number of jobs advertised in the area of horticulture. You may want to search according to categories (e.g., teaching jobs, greenhouse jobs, floriculture, turfgrass, and so on).

OUTCOMES ASSESSMENT

1. Briefly trace the history of horticulture.

2. Discuss, giving specific examples, the benefits of horticulture to society.

3. What is horticulture?

4. Discuss the roles of the seed and nursery industries in modern horticulture.

5. Give specific reasons for the distribution of horticultural production in the United States.

6. Horticulture is a science, an art, and a business. Discuss.

7. Distinguish among the divisions of the disciplines of horticulture.

8. Discuss, giving specific examples, how horticulture can be used in society to positively impact the environment.

9. Discuss specific ways in which horticultural applications are manifested on your campus or residential neighborhood.

2

Classifying and Naming Horticultural Plants

PURPOSE AND EXPECTED OUTCOMES

This chapter is designed to show the need and importance of a universal system for classifying and naming plants and to describe the various methods currently in use for accomplishing this goal.

After studying this chapter, the student should be able to

1. Define the term *taxonomy*.
2. Explain the need for a universal nomenclature.
3. Describe the binomial nomenclature.
4. Describe various operational systems of classification of plants based on growth form, fruits, life cycle, use, stem type, leaf characteristics, adaptation, and flower type.

[COLOR PLATES—*see color plate 2* for additional chapter photos]

OVERVIEW

Nature is characterized by diversity. No two individuals are exactly alike. Some individuals have identical *genomes* (arrays of genes). However, in appearance, even *clonal populations* (genetically identical individuals) or identical twins exhibit subtle differences. Every culture has a system for grouping individuals for a variety of practical purposes; names are attached to the groups and the component types of which they are comprised. As long as a culture remained closed to the outside world, there was no problem with the culture-based nomenclature. However, as cultures merged with each other and plant materials were moved across cultural and geographic lines, it became necessary, for effective cross-cultural communication, to have a universal system of naming plants. This system ensured that corn, called maize in another culture, would have a neutral name and mean the same crop to all people.

Some superficial differences automatically place organisms into distinct classes. For example, there are plants and there are animals. In plants, some bear flowers, others do not; some have broad leaves, others have narrow leaves; some bear fleshy fruits, others bear grains; and so on. These *natural systems* of classification are arbitrary and reflect the uses human cultures have for plants. Other forms of nomenclature are based on scientific principles that have universal application. This chapter explores the origin and nature of these different systems for grouping and naming plants.

2.1 SCIENTIFIC AND BOTANICAL SYSTEMS OF CLASSIFICATION

Taxonomy
The science of identifying, naming, and classifying plants.

Scientific systems of classification go beyond the superficial or natural system by employing a number of criteria that include morphological, anatomical, ultrastructural, physiological, phytochemical, cytological, and evolutionary (phylogenetical) criteria. Pyrame de Candole is credited with the introduction of the term **taxonomy** as the science of classifying and naming plants. Taxonomy is sometimes used synonymously with *systematics.* The latter, however, is a field of biology involved with the study of diversity among organisms to establish their natural (evolutionary) relationships, making taxonomy a discipline of systematics.

In plant identification, individuals are assigned to a descending series of related plants, based on their known common characteristics. For example, a marigold plant is first placed in a more distant group with plants that have seed, then among seed plants with flowers, and eventually in the most closely associated groups of varieties of marigold. In terms of *botanical nomenclature,* Carolus Linnaeus is credited with developing the current Latin-based system called the **binomial nomenclature,** because an individual is given two names, as opposed to the polynomial system, which was more descriptive. The international body that sets the rules for naming plants by this system publishes the *International Code of Botanical Nomenclature (ICBN)* to provide guidelines for standardizing the naming of plants. These rules are revised as new scientific evidence becomes available.

Binomial Nomenclature
A system of naming plants whereby a plant is given a two-part name representing the genus and species.

Kingdom
The highest taxonomic category.

2.2 TAXONOMIC GROUPS

Species
A category of biological classification ranking immediately below the genus or subgenus.

Several general classification categories have been defined in organisms. These classifications can be arranged in order from the most inclusive group (**kingdom**) to the least inclusive group (**species**) (Figure 2–1). Each of these groups constitutes a *taxon* (plural: *taxa*). In addition to these basic groups, subcategories are used in certain cases. These include levels such as *subdivision, subclass, suborder, subspecies,* and *variety* (or *cultivar*). An example of plant classification is presented in Table 2–1.

Order
A category of taxonomic classification ranking above the family and below the class.

Family
A group of related plants or animals forming a category ranking above a genus and below an order and usually comprising several to many genera.

TABLE 2–1 An Example of Scientific Classification of Plants

Taxon	Example	Common Name
Kingdom	Plantae	Plant
Division	Magnoliophyta	Flowering plant
Class	Liliopsida	Monocot
Order	Liliales	Lily order
Family	Liliaceae	Lily family
Genus	*Allium*	
Species	*Allium cepa*	Onion

Eight major taxa are commonly used in plant classification. The general basis of placing plants into each of these groups is as follows:	
Kingdom	Depends on whether the organism is a plant or animal
Division	Based on whether the plant bears seed or not
Class	Whether the seeds are borne in a fruit or are naked
Subclass	Assigned based on whether the seed contains one seed leaf or cotyledon (monocotyledon or monocot) or two cotyledons (dicotyledon or dicot)
Order	Based on differences and similarities in the vegetative and reproductive structures of plants
Family	Similar to order, family is assigned on the basis of differences and similarities of various vegetative and reproductive structure
Genus	Based on whether the species in a genus show close genetic affinities
Species	Assigned on the basis of plants being a population of related interbreeding forms

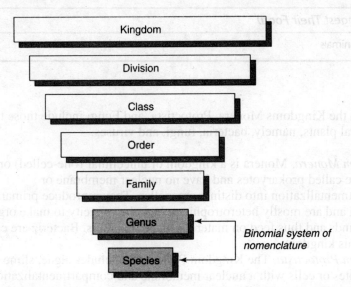

FIGURE 2–1 Major classification categories of living organisms.

According to the binomial nomenclature, each individual has a two-part name; the first part is called the **genus** (plural: *genera*) and the second part is called a *specific epithet* or *species*. This system is equivalent to surnames and first names in the naming of people.

Genus
A class, kind, or group marked by common characteristics or by one common characteristic.

2.2.1 KINGDOMS

Placing organisms into groups is a work in progress. Traditionally, living organisms are recognized as belonging to one of two categories or kingdoms: the *plant kingdom* or the *animal kingdom.* However, as science advances and knowledge increases, this scheme periodically comes under review. From the two-kingdom scheme evolved the three-, four-, and five-kingdom classifications of organisms. Even the five-kingdom scheme is deemed inadequate by certain scientists who propose a further breakdown into more kingdoms. The five-kingdom classification proposed by R. H. Whittaker in 1969 is presented in Table 2–2. The criteria for the classification are cellular structural complexity and forms of nutrition (photosynthesis, ingestion, or absorption of food in solution).

Even though horticulture focuses on organisms in Kingdom Plantae, other kingdoms are directly or indirectly important to the field. Horticulture exists because of humans (Kingdom Animalia). The field was developed by humans to serve humans.

TABLE 2–2 The Five Kingdoms of Organisms as Described by Whittaker

---

Monera (Have Prokaryotic Cells)

Bacteria

Protoctista (Have Eukaryotic Cells)

Algae
Slime molds
Flagellate fungi
Protozoa
Sponges

Fungi (Absorb Food in Solution)

True fungi

Plantae (Produce Own Food by the Process of Photosynthesis)

Bryophytes
Vascular plants

Animalia (Ingest Their Food)

Multicellular animals

Organisms in the Kingdoms Monera, Protoctista, and Fungi include those that are pests of horticultural plants, namely, bacteria, fungi, and viruses.

1. *Kingdom Monera.* Monera is a kingdom of unicellular (one-celled) organisms. They are called prokaryotes and have no nuclear membrane or compartmentalization into distinct organelles. They reproduce primarily by cell division and are mostly heterotrophic or lack the capacity to make organic compounds and thus feed on materials made by others. Bacteria are classified under this kingdom.
2. *Kingdom Protoctista.* The Kingdom Protoctista includes algae, slime molds, and eukaryotes or cells with a nuclear membrane and compartmentalization into membrane-bound organelles.
3. *Kingdom Fungi.* Fungi are filamentous eukaryotes that lack plastids and chlorophyll. Thus, they feed on dead or living organisms. Most plant diseases are caused by fungi.
4. *Kingdom Animalia.* Kingdom Animalia consists of multicellular organisms that are eukaryotes but without cell walls, plastids, and capacity for photosynthesis. Animals generally ingest their food and reproduce primarily by sexual means. Animals have the highest level of organization and tissue differentiation of any organism in any kingdom. They have complex sensory and neuromotor systems.
5. *Kingdom Plantae.* Organisms in the Kingdom Plantae are photosynthetic. They make food from inorganic materials. Few plants are heterotrophic, that is, feeding on organic material from other sources. They are multicellular, have cell walls, and live on land.

2.2.2 DIVISIONS OF KINGDOM PLANTAE

Several divisions are recognized in the Kingdom Plantae (Table 2–3). These divisions can be divided into two major categories: *bryophytes* and *vascular plants*. Vascular plants are large bodied and have three primary vegetative organs, *stem, leaves,* and *roots,*

TABLE 2-3 The Divisions of the Kingdom Plantae

	Divisions	Common Name
Bryophytes (non-vascular)	Hepaticophyta	Liverworts
(no seed)	Anthocerotophyta	Hornworts
Bryophyta	Mosses	
Vascular plants	Trachaeophyta	
a. Seedless (spore-bearing)	Psilotophyta	Whisk ferns
Lycophyta	Club mosses	
Sphenophyta	Horsetails	
Pterophyta	Ferns	
b. Seeded (cone-bearing)	Pinophyta	Gymnosperms (non-flowering)
Subdivision: Cycadicae	Cycads	
Subdivision: Pinicae		
Class: Ginkgoatae	*Ginkgo*	
Class: Pinatae	Conifers	
Subdivision: Gneticae	*Gnetum*	
c. Seeded (seed in fruits)	Magnoliophyta	Angiosperms (flowering plants)
Class: Liliopsida	Monocots	
Class: Magnoliopsida	Dicots	

and also *conducting tissues*. Vascular plants may produce seeds or be seedless. Most plants of horticultural interest are vascular plants.

In terms of relative abundance, more than 80 percent of all species in the plant kingdom are flowering plants. Even though *gymnosperms* (seed plants whose seeds are not enclosed within an ovary during development) make up only 0.2 percent of species in the plant kingdom, conifers (e.g., pines) occur on about one-third of forested lands of the world.

2.2.3 VARIETY VERSUS CULTIVAR

The lowest and least inclusive taxon is the species, as already indicated. Species may be subdivided into specific categories. A botanical variety is a naturally occurring variant of the species that is significantly different from the general species originally described. Botanical varieties may differ in subtle or more visible ways, such as in color, shape, size, chemical quality, or some other traits. Instead of two names, as expected in the binomial nomenclature, a variety requires the use of a third name after the introduction of the abbreviation *var.* (for **variety**). For example, broccoli is called *Brassica oleraceae* var. *botrytis*.

Through plant breeding, humans sometimes create new variants that are maintained under human supervision (as opposed to being naturally maintained, as is the case in varieties). The product of plant breeding is called a *cultivar,* a contraction of two terms—*cultiv*ated and *variety.* **Cultivars** are maintained as clones in vegetatively propagated species and as lines in species propagated by seed under specific conditions. Many flowers and vegetables have cultivars that are propagated by seed, whereas others are *hybrids* (F$_1$ seed from a cross of two different parents).

2.2.4 RULES IN CLASSIFICATION

In plant taxonomy, the ending of a name is often characteristic of the taxon. Classes often end in *-opsida* (e.g., Magnoliopsida). Names ending in *-ae* are subclasses of class names. Exceptions include several families such as Compositae (now called Asteraceae). Plant orders end in *-ales* (e.g., Rosales [roses]), while family names end in *-aceae* (e.g., Rosaceae).

Variety
Any of various groups of plants or animals ranking below a species.

Cultivar
Derived from the words cultivated and variety, often designating a product of plant breeding.

These higher-order taxa are not routinely encountered, unless one is conducting taxonomic studies. The binomial names are the most frequently encountered. When you walk through a botanical garden, or even a college campus where there is a good horticulture program or a good grounds and gardens department, you may find that some plants in the landscape are labeled with the correct binomial name or scientific name, as well as the common name (Figure 2–2). The family name is quite frequently indicated.

The rules for writing names become more stringent at the binomial level. The main rules are as follows:

1. The binary name must be underlined or written in italics to indicate that such names are non-English names.
2. The genus name starts with an uppercase letter, and the species name is written in lowercase throughout. The term *species* is both singular and plural. It may be shortened to "spp," for the plural "species."
3. In technical writing, an initial *L.* may follow the species, indicating that Linnaeus first named the plant. Other abbreviations may be encountered in the literature. An example of a full binary name for corn, for example, is Zea mays L., or *Zea mays* L. The genus may be abbreviated (e.g., *Z. mays* L.). Some plants may have a subspecies and hence have a third name added to the binary name. In such a case, the third name is also underlined or italicized.
4. Whereas the generic name can be written alone to refer to individuals in the group, the specific epithet cannot be used by itself (i.e., *Zea* but not *mays*).
5. At the bottom of the taxa hierarchy is variety, which is the naturally occurring and very closely related variant. As previously indicated, the binomial name is followed by the abbreviation *var.* and then the variety name. Cultivar names are not underlined or italicized (e.g., *Lycopersicon esculentum* Mill. cultivar 'Big Red' or L. esculentum cv. 'Big Red,' or L. esculentum 'Big Red').

Specific epithets are adjectival in nature. Many genera can have the same specific epithet. Some of them indicate color, such as *alba* (white), *variegata* (variegated), *rubrum* (red), and *aureum* (golden). Examples of frequently encountered epithets are *vulgaris* (common), *esculentus* (edible), *sativus* (cultivated), *tuberosum* (bearing tubers), and *officinalis* (medicinal).

In developing new horticultural cultivars, plant breeders employ a variety of techniques. The conventional techniques involve crossing or hybridizing plants that differ in desirable characteristics. In terms of taxonomic hierarchy, hybridization can be routinely performed at the base of the hierarchy, among varieties or cultivars of the same species. Crossing at other levels such as among species (*interspecies hybridization*) leads to genetic complications. Such a cross is problematic and has limited success, requiring the use of additional techniques, such as *embryo rescue*, in some cases.

FIGURE 2–2 Plants in the landscape may be identified by using a stake-mounted label, usually showing both the scientific and common names.

(Source: George Acquaah)

HISTORY OF PLANT TAXONOMY

PAUL R. FANTZ
North Carolina State University

Plant Taxonomy and the international rules currently governing plant names and classification had its origins in early Western civilizations. Several civilizations (China, India, Mexican Aztecs) in other areas of the world developed practices for plant identification, nomenclature and classification independently. The Chinese literature is rich in botanical treatises (3600-200 B.C.), and printing was developed some 400 years before Europeans. But, these works were unknown to Europeans.

PRELITERATE HUMANS

Knowledge of preliterate societies' botanical knowledge and taxonomic practice is unknown with any degree of accuracy. Much of what is reported has been inferred or deduced. Early stages of human evolution demonstrated that man utilized plants for food and shelter materials. This expanded to using plants for clothing, medicinal purposes, toxins (fish and arrowhead poisons; insecticides) and drugs (narcotics; kill "evil spirits"). Requirements for botanical knowledge necessitated that preliterate man become a practical taxonomist. It is assumed that those who didn't, failed to become our ancestors!

Modern studies by ethnobotanists with "primitive" societies occurring in remote areas of the world today support these inferences and deductions. Plant classification is based largely on useful and harmful properties of plants. The specialist in plant taxonomy has a different name in each culture, some of which include the shaman, witch doctor, medicine man or guru. They learned their trade through observation, experience, experimentation, and trial and error. Their knowledge was passed on through apprenticeship and training. Ethnobotanists currently are working to gain their trust, to learn from them as to which plants are utilized for treatment of human inflictions, and for other purposes.

These individuals possess the linguistic means to accurately distinguish between plants in their environment. Which plants should they use? The identification method has been designated as the **Doctrine of Signatures,** a belief that plants or plant parts resembling the human body must have been designed by the Creator for the purpose of furnishing remedies for ailments of these parts. One example is Clitoria, a genus of legumes comprising sixty species distributed worldwide, mostly in the tropics. Many species are reported to be used medicinally. Perennial roots resemble scorpion tails or cobras, thus used in India to treat scorpion stings and snake bites. There is some resemblance to a stomach with an elongated intestine basally, thus roots are used as a cathartic or laxative, a vomitive, for ascites (accumulation of abdominal fluids), or as an aperient. Also, there is some resemblance to a lung with pulmonary artery, hence the roots are used to remove phlem of bronchitis. Leaf juices or poultices are use for swollen joints, skin eruptions, earaches and headaches. Flower structure signatures result in the plant being used to enhance fertility in women and domesticated animals, control menstrual flow (antiperiodic or emmenagogue), and in treatment of gonorrhea. Flowers typically are blue, but the floral juice of white flower forms with medial bluish veins (resembles eye cornea and iris) is used to treat inflamed eyes. Seeds are in a single row in legume fruits, the fruit valves twisting on drying to expel the seeds away from the plant. Seeds are used to expel tapeworms, remove excess fluids (diruretic), poisons in the stomach, relief from constipation, or as fish poisons. Some plants are not attacked by insects as neighboring plants are, thus their juice is used to kill grubs and repel insects.

Civilization saw the rise of intellectual and social bases, supported by agriculture in areas where cultivation of crops was feasible. Botanic lore increased in importance. An important discovery was the Nile river sedge, *Cyperus papyrus*. The sheath was spread out and dried, providing a parchment for writing and recording data. This "fossilized speech" provided instant, accurate recall of data. Parchments were put together into books. Reproduction was time consuming, copied by hand, thus available to only the very rich. During the Middle Ages (500–1400 A.D.), many manuscripts were destroyed faster than they could be recopied. Three surviving books provided documentation of plant knowledge known in early civilizations.

Theophrastus (about 370–285 B.C.) was a Greek botanist of Eresus, and a disciple of Aristotle. He inherited Aristotle's Lyceum, a library, museum and botanic garden. He is known to have written over 200 titles, with two important botanical discourses. He often is cited as the "Father of Botany" in recognition of these contributions. *Enquiry into Plants* provides our 1st flora (an inventory of plants), describing 500 plants, plant communities and their distribution. Plants were classified by growth form (trees, shrubs, undershrubs, herbs). He distinguished between flowering and nonflowering plants, annuals and perennials, inflorescence types, ovary position (superior and inferior ovaries), and polypetalous(free petals) and gamopetalous (fusion) corollas. Many plant genera recognized today were Latinized from his aboriginal names (e.g., Aspharagos = *Asparagus;* Narkissos = *Narcissus;* Krataigos = *Crataegus*).

The Causes of Plants by Theophrasus provided knowledge on the anatomy and developmental morphology of plants. It demonstrated a foundational understanding of plant anatomy, distinguishing between organs and tissues, distinction between different types of tissues, pericarps of fruits, sexual and asexual modes of reproduction, and that sepals and petals were derived from modification of leaves. These works of Theophrastus were the authoritative references for 1800 years.

Caius Plinius Secundus (23–79 A.D.) Was a Roman naturalist, historian, lawyer and writer. He is known more commonly as "**Pliny the Elder**". He was given the task by the military government to record all the knowledge of the world. His *Historia naturalis* was a 37 volume treatise of which 9 volumes were devoted to medicinal and agricultural plants. Pliny the Elder was very gullible. Thus, his works are intermixed with myths and superstitions. Yet, his book was considered the authoritative source and profoundly influenced Western Europeans for nearly 1400 years.

Pedanius **Dioscorides** (about 20–70) was a Greek from Anajarabus, a Roman military physician and surgeon who traveled with the Roman armies. His *Materia Medica* was a pharmacopedia of medicinal plants recognized as the authoritative reference for 1400 years. He described some 600 species of plant based upon firsthand knowledge. He was the first to recognize natural plant relationships, particularly medicinal herbs today classified in the mint (Lamiaceae) and umbel/carrot (Apiaceae) families. Included were several new generic names utilized today (e.g. *Aloe, Anemone, Phaseolus*).

Plant names in these books were polynominal descriptions. Similar looking plants had more descriptive terms for segregation; hence, longer names. The language used was classical Greek or Latin, the language of the educated, affordable only to the very rich.

MIDDLE AGES

Albertus Magnus (1200–1280) was a German scholar, and Bishop of Ratisbon. His book, *De Vegetabilis,* included descriptions of non-medicinal plants. He was the first to distinguish vascular from nonvascular plants, and recognize monocots as different from dicots.

AGE OF HERBALISTS

Two major events increased the interest in plants and made more plants available to a wider audience. The first event in 1440 was the invention of printing and movable type. One of the earliest books to be printed was Pliny's *Historia naturalis*. Botanical discourses were cheap and easily obtained, and available to a wider audience of lower economic status. Especially popular were "Herbals" written by physicians interested in medicinal and agricultural plants. These books often had less than 1000 plants and provided descriptions to "diggers" who used the books to gathered the herbs sold to physicians and pharmacies. This "Age of Herbalists"led to a revival in the interest of plants from 1500-1580.

Otto Brunfels (1464–1534) was a German monk, schoolmaster, theologian and minister of Swiss lineage. His *Herbarum vivae Eicoones* described 700 plants, but was the first illustrated with woodcut engravings of high quality. Also, he was the first to distinguish between perfect versus imperfect flowers.

Jerome Boch (1489–1554) was a German writing under the Greek name of Hieronymus Tragus. His book *Neu Kreuterbuck* provided detailed descriptions based upon personal observation. Also, he included habitat and locality data for plants. This practice is utilized today as taxonomists collecting plant voucher specimens, will include habitat data and location collected on the label data.

Valerius Cordus (1515–1544) was dead when his *Historica Plaantarum* was published in 1561. His descriptions included details of flowers and fruits. The 446 plants were arranged in a more systematic format. **Leonhard Fuchs** (1501–1566) was a better documented herbalist in his book *De historia stiprium* with elaborated illustrations and descriptions.

AGE OF DESCRIPTION AND CLASSIFICATION

The second major event was the development of the science of Navigation in the 1600's. This led to aggressive exploration by the British, Dutch, French, Germans and Italians. Plants from Africa, China, India, Indonesia, Japan and the New World were brought back to Europe for naming and classification. Many authors had their own herbarium (library of dried plant vouchers specimens) from which they described the plants. Plant names were descriptive polnominals, and these increased exponentially. The bulging number of names and different characters utilized in the names provided problems in comparing plants between books. A need was growing for a formalized scheme of plant classification.

Andre Cesalpino (1519–1603) was an Italian botanist influenced by Aristotle's reasoning and logic. He concluded that some plant structures were more important than others. His book *De plantas libri* described 1520 plants, using fruits as the primary means of plant identification. His treatise greatly influence later botanists, Ray, Tournefort and Linnaeus.

Caspar Bauuhin (1560–1624) described 6000 plants. He was the first to recognize the concept of the genus and species. His names were descriptive polynominals, yet utilized a limited number of binominal names. He was the first to use synonomy, listing the names used by other botanists. Synonymy (alternative names) made it easy to compare treatments in different books.

John Ray, originally Wray (1627–1705) was a British naturalist, biologist and philosopher. He provided the first modern classification of animals (fishes, insects, mammals), geology and fossils, and the first British flora, an inventory of plants in the United Kingdom. He provided the greatest advancement in theoretical botany, and is regarded by some as the Father of Plant Physiology. His *Methodus Plantarum nova* described 18,000 species, included many non-European plants, and provided a four-tier hierarchal system of classification. The hierarchal system was Division (woody versus herbs), Subdivision (monocots versus dicots), Class (fruit types), Subclass (flower & leaf characters). Although criteria is different today, this was the beginning of a hierarchal scheme of classification, and regarded as the beginning of natural classification. **Pierre Magnol** (1638–1715) provided the first concept of modern families in his *Prodromus historiae generalis*.

Joseph Pitton de Tournefort (1656–1708) was a French botanists known as the "genus man". He describe 700 genera with 9000 species in his *Institutione rei herbariae*. The genus was the fundamental category of classification, base upon floral characters. Genera are artificial in modern concepts, having placed many non-related species together in the same genus. Genera were grouped into classes. Plant names included a large number of binominals, but inconsistently used along with polynominals.

THE LINNEAN ERA

Carl von Linné = Linnaeus (1707–1778) was the Swedish son of a Lutheran pastor and gardener. He studied pre-med under Professor Rudbeck, the physician to George Clifford, a wealthy banker interested in botany and horticulture. Linnaeus practice medicine while pursuing his true love with several plant expeditions. He lectured at the prestigious University of Upsalla, and was awarded a professorship in 1741. He restored the university's botanical garden, made plant expeditions, and inspi Included were Carl Thunberg (Japan), Daniel Solander (Cook's 1st world voyage), Andeds Sparrman (Cook's 2nd world voyage), and Pehr Kalm (NE American colonies). Linnaeus published 148 books, several financed by Clifford. His religious background influence his taxonomic philosophy, that the study of nature would reveal the Divine Order of God's creation, and it was the naturalist's task to construct a "natural classification" that would reveal this Order in the universe. In *Species plantarum*, his classification was based entirely upon the number and arrangement of the reproductive organs. A plant's class was determined by its stamens and its order by its pistils. This classification was controversial in its day, produced some unnatural grouping, but was easy to learn and use. A focus of prior authors was to replace past nomenclature with your own. Linnaeus won this competition.

Linnaeus made several taxonomic contributions with *Species plantarum* published on May 1, 1753. His classification scheme provided the first set of taxonomic keys, as one could identify unknown plant by counting the number of reproductive organs and noting their arrangement. He was the first to consistently use binominals, following Bauhin's concept of genus and species. He was the first to recognize varieties (by using Greek letters), natural populations within a species that bear a few distinctive traits different from typical species members. He segregated the name from the diagnosis (descriptive phrase of key character traits). For each species, Linnaeus included synonymy and abbreviated references to prior publications. He included the species nativity region. Using Latin, instead of his native Swedish, made his book immediately usable throughout Europe. Many botanists began adopting Linnaeus' nomenclature as the classification scheme was easy to use, and binominal names easier to remember. For his contributions, he is often called the Father of Taxonomy.

Michael Adanson (1727–1806) was a French naturalist of tropical Africa who rejected Linnaeus' philosophy. He rejected the idea of character weighing, that some characters such as reproductive organs were more valuable than others, such as vegetative traits. Taxonomists generally did not accept the Adansonian philosophy. However, recently numerical taxonomists were advocates of Adanson in preparing databases for computers (non biased by man) to delineate relationships. But, unacceptable results have led currently to character weighing by taxonomists entering data.

Jean Bergeret (1751–1813) was a French botanist who proposed a 15-letter uninomial system. Each letter would express a descriptive character. Thus *Belladona* (currently *Atropa belladona*) would be *Ieglyabiajisbey*. This was regarded as the worst possible system of nomenclature. However, it has been proposed that all plant names be reduced to a 7-letter acronym, easily used in computer databases. Four letters taken from the genus, three from the species. For example, CLITARB would be the name for *Clitoria arborescens*. However, this acronym also would fit *Clitoria arborea*. *Acer saccharum* and *Acer saccharinum* would be ACERSAC. It was not adopted. Then, a proposal for a 12-letter uninominal acronym has gathered little support.

Louis-Marie Aubert du Petit-Thouars (1793–1864) was a French botanist who specialized in orchids of the French islands of Bourbon (currently Reunion) and Madagascar (currently Mauritius). He proposed that generic names included a portion of the family name. Thus, the orchid genus *Habenaria* would become *Habenorchis*. It was not accepted. Today, paleobotanists find fossil nomenclature troublesome by mixing generic nomenclature with morphology.

Jean B.A.P.M. de Lamarck (1744–1829) was a French biologist who wrote the *Flora Francoise*. He made two important contributions. His flora included synoptic artifical keys for plant segregation and identification. Second, he introduced principles of natural system classification with a set of rules for natural grouping of species, and rules for treating families and orders.

Antoine-Laurent de Jussieu (1748–1836) was French and the nephew of three Jussieu botanists. He founded the Musee d'Historie Naturalelle de Paris. His *Genera plantarum* published 4 Aug 1789 resulted from his arrangement of the Versailles' garden in the Linnaean system. He arranged the genera into families, of which over 100 families are intact today and were described accurately.

Augustin Pyramus de Candolle (1778–1841) was a French educated Swiss. His *Prodromus systematis naturalis regni vegetabilis* (1816–1873) expanded the Jussieu system and demonstrated the inadequacy of the Linnean system. His objective was to describe and classify every known vascular plant. Seven volumes were produced before his death, ten by his son afterwards.

Charles Darwin (1809–1882) published the controversial *Origin of species*. He concluded that species are dynamic, viable population systems which change with time to form lineages of closely related organisms. This has led taxonomists to pursue a phylogenetic system of classification, from more primitive plants to more advance ones.

ERA OF INTERNATIONAL RULES

In 1843, an international zoological congress adopted a Zoological Code of Nomenclature. It emphasized priority, giving credit to the discoverer of the unknown **taxon** (general term to indicate any position at any rank). Also, scientific binominals would include an author citation, and rules for new combinations resulting from transfer.

Alphonse Louis Pyramus de Candolle (1806–1893) was a Swiss botanist and Augustin's son. He organized an international botanic congress in Paris in 1867. This was the first effort at standardization and legislation of taxonomic practices, with six principles. The objective was to put the past in order and provide for a stable future. Adoption resulted in the publication of the *Lois de la nomenclautre botanique*. **Priority** was the fundamental principle, and rules maintained usage of Linnaeus by principle of priority with some modification. Modern plant nomenclature would begin with Linnaeus. However, they did not designate a work nor a date, creating problems later. Plant nomenclature was **independent** of the Zoological Code. It established rules for valid (follows rules) and effective (accessible distribution) **publication**. **Latin** is used for scientific names regardless of their derivation. There is only one **correct name** for a taxon circumscribed at a rank, and rules were established for its determination and synonyms (rejected names). Plant categories (the hierarchal classification scheme) were established. Division was used, whereas zoologists used "phylum". Rules of nomenclature are **retroactive,** unless expressly limited. Also, examples were provided for fuller understanding of the rules. Author citation was adopted, with rules on name transfers. This is the most common author citation found in names today, the original author found in parenthesis followed by the author who transferred the name to the correct taxon. An example is *Centrosema virginianum* (L.) Benth., originally described as *Clitoria virginiana* by Linnaeus, but transfered to *Centrosema* by George Bentham.

George Bentham (1800–1884), a British botanist, and **Sir Joseph Hooker** (1817–1911), British director of Kew Botanic Gardens, published *General plantarum,* a 3-volume treatist describing all known seed plants. They were the first to recognize gymnosperms from angiosperms, and to recognized subgenera and sections.

Benjamin Dayton Jackson (1846–1927) was a British botanist and original compiler and editor of *Index Kewensis* (1895–present), a multivolume index enumerating all genera and species names of flowering plants published from the time of Linnaeus onward. He interpreted priority as the first species epithet published in the correct genus, not the earliest published name. This interpretation became designated as the **Kew Rule.**

Otto Kuntze (1843–1907) selected in his *Revisio* in 1891, Linnaeus' *Genera Plantarum* published in 1737 as the starting point for scientific names. This resulted in the replacement of 1074 generic names and transfer of over 30,000 species names, greatly upsetting nomenclatural stability.

North American botanists held a meeting in Rochester, New York, to discuss problems arising from the Paris Code of 1867. Leading the conference were **Asa Gray** (1810–1888), the Harvard University botanist, and **Nathanial Lord Britton** (1859–1934), botanist and founder of the New York Botanical Garden. The Rochester Code adopted the fundamental rules of the Paris Code. It selected Linnaeus' *Species Plantarum* as the starting point for scientific names of vascular plants. It introduce the principle of the **type** concept and rules relating to type. The nomenclatural type is an element to which the name is permanently attached, typically an herbarium voucher specimen. In cases of controversy or difficultly in interpretation of literature, the type can be examined to determine the circumscription of the name. Strict adherence to priority was adopted, not the Kew Rule interpretation. This created division amongst Americans as Gray and his supporters followed the Kew Rule in practice.

The **2nd Botanical Congress** (Vienna, 1905) adopted the 1867 rules and established Linnaeus' *Species Plantarum* (May 1, 1753) as the starting date for flowering plants. French was the official language, but a Latin diagnosis was required for new names. It established the conservation of generic names, exception to the rule of priority for obscure earlier generic names discovered in literature, or resulting from taxonomic judgement redefining a genus circumscription.

The **5th Botanic Congress** (Cambridge, 1930) promoted international stability with compromise amongst factions. It established the *International Code of Botanic Nomenclature* (ICBN), and its basic organization. Use of types were adopted in determination of the application of names. The **6th Botanic Congress** (Amsterdam, 1935) replaced French with English as the official language. The **7th Botanic Congress** (Stockholm, 1950) designated six type categories and suffixes for higher taxa (Table 1). Eight family names were conserved, lacking the suffixes (Table 3). It established *Taxon* and *Regum Vegetabile* as theofficial journals of the International Association of Plant Taxonomists. *Taxon* is the vehicle for proposed rule changes and rebuttal by peers. *Regum Vegetabile* is published irregularly, compiling a series of handbooks used by taxonomists and plant geographers.

The **15th Botanic Congress** (Tokyo, 1993) reorganized the ICBN arrangement, adopted "Phylum" in place of "Division", and clarified several rules concerning author citation and types. In addition, it established conservation of species names as an exception to priority, used for species of economic importance and rejection of a name that would cause a disadvantageous nomenclatural change when adopted. The **16th Botanic Congress** (St. Louis, 1999) standarized author citations with adoption of *Authors of plant names* by Brummit & Powell (1992), clarification of rules regarding types, and profound changes in fossil plant nomenclature.

TABLE 1 Type Categories for Plant Names. Types are based upon who is the author of the plant name and who designates the type.

A. The original author or a name designates the type specimen

Holotype.	One specimen or illustration used by the author or designated by him as the nomenclatural type. Currently, the author must cite herbarium of deposit.
Isotype.	Any duplicate of the holotype; always a specimen.
Paratype.	One or more specimens cited by the original author but not designated as the holotype or isotype.

B. The original author does not designate a type, but cites one or more voucher collections.

Syntype.	Any one of two or more specimens cited by the author in the protologue when no holotype was designated, or any one of two or more specimens simultaneously designated as types.

C. Type specimen designated by a later author, not the original author of a name.

Lectotype.	A specimen or illustration selected by a subsequent author from the original material to serve as the nomenclatural type when no holotype was indicated at the time of publication of the name, or when the holotype is missing, or when holotype belongs to more than one taxon. [Most common type as historical authors didn't designate types].
Neotype	A specimen or illustration selected to serve as nomenclatural type providing that all material on which the name of the taxon was based is missing.

TABLE 2 Plant Hierarchical Classification. Hierarchical ranks are descending. Suffixes cited are added to a genus in forming rank category name.

Rank	Suffix	Example - Maryland Butterfly Pea
Kingdom	-ae	Plantae
Phylum (Division)	-phyta	Magnoliop hyta [= angiosperms]
Subphylum (Subdivision)	-phytina	Magnoliophytina
Class	-opsida	Magnoliop sida [= dicots]
Subclass	-idae	Rosidae
Order	-ales	Fabales
Suborder	-ineae	Fabineae
Family	-aceae	Fabaceae [or Leguminosae]
Subfamily	-oideae	Papilionoideae
Tribe	-eae	Phaseoleae
Subtribe	-ineae	Clitoriineae
Genus–Intergeneric Hybrid		*Clitoria*
Subgenus		*Clitoria* subg. *Neurocarpum*
Section		*Clitoria* sect. *Neurocarpum*
Series		*Clitoria* ser. *Americana*

(Continued)

TABLE 2 *Continued*

Rank	Suffix	Example - Maryland butterfly pea
Species–Intrageneric Hybrid		*Clitoria mariana*
Subspecies		
Variety		*Clitoria mariana* var. *mariana*
Cultivar Group		
Forma–Cultivar		*Clitoria mariana* 'Mexicana'

TABLE 3 Conserved Plant Family Names. Plant family names that are exceptions to the suffix -aceae for family names through longtime usage, as specified in the ICBN Art. 18.5. The modern trend is to use the newer name.

Conserved name	Newer name	Vernacular name
Compositae	Asteraceae	sunflower family
Cruciferae	Brassicaceae	mustard family
Gramineae	Poaceae	grass family
Guttiferae	Clusiaceae	St. John's wort family
Labiatae	Lamiaceae	mint family
Leguminosae	Fabaceae	legume family
Palmae	Arecaceae	palm family
Umbelliferae	Apiaceae	carrot family

CULTIVATED PLANT NOMENCLATURE

In the twentieth century, a need developed for a precise, stable, internationally accepted set of rules for naming plants in cultivation. An International Commission for Horticultural Nomenclature and Registration met in London in 1952. Agricultural and silver cultural faculty were added. They produced the first Code published in 1953. The *International Code of Nomenclature for Cultivated Plants* (ICNCP) supplements the ICBN, not supplant it. Plants in cultivation take the same name as plants in the wild. The cultivar (derived from **culti**vated **var**iety) is the basic taxon of cultivated plants. Registration of cultivar names with an international registration authority was considered as of greatest importance.

The ICNCP is in its 8th edition. It establishes rules for naming cultivars and cultivar groups, intergeneric and intrageneric hybrids, graph-chimaeras, and hybrids of multiple parentage. Cultivar names published after 1 January 1935 require a fancy name, not a Latinized name as in the past. An appendix cites recognized registration authorities for different genera.

ADDITIONAL READINGS

Fantz, P.R. 1991. Ethnobotany of *Clitoria* (Leguminosae). Economic Botany 45:511-520.`

2.3 OTHER CLASSIFICATION SYSTEMS (OPERATIONAL)

A number of operational classification systems are employed simultaneously in the field of horticulture. The following are some of the major systems.

2.3.1 SEASONAL GROWTH CYCLE

Plants may be classified into four general groups based on growth cycle (Figure 2–3). Growth cycle refers to the period from first establishment (e.g., by seed) to when the plant dies. The four categories are as follows:

1. Annuals. An **annual** plant lives through only one growing season, completing its life cycle (seed, seedling, flowering, fruiting, and death) in that period. This group includes many weeds, garden flowers, vegetables, and wild flowers. The duration of a life cycle is variable and may be a few weeks to several months, depending on the species. Annuals are the basis of a major horticultural production group called annual bedding plants. These plants are produced largely for use in the landscape and also the vegetable garden. Popular annual flowers are geranium (*Geranium* spp.), zinnia *(Zinnia elegans),* marigold (*Tagetes* spp.), and pansy *(Viola tricolor).* In cultivation, certain vegetables such as tomato *(Lycopersicon esculentum)* are produced on an annual cycle.

2. Biennials. A **biennial** is a plant that completes its life cycle in two growing seasons. In the first season, it produces only basal leaves; it grows a stem, produces flowers and fruits, and dies in the second season. The plant usually requires some special environmental condition or treatment such as exposure to a cold temperature (*vernalization*) to be induced to enter the reproductive phase. Examples of biennials are sugar beet *(Beta vulgaris)* and onion *(Allium cepa).* Even though annuals and biennials rarely become woody in temperate regions, these plants may sometimes produce secondary growth in their stems and roots.

3. Perennials. **Perennials** may be herbaceous or woody. They persist year-round through the adverse weather of the nongrowing seasons (winter or drought) and then flower and fruit after a variable number of years of vegetative growth beyond the second year. Herbaceous perennials survive the unfavorable season as dormant underground structures (e.g., roots, rhizomes, bulbs, and tubers) that are modified primary vegetative parts of the plant. Examples of

Annual
A plant that completes its life cycle in one growing season or one year.

Biennial
A plant that completes its life cycle in two cropping seasons, the first involving vegetative growth and the second flowering and death.

Perennial
A plant that grows year after year without replanting.

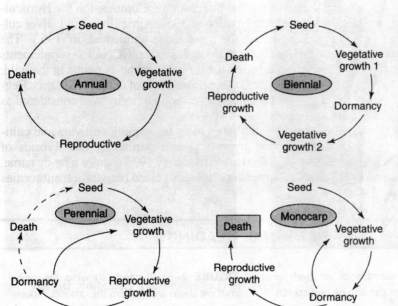

FIGURE 2–3 Classification of flowering plants according to the duration of their growth cycle from seed to seed. Variations occur within each category, even for the same species, due in part to the activities of plant breeders.

herbaceous perennials are turfgrasses such as Bermuda grass *(Cynodon dactylon)* and flowers such as daylilies (*Lilium* spp.) and irises (*Iris* spp.).

Woody perennials may be vines, shrubs, or trees. These plants do not die back in adverse seasons but usually suspend active growth. Although some perennials may flower in the first year of planting, woody perennials flower only when they become adult plants. This stage may be attained within a few years or even after 100 years. Woody perennials may be categorized into two types:

a. *Evergreen.* Evergreen perennials maintain green leaves year-round. Some leaves may be lost, but not all at one time. Examples of evergreen perennials are citrus (*Citrus* spp.) and pine (*Pinus* spp.).

b. *Deciduous.* Deciduous plants shed their leaves at the same time during one of the seasons of the year (dry, cold). New leaves are developed from dormant buds upon the return of favorable growing conditions. Examples of deciduous perennials are oak (*Quercus* spp.) and elm (*Ulmus* spp.). It should be mentioned that intermediate conditions occur in which some plants do not lose all of their leaves *(semideciduous).*

4. Monocarp. **Monocarps** are characterized by repeated, long vegetative cycles that may go on for many years without entering the reproductive phase. Once flowering occurs, the plant dies. A well-known example is the century plant (*Agave* spp.). More common examples are the bromeliads. When these plants bloom, the top parts die, and new plants arise from the root system of the old plant.

Monocarp
A plant (e.g., bromeliad, century plant) that lives for many years but flowers only once in a lifetime and then dies, new plants arise on the roots of the old plant.

2.3.2 KINDS OF STEMS

There are three general classes of horticultural plants based on stem type. However, intermediates do occur between these classes.

1. *Herbs.* Herbs are plants with soft, nonwoody stems (Figure 2–4). They have primary vegetative parts. Examples include corn *(Zea mays),* many potted plants, many annual bedding plants, and many vegetables. In another usage, the term *herbs* is associated with spices (plants that are aromatic or fragrant and used to flavor foods or beverages).

FIGURE 2–4 An example of an herb or herbaceous plant. Stems can also be herbaceous.
(Source: George Acquaah)

FIGURE 2–5 A shrub showing the typical multiple stems arising from the ground.   *(Source: George Acquaah)*

2. *Shrubs*. A shrub has no main trunk. Branches arise from the ground level on a shrub (Figure 2–5). It is woody and has secondary tissue. Shrubs are perennials and usually smaller than trees. Examples of shrubs are dogwood (*Cornus* spp.), kalmia (*Kalmia* spp.), and azalea (*Rhododendron* spp.).

3. *Trees*. Trees are large plants characterized by one main trunk (Figure 2–6). They branch on the upper part of the plant, are woody, and have secondary tissue. Examples include pine (*Pinus* spp.), oak (*Quercus* spp.), cedar (*Cedrus* spp.), and orange *(Citrus sinensis).*

2.3.3 COMMON STEM GROWTH FORMS

The criterion for classification is how the stem stands in relation to the ground (Figure 2–7). There are several types of stem growth forms, the most common ones including the following:

1. *Erect*. A stem is erect if, without artificial support, it stands upright (stands at a 90-degree angle to the ground level). Because of the effect of strong winds and other environmental factors, an erect plant may incline slightly. Trees have erect stems. To adapt crop plants to mechanized harvesting, plant breeders have developed what are called "bush" cultivars. These plants have strong stems and stiff branches.

2. *Decumbent*. The stems of decumbent plants are extremely inclined, with the tips raised. An example is the peanut *(Arachis hypogaea).*

3. *Creeping (or repent)*. A plant is described as creeping when it crawls on the ground, producing adventitious roots at specific points on the stem. Stems that grow horizontally in this fashion are called *stolons*. The strawberry plant (*Fragaria* spp.) has creeping stems.

4. *Climbing*. Climbers are vines that, without additional support, will creep on the ground. There are three general modes of climbing (Figure 2–8). *Twiners* are

FIGURE 2–6 A typical tree showing a well-defined, woody central axis. Certain species produce or can be manipulated to produce several stems. *(Source: George Acquaah)*

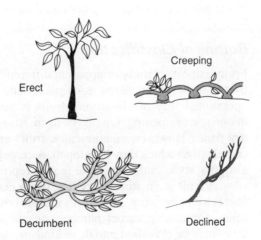

FIGURE 2–7 Examples of the variations in the direction or method of stem growth.

(a)

(b)

FIGURE 2–8 A climbing plant. To climb, such plants have various structural adaptations for holding onto physical support nearby, such as a (a) stake or a (b) wall. *(Source: George Acquaah)*

climbing plants that simply wrap their stringy stems around their support, as occurs in sweet potato *(Ipomea batatas)*. Another group of climbers develop cylindrical structures called *tendrils* that are used to coil around the support on physical contact. An example of a plant that climbs by this method is the garden pea *(Pisum sativum)*. The third mode of climbing is by *adventitious roots* formed on aerial parts of the plant, as found in the English ivy *(Hedera helix)* and *Philodendron*.

2.3.4 CLASSIFICATION OF FRUITS

Fruits can be classified on a botanical basis and for several operational purposes.

Botanical Classification

Fruits exhibit a variety of apparent differences that may be used for classification. Some fruits are borne on herbaceous plants and others on woody plants. A very common operational way of classifying fruits is according to fruit succulence and texture on maturity and ripening. On this basis there are two basic kinds of fruits—*fleshy fruits* and *dry fruits*. However, anatomically, fruits are distinguished by the arrangement of the carpels from which they developed. A carpel is sometimes called the *pistil* (consisting of a stigma, style, and ovary), the female reproductive structure.

    A **fruit** is a mature ovary. The ovary may have one or more carpels. Even though the fruit is a mature ovary, some fruits include other parts of the flower and are called *accessory fruits*. Combining carpel number, succulence characteristics, and anatomical features, fruits may be classified into three kinds, *simple, multiple,* or *aggregate* (Figure 2–9).

    Simple fruits develop from a single carpel or sometimes from the fusing together of several carpels. This group of fruits is very diverse. When mature and ripe, the fruit may be soft and fleshy, dry and woody, or have a papery texture. There are three types of fleshy fruits.

Fruit
A mature ovary.

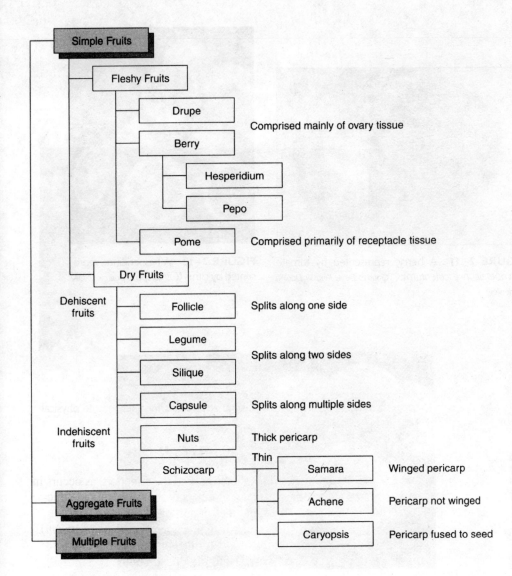

FIGURE 2–9 A classification of fruits.

FIGURE 2–10 A drupe, represented by nectarine (*Persica* spp.). (*Source:* Philip Dowell © Dorling Kindersley)

1. *Fleshy fruits.*

    a. *Drupe.* A drupe may comprise one to several carpels. Usually, each carpel contains one seed. The endocarp (inner layer) of the fruit is hard and stony and is usually highly attached to the seed (Figure 2–10). Examples are cherry (*Prunus* spp.), olive, coconut *(Cocos nucifera),* peach *(Prunus persica),* and plum *(Prunus domestica).*

    b. *Berry.* A berry is a fruit characterized by an inner pulp that contains a few to several seeds but not pits. It is formed from one or several carpels. Examples are tomato (*Lycopersicon esculentum*), grape (*Vitis* spp.), and pepper (*Capsicum anuum*) (Figure 2–11). If the exocarp (skin) is leathery and contains oils, as in the citrus fruits (e.g., orange [*Citrus sinensis*], lemon [*Citrus lemon*], and grapefruit [*Citrus paradisi*]), the berry is called a *hesperidium* (Figure 2–12). Some berries have a thick rind, as in watermelon (*Citrullus vulgaris*), cucumber (*Cucumis sativus*), muskmelon (*Cucumis melo*), and pumpkin (*Cucurbita pepo*) (Figure 2–13). This type of a berry is called a *pepo.*

    c. *Pome.* A pome is a pitted fruit with a stony interior. The pit usually contains one seed chamber and one seed. This very specialized fruit type develops from the ovary, with most of the fleshy part formed from the receptacle tissue (the enlarged base of the perianth) (Figure 2–14). Pomes are

FIGURE 2–11 A berry, represented by tomato (*Lycopersicon esculentum*): *(Source: Dave King © Dorling Kindersley)*

FIGURE 2–12 A hesperidium, represented by citrus (*Citrus* spp.). *(Source: USDA)*

FIGURE 2–13 A pepo, represented by muskmelon. *(Source: USDA)*

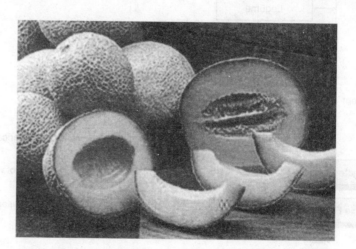

characteristic of one subfamily of the family Rosaceae (rose family). Examples of pomes are apple (*Pyrus malus*), pear (*Pyrus communis*), and quince (*Cydonia oblonga*).

2. *Dry fruits.* Dry fruits are not juicy or succulent when mature and ripe. When dry, they may split open and discharge their seeds (called *dehiscent fruits*) or retain their seeds (called *indehiscent fruits*).

   a. *Dehiscent fruits.* A fruit developed from a single carpel may split from only one side at maturity to discharge its seeds. Such a fruit is called a *follicle.* Examples are columbine (*Aquilegia* spp.), milkweed (*Asclepias* spp.), larkspur (*Delphinium* spp.), and magnolia (*Magnolia* spp.). Sometimes, the splitting of the ovary occurs along two seams, with seeds borne on only one of the halves of the split ovary. Such a fruit is called a legume (Figure 2–15), examples being pea *(Pisum sativum),* bean *(Phaseolus vulgaris),* and peanut *(Arachis hypogaea).* In a third type of dehiscent fruit, called *silique* or *silicle,* seeds are attached to a central structure, as occurs in radish *(Raphanus sativus)* and mustard *(Brassica campestris)* (Figure 2–16). The most common dehiscent simple fruit is the capsule, which develops from a compound ovary. In some species, seeds are discharged when the capsule splits longitudinally.

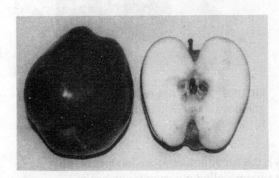

FIGURE 2–14 A pome, represented by apple (*Pyrus malus.*) *(Source: George Acquaah)*

FIGURE 2–15 A legume or pod, represented by garden bean (*Phaseolus vulgaris*). *(Source: George Acquaah)*

FIGURE 2–16 A silique and a capsule.

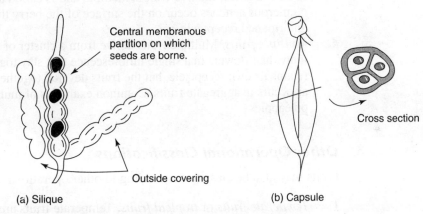

Central membranous partition on which seeds are borne.

Outside covering

Cross section

(a) Silique

(b) Capsule

In others, seeds exit through holes near the top of the capsule, such as in lily (*Lilium* spp.), iris (*Iris* spp.), and poppy (*Papaver* spp.).

b. *Indehiscent fruits.* Some indehiscent fruits may have a hard *pericarp* (exocarp + mesocarp + endocarp). This stony fruit wall is cracked in order to reach the seed. Such fruits are called *nuts,* as found in chestnut (*Castanea* spp.), hazelnut (*Corylus* spp.), and pecan *(Carya illinoensis)* (Figure 2–17). Nuts develop from a compound ovary. Sometimes the pericarp of the fruit is thin and the ovaries occur in pairs, as found in dill *(Anethum graveolens)* and carrot *(Daucus carota).* This fruit type is called a *schizocarp.* In maple (*Acer* spp.), ash (*Fraxinus* spp.), elm (*Ulmus* spp.), and other species, the pericarp has a wing and is called a *samara.* Where the pericarp is not winged but the single seed is attached to the pericarp only at its base, the fruit is called an *achene.* Achenes are the most common indehiscent fruits. Examples are the buttercup family (Ranuculaceae) and sunflower. In cereal

FIGURE 2–17 A nut, represented by pecan (*Carya illinoensis*). (*Source: David Murray © Dorling Kindersley*)

FIGURE 2–18 Aggregate fruit, represented by strawberry. (*Source: Lan O' Leary © Dorling Kindersley*)

grains (Poaceae or grass family), the seed, unlike in an achene, is fully fused to the pericarp. This fruit type is called a *caryopsis* or *grain*.

3. *Aggregate fruits.* An aggregate fruit is derived from a single flower with several to many pistils. The individual pistils develop into a cluster of tiny fruitlets or drupes, instead of independent units, but remain on a single receptacle. Species that produce this kind of fruit include strawberries, raspberries, and blackberries. In strawberries, the true fruit is inedible and is called an *achene* (Figure 2–18). Numerous achenes occur on the surface of the berry that consists of an enlarged and ripened receptacle.

4. *Multiple fruits.* Multiple fruits derive from a cluster of several to many individual flowers in a single inflorescence that stay together. Each flower retains its own receptacle, but the fruits develop together into a single larger fruit, as occurs in aggregate fruits. Common examples of multiple fruits include figs and pineapples.

Other Operational Classifications

Fruits may also be classified according to other operational uses.

1. *Temperate fruits* or *tropical fruits.* Temperate fruits are fruits from plants adapted to cool climates, and tropical fruits are produced on plants adapted to warm climates. For example, apple *(Pyrus malus)*, peach *(Prunus persica)*, and plum *(Prunus domestica)* are temperate fruits, whereas mango *(Mangifera indica)* and coconut *(Cocos nucifera)* are tropical fruits.

2. *Fruit trees.* Tree fruits are fruits borne on trees, such as apple *(Pyrus malus)* and mango *(Mangifera indica)*.

3. *Small fruits.* Small fruits are predominantly woody, perennial, dicot angiosperms. They are usually vegetatively propagated and bear small- to moderate-sized fruits on herbs, vines, or shrubs. Examples are grape *(Vitis* spp.), strawberry *(Fragaria* spp.), and blackberry *(Rubus* spp.). Small fruits require training and pruning (removal of parts of the shoot) to control growth and remove old canes (branches) to obtain desired plant shape and high productivity.

4. *Bramble fruits.* Bramble fruits are nontree fruits that usually require physical support (such as a trellis) during cultivation. Examples are raspberry *(Rubus* spp.), blackberry *(Rubus* spp.), and boysenberry *(Rubus* spp.). Bramble fruits also require training and pruning in cultivation.

2.3.5 CLASSIFICATION OF VEGETABLES

Vegetables may be classified on the basis of life cycle, edible or economic parts of the plant (use), adaptation, and botanical features.

1. *Life cycle.* Based on life cycle, vegetables may be classified as annuals, biennials, or perennials.

   a. *Annual.* Most vegetable garden crops are true annuals, such as corn *(Zea mays)*, or are cultivated as annuals, such as tomato *(Lycopersicon esculentum)*. These plants are selected for either fall or summer gardening. They require a few weeks to several months to matur, depending on the cultivar.

   b. *Biennial.* Few popular vegetable garden crops are biennials, and, even then, they are frequently cultivated as annuals and replanted each season. Examples are sugar beet *(Beta vulgaris)* and carrot *(Daucus carota)*.

   c. *Perennial.* Whenever perennial vegetable garden crops are cultivated, they must be strategically located so as not to interfere with seasonal land preparation activities needed for planting annual crops. These plants may be pruned to control growth or to remove dead tissue. Examples are asparagus *(Asparagus officinalis)* and horseradish *(Rorippa armoracia)*.

2. *Edible or economic parts.* Vegetables may be operationally classified according to the parts of the plant harvested for food or other uses.

   a. *Pods.* Pods are legumes that are harvested prematurely, cooked, and eaten with the seeds inside. When harvesting is delayed, pods develop fiber and become stringy and undesirable for fresh use. Examples are green bean and okra (see Figure 2–15).

   b. *Roots.* Sometimes primary plant parts (stem, root, and leaf) may become modified as storage organs for food. Roots may become enlarged as a result of the accumulation of stored food (Figure 2–19). The roots are dug and eaten baked, boiled, or fried. An example is the sweet potato.

   c. *Bulbs.* Like roots, bulbs are modified stems and leaves, as found in onions (Figure 2–20). The stem is highly compressed to form what is called a *basal plate,* while the leaves are storage organs.

FIGURE 2–19 A root, represented by sugar beet *(Beta vulgaris).* *(Source: George Acquaah)*

(a)

(b)

FIGURE 2–20 A bulb, represented by onion *(Allium cepa)*: (a) whole bulb and (b) vertical cross section. *(Source: George Acquaah)*

FIGURE 2–21 A tuber, represented by Irish potato (*Solanum tuberosum*).

(Source: George Acquaah)

Cool-season Plant
A plant that grows best at daytime temperatures of between 15° to 18°C (60° to 65°F).

Warm-season Plant
A plant that grows best at daytime temperatures of between 18° to 27°C (65° to 81°F).

    d. *Tubers.* Tubers look like modified roots. The difference between them is that tubers are swollen stems, whereas roots are swollen roots (Figure 2–21).

    e. *Greens.* Greens are vegetable crops whose leaves are usually picked at tender stages to be used for food. The leaves are generally cooked before being eaten.

3. *Adaptation.* Just like fruits, certain vegetable species prefer cool temperatures during production, and others prefer warm temperatures. Based on seasons in which they grow best, vegetables may be classified into two groupings.

    a. *Cool season.* **Cool-season** crops require monthly temperatures of 15 to 18°C (60 to 65°F). Examples are sugar beet *(Beta vulgaris)* and cabbage *(Brassica oleracea).*

    b. *Warm season.* **Warm-season** crops prefer monthly temperatures of 18 to 27°C (65 to 81°F). Examples are okra *(Hibiscus esculentus),* eggplant *(Solanum melongena),* corn *(Zea mays),* and shallot *(Allium cepa).* It should be mentioned that plant breeders have developed cultivars with wide adaptation for many crop species. For example, popular garden crops including corn, tomato, and pepper are grown over a wide range of climates. Even though cultivars with cold or heat tolerance may have been bred for different crops, commercial large-scale production occurs in regions of best adaptation of these crops, unless production is under a controlled environment (greenhouse).

4. *Botanical features.* Vegetables may be classified according to specific botanical characteristics they share in common.

    a. *Vines.* Vines are plants with stems that need physical support; without it they creep on the ground or climb onto other nearby plants in cultivation. Examples are squash, pumpkin, and cucumber.

    b. *Solanaceous plants.* Solanaceous plants belong to the family Solanaceae. Examples are eggplant, tomato, and pepper.

    c. *Cole crops.* Cole plants belong to the Brassica family. Examples are cabbage, cauliflower, and broccoli *(Brassica oleracea* var. *botrytis)* (Figure 2–22).

2.4 CLASSIFICATION OF ORNAMENTAL PLANTS

Ornamental plants may also be classified based on stem type, growth cycle, leaf form, use, and other characteristics.

(a)

(b)

FIGURE 2–22 Cole crops, represented by (a) broccoli (*Brassica oleracea* var. *botrytis*) and (b) cabbage (*Brassica oleracea*). (*Source: George Acquaah*)

2.4.1 HERBACEOUS ORNAMENTAL PLANTS

Herbaceous plants are nonwoody. Many horticultural plants, especially those grown indoors, are nonwoody. They have a wide variety of uses in landscapes as well. They may be classified in various ways.

1. *Growth cycle*
   a. *Annuals.* Annual ornamentals are planted each season. Flowering annuals are prominent in the landscape in favorable seasons, providing most of the color (Figure 2–23). Versatile landscape plants can be used to fill in gaps, provide color in bulb beds after the bulbs have bloomed, and create colorful flower beds, hanging baskets (flowers grown in containers and hung), and cut flowers (flowers grown and cut for use). Examples include petunia (*Petunia* spp.), zinnia *(Zinnia elegans),* and marigold (*Tagetes* spp.).
   b. *Biennials.* Biennial ornamentals are vegetative in their first year of growth and bloom in the next season. Examples are foxglove (*Digitalis* spp.) and hollyhock.
   c. *Perennials.* Since perennials live for a long time in the landscape, locating them requires a great deal of thought and planning. Perennials may be flowering or nonflowering.
   d. *Flowering.* Flowering perennials may be planted in flower beds in the fall season to provide early blooms, after which annuals may be planted. Examples are geranium (*Geranium* spp.), lily (*Lilium* spp.), and tulip (*Tulipa* spp.).
   e. *Foliage.* Foliage, or nonflowering, perennials are popular for indoor use in houses and offices as potted plants (Figure 2–24). Examples are coleus *(Coleus blumei),* sansevieria (*Sansevieria* spp.), and dumbcane *(Dieffenbachia).*
2. *Other operational classifications.* Herbaceous plants may be used in a variety of other ways, both indoors and outdoors.
   a. *Bedding plants.* Bedding plants are annual plants raised for planting outdoors in flower beds. They are usually started from seed indoors in the off-season and transplanted later in the growing season. Examples include petunia (*Petunia* spp.), zinnia *(Zinnia elegans),* pansy *(Viola tricolor),* and marigold (*Tagetes* spp.).

FIGURE 2–23 Flats of annual bedding plants. Annual plants provide a tremendous amount of variety in color in the landscape. *(Source: George Acquaah)*

FIGURE 2–24 A foliage plant. Foliage plants are usually green, but certain species have streaks of color or variegation. *(Source: George Acquaah)*

    b. *Hanging plants.* Hanging basket plants are plants, annual or perennial, flowering or foliage, that are grown in decorative containers and hung by equally elegant ropes from the ceiling in the patio, in the doorway area, or from decorative plant poles. Examples are geranium *(Geranium* spp.) and spider plant *(Chlorophytum comosum).*

    c. *Houseplants.* Indoor plants or houseplants, are plants adapted to indoor conditions. They are grown in containers, are usually slow growing, and may be flowering or foliage plants. Examples are sansevieria *(Sansevieria* spp.) and Indian rubber plant *(Ficus elastica).*

2.4.2 WOODY ORNAMENTAL PLANTS

Woody ornamentals differ in size and growth pattern. Some shed their leaves and are called *deciduous,* whereas others maintain fresh leaves year-round and are called *evergreen.* Some are shrubs, and others are trees. Woody ornamentals may be grown in a perennial garden along with herbaceous perennials. When choosing these plants, attention should be paid to growth habit, color, texture, shape, and adaptation.

1. *Shrubs.* As previously described, a shrub is a perennial woody plant of relatively low stature and usually produces multiple stems that arise from the ground or very close to it. Shrubs, which may be used as hedge plants or ground cover, can be classified as deciduous or evergreen.

    a. *Deciduous shrubs.* Deciduous shrubs shed their leaves at some point in the year. Examples are lilac *(Sylinga vulgaris),* honeysuckle *(Lonicera japonica),* and barberry *(Berberis* spp.).

    b. *Evergreen shrubs.* Evergreen shrubs may be further divided into two groups according to leaf size.

Narrowleaf.

Narrowleaf shrubs have needlelike leaves (Figure 2–25), as in pine *(Pinus* spp.) and juniper *(Juniperus* spp.).

Narrowleaf
A group of evergreen plants having needlelike leaves.

FIGURE 2–25   A narrowleaf plant.   *(Source: George Acquaah)*

FIGURE 2–26   A broadleaf plant.
(Source: George Acquaah)

Broadleaf.
  Broadleaf shrubs have large leaf lamina (Figure 2–26), as in gardenia (*Gardenia* spp.) and rhododendron.
2. *Trees.* Trees are the largest plant materials in the landscape and thus should be located with care. They can overwhelm a house in the adult stage if inappropriate tree species are planted. Trees can also modify the local climate (e.g., as shade trees or wind breaks).
  a. *Deciduous trees.* Examples of deciduous trees are birch *(Betula papyrifera),* elm (*Ulmus* spp.), and willow (*Salix* spp.).
  b. *Evergreen trees.*
    Narrowleaf. Examples of narrowleaf evergreen trees are spruce (*Picea* spp.) and red cedar *(Juniperus virginiana).*
    Broadleaf. Examples of broadleaf evergreen trees are holly *(Ilex opaca)* and citrus (*Citrus* spp.).
3. *Vines.* Vines are climbers (Figure 2–27) and can be manipulated to create a variety of structures and for various functions in the landscape. Like trees and shrubs, vines can be deciduous or evergreen.
  a. *Deciduous vines.* An example of a deciduous vine is clematis *(Clematis recta).*
  b. *Evergreen vines.* An example of an evergreen vine is English ivy *(Hedera helix).*

Broadleaf
A group of evergreen plants having a large leaf lamina.

2.4.3   CLASSIFICATION BASED ON HARDINESS (ADAPTATION)

Plants can be classified according to their hardiness or adaptation to local climate. Certain trees are able to thrive under cold temperatures, whereas others prefer warm or tropical conditions. The U.S. Department of Agriculture (USDA) Plant Hardiness Zone map

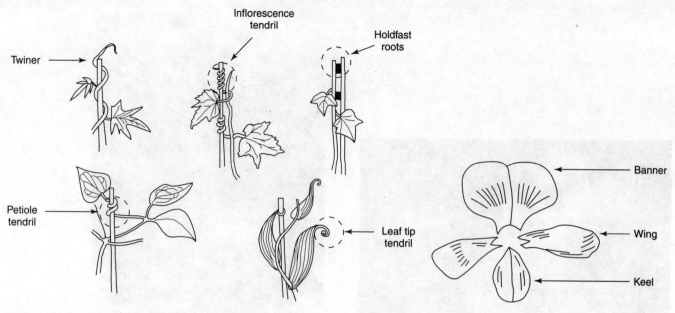

FIGURE 2–27 Twiners. Twining species have a variety of adaptive features for attaching to nearby physical supports. These are modifications of stems, leaves, or roots.

FIGURE 2–28 Petals of a typical legume flower.

divides the United States into ten zones. Zone 1 is the coldest, and zone 10 is the warmest. Plants' adaptive ranges may be narrow or broad. For example, a shrub such as cinquefoil *(Potentilla fruticosa)* is adaptable to zones 2 through 7, and lantana *(Lantana camara* 'Nivea' L.) is adapted to zones 9 and 10. All plants may be placed into one or more of these hardiness zones.

2.5 FLOWERS IN CLASSIFICATION

Flowers are described in detail in Chapter 3. They play a major role in the classification of flowering plants (angiosperms) because flowers have very stable plant parts in different environments.

Flower characteristics may vary within certain families. However, specific flowers are characteristic of certain families. For example, the legume family (Fabaceae) is characterized by an irregular flower with a keel petal, two wing petals, and a banner petal (Figure 2–28). These flowers develop into a fruit, the legume. The grass family (Poaceae) is also characterized by a flower with a spike inflorescence (Figure 2–29). In the nightshade family (Solanaceae), the petals of the flower are fused into a corolla tube with stamens (male flower parts) fused to the corolla (Figure 2–30).

The sunflower family (Asteraceae) has a compact inflorescence in which numerous tiny flowers (florets) are arranged in a manner to resemble a single large flower (Figure 2–31). The spurge family (Euphorbiaceae) has a rather unique inflorescence (Figure 2–32).

2.6 SOME FAMILIES OF HORTICULTURAL IMPORTANCE

The following is a partial listing and brief discussion of important crop families of horticultural interest.

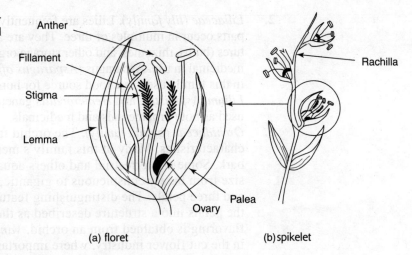

FIGURE 2–29 Parts of a typical grass flower: (a) a floret and (b) a spikelet.

Anther
Fillament
Stigma
Lemma
Palea
Ovary
Rachilla

(a) floret

(b) spikelet

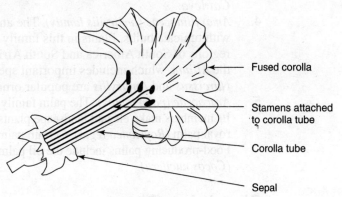

FIGURE 2–30 Fused petals of the family Solanaceae (nightshade family).

Fused corolla
Stamens attached to corolla tube
Corolla tube
Sepal

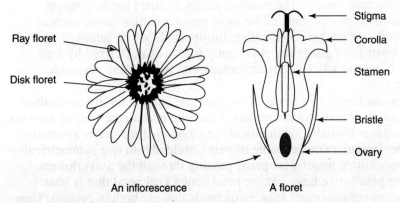

Ray floret
Disk floret
An inflorescence

Stigma
Corolla
Stamen
Bristle
Ovary
A floret

FIGURE 2–31 An inflorescence and single floret of the family Asteraceae (sunflower family).

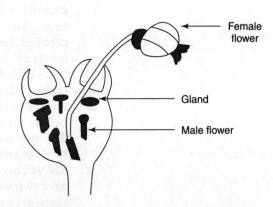

Female flower
Gland
Male flower

FIGURE 2–32 A cyathium of the family Euphorbiaceae (spurge family).

2.6.1 ANGIOSPERMS (FLOWERING PLANTS)

Monocotyledons (Monocots)

1. *Poaceae (grass family)*. In terms of numbers, the grass family is the largest of flowering plants. It is also the most widely distributed. This family includes all of the cereals (e.g., wheat, barley, oats, rice, and corn). In horticulture, most grasses are ornamental and especially noted for their role as lawn material in the landscape. Important grasses include the fescues (*Festuca* spp.) and bluegrass (*Poa* spp.). A popular grass used as a vegetable is sweet corn (*Zea mays*).

2. *Liliaceae (lily family).* Lilies are frequently characterized by large flowers whose parts occur in multiples of three. They are also known by their underground structures (bulbs, rhizomes, and other storage organs). They are mostly ornamental or medicinal in use. Asparagus *(Asparagus officinalis)* is the rare example of a plant in this family used as a food source for humans. Important ornamentals include *Lilium, Aspidistra,* and *Hemerocallis* genera. The *Aloe* genus provides species used as both ornamentals and medicinals.

3. *Orchidaceae (orchid family).* The orchid family is very large, with diverse characteristics. Many of this family's members are epiphytes found on tree bark. Some are terrestrial and others aquatic. The flowers, which can range in size from barely conspicuous to gigantic, are characterized by three sepals and three petals. The distinguishing feature is a unique formation of one of the petals into a structure described as the lip. The widely used vanilla flavoring is obtained from an orchid, *Vanilla planifolia.* Orchids are also used in the cut flower industry, where important genera include *Dendrobium* and *Cattleya.*

4. *Amaryllidaceae (amaryllis family).* The amaryllis family is characterized by plants with tunicate bulbs. Plants in this family are adapted to temperate and warm regions of South America and South Africa. One of the most important genera is the *Allium,* which includes important species such as onion, garlic, and chives. *Narcissus* and *Amaryllis* are popular ornamental genera.

5. *Aracaceae (palm family).* The palm family is tropical and subtropical in adaptation. Its members make elegant landscape plants; the most popular ones include the royal palm *(Roystonea regia).* Certain palms are shrubs that can be grown indoors. Food-producing palms include the oil palm *(Elaeis guineensis)* and the coconut *(Cocos nucifera).*

Dicotyledons (Dicots)

1. *Brassicaceae (mustard family).* The mustard family is noted for its pungent herbs. This family contains some of the most popular garden crops, such as cabbage, brussels sprout, broccoli, radish, turnip, cauliflower, rutabaga, and horseradish. Apart from pungency, this family is also characterized by fruit types called siliques or silicles. Certain ornamental types of the vegetable species occur.

2. *Fabaceae (legume family).* In terms of number, the legume family ranks third behind the sunflower and orchid families. Fabaceae is characterized by flowers that may be *regular* (radially symmetrical) or *irregular* (bilaterally symmetrical) in shape. Irregular (i.e., capable of being divided into two symmetrical halves only by a single lengthwise plane passing through the axis) flowers have two wing petals, one large banner petal, and a keel petal that is boat shaped. Legumes are important sources of foods that are high in protein. They are used in improving the protein quality and quantity of forage for livestock. Important garden legumes include pea, lima bean, garbanzo bean, and mung bean.

3. *Cactaceae (cactus family).* Cacti are native to North and South America. They vary in size from the pinheadlike forms to the giant saguaro forms, which may be as tall as 15 meters (50 feet) and weigh in excess of 4.5 metric tons (5 tons). They have large and brightly colored flowers. Cacti grow very slowly and require little care when grown as houseplants. Their leaves are usually small, and their fleshy stems may be flattened or cylindrical, with the capacity to photosynthesize.

4. *Lamiaceae (mint family).* Most plants in the mint family produce aromatic oils in their leaves and stems. They are also characterized by their angular stems, opposite leaves, and irregular flowers. The mint family includes popular herbs

such as rosemary, sage, thyme, marjoram, basil, catnip, peppermint, lavender, and spearmint. Apart from being useful for medicinal and culinary purposes, mints are used as ornamentals in landscaping.

5. *Solanaceae (nightshade family).* The nightshade family is noted for the poisonous alkaloids many of them produce (e.g., the deadly drug complex called *belladonna* that is extracted from the nightshade plant). Other drugs produced by this family are atropine, scopolamine, nicotine, solanine, and hyoscyamine. Important vegetable plants in this family are tomato *(Lycopersicon esculentum)*, eggplant *(Solanum melongena)*, pepper *(Capsicum* spp.), and potato *(Solanum tuberosum)*. Other important plants are tobacco *(Nicotiana tabacum)* and petunia *(Petunia hybrida)*. When potato tubers are exposed to the sun, they produce a green color at the surface. These green areas are known to contain toxins.

6. *Apiaceae (carrot family).* Plants in the carrot family frequently produce numerous tiny flowers that are arranged in umbels. The plants of horticultural importance include vegetables and herbs such as parsley, carrot, celery, dill, coriander, and parsnip.

7. *Cucurbitaceae (pumpkin family).* The pumpkin or gourd family is characterized by prostrate or climbing herbaceous vines with tendrils and large, fleshy fruits containing numerous seeds. Important plants include pumpkin *(Cucurbita maxima)*, melon *(Cucumis melo)*, watermelon *(Citrullus lunatus)*, and cucumber *(Cucumis sativus)*.

8. *Asteraceae (sunflower family).* The sunflower family has the second largest number of flowering plant species. Flowers in this family occur in a compact inflorescence or head (Figure 2–31). Some of the members are edible and others ornamental. Important plants include sunflower *(Helianthus annuus)*, marigold *(Tagetes* spp.), *Dahlia* spp., *Chrysanthemum* spp., *Aster* spp., and edible plants such as lettuce *(Lactuca sativa)*, Jerusalem artichoke *(Helianthus tuberosus)*, and endive *(Cichorium intybus)*. The common dandelion, *(Taraxacum officinale)*, a noxious weed in lawns, belongs to this family.

9. *Euphobiaceae (spurge family).* Most members of the spurge family produce milky latex, and the family includes a number of poisonous species. The largest genus in this family is the *Euphorbia*. Important plants include the Christmas plant, or poinsettia *(Euphorbia pulcherrima)*; a root crop, cassava *(Manihot esculenta)*; and the castor bean *(Ricinus communis)*.

10. *Rutaceae (rue family).* Most of the species in the rue family are aromatic shrubs or trees. An important and popular genus is the *Citrus,* which includes plants such as mandarin, lemon, lime, grapefruit, and sweet orange.

11. *Ericaceae (heath family).* The heath family consists of shrubs that are adapted to acidic soils. The genera of horticultural importance include *Rhododendron* (rhododendron and azalea) and *Vaccinium* (blueberry and cranberry).

2.6.2 GYMNOSPERMS

Gymnosperms have naked seed. There are four divisions of gymnosperms with living representatives: Cycadophyta (cycads), Ginkgophyta (ginkgo, maidenhair tree), Coniferophyta (conifers), and Gnetophyta (gnetophytes). The most widespread of these divisions is the Coniferophyta, which consists of about 50 genera and 550 species. The most familiar of all conifers are the pines of the family Pinaceae. The important genera of conifers other than the pines are the firs (Abies), spruces (Picea), hemlocks (Tsuga), Douglas firs (Pseudotsuga), cypresses (Cupressus), and junipers (Juniperus). These predominantly evergreen trees and shrubs occur primarily in temperate areas.

Gymnosperms
Plants that bear seeds that are not within fruits (naked).

SUMMARY

The science of classifying and naming plants is called *plant taxonomy*. Carolus Linnaeus developed the current Latin-based binomial nomenclature in which plants are given two names, the first name called the *genus* and the second name called the *species*. The International Code of Botanical Nomenclature (ICBN) provides guidelines for the naming of plants. The taxonomic groups in order of descending hierarchy are kingdom, division, class, subclass, order, family, genus, species, and variety. Kingdom is the most genetically divergent level, and variety represents the level at which individuals are most similar in genotype and external features.

There are three plant kingdoms—Monera, Protoctista, and Fungi. Most plants of horticultural interest are vascular plants (having conducting tissues—xylem and phloem). Apart from classifying plants on a scientific basis, there are a number of operational classifications based on (1) stem type (herbs, shrubs, and trees), (2) kind of herb (annual, biennial, or perennial), (3) stem growth form (erect, decumbent, creeping, or climbing), (4) fruit type (herbaceous fruiting plants versus woody fruiting plants), (5) adaptation (cool season or warm season), and (6) edible parts (roots, bulbs, pods, greens, and so forth).

REFERENCES AND SUGGESTED READING

Benson, L. 1979. *Plant classification,* 2d ed. Lexington, Mass.: Heath.

Esau, K. 1977. *Anatomy of seed plants,* 2d ed. New York: John Wiley & Sons.

Glendfill, D. 1989. *The names of plants,* 2d ed. New York: Cambridge University Press.

Hartman, H. T., A. M. Kofranek, V. E. Rubatzky, and W. J. Flocker. 1988. *Plant science,* 2d ed. Englewood Cliffs, N.J.: Prentice Hall.

Radford, A. E. 1986. *Fundamentals of plant systematics.* New York: Harper & Row.

Rice, L. W., and P. R. Rice, Jr. 1993. *Practical horticulture,* 2d ed. Englewood Cliffs, N.J.: Prentice Hall.

Stern, K. R. 1997. *Introductory plant biology,* 2d ed. Dubuque, Iowa: Wm. C. Brown Publishers.

About Linnaeus, the father of plant classification
http://www.ucmp.berkeley.edu/history/linnaeus.html

Classifying plants—Simplified—Both scientific and operational classifications with photos *http://www.pssc.ttu.edu/pss1321/Web%20topics/plantclassificationnew.htm*

Gives English meaning of Latin names used to classify plants
http:www.thewildflowersociety.com/wfs_new_pages/1k2_flower_names.htm

Good general information on classification
http:www.botany.utoronto.ca/courses/bot307/B_How/janename.html

PRACTICAL EXPERIENCE

1. Visit a grocery store and purchase different horticultural produce in the following classes:
   a. Fruits:
      drupes
      berries
      nuts
   b. Roots

    c.   Leaves

    d.   Bulbs

2.   Cut across (transverse section) the fruits to expose the inside and compare them.

3.   Complete the plant taxonomic classification of sweet corn, following the example given in Section 2.2.

4.   Field trip

    a.   Take a walk on campus, bringing along copies of figures to use in identifying the variety of characteristics that are the basis of plant taxonomy. Record as many distinguishing features as are represented in the plants on campus (e.g., flower arrangement, leaf shape, and margin).

    b.   Take a trip to a botanical garden and repeat the exercises in part a.

OUTCOMES ASSESSMENT

1.   What is plant taxonomy?

2.   Discuss the rationale for classifying plants.

3.   Briefly discuss the history of plant classification.

4.   Distinguish between a pome and a drupe.

5.   Tomato is a fruit, and so are peanut and cashew. Explain.

6.   What is the binomial nomenclature? Who invented it?

7.   Distinguish between warm-season crops and cool-season crops.

8.   Discuss how a plant breeder might be guided by the classification categories in his or her professional work.

9.   Certain plants can be classified as annual, biennial, or perennial, on different occasions. Explain.

10. Discuss the benefits of operational classification of plants.

3

Plant Anatomy

PURPOSE AND EXPECTED OUTCOMES

This chapter is designed to describe the physical and structural organization of higher plants and to show how plant anatomy is used as a basis of classifying horticultural plants.

After studying this chapter, the student should be able to

1. Describe the levels of eukaryotic organization.
2. Describe the cell structure and function of major organelles.
3. List and describe the primary tissues of higher plants and their functions.
4. Describe various plant organs and how they are used as a basis for classifying horticultural plants.

[COLOR PLATES—*see color plate 3* for additional chapter photos]

OVERVIEW

Plant Anatomy
The study of the structure of cells, tissues, and tissue systems.

The scientific discipline of **plant anatomy** deals with cataloging, describing, and understanding the function of plant structures. The functional aspect of the study of anatomy overlaps with *plant physiology* (Chapter 5). Plant anatomy can be studied at various levels of eukaryotic organization, the most fundamental being the molecular level, which deals with macromolecules (Figure 3–1). These basic molecules are organized into *organelles*. The next level of complexity of organization is *tissues*. Cellular substructures are not visible to the naked eye, requiring the aid of magnifying instruments to be seen. Even though organs and whole-plant structures are the most readily visible to the naked eye, it is important to know that what we see are products of subcellular function involving the effects of physiological processes.

A good understanding of plant anatomy helps horticultural scientists in manipulating plants for increased productivity and aesthetic value. Before nudging nature, one needs to know and understand the norm, how it responds to change, and how to effect change.

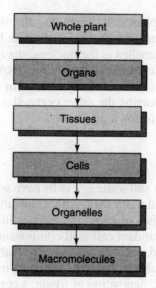

FIGURE 3–1 Levels of organization of eukaryotes. The study of eukaryotes below the level of organs usually requires the aid of special equipment such as microscopes to observe and manipulate.

3.1 CELL

3.1.1 THE UNIT OF ORGANIZATION OF LIVING THINGS

The **cell** is the unit of organization of living things. Some organisms have only one cell (*unicellular*), and others are made up of many cells (*multicellular*). Unicellular organisms are also called *prokaryotes*, or lower organisms, an example being the algae. They lack a distinct nucleus because of the absence of a nuclear membrane. Higher organisms, or *eukaryotes*, have distinct nuclei and cells that are compartmentalized by means of membranes such that each compartment has a different function. They may be unicellular or multicellular. Plants of horticultural interest are eukaryotes, or higher plants.

Under appropriate laboratory conditions, a single cell may be nurtured to grow and develop to produce the entire plant from which it was derived. This capability is called *totipotency* and results because each cell has the complete *genome* (the complete set of genes for the particular organism) to direct the development of the whole plant. This capacity is exploited in propagating certain horticultural plants and manipulating the genetic structure of others to produce new and improved types.

Cells, like all living things, grow and age. There are different sizes and shapes of cells. Through the process of *cell division,* a single cell rapidly divides and multiplies to produce a uniform mass of cells. These cells subsequently undergo changes through the process of **differentiation** to perform specific functions in the plant, as needed. For example, some cells change to produce strengthening tissues, while others produce flower or leaf buds. During this differentiation process, the shapes and sizes of cells are modified appropriately, as is their structural strength. Horticultural products are harvested in time to obtain products that have the optimal quality desired by consumers. A delay in harvesting a product may reduce its quality and consequently the market value. As cells age, their physical structures change such that products that should be juicy and succulent, for example, become less juicy and more fibrous.

3.1.2 CELL STRUCTURE

The plant cell may be divided into three parts—the *outer membrane* (**plasma membrane** or *plasmalemma*), the *cytoplasm,* and the *nucleus.* The plasma membrane functions as a selective barrier to the transport of substances into and out of the protoplast.

Cell
The basic structural and physiological unit of plants and animals.

Differentiation
Physical and chemical changes associated with the development and/or specialization of an organism or cell.

Plasma Membrane
The membrane that surrounds the entire protoplast.

The content of a living plant cell, excluding the wall, is called the protoplasm (or protoplast). Embedded in the protoplasm are discrete bodies called **organelles.** The most prominent of cellular organelles is the nucleus, the *organelle* that houses most of the cell's genetic material (deoxyribonucleic acid, or DNA). DNA is responsible for directing cellular functions. Some old cells lack nuclei. The area outside of the nucleus is called the cytoplasm, and it contains the other organelles (Figure 3–2). Some of these organelles are described in the following sections.

The Cell Wall

All plant cells except the sperm and some egg cells have walls. When the protoplast dies and degenerates, what is left is the *cell wall,* which constitutes the bulk of woody plants. Chemically, the cell wall consists of *cellulose, hemicellulose, protein,* and *pectic substances.* Cellulose, the most abundant cell wall component, is a polysaccharide (a polymer of sucrose molecules) and nutritionally of little value to humans since it is not digestible. Pectins are acidic polysaccharides (polymers of galacturonic acid). At a particular stage in the life of a cell, deposition of *lignin,* a complex mixture of polymers of phenolic acid occurs. This hardens the cell wall, rendering it rigid and inelastic. This process is called *lignification.*

The thickness and other structural features of a cell wall vary according to the age and type of cell. All cells have a standard *primary cell wall,* which is the first to form when a cell is developing. This type of cell wall is found where cells are actively growing and dividing. Chemically, it is composed predominantly of cellulose and pectic substances. When cell growth ceases, a *secondary cell wall* is deposited inside of the primary cell wall. With this new layer of cellulose and lignin, the cell wall becomes rigid. Adjacent cell walls are held together by a pectin-rich material called the *middle lamella.* When fruits rot under fungal attack, the middle lamella breaks down into the characteristic slimy fluid associated with rotting. Cell-to-cell interconnections are produced by cytoplasmic strands called *plasmodesmata.*

Nucleus

Upon staining a cell in the resting stage (interphase), the *nucleus* usually shows up as a spheroidal and densely stained body. This structure is the fundamental organelle of a cell since it is the primary repository of genetic information for the control and maintenance of cellular structure and function. The nucleus is composed of DNA,

FIGURE 3–2 The parts of a plant cell.

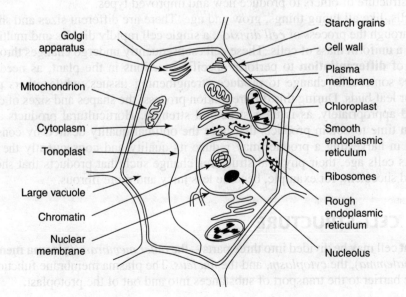

Golgi apparatus

Mitochondrion

Cytoplasm

Tonoplast

Large vacuole

Chromatin

Nuclear membrane

Starch grains

Cell wall

Plasma membrane

Chloroplast

Smooth endoplasmic reticulum

Ribosomes

Rough endoplasmic reticulum

Nucleolus

ribonucleic acid (RNA), proteins, and water. The DNA occurs in defined structures called **chromosomes** that allow it to be replicated accurately (except in occasional alterations called *mutations*).

Chromosomes are visible as strands when the DNA-histone complex coils and appears to condense. Chromosomes stain differentially to reveal dark and light sections. The dark sections are called *heterochromatin* and represent DNA-containing genes that are not actually directing the synthesis of RNA. The light-staining sections are called *euchromatin* and contain active genes. The chromosome number per cell is characteristic of the species (Table 3–1). The number of chromosomes in the *gametic cell* (sex cell, such as pollen) is half that of the *somatic cell* (body cell). When two *homologous pairs* (identical mates) occur in a cell, it is called a *diploid*. Sometimes, in certain plant species, cells may contain multiple copies beyond the diploid number, a condition called *polyploidy*.

Vacuoles

Vacuoles are cavities in cells that contain a liquid called the *vacuolar sap,* or *cell sap,* within the vascular membrane called *tonoplast*. The sap consists mainly of water, but other substances such as salt, sugars, and dissolved proteins occur, according to the physiological state of the cell. Vacuoles also store water-soluble pigments called *anthocyanins*. These pigments are responsible for the red and blue colors of many flowers (e.g., geranium, rose, and delphinium), fruits (e.g., cherry, apple, and grape), and vegetables (e.g., cabbage, turnip, and onion). Anthocyanins are also involved in the fall colors of some leaves. Vacuoles vary in size: In meristematic cells (young and actively dividing), the vacuoles in a single cell are small in size but numerous. In mature cells, however, these numerous small vacuoles usually fuse into large cavities that may occupy about 90 percent of the cell, pushing the remainder of the protoplasm against the cell wall. Vacuoles absorb water to create the **turgor pressure** required for physical support in plants. Plants under moisture stress wilt for lack of turgor pressure. A variety of rapid movements in plants such as flower opening, leaf movement in response to touch (e.g., in *Memosa pudica*), and the opening and closing of guard cells are attributed to functions of the vascular vacuoles. Vacuoles have some digestive functions similar to those of lysosomes in animal cells; macromolecules are broken down in vacuoles and their components recycled within the cell.

Turgor Pressure
The pressure on a cell wall that is created from within the cell by the movement of water into it.

TABLE 3–1 The Number of Chromosomes Possessed by a Variety of Plant Species

Species	Scientific Name	Chromosome Number (n)
Carrot	*Daucus carrota*	18
Garden pea	*Pisum sativum*	7
Evening primrose	*Oenothera biennis*	7
Broad bean	*Vicia faba*	6
Potato	*Solanum tuberosum*	24
Snapdragon	*Antirrhinum majus*	8
Tomato	*Lycopersicon esculentum*	12
Corn	*Zea mays*	10
Lettuce	*Lactuca sativa*	18
Garden onion	*Allium cepa*	8
White oak	*Quercus alba*	12
Yellow pine	*Pinus ponderosa*	12
Cherry	*Prunnus cerasus*	16
Bean	*Phaseolus vulgare*	11
Cabbage	*Brassica oleracea*	9
Cucumber	*Cucumis sativus*	7

Plastids

Plastids are very dynamic plant cell organelles capable of dividing, growing, and differentiating into different forms, each of which has a different structure and function. Plastids contain their own DNA. They are said to be *semiautonomous* because they synthesize some of their own proteins. The genes they contain are not inherited according to Mendelian laws (they have extrachromosomal inheritance, meaning that it does not occur in chromosomes in the nucleus). *Chloroplasts* are plastids that contain *chlorophyll,* the green pigment that gives plants their characteristic green color and, more importantly, is involved in photosynthesis. A chloroplast contains saclike vesicles called *thylakoids,* which are stacked in units called *grana* (singular: *granum*). The grana are suspended in a fluid called *stroma.* Chloroplasts occur only in plants, not in animals. During cell division, no special mechanism ensures equal distribution of plastids. Consequently, certain cells may receive no plastids at all; the parts of the leaf that have cells without chloroplasts develop no green color. Instead, they produce white, pink, or purple coloration. Leaves showing such patches of color are said to be *variegated* (Figure 3–3). Colorless plastids are generally called *leucoplasts.*

Whereas nonangiosperms are generally not colorful, being predominantly green, angiosperms (flowering plants whose seeds develop within ovaries that mature into fruits) have certain plastids with the capacity to produce large amounts of *carotenoids* (bright yellow or orange and red pigments). These plastids are called *chromoplasts* (*chroma* means color). More than 30 different types of pigments have been found in the chromoplasts of pepper (*Capsicum* spp.). The pigments are diverse in their composition and in the colors they produce. Flowers display a spectacular array of colors. Colors found in petals and fruits are caused by plastids. Although leaves are predominantly green, they may also exhibit other colors. The presence of chlorophyll overwhelms other colors and masks their expression; however, under the right conditions (such as occurs seasonally in fall), the chlorophyll breaks down, allowing the masked colors to be expressed as beautiful colors during the fall season in temperate regions. All types of plastids, especially chloroplasts and chromoplasts, are interconvertible. When plants are grown in darkness, chloroplasts change into *etioplasts,* resulting in a deformation called *etiolation* (spindly growth due to excessive elongation of internodes). Light is required to reverse this abnormal growth. To prevent etiolation, plants grown under conditions of insufficient daylight (such as houseplants and greenhouse plants) are provided with supplemental light from an artificial source.

Mitochondria

A cell may survive without plastids, but all cells must have *mitochondria,* organelles that provide the energy (adenosine triphosphate, ATP) required for plant processes. These organelles are bound by a double membrane. The inner membrane is folded into projections

FIGURE 3–3 Variegation of the leaf of dumbcane (*Dieffenbachia* spp.). *(Source: George Acquaah)*

called *cristae;* this extreme folding increases the internal surface area of mitochondria for biochemical reactions. Mitochondria have their own DNA, just like chloroplasts. They are sites of respiration, the cellular process responsible for producing energy for living organisms.

Ribosomes

Ribosomes are sites of protein synthesis. These tiny structures consist of approximately equal amounts of RNA and protein. Ribosomes may occur freely in the cytoplasm or attached to the endoplasmic reticulum (described next). When engaged in protein synthesis, ribosomes tend to form clusters called *polyribosomes* or *polysomes.*

Endoplasmic Reticulum

The *endoplasmic reticulum* is a membranous structure distributed throughout the cytoplasm as a system of interconnected, flattened tubes and sacs called *cisternae.* The extent of folding and the amount of endoplasmic reticulum depend on the cell type and function and the cell's stage of development. A transverse section of this organelle shows two parallel membranes with a space between them. When ribosomes are attached to the surface, it is called *rough endoplasmic reticulum;* otherwise it is called *smooth endoplasmic reticulum.* This organelle also serves as a channel for the transport of substances such as proteins and lipids to different parts of the cell and as the principal site of membrane synthesis.

Golgi Apparatus

The *Golgi apparatus* is a collective term for structures called *Golgi bodies* or *dictyosomes,* which consist of a stack of about four to eight flattened sacs, or cisternae. In higher plants, dictyosomes have secretory functions. They secrete new cell wall precursors and other substances.

Microbodies

Microbodies are single-membraned, spherical bodies that have roles in metabolic processes. A group of microbodies associated with mitochondria and chloroplasts are called *peroxisomes.* These microbodies contain the enzyme glycolate oxidase and function in glycolate oxidation during photorespiration (light-dependent production of glycolic acid in chloroplasts and its subsequent oxidation in peroxisomes). Another group of microbodies called *glyoxysomes* contain enzymes involved in the breakdown of lipids to fatty acids. The fatty acids are converted to carbohydrates that are used for growth and development during the germination of many seeds.

Ergastic Substances

Ergastic substances are miscellaneous substances in the cell that include waste products and storage products such as starches, anthocyanin, resins, tannins, gums, and protein bodies. These substances may be classified as either *primary metabolites* (e.g., starch and sugars that have a basic role in cell metabolism) or *secondary metabolites* (e.g., resins and tannins that have no role in primary metabolism). Secondary metabolites are known to play a role in protecting the plant from herbivores and insect attack. Tannins are toxic to animals. For example, the rhubarb leaf blade contains calcium oxalate crystals, but the petiole does not; thus, while the petioles are edible, the leaf blade is toxic to animals. Similarly, *Philodendron* stems and shoots and *Dieffenbachia* (dumbcane) leaves contain calcium oxalate in the raphides (sharp needles on the plant) that is very irritating to the throat. Noncrystalline ergastic substances such as silica deposits occur in the cell walls of some grasses and sedges. These deposits strengthen the tissue and also protect the plant against insects and other pests.

3.2 TYPES OF PLANT CELLS AND TISSUES

Different types of cells are used to construct the different tissues and organs to meet the variety of functional needs of the plant. These cells can be classified into three basic types: *parenchyma, collenchyma,* and *sclerenchyma.* The three types of cells differ from each other in their cell wall characteristics. Simple cells aggregate in certain characteristic patterns to form **tissues.** When the tissue consists of one type of cell, it is described as a *simple tissue;* when more than one type of cell is present, the tissue is called a *complex tissue.*

3.2.1 SIMPLE TISSUES

Tissue
A set of cells that function together.

1. *Parenchyma.* Parenchyma cells are characterized by their thin wall. The tissue they form is described as *parenchyma (parenchymatous) tissue.* This cell type occurs extensively in herbaceous plants. Functionally, parenchyma cells are found in actively growing regions of plants called **meristems.** Meristematic cells are undifferentiated. The parenchyma cells in meristematic regions are also called *meristematic parenchyma.* Some parenchyma cells have synthetic functions, such as in the chloroplasts, where they are called *photosynthetic parenchyma,* or *chlorenchyma* cells, and function in photosynthesis. Some parenchyma cells have secretory roles and are called *secretory parenchyma.* The fleshy and succulent parts of fruits and other swollen parts such as roots and tubers consist of large amounts of parenchyma tissue.

Meristem
A cell or region of specialized tissue whose principal function is to undergo cell division.

2. *Collenchyma.* Collenchyma cells have a thick primary wall that plays a mechanical role in the plant support system by strengthening tissues. This role is confined to regions of the plant where active growth occurs so as to provide the plant some protection from damage. Collenchymatous tissue occurs in the stem below the epidermis (outermost layer of the cells in the particular plant part) in leaves, it occurs in the petiole (or leaf stalk), leaf margins, and main veins of the leaf blade or lamina. Fruit rinds that are soft and edible contain collenchyma tissue. As these cells age, they accumulate hardening substances and become unevenly sclerified, or thickened.

3. *Sclerenchyma.* Sclerenchyma cells have two walls, primary and secondary, the latter being thicker. They also have a mechanical function in plants, serving as reinforcement for tissues. Sclerenchyma cells have elasticity and resiliency and thus can bend without snapping. Naturally, therefore, they are found in places in the plant, such as the leaf petiole, where bending and movement occur. There are two basic types of sclerenchyma cells—short cells, called *sclereids,* and long cells, called *fibers.* The primary cell wall is made up of cellulose, hemicellulose, and other pectic substances. The secondary wall is formed from large deposits of lignin; cells with deposits of lignin are said to be lignified. Sclerenchyma occurs, for example, in the stones of fruits, around the seeds, or in immature fruits. Sclerenchyma cells abound in plants that yield fiber such as kenaf, flax, and hemp.

3.2.2 COMPLEX TISSUES

The three basic cell types may aggregate separately or in combination to form complex tissues that perform a variety of functions in the plant. Some of these tissues are *epidermis, secretory tissue,* and *conducting tissue.*

Epidermis

Epidermis
The outermost layer of cells on all parts of the primary body—stems, leaves, roots, flowers, fruits, and seed—but absent from root tips and apical meristems.

The **epidermis** is the outermost layer of the plant that separates its internal structures from its external environment. Since a plant's environment changes, its epidermis should possess developmental plasticity or flexibility such that it adapts to a wide range of conditions. Such flexibility may involve physiological, structural, and anatomical variability.

By virtue of its position, the primary function of the epidermis is to regulate water and gas movement into and out of the plant. Some plants have a waterproof epidermis, whereas others are permeable to moisture and gases. Waterproofing is caused by the occurrence of a hydrophobic (water-repelling) substance called *cutin* (polymerized fatty acids) that is deposited on the outside of the epidermal wall. Waterproofing occurs in most rain forest epiphytes, such as cactus, orchid, and philodendron, where protection against leaching of minerals is critical. The resulting layer is called a *cuticle* and is waxy in nature. The epidermis protects the plant against sunlight. Intense sunlight can overheat the protoplasm and bleach the chlorophyll. Sometimes orchardists paint the exposed trunks of fruit trees to reflect sunlight and thus prevent damage from excessive heat. The epidermal layer also has a protective role, resisting the intrusion of biological pests such as bacteria and fungi. Some layers protect the plant against chewing insects, and others have hairlike structures (pubescence) called *trichomes* that interfere with oviposition (deposition of eggs). Some of these epidermal outgrowths **secrete** a variety of substances for many different purposes.

In the green parts of plants, especially in leaves, the epidermis has pores called *stomatal pores,* or *stomata* (singular: *stoma*). The pores occur predominantly on the abaxial (lower surface) part of the leaf and are bordered by structures called *guard cells.* The guard cells control the opening of the stoma. These pores function in gaseous and moisture exchange. In some horticultural practices, certain chemicals are administered to plants by foliar application. Such chemicals enter the plant through the stomata.

Secretion
The movement, either by diffusion or active transport, of materials out of a plant or into a space where they can accumulate for storage.

Secretory Tissue

According to the nature of the material secreted, secretory systems may be classified according to where they are found (i.e., whether outside or inside of the plant).

Found Outside of the Plant

1. *Nectaries.* Nectaries are found on parts of the plant. When they occur in flowers they are called floral nectaries, and when they occur elsewhere they are called extrafloral nectaries. They secrete a fluid called *nectar* that consists of sugars (especially glucose, sucrose, and fructose) and numerous other organic compounds. Certain insects including butterflies and bees feed on nectar and in the process aid in the pollination of the flowers.
2. *Hydathodes.* Secretory structures called hydathodes secrete almost pure water. They are thus thought to play a role in the transport of minerals to young tissues, in addition to the role played by transpiration. Under conditions of moist soil, high humidity, and cool air, the leaves of many plants, especially grasses, are known to produce droplets of water along their margins that appear similar to dew. However, the moisture is due to a special secretory process called *guttation.*
3. *Salt glands.* Salt glands, which secrete inorganic salts, occur in plants that grow in desert and brackish areas that are high in salts. These salts may accumulate on the leaves of certain plants and thereby make them unattractive to herbivores.
4. *Osmophores.* Osmophores are fragrance-secreting glands found in flowers. They secrete odors and perfumes (predominantly oily compounds belonging to the class of volatile, small terpenes). The repulsive odor of aroids is attributed to the amines and ammonia produced by osmophores.
5. *Digestive glands.* Digestive glands are found in insect-eating (insectivorous) plants. They secrete enzymes used in digesting the animal materials trapped by such plants (e.g., pitcher plant).
6. *Adhesive cells.* Adhesive cells secrete materials that allow for attachment between host and parasite. The strong attachment due to adhesive material helps parasites during penetration of their host.

Found Inside of the Plant

1. *Resin ducts.* Resin ducts are long canals that contain sticky resin. They are most abundant in the wood and leaves of conifers.
2. *Mucilage cells.* Mucilage cells are slimy secretions high in carbohydrate and water content. The mucilage secreted by the growing root tip, called mucigel, is believed to be important in lubricating the passage of the root through the soil.
3. *Oil chambers.* Certain glands secret compounds that are commonly deposited in large cavities in the plant. However, these oils are moved outside of the plant, where they are aromatic.
4. *Gum ducts.* Cell wall modification results in the production of gums in certain tree species.
5. *Laticifers.* Laticifers are latex-secreting glands. They occur in species such as milkweed, poppy, and euphorbia. The latex may contain diverse compounds including carbohydrates, lipids, tannins, rubber, protein, and crystals. Even though the secretion from poinsettia *(Euphorbia pulcherrima)* has been found to be nontoxic to humans, "plant milk" should not be ingested.
6. *Myrosin cells.* Myrosin cells contain a neutral enzyme called myrosinase. However, when this harmless protein is mixed with its substrate (thioglucosides), a toxic mustard oil (isothiocyanate) is produced. This mixing occurs when myrosin cells are ruptured during chewing by insects or other animals.

Since all cells are capable of transporting materials across their boundaries, all cells may be said to have secretory functions. Secretory functions are needed by cells for a variety of reasons. Accumulation of metabolic waste in the cell may be toxic, and so the waste must be excreted. Compounds that are actively transported out of the cell include sugars, inorganic salts, hormones, nitrogenous compounds, and sulfur-containing compounds. However, deposits in the cell wall such as cuticle, suberin, lignin, and waxes are products of secretory activities that are desired for specific roles in the plant, as previously mentioned. In carnivorous plants, secretions are needed to digest trapped animals.

Apart from secretory activities that are related to cellular metabolism, cells secrete other chemicals. Some glands in flowering plants secrete scents to attract pollinators. Some flowers produce very sweet fragrances that people enjoy. Other plant secretions are substances that repel animals that may be pests.

Conducting Tissues

Vascular Plant
Any species that has vascular tissue—xylem and phloem.

Vascular plants have an elaborate system of vessels used in conducting organic and inorganic solutes from place to place in the plant. These systems are complex tissues consisting of a variety of cell types. There are two conducting tissues in plants: *xylem* and *phloem*.

Xylem Tissue The xylem tissue conducts water and solutes from the roots up to the leaf, where food is manufactured by the process of photosynthesis. Since it consists of sclerenchyma cells, it also provides structural support to the plant as a whole, and it stores nutrients or new materials for photosynthesis. The conducting cells of the xylem are of two types, *tracheids* and *vessel elements*. These two types of cells are collectively called *tracheary elements,* which vary widely in size, shape, and types of secondary walls.

Water is moved up the xylem tissue by water potential. This movement is caused by passive transport because the xylem cells have no protoplasm, just the cell wall, and hence function essentially as dead cells. Tracheids tend to be long and spindle shaped; vessel elements may be narrow or wide. Both cell types have lateral perforations (or *pits*) to permit flow of cell sap from cell to cell. The elements may have large holes in the primary wall and thus are classified as tracheids, or they may lack such holes and be called vessel elements. Tracheids are the only conducting elements in gymnosperms. In angiosperms, vessel elements are good conductors when water is abundant and flows in high volume. Wood is predominantly xylem tissue. In nonwoody (herbaceous) plants, xylem occurs in amounts necessary for the conduction of water.

Phloem Tissue Structurally, phloem tissue may be made up of parenchyma cells or a combination of parenchyma and sclerenchyma cells. The conducting elements are called *sieve elements* and are of two types, *sieve cells* (primarily parenchyma) and *sieve tube members*. In angiosperms, sieve elements are closely associated with spindle cells called *companion cells*. In nonangiosperms, these cells are called *albuminous cells*. They are believed to be involved in *phloem loading* (in which newly synthesized sugars are loaded for export to other plant parts). This loading occurs in the minor veins of leaves. Phloem cells, of necessity, function as living cells. The general function of phloem tissue is to move food from the leaves, where it is manufactured, to other parts of the plant, where it is used or stored. A significant difference between xylem and phloem tissue function is that the plant actively controls the distribution of photosynthates as conducted by the phloem tissue system but has a passive role in the movement of raw materials up to the leaves. The active (under the plant's control) movement of food by plants enables food to be transported to the parts of the plant where it is needed and similarly be extracted in other areas (*source-sink* relationship). This dynamic nature of the movement of sugars, amines, and other nutrients enables the plant to reallocate resources as it grows through various phases. Phloem cells are not durable and must be replaced constantly.

Apical Meristems

In animals, growth occurs by means of the *diffuse growth* process. In this process, growth occurs throughout the entire individual, all parts growing simultaneously. In plants, however, the means of growth is by the *localized growth* process, whereby growth is limited to certain regions called meristems.

Meristems are areas of active growth where cells are dividing rapidly. The cells in these regions are undifferentiated (sources of *developmental plasticity*). In organs, such as the root and the shoot, the meristems are located at the tip (apex) and hence are called *apical meristems*. Some meristematic cells occur in the leaf axil and are called *axillary meristems*. Meristems also occur in other parts of the plant (e.g., *basal, lateral,* and *intercalary*). The localized growth process makes it possible for juvenile and mature adult cells to coexist in a plant provided good environmental conditions exist. The plant can continue to grow while certain organs and tissues are fully mature and functional and can grow indefinitely without any limit on final size. This growth pattern is called *open* or *indeterminate*. In reality, many plants appear to have predictable sizes that are characteristic of the species, but this feature is believed to be largely an environmental and statistical phenomenon. Under controlled environmental conditions in which optimal growth conditions prevail, many annual plants have been known to grow perennially.

In some species, the apical meristem dies after it has produced a certain number of leaves. The plant then ceases to grow and is said to be *determinate* (as opposed to indeterminate). In flowering species, plants go through a vegetative growth phase of variable duration (depending on the species) before flowering.

3.3 STEM

The *stem* is the central axis of the shoot of a plant.

3.3.1 FUNCTIONS

The functions of the stem include the following:

1. Stems produce and provide mechanical support for holding up the branches, leaves, and reproductive structures. Leaves of plants need to be displayed such that they intercept light for photosynthesis.

2. Stems move water and minerals through their conducting vessels up to the leaves for the manufacture of food and then conduct manufactured food down from the leaves to other parts of the plant.
3. Stems may be modified to serve as storage organs for food, water, and minerals. Succulents such as cacti have stems that are designed for storage. The Irish potato is a swollen stem.
4. Certain plants are propagated through asexual means by using pieces of the stem as cuttings. These cuttings are rooted and then planted as seedlings to raise new plants.

3.3.2 STEM TYPES

There are two basic types of stems in vascular plants: *dicots* (*dicotyledons,* or two cotyledons) and *monocots* (*monocotyledon,* or one cotyledon). They differ in how the primary tissues (xylem and phloem) are arranged. The outermost layer of the stem is the *epidermis,* which borders the internal part called the *cortex.* The cortex is usually composed predominantly of parenchyma cells. It may contain sclerenchyma cells in some plants. The cortex is usually narrow, except in herbaceous stems of monocots, in which it is often extensive. The cortex surrounds the *vascular tissues,* which form a central cylinder called the *stele.* The stele consists of *vascular bundles* and is made up of xylem and phloem tissues. In dicots and gymnosperms, vascular bundles are arranged in a ring (Figure 3–4). In the center of the stem lies a region of purely parenchyma cells called the *pith.* In monocots, the bundles are distributed throughout the cortex, and there is no pith (Figure 3–5).

3.3.3 MODIFIED STEMS

Stems do not always grow upright or vertically. Other forms of stems occur either above or below ground.

1. *Crowns.* The crown may be likened to a compressed stem, as found in bulbs. Leaf and flower buds occur on the crown and give rise to leaves and flowers. In plants such as asparagus, the crown may be further modified into a food storage organ.
   a. Plants with modified or specialized underground storage organs are called bulbous plants. There are different types of these plants—true bulbs, corms, crowns, tubers, rhizomes, stolons, pseudobulbs, and tuberous roots. These structures are further discussed in Chapter 10 (vegetative propagation).

FIGURE 3–4 A cross section of a dicot stem.

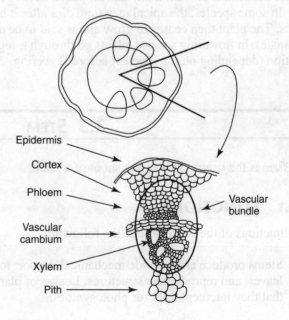

Epidermis

Cortex

Phloem

Vascular cambium

Xylem

Pith

Vascular bundle

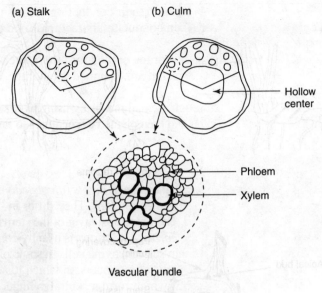

(a) Stalk   (b) Culm

Hollow center

Phloem
Xylem

Vascular bundle

FIGURE 3–5 Cross sections of monocot stems: (a) a stalk and (b) a culm with a hollow center. A corn plant has a stalk and a bamboo has a **culm**.

FIGURE 3–6 Runner of strawberry.

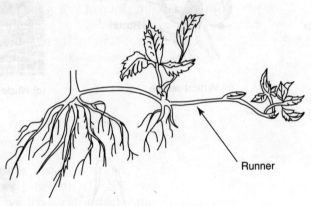

Runner

Culm
Stem of grasses and bamboos, usually hollow except at the swollen nodes.

2. *Stolons.* Stolons are stems that grow horizontally above ground and occur in plants such as strawberry and Bermuda grass (Figure 3–6). Roots may arise at the nodes of the stem as it creeps on the surface of the soil. When stolons have long internodes that originate at the base of the crown of the plant (as in strawberry), the stolon is called a *runner.*

3. *Spurs.* Spurs are found on branches of woody plants such as pear and apple. They are stems whose growth has been severely restricted due to shortened internodes. Spurs may resume normal growth at a later stage.

4. *Rhizomes.* Plants such as bamboo, banana, and canna produce horizontally growing underground stems called rhizomes (Figure 3–7). Most rhizomatons species are monocots. Rhizomes differ in size, as in the species ginger *(Zingiber officinale),* in which they perform storage functions.

5. *Corms.* Corms are underground structures that are compressed and thickened stems (Figure 3–8). They occur in only some monocots. Ornamentals including crocus and gladiolus produce corms. Corms are not true bulbs. They comprise a solid stem with distinct nodes and internodes, covered by dry, scale-like leaves. Corms produce roots for anchorage and to pull the corm deeper into the ground, and a set of fibrous roots for water and nutrient absorption. They also produce branches called *cormels* that can be used for propagation.

6. *Bulbs.* Like corms, bulbs have compressed stems (based plates). They are so highly compressed that the prominent part of the structure is not the stem but rather modified leaves that are attached to the stem and wrapped up into a round

FIGURE 3–7 Rhizomes. These underground structures differ in size and may be significant storage organs of the plant where they are thick, as in ginger (*Zingiber officinale*).

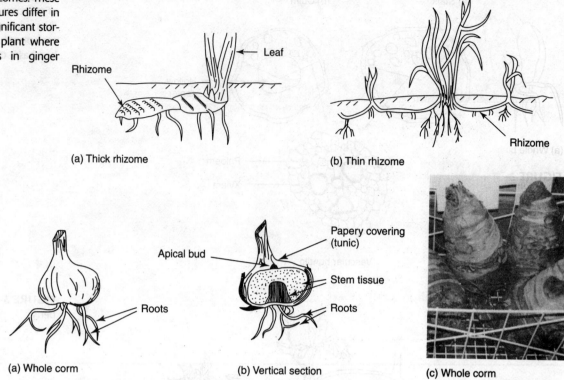

(a) Thick rhizome

Rhizome

Leaf

(b) Thin rhizome

Rhizome

(a) Whole corm

Roots

(b) Vertical section

Apical bud

Papery covering (tunic)

Stem tissue

Roots

(c) Whole corm

FIGURE 3–8 A corm. *(Source: George Acquaah)*

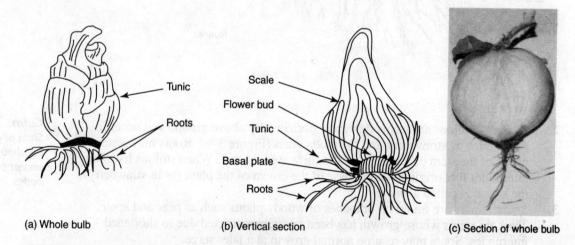

(a) Whole bulb

Tunic

Roots

(b) Vertical section

Scale

Flower bud

Tunic

Basal plate

Roots

(c) Section of whole bulb

FIGURE 3–9 Tunicate bulb.

structure called a bulb. These scale leaves store food. Plants including tulip, lily, onion, and hyacinth produce bulbs. Unlike corms, bulbs lack distinct nodes and internodes. There are two basic types of bulbs. A bulb is described as tunicate (as in onion) when the modified leaves completely cover the stem in concentric layers with addtional protective tunic that dries up into a relatively thin membrane upon harvesting. Bulbs like iris, tulip, and hyacinth are described as cold-hardy and planted in the fall season to flower in springtime. Others like *Amarylis* and *Hymerocallis* are tender bulbs that are planted in summer. Bulbs produce side branches called bulblets or offsets that are used as propagules (Figure 3–9). In Easter lily, the attachment of the leaves is only partial, not concentric, and irregular. This type of bulb is called a scaly bulb and lacks a protective tunic. They are more prone to damage and dessication (Figure 3–10).

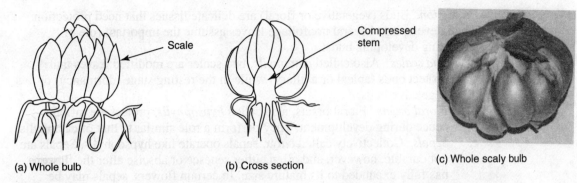

(a) Whole bulb   (b) Cross section   (c) Whole scaly bulb

FIGURE 3–10 A scaly bulb. *(Source: George Acquaah)*

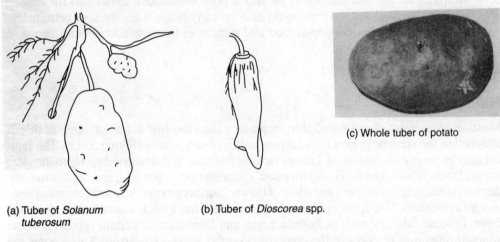

(c) Whole tuber of potato

(a) Tuber of *Solanum tuberosum*   (b) Tuber of *Dioscorea* spp.

FIGURE 3–11 Tubers. These swollen stems vary in size and shape depending on the species. The flesh color is also variable and may be creamish, whitish, yellowish, or some other color. *(Source: George Acquaah)*

7. *Pseudobulbs.* Also called false bulbs, these modified stems are commonly produced by orchids and are variable in appearance. The *Dendrobium* orchid produces an elongated and jointed structure with offshoots at the upper nodes. Once roots form at the base of these offshoots, they may be removed and transplanted. The most popular orchids (e.g., *Cattleya, Miltonia, Laelia*) can be propagated by using rhizomes or stolons divided into sections containing about five pseudobulbs.

8. *Tubers.* In plants such as yam (*Dioscorea* spp.) and white (or Irish) potato (*Solanum tuberosum*), the underground stems are highly enlarged as storage organs (Figure 3–11). Caladium is a popular tuber plant. Whereas Irish potato tubers are generally small in size, yam tubers vary widely in size and shape, according to the species, some attaining lengths of several feet. Tubers have nodes and axillary buds called eyes. Tubers develop best under reduced photoperiod (short days) and lower night temperatures. However, shoot development is vigorous under long-day conditions.

9. *Tuberous roots.*   They lack nodes and axillary buds, the buds are present only at the shoot (proximal) end.

3.4 Leaf

There are five types of leaves: *foliage leaves, bud scales, floral bracts, sepals,* and *cotyledons.*

3.4.1 FUNCTIONS

The major functions of leaves are the following:

1. *Food manufacture.* The most widely known function of the leaf is photosynthesis. This function is performed by *foliage leaves,* which are the most readily visible type of leaf.

2. *Protection.* Buds (vegetative or floral) are delicate tissues that need protection while developing. Several nonfoliage leaves assume the important role of protecting developing buds:

   a. *Bud scales.* Also called *cataphylls,* bud scales are modified leaves that protect buds (apical or axillary) while in the resting stage (dormancy) or vegetative buds.

   b. *Floral bracts.* Floral bracts, also called *hypsophylls,* protect the inflorescence during development. They perform a role similar to that of cataphylls.

   c. *Sepals.* Collectively called *calyx,* sepals operate like hypsophylls. Sepals are not durable, however, and often either senesce or abscise after the flower has fully expanded to its mature size. In certain flowers, sepals may be brightly colored like petals and may exude fragrances and produce nectar.

3. *Storage.* Storage as a function of the leaf is often overlooked. *Cotyledons* (or seed leaves) store food that the embryo depends on early in life while the seed germinates until the seedling has developed roots and sometimes leaves to start photosynthesis.

3.4.2 STRUCTURE

Foliage Leaves

Most leaves consist of a flat and thin structure called the *leaf blade,* or *lamina,* that is attached to the stem or branch by a narrow stalk called a *petiole* (Figure 3–12). The lamina may be *simple* or *compound.* Leaves lacking this stalk and attached directly to the stem are said to be *sessile.* The leaf is *dorsoventral* (flattened top to bottom), and as such the epidermis on the *adaxial* (upper) and *abaxial* (lower) surfaces experiences different environmental conditions. The upper epidermal layer of a leaf has a thicker cuticle than the lower layer. In some families, such as Portulacaceae and Begoniaceae, certain species have no *stomata* (openings or pores in the epidermis) on the adaxial epidermis. These pores are bordered by specialized cells called *guard cells* (Figure 3–13). In floating species of families such as Ranuculaceae, abaxial stomata are lacking; in completely submerged plants, such as certain species of Nymphaeaceae, stomata may be absent altogether.

Most stomata occur on the abaxial surface, as do trichomes. The internal part of the leaf, the *mesophyll,* is equivalent to the cortex in the stem (Figure 3–14). Directly below the upper epidermis are columns of cells called *palisade parenchyma.* There may be

FIGURE 3–12 A typical broad leaf. The size, shape, and other features vary widely among species.

FIGURE 3–13 (a) A surface view and (b) cross section of a stoma.

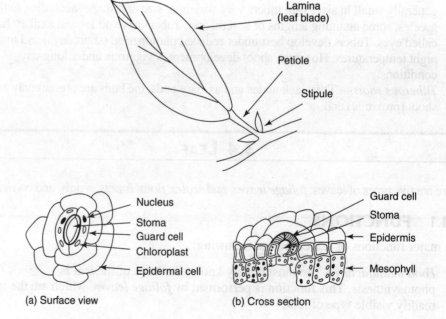

Lamina (leaf blade)

Petiole

Stipule

Nucleus
Stoma
Guard cell
Chloroplast
Epidermal cell

(a) Surface view

Guard cell
Stoma
Epidermis
Mesophyll

(b) Cross section

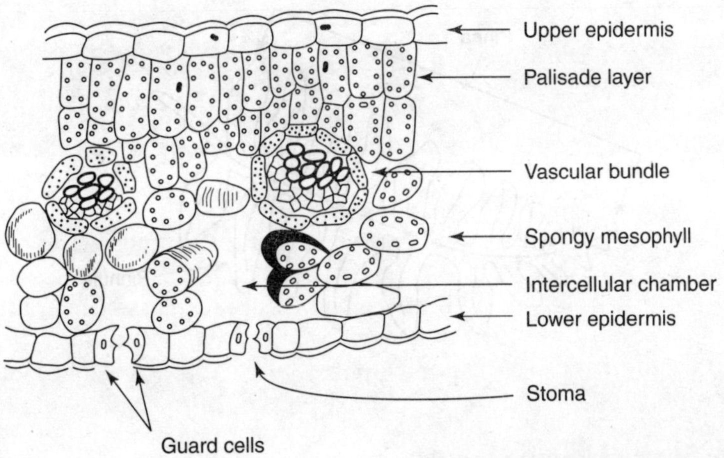

FIGURE 3–14 A transverse section of a typical dicot leaf showing internal structure.

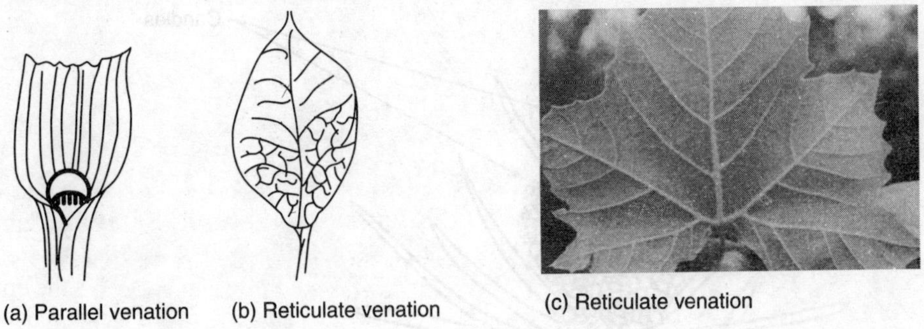

Upper epidermis
Palisade layer
Vascular bundle
Spongy mesophyll
Intercellular chamber
Lower epidermis
Stoma
Guard cells

(a) Parallel venation
(b) Reticulate venation
(c) Reticulate venation

FIGURE 3–15 Leaf venation in a (a) monocot, (b) dicoty, (c) an actual dicot leaf venation. *(Source: George Acquaah)*

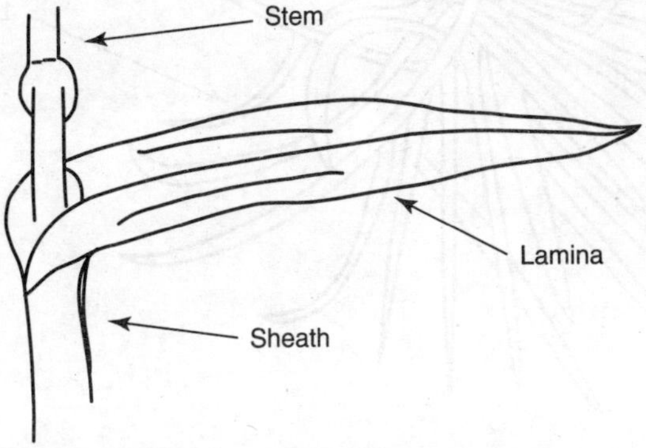

Stem
Lamina
Sheath

FIGURE 3–16 A typical grass leaf.

more than one row of this tissue if the plant is exposed to intense sunlight. Palisade tissue cells contain chloroplasts used in photosynthesis. Next to the lower epidermis is a layer of widely spaced cells called *spongy mesophyll.* This tissue provides flexibility of the lamina as it moves in the wind.

The vascular system of the stem extends to the leaf. Dicot leaves generally have a single, large *central vein,* or *midrib,* from which secondary and tertiary veins branch out into the lamina. This vascular system provides the framework of the leaf. The pattern of veins (called *venation*) is a basis for classifying plants. Dicots have *reticulate venation* (weblike), while monocots have *parallel venation* (Figure 3–15).

Leaves drop after a period of being on the stem. In dicots, a zone called the *abscision zone,* located at the base of the petiole, is responsible for the dropping of leaves as they age or as a result of adverse environmental conditions. The base of the petiole is a swollen structure called a *pulvinus,* enlarged as a result of water imbibed by the parenchyma cells in that region. Under moisture stress, the pulvinus cells lose water and collapse, resulting in drooping of the petiole. When the pulvinus becomes turgid again, the leaf is lifted up.

Monocot leaves lack a petiole (Figure 3–16). Instead, they have a base *(sheath)* and a lamina with parallel venation. The junction where the lamina attaches to the sheath may have a structure called a *ligule.* An *auricle* or *stipule* may also be present.

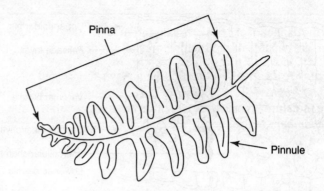

FIGURE 3–17 A fern leaflet (pinna). The fern leaf, called a frond, is typically dissected. The leaf blade is usually segmented into pinnae, which are attached to the main axis (rachis) of the frond. The lower surfaces of the pinnae may be covered with clusters of sporangia enclosed in structures called indusia (singular: *indusium*). These structures give a rust-colored appearance to the pinnae.

FIGURE 3–18 Pine leaves are also referred to as needles. If a number of leaves are held together, each cluster or fascicle of needles forms a cylindrical rod.

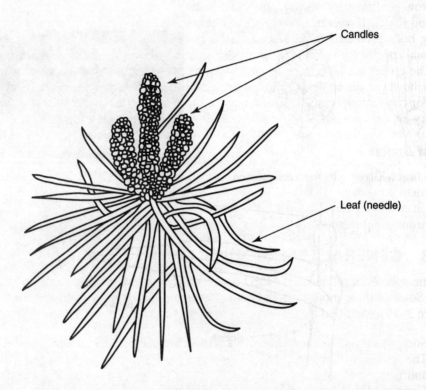

Xerophyte
A plant adapted for growth in arid conditions.

Leaf organization in ferns is similar to that of dicots. However, the lamina is usually compound (Figure 3–17). The venation of mature fern leaves is open and dichotomously branched. Few ferns have reticulate venation. The leaves of conifers are always simple and perennial. They are leathery, tough, and sclerified. The epidermis consists of thick-walled cells. In the pine family (Pinaceae), the leaves are long and needlelike (Figure 3–18). *Transfusion tissue* occurs around the conducting tissue, and resin canals are also characteristic of conifer leaves.

Modified Foliage Leaves

Xeromorphic Foliage Leaves
Certain plants have leaf anatomy and growth forms that are adapted to desert conditions. These plants are called **xerophytes** and are characterized by a thick-walled epidermis and hypodermis. The epidermis is covered by a dense and waxy cuticle. A large number of trichomes are found, and many have salt glands. To decrease transpirational loss under xeric conditions, the external surface of xeromorphic leaves is small. The leaves may be small in size, cylindrical, and succulent. The internal packaging of cells is also tight so as to reduce the surface area for moisture loss. The spongy mesophyll may be completely absent in some cases. Water storage cells

usually occur in xerophytes. In certain species, leaves are shed after only a few weeks. This strategy reduces the danger of excessive transpiration in the event of a severe drought. Such species, however, are capable of producing a fresh flush of leaves when the rains return.

Submerged Foliage Leaves Aquatic plants have submerged foliage leaves. These plants are called *hydrophytes* (e.g., *Eleocharis, Najas,* and *Sagittaria*). Since they do not need to conserve moisture, their leaves have thin cuticles. Similarly, other cell walls tend to be thin. *Gas chambers* in the spongy mesophyll trap internally generated gases, making the leaves buoyant.

Bud Scales

Bud scales (cataphylls) are leaves designed for protecting buds (apical or axillary). This type of leaf is absent in annual plants in which there are no terminal resting buds. Plants that grow continuously or have only brief resting periods (such as tropical plants) also lack bud scales. However, some types of plants such as mango *(Mangifera indica)* have resting buds protected by bud scales. Bud scales are especially critical in temperate perennial species for protection against desiccation from winter winds and insect damage. The epidermal layer may be composed of cells with thickened walls. More commonly, however, the epidermis forms a protective layer of corky bark. Since there is little need for conduction, vascular tissue may occur in limited amounts. Similarly, stomata are very uncommon and, if present, eventually are lost when cork forms.

Floral Bracts

Floral bracts (hypsophylls) are leaves designed to protect the inflorescence during development, as previously stated. They are similar to bud scales but are weaker. Usually green in color and thus capable of photosynthesis, they are less resistant than bud scales to environmental factors.

3.4.3 GENERAL LEAF MODIFICATIONS

In some species, modified leaf forms occur along with the normal forms on the same plant. Some of these modifications bear no resemblance to leaves when viewed casually (Figure 3–19). Modified leaves serve a variety of functions:

1. Some are glands for secretion of various substances.
2. The spines or thorns found on some plants protect the plant against pests and animals.
3. Some modified stems (such as bulbs) have leaves that store food.
4. Under arid or xeric conditions, xerophytes develop a thick-walled epidermis and hypodermis. These structures are covered with wax that resists the attack of chewing insects and also protects the leaves from excessive light.
5. Plants that grow under submerged conditions (hydrophytes) have very thin cuticles and cell walls.

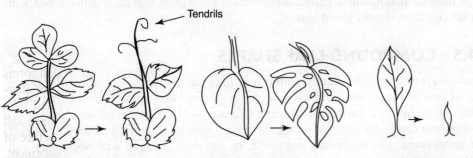

(a) Tendrils of *Pisum*

(b) Fenestrated leaf of *Monstera*

(c) *Berberis* leaf reduced to spine

FIGURE 3–19 Modified leaves. (a) The terminal leaflets of a pea compound leaf may change to become stringy tendrils. (b) When grown under intense light, the solid leaf of *Monstera* develops holes. (c) In certain species, the leaf lamina may be drastically reduced to become a spine.

FIGURE 3–20 Selected common leaf forms: (a) filiform, (b) linear, (c) elliptic, (d) lanceolate, (e) ovate, (f) obvate, (g) hastate, (h) cordate, (i) peltate, (j) spatulate.

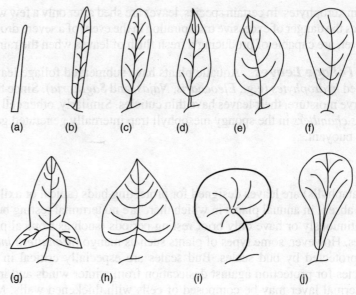

(a)   (b)   (c)   (d)   (e)   (f)

(g)   (h)   (i)   (j)

FIGURE 3–21 Selected common leaf shapes.

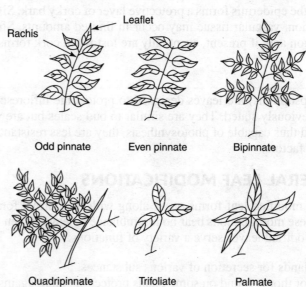

Rachis   Leaflet

Odd pinnate   Even pinnate   Bipinnate

Quadripinnate   Trifoliate   Palmate

3.4.4 FOLIAGE LEAF FORMS

The form of a leaf refers to the shape of the lamina. Leaves range from narrow needles (as in pines) to circular shapes as in water lily *(Victoria amazonia)*. The most common leaf forms are shown in Figure 3–20. Each shape is representative of only the particular class, since there are degrees of expression as well as size in each group. Certain leaf forms involve incomplete or partial separation of the lamina into parts called lobes. Certain species have deeply lobed leaves.

3.4.5 COMPOUND LEAF SHAPES

Simple leaves occur individually with one lamina (single leaf). A *compound leaf* consists of two to many small leaves (leaflets or *pinnae*) arranged on either side of the midrib or rachis in a variety of patterns (Figure 3–21). Compound leaves with this arrangement are called *pinnate leaves*. In certain species (e.g., ferns), the pinna is further subdivided into secondary segments, or *pinnules*. Leaves with secondary segments are called *bipinnate leaves*. Further subdivision produces *tri-* and *quadripinnate leaves*.

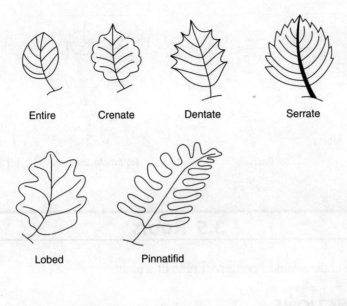

Entire   Crenate   Dentate   Serrate

Lobed   Pinnatifid

FIGURE 3–22 Selected common leaf margins.

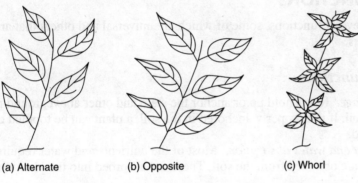

(a) Alternate   (b) Opposite   (c) Whorl

FIGURE 3–23 Selected common leaf arrangements.

3.4.6 LEAF MARGINS

A leaf may have an unindented margin or border or an indented one. In the latter case, there are also degrees of expression, some being more deeply incised than others (Figure 3–22). Some leaf margins or edges are smooth, whereas others are jagged or serrated.

3.4.7 LEAF ARRANGEMENTS

The three basic leaf arrangements are *alternate, opposite,* and *whorl* (Figure 3–23). An alternate arrangement involves leaves set on opposite sides of the branch or stem in a staggered pattern. In opposite arrangement, the placement of leaves is in opposite pairs; in a whorl arrangement, leaves are placed around the stem at each node.

3.4.8 LEAF ATTACHMENT

Figure 3–24 shows a variety of leaf attachments in plants. Grasses have sheathing *(sheath)* attachment to the stem of the plant, as in the case of corn, in which a tubular structure protectively surrounds the stem. Some leaves arise directly from the plant stem and are called *sessile.* Other are attached to the stem by a stalk called a *petiole.*

3.4.9 LEAF TIPS AND BASES

Plants exhibit a wide variety of shapes in the leaf tip and base (Figure 3–25). Tips may be pointed or rounded. In the leaf base, certain species have an indented lamina at the petiole-lamina junction (e.g., *cordate*), and others are straight (e.g., *hastate*).

FIGURE 3–24 Selected common leaf attachments.

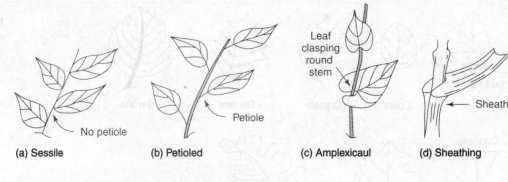

(a) Sessile   (b) Petioled   (c) Amplexicaul   (d) Sheathing

No petiole / Petiole / Leaf clasping round stem / Sheath

3.5 ROOTS

The root is the underground vegetative organ of a plant.

3.5.1 FUNCTIONS

Roots have several functions, some of which are universal and others that are limited to certain species.

General Functions

1. *Anchorage.* Roots hold up or anchor the stem and other aboveground plant parts to the soil. If not properly anchored in the soil, a plant can be toppled easily by the wind.
2. *Nutrient and water absorption.* Most of the nutrients and water required for plant growth are obtained from the soil. These are absorbed into the plant through its roots.
3. *Hormone synthesis.* Some hormones (cytokinins and gibberelins) required for shoot development and growth are synthesized in the roots.

Specialized Functions

1. *Storage of carbohydrates.* Some species (e.g., sweet potato) have swollen roots that store carbohydrates (Figure 3–26). The plant falls back on such food reserves during times of limited food.
2. *Aerial support.* Even though roots are mostly underground, some species have *aerial roots*. In some grasses, such as corn, modified roots called **prop roots** provide additional anchorage for the plant to its growing medium (Figure 3–27). In climbers, including some ivy, aerial roots enable plants to cling to walls and other structures that they climb (Figure 3–28).

Prop Roots
Adventitious roots that originate from the shoot and pass through the air before entering the soil.

3.5.2 TYPES OF ROOTS AND ROOT SYSTEMS

Roots that develop from a seed are called *seminal roots*. Seminal roots are called the true roots of the plant. A germinated seed produces a young root called a *radicle*. The radicle grows to become the *primary root* of the plant from which *lateral roots* (or *secondary roots*) emerge (Figure 3–29). Any "root" (other than the true root) that originates from other parts of the plant is said to be *adventitious* (e.g., the prop roots in corn or nodal roots or crown roots in other plants). There are two basic root systems.

Tap Root
The radicle is more prominently enlarged than any of the laterals.

1. *Tap root.* The **tap root** system, also called the *primary root* system, is characterized by a large central axis that is larger than the lateral roots that develop from it (Figure 3–30). A tap root grows deep into the soil as the

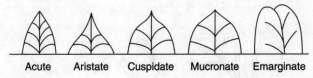

Acute   Aristate   Cuspidate   Mucronate   Emarginate

(a) Leaf tips

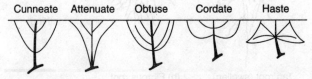

Cunneate   Attenuate   Obtuse   Cordate   Haste

(b) Leaf bases

FIGURE 3–25 Selected common leaf tips and bases.

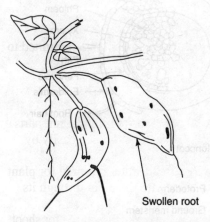

Swollen root

FIGURE 3–26 A swollen root. This root modification may assume a conical and elongated shape, as in carrot (*Daucus carota*), or a round shape, as in radish (*Raphanus sativus*).

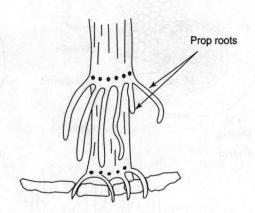

Prop roots

FIGURE 3–27 Prop roots of corn (*Zea mays*).

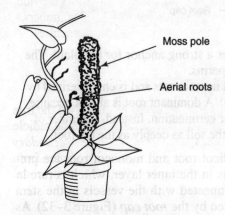

Moss pole

Aerial roots

FIGURE 3–28 Aerial roots are used in certain species to aid in the climbing of vines onto nearby physical supports.

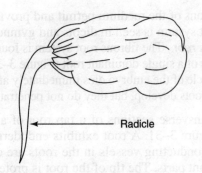

Radicle

FIGURE 3–29 A radicle of a germinating seed.

FIGURE 3–30 (a) Tap root system. A tap root may be a swollen root, as found in carrot (*Daucus carota*) and radish (*Raphanus sativus*). (b) Fibrous root system.

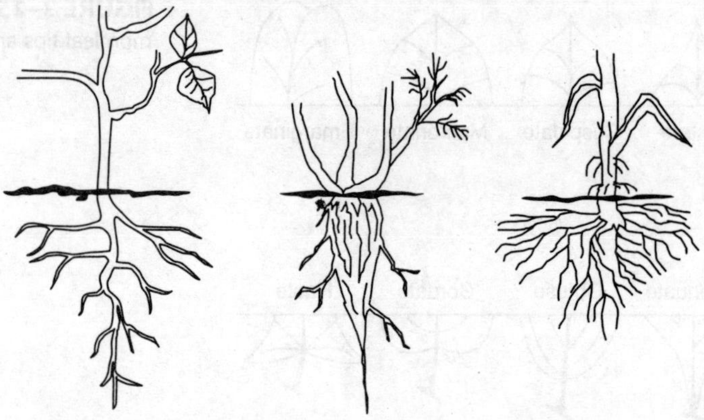

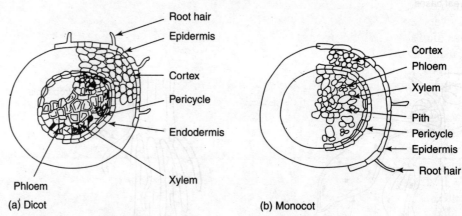

(a) Tap root   Tap root (swollen)   (b) Fibrous root

FIGURE 3–31 Transverse sections of dicot and monocot roots.

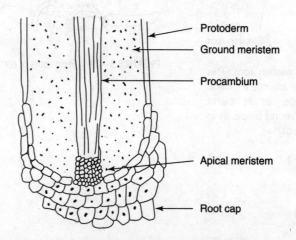

FIGURE 3–32 A longitudinal section of a root cap region.

conditions of the medium permit and provides a strong anchor for the plant. The tap root system is seen in dicots and gymnosperms.

2. *Fibrous root.* The fibrous root system is found in monocots and is characterized by the lack of a single dominant root (Figure 3–30). A dominant root is absent because the radicle of the embryo dies immediately after germination. Instead, a number of lateral roots develop, but they do not penetrate the soil as deeply as the tap root.

The transverse sections of a tap root of a dicot root and monocot root are presented in Figure 3–31. A root exhibits endodermis in the inner layer, which is rare in stems. The conducting vessels in the roots are connected with the vessels in the stem and other plant parts. The tip of the root is protected by the *root cap* (Figure 3–32). As the root pushes its way through the soil, it sheds its peripheral cells. These cells are replaced as they are shed. The root epidermis is usually one cell layer thick. One feature of the root system is the occurrence of *root hairs,* structures often associated with absorption of water and minerals from the soil. The density of these hairs within the soil depends on the environmental conditions. Roots usually produce more hairs under dry conditions and less under moist conditions and are relatively short-lived. When roots grow through a medium of differential nutritional quality and moisture, the parts in more favorable conditions (high moisture, high fertility) assume an accelerated growth period called *compensatory growth,* while the growth of other parts slows down.

3.6 STRUCTURE OF WOOD

All plants consist of what is called a *primary vegetative body.* This body is made up of the three basic organs—stem, leaf, and root. These organs, however, occur in their soft form (i.e., they have no wood). In herbaceous dicots, ferns, and most monocots, this primary vegetative phase persists throughout the lifetime of the plant. However, nonherbaceous dicots and gymnosperms are able to initiate a secondary body within the primary one using *secondary tissues.* The result is a woody plant with a large body. For example, instead of being like an herb, a tree is the result of secondary growth. It is important to note that even in woody plants, primary vegetative tissue may occur in certain parts.

The tissue responsible for part of the secondary growth in woody plants is called the **vascular cambium.** This tissue occurs as a continuous ring of several layers of cells located between the xylem and the phloem tissues. The region where it occurs is called the *cambial region.* In plants such as cactus and euphorbia, the cambial layer is less pronounced and confined to the vascular bundles.

In active plants, the cells in the cambial region divide to produce cells that differentiate into conducting tissues. The secondary growth that occurs to the interior of the vascular cambium produces the secondary xylem, or **wood.** The activity of the vascular cambium is influenced by the environment, specifically by moisture and temperature. Under favorable conditions the cambium is active, but it is dormant under adverse weather conditions such as drought and cold temperature. Once formed, the secondary xylem remains in the stem. As the new layer develops, the older layer is pushed outward in a radial manner. This process makes the plant grow larger and stronger. In situations in which cambial activity is influenced by the environment (especially temperature), a cyclical pattern develops such that **annual rings** representing the previous secondary xylem tissues are observable (Figure 3–33). In such cases, the age of woody plants can be estimated from the number of such rings found in the wood. However, in species such as ebony (*Diospyros ebenum*) that grow in benign or seasonless tropical regions, annual rings are not formed. On the other hand, plants that grow under conditions of erratic moisture, such as that in arid and semiarid regions, may produce more than one growth ring per year in response to moisture patterns. The science of studying growth rings is called *dendrochronology.*

Wood may be classified according to the kind of plant that produces it. Nonflowering plants found in temperate regions (e.g., spruce, pine, fir, and larch) produce wood

Vascular Cambium
A sheetlike fundamental type of meristem that produces secondary xylem and phloem.

Wood
Secondary xylem.

Annual Rings
Cylinders of secondary xylem added to the stem of a woody plant in successive years.

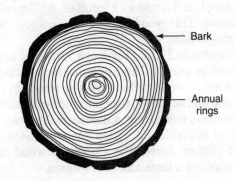

- Bark
- Annual rings

FIGURE 3–33 Annual rings of a woody dicot stem. A ring is equivalent to one year's growth of the xylem tissue.

FIGURE 3–34 Heartwood and sapwood. Heartwood consists of nonconducting tissue; sapwood is still-functioning xylem tissue.

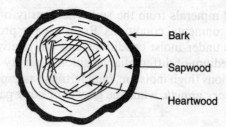

FIGURE 3–35 Tension wood. This reaction wood of dicots is found on the upper side of the branch and consists of large amounts of gelatinous fibers.

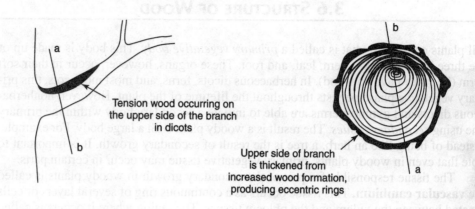

Tension wood occurring on the upper side of the branch in dicots

Upper side of branch is thickened from increased wood formation, producing eccentric rings

FIGURE 3–36 Compression wood. In conifers the reaction wood forms on the lower side of the branch. This wood is heavier and more brittle than normal wood.

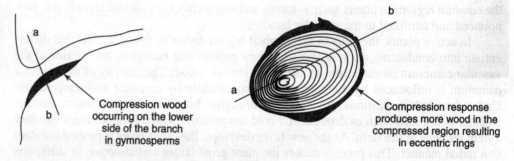

Compression wood occurring on the lower side of the branch in gymnosperms

Compression response produces more wood in the compressed region resulting in eccentric rings

Softwood
Wood produced by a conifer.

Reaction Wood
Wood produced in response to a stem that has lost its vertical position.

that is relatively homogeneous. This wood, called **softwood,** is composed predominantly of tracheids without vessels. Because softwoods are readily penetrable by nails, they are widely used in construction. They contain large amounts of lignin, which makes them desirable for use as lumber, because lignin stabilizes the wood and reduces warping.

The wood of dicots found in temperate and tropical zones is composed predominantly of fibers and vessels. These structures make the wood stronger and denser, the resultant wood being called *hardwood*. Examples of hardwood include walnut, oak, maple, ash, and hickory. These woods are characteristically hard to nail and hence not preferred for construction.

Wood may also be classified on the basis of location and function. Conduction of sap occurs only in outer secondary xylem where the wood is relatively weak. This part of the wood is called *sapwood* and is light and pale colored (Figure 3–34). The center of the wood is dry, dark colored, and dense as a result of the deposits of metabolites such as gums, tannins, and resins. This wood is called *heartwood*. Sapwood converts into heartwood as the plant grows older.

Branches of trees are attached to the trunk at a variety of angles. They sway in the wind and are weighed down by gravity. These external factors cause the plant to respond by developing a special kind of wood called **reaction wood.** In dicots, this specialized wood is called *tension wood* and occurs on the upper side of the stem (Figure 3–35). This wood contains gelatinous fibers made from cellulose, making the wood brittle and difficult to cut. Reaction wood in conifers is called *compression wood* and occurs on the lower side of the branch (Figure 3–36). The amount of wood in the compressed area increases with time and contains a large amount of lignin.

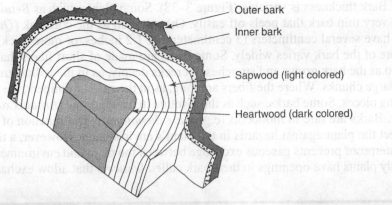

Outer bark
Inner bark
Sapwood (light colored)
Heartwood (dark colored)

FIGURE 3–37 Tree bark, which is comprised of the tissues outside the cambium, including the phloem.

(a)

(b)

(c)

FIGURE 3–38 Tree bark differs in thickness and roughness. Some are thin and flaky, whereas others are thick and firm.   *(Source: George Acquaah)*

3.7 BARK

As previously stated, the secondary xylem produces wood. The secondary phloem is a major part of the **bark** of a tree (Figure 3–37). The bark develops in perennial plants as the epidermis is replaced by a structure called the *periderm*. The periderm is composed of a mixture of cells, some of which are meristematic and are called the *phellogen*, or *cork cambium*. The bark includes the cork cambium and the secondary phloem tissue.

Bark
The part of the stem or root exterior to the vascular cambium.

Bark thickness is variable (Figure 3–38). Some plants, such as *Betula platyphylla*, have very thin bark that peels off easily. Others, such as the cork oak *(Quercus suber)*, may have several centimeters (3 centimeters, or 1.2 inches, or more thick) of bark. The texture of the bark varies widely. Some barks are made of short fibers that are not elastic, so as the bark grows and stretches, it cracks deeply, as in the willow tree, and breaks into large chunks. Where the fibers are long, as in the case of junipers, the bark peels off in long pieces. Some barks, such as those found in the madrone *(Arbutus xalapensis),* are flaky. Barks are rare in monocots (e.g., *Aloe dichotoma*). The function of the bark is to protect the plant against hazards in the plant's environment. However, a thick bark that is waterproof prevents gaseous exchange between the plant and environment. Therefore, woody plants have openings in their bark called *lenticels* that allow exchange of gases.

3.8 FLOWERS

The *flower* is the part of the plant most readily associated with the field of horticulture. It contains the reproductive organs of flowering plants (angiosperms). A typical flower has four parts: *sepal, petal, stamen,* and *pistil.* A developing flower bud is protected by leaflike structures called *sepals,* which are collectively called *calyx.* The most showy parts of the flower are the petals, which collectively are called a *corolla* (Figure 3–39). Petals have color and fragrance that attract pollinators to the flower. The texture of petals may be smooth, or the epidermis may have trichomes (hairs). Usually, petals drop soon after the flower has been pollinated.

The petals in some flowers are about the same size and shape, such as those found in magnolia. These flowers are said to be *actinomorphic* (Figure 3–40). In families that have different types of petals on one flower (such as occurs in clover) the plants are said to be *zygomorphic*. Sometimes the corolla is made up of individual petals, and the flower is described as *apopetalous*. Some flowers (e.g., honeysuckle) have a fused corolla *(sympetalous),* forming a *corolla tube.*

The collective term for the male reproductive organ parts is *androecium*. The stamen is comprised of a stalk called the *filament* that is capped by a structure called an

FIGURE 3–39 Parts of a typical flower.

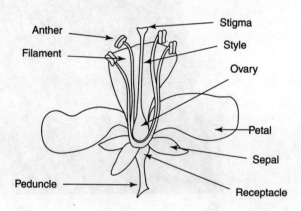

FIGURE 3–40 Selected flower shapes.

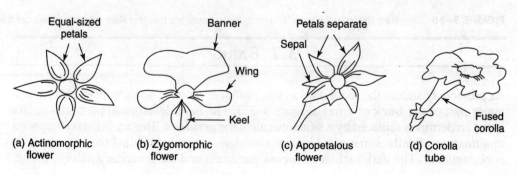

(a) Actinomorphic flower   (b) Zygomorphic flower   (c) Apopetalous flower   (d) Corolla tube

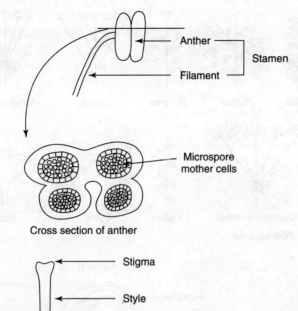

FIGURE 3–41 Whole and cross-sectional view of male flower parts.

Anther

Stamen

Filament

Microspore mother cells

Cross section of anther

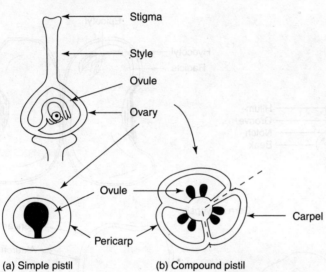

FIGURE 3–42 Whole and cross-sectional view of female flower parts.

Stigma

Style

Ovule

Ovary

Ovule

Carpel

Pericarp

(a) Simple pistil   (b) Compound pistil

anther, the sack that contains the pollen grains (Figure 3–41). The female reproductive parts are collectively called *gynoecium.* The *carpel* consists of three structures: the *style,* which is similar to the filament; is tubular and capped by the *stigma,* a receptacle for receiving pollen grains; and the third structure is the *ovary,* which contains ovules (Figure 3–42). Gymnosperms have no flowers. Instead, their reproductive structures are called *strobili* (singular: *strobilus*).

If a flower has both male and female parts it is said to be *perfect.* When all of the four parts of a flower are present, a *complete flower* exists. If one or more parts are missing, the flower is said to be *incomplete.* Certain flowers are either male or female and, therefore, *imperfect.* In plants described as *monoecious,* both male and female flowers occur in one plant but are physically located on different parts. In sweet corn, the male flowers *(tassel)* occur at the terminal parts while the female flowers *(silk)* occur on the middle region on the leaf axil. Cucumber, walnut, and pecan are also monoecious, and as such both sexes are required for fruiting to occur in cultivation. In *dioecious* plants, such as date palm, holly, and asparagus, however, one plant is exclusively either male or female.

Flowers may occur individually *(solitary)* or in a bunch or cluster *(inflorescence,* as in urn plant, lupine, and snapdragon). The main stalk of an inflorescence is called a *peduncle;* the smaller stalks are called *pedicels.* There are three basic types of inflorescence: *head* (e.g., daisy and sunflower), *spike* (e.g., gladiolus and wheat), and *umbel* (e.g., onion and carrot). These and other types of flower clusters are shown in Figure 3–43.

The physical structure and display of certain flowers make them capable of *self-pollination* (pollen grains from the anther are deposited on the stigma of the same flower). Since the mating system excludes foreign pollen, the species tends to be genetically pure,

FIGURE 3-43 Inflorescence type.

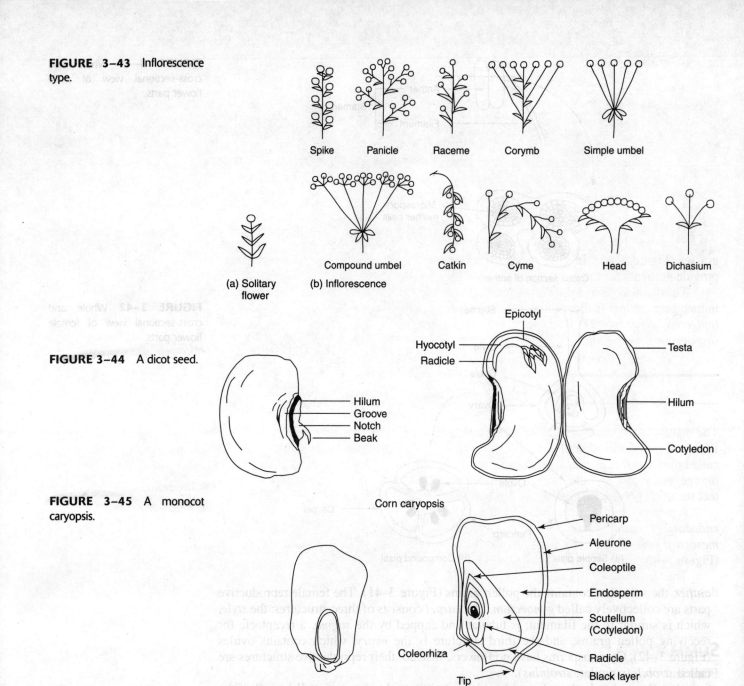

Spike   Panicle   Raceme   Corymb   Simple umbel

(a) Solitary flower   Compound umbel   Catkin   Cyme   Head   Dichasium

(b) Inflorescence

FIGURE 3-44 A dicot seed.

Hilum, Groove, Notch, Beak

Epicotyl, Hyocotyl, Radicle, Testa, Hilum, Cotyledon

FIGURE 3-45 A monocot caryopsis.

Corn caryopsis

(a) Whole   (b) Transverse section

Pericarp, Aleurone, Coleoptile, Endosperm, Scutellum (Cotyledon), Radicle, Black layer, Coleorhiza, Tip

or homozygous. Imperfect flowers have no choice but to engage in *cross-pollination* (pollen transferred from one flower and deposited on a different flower). Insects, birds, mammals, and wind are all agents of this process that promotes heterozygosity by permitting foreign pollen to be deposited.

3.9 SEED

Monocot
A type of angiosperm characterized by seeds with only one seed leaf or cotyledon.

Horticultural plants may be seed bearing (gymnosperms and angiosperms) or nonseed bearing *(cryptogams)*. Seeds remain dormant until the proper environmental conditions for germination prevail. A seed contains an *embryo,* or miniature plant (sporophyte), that is encased in a seed coat, or *testa,* in dicots and a pericarp in **monocots.** In dicots, the embryo is sandwiched between two structures called cotyledons, which function as storage organs (Figure 3-44). Monocots have one cotyledon, which is called a *scutellum* in

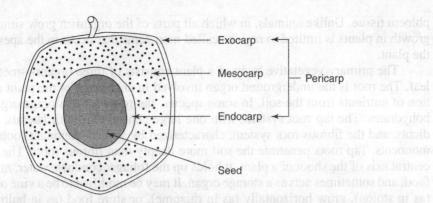

FIGURE 3–46 Parts of a typical fruit.

grasses (Figure 3–45). In grasses, the *endosperm* is the storage organ. The cotyledons provide nutrients for the growing embryo until the seedling is able to photosynthesize.

The **dicot** seed has a tiny opening called a *hilum,* through which water and air enter to initiate germination. In dicots, the cotyledons are pushed above the soil during germination (*epigeous germination*), whereas in monocots, the cotyledon remains underground (*hypogeous germination*).

Dicot
A type of angiosperm characterized by seeds with two seed leaves or cotyledons.

3.10 FRUITS

The mature ovary, together with the associated parts, form the *fruit*. In most species, the fruit bears *seeds*. In others, the fruit may develop without fertilization, a phenomenon called **parthenocarpy**. Parthenocarpic fruits (e.g., Cavendish banana, Washington navel orange, and many fig cultivars) are seedless. The natural function of the fruit is to protect the seed; however, animals and humans most desire the fruit.

A typical fruit has three regions: the *exocarp* (the outer covering or skin), the *endocarp* (a boundary around the seed and may be hard and stony or papery), and the *mesocarp* (the often fleshy tissue that occurs between the exocarp and the endocarp) (Figure 3–46).

The anatomy of fruits is discussed in great detail in Chapter 2, where such description was necessary to help in the classification of fruits.

Parthenocarpy
Development of fruit without sexual fertilization.

SUMMARY

Plant anatomy is the science of cataloging, describing, and understanding the functions of plant structures. Eukaryotes have various levels of structural organization. The cell is the fundamental unit of organization of living things. It is totipotent, grows, and ages. Cells consist of a variety of organelles such as mitochondria, chloroplasts, and nuclei, each with specific functions. The mitochondria are involved in energy-related functions, and the chloroplasts in photosynthesis, or food manufacture. The nucleus houses the chromosomes that contain most of the genetic material of the plant.

Plant cells undergo differentiation to produce a variety of types, namely, parenchyma, collenchyma, and sclerenchyma. These types differ in cell wall characteristics and have specific structural roles. Cells aggregate to form tissues with specific functions. Parenchyma cells are thin walled and occur in tissues that have secretory, photosynthetic, and growth functions. Collenchyma and sclerenchyma are thicker walled and have mechanical roles in plant-strengthening tissues. Apart from simple tissues, cells aggregate to form complex tissues such as the epidermis (protective role) and those with secretory functions as found in nectaries. Some complex tissues are involved in the movement of organic and inorganic solutes through the plant. The xylem tissues move water and minerals from the roots to the leaves, where they are used in photosynthesis. The photosynthates are transported from leaves to other parts of the plant through the phloem tissue. Unlike animals, in which all parts of the organism grow simultaneously, growth in plants is limited to regions called meristems that occur in the apex or axils of the plant.

The primary vegetative body of a plant consists of three organs—root, stem, and leaf. The root is the underground organ involved in anchorage of the plant and absorption of nutrients from the soil. In some species, the roots act as storage organs for carbohydrates. The tap root system, with one large central axis with laterals, is found in dicots, and the fibrous root system, characterized by several dominant roots, is seen in monocots. Tap roots penetrate the soil more deeply than fibrous roots. The stem is the central axis of the shoot of a plant. It holds up the foliage; conducts water, minerals, and food; and sometimes acts as a storage organ. It may be modified to be a vine or may creep (as in stolon), grow horizontally (as in rhizome), or store food (as in bulb, tuber, and corm). The leaf is the primary photosynthetic apparatus of the plant and is usually green in color. It may also be modified to be a storage organ. It varies in shape, size, form, margin, and arrangement.

In dicots, secondary growth in nonherbaceous species produces wood, or secondary xylem. The inner layers of the wood that have lost conducting ability constitute the heartwood, and the outer layer forms the sapwood. Gymnosperms produce softwood because they lack certain strengthening fibers. The secondary phloem produces a tough outer layer called bark that replaces the epidermis. The bark in oak species may be several centimeters thick.

The flower, showy and colorful, is the reproductive organ of the flowering plant. The male organ comprises the filament and the anther (contains pollen grains). The female organ, the carpel, consists of a style that is capped by a stigma and an ovary that contains ovules. After fertilization, a seed is produced. It contains an embryo, or a miniature plant. In dicot seeds, the embryo is sandwiched between two storage organs called cotyledons. Only one cotyledon occurs in monocots. When dicot seeds are planted, they germinate by pushing the cotyledons above the soil surface (epigeous germination). Monocots leave one cotyledon below the ground (hypogeous germination).

REFERENCES AND SUGGESTED READING

Esau, K. 1977. *Anatomy of seed plants*, 2d ed. New York: John Wiley & Sons.

Hartmann, H. T., A. M. Kofrnek, V. E. Rubatzky, and W. J. Flocker. 1988. *Plant science: Growth, development, and utilization of cultivated plants*, 2d ed. Englewood Cliffs, N.J.: Prentice Hall.

Hayward, H. E. 1967. *The structure of economic plants*. New York: Lubrect & Crammer.

Moore, R., and W. D. Clark. 1994. *Botany: Form and function*. Dubuque, Iowa: Wm. C. Brown Publishers.

Stern, K. R. 1997. *Introductory plant biology*, 2d ed. Dubuque, Iowa: Wm. C. Brown Publishers.

Wilson, L., and W. E. Loomis. 1967. *Botany*, 4th ed. New York: Holt, Rinehart & Winston.

Excellent and well-illustrated presentation of plant anatomy
  http://dallas.tamu.edu/weeds/anat.html

Excellent microscope slides of cross sections of plant parts
  http://www.unlv.edu/Colleges/Sciences/Biology/Schulte/Anatomy/Anatomy.html

Simple and well-illustrated description of plant structure
  http://www.emc.maricopa.edu/faculty/farabee/biobk/BioBookPLANTANAT.html

PRACTICAL EXPERIENCE

LABORATORY

1. Obtain prepared slides of transverse sections of dicot stems and roots. Compare and contrast the two kinds of stems and the two kinds of roots.

2. Obtain samples of modified roots:
   a. rhizome
   b. corm
   c. stolon
   d. bulb

3. Obtain samples of leaves from different species showing a variety of forms, arrangement, and margin types.

GREENHOUSE

Plant a legume seed and a grass seed. Compare and contrast germination or emergence types, the root systems, leaf characteristics, and other anatomical differences.

FIELD TRIP

1. Take a walk across your campus and observe the variety of types of tree bark.

2. Visit a botanical garden or a greenhouse to observe the following:
   a. flower types
   b. leaf types—arrangement, form, and margins

OUTCOMES ASSESSMENT

1. How can an understanding of plant anatomy help one to become a better horticulturalist?
2. Distinguish, giving examples, between a bulb and a corm.
3. Distinguish, giving examples, between a tunicate bulb and a scaly bulb.
4. Discuss the importance of modified stems and roots in the horicultural industry.
5. Discuss the diversity in leaf margins in plants.
6. Describe how wood is formed. What are annual rings?
7. Besides ornamental value, in what ways are flowers important in horticulture?
8. Compare and contrast monocot and dicot seeds.
9. What are adventitious roots? How important are they to plants?

Plant Growth Environment

PURPOSE AND EXPECTED OUTCOMES

The purpose of this chapter is to list and discuss the nature and roles of the essential plant growth environmental factors and how they can be manipulated to enhance the performance of plants.

After studying this chapter, the student should be able to

1. List the important plant growth factors in both the aboveground and belowground environments.
2. Discuss the roles of each environmental factor in plant growth and development.
3. Describe how each environmental factor may be managed for better plant performance.

[COLOR PLATES—*see color plate 4* for additional chapter photos]

OVERVIEW

Plant growth and development do not occur in a vacuum but in an environment. The genetic blueprint directs the development of the plant within an environment. Two individuals of identical genotype are likely to manifest differences in appearance (phenotype) if they develop in different environments. In other words, one can alter the course of a plant's growth and development by manipulating its environment. Such manipulation of plants can be advantageous for humans. The implication and practical application for horticulture are that the output, in terms of yield and quality of produce of a plant, to some extent is within the control of the grower. To manipulate the plant's environment, it is important first to know what elements of the general environment affect plant growth and how they exert their influence.

Factors that affect plant growth may be divided into two broad categories, namely, those that occur in the *aboveground environment* and those that occur in the *belowground environment*. Some factors occur in both categories.

4.1 CLIMATE, WEATHER, AND HORTICULTURE

Climate is a combination of aboveground environmental factors—*temperature, moisture, sunlight,* and *air*—and is characteristic of a region. It determines what crops can be cultivated in a given area. Some regions receive 0 to 25 centimeters (0 to 9.9 inches) of precipitation per annum and are said to be *arid,* or dry, whereas other regions may receive 75 to 100 centimeters (29.5 to 39.4 inches) of precipitation and are called *humid* regions. The immediate environment of plants is called the *microclimate.* This environment plays a role in plant processes such as *evaporation* (loss of moisture from any surface) and *transpiration* (loss of moisture by plants) and also in the incidence of disease.

    Weather is the composite effect of the interplay of temperature, precipitation, wind, light, and relative humidity as it pertains to a specific locality. These weather factors are dynamic, having daily, weekly, monthly, and seasonal patterns of variation. These local patterns are repeated year after year, creating the *climate* of the specific area. Regional weather patterns are affected by factors including altitude, latitude, and geographic features such as mountains and large bodies of water. The higher you go, the cooler it becomes. Oceans and large lakes moderate temperature extremes of nearby land masses. Vegetables and fruit crops are delicate and require stable climates for optimal production. They are grown on the leeward side of large lakes; grain crops, which perform well under drier and less stable climatic conditions, are grown on the windward side. Large bodies of water also store heat in fall and are cold reservoirs in spring. The stored heat has a warming effect on the land around the lake by delaying the onset of frost on the leeward side (Figure 4–1). Valley floors are colder than hillsides because cold, dense air sinks to lower levels. A belt of warm air above the cold air in the valley is called a *thermal belt* and is a region where conditions are conducive to fruit production (Figure 4–2).

4.2 ABOVEGROUND ENVIRONMENT

The aboveground environmental factors may be classified into two types—*abiotic* (nonliving) and *biotic* (involving living organisms).

4.2.1 ABIOTIC FACTORS
The abiotic factors in the environment are air, water, temperature, and light.

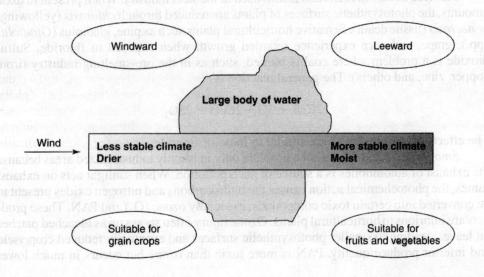

FIGURE 4–1 The role of large bodies of water in altering the climate.

FIGURE 4–2 The formation of thermal belts. Colder and heavier air occurring at higher altitudes moves down and pushes the warmer and lighter air upward. This air convection leaves the higher band of land warmer. This thermal belt is warm and permits the culture of frost-sensitive crops on certain parts of slopes in areas that are normally too cold for growing crops.

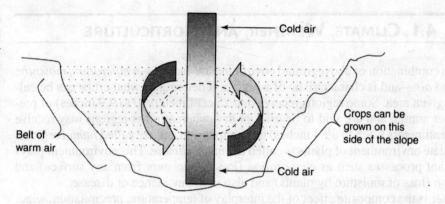

Cold air

Crops can be grown on this side of the slope

Belt of warm air

Cold air

Air

Air is a gaseous environment that consists of many components—most importantly, nitrogen, carbon dioxide, hydrogen, and oxygen. Oxygen is required for respiration, the process by which energy is released from stored plant food for use by plants. The other role of air in plant growth is in the amount of water it holds. The water content of air is called *humidity* and is measured in units of **relative humidity** (*RH*) by using an instrument called a *psychrometer*. Humidity depends on *vapor pressure* (concentration of water vapor in the air) and temperature. Relative humidity decreases when temperature increases and water vapor remains constant. The amount of water needed by a plant for normal growth is directly related to the humidity or water content of the air. Plants lose moisture through the process of transpiration, and soil loses moisture through evaporation. A combination of these two processes is called **evapotranspiration.** When the air is dry, evaporation occurs at a much more rapid rate than when the air is moist. Although soil-stored moisture is depleted slowly, high humidity encourages the incidence of disease.

Air movement is also important to crop production. Strong winds can damage trees in the landscape as well as food crops. *Wind breaks* may be erected in windy regions to reduce wind velocity so that crops can be produced successfully. Windy conditions, combined with high temperatures, increase moisture loss by transpiration. Strong winds adversely affect the success of pollination involving insects and may damage tender leaves and young fruits and consequently reduce crop yield.

Relative Humidity
The ratio of the weight of water vapor in a given quantity of air to the total weight of water vapor that quantity of air can hold at a given temperature, expressed as a percentage.

Evapotranspiration
The total loss of water by evaporation from the soil surface and by transpiration from plants, from a given area, and over a specified period.

Ozone
A form of oxygen found in the stratosphere that is more effective than ordinary oxygen in shielding living organisms from the adverse effects of intense ultraviolet radiation.

Air Pollution   Environmental pollutants are a problem, especially in areas where heavy industrialized activities occur. At significant levels, air pollutants inhibit photosynthetic processes, resulting in reduced crop yield. The major air pollutants are *fluoride, sulfur dioxide,* **ozone,** *peroxyacetyl nitrate (PAN),* and *pesticides.*

Fluoride occurs in rocks and is also used in the steel industry. When present in toxic amounts, the photosynthetic surfaces of plants are reduced through *chlorosis* (yellowing) or *necrosis* (tissue death). Sensitive horticultural plants such as pine, gladiolus (*Gladiolus* spp.), grape, and corn experience retarded growth when exposed to fluoride. Sulfur dioxide is a problem where coal is burned, such as in the ore-smelting industry (iron, copper, zinc, and others). The general reaction is

$$2CuS + 3O_2 - 2CuO + 2SO_2$$

The effects of sulfur dioxide are similar to those of fluoride.

Smog (*smoke* and *fog*) is not a problem only in heavily industrialized areas because the exhaust of automobiles is a source of such pollution. When sunlight acts on exhaust fumes, the photochemical action causes the hydrocarbons and nitrogen oxides present to be converted into certain toxic compounds, especially ozone (O_3) and PAN. These products are injurious to horticultural plants. Ozone injury often shows up as bleached patches on leaves, leading to smaller photosynthetic surfaces and eventually reduced crop yield and inferior produce quality. PAN is more toxic than ozone but occurs in much lower concentration in the atmosphere. A class of compounds called *chlorofluorocarbons (CFCs)* release chlorine upon breaking down. This chlorine rises and, upon reaching the upper atmosphere, reacts with ozone, reducing it to oxygen gas. The ozone layer thus becomes depleted, allowing more harmful ultraviolet radiation to reach the earth. An example of CFC is *freon,* a refrigerant and propellant in aerosol cans. Aerosols used in homes (coolants in refrigerators and some cosmetic sprays) also can deplete the ozone layer. Pesticides are sources of environmental pollution. Arsenic-based insecticides, for example, cause chlorosis and necrosis, resulting in poor growth and quality of plant products.

Acid Rain   Acid rain is a consequence of air pollution, because the pollutants in the atmosphere are brought down in the various kinds of precipitation (rain, ice, and snow). When the pH of rain is below 5.6, it is described as **acid precipitation.** Acid rain is produced when sulfur oxide and nitrogen oxide react with water in the atmosphere to form sulfuric acid and nitric acid, respectively. Normal (unpolluted) rain has a pH of about 6.0. Acid rain with a pH of less than 3 has been recorded in heavily industrialized and polluted parts of Scotland, Norway, and Ireland. The eastern United States and southeastern Canada record an average pH of 4 to 4.5 in rain water. Pollutants can remain airborne for long distances. Thus, nonindustrial areas can experience acid rain because of a drift effect from polluting sources in neighboring countries.

> **Acid Precipitation**
> Precipitation (e.g., rain, snow, sleet, and hail) with a pH of less than 5.6.

Mychorrhizal fungi are known to be affected adversely by acid rain. Acidified lakes have shown dramatically reduced fish populations. This decline is attributed in part to aluminum toxicity. Aluminum is a trace element in plant nutrition but comprises about 5 percent of the earth's crust. It is not soluble under alkaline conditions. Acid rain provides the low pH required to dissolve soil aluminum and other heavy metals such as lead, mercury, and cadmium. Acid rain is also suspected in chemical damage to certain forests.

Water

Role   Water is required for germination, the first step in plant growth. Water from the aboveground environment comes from precipitation (including rain and snow) and evaporation. In terms of plant growth needs, the distribution of precipitation throughout the crop growth period is as important as the total amount. Water is needed for photosynthesis, the process by which plants manufacture food. Water is the medium by which minerals and photosynthates are transported through the plant. Plants are cooled through the process of transpiration.

Moisture Stress   The effect of **moisture stress** on horticultural plants is discussed more fully later in this chapter. Lack of moisture in the aboveground environment makes the air less humid, thereby increasing its drying power. The rates of plant processes such as transpiration, diffusion, and evaporation are affected directly by the vapor pressure of the air (the part of the total air pressure attributable to the water molecules present in the air). As previously indicated, if air temperature is increased but the amount of water vapor in the air stays the same, the relative humidity of the air decreases. Excessive moisture in the microclimate of plants predisposes them to disease. Horticultural plants grown indoors are sometimes given a misty spray of water to increase the humidity of the microclimate, especially in winter when the heaters are turned on to warm the building.

> **Moisture Stress**
> Occurs when a plant is unable to absorb adequate water to replace that lost by transpiration.

Temperature

Temperature, the intensity factor of heat energy, is important in all plant biological, chemical, and physiological processes. It regulates the rate of chemical reactions and consequently regulates the rate of plant growth. As a contributing factor to climate, it plays a major role in plant adaptation and the length of the growing season. The kind of horticultural plants that can be grown in an area therefore depends on temperature (in conjunction with rainfall, light, and air movements). As previously indicated,

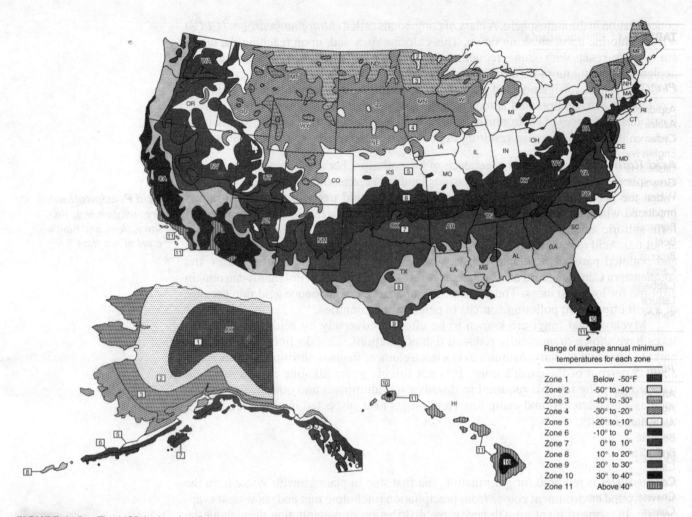

Range of average annual minimum
temperatures for each zone

Zone 1	Below -50°F	
Zone 2	-50° to -40°	
Zone 3	-40° to -30°	
Zone 4	-30° to -20°	
Zone 5	-20° to -10°	
Zone 6	-10° to 0°	
Zone 7	0° to 10°	
Zone 8	10° to 20°	
Zone 9	20° to 30°	
Zone 10	30° to 40°	
Zone 11	Above 40°	

FIGURE 4–3   The USDA plant hardiness zone map. *(Source: USDA)*

Hardy Plants
Plants adapted to cold temperatures or other adverse climatic conditions of an area.

the U.S. Department of Agriculture (USDA) has developed a *plant hardiness zone* map that shows crop adaptation in the United States (Figure 4–3). **Hardy plants** are those that are tolerant of cold temperatures and adverse climate. Most plants can live and grow within temperature ranges of 0 to 50°C (32 to 122°F). However, sensitivity to cold temperature limits the regions in which crops can be cultivated successfully. High temperatures may kill plants outright or reduce production when they coincide with flowering and fruiting periods. Plants representative of those adapted to the various hardiness zones are presented in Table 4–1.

The damage caused depends on the physiological state of the plant. If actively growing, succulent tissue in plant parts such as flower buds are more susceptible than dormant tissue to cold damage. *Frost damage* is critical when flower buds start to open. Warm-season crops are more prone to frost damage. Although low temperatures may harm some plants, others flower only after receiving cold treatment to break dormancy. Chilling is part of the culture of some ornamental bulbs such as daffodil *(Narcissus)* and hyacinth *(Hyacinthus)*. Biennial plants frequently require cold treatment or winter chilling to flower.

To improve plants' response to cold temperatures, growers may put them through a process called **hardening**. This process involves exposing plants gradually to an increasingly harsh environment so that they slowly acquire resistance to the adverse conditions.

Hardening Off
Adapting plants to outdoor conditions by withholding water, lowering the temperature, or altering the nutrient supply.

Protection against Cold Temperature–Related Losses   The best protection against frost damage is to plant *after* the threat of frost has passed. However, this

98   *Chapter 4   Plant Growth Environment*

TABLE 4–1   Climatic Adaptation of Selected Plants

Cool-Temperature Plants

Plant	Scientific Name
Aspidistra	*Aspidistra* spp.
Azalea	*Rhododendron* spp.
Cyclamen	*Cyclamen* spp.
English ivy	*Hedera helix*
Fatshedera	*Fatshedera lizei*
Geranium	*Pelargonium* spp.
Hydrangea	*Hydrangea* spp.
Impatiens	*Impatiens* spp.
Primrose	*Primula* spp.
Beet	*Beta vulgaris*
Broccoli	*Brassica oleraceae* var. *botrytis*
Carrot	*Daucus carota*
Cabbage	*Brassica oleraceae*
Lettuce	*Lactuca sativa*
Radish	*Raphanus sativa*

Warm-Temperature Plants

Plant	Scientific Name
African violet	*Saintpaulia* spp.
Agave	*Agave* spp.
Aluminum plant	*Pilea cadierei*
Begonia	*Begonia* spp.
Bromeliads	Many species
Cacti	Many species
Caladium	*Caladium* spp.
Chinese evergreen	*Aglaonema costatum*
Coleus	*Coleus blumei*
Croton	*Codiaeum* spp.
Corn plant	*Dracaena fragraus 'Massangeana'*
Dwarf banana	*Musa cavendishii*
Dumbcane	*Dieffenbachia* spp.
Jade plant	*Crassula argenta*
Palms	Many species
Pineapple	*Ananas comosus*
Petunia	*Petunia* spp.
Corn	*Zea mays*
Cucumber	*Cucurbita sativus*
Eggplant	*Solanum melongena*
Melon	*Cucumis melo*
Tomato	*Lycopersicon esculentum*
Sweet potato	*Ipomea batatas*

period is not always predictable and it may not be economical to wait that long. Most crop damage from frost occurs when the temperature drops unexpectedly in early spring. Just-opened flower buds and young seedlings are most vulnerable. Growers obtain premium prices if they have produce available for sale early in the season. Rather than waste time, many growers prefer to take the risk to plant early and adopt a variety of strategies to minimize frost damage when it occurs. Such strategies include the following:

1. *Use frost forecast.*   USDA publications of maps and tables showing predicted patterns of frost occurrence throughout the nation are available. These charts show average dates for the last killing frost (in spring and in fall), after which

frost damage is not likely. Sometimes, certain plants in the locality may act as indicator plants to guide growers as to when it is safe to plant crops outside. For example, when the American dogwood blooms, it is safe to plant outside.

2. *Protect plants.*

   a. *Hot caps.* Hot caps are dome-shaped, moisture-resistant paper caps used to cover plants individually in the field. As plants grow taller, the tops can be torn off to give more room for plant growth. When the threat of frost is over, the caps are removed. Because of its high cost, this protective measure is cost effective only in the production of high-premium crops such as tomato, summer squash, and pepper.

   b. *Sprinkler application.* Growers may provide additional heat for frost protection by sprinkling water on plants. The principle behind this strategy is that water releases *latent heat* for fusion when it changes state from liquid to solid (ice). This heat energy is enough to protect some plants against frost damage. The amount of heat generated is even greater if warmer water (above 0°C or 32°F) is applied. Further protection of the buds is derived from insulation provided by ice as it encases the young bud. Sprinkling is necessary throughout the duration of the frost period. However, too much sprinkling may lead to excessive ice formation on plants that may cause limbs to break under the weight of the ice. The soil may also be in danger of flooding under conditions of continuous sprinkling.

   c. *Plastic mulching.* Spreading polyethylene sheets over the seedbed provides warmth for germination and seedling growth. Opaque sheets minimize weed problems, since weeds receive partial light while germinated seeds receive full light.

   d. *Row covers.* Polyethylene sheets or other fabric may be used to cover rows of crops for protection from frost. These materials may be laid directly on plants in certain cases or they may be supported with wire hoops. Row covers also protect plants against certain insect pests. Plants under the cover are warmed and experience early and increased growth.

   e. *Polyethylene tunnels.* Polyethylene tunnels are a kind of row cover, but the top is designed to be opened (if necessary) during the daytime when temperatures are too high.

   f. *Wind machines.* Wind machines are like giant fans erected in crop fields to be used for mixing up the colder bottom (near the soil) layer of air with the warmer top layer of air. The air is colder near the soil surface because the soil radiates heat into the atmosphere at night. The condition in which colder air underlies warmer air is called *air inversion.* The temperature differential (between the colder and warmer air) may be small such that normal daytime conditions can eliminate the temperature inversion. However, when the temperature near the surface of the soil is very low, it may be necessary to use mechanical processes such as a strong draft from a fan to mix the air.

   g. *Heaters.* Orchards may be heated by using portable burners (gas burners). This practice is not common because of the high cost of fuel and the pollution that results from its combustion.

Temperature has a diurnal pattern; that is, it varies between the daytime and nighttime, rising in the day and falling at night. In some horticultural operations, especially under controlled environments in the greenhouse, success depends on maintaining a certain nighttime temperature.

As a general rule, planting dates for horticultural crops are delayed as one moves northward. This generalization is embodied in the *Hopkins bioclimatic law,* which states that crop production activities (such as planting and harvesting) and specific morphological developments are delayed four days for every one degree of latitude, five degrees of longitude, and 122 meters (400 feet) of altitude as one moves northward, eastward, and upward. Another important generalization is that within the normal temperature range for plant growth and development, the growth rate is doubled for every 10°C (18°F) increase in temperature. Plant metabolic rate is slowed as temperatures decrease and accelerated as temperatures rise. Therefore, plant growth is slower in the cool season.

Temperature Stress Biochemical reactions have an optimal temperature at which they occur. Photosynthesis declines as the temperature rises to excessive levels, with negative consequences. High temperatures cause plants to transpire excessively. The moisture in the soil is lost rapidly through evaporation, causing moisture stress to plants.

Dormancy Low temperatures are required for purposes other than flower induction in plant growth and development. Horticultural plants with corms or tubers and many flowering shrubs and fruit trees require low temperatures to break dormancy. Dormancy is discussed in detail later in the text.

Other Temperature Effects Cool temperature is required by bulb plants such as narcissus, tulip, and hyacinth for good flower development.

Heat Units Temperature may be used to quantify the amount of growth that occurs in a plant because the two factors are correlated. This relationship is used by scientists to predict the harvest dates of crops and also to determine the adaptability of plants to various climatic zones. Plant development can be measured in *heat units*. A heat unit is the number of degrees Fahrenheit by which the mean daily temperature exceeds a base minimum growth temperature. It is calculated using the following formula:

$$\text{heat unit} = [(\text{daily minimum temperature} + \text{daily maximum temperature})/2] - \text{base temperature (°F)}$$

The base temperature used in the calculation of heat units varies among species. For example, a value of 50°F (10°C) is used for corn and many fruit trees. A plant requires a certain number of hours of warmth for a specific growth phase to occur. Dormant buds on temperate fruit trees require winter chilling and a specific heat unit for the buds to break. Species such as high-bush blueberry have high (long) winter chilling and low heat unit requirements, whereas others such as pecan have low chilling and high heat unit requirements.

Light

Light for plant growth comes primarily from the sun. The role of light in the growth and development of horticultural plants depends on its *quality, quantity,* and *daily duration.* When plants are grown indoors, artificial lighting is required. The most readily recognized role of light is in photosynthesis, but it also has other important functions, such as seed germination in some horticultural species. *Solar radiation* is electromagnetic in nature. Radiant energy is described by its *wavelength* and *frequency.* The shorter the wavelength and higher the frequency, the higher the energy transmitted. Cosmic rays have the most energy, and radio waves have the least energy (Figure 4–4).

Because of the curvature of the earth's surface, incoming solar radiation strikes the earth directly at the equator but obliquely toward the pole. The rays at the poles are spread over a wider surface and pass through more air mass and thus are more filtered than at the equator. Hence, polar radiation has less energy (colder). The duration of the radiation reaching the earth varies with the season, since day length is also seasonally variable. Sunrise and sunset patterns differ from one season to another. The amount and duration of sunlight are affected by the angle of the sun. The angles are wider in summer than in winter. A knowledge of these seasonal changes in the sun angles is important in the orientation of a greenhouse and other solar collectors for maximum exposure to sunlight. Cloud cover can also reduce effective solar radiation. To increase light interception by plants, growers may use closer spacing (increase plant density). In row crops, provided

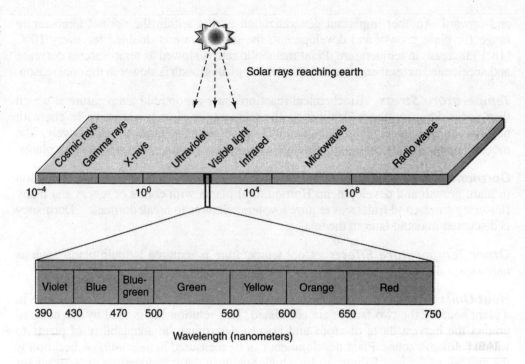

it is convenient and slope is not a factor, rows should be oriented in the east-west direction. Plants in north-south–oriented rows are self-shading as the sun moves. Shade cast by plants in east-west rows falls to the ground.

Light Intensity Sunlight *intensity* (brightness or quantity) is highest at noon. The sun may shine brightly, but the percentage intercepted by the plant's photosynthetic apparatus (mainly leaves) is what is important. Leaves in the upper parts of plants may be able to fully intercept light while shading those below. Horticultural practices such as *pruning* open up the plant canopy for penetration of light to lower leaves for increased photosynthetic efficiency. By adopting an appropriate row spacing and plant density and using cultivars with desirable plant architecture (erect plant with leaves displayed at less than a 90-degree angle), more light can be intercepted for increased photosynthesis and subsequent higher yield.

Sunlight intensity at midday is about 10,000 foot-candles. Of this quantity, many plants can effectively utilize only about 50 percent for photosynthesis. A relatively low light intensity is more efficiently utilized by plants for photosynthesis than high-intensity light. Therefore, two leaves, each receiving 50 percent of full sunlight, together are more efficient in photosynthesizing than one leaf receiving full sunlight. Most houseplants and trees such as maple and oak do not increase their photosynthetic rate significantly as light intensity increases, which occurs with grasses such as corn and Bermuda grass (Figure 4–5). Therefore, many ornamental houseplants need subdued light to survive and develop properly. A selected list of plants for various light intensities is presented in Table 4–2.

ETIOLATION Even though a relatively low-intensity light is utilized more efficiently than a high-intensity light, very low light intensity can be detrimental to the growth and development of plants. Plants grown in the dark or dim light (shade) may exhibit difficulties, including growing tall and spindly with yellowing of leaves, a condition called **etiolation** (Figure 4–6). Plant *hormones* play a role in etiolation. *Auxins* (plant growth hormones, especially indoleacetic acid [IAA]) accumulate under shaded or dark conditions; sunlight destroys IAA. The high concentration of IAA induces accelerated growth, leading to the rapid gain in height. Plants grown in dense populations shade each other, leading to etiolated growth.

Etiolation
Abnormal elongation of stems caused by insufficient light.

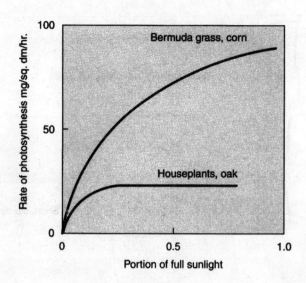

FIGURE 4–5 Light utilization of plants in photosynthesis.

TABLE 4–2 Adaptation of Plants to Light

Full Sunlight–Loving Plants

Plant	Scientific Name
African lily	*Agapanthus* spp.
Agave	*Agave* spp.
Aluminum plant	*Pilea cadierei*
Avocado	*Persea* spp.
Cactus	Many species
Cape jasmine	*Gardenia jasminoides*
Calla lily	*Zantedeschia aethiopica*
Coleus	*Coleus blumei*
Dwarf banana	*Musa cavendishii*
Hibiscus	*Hibiscus rosa-sinensis*
Hen and chickens	*Sempervivum tectorum*
Geranium	*Perlargonium* spp.
Corn	*Zea mays*
Melon	*Cucumis melo*
Tomato	*Lycopersicon esculentum*
Squash	*Cucurbita mixta*
Pepper	*Capsicum anuum*
Marigold	*Tagetes* spp.
Rose	*Rosa* spp.

Partial Shade–Loving Plants

Plant	Scientific Name
Azalea	*Rhododendron* spp.
Bird's-nest fern	*Aspleniun nidus*
Boston fern	*Nephrolepis exaltata*
Chrysanthemum	*Chrysanthemum* spp.
Fatsia	*Fatsia japonica*
Fatshedera	*Fatshedera lizei*
Prayer plant	*Maranta leuconeura*
Primrose	*Primula* spp.
Spider plant	*Chlorophytum comosum*
Sansevieria	*Sansevieria* spp.

FIGURE 4–6 The effect of low light intensity or darkness on plants.

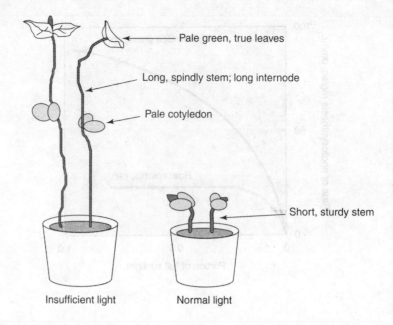

Pale green, true leaves

Long, spindly stem; long internode

Pale cotyledon

Short, sturdy stem

Insufficient light   Normal light

COLOR DEVELOPMENT In apples, fruits formed on the inner branches do not develop to their full intense color because the reduced light intensity experienced inside the canopy is not adequate for the anthocyanin pigments to develop. Chlorophyll development is light dependent. In the absence of light, asparagus and celery become blanched (white). These white products are preferred in certain cultures and markets; therefore, some growers in such areas deliberately cover the base of the plants by mounding with soil or using paper to block out light.

TILLERING AND BRANCHING Plants such as grasses produce additional shoots or secondary stems from the crown, called *tillers,* when the IAA concentration in the plant falls below the optimum for vegetative elongation. Unless the IAA level is reduced, plants will not tiller, branch, or produce seed. The role of light in these responses is related to regulating the concentration of IAA.

Light Quality Light quality relates to its wavelength. For photosynthesis, plant leaf chlorophyll is able to absorb light wavelength in the visible portion of the radiant light spectrum (see Figure 4–4). The visible light ranges between about 400- and 735-nanometer wavelengths. In fact, most of the radiation reaching the earth from the sun falls within this range. Oxygen and ozone in the atmosphere filter out much of the high-energy radiation, and water vapor and carbon dioxide effectively screen out much of the infrared radiation before it reaches the earth's surface. This radiation is involved in the interconversion of oxygen and ozone. When oxygen absorbs short-wavelength ultraviolet radiation, it is converted to ozone. Conversely, when ozone absorbs long-wavelength ultraviolet waves, it is converted to carbon dioxide.

Of the minute fraction of light reaching the earth, plant pigments selectively absorb various wavelengths. A green leaf absorbs light through the visible spectrum but most strongly in the blue (approximately 430 nanometers) and red (approximately 660 nanometers) areas. It absorbs most poorly in the green (approximately 540 nanometers) area and thus reflects mostly green light, making most leaves appear green to the eye. Plant pigments absorb sunlight and use it as a source of energy in carbon dioxide fixation (the incorporation of carbon dioxide into an energy-rich organic product). The important light pigments include chlorophyll and carotenoids. Photosynthesis (the process by which plants utilize sunlight to make food) is described in detail in Chapter 5.

Photoperiodism
Response to the duration and timing of day and night.

Daily Duration of Light The length of day has an effect on two plant processes—time of flowering and plant maturity. This light-induced response is called **photoperiodism,** and plants that flower under only certain day-length conditions are called *photoperiodic*. Four photoperiodic responses in plants are a basis for classifying horticultural plants.

1. *Short-day plants (or long-night plants)*. Short-day plants will not flower under continuous light. They require a photoperiod of less than a certain critical value within a 24-hour daily cycle. For example, strawberry *(Fragaria x ananasia)* requires 10 hours of light or less and violet *(Viola papilionacea)* requires 11 hours. Poinsettia *(Euphorbia pulcherrima)* requires 12.5 hours of daylight and cocklebur *(Xanthium strumarium)* requires about 16 hours or less of light. When planted in the field, short-day plants flower in early spring or fall (Table 4–3).
2. *Long-day plants (or short-night plants)*. Long-day plants are plants that flower only when light periods are longer than a certain critical length (Table 4–4). These plants flower mainly in summer and include annuals such as henbane *(Hyoscyamus niger)*, which requires more than 10 hours of light, and spinach *(Spinacia oleracea)*, which requires 13 hours of light. Baby's breath *(Gypsophila paniculata)* requires 16 hours or more of daylight in order to flower.
3. *Day-neutral plants*. Day-neutral plants are not responsive to photoperiod and flower according to the developmental stage. Plants in this category include tomato, corn, and cucumber (Table 4–5).
4. *Intermediate-day plants*. Certain grasses such as Indian grass do not flower if the days are too short or too long. These plants are said to have two critical photoperiods and are categorized as intermediate-day plants.

The Role of Darkness in Photoperiodism Photoperiodic plants in actuality track or measure the duration of darkness or dark period rather than duration of light. Thus, short-day plants (or long-night plants) flower only if they receive continuous darkness for equal to or more than a critical value (Figure 4–7). If the dark period is interrupted by light of sufficient intensity for even a minute, flowering will not be induced. Similarly, a long-day plant (or short-night plant) will not flower if the critical duration of darkness is exceeded. However, if a long-night period is interrupted by light, flowering will be induced.

TABLE 4–3 Selected Short-Day Plants

Plant	Scientific Name
Chrysanthemum	*Chrysanthemum x morifolium*
Gardenia	*Gardenia jasminoides*
Poinsettia	*Euphorbia pulcherrima*
Kalanchoe	*Kalancho blossfeldiana*
Bryophyllum	*Bryophyllum pinnatum*
Orchid	*Cattleya trianae*
Strawberry	*Fragaria x ananasia*
Violet	*Viola papilionaceae*

TABLE 4–4 Selected Long-Day Plants

Plant	Scientific Name
Baby's breath	*Gypsophila paniculata*
Spider plant	*Chlorophytum comosum*
Sedum	*Sedum spectabile*
Evening primrose	*Oenothera* spp.
Bentgrass	*Agrostis palustris*
Fuchsia	*Fuchsia x hybrida*
Rex begonia	*Begonia rex*

TABLE 4–5   Selected Day-Neutral Plants

Plant	Scientific Name
Bluegrass	*Poa annua*
Corn	*Zea mays*
Cucumber	*Cucumis sativus*
Pea	*Pisum sativum*
English holly	*Ilex aquifolium*
Tomato	*Lycopersicon esculentum*
Kidney bean	*Phaseolus vulgaris*

FIGURE 4–7 Photoperiodic response in flowering species. Light interruption of darkness affects short- and long-day plants differently.

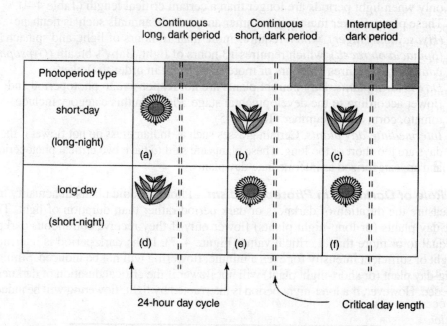

Interrupting the long night with such a short period of lighting is called *flash lighting*. The responses of short-day plants and long-day plants to light interruption are opposite in the two categories of plants.

The most sensitive part of the dark period regarding its response to light interruption appears to be the middle of the period of exposure. The effect diminishes before or after the midperiod. Further, the photoperiodic response can be very precise in that a deviation of even less than 30 minutes from the critical value of required exposure can cause failure to produce an induction of flowering. In henbane, for example, a photoperiod of 10 hours, 20 minutes, induces flowering, whereas a photoperiod of 10 hours does not. Further, environmental factors such as temperature can modify the photoperiodic behavior of a plant. For example, flowering in henbane is induced by exposure to 11.5 hours of light at 28.5°C, but it takes only 8.5 hours of exposure to light to induce flowering at 15.5°C.

The photoperiodic response varies among species with respect to the number of cycles of day-night treatment needed to induce flowering. Some species require only one exposure to the appropriate photoperiod to be induced to flower, whereas others require several days or even weeks (as in spinach) of exposure to the critical day-night cycle to induce flowering. Further, the stage in development (age) affects the way the photoperiod treatment is administered. Some plants respond as seedlings, but others need to attain a certain age.

Growers manipulate the photoperiod requirements of certain seasonal and high-income greenhouse plants to produce plants in a timely fashion. Short-day plants such as poinsettia, chrysanthemum, and Christmas cactus are in high demand during specific times of the year. Growers start these plants under long-day conditions and then finish them under appropriate photoperiods. The required photoperiod is provided by covering the plants with a black cloth between 5 P.M. and 8 A.M. The photoperiod may be prolonged during the natural short days by artificial lighting. This extended day length keeps the plants vegetative.

Greenhouse Effect

The earth is warmed to a limited extent by the solar radiation that strikes it directly. As indicated earlier, the earth's atmosphere filters out most of the short-wave radiation. After striking the earth, some of the solar radiation is reradiated into the atmosphere by the earth. Much of this secondary radiation is long wave (infrared). Much (85 percent) of the solar radiation is absorbed by the water vapor in the atmosphere, while the remainder is reflected back to Earth (Figure 4–8). The reflection back to Earth is caused by the accumulation of gases (especially carbon dioxide, methane, and nitrous oxide—commonly called *greenhouse gases*), which prevents the heat from escaping. Consequently, there is a global rise in temperature. This phenomenon is primarily responsible for warming (indirectly) the earth and is called the *greenhouse effect*.

4.2.2 BIOTIC FACTORS

Climate influences plant diseases and insect pests. For an epidemic to occur, there must be a susceptible host, pathogen, and favorable environment, called the *disease triangle*. Disease will not occur unless all three factors are present. However, disease can occur to varying degrees. Local weather conditions may favor the development of certain pathogens or predispose plants to diseases by lowering their resistance. Many insects have a short life span. Changes in the climate can adversely affect their population and effectiveness at any stage of their life cycle. Certain insects proliferate in specific seasons and occur in low populations in others. For example, the San Jose scale *(Aspidiotus perniciosus)* is a problem in the warm temperatures of summer but not in cold climates.

The aboveground environment contains organisms that are microscopic and largely pathogenic to plants. Plant diseases and pests are described later in this book. Other large-bodied organisms that occur in the environment can help or harm plants. Birds help in seed dispersal and bees and butterflies in flower pollination. On the other hand, rodents harm plants in the field in a variety of ways. Seeds may be eaten before they have a chance to germinate. Mature produce may be eaten before harvest; plant stems and foliage may be eaten by herbivores such as deer and rabbits.

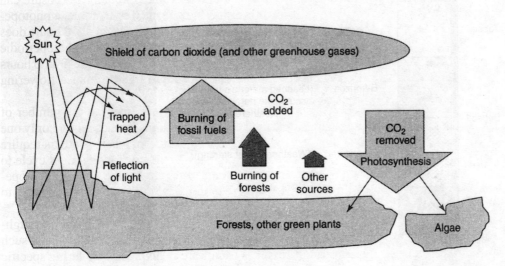

FIGURE 4–8 The greenhouse effect of carbon dioxide.

The *soil* is the primary medium for crop growth, although modern technology allows crops to be grown in other media. The role of climate in determining crop adaptation was discussed earlier in this chapter but was limited to the aboveground environment. Climate plays a significant role in determining the types of soils in which crops may be grown. This role comes from the fact that climate is a primary factor in the dynamic process of soil formation called *weathering,* the process by which *parent material* (the rocks from which soils are formed) is broken down into small particles. The type of soil formed affects the kind of vegetation it can support, which in turn further impacts the process of soil formation by influencing the organic matter and nutrient content of the soil. Soil formation is a continuous process.

4.3.1 SOIL

Role of Soil in Horticulture

The role of soil in horticultural crop production is to provide physical support and a reservoir of nutrients and moisture for growing plants. In terms of nutrition, soils may be described as fertile, marginal, or infertile. Soil nutrients are depleted with years of use and need to be replenished periodically. The soil may not be rich in native nutrients, but to be useful for crop production, it should at least be capable of holding water and nutrients for some time. If this condition does not exist, the grower should make provisions to supply supplemental nutrition to prevent deficiency problems. To be of any use for crop production, the soil should be deep enough to permit root development for good anchorage while supplying adequate nutrition.

Soil Profile

Soil Profile
A vertical cross section of the soil showing the various layers or horizons that have developed over the period of soil formation.

When a deep trench is dug to expose a vertical cross section of the soil, one usually can observe different layers called *soil horizons.* These layers together constitute the **soil profile.** The degree of profile development depends on the age of the soil, young soils showing less development than older ones.

A soil profile can be described in great detail, but for our purposes, a profile is considered to consist of three general sections (Figure 4–9):

1. *Topsoil (or A-horizon).*   Topsoil is the upper layer of soil, where most plant roots are found. It is usually darker in color because of the high organic matter

FIGURE 4–9   (a) A simplified illustration of a typical soil profile. (b) An actual profile of a Mollisol showing a dark surface horizon and white subsoil.
(Source: For (b), USDA)

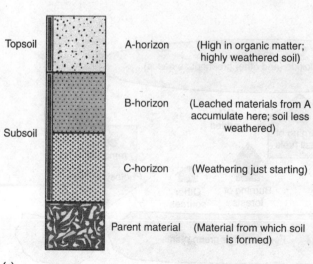

(a)

(b)

content. This section is sometimes called agricultural soil and is the portion disturbed during *tillage* and other soil-preparation practices for planting crops. The topsoil is also the part of the soil that experiences the most leaching and weathering.

2. *Subsoil (or B- and C-horizons).* Subsoil is a transitional zone in the soil profile, a "catch zone" for particles and mineral elements that have moved down from the topsoil by water action. This horizon may accumulate clays, calcium carbonates, and mineral oxides. Organic matter content is minimal in this zone; some roots may occur.

3. *Parent material (substratum or R-horizon).* The R-horizon consists of the primary parent material from which the soil above was formed. With time, soil-forming factors will act on this material to produce more soil.

Properties of Soil

Some soils may consist almost entirely of organic matter, such as peat bogs, while others may consist almost entirely of mineral elements, such as sandy soils in deserts. A good agricultural soil has both mineral and organic constituents. A typical soil (mineral soil) has four principal constituents—mineral, water, air, and organic matter (Figure 4–10).

The soil is truly a dynamic system in which three factors (physical, chemical, and biological) interact to affect plant growth and development; soil is affected in turn by the plants. Understanding the roles of each of these factors in the soil system and their effects on plants is important in making an appropriate choice of soil for crop cultivation and knowing the best way to amend or manipulate the soil for better crop production. Aspects of these three soil properties that affect crop production are discussed next.

Physical Properties The physical properties of interest in soil include soil texture and soil structure.

SOIL TEXTURE Soil may be physically separated on the basis of particle size. Three basic particle size classes, called *soil separates,* are recognized; they include *sand, silt,* and *clay* (Table 4–6). An agricultural soil normally contains all three soil textural classes but in varying proportions. **Soil texture** may be defined as the proportions (percentages) of sand, silt, and clay particles in a soil. When the three soil separates occur in equal proportions, the substance is called *loam.* A perfect loam does not occur in the field. Instead, one of the separates often predominates in the soil. Soils are therefore described as, for example, sandy loam or sandy clay loam to indicate the predominant separate or separates in the soil.

Soil texture affects soil drainage. Clay soils do not drain well and are easily waterlogged. Clay soils are also described as heavy soils and are difficult to till. They often crack upon drying. Because root growth is hampered in heavy soils, crops whose

Soil Texture
The relative percentages of sand, silt, and clay in a soil.

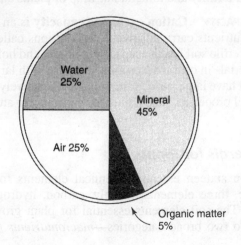

Water 25%

Mineral 45%

Air 25%

Organic matter 5%

FIGURE 4–10 The composition of a typical mineral soil.

TABLE 4–6 Selected Soil Properties and How They Are Affected by Soil Texture

Textural Class (Soil Separates)	Particle Size (mm)	Cation Exchange	Drainage	Water-Holding Capacity	Aeration
Sand	2.0	Low	Excellent	Poor	Excellent
Silt	0.05	Medium	Very good	Very good	Good
Clay	0.002	High	Poor	Excellent	Poor

economic parts are roots or tubers, such as sugar beet and carrot, should not be grown in clay soils. When crops are grown in sandy soils, frequent watering is necessary because these soils drain well. Well-drained soils are preferred by soil microbes and other organisms that are beneficial to plants.

Soil texture, in practice, cannot be changed in the field. However, the water-retention capacity of sandy soils can be improved by adding organic matter. Excess moisture in clay soils can be drained by using tile drains or raised beds to grow crops.

Soil texture has implications in soil fertility. Clay soils have high *cation exchange capacity (CEC)*, the ability of soil to attract and hold cations. Sandy soils have low CEC, which indicates low soil nutritional status. Sandy soils have large pore spaces and dry faster than clay soils. They also warm up much faster, making them suitable for early spring production.

SOIL STRUCTURE   **Soil structure** is determined by the arrangement of soil particles in the soil. The soil separates (primary particles) are arranged into secondary particles called *peds* or simply *aggregates* of different shapes and sizes.

The effects of texture on a soil are modified by its structure. Soil structure affects the pore size, water-holding capacity, infiltration rate, and permeability of water and air. A soil that drains poorly, crusts, and has poor water-holding capacity or permeability may have poor aggregation.

Peds may not be durable and thus change when the soil is disturbed. In other words, soil structure can be changed. Factors of change include raindrops, tillage, and traffic. Soils must not be tilled when wet, because the soil structure will be destroyed. The use of heavy equipment and walking over soil causes soil compaction, which impedes drainage and rooting. On the other hand, the incorporation of organic matter into the soil improves soil structure. Granular and crumb soil structures are desirable for most agricultural purposes, and they also respond to soil management. They are well aerated and have good infiltration and water-holding capacity. Compaction increases the soil *bulk density* (the weight of oven-dried soil divided by the volume of soil) and subsequently decreases the pore space, water infiltration rate, and air space.

Chemical Properties   The soil chemical properties relevant for our purposes are those that influence soil fertility and mineral nutrition of plants and soil reaction, or pH.

CATION EXCHANGE CAPACITY   **Cation exchange capacity** is an index of soil fertility. Many essential plant nutrients carry positively charged ions called *cations* (e.g., Ca^{2+}, Na^+, K^+, and Mg^{2+}). A fertile soil has the capacity to attract and hold these nutrients. The most efficient soil materials in cation adsorption are those with large surface areas. Clay particles called *colloids* have large surface areas that are negatively charged. Soil organic matter also has colloidal properties. The higher the capacity for attraction of cations, the higher the CEC.

Essential Soil Minerals for Plants

Most plants depend on sixteen essential chemical elements for proper growth and development. Of these, three elements, namely, carbon, hydrogen, and oxygen, are obtained from the air. The soil elements essential for plant growth and development are often classified into two broad categories—*macronutrients (major nutrients)* and

Soil Structure
The arrangement of primary soil particles into secondary particles, units, or peds.

Cation Exchange Capacity
The base-exchange capacity or measure of the total exchangeable cations a soil can hold.

TABLE 4–7 Soil Mineral Nutrients Essential for Plant Growth and Development

Macronutrients		Micronutrients
(Major, Primary)	Secondary Nutrients	(Minor, Trace)
Nitrogen (N)	Calcium (Ca)	Iron (Fe)
Phosphorus (P)	Magnesium (Mg)	Manganese (Mn)
Potassium (K)	Sulfur (S)	Molybdenum (Mo)
		Copper (Cu)
		Boron (B)
		Zinc (Zn)
		Chlorine (Cl)

micronutrients (minor elements or trace elements). The macronutrients may be subdivided into primary nutrients and secondary nutrients (Table 4–7). Primary nutrients are utilized in large amounts by plants and are often prone to deficiency in the soil. Secondary elements are used by plants in much smaller amounts than the primary elements. Micronutrients are needed in only trace or minute amounts by plants and are not frequently deficient in soils. Trace elements are especially critical in greenhouse cultivation, where artificial mixes are often used. Sandy soils and soils that experience prolonged heavy precipitation or prolonged intensive cultivation provide conditions under which micronutrient deficiency is likely.

Primary Nutrients (Macronutrients)
The three primary **macronutrients** are nitrogen, phosphorus, and potassium.

Macronutrient
A chemical element that is required in large amounts (usually greater than 1 ppm) for the growth and development of plants.

NITROGEN (N) Nitrogen is one of the most widely used elements in plant nutrition. Plants absorb this element in its inorganic form as nitrate ions (NO_3^-) and occasionally as ammonium (NH_4^+). A natural cycle (nitrogen cycle) exists for recycling nitrogen. When plants absorb nitrate ions, they become immobilized (mineral form is changed into organic form) by becoming part of the plant tissue. When plants die, their tissue is decomposed to release the organic form of nitrogen into inorganic ions by the process of mineralization. Microbes decompose dead tissue to release nitrates, and some are capable of fixating atmospheric nitrogen by the process of nitrogen fixation. This process, part of a symbiotic relationship between bacteria (Rhizobia) and legume roots, involves two chemical reactions: ammonification and nitrification.

Nitrogen is used in the synthesis of amino acids and proteins and is a component of chlorophyll and enzymes. It promotes vegetative growth and as a result may delay maturity. Its deficiency causes stunted growth, especially lateral shoots with leaves turning light green then yellow (**chlorosis**), the most visible deficiency symptom. Entire leaves are chlorotic, starting with lower foliage. Older leaves later defoliate; stems are thin. Nitrogen is readily lost from the soil through leaching and soil erosion and is also readily removed by plants. Deficiency can be corrected by applying organic or inorganic fertilizers.

Nitrogen is mobile in the plant. Thus, if the element is in short supply in the soil, protein nitrogen in older leaves is converted into a soluble form and translocated to younger leaves, where it is most needed. The older leaves then lose color while younger leaves remain green.

Chlorosis
A condition in which a plant or a part of a plant turns greenish-yellow due to poor chlorophyll development or the destruction of the chlorophyll resulting from a pathogen or mineral deficiency.

PHOSPHORUS (P) Phosphorus is absorbed primarily as orthophosphate ions (mainly $H_2PO_4^-$ and also HPO_4^{2-}). Phosphorus is found in proteins and nucleic acids (DNA and RNA) and is critical in the energy transfer process (adenosine triphosphate [ATP] and adenosine diphosphate [ADP]). Phosphorus is found to induce root proliferation and early crop maturity.

When phosphorus is deficient in the soil, leaves become dark bluish or greenish and plants become stunted. This deepening of color is caused by an increase in nitrates in the leaves. Yield is subsequently reduced. Purplish color, especially of older leaves, or reddish-purple color on some grasses indicates phosphorus deficiency. Phosphorus is also mobile in the plant and is regularly recycled from older parts to younger growing parts. It has a tendency to be rendered readily unavailable (fixed) in the soil. It is most available at a pH of 5.5 to 7.0.

POTASSIUM (K)   Sandy soils may be deficient in potassium since the element is readily leached. Potassium is absorbed by plants in its ionic form (K^+). It is a catalyst for enzyme reactions and is also important in protein synthesis, translocation, storage of starch, and growth of meristematic tissue. Whereas nitrogen and phosphorus are converted into compounds for plant growth, potassium occurs in the plant tissue as a soluble inorganic salt. It is very mobile. Luxury consumption of potassium is common in plants, even though the element is required in large amounts. When potassium is deficient in the soil, the root system and stems become weak and prone to lodging; yield is reduced. Readily visible deficiency symptoms vary among species. Some plants show marginal burning of leaves (*marginal* **necrosis**), speckled or mottled leaves, interveinal chlorosis, and leaf curling. These symptoms occur in older leaves and spread upward. Potassium is removed by plants, but it is also prone to fixation and leaching, especially in soils low in organic matter and from soilless growing media.

The most abundant monovalent ion in plants is K^+, whose concentration may be equal to or more than that of nitrogen. Plants such as carnation may have as high as 9 percent potassium on a dry-weight basis. Roses have about 2 to 3 percent potassium on the average. Potassium appears to have a role in nitrogen metabolism; when deficient, plants show a high level of water-soluble nitrogen. When ammonium forms of nitrogen are used to fertilize plants in case of deficiency, the deficiency symptom is intensified and the plants become severely injured. This injury may be due to the accumulation of nitrogen (that has not been changed into protein) to excessive and toxic levels.

Secondary Nutrients **Calcium (Ca)**   Calcium is not only an essential plant nutrient but is also used in correcting soil acidity so that other soil nutrient elements can be made available to plants in appropriate amounts. It is absorbed as Ca^{2+} ions by plants. Calcium is important in cell growth and division, cell wall formation (calcium in the form of pectate), and nitrogen accumulation. The element also forms organic salts with organic acids in plants. For example, in dumbcane *(Dieffenbachia)* calcium forms calcium oxalate, which is irritating to the tongue and throat of humans when ingested.

When deficient, plant tissue formation is incomplete. The terminal bud may cease to grow, leaving a blunt end. Deficiency symptoms for calcium are manifested frequently as defective terminal bud development. The margins of young leaves may not form, resulting in strap leaves. Slight chlorosis followed by brown or black scorching of new leaf tips and die-back of growing points are also characteristic of this deficiency. Roots grow poorly and are short and thickened.

MAGNESIUM (MG)   Magnesium is released when rock minerals such as dolomite, biotite, and serpentine decompose. Absorbed as Mg^{2+} ions, magnesium is the central atom in the structure of a chlorophyll molecule. It is also essential in the formation of fats and sugars.

Magnesium is mobile in plants, and thus deficiency appears first in older leaves. Large amounts of potassium ions may interfere with its uptake due to ion antagonism created by this situation. This antagonism is prevented when the potassium to magnesium ratio in the growing medium is about 3:1 to 4:1. There is interveinal chlorotic mottling or marbling of the older leaves, proceeding to younger leaves as the deficiency intensifies.

SULFUR (S)   Sulfur is obtained primarily from the decomposition of metal sulfides in igneous rocks. It occurs in the soil as sulfates and sulfides, as well as in humus. It is absorbed by plants as sulfate ions (SO_4^{2-}). The unique flavors of certain vegetables, such as onion and cabbage, as well as other cruciferous plants, are due to certain sulfur compounds. Sulfur is an ingredient in vitamins and amino acids. The dominant symptom of sulfur deficiency is chlorotic foliage. In addition, the stems of affected plants are weak, thin, hard, and woody. Sulfur is not usually added as a fertilizer element but is added indirectly when sulfate forms of other elements are applied. Sulfur is also available from air pollution.

Necrosis
Death of tissue associated with discoloration and dehydration of all or parts of a plant organ.

Micronutrients (Trace Elements) Micronutrients (trace elements or microelements) are essential elements utilized by plants in very small amounts. Low-analysis fertilizers such as 5-10-5 have trace elements as impurities. High-analysis fertilizers may be fortified with micronutrients.

BORON (B) Boron is absorbed by plants as borate (BO_4^{2-}). Mobile in the plant system, it affects flowering, fruiting, cell division, water relations (translocation of sugars), and other processes in the plant. When deficient, symptoms appear at the top of the plant. Terminal buds die, producing growth described as *witches'-broom*. Lateral branches grow and form rosettes; young leaves thicken and become leathery and chlorotic. Stems become hollow and may crack.

IRON (FE) Though more abundant in most soils than other trace elements, iron deficiency occurs in alkaline or acidic soil. It can be absorbed through leaves or roots as Fe^{2+} ions (and also as Fe^{3+} ions to a much smaller extent since availability is reduced by being bound in plant tissue). Iron chelates can also be absorbed. Iron is a component of many enzymes and a catalyst in the synthesis of chlorophyll. Iron deficiency shows up as interveinal chlorosis of young leaves. In severe cases, leaves may become whitish, since iron plays a role in photosynthesis, as indicated previously. Iron is immobile and thus deficiency appears first in younger leaves.

MOLYBDENUM (MO) Vegetables, cereals, and forage grasses are among a number of species that are known to show very visible symptoms when molybdenum is deficient in the soil. This element is unavailable to plants grown under very low pH (highly acidic) conditions. In such cases, *liming* is employed as a corrective measure.

Molybdenum is involved in protein synthesis and is required by some enzymes that reduce nitrogen. The leaves of cauliflower and other cruciferous plants become narrow *(whiptail)* when the element is lacking in the soil. Plant leaves may also become pale green and roll up.

MANGANESE (MN) Manganese, absorbed as Mn^{2+} ions, is crucial to photosynthesis because of its role in chlorophyll synthesis. It is also important in phosphorylation, activation of enzymes, and carbohydrate metabolism. It is not mobile in plants. When deficient, interveinal chlorosis is observed in younger leaves, just as in iron deficiency.

ZINC (ZN) Zinc is an enzyme activator. It is absorbed as Zn^{2+} ions by plant roots and tends to be deficient in calcareous soils that are high in phosphorus. When deficient, plant leaves are drastically reduced in size and internodes shortened, giving a rosette appearance. Interveinal chlorotic mottling may occur in young leaves. Kalanchoe is particularly susceptible to zinc deficiency as a greenhouse plant. In species such as peach and citrus, deficiency of zinc produces a type of chlorosis called *mottled leaf.*

COPPER (CU) Soils that are high in organic matter are prone to copper deficiency. Copper is important in chlorophyll synthesis and acts as a catalyst for respiration and carbohydrate and protein metabolism. Younger leaves may show interveinal chlorosis while the leaf tip remains green; with time, the leaf blade becomes necrotic. Terminal leaves and buds die, and the plant as a whole becomes stunted. Copper sulfate or copper ammonium sulfate may be administered to leaves or soil to correct deficiency problems.

CHLORINE (CL) Chlorine is absorbed by plants as chloride ions (Cl^-). Deficiency in the field is rare. An excessive level of chlorine is more often a problem than its absence. When deficiency occurs in the soil, plants may be stunted and appear chlorotic, with some necrosis.

4.3.2 SOIL ORGANIC MATTER

Organic matter in the soil may result from plant or animal materials. Plant residue or green manure crop incorporated into the soil by tilling the decaying plant roots is a good source of organic matter. Plant matter such as dried leaves on the surface of the soil is not

Soil Erosion
The wearing away of the land surface by geological agents such as water, wind, and ice.

considered organic matter until it is incorporated into the soil. **Soil erosion** depletes soil organic matter. Organic matter is important to soil productivity since it is a source of nutrients when it decomposes. It improves soil structure by binding together mineral particles into aggregates for better aeration and drainage. It helps to buffer soils against rapid changes in pH. Organic matter increases the water-holding capacity of soils and gives them their characteristic dark brown or black color. Microorganisms (e.g., bacteria, fungi, and actinomycetes) are responsible for decomposing plant parts for easier incorporation into the soil. Sugars, starches, proteins, cellulose, and hemicellulose decompose rapidly, whereas lignin, fats, and waxes are slow to decompose. Organic matter acts as a *slow-release fertilizer*, since its nutrients are released gradually over a particular period.

Humus is a very stable part of the soil organic matter. Much of humus is formed from two general biochemical processes. The chemicals in the plant residue undergo *decomposition* by microbial action to produce simpler products. These breakdown products undergo *synthesis,* by which the simpler products are enzymatically joined to make more complex products such as polyphenols and polyquinones. These synthetic products interact with nitrogen-containing amino compounds to produce a great portion of resistant humus. Further, the synthetic process is aided by the presence of colloidal clays. Humic particles (or humic micelles) carry a large amount of adsorbed cations (e.g., Ca^{2+}, Mg^{2+}, H^+, and Na^+) as clay micelles.

4.3.3 SOIL REACTION AND NUTRIENT AVAILABILITY

A *soil test* showing that adequate amounts of a nutrient are present does not indicate its availability to the plant. In addition to adequate amounts, the presence of moisture is critical, because water is the medium in which solutes are transported through the plant. Other factors that interfere with nutrient availability are soil temperature and *soil reaction, or pH*. Plant processes are generally slowed down by low temperatures.

Soil reaction, or pH, is a measure of the hydrogen ion concentration as an indication of the soil's degree of *acidity* or *alkalinity*. A pH of 7 is neutral. Values above 7 are considered alkaline, and values below 7 are acidic. The pH scale is logarithmic (Figure 4–11), meaning that a soil pH of 5 is 10 times more acidic than a soil pH of 6 and a pH of 4 is 100 times more acidic than a pH of 6. Most horticultural crops tolerate a soil pH within the range of 4 to 8. Soil pH regulates nutrient availability. Figure 4–12 shows the relationship between pH and nutrient availability to plants. A pH of 7 ± 1 appears to be a safe range for most nutrient elements in the soil. Only iron is available at a strongly acidic pH. Conversely, iron is deficient in the soil under alkaline conditions. Sensitive plants (such as bluegrass [*Poa pratensis*]) develop iron-deficiency symptoms called *iron chlorosis,* a condition in which young leaves lose their green color and become yellowish. The difference between this kind of chlorosis and that associated with nitrogen deficiency is that iron chlorosis occurs between the veins of the leaves (interveinal chlorosis) and nitrogen causes a more uniform yellowing of leaves. Soil pH affects the biotic population of soil. Fungi tend to prefer highly acidic conditions (pH of 4 to 5), and nitrogen-fixating bacteria (*Rhizobia*) prefer a pH range of between 6 and 8. Table 4–8 shows the pH requirements of various horticultural plants.

Factors That Affect pH

Soil pH may rise in a soil that experiences low rainfall or is poorly drained. Salts tend to accumulate under these conditions. Soils formed on calcareous parent material have high alkalinity. Acidic soils (low pH) occur when soils are exposed to heavy rainfall and good drainage such that the bases are leached into lower depths or washed away in the runoff.

Correcting pH

Low soil pH may be corrected in practice by adding limestone ($CaCO_3$) or gypsum ($CaSO_4$) to the soil to raise the pH. The choice depends on the soil pH and other characteristics. To lower soil pH, sulfur compounds are added to the soil. Nitrogen fertilizers also tend to

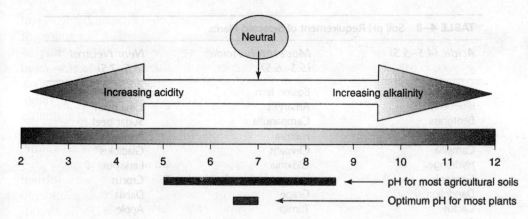

FIGURE 4–11 A representation of the pH scale. The scale is logarithmic and divided into 14 units, ranging from 1 to 14.

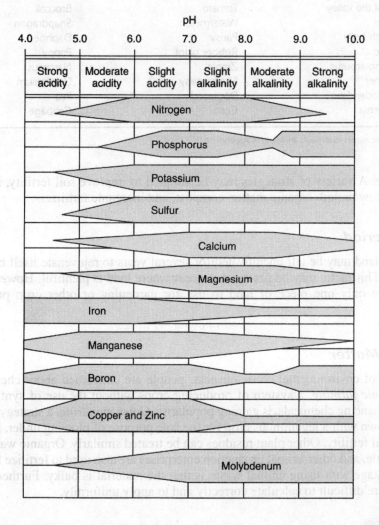

FIGURE 4–12 An illustration of the soil nutrient availability as affected by pH. The range of availability for each nutrient element depends on whether the soil is mineral, organic, or in between.

increase soil acidity. Liming has other added benefits: It increases the availability of phosphorus and potassium to plants, while adding calcium and magnesium to the soil. It also improves soil structure and reduces the potential toxicity of aluminum (Al) and iron (Fe), which are soluble at low pH.

4.3.4 IMPROVING SOIL FERTILITY

Soil nutrients for plant growth become depleted over years of crop production. Crops remove some nutrients, and a portion is lost through leaching and fixation. After a period of continuous farming, the nutrients in the soil must be replenished or crop productivity

TABLE 4–8   Soil pH Requirement of Selected Plants

Acidic (4.5–5.5)	Moderately Acidic (5.5–6.5)	Near Neutral (6.5–7.5)
Azalea	Boston fern	Artichoke
Blueberry	Amaryllis	Lima bean
Bentgrass	Campanulla	Sugar beet
Cranberry	Fuchsia	Poinsettia
Camellia	Clematis	Gladiolus
Hydrangea	Gloxinia	Larkspur
Gardenia	Impatiens	Crocus
Dandelion	Grape	Dahlia
Cactus	Turnip	Apple
Strawberry	Shallot	Cabbage
Lily of the valley	Tomato	Broccoli
Laurel	Watermelon	Snapdragon
English holly	Pansy	Daphne
Potato	Rubber plant	Poppy
Trailing arbutus	Zinnia	Narcissus
Heather	Shasta daisy	Delphinium
Rhododendron	Dogwood	Pea
Gardenia	Corn	Cabbage

Scientific names of all plants are found in Appendix 4-D.

will decline. A variety of strategies may be adopted to improve soil fertility, including use of a fallow period, organic matter, compost, and inorganic fertilizers.

Fallow Period

A piece of land may be left uncultivated for several years to rejuvenate itself by natural processes. This tactic may be practical in areas where land is plentiful. However, most people have only one piece of land to use for gardening or other crop production activities.

Organic Matter

In this age of environmental consciousness, people are concerned about chemicals in food. *Organic farming*, a system of producing crops without the use of synthetic soil nutrient-enhancing chemicals, is gaining popularity. *Green manuring,* a strategy in which a field is sown with a leguminous crop for the sole purpose of plowing under, is used to improve soil fertility. Other plant residues can be treated similarly. Organic wastes from poultry, cattle, and other animal production enterprises are also used to fertilize farmland. A disadvantage with using animal waste is that the material is bulky. Further, organic fertilizers are difficult to calculate correctly and to apply uniformly.

Compost

Home gardeners may prepare *compost,* which is simply partially decomposed plant material. Composting is discussed in detail in Chapter 22.

Inorganic Fertilizers

Most soil amendments are accomplished by applying inorganic fertilizers. Inorganic fertilizer amounts are easier to calculate correctly and apply uniformly, and they are less bulky.

4.4 FERTILIZERS

Fertilizer sources may be *organic* or *inorganic*. Most of the fertilizers applied in horticulture are inorganic in nature.

4.4.1 ORGANIC FERTILIZERS

Organic fertilizers are derived from plant and animal residues. Sources of organic fertilizers include animal droppings (or *manure* from the barnyard or poultry house, bird droppings, and other animal wastes), dried blood, and bonemeal. *Guano* is an organic fertilizer consisting of bird droppings collected off the shores of South American islands. Other sources of organic fertilizers are cottonseed meal and liquid waste from meat- and poultry-processing factories. One of the commonly used nitrogen fertilizers, urea (46-0-0), is actually a synthetic organic fertilizer.

Organic fertilizers are not commonly used in horticulture for several reasons, including the following:

1. They are bulky to handle, requiring large amounts of space to store the required quantity.
2. Their nutrient content is low (low analysis). Large quantities are thus required to provide appreciable amounts of the nutrients needed.
3. They are difficult to quantify and apply according to a specified rate of desired amounts of nutrient elements.
4. The nutrients they contain are released too slowly. They are released as the material decomposes, and decomposition is variable and dependent on the environmental conditions.
5. They are difficult to apply uniformly.
6. They are applied only to the soil.
7. Their use is often accompanied by foul odor that could be slight or very intense as is the case of fish emulsion.
8. Fresh manures need to be composted to avoid burning plants from the high salts they contain.
9. Some sources such as sewage sludge may contain heavy metals (e.g., cadmium) that are injurious to plants.

Although these disadvantages usually disallow organic fertilizers in horticulture, the following advantages for use do exist:

1. Organic fertilizers provide nutrients as well as increase organic matter content of the soil, thereby improving soil physical structure and microbial activity.
2. Composted manures are often marketed as soil conditioners.
3. They supply micronutrients in addition to macronutrients.

4.4.2 INORGANIC FERTILIZERS

Inorganic fertilizers are most widely used to provide supplemental nutrition to horticultural plants during production in the field or in containers indoors. They are popular for reasons including the following:

1. They are easy to store.
2. They have higher analysis than organic fertilizers.
3. They can be custom formulated for specific purposes.
4. Inorganic fertilizers are easy to apply and can be applied uniformly.
5. They are available in liquid and solid forms.

6. They can be applied to both soil and leaves.
7. Accurate quantitative application is facilitated.
8. Nutrients are readily available to plants.
9. Growers can mix their own formulations accurately.

Fertilizer Formulations

Commercial fertilizers formulated to supply one nutrient element are called *straight* (or *simple* or *incomplete*) fertilizers (e.g., urea supplies only nitrogen). Some formulations supply two or three major elements and are called *compound* (or *mixed, balanced,* or **complete** if all major elements are present) **fertilizers.** A grower may produce homemade mixed fertilizers from straight ones.

Complete Fertilizer
A fertilizer formulation that supplies nitrogen, phosphorus, and potassium.

Fertilizer Nomenclature

The major elements (nitrogen, phosphorus, and potassium) are considered in this order in describing fertilizers. Technically, phosphorus is P_2O_5 and potassium is K_2O. A label on a fertilizer bag that reads 60:0:0 means that the fertilizer supplies only nitrogen, at the rate of 60 percent by weight of the total contents of the bag, the remainder being inert fillers added during the manufacturing process to aid in fertilizer handling. Similarly, a label reading of 0:15:0 means that the fertilizer supplies only phosphorus, at 15 percent by weight. A label reading 14:14:14 indicates that this mixed fertilizer supplies 14 percent each of nitrogen, phosphorus, and potassium. Except for nitrogen, the other major nutrients are not used in the elemental form. To convert phosphorus from its elemental form to phosphate, the conversion calls for multiplication by 2.29; to achieve the reverse (convert phosphate to phosphorus) the weight of phosphate is multiplied by 0.49. Similarly, to convert potash to elemental potassium, the weight is multiplied by 0.83; to obtain the reverse, elemental potassium is multiplied by 1.20. The proportion of the elements as illustrated earlier (e.g., 15:30:15) is called the **fertilizer analysis** or *fertilizer grade.* A fertilizer analysis is the minimum guaranteed analysis; an analysis of 60-0-0 means that a 100-pound bag supplies 60 pounds of nitrogen, *not* 59.9 pounds. (However, the weight could be higher than 60 pounds.) When the grade is divided by the highest denominator for the grade, the result is called the *fertilizer ratio* (e.g., 15:30:15 divided by 15 becomes 1-2-1).

Fertilizer Analysis
The proportions of nutrient elements supplied by a fertilizer formulation.

Fertilizer Forms

Mixed fertilizers are obtained in the form of *granules* (granular—all components are processed together in the factory into one compound), *bulk blends* (similar to granular, but components are physically blended such that they may segregate, leading to nonuniform application), or *fluids.* Fluid fertilizers allow micronutrients and pesticides to be incorporated into one application. They may be applied through irrigation water, directly to leaves (*foliar application*).

Slow- or Controlled-Release Fertilizers

Ordinary fertilizers dissolve quickly to release their nutrients into the soil, necessitating frequent application of fertilizers. It is estimated that one month after application of the regular type of nitrogen fertilizer to a lawn, little remains. In greenhouses where watering is frequent, regular fertilizers quickly leach out of the pots into the drain. Industrial processes enable fertilizers to be specially coated to release nutrients at a slow rate. For example, instead of "naked" urea, this fertilizer is coated with formaldehyde or sulfur. Such fertilizers are called *slow release* and are expensive. Sulfur-coated fertilizers may be designed for various rates of release. For example, sulfur-coated urea (SCU_{10}) releases 10 percent of the nitrogen in the first seven days, whereas SCU_{40} releases 40 percent of the nitrogen in seven days. Slow-release fertilizers are used widely in the horticultural industry in greenhouses and for lawns and golf courses.

One of the most commonly used controlled-release fertilizers is Osmocote, which is a high-analysis fertilizer (14:14:14 or 19:6:12). It is packaged in a plastic coat. The 14:14:14 analysis is formulated to release nutrients over about four months, and the 19:6:12 releases nutrients over six to nine months.

Another controlled-release fertilizer is *urea formaldehyde,* which contains 38 percent nitrogen. About 85 percent of this nutrient is available to plants over a period of six months or more. The remaining 15 percent is released so slowly that the plants may not be able to benefit from it during the growing season. This fertilizer is recommended for use under warm conditions (or in spring, summer, or early fall) because of the warm temperature needed to make nitrogen available. Urea formaldehyde should be added after pasteurization of the soil or growing medium to prevent complete release of all of the nitrogen at once.

Magnesium ammonium phosphate (Magamp) is a controlled-release fertilizer of analysis 7:40:6 plus about 12 to 14 percent magnesium. This fertilizer uses particle size to control the release of the nutrients. The finer form may release the nutrients over a period of three months, whereas the coarse form may release the nutrients over about a six-month period. The nitrogen in fertilizer is in the ammonium form; thus, when applied to media such as soilless mixes where the rate of nitrification is slow, plants may experience nitrogen deficiency.

Commercial Sources of Inorganic Fertilizers

A summary of the common sources of commercial inorganic fertilizers is provided in Table 4–9.

Nitrogen   Organic sources of nitrogen include animal manures and wastes and green manures (legumes and other species grown and plowed under the soil). Commercial inorganic sources include salts of ammonia and potassium.

Phosphorus   Animal manures are a source of phosphorus. Commercial fertilizers are made primarily from rock phosphate (apatite). The most common fertilizer source of phosphorus is superphosphate, which contains 16 to 20 percent phosphoric acid. Other commercial forms are ammonium phosphate and triple superphosphate.

Potassium   Inorganic fertilizers are used to replenish soil supplies. Commercial fertilizers may be purchased as potassium sulfate (K_2SO_4, or sulfate of potash), potassium chloride (KCl, or muriate of potash), or potassium nitrate (KNO_3, or saltpeter). The nitrate form is the most expensive and as such is cost effective only when applied to high-premium crops such as vegetables and orchard plants.

Calcium   Calcium is added to soil by using commercial compounds collectively called *agricultural limes.* They are available in various forms. Sources of carbonate of lime include calcite (primarily $CaCO_3$) and dolomite (primarily $CaMg[CO_3]_2$). Sources of oxide lime are called burned lime or quicklime (CaO). This form is more expensive and difficult to handle than limestone. The hydroxide form of lime is called hydrated lime ($Ca[OH]_2$). Like CaO, it is caustic and expensive.

Magnesium   Magnesium deficiency shows up as interveinal chlorosis (yellowing between veins) of older leaves. A common source of magnesium is dolomitic limestone ($CaCO_3 \cdot MgCO_3$). Others are magnesium sulfate ($MgSO_4$) and potassium magnesium sulfate ($K_2SO_4 \cdot 2MgSO_4$). Magnesium sulfate may be purchased as a foliar spray.

Sulfur   Sulfur deficiency may be corrected by adding elemental sulfur, lime sulfur, or sulfate salts of aluminum, ammonia, calcium, sodium, and others.

Boron   Boron occurs in animal manure and superphosphate and is available as sodium or calcium borate.

TABLE 4–9 Common Inorganic Fertilizers That Supply Essential Nutrients for Plant Growth and Development

Fertilizer Element	Fertilizer	Analysis
Nitrogen (N)	Ammonium sulfate	20-0-0
	Ammonium nitrate	33-0-0
	Diammonium phosphate	18-46-0
	Sodium nitrate	15-0-0
	Potassium nitrate	13-0-44
	(Ammonia gas)	(82-0-0)
Phosphorus (P)	Superphosphate	0-20-0
	Triple (treble) superphosphate	0-40-0
	Dicalcium phosphate	0-52-0
	Diammonium phosphate	18-46-0
	Monoammonium phosphate	11-48-0
Potassium (K)	Potassium chloride	0-0-60
	Potassium nitrate	13-0-44

Chemicals that provide micronutrients include magnesium sulfate (Mg), iron sulfate (Fe), borax (Bo), copper sulfate (Cu), epsom salt (Mg), sulfur (S), manganese sulfate (Mn), and calcium nitrate (Ca).

Iron   For foliar application, iron chelates or ferrous sulfate may be used.

Molybdenum   Foliar spraying of sodium molybdate or application to seed or soil is effective in correcting the deficiency problem.

Manganese   Like other trace elements, foliar application of manganese sulfate is commonly used to remedy any deficiency.

Zinc   Foliar application of a zinc sulfate solution or a chelate may be used to correct deficiency problems.

4.4.3   SOIL NUTRITIONAL MONITORING

The grower must regularly monitor plants in production to ensure that the best nutrition required for optimum productivity is being provided. A timely intervention can usually save the season's production from being mediocre in terms of quality and quantity. Three systems are used to monitor the nutrient status of a soil or growing medium— visual diagnosis, soil testing, and foliar analysis. These systems differ in scope, accuracy, cost, and ease of implementation. It is best to use a combination of systems in making a diagnosis.

Visual Diagnosis

As its name implies, visual diagnosis is based strictly on observation. Since it is an after the-fact test, significant damage may already have been inflicted. The seriousness of the damage depends on the nature of the operation and the stage at which the deficiency is observed. Some symptoms are observed early in the development of the plant, whereas others manifest themselves when the plant is mature. For problems with early signals, the damage may be completely reversible; however, usually the damage is only partially reversible.

The deficiency symptoms associated with the various essential nutrients have been discussed previously in the section on nutrient elements. These symptoms range from color changes to physical deformities and death of tissue *(necrosis)*. One weakness of visual diagnosis is the lack of specificity. Often, one symptom may be unique and typical of specific nutrient deficiencies. For example, witches'-broom is typical of boron deficiency.

Chlorosis (the yellowing of green leaves) is associated with deficiencies in nitrogen, sulfur, magnesium, iron, and other elements. The differences among the elements lie in the pattern of chlorosis (interveinal, veinal, or uniform), the part of the leaf (marginal or whole leaf), the age of the leaf (young or old), and whether it is the dominant symptom. Plants often become stunted in growth under conditions of poor nutrition. Deficiency symptoms are easier to spot in certain species than in others. In short, it takes experience to be able to utilize the visual diagnosis precisely. Further, deficiency associated with micronutrients is more common in greenhouse production. Other weaknesses of visual diagnosis are that pH cannot be observed, and more importantly the level of soluble salts and general nutritional status cannot be ascertained for appropriate amendments.

Soil Test

A *soil test* is a more effective and useful diagnostic evaluation than visual diagnosis for soil nutritional status. A soil test (depending on what is actually done) (1) provides a measure of soil pH (deficiency may be due to improper pH affecting the availability of the nutrient element) and (2) measures the total amount of a nutrient present in the soil; it also provides information on the proportion of the nutrient that is readily available.

A soil test can be conducted before planting, during soil preparation, or during production as the need arises. Soil testing is recommended as a routine part of a production operation. When done before planting, it allows the grower to adopt a preventive strategy rather than a curative one to nutritional problems in production. If soil pH is the problem, liming is easier and more effectively applied before planting so that it can be thoroughly mixed with the soil. A soil test helps in planning so that the needed types and amounts of fertilizers are purchased. It also helps in determining what crop production operation the soil will support naturally or what it will take to amend it for another production operation.

In a greenhouse operation, a fertilizer regime should be developed for the medium, type of plant, and specific production operation. Greenhouse media components react differently with plant nutrients. For example, pine bark– and peat moss–based soilless media (plant growth media containing no natural soil) tend to experience micronutrient deficiency, especially involving iron. It is critical for a greenhouse operation to periodically monitor the pH and soluble-salt content of growing media to prevent injury to plants. Excessive salts can build up in the root medium from the application of soluble fertilizers. This high salt concentration prevents water from entering plant roots because of a drastically reduced osmotic potential. Normally, root cells have higher salt concentration than the soil solution; thus osmosis can occur and roots are able to absorb water. A signal that a soil is high in soluble salt is indicated when plants appear to be wilting on a bright day in spite of adequate moisture in the soil. Seedlings are more prone to injury from high soluble-salt levels than established plants. Salt tolerance of selected plants is presented in Table 4–10.

One can conduct a soil test by purchasing a *home soil test kit*. However, for more detailed analysis, the soil sample may be sent to a commercial or university laboratory designated by the state or county, either for a fee or free of charge, depending on the particular policies of the state department of agriculture and the testing center. A good soil test starts with good *soil sampling;* the results of a test are only as good as the samples used. Samples must be representative of the field. For a small garden, about 10 to 12 samples taken to include 8 to 12 inches (20.3 to 30.5 centimeters) of the soil profile (ensuring that both the topsoil and the soil in the root zone are included), and spread over the piece of land, should be adequate. These subsamples are mixed together in a container, and from this mixture, a small sample is taken and sent to the laboratory for analysis.

A representative sample can be taken just by observing certain general guidelines. First, look at the general area to be sampled, and, if necessary, divide it into sections based on their level of uniformity. Sample these different sections separately. Avoid sampling distinctly unusual sites (e.g., waterlogged land).

TABLE 4–10 Soil Salt Tolerance of Selected Plants

Relatively Salt Tolerant	
Plant	Scientific Name
Bermuda grass	Cynodon dactylon
Beet	Beta vulgaris
Broccoli	Brassica oleraceae
Tomato	Lycopersicon esculentum
Cucumber	Cucumis sativus
Muskmelon	Cucumis melo
Rose	Rosa odorata

Relatively Salt Intolerant	
Plant	Scientific Name
Bentgrass, colonial	Agrostis tenuis
Kentucky bluegrass	Poa pratensis
Strawberry	Fragaria spp.
Avocado	Persea americana
Grape	Vitis spp.
Carrot	Daucus carota
Onion	Allium cepa
Gardenia	Gardenia jasminoides
Geranium	Pelargonium x hortorum
Azalea	Rhododendron spp.
Sweet corn	Zea mays var. saccharata
Pepper	Capsicum annuum

Foliar Analysis

Foliar analysis is like a soil test performed on leaves. One difference between the two tests is that while a soil test provides information on nutrients available for uptake, foliar analysis provides information on nutrients taken up and accumulated in the leaf. A foliar test does not provide information on the growing medium pH or soluble-salt content, but it offers a complete analysis of all essential nutrients. The rationale of foliar analysis is that the nutrient content of the plant's tissue affects its growth. Up to a point, increasing the content of essential nutrients will result in increased growth. However, plants are able to take in large amounts of nutrients without corresponding changes in growth, a situation called *luxury consumption*. Excessive amounts of nutrients (beyond luxury consumption) can be injurious to the plant.

To conduct foliar analysis, representative samples of leaves are obtained from the plant. Species differ in which leaves are most representative of the whole plant. The age of the leaves also affects the nutrient content. Samples of foliar analysis should be obtained at intervals of four to six weeks. The results of analysis are compared with standards developed from testing a wide variety of sources. The standards for macronutrients are crop specific and vary widely; micronutrient standards are widely applicable.

4.4.4 APPLYING FERTILIZERS

The first step in a fertilizer program is to determine the type and amount of fertilizer needed. Excessive fertilization is economically wasteful and may even injure or kill the plants. A fertilizer program should take into account the cropping history of the field, the soil type, and the needs of the crop being grown. Since vegetables generally are heavy users of soil nutrients, fields that have been cropped with vegetables on a repeated basis may require fertilization.

Fertilizers may be applied before planting *(preplant)*. The recommended amount may be distributed over the area and then plowed in. Fertilizer may also be applied after germination has occurred and at various times during the growth of the crop. Whatever the time of application, fertilizers may be applied to a crop in a variety of ways.

Methods of Placement in the Field

The method of placement depends on the fertilizer form—liquid or solid (dry). Fertilizers may be applied to the soil or the plant leaves; they may be spread out or confined to a small area. Nitrogen fertilizers are available as single-element or compound forms. When applying nitrogen, one should consider, among other factors, the stage of development of the crop and the season. Nitrogen is needed most by almost all crops in the early stages of growth and development. When applied in cold conditions in ammonium form, the change to usable nitrate form is slow. Nitrogen fertilizers may be acidic, alkaline, or neutral in reaction.

Dry Application Dry fertilizers are applied to the soil. They may be spread out or concentrated in bands or spots. The general methods of placement of dry fertilizers are as follows:

1. *Broadcast application.* Broadcasting entails spreading the fertilizer, mechanically or manually, over the general surface area of the soil as evenly as possible (Figure 4–13). If it is done during soil preparation, a plow or disk may be used to incorporate it into the soil. Seasonal or periodic fertilizing of lawns may be accomplished by this method. It is a very speedy way of fertilizing. The disadvantage is that every part of the field is equally fertilized, and hence for widely spaced horticultural plants, such as watermelon, much of the fertilizer is not utilized by the crop.

2. *Banding.* As the name implies, banding is a method of fertilizer placement whereby the fertilizer is localized near the seed or plant. Care must be taken to place it either about 2 to 3 inches (5.1 to 7.6 centimeters) beside or the same distance below the seed or plant to prevent injury to the seedlings from the excessive presence of salts. This excess of salts is usually a concern when using especially strong nitrogen and potassium fertilizers.

3. *Sidedressing.* Because the soil is not disturbed during fertilizer application in sidedressing, the time of application is important. For example, when urea is applied on a hot summer day, the area must be irrigated to reduce the loss to the atmosphere through volatilization. Crops planted on beds such as cole crops are fertilized this way. However, care must be taken not to bring the dry fertilizer into direct contact with the plant foliage.

4. *Drill hole.* Trees have roots that penetrate deep into the soil. To make fertilizers readily available, they may be placed close to the roots by drilling holes to reach the root zone and filling the holes with the granular fertilizer at the recommended rate.

FIGURE 4–13 An operator applies a soil amendment (lime) by broadcast application.
(Source: USDA)

Liquid Application Liquid fertilizer applications involve applying water-soluble forms of fertilizer to either the soil or the leaves.

1. *Starter fertilizer application.* In the vegetable industry, where seedlings are transplanted, new transplants benefit from a diluted concentration of complete fertilizer that is applied through the transplant water. Phosphorus is especially desirable in the *starter fertilizer solution,* and a general recommendation is about 3 pounds (1.4 kilograms) of 15:30:15 fertilizer in 50 gallons (201.9 liters) of water, applied at one cup per plant.
2. *Foliar application.* Soluble fertilizers may be applied in diluted amounts to plants by spraying directly onto the leaf surface. Since only small amounts of chemicals are applied, the method is not adequate to meet the nutritional needs of plants. Supplementary soil application is usually required.

Application of Gas

Application of fertilizer as gas is possible in certain cases, such as the application of nitrogen in the form of ammonia gas under pressure. This form of nitrogen has a very high analysis. Application is accomplished by injecting the compound as pressurized gas into the soil.

4.4.5 METHODS OF APPLICATION

Fertilizers may be applied by using bare hands, machinery, or through irrigation water when water is administered by sprinklers or tubes. The method chosen depends on factors such as the size of the area to be fertilized, the form of fertilizer, the placement method, the crop, and the stage of application.

Dry Application

Manual For a small garden, fertilizers may be manually applied, regardless of the method of placement chosen. However, the uniformity of application may be questionable with placement methods such as broadcasting. Manually held or pushed spreaders are available to facilitate the broadcast operation and for improving uniformity of application. When applying fertilizer to trees in the landscape or potted plants using dry formulations, the operation is done by hand.

Mechanized Sometimes fertilizer can be applied at the time of planting seed. This method of application entails inserting the fertilizer along with the seed using a seed drill and is called *pop-up* application. When applied with the seed drill, the fertilizer is placed in the seed furrow. When applying fertilizer to a large area, it is done more efficiently and uniformly by using a mechanized system. Mechanized systems enable calibration of equipment to deliver fertilizer at a uniform rate over an entire area.

Liquid Application

Liquid application of fertilizer to containers on a small scale (e.g., at home) may be accomplished by dissolving the fertilizer in water and dispensing it with a calibrated container to the potted plants. A dispenser containing fertilizer may be attached to a watering hose and used for irrigation (see later section). In greenhouses and fields, liquid fertilizers are applied through irrigation water.

Foliar Application Most fertilizer applications involve the use of major nutrients, or macronutrients, applied to the soil. The rates of application are often large and can injure vegetative tissue on direct contact. Hence, caution should be exercised in applying dry fertilizer elements by avoiding placing the elements too close to the plant.

It is neither practical nor safe to apply major elements to leaves directly. Foliar spraying is often used to correct deficiency problems of trace elements. Since trace elements are required in minute amounts, it is safe to administer them by foliar application.

Fertigation Fertigation, also called *chemigation,* entails applying fertilizer to crops through the irrigation water. This method is usually used in the greenhouse. The drip irrigation method is particularly suitable for fertigation. In effect, it is a kind of topdressing application. Critical issues of concern in fertigation include the solubility of the fertilizer and the quality of irrigation water. Water-soluble fertilizers should be used in fertigation. Hard water with excessive amounts of dissolved calcium can be problematic if the irrigation system is incapacitated through blockage of holes by calcium deposits. The advantage of this method is that in soils that drain very freely (e.g., sandy) and for fertilizer elements that are prone to leaching (e.g., nitrogen), irrigation can be controlled to deliver the right amounts of moisture and fertilizer at rates that the plant can utilize efficiently.

Small-scale fertigation systems are available for home use. They usually consist of a handheld unit containing a dry formulation of the fertilizer. The unit is connected to a watering hose that runs water through the container before sprinkling on the area to be irrigated. These units are used for watering vegetable gardens, flower beds, lawns, and other plants in the landscape.

4.4.6 TIMING OF APPLICATION

Fertilizers are applied supplementarily to the nutrition plants obtain from the soil. Plants go through growth phases, each phase with special nutritional needs to support the growth and development activities taking place. Fertilizers are subject to a variety of environmental factors that cause them to be depleted in the soil. For example, under aerobic conditions, nitrogen is lost through *denitrification* (a process whereby bacteria convert nitrates into unusable nitrogen gas). Nitrogen fertilizers are readily leached or, in some cases, volatilized. Phosphorus and potassium are prone to fixation. Appropriate rate and type of fertilizer must therefore be chosen, and the application must be timely. Fertilizers are most beneficial to plants when applied as close as possible to the time of maximum need.

Fertilizers release their nutrients at various rates and over varying periods of time. Organic fertilizers release their nutrients as the material decomposes; consequently, they are not useful when immediate supplemental nutrition is required. Dry application of fertilizers requires moisture availability to enable use of the nutrients. Rain or irrigation is needed after application of dry fertilizer. On the contrary, irrigation or rain is undesirable after foliar application because it will wash the nutrients into the soil.

4.4.7 FERTILIZER RECOMMENDATIONS

After a soil test, fertilizer recommendations are made based on a number of factors, including the following:

1. The regional information on weather and soils.
2. The cropping history of the land.
3. The crop yield target or goal desired by the grower.
4. The crop to be fertilized (in terms of how it responds to fertilization).

For small-scale growers such as home gardeners who have no set yield and profit targets, the general goal of gardening is to produce a good, healthy, and attractive crop. Homeowners and gardeners often overfertilize their gardens and lawns. For some, it is a seasonal ritual or tradition to fertilize the lawn and garden crops. Many people do not conduct soil tests on their plots and hence may not derive optimum benefits from their efforts. Since no specific yield goal is set in home gardening projects, a moderate application of fertilizer is all that may be needed. A general application may be 10 to 20 pounds per 1,000 square feet (4.5 to 9 kilograms per 92.9 square meters); a complete fertilizer (10:10:10) is often sufficient for gardens and lawns.

4.4.8 GREENHOUSE FERTILIZATION

Most greenhouse production occurs in containers, which restricts the amount of soil or growth medium from which a plant can obtain nutrition. Further, greenhouse media used in greenhouses for plant cultivation are often artificial and have little or no nutrition to support plants. As a result, fertilization is critical in greenhouse production. Fertilization programs should include minor or trace elements in addition to major elements. Liquid fertilizers, applied through irrigation water, are important in greenhouse fertilization. The subject is discussed further in Chapter 12.

4.4.9 FERTILIZER CALCULATIONS

Following a soil test, recommendations are made as to the type and amounts of fertilizer the producer may apply. An amount of a certain nutrient may be purchased. However, the weight of fertilizer applied depends on the source, since fertilizers come in all kinds of grades. The three common calculations involving dry fertilizer formulations are (a) nutrient percentage, (b) amount or weight of source (commercial) fertilizer to apply, and (c) the amounts or weights of component materials to use in preparing a bulk of mixed fertilizer.

1. **Nutrient percentage**

   Problem: What is the percentage of nitrogen in the fertilizer urea?

   Solution: Urea has a formula of $(NH_2)_2 CO$, and molecular weight of 60.056 g Molecular weight of nitrogen $(N_2) = 28.014$
   Percentage of nitrogen = $[28.014/60.056] \times 100 = 46.6$ or 46% approximately (round down to nearest whole number).

2. **Simple fertilizer mixture**

   Problem: Given ammonium nitrate (34-0-0) and treble super-phosphate (0-45-0), prepare 1,000 kg of fertilizer of grade 15-10-0.

   Solution: Final mixture will contain 150 kg of nitrogen (i.e., 15% of 1,000 kg).
   It will also contain 100 kg P_2O_5 (i.e., 10% of 1,000 kg).
   Amount of ammonium nitrate needed (p.s., it contains 34 kg of N per 100 kg): $[100 \times 150]/34$ = 441 kg of 34-0-0
   Similarly, for phosphorus (contains 45 kg of P_2O_5 per 100 kg)$[100 \times 100]/45$ = 222 kg of 0-45-0
   Total nutrients = 441 + 222 = 663 kg (leaving 337 balance of the desired 1,000 kg).

The balance is satisfied by adding a filler (inert material) or lime. The procedure is the same for compounding a mixture of three components (i.e., N-P-K).

What if calculated proportions of nutrient components add up to more than total desired weight? In this example, what if the two amounts exceeded 1,000 kg? The component amounts cannot exceed the total desired weight. If that happens, the desired grade should be lowered or a source with higher analysis (e.g., for nitrogen, use urea with 46% N) should be used.

3. **Amounts (weights) of sources (fertilizers) to apply**

   Problem: It has been recommended that a producer apply 80 kg of nitrogen and 40 kg of phosphorus per acre to his field.

How much of ammonium nitrate and treble superphosphate should be applied to achieve the recommended rate?

Solution: Ammonium nitrate contains 34% N; treble superphosphate contains 45% P_2O_5. From example (2), the amount of source to be added to provide 80 kg of N

= [80 × 100]/34

= 235 kg of 34-0-0 per hectare.

Similarly, for 40 kg of P_2O_5

= [40 × 100]/45

= 88.9 kg of 0-45-0 kg per hectare.

Total of mixture = 235 + 89 = 324 per hectare.

To convert from kg per hectare to pounds per acre, multiply by 0.89.

4.4.10 SOIL SALINITY

Soil salinity refers to the presence of excessive amounts of soluble salts (Na^+, Mg^{2+}, Ca^{2+}, Cl^-, SO_4^{2-}) in the soil. High soil salinity inhibits water extraction by plants. Plants differ in their tolerance of soil salinity. Soil salinity is more of a problem under hot and dry weather conditions. It is measured in electrical conductivity units (decisiemens per meter or dS/m). Salinity of 0–2 units is tolerable to plants. However, at 4–8, most crops experience yield decreases, whereas at 8–16 or higher, only tolerant plants can produce acceptable yields. The sodium hazard of irrigation water is measured as sodium adsorption ratio (SAR), where SAR is calculated as follows:

$$SAR = Na^+\sqrt{Ca^{2+}\ Mg^{2+}}$$

Irrigation water that is high in SAR leads to breakdown in soil physical structure.

4.5 Soil Organisms

The soil is teeming with life. Some soil organisms improve the plant environment for good crop growth, whereas others are pests that damage or kill plants. Soil organisms may be divided into several operational groups.

4.5.1 MICROORGANISMS

Soil *microorganisms* (or microbes) include bacteria and fungi, as well as actinomycetes. They perform very useful functions to the benefit of plants. Bacteria, through enzymatic digestion, decompose dead organic material. This action increases the soil's organic matter content and improves its physical properties. Microbes in the soil are also involved in nutrient cycling processes (such as the nitrogen cycle).

Fungi are also important decomposers. In acidic soils, fungi are crucial because they tolerate acidity. The most prominent fungi of interest are the *molds* and *mushrooms*. Microbes, although useful, can also be a menace by causing diseases that are responsible for economic loss to producers.

4.5.2 NONARTHROPOD ANIMALS

Arthropods are animals with exoskeletons and jointed legs; *nonarthropods* lack these features. Nonarthropods of horticultural interest are *nematodes* (roundworms) and *earthworms.* Nematodes are round, microscopic, and the most abundant animals in soil. Nematodes are parasitic to a wide host of horticultural plants, including tomato, carrot, turfgrass, fruit trees, and ornamentals. They inhabit the roots of their hosts and cause the development of amorphous structures that resemble nodules formed by *Rhizobia.* These growths not only deform the roots but, more importantly, stifle the growth of plants.

Earthworms, on the other hand, have positive roles in relation to soil. They improve soil water infiltration and aeration by their earth-moving activities and increase the organic matter content of the soil through the plant materials they drag into the holes they dig. They are important in lawns, because they feed on the *thatch* (dead plant material on the soil surface) that builds up with the mowing of lawns. Earthworms thrive in areas that are moist and high in organic matter, avoiding dry and acidic soils.

4.5.3 ARTHROPOD ANIMALS

Examples of *arthropods* (animals with exoskeletons and jointed legs) of importance to horticulture include *termites, millipedes, centipedes, butterflies, ants, grubs,* and other insects. Termites improve drainage of the soil by the pore spaces they create. Ants and termites are also earth movers like earthworms, except that these insects can move huge quantities of material from within the soil to the surface, creating unsightly hills in lawns. Grubs are a menace in lawns because they feed on grass roots, causing dead spots to appear.

4.5.4 VERTEBRATE ANIMALS

Soil-inhabiting vertebrate animals include rodents, such as ground squirrels, mice, gophers, and rabbits. They are known for their earth-moving activities, some of which can create unsightly structures. However, the holes they burrow help in soil drainage. Rodents can ravage crops in the field, which results in economic loss for the grower.

4.6 SOIL AIR

A typical mineral soil, as previously indicated, consists of 25 percent air. Air is required for respiration by plant roots. Waterlogged conditions cause pore spaces to be filled with water and thus force plants to respire anaerobically (respiration in the absence of oxygen). Seeds require oxygen for germination. Clay soils are very susceptible to poor soil aeration, whereas sandy soils are well aerated. To improve aeration of clay soils, crops may be planted on raised beds, which helps to drain the soil pore spaces so that air can occupy them. Vegetables such as tomato and pea are susceptible to oxygen deficiency, which occurs in soils that are water saturated. These plants wilt and eventually die if the situation is not promptly corrected. Soil oxygen levels of less than about 10 to 12 percent are stressful to most plants. Plants such as water lilies have adaptive structures for respiration under water. Crops grown in water as a medium require aeration to aid in root respiration.

Air is also required for decomposition of organic matter by soil bacteria (Chapter 22). Under waterlogged conditions, plant materials do not decompose properly and form materials such as peat (partially decomposed organic matter).

4.7 SOIL TEMPERATURE

Temperature regulates the rates of all chemical reactions. Plant roots do not grow when the soil temperature is 5°C (41°F) or colder. Even though small grains can germinate at

1°C (34°F), the optimum temperature for germination is 18°C (64°F) and warmer for most crops. Soils warm up much more quickly than water. Sandy soils are said to be warm, whereas clay soils are cold. This situation results because sandy soils drain more quickly, retain less moisture (more air spaces), and warm up more quickly than a soil that has a high capacity for water retention.

Large bodies of water moderate the temperature responses of the soil near them. Since water heats or cools more slowly than soil, the land around large bodies of water tends to experience slow rates of temperature changes. Such a condition occurs in the Great Lakes region. Fruit trees blossom late and are able to escape the onset of killing frosts. In fall, the killing frosts are delayed, thereby extending the growing season. Vegetables and fruit trees are grown in this region along Lake Erie.

Soil temperature can be modified for crop production. Applying a mulch to a soil surface can modify its temperature; draining a soil enables it to warm up quickly. Raised beds help to improve soil drainage. Light-colored mulches reflect sunlight, whereas dark mulch absorb it. Soil temperature can be lowered under light-colored mulch. Some growers use black mulches to raise soil temperature in order to grow an early crop of vegetables and melons in fall. Pale mulches are also used for weed control.

4.8 SOIL WATER

Soil water is critical to plant growth and development. It is the solvent in which soil nutrients are dissolved before they can be absorbed by plant roots. Once in the plant, water is the medium of transportation of solutes and is required in photosynthesis. Plants lose large amounts of water from their surfaces by the process of transpiration. Soil is the primary source of water for plant use. Soil water also affects soil air and soil temperature and thereby influences plant growth and development. Soil water plays a role in the loss of soil by soil *erosion*.

4.8.1 HOW SOIL RETAINS WATER

The goal of irrigation is to provide and retain moisture in the root zone of the plant. After a heavy irrigation or rain, the soil may receive water to fill all pore spaces and become saturated. The soil at this stage is at its *maximum retentive capacity*. Under this condition, water drains freely under the force of gravity (Figure 4–14). The matric potential at this stage is high. After a period of time, drainage ceases. The water drains out of the macropores first, leaving only the micropores to remain filled with water. This remnant water is resistant to gravitational force. The soil at this stage is said to be at **field capacity**. The water at field capacity may be depleted by evaporation from the surface of the soil or transpiration from the plant leaf surface. These two processes together are called *evapotranspiration* (discussed later in this chapter).

There comes a stage where soil moisture cannot be readily absorbed by roots. At this point the plants show signs of moisture stress and start to wilt. If this condition persists for a long time, the plants remain wilted both day and night. They will recover if water is provided soon. The status of soil moisture at this stage is called the *wilting coefficient* or *permanent wilting percentage*. The remnant water occurs only in the smallest of micropores.

4.8.2 TYPES OF SOIL MOISTURE

From a physical point of view, three forms of water are recognizable—*gravitational, capillary,* and *hygroscopic*. Gravitational water is temporary and not of much use to plants; it can be detrimental to plants unless rapidly drained. Similarly, hygroscopic water is not useful to plants because it is largely in vapor form. Capillary water is thus

Field (Water) Capacity
The amount of water remaining in the soil after the soil layer has been saturated and the free (drainable) water has been allowed to drain away.

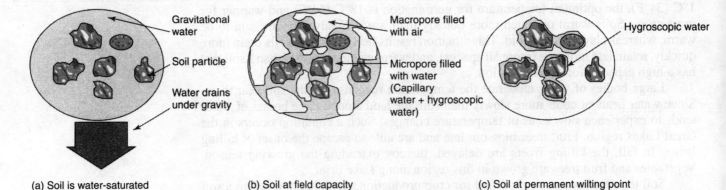

Gravitational water	Macropore filled with air	Hygroscopic water
Soil particle	Micropore filled with water (Capillary water + hygroscopic water)	
Water drains under gravity		

(a) Soil is water-saturated   (b) Soil at field capacity   (c) Soil at permanent wilting point

FIGURE 4–14 Drainage and retention of water in soil. (a) Water-saturated soil drains largely under gravitational force. (b) After the gravitational water has drained out of the macropores, or large pores, the soil is said to be at field capacity. (c) Hygroscopic water is tightly bound to soil particles.

the most useful form of soil water for plant growth and development. The difference between soil moisture at field capacity and wilting coefficient is described as *available water.* Any water held at a potential of lower than −15 bars is unavailable to most plants. Generally, as soil texture decreases, its ability to hold water increases. Sand holds the least amount of water, whereas silt loam retains the most moisture. Soil organic matter contributes to soil moisture retention indirectly through its effect on soil structure. Plants grow best when soil moisture is near field capacity.

It should be mentioned that a combination of factors affect the availability of soil moisture to plants, including soil structure and texture, soil moisture suction, humidity, wind velocity, air and soil temperature, and density of plant roots. Some plants use up more soil water than others to produce an equal amount of dry matter.

4.8.3 WATER TABLE

Water Table
The upper surface of ground water; that level below which the soil is saturated with water.

Water drained from upper horizons of the soil accumulates below. As the accumulation continues, the soil and underlying parent material become saturated with water, creating what is called *groundwater.* The top of the saturated zone in the soil is called the **water table.** The water table varies with seasons and is usually highest in winter. A high water table means water is close to the soil surface, a situation occurring in areas called *wetlands.* Without drainage (removal of excess water from the soil), such soils cannot be used to produce horticultural plants. Most plant roots cannot thrive under waterlogged conditions.

Sometimes, water accumulates in the soil profile because the downward flow is impeded by an impervious layer (e.g., clay pan). This condition, described as a *perched water table,* develops when plants are grown in containers. A perched water table means that the pore spaces at the bottom of the pot are all filled with water. Shallow pots thus have less room for plants to grow in before they reach this induced water table (Figure 4–15). To prevent the formation of a perched water table, the growing media must be properly constituted to allow complete drainage of the entire depth of the soil in the container. The soil should be porous, and drainage holes in the bottom of the pot should be open at all times.

4.8.4 HOW SOIL LOSES MOISTURE

Soil water is subject to loss by a variety of ways. Some of it (up to about 50 percent) may be lost to drainage of water from the plant root zone. Percolating water is not permanently lost, since some of it can be returned to the root zone by capillary rise. Some of the remaining soil water is moved to the soil surface by capillarity and lost by evaporation. Another avenue to soil water loss is from the root zone via the process of transpiration (plants absorb water and lose it, especially through their leaves).

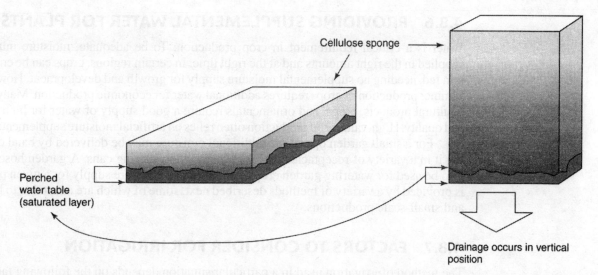

FIGURE 4–15 Demonstration of a perched water table. After drainage ceases when the piece of foam is in the horizontal position, a water-saturated layer occurs at the bottom. When stood on its shorter end, water drainage resumes because of increased space above until a new perched water table develops.

4.8.5 EVAPOTRANSPIRATION

Loss of moisture by the process of evaporation and transpiration together produces a combined effect called *evapotranspiration*. As moisture is lost from the soil surface, water moves slowly below to restore the equilibrium. However, if the rate of evaporation is so rapid that it overwhelms the rate of replacement of water from below, the surface layer can become so dry that the continuity of water flow from below is interrupted. This dry surface layer serves to protect the lower layers and conserves moisture.

Evapotranspiration is influenced by certain factors. The rate of evaporation is directly related to the net radiation from the sun. Solar radiation is higher on a clear day than a cloudy one. Further, plant cover or shading by plant leaves reduces the effective soil surface for evaporation. This factor, called *leaf area index* (leaf area of plants per soil surface area occupied by plants measured), affects the amount of radiant energy reaching the soil surface. Evaporation is thus higher in a field of newly planted seedlings than in an established one with more dense leaf cover.

Evapotranspiration is also affected by atmospheric vapor pressure. When the atmospheric vapor pressure is less than that at the plant and soil surfaces, evaporation occurs. Temperature increases the vapor pressure at the leaf and soil surfaces, with little effect on the vapor pressure of the general atmosphere. With a drier atmosphere, evaporation proceeds rapidly. Similarly, wind tends to remove moisture vapor from wet surfaces. Thus, leaves and soil surfaces lose moisture more rapidly on dry, windy days. Evapotranspiration is higher in soils near field capacity than in soils with low moisture content.

Evapotranspiration can be controlled by crop selection and cultural management. Application of mulch can significantly reduce evaporation and conserve moisture. Cover crops or ground cover also reduce evaporation from the soil. Tillage as a method of weed control eliminates the wasteful use of water by weeds.

Plants may need supplemental moisture during cultivation. Evapotranspiration losses can be reduced when plants are irrigated because the timing of application and amount of water applied can be controlled. Watering should be done at a time of day when the water vapor gradients are low. In this regard, crops are best grown in the cool season, whenever possible. In the dry period when irrigation is needed, the soil surface should be kept only as moist as is needed by the particular plant. However, the watering schedule should allow water to penetrate to the root zone. Methods that allow water to be concentrated around the roots (drip irrigation) are most efficient in this regard. To further reduce surface moisture loss, subsurface irrigation is even more efficient because the pipes are buried in the ground to supply water to the root zone.

4.8.6 PROVIDING SUPPLEMENTAL WATER FOR PLANTS

Water is a critical requirement in crop production. To be adequate, moisture must be supplied in the right amounts and at the right time. In certain regions, crops can be entirely rain fed, needing no supplemental moisture supply for growth and development. However, summer production of crops requires additional water for economic production. Many horticultural products, crops, and ornamentals require a good supply of water for high yield and quality. High-value crop production often relies on artificial moisture supplementation.

For a small garden operation, additional moisture may be delivered by hand carrying it in a variety of receptacles such as buckets and watering cans. A garden hose may also be used for watering garden crops. A continuous moisture supply for a given period is provided by a variety of methods described next, some of which are adaptable to large- and small-scale productions.

4.8.7 FACTORS TO CONSIDER FOR IRRIGATION

The method of irrigation used in a particular situation depends on the following factors:

1. *Crop.* The method used to irrigate depends on the type of crop or plant and its water needs, size, and way it is being cultured. Because plants that creep on the ground cannot lie in water, the method of irrigation should not permit water to pond on the soil surface. When growing trees that are spaced widely, it is efficient to supply water to the trees individually rather than watering the large spaces in between plants. Irrigating tall trees from above is difficult. Overhead systems of irrigation are unsuitable for tree irrigation. Certain plants prefer or need large volumes of water to perform well, and the irrigation system should be capable of providing this volume.

2. *Source of water.* Different sources of irrigation water vary in cost and availability. Certain methods of irrigation (flood) require the entire soil surface to be covered with water. This method is not practical when the source of water is the domestic water supply. It is more suited to water from rivers or other large bodies of water. Tap water is adequate for watering lawns and residential and urban landscape plants.

3. *Soil type.* Soils differ in water infiltration rate. If the soil is sandy, the water infiltration rate is high, making the area unsuited to flood irrigation. Much of the water is wasted near the supply source because of deep and rapid infiltration. Water moves slowly over the surface.

4. *Slope of the land.* Certain irrigation methods require water to be moved by gravity and thus are adaptable to fields in which the ground slopes.

5. *Rainfall regime of the region.* In areas of erratic rainfall and low annual totals, moisture must be administered efficiently. The drip system places less demand on the scarce water supply.

6. *Crop rotation.* If crops rotated in the production system require different land preparation and other cultural practices, a method that is flexible and adaptable should be selected. Not all plants can tolerate flooding. The differences in spacing requirements necessitate a flexible system that can be adjusted readily.

7. *Surface of the land.* Installation of an irrigation system is affected by the nature of the terrain. Certain methods such as flooding require grading and leveling of the land. Where pumps are needed to lift water, the relief of the area determines the kind of pump needed to move water from the source to the field.

8. *Cost.* Irrigation methods differ in cost in terms of initial installation and maintenance.

4.8.8 METHODS OF IRRIGATION

Irrigation systems for applying supplemental moisture to plants may be grouped into three categories—sprinkler irrigation, drip or trickle irrigation, and surface irrigation.

Overhead Sprinkler Irrigation

Water is usually moved under high pressure through a simple or more elaborate network of pipes. For home gardens and landscapes, the pressure used is from the municipal water source. Municipal water is delivered at very high pressure (more than 80 psi), which can damage equipment unless it is reduced by installing pressure-reducing valves. A network of pipes is installed underground and fitted with pop-up sprinkler heads to deliver a spray of water to the area.

Some overhead irrigation systems are designed to be mobile. They are used temporaily in a location and then moved to another area or removed for storage. It may be as simple as a garden hose sprinkler. There are different designs of this kind of sprinkler, which is easy to use and adapted to irrigating lawns, vegetable gardens, and flower beds. Their use is limited by the length of the hose to which the sprinkler is attached. For irrigating a large area, a *drum-mounted hose* (Figure 4–16) may be used. A disadvantage of this system is that it must be set up for use and then removed afterward or moved periodically until the area is completely irrigated. Certain models allow the sprinkler to move (*moving sprinklers*) automatically across the landscape, thus eliminating the need for human intervention. A *perforated hose (porous hose)* may also be used to distribute water to plants in the landscape.

Watering Cans are used for watering flower beds in the absence of sprinkler systems.

Sprinkler irrigation is a method of mimicking the rain by supplying moisture from above. The equipment may be as simple as a *lawn* or *garden sprinkler* or as elaborate as a large, self-propelled *center pivot* system used on large commercial farms (Figure 4-16). The sprinkler system may consist of portable or fixed pipes. Water is distributed through a network of pipelines under high pressure. Equipment costs can be high. Sprinklers are desirable where soils have high infiltration rates or uneven surfaces. Sprinklers are also used where irrigation is not the primary source of moisture for crop growth. In this case, a portable system may be transported to the area when needed. Center pivot systems that are equipped with LEPA heads have high water application efficiency and also multiple modes of operation (bubble, sprays, chemigation).

(a)

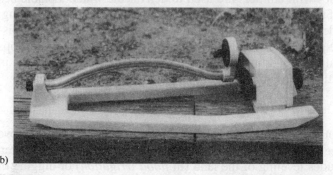
(b)

(c)

FIGURE 4–16 (a) A center pivot irrigation system. (b) Common lawn oscillating sprinkler. (c) Portable pipes sprinkler system.
(*Source: For* (a) and (c) USDA, (b) George Acquaah)

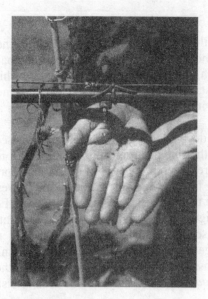

FIGURE 4–17 A drip irrigation system may be suspended on a cable or laid on the ground. Drops of water are delivered to the base of the plant, wetting only a limited area. *(Source:* USDA)

FIGURE 4–18 Flood irrigation of citrus field. *(Source:* USDA)

Sprinkler irrigation has the effect of modifying the microclimate of plants, since water has a high specific heat. Sprinkler irrigation is used in the horticultural industry for frost protection in the production of vegetables and fruits in winter.

Drip or Trickle Irrigation

In methods of irrigation besides drip irrigation, water is applied perhaps to areas where it is not needed. *Drip irrigation* is a spot application system for watering plants in which minute amounts of water are applied almost continuously to plants throughout the growing period (Figure 4–17). Precise water volume is applied to the root zone of the plant. If well designed and managed, its efficiency can be 90–95 percent (i.e., only 5–10 percent of the applied water is wasted). It operates under lower pressure than sprinkler irrigation systems. The producer can conduct other operations (e.g., harvesting and spraying with pesticides) while irrigation is in progress. This method of irrigation is also suited for chemigation. However, the initial investment is high for this system. Furthermore, it is prone to damage by rodents and is also management intensive. It is economical to use and also highly desirable in areas where the water supply is limited and water cost is excessive. Plastic pipes with emitters are used to deliver the water. These tubes may be laid on the surface of the land or buried, the latter being more prone to clogging. Drip irrigation is especially desirable for high-value crops that require uniform soil moisture for good development (e.g., vineyards and orchards). For example, when tuber crops such as potatoes are grown under conditions where the soil experiences fluctuations in moisture levels, tuber formation is irregular, leading to low market value.

Surface Irrigation

In sprinkler and drip irrigation, a pump may be required for appropriate pressure to move water through pipes. Surface systems depend on the slope of the land to move water. Initial land preparation includes leveling of the land (in *flood irrigation*) or digging of ditches (in *furrow irrigation*). These methods are not suitable for sandy soils or soils that have a high infiltration rate, especially if water is to be moved over long distances. Flood

FIGURE 4–19 Furrow irrigation of lettuce. *(Source: USDA)*

irrigation is commonly used in orchards (Figure 4–18). Furrow irrigation is a version of flood irrigation in which the surface flow is limited to channels between ridges. Vegetables may be irrigated in this way (Figure 4–19).

4.8.9 SOURCE OF WATER

For home gardening, municipal water is the most frequent source of water for irrigation. The advantage of this source is that it is ready for use, provided the user has a means of connecting to it, eliminating the initial cost of providing an irrigation system. The source is reliable, since water is needed each day for a variety of uses in the home; the city ensures a continued supply. The disadvantages of this source of water are its high cost, the possibility of rationing in certain areas at times when plants need water the most, and the sensitivity of certain plants to municipal water treatments (chlorine and fluoride).

For a large landscape, a well may be an alternative source of water. Wells are practical where the water table is at a readily accessible level. Sinking a well is expensive, and the quality of water is affected by soil and rock materials and may yield hard water (containing rock mineral deposits). Underground water may be contaminated by soil surface pollutants. Three types of wells may be used for irrigation. **Driven wells** are relatively inexpensive and easy to install. The unit is small and thus unobtrusive in the landscape. However, it yields a limited amount of water and is prone to blockage from debris over time. Driven wells are practical in areas where the water table is high. A well point must be found, which is perhaps the most difficult aspect of the whole process. Once found, shafts are driven into the soil using a sledgehammer. Shafts may each be about 5 feet long (1.5 meters) and are driven one after another, connecting the sections as one proceeds. *Dug wells* take up more space but also yield more water. If the site is properly selected, a dug well produces good-quality water year-round. A pump is needed to lift the water for use; dug wells may be lined with rock or concrete. The third type of well, a *drilled well*, is rather expensive and not a common option for homeowners. It is installed by using large drilling equipment similar to that used for prospecting oil.

Driven Well
A method of drawing groundwater by driving shafts into the water table.

4.8.10 WATER QUALITY

Water quality for irrigation is not only critical to the success of growing plants but it also affects the design of irrigation systems. The issue is less critical if municipal water is the water source for irrigation. Water quality problems may be physical, biological, and chemical. The physical problems relate to the presence of mineral particles—sand, silt, and clay—in the water source. These sediments can clog pipes and sprinkler nozzles. Chemical problems pertain to the presence of dissolved salts like calcium, magnesium, bicarbonate, and iron. These chemicals can precipitate out of the water, causing clogging of pipes and nozzles as in the case of physical pollutants, as well as corrosion of metal parts if water pH is low. Also, chemicals like iron and manganese can stain walls and sidewalks. Untreated water can carry a variety of microbes and algae. These problems are associated with water wells and surface water sources of irrigation water.

Polluted irrigation water is more problematic for drip irrigation systems than sprinker systems because of the tiny orifices of the emitters and tubes used in microirrigation. Some filtration is required for such pollution-sensitive systems.

4.8.11 EVAPOTRANSPIRATION AND ITS EFFECT ON IRRIGATION

Moisture in the root zone of the soil is lost through plants by the process of transpiration through plant surfaces. Soil moisture is also lost from the soil when water vapor is lost by evaporation from the soil surface. These two processes produce a combined effect, called evapotranspiration, that is responsible for most of the water removal from the soil. The efficiency of irrigation is dependent on evapotranspiration. To minimize this factor, water must be applied at the right time of day by the most water-efficient method and protected from rapid loss. Water applied to bare soil is rapidly lost by evaporation from the soil surface. Mulching, where practical, may be applied to reduce this moisture loss. Irrigation in the early morning allows water to seep into the soil and thereby reduces the loss that occurs at high noon. Methods of irrigation vary in water use efficiency; drip irrigation provides water in the most efficient manner.

4.8.12 BEST TIME OF DAY TO IRRIGATE

The critical considerations in watering plants in the landscape or garden are to deliver adequate moisture to the root zone, reduce waste, and avoid the persistence of a microclimate conducive to disease organisms. Water should be delivered at a rate at which it can infiltrate the soil and for a long enough time to achieve deep wetting of the root zone. Such watering can happen any time of day. In terms of waste, certain times of day, especially around noon, provide the greatest opportunity for water loss from the soil and other surfaces due to evapotranspiration (see next section). Contrary to popular belief, plant leaves will not be scaled when they are watered at high noon. Rather, moisture loss is very high at this time of day. The other important consideration is avoiding the persistence of high humidity and high moisture, which predisposes plants to diseases. Watering plants such that there will be time for leaves to dry before nightfall reduces disease incidence. Most landscapes are watered in the early part of the day for the reasons given.

4.8.13 PRECIPITATION RATE

It is important that an automatic lawn irrigation system be carefully designed for efficient and effective high water use. The topography of the area, soil water-holding capacity, and plant needs must be considered in the design. One factor of paramount importance is the **precipitation rate**, the measure of the amount of rainfall received by the area within one hour. A high precipitation rate is considered to occur when more than 1 inch (2.5 centimeters) of rain falls within an hour; a low rate is less than 1 inch per hour. An area of predominantly sandy soil has a high soil infiltration rate and thus requires a high precipitation rate to satisfy plants' water needs. Using this information, one can select a system that will not be overworked (because of use for an excessively long period at one time).

Sprinkler heads used in subirrigation systems may be divided into three groups according to precipitation rates. Low-precipitation-rate sprinklers are used where the soil can tolerate a large amount of water in a short period. Moderate-precipitation-rate sprinklers are run for a longer time and can have variable output. They are located in areas that are average in infiltration rate. It should be mentioned that although a homeowner

Precipitation Rate
The amount of rainfall received by an area within one hour.

can self-install an underground irrigation system, certain decisions are best made by a professional, unless one has sufficient knowledge about the system. For example, one should know the *running time* for the system, a calculation based on the precipitation rates, which in turn is dependent on the infiltration rate of the soil in the area. Further, one should determine where to locate the sprinklers in the landscape. A sprinkler system does not utilize identical sprinkler heads throughout the landscape, which are varied according to site characteristics. The general rule is that the precipitation rate of a particular system is inversely related to the head spacing (spacing between sprinkler heads on a lateral) or row spacing (between lateral pipes). For best results, a design should ensure even or balanced water coverage. Uniform coverage requires that sprinkler heads be properly matched; failure to do so will result in dry spots in the lawn.

Irrigation Kits

For the do-it-yourself grower, misting, watering, and drip irrigation kits can be purchased for use. These units are designed for application in greenhouses, nurseries, and general landscapes. A unit consists of the pipes and outlets (risers, sprinklers, or tubules) and all necessary connectors. Installation of irrigation systems in the landscape and garden is discussed later in this chapter.

4.8.14   CONSERVING SOIL MOISTURE

Water loss in the landscape during irrigation can be minimized by observing several simple practices:

1. Water in the early morning when the temperature is lowest to reduce evaporative loss.
2. To avoid runoff, apply water at the rate of soil infiltration.
3. Improve the water-retention capacity of soil by incorporating organic matter as needed.
4. Do not overwater. Water that cannot be used by plants is wasted.
5. Adjust timers on automatic sprinklers on a seasonal basis to avoid use when water is not needed.
6. Wetting of soil should be confined to the diameter of the plant canopy.
7. Use a mulch, whenever appropriate, to reduce evaporation.
8. Apply the concept of hydrozoning in designing the landscape.

4.8.15   FACTORS AFFECTING WATERING FREQUENCY

The frequency of watering depends on a combination of several factors:

1. *Species.* Certain species such as cacti are drought tolerant, as are deep-rooted plants that are adapted to tropical and dry climates. Drought-tolerant cultivars of various horticultural plants have been bred by scientists. Annual bedding plants, including garden vegetables such as tomato, pepper, and cole crops, need to be watered frequently.
2. *Soil properties.* Sandy soils are well aerated, drain freely, and have lower moisture-retention capacities than loams or clays. When sandy soils are used for any type of plant production, watering is a major production input. Clay soils are more prone to waterlogging than sandy soils. The moisture-retention capacity of sandy soils may be improved by incorporating organic matter and using mulch.
3. *Stage in plant growth.* Frequent watering is needed during the period of plant establishment. In some cases, plants may require watering twice a day. Once established, watering frequency may be reduced according to the capacity of the plants to forage for water. Water is needed at critical times such as flowering and fruiting. Drought at these times can cause flower and fruit drop.

4. *Season.* Certain trees and shrubs can be solely rain fed during their cultivation. However, annual species and smaller plants need supplemental moisture to survive the summer. In summer, especially in areas with less than 40 inches of annual rainfall, lawns need to be irrigated more frequently, sometimes every other day or even daily if a luxuriant lawn is desired.

5. *Conservation practice.* Installation of a mulch reduces evaporation and increases soil water retention. Similarly, the presence of a ground cover improves water retention. The concept and practice of xeriscaping minimizes the use of water in the landscape.

4.8.16 SPRAY HEADS FOR SPRINKLERS

Nozzle
A device through which a spray is delivered; it is designed to deliver a spray in a certain pattern, rate, and uniformity.

There are a variety of sprinkler heads to select from to suit the needs of the landscape. The heads vary in versatility, cost, design, and other features. A sprinkler head contains a **nozzle**, a device through which a spray is delivered in a specific pattern, rate, and uniformity. For areas where high precipitation is needed, one may choose a *fixed-spray sprinkler*, a *bubbler*, or a *microsprayer*. Bubblers are able to soak the soil deeply in a small area. In areas where low to medium precipitation is needed, the choice can be made from *rotating-stream heads, stream-spray heads, impact-rotor heads, gear-rotor heads*, and *pop-up heads*. Pop-up sprinklers are very unobtrusive in the landscape. They pop up under pressure when the system is turned on and sink back into their shells out of view after use. Some of these heads can be installed at angles to enable effective and efficient watering of slopes. Some are designed to water a variety of plant arrangements, including low plants in the foreground and tall plants in the background.

An irrigation system is not complete without control panel valves. This aspect of the system varies widely, and the choice is best left to professionals. The purpose of this section, then, is to make the reader knowledgeable about what an underground system consists of in order to be able to participate in its design and supervise its installation to a reasonable degree.

4.8.17 PUMPS FOR IRRIGATION SYSTEMS

Landscape and garden irrigation systems depend on pressure to move and distribute water. If one is depending on a municipal water supply for irrigation, there is no need to obtain and install a pump for irrigation. A pump is invariably required to lift water from a low level (e.g., a well) and distribute it throughout the landscape in pipes. There are several types of pumps from which to choose, a decision that must be made with great care for best results. *Effluent pumps (utility* or *sump pumps)* are relatively inexpensive. They are designed for use in pumping water that contains no solids (e.g., pumping water from a basement after flooding or emptying a pond or pool). For irrigation purposes, this pump is adequate when the source of irrigation water is a shallow pond or well. A disadvantage with this pump is the need for an outside power supply. Also, the pump works at a constant, nonadjustable water pressure.

Single-pipe jet pumps (or *shallow-well jet pumps*) have adjustable water pressure capability. Designed for use in shallow wells of less than 25 feet (7.5 meters) deep, they are not submersible and are more expensive than effluent pumps. However, they are automatic and not restricted by power cables and the need for an outside power supply. To utilize water from a well that is deeper than 25 feet (up to about 125 feet), a *dual-pipe jet pump (deep-well jet pump)* is needed. This pump is not submersible and is less efficient than the more expensive *submersible deep-well pump*, which can pump water from a depth of about 500 feet (150 meters).

4.8.18 SOIL DRAINAGE

Plant roots do not tolerate excessive moisture. *Drainage* is the method by which excess moisture (gravitational) is removed from the soil to enable the soil to be adequately aerated. An area of land can be drained by one of two systems—surface drainage or subsurface drainage.

1. *Surface drainage.*   Surface drainage uses open ditches to remove surface running water before it infiltrates the soil. The land is prepared such that it slopes very gently toward the ditches. Large amounts of water can be drained by surface irrigation in a short period. These ditches require maintenance to keep them open; open drains occupy land that could otherwise have been cropped and also interrupt the continuity of the land.

2. *Subsurface drainage.*   In subsurface, or underground, drainage systems, channels are provided in the zone of maximum water accumulation to drain the excess water. The system must be placed below the plow depth. In one system, that most commonly used, the channels consist of perforated plastic pipes laid at predetermined intervals across the field. Water enters the pipes through the perforations and is moved to an outlet ditch. Other less common systems are the mole drainage and the clay-tile drainage systems. Installation of the mole system is less expensive than clay tiles, which are very costly. Outlets of the subsurface systems of drainage must be protected from clogging by sediments, dead animals, bird nests, and other obstructions.

Advantages of Drainage

Drainage is beneficial to plants and horticultural operations in several ways.

1. *Strong structural foundation.*   Greenhouses and other structures constructed for horticultural use are more stable when located on well-drained soils. Greenhouses typically use large amounts of water for a variety of activities— washing, irrigation, and the like. The site of the facility should be well drained to handle the excess water.

2. *Aeration.*   By draining the root zone, plant roots grow in an environment with a good balance of air and moisture. Aerobic bacteria are able to function properly to decompose organic matter to release nutrients for plant use.

3. *Warm soil.*   Drainage of excess water decreases the specific heat of soil, allowing it to warm up more quickly. In clay soils and poorly drained areas, plants should be grown in raised beds. Raised beds improve drainage and free up pore spaces for air to warm the soil.

4. *Timely field planting.*   Seeds require warm soil to germinate. Seeds can be planted at the usual time in the season if cold soils are drained to make them warmer.

4.8.19   ENVIRONMENTAL CONCERNS

Land is irrigated mostly in drought-prone areas. In these areas, leaching is minimal, leading to the accumulation of salts in irrigated soil. Excessive fertilization predisposes soil to salinity. Crops have different salt tolerance levels.

The use of fertilizers and irrigation water, while desirable for high economic production, has both short- and long-term environmental consequences. Groundwater and surface waters are polluted as a result of this crop production activity. Excess water from irrigation, either as runoff or drainage, ends up in the groundwater or rivers. This water is loaded with salts and as such causes the salt concentration of rivers to rise.

Phosphates are readily fixed in the soil (adsorbed to soil particles). Phosphate pollution occurs in surface water as a result of soil erosion, which moves soil into surface waters. Nitrates, on the other hand, are readily leached and hence end up in the groundwater. Nitrates may accumulate in some leafy vegetables beyond normal levels. Nitrate toxicity is a problem in ruminants.

4.8.20   GREENHOUSE IRRIGATION

Greenhouse irrigation is discussed in Chapters 12 and 13.

Most horticultural plants are grown in solid media, in the field, in containers outside or inside of the house, or in controlled-environment greenhouses. Soil properties have implications in the way they are managed for optimum productivity. Most plant production or display occurs in the field in real soil. Depending on the soil properties and the needs of the plant to be cultivated, soils are physically and sometimes chemically manipulated to provide the best medium for growth. Growing plants indoors either at home or in the greenhouse requires the growth medium to be placed in a container. This situation poses new challenges in managing the growth medium, which should drain freely while holding adequate moisture and nutrients for plant use. Potting media frequently consist either entirely or partly of artificial or *soilless* components.

Soils are disturbed to varying degrees to prepare them for crop production. *Tillage* is the term used for the manual or mechanical manipulation of soil to prepare it for use in crop cultivation. Conventional soil preparation *(conventional tillage)* involves turning over all of the soil in an area of land. Other conservative systems such as the *minimum tillage (zero tillage* or *no-till)* disturb only the spots where seeds or plants are to be located.

4.9.1 PURPOSES OF TILLAGE

How soil is tilled depends on its intended use.

1. *Seedbed preparation.* A seedbed provides an environment in which a seed can germinate and grow. It is loose, well drained, deep enough, makes good contact with the seed, retains adequate moisture, and is free of weeds. If the seeds to be sown are tiny, such as those of carrot and lettuce, the *tilth* should be fine. A rough finish is sufficient for large seeds and transplants.
2. *Level land.* Land leveling may be required while preparing the land to make it amenable to a chosen method of irrigation.
3. *Weed control.* Weeds are a menace to crop production and compete with crops for plant environmental growth factors. They must be controlled before planting and during the growth of the crop by appropriate tillage methods.
4. *Incorporation of organic matter and soil amendments.* Green manures, crop residues, fertilizers, and other chemicals may be added to the soil by plowing them under or mixing them in at the time of preparation.
5. *Improved physical properties of soil.* Compaction of the field impedes drainage, rooting, and general crop growth. A **pan** caused by traffic or tillage may be broken up by tillage methods.
6. *Erosion control.* The soil surface after tillage may be such that it impedes runoff. Stubble may be incorporated into the topsoil or ridges constructed to curb erosion. On a slope, the ridges or direction of plowing should be across the slope to impede surface runoff.

Pan
A layer in the soil that is highly compacted or very high in clay content.

4.9.2 TYPES OF TILLAGE

In terms of the depth to which a soil is tilled and the purpose of tillage, there are two general classes of tillage. Each requires different implements.

Primary Tillage

In primary tillage, the soil is tilled to a depth of about 6 to 14 inches (15 to 36 centimeters). The topsoil is turned over, burying the vegetation and other debris. Primary tillage may be used to incorporate fertilizer and also to aerate the soil. The end product is a rough, cloddy soil surface. Because of the depth of plowing, heavy machinery and implements are used in primary tillage operations. The end product is meant to be transitional and is not ready for planting seeds or seedlings.

Secondary Tillage

Primary tillage is usually followed by a secondary tillage operation to break up the clods to produce a finer tilth for a good seedbed. Another purpose of secondary tillage is to control weeds. The implements used work up to about half the depth (2 to 6 inches or 5 to 15 centimeters) of primary tillage implements.

4.9.3 TILLAGE SYSTEMS

The term *tillage system* refers to the nature and sequence of tillage operations adopted in preparing a seedbed for planting. Each system has specific objectives relating to the condition of the seedbed and soil conservation strategies emphasized.

Conventional Tillage

The goal of conventional tillage is to obtain a clean field in which all weeds and stubble are plowed under the soil. The soil is deeply plowed, requiring both primary and secondary tillage operations and benefiting from both methods. Three general steps are involved in conventional tillage:

1. A preliminary clearing of the land to remove excessive amounts of plant debris. This step depends on the kind of vegetative cover. Shrubs and trees usually must be removed. Grasses can be plowed under the soil without difficulty, unless the plants are very tall.
2. Primary tillage is then conducted to turn the soil over to bury the remaining debris. This activity is called plowing and involves the use of heavy implements.
3. Secondary tillage completes the tillage by providing a fine seedbed. The operation requires several passes of various light implements.

In conventional tillage, the soil is completely exposed to environmental factors. Further, because several trips are made over the land by the various tillage equipment, the soil is prone to compaction, a condition that impedes soil drainage. Deep tillage is thus required periodically under conventional tillage to break the hardpan formed as a result of soil compaction. Conventional tillage is expensive.

Conservation Tillage

The goal of conservation tillage is to conserve the soil in terms of soil loss to erosion and moisture loss. It may entail producing a fine tilth that breaks capillarity and reduces moisture loss from evaporation, or plant matter may be left on the surface for mulching and impeding soil erosion.

Minimum Tillage

The goal of minimum tillage (also called *zero tillage* or no-till) is to disturb the soil as little as possible during the entire soil preparation and crop growth periods. Only the spot where the seed or plant will be located is disturbed. Minimized soil disturbance requires special equipment and also relies on chemicals to control weeds.

Listing

Listing is a tillage operation in which an implement called a *lister* is used to create beds or form ridges on which seeds or plants are sown. Sometimes, in well-drained soil, seeds are sown in the furrows between the ridges instead of on the ridges. The soil in the ridge is warmer and has a quick infiltration rate. Ridges also help to prevent soil erosion.

Cultivation

Cultivation is a tillage operation performed as needed during the crop production cycle, anytime between seed germination and crop harvest. The primary goal of cultivation is to control weeds. However, soil is also cultivated to improve infiltration and aeration.

4.10 POTTING MEDIA

Soils, as they occur in nature, consist of mineral elements. They are dense and bulky. Plants are not always grown outdoors in fields. Some are grown indoors and require containers to hold the soil. Because of the bulky nature of natural soil, scientists have developed methods for synthesizing growing media for a variety of purposes. The ingredients in such mixes may be natural or artificial. The goal of such creations is to use proportions of these ingredients in mixes such that the results mimic the environment that a natural soil would provide for a seed or plant. In fact, since humans are in control, they are able to manipulate the proportions of ingredients to create a wide variety of growing conditions not available in nature. These mixes are sometimes called *soilless mixes* because they consist of materials that are not true soil ingredients. However, certain mixes contain real or true soil material.

4.10.1 FORMULATING A MIX

Properties of a Good Mix

Potting mixes are formulated according to need. Certain mixes are constituted for germination and others for growth. Various plants prefer various characteristics in mixtures. Difference notwithstanding, all mixtures should have certain basic physical, chemical, and biological properties.

1. Physically, the mix should drain freely (good infiltration) and be well aerated.
2. The materials used should have high particle stability (i.e., it should not decompose rapidly) and be easily wetted.
3. It should have good moisture-holding capacity and good bulk density.
4. For use in automated pot-filling machines, the mix should flow easily.
5. Chemically, the material used should not produce any toxins. For example, sawdust or chipping from treated lumber should be washed before use. Natural toxins in plants usually break down when plant materials decompose properly.
6. The mix should have good CEC (about 50 to 100 mEq/100 g of soil) and buffer capacity. The pH should be about 5.5 to 6.0 or according to the need of the plant to be grown.
7. Nutrient element needs for proper growth and development should be provided in a balanced amount. Certain mixes include special fertilizer conditioners.
8. Artificial soil mixes are usually pasteurized to kill pathogens. However, beneficial microbes should be present in the soil.

Materials

Materials used in formulating a mix include those of organic and inorganic origin (Figure 4–20.)

FIGURE 4–20 Materials for a soilless mix, (a) Wood bark, (b) Perlite, (c) Sphagnum moss, and (d) A soilless mix of ingredients. *(Source: George Acquaah)*

Materials of Plant Origin In natural soils, plant roots and other plant remains, along with decaying animal material, provide the organic matter content. In artificial mixes, plant materials are incorporated to fulfill the role of organic matter. The common sources of organic matter in soilless mixes are peat moss, wood by-products, and bark.

PEAT MOSS *Peat moss,* or simply *peat,* is an organic material composed of partially decomposed plant matter that has been preserved under water. It is recovered from underneath bogs and swamps, for example, and has a high water-holding capacity. It also supplies some nutrients, especially nitrogen. The types of peat differ according to plant material acidity and degree of decomposition. The best and most widely used is *sphagnum peat.* It can absorb 10–20 times its weight in water.

Sphagnum peat consists of partially decomposed plant material *(Sphagnum moss)* that is dehydrated. Its varying degrees of decomposition form the basis for material grading. Grade H1 occurs at the top of the bog and is the most decomposed. Grade H10 occurs at the bottom of the pile and is least decomposed. The highest-quality horticultural peat is obtained from layers H3 through H5. This peat has high moisture- and nutrient-holding capacity. It is recovered from acidic bogs. The grades used in horticulture have a pH between 4.0 and 4.5. Sphagnum moss is lightweight and relatively disease free. It inhibits the growth of the organisms responsible for damping-off disease in seedlings. It holds nutrients well and can be pasteurized without being destroyed.

When applied, sphaghum peat improves drainage and aeration in heavier soils while improving moisture and nutrient retention in lighter soils. Apart from sphagnum peat, other peats differ according to the plant material from which they are formed. These types include sedge peat, hypnum peat, and reed peat, which are not commonly used in greenhouse operations. Many of the peat deposits in the northern United States are hypnaceous. They are more decomposed and have a pH range between 4.0 and 7.5 or even higher.

WOOD BY-PRODUCTS Wood shavings and sawdust may be used in soilless mixes. The source of wood products is important since certain woods, such as redwood, contain high levels of manganese, an element injurious to young plants. Before use, such problem material should be leached (watered heavily for several hours) to remove this element and other toxins that may exist. Not all toxins can be leached out of the plant material. Sawdust from cedar and walnut should be avoided because leaching is not effective in removing the toxins they contain. Sawdust may be acidic or alkaline in reaction. Including sawdust in a growing medium often creates temporary nitrogen deficiency because the bacteria that decompose sawdust first utilize some of the existing nitrogen. Thus, some nitrogen fertilizer should be included in the mix when sawdust is used as an ingredient.

In areas of certain crop production, by-products of the industries may be good sources of material for soil mixes. Usable plant by-products include peanut shells, bagash (from crushing sugarcane), straw, and corncobs.

BARK Bark from hardwoods such as oak and maple or softwoods such as conifers may be used in a growing mix. Bark consists primarily of lignin, which decomposes slowly. Hardwood bark tends to be higher in nitrogen, phosphorus, and potassium and lower in calcium content than softwood bark. Softwood bark, on the other hand, is higher in micronutrients, especially manganese. Just like wood by-products, bark from certain species may contain toxins. Growth inhibitors have been found in the barks of walnut, cherry, cedar, and white pine. Loblolly pine *(Pinus taeda)* and slash pine *(Pinus caribaea)* barks do not have growth inhibitors and thus are the most widely used in artificial soil mixes.

OTHER MINOR SOURCES Leaf mold (especially from maple, oak, and sycamore) is composted material that can improve drainage, aeration, and water-holding capacity of the medium. Bagasse (by-products of the sugar industry) has potential for use in media formulation. However, its high sugar content triggers a high microbial activity leading to reduced media quality over time. Rice hulls, corn cobs, peanuts shells, and others are also organic materials that are less commonly used in media formulation.

Carbon to nitrogen ration (C:N) is an indication of the susceptibility to decomposition of an organic matter, a lower ratio indicating that the material can decompose rapidly, while a high ratio indicates the material is highly resistant to decomposition. High cellulose (high carbon) is the reason for resistance to decay of organic matter. Rapid decay of organic matter in a container medium can result in decreased volume, increased compaction, and reduced aeration.

Materials of Mineral (Rock) Origin
A variety of inorganic materials (containing no carbon) are used in soil mixes.

SAND *Sand* is a heavy ingredient in growing mixes. Easy to pasteurize, its role in the mix is to improve drainage and infiltration; it does not hold moisture. Sand does not supply any nutrients to the mix. Silica sands with particle sizes between 0.5 and 2.0 millimeters are desirable. If larger particles are used, the mix may settle and become compacted, thus reducing infiltration. Sand may be obtained from the riverbed or mined from white mountain sand deposits. The latter source produces particles that have flat sides (called sharp sand). This angular property gives preference to this kind of sand because it does not settle or pack down in a mix as does sand with rounded particles such as that from riverbeds. Packing down reduces the pore spaces in the soil.

PERLITE *Perlite* is a light rock material of volcanic origin. It is essentially heat-expanded aluminum silicate rock. The volcanic ore is heated to extreme temperatures of about 982°C (1,800°F) to cause the rock particles to expand to produce the white product used in mixes. Its role in a mix is to improve aeration and drainage. It can be pasteurized. If this ingredient is required in a mix, the horticultural grade should be selected since it has larger particle size and is thus more effective.

Perlite is neutral in reaction and provides almost no nutrients to the mix (except for small amounts of sodium and aluminum). A disadvantage of the use of perlite is its low weight, which makes it float when the medium is watered. Further, during mixing, it produces dust, which can be eliminated by wetting the material lightly before use.

VERMICULITE *Vermiculite* is heat-expanded mica. This mineral is heated at temperatures of about 760°C (1,400°F) to produce the folded structure associated with the material. It is very lightweight and has minerals (magnesium and potassium) for enriching the mix, as well as good water-holding capacity. Neutral in reaction (pH), it is available in grades according to sizes. Grade 1 includes the largest particles, and grades 4 and 5 are fine in texture. The most commonly used grades are 2 through 4. Its fineness, incidentally, makes it prone to being compressed easily in the mix. To reduce this potential, a mix including vermiculite should not be pressed down hard.

ROCK WOOL Rock wool is produced from a mixture of basalt, coke, and limestone heated at extremely high temperatures of about 1,482 to 1,600°C (2,700 to 2,900°F). Rock wool fibers are molded into different shapes (e.g., cubes or slabs) and sizes for a variety of uses in horticultural production in the greenhouse. Rock wool supplies small amounts of micronutrients (calcium, magnesium, sulfur, iron, zinc, and copper). Since this material is not biodegradable, its use in media is problematic from an environmental perspective.

Other Additives for Mixes In addition to the four inorganic materials described previously, several materials are added to improve the quality of the general mix from the standpoint of nutrition, soil reaction, and stability. These materials include the following:

1. *Fertilizer.* Because most of the component materials of a soilless mix do not supply plant nutrition, it is important to include some fertilizer to provide at least a starter nutrition for plants when these materials are used in a soil mix. Slow-release fertilizer is often included in a mix for this purpose. Fluoride-containing fertilizers (such as superphosphates) should be avoided, since the fluoride is injurious to certain greenhouse-cultivated foliage plants such as chlorophytum.
2. *Limestone.* Limestone, or calcium carbonate, is an ingredient in soil mixes whose principal role is to correct the pH of the mix. It is added in the form of a powder.
3. *Wetting agent.* To transport commercial soilless mixes at reduced cost, manufacturers prefer to use dry ingredients because of their lighter weight. However, dry peat moss repels water. To correct this problem, manufacturers of soil mixes include a wetting agent in their products. Wetting agents are easiest to apply in granular form. Liquid formulations of these agents are also available.
4. *Polystyrene pieces.* The major use of the inert material polystyrene is to lighten the weight of the mix. It has no nutritional value. When watered, particles of this ingredient are found floating on the surface of the water that pools above the soil in pots that contain this material.

4.10.2 FACTORS TO CONSIDER IN CHOOSING MATERIALS FOR A MIX

A large variety of ready-made mixes can be purchased from reputable suppliers. However, if a grower decides to prepare a homemade mix, the following factors should be considered.

Quality of Ingredients

Since mixes vary in physical and chemical characteristics, growers usually adapt specific production practices to soil mixes (e.g., watering and fertilizing regimes). Changes in the quality of the ingredients alter the physical and chemical properties of the mix, making it less responsive to the production practice in use.

Availability

If one is operating in a peanut-growing region, peanut shells could be used in formulating mixes. Establishing sources of regular and ready supplies of raw materials is important to prevent interruption in the production cycle of an enterprise.

Cost

Materials vary in cost. Inorganic components can be especially expensive. Substitutes can be made, as previously indicated, if one understands the role of ingredients in the mix.

Use

The mix prepared should meet the needs of the operation in terms of plant requirements and any automation available. Certain mixes are not conducive for use in potting machines.

Ease of Preparation

Pasteurization is critical to the formulation of mixes. Certain ingredients are difficult to pasteurize. If chemicals (i.e., fertilizers) are to be added, care should be taken to avoid hazards from incorrect calculations and mixing.

4.10.3 CONSTITUTING MIXES

All of the ingredients previously described do not have to be included in each mix. Mixes are formulated for specific purposes, based on the needs of the plant. Certain mixes have broad application. Examples of such mixes are

1. 1:1 of sphagnum moss and vermiculite
2. 1:1:1 of sand, sphagnum moss, and a wood product (e.g., bark or wood shavings)
3. 3:1:1 of peat, perlite, and vermiculite
4. 2:1:1 of peat, bark, and sand
5. 2:1:1 of peat, perlite, and vermiculite
6. 2:1 of peat and perlite

The appropriate amounts of lime and fertilizer should be added to these mixes. These ingredients are included in these proportions on the basis of volume rather than weight, since they all vary in bulk density. It is important that the mix be disease free; therefore, commercial products are often sterilized by either *heat (steam) pasteurization* or chemical treatment (e.g., methyl bromide).

Standard Mixes

Certain growing mixes have been developed and popularized over the years. These media form the standard, which may be modified for specific purposes. The advantages of these standard mixes include first the fact that they have been thoroughly researched and proven to be successful and second that using standard mixes removes the guesswork from the formulation of mixes. They can be reproduced and thus are useful in quantitative studies where uniformity of research materials is needed. These standard mixes are predictable in their effects. Two of the commonly utilized standard mixes are described in Table 4–11. Soil mixing can be done on a large scale using commercial-batch soil mixers or continuous media mixing systems.

Roles of Ingredients in a Mix

Each soilless mix ingredient has a specific role to play in the mix. The property of a mix and the ingredient responsible are as follows:

1. *Good water retention.*   Soilless mixes are utilized mainly in plants cultured in containers. The volume of soil is usually limited. The mix materials should be able to retain moisture so that the medium does not dry out too quickly. Organic materials are used as ingredients for increasing the water retention of the medium.

TABLE 4–11 Selected Standard Mixes

1. Cornell Peat-Lite Mix A

	Quantity	
Materials	*Per Cubic Yard*	*Per Cubic Meter*
Sphagnum peat moss	0.5 yd^3	0.5 m^3
Vermiculite	0.5 yd^3	0.5 m^3
Ground dolomitic limestone	5 lb	3 kg
Single superphosphate	1–2 lb	0.6–1.2 kg
Calcium of potassium nitrate	1 lb	0.6 kg
Fritted trace elements	2 oz	74 g
Wetting agent	3 oz	111 g

2. Cornell Peat-Lite Mix B

Substitute horticultural perlite for vermiculite

3. The University of California Mix

	Quantity	
Materials	*Per Cubic Yard (lb)*	*Per Cubic Meter (kg)*
Hoof and horn or blood meal (13%)	2.5	1.47
Potassium nitrate	0.25	0.15
Potassium sulfate	0.25	0.15
Single superphosphate	2.5	1.47
Dolomitic lime	7.5	4.42
Calcium carbonate	2.5	1.47

The University of California Mix, as constituted above, should be used fresh; if storage is needed, the mix should exclude the hoof and horn or blood meal.

2. *Good drainage and aeration.* The mix should be well drained to reduce the danger of overwatering, which can cause a perched water table. Most plant roots are intolerant of anaerobic conditions. Materials such as perlite and sand are used for good aeration. Good soil drainage guards against the buildup of harmful salts.
3. *Proper pH.* Improper soil reaction interferes with nutrient availability for plants. Certain organic materials used in mixes produce acidity or alkalinity in the medium. The use of lime is necessary to correct soil acidity.
4. *Fertility.* Most soil mix ingredients do not contribute appreciably to the fertility of the growing medium. Additional materials such as fertilizers are needed to provide the required nutrition for proper plant growth and development.

Advantages of Soilless Mixes

The major advantages of soilless mixes include the following:

1. *Uniformity of mix.* The physical and chemical properties of a mix are uniform throughout the mix, a condition not found in field soil. The homogeneity of the medium makes it possible for plants to grow and develop uniformly, provided other growth factors are also consistent.
2. *Ease of handling.* Mixes are lightweight and easy to transport. Ingredients are easy to scoop and move around during manual preparation.
3. *Versatility.* Mixes can be made to order (custom mixed) for specific needs; can be used to amend soils in the field by mixing into flower beds, lawns, or garden soil; and are convenient to use in container plants.

4. *Sterility.* Mixes, initially at least, are free from diseases and pests. Seedling germination is less prone to diseases such as damping-off.
5. *Good drainage and moisture retention.* A mix can be custom-made to provide the appropriate degree of drainage and moisture retention.
6. *Convenience of use.* Mixes are ready to use when purchased.

Disadvantages of Soilless Mixes

Disadvantages of soilless mixes include the following:

1. *Light weight.* Some mixes are very light, especially when dry. When used in potted plant production, they are easily toppled over by even a gentle wind or push.
2. *Limited nutritional supply.* Mixes that incorporate fertilizers provide nutrition for a limited period of time. The component ingredients of mixes are generally void of any appreciable amount of plant growth nutrients. Micronutrients are especially lacking and should be supplemented with an appropriate fertilizer program when growing a crop.
3. *Lack of field correspondence.* Mixes are constituted to provide minimal problems to germinating seeds and rooting plants. As such, the physical conditions of mixes are different than field soil conditions. Roots grow rapidly and ball up in pots. During transplanting into the field, care should be taken to create good root contact with the soil. Some plants may not establish quickly if root contact with the soil is poor.
4. *Cost.* Some mixes are expensive (but worth the investment).

4.11 Soil Sterilization

4.11.1 FIELD STERILIZATION

Sterilizing field soil can be accomplished by harnessing the energy of the sun. *Solar pasteurization,* or *soil solarization,* is a method of pasteurizing the soil by using solar energy. The goal of pasteurization is to rid the soil of harmful bacteria, fungi, nematodes, and weeds. The area to be treated is first cleared of grass and weeds. The soil is then cultivated, raked, and watered uniformly to a depth of about 12 inches (30 centimeters). A clear plastic is stretched tightly over the area and tucked under a border of soil. The plastic cover should be left in place for about four to eight weeks for effective solarization. Black plastic reflects heat, even though it controls weeds much better. Beds with north-south orientation receive sunlight most of the day, and the effect is better. Field temperature under solarization can exceed 120°F.

Plant diseases known to be controlled by this treatment include fusarium wilt, verticilium wilt, pinkroot, and southern blight. Weeds effectively controlled include cheeseweed *(Malva neglecta),* annual bluegrass *(Poa annua),* and pigweed *(Amaranthus* spp.). Plants grown in recently solar-pasteurized soil grow faster and larger than those in nonpasteurized soil. The soluble nutrient levels in soil with reference to nitrogen, calcium, and magnesium have been found to increase after solarization. Solarization is used by organic gardeners.

4.11.2 STERILIZATION OF GREENHOUSE SOIL

Growing media for indoor use can be sterilized by a variety of methods. The goals are identical to sterilization of field soil.

Steam Pasteurization

Steam pasteurization is a nontoxic method of sterilizing soil by which steam is passed through a pile of soil. Soil to be steamed should be prepared by mixing thoroughly and readied for planting. Fertilizers and lime should be mixed in before sterilizing. Certain fertilizers, such as Osmocote, cannot be sterilized and should be added after the process is complete. The soil to be steamed is covered with a tarpaulin or some other appropriate material. The soil should not be too dry or too wet; either condition requires additional heating time to properly sterilize the soil. The hot steam may be introduced via buried pipes with perforations. Alternatively, in surface steaming, a porous canvas hose may be laid on top of the evenly graded topsoil and covered. The buried pipe method is more effective when ground beds are to be sterilized.

Steam aerated by introducing air into the steam flow is preferred to using steam alone. At a temperature of 60°C (140°F), the aerated steam is administered for 30 minutes. In the pure steam method, the soil temperatures are higher (84°C, or 180°F). Overheating is detrimental to the soil because it can kill beneficial organisms and cause buildup of toxic substances, especially in soils that have a high organic matter content. Heating results in a high soluble-salt level in the soil. Further, since beneficial organisms are killed, soilborne diseases that occur after pasteurized soil has cooled tend to spread quickly.

The advantages of using steam pasteurization include the ability of the grower to plant immediately after the soil has cooled. Although it may kill undesirable pests and disease organisms, if done at the proper temperature, the beneficial organisms are not harmed. Further, applying steam is relatively inexpensive. Soil drainage and aeration have been known to improve after steam pasteurization due to aggregation of particles. Steam sterilization is also applicable to containers, tools, and other equipment.

Chemical Sterilization

Soil can be sterilized by using certain fumigants. Chemical sterilization is less effective than steam sterilization and is toxic. The soil cannot be planted immediately after the process, unlike after steaming. Depending on the chemical used, a waiting time of about 24 hours to several weeks may be needed. Further, during the application, the room must be vacated to prevent worker poisoning. To effectively permeate the soil, it must not be cold but a desirable warm temperature that differs according to the type of chemical used. Chemicals used include *chloropicrin* (or tear gas). Because of the effect on humans, precautions must be taken to control the gas, such as watering the area after application to provide a water seal or providing the treatment under airtight cover. Further, chemical sterilization should be used only when the greenhouse is vacant (no plants).

Other chemicals used in sterilization include formalin and vapam. Vapam is not toxic to humans but must not be used in their presence. Treated growing media are ready for use only after several weeks. Some plants are sensitive to the residual effects of certain chemical treatments. For example, carnations are damaged when grown in media treated with Dowfume MC-2 (a mixture of methyl bromide and 2 percent chloropicrin). This chemical is extremely toxic to humans and must be used with great caution.

4.12 LIQUID MEDIA

As indicated earlier, soil is the most popular medium for the cultivation of crops. Soil, or any solid medium, provides physical support for plants to grow. Today, plants are cultivated on a large scale under controlled-environment conditions indoors. A variety of media have been developed to facilitate such an undertaking. Perhaps the most revolutionary is growing plants in liquid media (water fortified with nutrients). The science and methods of water culture, or *hydroponics,* are presented in detail in Chapters 4–13.

One of the earliest and still widely used liquid media in plant culture is *Hoagland's nutrient solution,* an all-nitrate solution. Various *nutriculture systems* have their own unique liquid media recipes. Crop needs and cultural conditions call for special nutrient systems to be used for the successful production of specific crops.

SUMMARY

Plants require appropriate temperature, moisture, light, and air for good growth and development. These conditions occur both above- and belowground. In addition, plants need a medium in which to grow, the common one being soil, even though modern technology enables plants to be grown in soilless media. Air is required for respiration (for energy); water is needed for germination, photosynthesis, and translocation of solutes within the plant, among other functions. Light is needed for photosynthesis and also affects reproductive activities in some species through photoperiodism. Light affects plants through its intensity, duration, and quality. Long-day plants require more than twelve hours of daylight to flower. Short-day and day-neutral plants have varying daylight requirements. Temperature is the intensity factor of heat energy and regulates the rate of chemical reaction. Soil has layers called horizons that make up a soil profile. The topsoil is of most importance to horticulture. Soils vary in texture (particle size distribution) and structure (particle arrangement), as well as in chemical characteristics such as soil reaction (pH) and nutrient level. The nutrients used by plants in large amounts, called major nutrients, or macronutrients, are nitrogen, phosphorus, and potassium. Those required in small or minute amounts are called micronutrients, minor nutrients, or trace elements and include copper, molybdenum, zinc, chlorine, manganese, magnesium, and calcium. Nutrient elements can be artificially supplied by fertilizers. The soil is home to a large number of organisms, some of which are beneficial to plants.

Soil is the primary medium in which plants are grown. Plants may be grown directly in the soil in the field or in soil placed in containers. Sometimes the medium used for potting may be entirely or partially nonsoil or artificial. Before use, the soil has to be prepared. This preparation is called tillage. Primary tillage (rough) precedes secondary tillage (finer tilth). Several concepts are important in tillage. In conventional tillage, the field or plot is deeply plowed using primary or secondary operations before use. In minimum tillage, only the spot where the seed is to be placed is disturbed. Conservation tillage includes practices that conserve soil moisture and prevent erosion. Different implements, including plows, harrows, listers, and tillers, are available for various tillage operations. Potting soil frequently includes artificial ingredients such as perlite and vermiculite. Organic materials used include peat moss, sphagnum moss, and wood products; inorganic ingredients include sand and limestone.

REFERENCES AND SUGGESTED READING

Boodley, J. W. 1998. *The commercial greenhouse,* 2d ed. Albany, N.Y.: Delmar.

Bunt, A. C. 1976. *Modern potting composts: A manual on the preparation and use of growing media for pot plants.* University Park: Pennsylvania State University Press.

Janick, J. 1986. *Horticultural science,* 4th ed. San Francisco: W. H. Freeman.

Kramer, J. 1974. *Plants under lights.* New York: Simon & Schuster.

Maracher, H. 1986. *Mineral nutrition in higher plants.* New York: Academic Press.

McMahon, R. W. 1992. *An introduction to greenhouse production.* Columbus Ohio Agricultural Education Curriculum Materials Services.

Nelson, P. V. 1985. *Greenhouse operation and management,* 3d ed. Reston, Va.: Reston Publishing Co.

Rice, L. W., and R. P. Rice, Jr. 1993. *Practical horticulture.* Englewood Cliffs, N.J.: Prentice Hall.

Singer, M. J., and D. N. Munns. 1987. *Soils: An introduction.* New York: Macmillan.

Excellent and well-illustrated site on plant nutrient deficiency symptoms

http://www.ces.ncsu.edu/depts/hort/floriculture/def/

General discussion of fertilizers

http://www.answers.com/topic/fertilizer?cat=technology

Soil test

http://www.agr.state.nc.us/cyber/kidswrld/plant/soiltest.htm

Soilless mixes

http://hgic.clemson.edu/factsheets/hgic1456.htm

USDA plant hardiness zone interactive map

http://www.usna.usda.gov/Hardzone/ushzmap.html?

PRACTICAL EXPERIENCE

1. Plant sixteen pots of a selected plant. Group pots into sets of four. Select a source of nitrogen fertilizer and four different levels (0, 1, 2, 3). The amount chosen depends on the size of the pot and the type of plant. Your instructor will give you guidance. Apply one level to each set of pots. Observe the differences in plant growth at the end of the course by measuring a selected number of plant characteristics.
2. Repeat exercise 1 using other nutrients (phosphorus and potassium) and different plant species. You may increase the number of pots per set so that you can measure plant weight and other characteristics at periodic intervals. These intermediate measurements are destructive, requiring the samples to be uprooted or cut and dried. You may also take measurements at periodic intervals without destructive sampling.
3. Collect samples of soil from various areas—a garden, a flower bed, and a lawn. Test for soil reaction (pH) and other macroelements by using a simple garden soil testing kit.
4. Place a set of seedlings of corn and one set of beans under bright light. Place similar sets of plants in darkness. Observe the differences in plant growth and development after three weeks (or more) and explain the results.
5. Visit a farm equipment rental company or dealership to see the various available tillage implements and learn about their functions.
6. Obtain samples of the various components of soilless mixes—vermiculite, perlite, peat moss, and sphagnum moss—and create your own mixes. Test the physical properties of the mixes, including weight per unit volume, texture, and drainage.

OUTCOMES ASSESSMENT

1. Distinguish between climate and weather as it relates to plant production.
2. Discuss how horticulturalists protect field-grown plants against adverse temperature conditions.
3. Give the importance of the USDA hardiness zone map in the horticultural industry. In what zones does your state fall?
4. Distinguish between the role of light in plant growth and development based on its intensity and duration.
5. Discuss light-induced abnormalities in plants and how horticulturalists manage light in plant production for high-quality products.
6. Discuss the role and importance of soil pH in plant nutrient management.
7. What is a soil test and how is it used in crop production?
8. Discuss the factors to consider in selecting and applying a method of supplemental moisture application in a crop production enterprise.
9. What is the importance of soilless mixes in modern horticulture? What is the rationale of the formulation of a soilless mix?
10. What is the concept of the C:N ratio and its application in horticulture?

Plant Physiology

PURPOSE AND EXPECTED OUTCOMES

The purpose of this chapter is to discuss the primary plant physiological processes and to show how they affect the growth and development of horticultural plants. The discussion includes how an understanding of these processes enables scientists and growers to manipulate them for the higher quality and productivity of plants.

After studying this chapter, the student should be able to

1. Describe the generalized pattern of growth in organisms (sigmoid curve).
2. Describe the generalized phases of plant growth.
3. Discuss vegetative growth and development in plants and how growth patterns are used as a basis for the classification of plants.
4. Describe reproductive growth and development in plants.
5. Describe the role of environmental factors on plant growth and development.
6. Describe specific growth processes—photosynthesis, respiration, transpiration, translocation, and absorption—and their roles in plant growth and development.
7. Discuss specific ways in which growers may manipulate physiological processes for increased plant productivity and quality.

OVERVIEW

The genotype of an organism specifies its course of development within a given environment. A tall plant will grow tall, first because it has the *genes* for tallness, and second because it is provided with the appropriate *environment* to support the expression of the tallness trait. In growing to become tall, certain specific physiological activities must occur to provide the materials and energy required to translate genetic information into a physical appearance or phenotype. In other words, it is through physiological processes that genes are expressed.

Physiological processes allow the embryo in a seed to develop into a mature plant. As a plant grows and develops, it does so because of the roles of physiological processes such as *photosynthesis, respiration, transpiration, translocation,* and *absorption.* A variety of external and internal factors affect physiological processes. Light and hormones are notable factors that affect the growth of plants. By understanding how these factors and the processes themselves function, scientists, and eventually growers, are able to manipulate plants to their advantage by altering certain environmental conditions. Some processes may be slowed down and others speeded up. The major physiological processes that affect plant growth and development are discussed in this chapter.

5.1 GROWTH AND DEVELOPMENT

Growth and development involve three basic activities:

1. Cellular division
2. Enlargement
3. Differentiation

5.1.1 GROWTH

Growth
A progressive and irreversible increase in size and volume through natural development.

Growth is an irreversible phenomenon that occurs in a living organism, resulting in an increase in its overall size or the size of its parts. Growth is accompanied by energy-dependent metabolic processes. As such, whereas producing a leaf or root is growth, an increase in size due to swelling from water absorption is not.

Cellular Division and Enlargement

Osmosis
The diffusion of water or other solvents through a differentially permeable membrane from a region of higher concentration to a region of lower concentration.

The processes of cell division and enlargement are frequently associated. Cellular enlargement often precedes cellular division, as found in meristematic cells. However, the two processes are regulated independently. Cell enlargement does not induce cell division, and the latter is not always preceded by the former. For cells to enlarge, the rigid cell walls (which are rigid) must first be "loosened." This loosening occurs when certain acids are secreted into the cell walls (cell wall acidification). These acids in turn activate certain pH-dependent enzymes that act on cellulose in the walls. This cell-loosening process is influenced by a plant hormone called *auxin.* In addition to loosening of the cell wall, cellular enlargement requires *positive turgor pressure,* which results as a cell takes in water by **osmosis.** Because enlargement is required for growth and turgor is required for enlargement, the water status of a plant is critical to its growth and development. Cellular enlargement usually occurs in only one direction. Expansion occurs where the cell wall is most elastic. Cell wall elasticity is dependent on the orientation of the cellulose *microfibrils* in the wall. Where longitudinal cellulose microfibrils occur, the cell wall enlarges in a transverse fashion. On the other hand, transverse deposition of microfibrils in the cell walls produces longitudinal expansion. Random cellulose microfibrils produce equal expansion in all directions.

Growth produces an increase in dry matter when the plant is actively *photosynthesizing.* It is influenced by genetic, physiological, and environmental factors. Some plant cultivars are bred to be tall and large bodied, whereas miniature cultivars are bred for other purposes. For example, tomato cultivars used in salads produce small and near bite-size fruits; those used in canning are much larger in size. Plants can be manipulated by the application of chemicals to change their size by either enhancing or inhibiting growth. By changing the environment of the plant (e.g., soil, water, nutrients, temperature, photoperiod, and light intensity), a plant's growth can be enhanced or hindered. These environmental factors of plant growth and development are discussed in Chapter 4.

Growth in an organism follows a certain general pattern described by a *sigmoid curve* (Figure 5–1). The pattern and corresponding developmental stages as they occur in plants are as follows:

1. *Lag growth phase.* The lag phase includes activities in preparation for growth. Dormant cells become active; dry tissue imbibes moisture; cells divide and increase in size; the embryo differentiates.
2. *Logarithmic growth phase.* The logarithmic growth phase is characterized by an increasing growth rate and includes seed germination and vegetative plant growth periods.
3. *Decreasing growth phase.* During the decreasing growth phase, growth slows down. This stage includes flowering, fruiting, and seed filling.
4. *Steady growth phase.* Growth rate either declines or stops during the steady growth phase. This phase is associated with age, or the plant's maturity.

The characteristics of the sigmoid growth pattern vary among species and plant parts. In fruit growth, food materials are translocated from one part of the plant to another. In species such as apple, orange, pear, tomato, and strawberry, fruit growth follows the simple sigmoid growth curve, with variations in characteristics. However, in certain species, including stone fruits, such as plum, peach, and cherry, fruit growth follows a *double sigmoid curve* pattern whereby the single pattern is repeated (Figure 5–2). During the plateau of the first sigmoid curve, the fruit size barely changes; most of the activities involve seed development. In stone fruits, the hardening of the endocarp (pit) occurs during the second phase of fruit development.

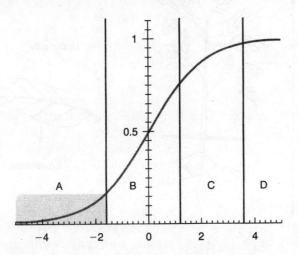

FIGURE 5–1 A typical sigmoid growth curve. (a) lag phase, (b) log phase, (c) decreasing phase, (d) steady phase.

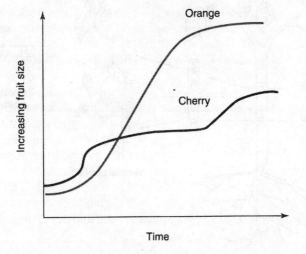

FIGURE 5–2 The sigmoid and double sigmoid growth curves. Stone fruits are characterized by the double sigmoid curve growth pattern. The characteristics of either curve differ from one species to another.

Development

Cellular Differentiation and Dedifferentiation

Differentiation is the process by which meristematic cells (genetically identical) diverge in development to meet the requirements for a variety of functions. The specialization of cells occurs as a result of differential activation of the cell's genome (total number of genes), resulting in the structure and function of previously genetically identical cells becoming different.

Differentiated cells can revert to meristematic status; when this happens they are said to be *dedifferentiated*. Cells dedifferentiate when the plant structural pattern is disrupted by, for example, wounding. To repair the damage, the cells in the damaged regions first become "deprogrammed" so that they can be reprogrammed to form the appropriate types of cells needed for the repair.

Polarity

Plants and their parts exhibit strong directional differences that are described as polarity. Classic examples of such directional growth and development are the existence of abaxial and adaxial parts of a leaf and the shoot and root ends of a full plant that are very different in structure and function (Figure 5–3). *Polarity* may be influenced by environmental factors such as gravity and light or it may be genetic in origin. In angiosperms, polarity appears to be fixed and difficult to alter. Thus, a stem cutting will always produce roots at the basal end and shoots at the apical end (Figure 5–4). Polar transport of growth hormones (such as auxin) is implicated in this phenomenon.

Differentiation
The process of change by which an unspecialized cell becomes specialized.

FIGURE 5–3 Polarity in plants.

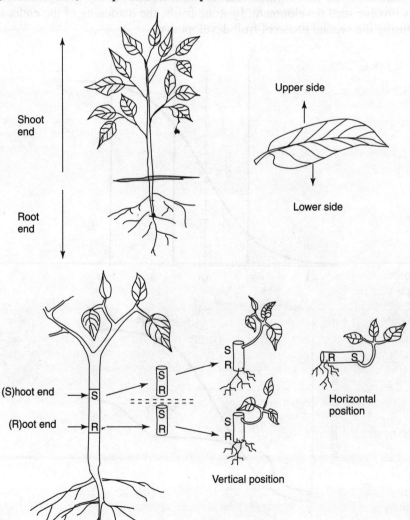

FIGURE 5–4 Polarity in the stem. Auxin transport in the stem is polar. No matter the orientation, rooting will occur only at the root end of the segment of the stem.

5.1.2 THE ROLE OF SIGNALS IN GROWTH AND DEVELOPMENT

Plant growth and development are regulated by complex signals. Plant hormones have been shown to stimulate differentiation of procambium. In tissue culture, the addition of a hormone such as auxin stimulates leaf formation in callus (a mass of undifferentiated tissue). In plants, removing the shoot apex stimulates lateral bud growth. Genetic control similar to that found in animals has been seen in maize studies. Other known control signals are *positional control* (caused by the position of a cell in plant tissue), *biophysical control* (caused by physical pressure generated by growing organs), and *electrical currents* (generated by growing plants).

5.2 ORGANIC COMPOUNDS OF PLANT CELLS

Major and minor inorganic chemicals obtained by plants from the soil are discussed in Chapter 4. These inorganic elements are utilized by the plant to synthesize the organic components of cells. Water is one of the most abundant inorganic compounds in plant cells. Carbon, hydrogen, and oxygen occur in all organic molecules. Sulfur and phosphorus occur in very few organic molecules and, even then, only in small amounts. The major classes of cellular organic constituents are *carbohydrates, lipids, proteins,* and *nucleic acids.* Of these, proteins and nucleic acids are relatively large molecules and hence are called *macromolecules.*

5.2.1 CARBOHYDRATES

Carbohydrates are the most abundant organic molecules in nature. In plants, they are the principal components of cell walls. They are also the primary energy-storage molecules in most organisms. Carbohydrates are made up of three elements—carbon (C), hydrogen (H), and oxygen (O)—usually in the ratio of 1:2:1 of carbon to hydrogen to oxygen. The general molecular formula of carbohydrates is thus $(CH_2O)_n$. The three principal kinds of carbohydrates—*monosaccharides, disaccharides,* and *polysaccharides*—are classified on the basis of the number of sugar molecules they contain.

Monosaccharides

Monosaccharides ("one sugar"), or *simple sugars,* consist of a chain of subunits with the basic structure $(CH_2O)_n$. Simple sugars are thus the building blocks of carbohydrates. Sugar names have the suffix *-ose* and a prefix that indicates the number of carbon atoms each sugar contains. For example, a *pentose sugar* has five carbons, and a *hexose sugar* has six carbons. Hexoses and pentoses are the most important simple sugars in plants. They occur as cell wall constituents and are important in energy aspects of cellular function. Glucose, a hexose, is used in the synthesis of other complex molecules such as starch (see polysaccharides). It is a major product of photosynthesis. The sweet taste of ripened fruits is due in part to the glucose and fructose sugars, as well as hexose sugars. Fructose can be converted to glucose and hence perform the functions of glucose. Ribose sugar is a constituent of deoxyribonucleic acid (DNA) and ribonucleic acid (RNA).

Disaccharides

Disaccharides consist of two monosaccharides joined by the process of *condensation* (removal of a water molecule by an enzyme-catalyzed process). Disaccharides can be broken down into component molecules by **hydrolysis** (addition of a water molecule to each linkage). *Sucrose,* or common table sugar from sugarcane or sugar beet, is a disaccharide consisting of glucose and fructose. Whereas the sugar transported in animal systems is commonly glucose, sucrose is the form in which sugars are most often transported in plants.

Hydrolysis
The breakdown of complex molecules to simpler ones, resulting from the union of water with the compound.

Polysaccharides

A *polymer* is a large molecule consisting of identical or similar molecular subunits called *monomers*. These monomers can polymerize into long chains. When three or more sugar molecules polymerize, the product is a polysaccharide. In most plants, accumulated sugars are stored in seed, leaves, stems, and roots in the form of a polysaccharide called *starch*. Starch is made up of two different polysaccharides—*amylose* and *amylopectin*. Amylose consists of glucose molecules linked in a nonbranching pattern (1,4-linkages), whereas amylopectin consists of molecules linked in a branching pattern (1,6-linkages). The figures in the linkage patterns refer to the position of carbons in the rings involved in the linkage. In certain species, such as temperate grasses, the commonly stored polysaccharides in leaves and stems are polymers of fructose called *fructans*.

Polysaccharides are important structural compounds. The most important in plants is cellulose, a polymer of β-glucose monomers (instead of α-glucose, as in starch) in 1,4-linkages. Cellulose is the most abundant polymer in nature. The molecular arrangement in this compound makes cellulose chains more rigid than starch, even though they consist of the same monomers. Cellulose is resistant to enzymes that readily hydrolyze starch and other polysaccharides. The biological functions of starch and cellulose are thus different. In fact, once incorporated into the cell wall as a constituent, cellulose cannot be utilized as a source of energy by plants. In ruminant animals such as cattle, it takes the action of microbes in the digestive tract to make cellulose an energy source. Other important polysaccharides in plants are *pectin*, a polymer of *galacturonic acid*, a six-carbon sugar containing an acid group, and *hemicellulose* (composed of a complex mixture of sugars).

5.2.2 LIPIDS

Lipids are a group of fats and fatlike substances. They differ in two major ways from carbohydrates. Lipids are not water soluble, unlike most carbohydrates. Also, lipids structurally contain a significantly larger number of C-H bonds and as a result release a significantly larger amount of energy in oxidation than other organic compounds. Lipids can be classified as follows.

Fats and Oils

Fats and *oils* have a similar chemical structure, consisting of three fatty acids linked to a *glycerol*, a three-carbon alcohol molecule. This structural arrangement is the origin of the term *triglyceride*. Fats and oils are storage forms of lipids called *triglycerides*. Whereas fats are solid at room temperature, oils remain liquid. Cells synthesize fats from sugars. Plants, as previously indicated, store excess food as starch. To a limited extent, fat is stored as droplets within the chloroplasts of some species of plants such as citrus.

Triglycerides differ in nature by the length of their fatty acid chains and the number of hydrogen atoms to which their carbons are linked. They are said to be saturated when most carbon atoms are linked to hydrogen atoms, or unsaturated, when some carbon atoms are double-bonded to hydrogen. Triglycerides containing unsaturated fatty acids tend to behave like oils, and are fluid or liquid at room temperature. Unsaturated fatty acids are found in plants such as corn and peanut, both of which are sources of edible oil.

Phospholipids

Phospholipids differ from triglycerides in that only two of the three fatty acids are attached to glycerol, the third one being attached to a phosphate group. The presence of the phosphate at the end of the phospholipid molecule makes this end of the fatty acid molecule water soluble (the other end remains water insoluble). Phospholipids are important cellular membrane constituents.

Cutin, Suberin, and Waxes

Cutin, suberin, and *waxes* make up a group of lipids that are insoluble and create a structural barrier layer in plants. Cutin and suberin form the structural matrix within which waxes are embedded. Waxes consist of fatty acids combined with a long-chain alcohol. The cutin-wax complex forms a water-repellent layer that prevents loss of water from the protected area. The outer walls of epidermal cells have a protective layer called a cuticle that consists of cutin embedded with wax. Suberin occurs in significant amounts in the walls of cork cells in tree bark.

5.2.3 PROTEINS

Proteins are structurally more complex than carbohydrates and lipids. They are composed of building blocks called *amino acids,* which are nitrogen-containing molecules. Amino acids polymerize by linkage of *peptide bonds* (a bond formed between two amino acids) to produce chains called *polypeptides.* The twenty commonly occurring amino acids are used to form all proteins by bonding in a variety of sequences. The basic structure is the same for all amino acids—an *amino group,* a *carboxyl group,* and a *hydrogen atom* bonded to a *central carbon atom.* What distinguishes amino acids is the unique *R group.* The R group may be *polar* or *nonpolar* (according to its tendency to dissolve in a polar solvent such as water), polar groups being more soluble in water than nonpolar ones. An amino acid may have a *net charge* (either positive or negative) or be *neutral* (no net charge). Of the twenty commonly occurring amino acids, fifteen are neutral, three are basic, and two are acidic.

Enzymes

Enzymes are large, complex, globular proteins that act as *catalysts* in biochemical reactions. Catalysts accelerate the rate of chemical reactions by lowering the energy required for activation. That is, reactions can be sped up while occurring at relatively low temperatures. In the process of the reaction, these substances remain unaltered and are hence reusable. An enzyme has an *active site* to which the *substrate* (the substance acted on by the enzyme) attaches to form an enzyme-substrate complex. A substrate might be a compound such as glucose or adenosine triphosphate (ATP). These substances are changed into new products at the end of the reaction.

> **Enzyme**
> *A complex protein that speeds up a chemical reaction without being used up in the process.*

About 2,000 enzymes are known to occur in nature. Each enzyme catalyzes a specific reaction. Sometimes an enzyme-catalyzed reaction requires the presence of a third substance in order to proceed. These additional substances are called *cofactors* and may be organic or inorganic. Inorganic cofactors are also called *activators* and are usually metallic ions required in trace amounts in plant nutrition, such as iron, magnesium, and zinc. Organic cofactors (e.g., nicotinamide adenine dinucleotide [NAD$^+$] and nicotinamide adenine dinucleotide phosphate [NADP$^+$]) are called *coenzymes.* These substances accept atoms that are removed by the enzyme during the reaction. Enzymes that remove hydrogen atoms from substrates are called *dehydrogenases.*

5.2.4 NUCLEIC ACIDS

Nucleic acids are chemicals involved in hereditary aspects of cellular life. They are polymers of nucleotides that consist of a *phosphate group,* a *five-carbon sugar,* and a *nitrogenous base.* The two major types of nucleic acids are *DNA* and *RNA.*

Deoxyribonucleic acid (DNA) is the genetic material of living organisms. It consists of *nitrogenous bases, sugar,* and *phosphate.* There are four bases: *adenine (A), cytosine (C), guanine (G),* and *thymine (T).* Adenine and guanine are called *purines,* and cytosine and thymine are *pyrimidines.* The letters *A, C, G,* and *T* are the genetic alphabets. The sugar is a *pentos* (five-carbon ring) and is of the *deoxyribose variety.* The sugar and base link up to form a *nucleoside,* which then combines with a phosphate to form a *nucleotide.* Nucleotides link up to produce a chain called a *polynucleotide,* in which the sugar and phosphate form a backbone from which the bases extend. Two polynucleotide chains pair up in an antiparallel (running in opposite sequence) and complementary fashion. That is, *A* always pairs with *T* (by a double hydrogen bond), and *G* always pairs with *C* (by a triple bond). The pair of chains then winds or coils up into a *double helix.*

> **DNA**
> *Deoxyribonucleic acid (DNA) is the genetic material organisms inherit from their parents.*

TABLE 5–1   Selected Examples of C3, C4, and CAM Plants

Common Name	Scientific Name
C_3 Plants	
Kentucky bluegrass	*Poa pratensis*
Creeping bentgrass	*Agrostis tenuis*
Sunflower	*Helianthus annuus*
Scotch pine	*Pinus sylvestris*
Tobacco	*Nicotiana tabacum*
Peanut	*Arachis hypogaea*
Spinach	*Spinacia oleracea*
Soybean	*Glycine max*
Rice	*Oryza sativa*
Wheat	*Triticum aestivum*
Rye	*Secale cereale*
Oats	*Avena sativa*
C_4 Plants	
Crabgrass	*Digitaria sanguinalis*
Corn	*Zea mays*
Bermuda grass	*Cynodon dactylon*
Sugarcane	*Saccharum officinale*
Sorghum	*Sorghum vulgare*
Pigweed	*Amaranthus*
Euphorbia	*Euphorbia* spp.
Millet	*Pennisetum glaucum*
Sedge	*Carex* spp.
CAM Plants	
Wax plant	*Hoya carnosa*
Snake plant	*Sansevieria zeylanica*
Maternity plant	*Kalanchoe diagremontiana*
Pineapple	*Ananas comosus*
Spanish moss	*Tillandsia usneoides*
Jade plant	*Crassula argentea*
Ice plant	*Mesembryanthemum* spp.
Century plant	*Agave americana*
Cacti (many spp.)	

The information in the DNA is decoded by the process of *protein synthesis*. The genetic message occurs in the sequence of nitrogenous bases. The sites of protein synthesis are outside of the nucleus on the ribosomes in the cytoplasm. Copies of the nuclear DNA must first be made and transported to the ribosomes to serve as *templates*. Another nucleic acid, called *ribonucleic acid (RNA)*, is responsible for this genetic transport. The RNA differs from DNA in the types of sugar.

5.3 PLANT GROWTH PROCESSES

Plant growth processes provide the raw materials and the energy required for building new tissues and nurturing them to maturity. The major processes are discussed in the following sections.

5.3.1 PHOTOSYNTHESIS

Photosynthesis accounts for more than 90 percent of the dry matter yield of horticultural plants and is the ultimate source of food and fossil fuel. Photosynthesis is the single most important chemical reaction in nature. It impacts the environment significantly through its effects on the oxygen content of the air. This major physiological process is important not only because of its tremendous impact on a variety of functions in nature but also because an understanding of the process enables scientists to maximize its rate for higher crop productivity.

Photosynthesis is a reaction occurring in green plants whereby plants utilize water and the energy of sunlight to fix inorganic carbon dioxide in the form of organic compounds, releasing oxygen in the process. In other words, the sun's energy is transformed by plants through photosynthetic processes into chemical energy usable by other living organisms. The importance of this process is more readily apparent when we understand that plants are ultimately the source of all food. Plants may be used *directly* as food (e.g., vegetables, fruits, grains, nuts, and tubers) or may be used by animals and then *indirectly* become available through animal products (e.g., poultry, fish, meat, and dairy products). Lest we limit the importance of plants to food, it should be made clear that plants are also sources of materials for fuel, clothing, and medicines. They are utilized widely in the beautification of the landscape and performance of other functional roles.

The general chemical reaction of photosynthesis is

$$6CO_2 + 12H_2O \xrightarrow[\text{light energy}]{\text{green plant}} C_6H_{12}O_6 + 6O_2 + 6H_2O$$

This reaction occurs in the chloroplasts, using chlorophyll as an enzyme. Carbon dioxide comes from the air and water from the soil.

Phases of Photosynthesis

Light-Dependent Reactions LIGHT The nature of the electromagnetic spectrum is discussed in Chapter 4. Figure 4–4 shows that visible light is only a small portion of the vast electromagnetic spectrum. Only certain wavelengths of light are involved in photosynthesis. These specific wavelengths depend on the *absorption spectrum* (the range of wavelengths of light absorbed) of the various pigments involved in photosynthesis. A pigment may absorb a broad range of wavelengths, but certain ones are more effective than others in performing specific functions. The *action spectrum* of a pigment describes the relative effectiveness of different wavelengths of light for a specific light-dependent process such as flowering or photosynthesis.

Light-Independent Reactions The light-independent reactions stage is also collectively called the *dark reaction* of photosynthesis. At this stage, carbon dioxide is reduced to carbohydrate, a process called **carbon dioxide fixation.** This stage does not depend directly but rather indirectly on light, since the ATP and NADPH required are produced by the light-dependent reactions. Further, the two chemicals do not accumulate in the cell but are used up as fast as they are produced. The fixation of carbon dioxide (CO_2) comes to a halt soon after the light supply is terminated.

Carbon dioxide fixation occurs by one of two major pathways, which are distinguished by the first product formed. These are the three-carbon (C_3) pathway and the four-carbon (C_4) pathway.

1. *The Calvin cycle.* Named after its discoverer, the first product of the *Calvin cycle* is a three-carbon compound. Thus this pathway is also called the *C_3 pathway*. Plants that photosynthesize by this pathway are called *C_3 plants*. Carbon dioxide enters the cycle and becomes covalently bonded to a five-carbon sugar with two phosphate groups called *ribulose 1,5-bisphosphate (RuBP)* (Figure 5–5). This process (fixation) is catalyzed by the enzyme *RuBP carboxylase,* also commonly

called *rubisco*. Because this enzyme is abundant in chloroplasts, rubisco is said to be the most abundant protein in nature. The overall process can be summarized by the following equation:

$$6CO_2 + 12NADPH + 12H^+ + 18ATP \rightarrow 1 \text{ glucose} + 12NADP^+ + 18ADP + 18P_i + 6H_2O$$

The intermediate product is *glyceraldehyde 3-phosphate*.

Glucose is indicated in the preceding summary equation, but in practice, photosynthesizing cells generate a minimal amount of this sugar. Most of the fixed carbon dioxide is either converted to sucrose (which is the principal form in which sugar is transported in plants) or stored in the form of starch.

2. *The four-carbon pathway.* Many plants are known to be able to fix carbon dioxide by a pathway whose first product is a four-carbon substance. This pathway is also called the C_4 *pathway,* and plants that photosynthesize by this pathway are called C_4 *plants.* First, a CO_2 molecule is bonded to *phosphoenol pyruvate (PEP),* a three-carbon acceptor compound, resulting in the production of *oxaloacetate.* The reaction is catalyzed by the enzyme *PEP carboxylase* (Figure 5–6).

C_4 plants are less efficient than C_3 plants in terms of the energy requirements in fixing CO_2. To fix one molecule of CO_2, C_4 plants need five ATPs, whereas C_3 plants need only three. However, C_4 plants have higher photosynthetic rates than C_3 plants and also are able to continue photosynthesizing under conditions such as high temperatures and high light intensity when C_3 plants cannot (Figure 5–7). Generally, C_4 plants are adapted to tropical conditions. Select examples of both categories of plants are presented in Table 5–1. Under hot, sunny skies, C_3 plants undergo a process called *photorespiration* (light-dependent production of glycolic acid in chloroplasts and its subsequent oxidation in peroxisomes). C_4 plants use CO_2 more efficiently and hence are able to function at only partially closed stomata, as occurs on hot, sunny days.

C_3 and C_4 plants are different structurally. The bundle sheath cells of C_3 leaves have small chloroplasts. Photosynthesis occurs only in the mesophyll cells. However, the bundle sheath cells of C_4 plants are large and contain large chloroplasts. These chloroplasts exhibit the Calvin cycle, while the mesophyll cells exhibit the C_4 pathway. All plants known to use the C_4 pathway are flowering plants. In

FIGURE 5–5 The Calvin cycle or C_3 pathway of carbon dioxide fixation.

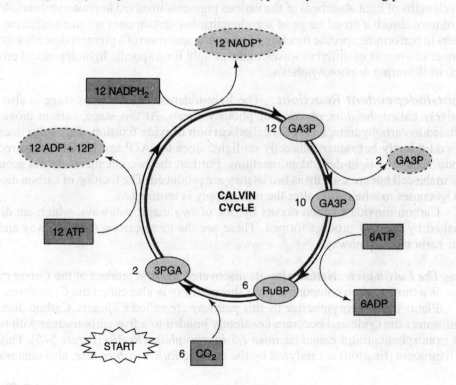

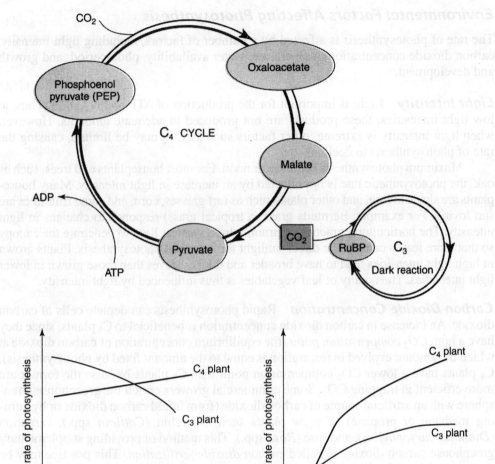

FIGURE 5–6 The C$_4$ pathway of carbon dioxide fixation.

FIGURE 5–7 The relative rates of photosynthesis in C$_3$ and C$_4$ plants as influenced by (a) temperature and (b) light intensity.

(a) Leaf temperature — Net rate of photosynthesis — C$_4$ plant, C$_3$ plant

(b) Light intensity — Net rate of photosynthesis — C$_4$ plant, C$_3$ plant

lawns, where C$_4$ species such as crabgrass *(Digitaria sanguinalis)* occur among C$_3$ species such as Kentucky bluegrass *(Poa pratensis)*, the crabgrass grows rapidly in summer and tends to suppress the fine-leafed species with its broad leaves.

3. *The Crassulacean acid metabolism.* The Crassulacean acid metabolism (CAM) is a photosynthetic pathway that allows certain plants to fix carbon dioxide in the dark by the activity of PEP carboxylase. Because the stomata of leaves are closed during the hot day, CAM plants depend on CO$_2$ that accumulates in the leaf during the nighttime. This reaction provides *malic acid,* which accumulates in the vacuoles of cells. During the next light period, the malic acid is decarboxylated. The resulting CO$_2$ is transferred to the Calvin cycle within the same cell.

Most CAM plants inhabit environments in which moisture stress and intense light prevail. Many are succulents such as members of the cactus (Cactaceae), stone crop (Crassulaceae), and orchid (Orchidaceae) families. Houseplants with CAM include wax plant *(Hoya carnosa)* and snake plant *(Sansevieria zeylanica)*.

CAM plants are relatively slower growing than C$_3$ or C$_4$ plants under favorable conditions. They grow more slowly because plants, by nature, tend to conserve moisture and in so doing close the stomata most of the day, thus limiting the CO$_2$ intake needed for fixation.

Environmental Factors Affecting Photosynthesis

The rate of photosynthesis is affected by a number of factors, including light intensity, carbon dioxide concentration, temperature, water availability, photoperiod, and growth and development.

Light Intensity   Light is important for the production of ATP and NADPH. Thus, at low light intensities, these products are not produced in adequate amounts. However, when light intensity is extreme, other factors such as CO_2 may be limited, causing the rate of photosynthesis to decline.

   Maximum photosynthesis occurs near noon. For most houseplants and trees, such as oak, the photosynthetic rate is not affected by an increase in light intensity. Many houseplants are shade loving, and other plants such as turf grasses, corn, and some fruit trees are sun loving. For example, Bermuda grass (a tropical grass) responds to changes in light intensity. The horticultural practice of pruning trees permits light to penetrate the canopy so that more leaves can receive direct sunlight for increased photosynthesis. Plants grown in high light intensities tend to have broader and thicker leaves than those grown in lower light intensities. The quality of leaf vegetables is thus influenced by light intensity.

Carbon Dioxide Concentration   Rapid photosynthesis can deplete cells of carbon dioxide. An increase in carbon dioxide concentration is beneficial to C_3 plants, since they have a high *CO_2 compensation point* (the equilibrium concentration of carbon dioxide at which the amount evolved in respiration is equal to the amount fixed by photosynthesis). C_4 plants have a lower CO_2 compensation point than C_3 plants because the former are more efficient in trapping CO_2. Some commercial growers enrich the greenhouse atmosphere with an artificial source of carbon dioxide (from liquid carbon dioxide or by burning methane or propane) to grow plants such as orchid (*Cattleya* spp.), carnation (*Dianthus caryophyllus),* and rose (*Rosa* spp.). This method of providing supplementary greenhouse carbon dioxide is called *carbon dioxide fertilization*. This practice may be necessary during the winter when carbon dioxide levels in airtight greenhouses may be lowered to a degree where photosynthesis could be limited on sunny days. However, unless the purpose of providing additional carbon dioxide is to increase productivity, the carbon dioxide concentration in winter may be readily restored by frequent ventilation of the facility rather than adopting carbon dioxide fertilization.

Temperature   Photosynthetic rate is decreased in cold temperatures because the fixation stage is temperature sensitive. However, under conditions in which light is a limiting factor (low light conditions) the effect of temperature on photosynthesis is minimal. Generally, if light is adequate, the photosynthetic rate is found to approximately double the rate in plants in temperate areas for each 10°C (18°F) rise in temperature. The quality (sugar content) of certain fruits such as cantaloupe is reduced when they are grown under conditions in which the photosynthetic rate is reduced but respiration is high because of high temperatures. C_3 plants grow poorly at high temperatures. For example, lawn grasses that follow the C_3 pathway perform poorly in summer, whereas C_4 plants that are weeds, such as crabgrass, thrive.

Water Availability   When plants grow under conditions of moisture stress because of low soil moisture or dry winds that accelerate transpiration, enzymatic activities associated with photosynthesis in the plants slow down. Stomata close under moisture stress, reducing carbon dioxide availability and consequently decreasing the photosynthetic rate.

Photoperiod   The duration of day length (photoperiod) affects photosynthesis in a directly proportional way. Generally, plants that are exposed to long periods of light photosynthesize for a longer time and as a result tend to grow faster. In the winter season when sunlight is less direct and of shorter duration, growing plants indoors is more successful if additional lighting at appropriate intensity is provided to extend the period of natural light.

Growth and Development The general plant growth and development needs also influence the rate of photosynthesis. The photosynthetic rate is lower in a young expanding leaf than in a fully expanded one. On the other hand, as plant leaves begin **senescence** (an aging process involving degradation of proteins), the photosynthetic rate in mature leaves declines and eventually ceases in certain species.

Other factors affect the rate of photosynthesis. One such factor is nutrition (deficiency of nitrogen and magnesium, which are both required by chlorophyll, can decrease the rate). Environmental pollutants such as ozone and sulfur damage horticultural plants by causing loss of chlorophyll in leaves and thus reducing the available photosynthetic surface.

Senescence
The breakdown of cell components and membranes that leads to the death of a cell.

5.3.2 RESPIRATION

Respiration may occur in an environment that is oxygen rich or oxygen deficient.

Aerobic Respiration

Aerobic respiration accomplishes the reverse of photosynthesis by using oxygen from the air to metabolize organic molecules into carbon dioxide and water to release stored energy in the form of ATP. In fact, the primary purpose of respiration is this energy-production function. *Polysaccharides* are stored in different forms by different organisms; for example, bananas store it as sucrose, whereas onions store it as fructose. The general reaction that occurs in mitochondria in the cytoplasm is as follows:

$$C_6H_{12}O_6 + 6O_2 \rightarrow 6CO_2 + 6H_2O + energy$$

Respiration consists of three distinct stages. The first reaction, *glycolysis*, occurs in the cytoplasm, where glucose is broken down into pyruvic acid. In the first part, ATP is converted to ADP; in the second part, ADP is converted to ATP. Pyruvic acid from glycolysis enters the mitochondria to complete the next two phases, which are the *Krebs cycle (tricarboxylic acid cycle or citric acid cycle)* and the *electron transport chain* (requires oxygen). This three-phase process is called *aerobic respiration,* since it requires oxygen. When oxygen is limited, another form of respiration, called *anaerobic respiration* (or *fermentation*), occurs, the end product being alcohol.

Glycolysis Glycolysis ("sugar splitting") occurs in the cytoplasm of the cell. It involves the breaking down of glucose into pyruvic acid (Figure 5–8). In a series of reactions two, three-carbon sugar phosphates are produced from one, six-carbon glucose molecule. The sugar phosphates are then converted to pyruvic acid (a pyruvate), accompanied by the production of ATP and the reduction of NAD^+ to NADH. The overall equation for glycolysis is as follows:

glucose $+ 2NAD^+ + 2ADP + 2P_i \rightarrow 2$ pyruvic acid $+ 2NADH + 2H^+ + 2ATP + 2H_2O$

Glycolysis
The initial phase of all types of respiration in which glucose is converted to pyruvic acid without involving free oxygen.

In effect, one glucose molecule is converted into two molecules of pyruvic acid. The formation of ATP by the enzymatic transfer of a phosphate group from a metabolic intermediate to ADP is called *substrate-level phosphorylation.*

Krebs Cycle The Krebs cycle occurs in the mitochondrion, following the entry of pyruvic acid from glycolysis. The series of enzyme-catalyzed reactions involved in this cycle constitute what is called *oxidative decarboxylation* (Figure 5–9). The reactions may be summarized by the following equation:

oxaloacetic acid $+$ acetyl CoA $+$ ADP $+ P_i + 3NAD^+ +$ FAD $\rightarrow$ oxaloacetic acid $+$ $2CO_2 +$ CoA $+$ ATP $+ 3NADH + 3H^+ +$ FADH$_2$

FIGURE 5–8   A summary of glycolysis.

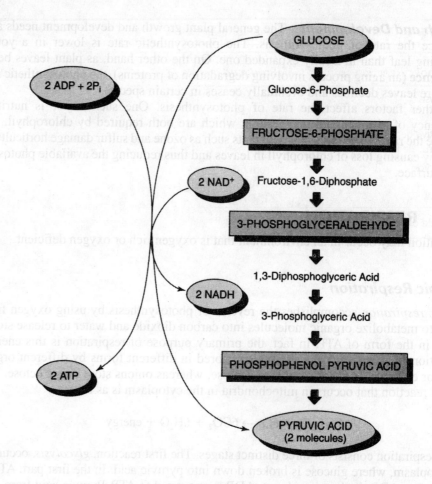

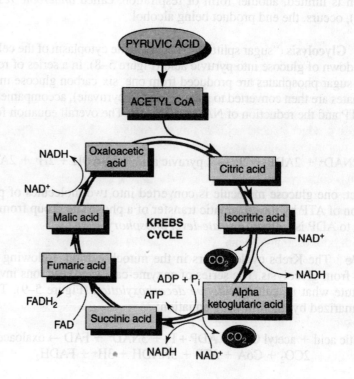

FIGURE 5–9   A summary of the Krebs cycle. The cycle always begins with acetyl CoA, which is its only real substrate.

TABLE 5–2 Energy Produced from Aerobic Respiration

Metabolic Reaction	Coenzyme Type Produced	ATP Yield Coenzyme	Total
Glycolysis	(Direct)	2	2
	2 NADH	2	4
Oxydative decarboxylation of pyruvate to acetyl CoA	2 NADH	3	6
Krebs cycle	(From GTP)		2
	6 NADH	3	18
	2 FADH$_2$	2	4
Net yield of ATP			36

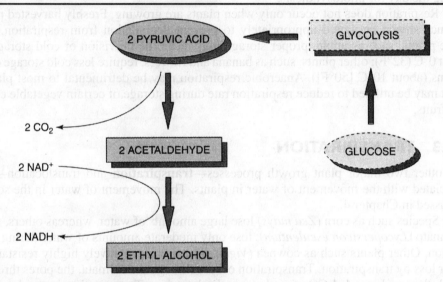

FIGURE 5–10 A summary of the process of fermentation.

Energy Yield in Respiration   The energy yield from the respiration of one molecule of glucose is presented in Table 5–2. The net yield of 36 ATPs from aerobic respiration of one molecule of glucose is common to most organisms.

Anaerobic Respiration

Aerobic respiration results in the complete oxidation of pyruvic acid to CO_2 and water. When oxygen is absent, pyruvic acid (or pyruvate) is not the end product of glycolysis. Instead, pyruvate is broken down to *ethyl alcohol* (ethanol) and CO_2 in most plant cells (Figure 5–10). This anaerobic process is called *anaerobic respiration,* or alcoholic fermentation. In some bacteria, the end product is lactic acid, and thus the process is called *lactate* **fermentation.** The anaerobic respiratory pathway is very inefficient. In aerobic respiration, the initial energy of 686 kilocalories (kcal) per mole of glucose yields 263 kcal (39 percent) at the end of the process, which is conserved in 36 ATP molecules. In fermentation, only 2 ATP molecules are produced, representing about 2 percent of the available energy in a molecule of glucose.

When horticultural plants are grown in mud (air is limited), they are forced to respire anaerobically. Similarly, houseplants die when they are overwatered or grown in containers with poor drainage because they are unable to respire aerobically; instead they resort to anaerobic respiration, which yields very little or no energy at all. Fermentation, however, is a very important process utilized in the alcoholic beverage industry. Wine (from grapes) and apple cider are a few products that depend on anaerobic respiration. Respiration is the source of energy for all life processes. Since it depends on products of photosynthesis (the two processes work in opposite directions), it is critical that a desirable relationship between them be maintained for proper growth and development of plants. If food is broken down faster than it is manufactured, plant growth will be

Fermentation
The metabolic breakdown of an organic molecule in the absence of oxygen or with low levels of oxygen to produce end products such as ethanol and lactic acid.

severely hampered. This imbalance may cause the eventual death of certain plants when they are grown in the shade. Whereas light is required for photosynthesis, it is not required for respiration, and hence the latter proceeds even in shade. Fortunately, photosynthesis generally occurs at a higher rate than respiration, such that there are excess photosynthates for growth or production of fruits and seed through storage. It is estimated that a photosynthetic rate of about 8 to 10 times higher than the respiration rate is required for good production of vegetables.

To decrease respiration of carbohydrates, the temperature may be lowered to slow the reaction. However, this action also slows the photosynthetic rate. A warm temperature, moderate intensity of light, and adequate supply of water are desired for maximizing the photosynthetic rate. This condition occurs on warm, bright days with cool night temperatures of about 5°C (9°F) colder than day temperatures. Respiration is reduced during the cool period of the night, while adequate duration and intensity of light exist during the day for photosynthesis.

Respiration does not occur only when plants are growing. Freshly harvested plant produce should be stored appropriately to prevent degradation from respiration. For some plants, such as apple, proper storage may mean the provision of cold storage at about 0°C (32°F); other plants, such as banana and flowers, require less cold storage conditions (about 10°C [50°F]). Anaerobic respiration may be detrimental to most plants, but it may be utilized to reduce respiration rate during storage of certain vegetable crops and fruits.

5.3.3 TRANSPIRATION

Transpiration
The loss of water from plant surfaces by evaporation and diffusion.

The other two major plant growth processes—**transpiration** and translocation—are associated with the movement of water in plants. The movement of water in the soil is discussed in Chapter 4.

Species such as corn *(Zea mays)* lose large amounts of water, whereas others, such as tomato *(Lycopersicon esculentum),* lose only moderate amounts of water during cultivation. Other plants such as cowpea *(Vigna sinensis)* are relatively highly resistant to water loss by transpiration. Transpiration occurs through the stomata, the pores through which the much-needed CO_2 for photosynthesis passes. Transpiration is regulated by closure of the stomata, an event that excludes CO_2 and reduces the rate of photosynthesis. However, respiration produces some CO_2 that can be trapped and used by plants after the stomata have closed.

The stomata open or close according to changes in turgor pressure in the guard cells. Water in most cases is the primary factor that controls stomatal movements. However, other factors in the environment also affect stomatal movements. Generally, an increase in CO_2 concentration in the leaf causes stomatal closure in most species. Some species are more sensitive than others to the effects of CO_2. Similarly, the stomata of most species open in light and close in the dark. An exception to this feature is plants with CAM pathways of photosynthesis. Photosynthesis uses up CO_2 and thus decreases its concentration in the leaf. Evidence suggests that light quality (wavelength) affects stomatal movements. Blue and red light have been shown to stimulate stomatal opening. The effect of temperature on stomatal movements is minimal, except when excessively high temperatures (more than 30°C [86° F]) prevail, as occurs at midday. However, an increase in temperature increases the rate of respiration, which produces CO_2 and thereby increases the CO_2 concentration in the leaf. This increase in CO_2 may be part of the reason stomata close when the temperature increases.

Apart from environmental factors, many plants have been known to accumulate high levels of abscisic acid, a plant hormone. This hormone accumulates in plants under conditions of moisture stress and causes stomata to close.

Transpiration is accelerated by several environmental factors. The rate of transpiration is doubled with a more than 10°C (18°F) rise in temperature. Transpiration is slower in environments of high humidity. Also, air currents may accelerate the transpiration rate by preventing water vapor from accumulating on the leaf surface.

(a)

(b)

(c)

(d)

(e)

Myriad Botanical Gardens – Oklahoma City: The Crystal Bridge, north view (a), close up of north view (b), and Plaza view (c). The world's largest unbranched inflorescence, *Amorphophallus titanum*, also known as Titan arum or corpse flower, bloomed in the Crystal Bridge Tropical Conservatory on June 29, 2005. The 42-inch tall corpse flower lasted through Tuesday, July 5 before it collapsed (d). A section of the palms collection in the garden (e). *(Source:* Dr. Allan Storjohann, Manager, Myriad Botanical Gardens, 100 Myriad Gardens, Oklahoma City.)

(a)

(b)

(c)

(d)

(e)

(f)

(g)

Fruits and nuts: (a) Pome, represented by apple; (b) Multiple fruit, represented by pineapple; (c) Drupe, represented by nectarine; (d) Berry, represented by tomato; (e) Hesperidium, represented by lime; (f) Aggregate fruit, represented by strawberry; and (g) Nut, represented by almond. *(Sources:* (a) Pearson Education/PH College; (b,c) Philip Dowell © Dorling Kindersley; (d) Dave King © Dorling Kindersley; (e) Geoff Dann © Dorling Kindersley; (f) Ian O'Leary © Dorling Kindersley; (g) David Murray © Dorling Kindersley.)

Wood: (a) Disease infection of the stem from improperly healed wound; (b) transverse section of a stem showing a thick bark; (c) transverse section of a stem showing an inner dark region of heartwood and outer region of sapwood; (d) transverse section of a stem showing annual rings. **Soilless mix materials**: (e) wood bark, (f) perlite, (g) peat moss, (h) compounded commercial soilless mix. **Fertilizer**: (i) fertilizer bag showing analysis, (j) a commercial potting mix with fertilizer, and (k) slow-release fertilizer (left) and fertilizer sticks for potted plants (right). *(Sources:* (a, c) Peter Chadwick © Dorling Kindersley; (b) PurestockX; (d) Dave King / Dorling Kindersley © Weald and Download Open Air Museum, Chichester.)

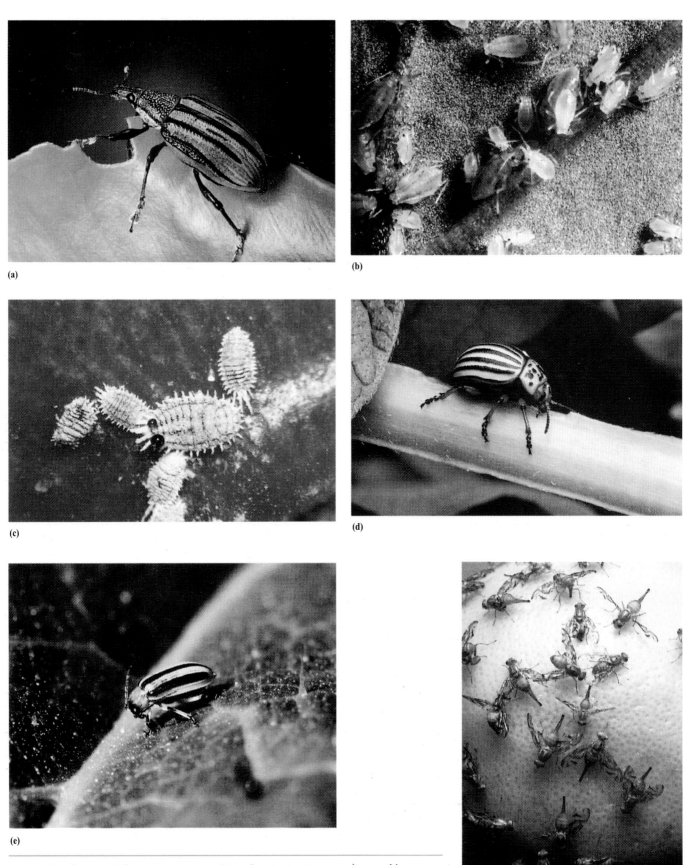

Horticultural pests: (a) Typical damage caused by a chewing insect pest such as a cabbage worm, (b) aphids (sucking insects), (c) mealybugs (sucking insects), (d) Colorado potato beetle, (e) cucumber beetle, and (f) Mexican fruit fly. *(Source:* Courtesy of USDA.)

Biological pest control: Green lacewing larva eating whitefly nymphs; (b) *Aleiodes indiscretus* wasp parasiting on a gypsy moth caterpillar; (c) P-14 lady beetle devours a pea aphid; (d) Adult *Delphastus pusillus* beetle eating whitefly nymphs; (e) Spined soldier bug feeds on Mexican beetle larva; (f) *Calsoma sycophanta* beetle feeding on a gypsy moth caterpillar. *(Source:* Courtesy of USDA.)

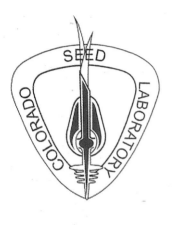

(a)

(b)

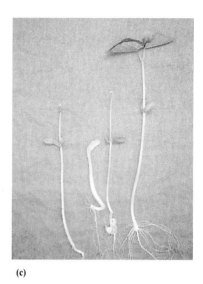

(c)

(d)

(e)

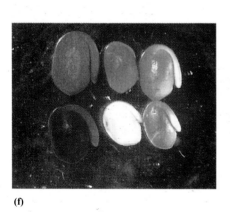

(f)

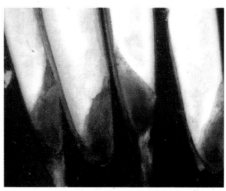

(g)

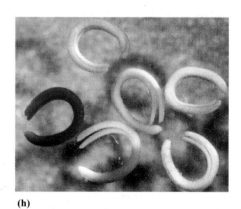

(h)

Selected seed testing activities at Colorado Seed Laboratory: (a) CSL logo. (b) Triticale is grown on towels; this sample is ready to be evaluated. (c) The three beans on the left have sprouted, but are missing primary leafs—thus they are considered abnormal. (d) The four components of seed purity. (e) Safflower planted in special seed germination towels. (f) These lupine seeds have varying degrees of stain. The root tips on three of the seeds have not stained, and the cotyledons of the lower middle seed are also void of stain: this indicates that the seed is dead or abnormal. (g) The essential structures of these embryos have all stained, indicating that this seed is viable. (h) Pigweed (*Amaranthus spp.*) has a peripheral embryo that must be extracted from the seed to stain. The embryo on the left is viable. *(Source: Courtesy, Annette Miller, USDA-ARS National Center for Genetic Resources Preservation. Fort Collins, Colorado.)*

Vegetative propagation: (a) Cut tongue opened with a match stick; (b) two tongues fitted together in an approach graft prior to taping; (c) grafting cactus; (d) bark grafting using three scions; (e) chip budding; and (f) a healed graft union; (g) callus tissue; (h) multiple root formation; (i) single root; (j) roots formed on shootlet kept on root-inducing medium. *(Sources:* (a–c) Peter Anderson © Dorling Kindersley; (d–f) © Dorling Kindersley; (g–j) Kanyand Matand, Langston University, Center for Biotech Research and Education.)

(a)

(b)

(c)

(d)

(e)

(f)

Containers for houseplants: Containers are as important as the plants they hold. They come in all shapes, sizes, and colors. Some are made of synthetic materials (a); others are made of natural materials like clay (b). Pots can be colorful, and some are simply works of art (c, d, e). There are various accessories, such as saucers with coasters to allow plants to be easily moved around (f).

Hanging baskets: Some plants have unique features that are best displayed by hanging them in baskets. Examples include the rabbit's foot fern (a), Bead plant (b), Boston Fern (c), Pitcher plant (d), Spider plant (e), Ivy (f), Orchid (g), Pothos (h), and Staghorn fern (i).

Steps in repotting: (a1) insert old pot into new bigger pot and fill space to create mold; (a2) remove plant from old pot and separate roots; (a3) place plant into hole molded in the bigger pot and fill up space. **Window display**: (b) several potted plants displayed in the window pane; (c) widow garden outside the window. **Creating a hanging basket**: (d1) seedlings are inserted through wall of basket containing potting mix; (d2) fully planted and blooming hanging basket. *(Sources: (a) Matthew Ward © Dorling Kindersley; (b, d2) © Dorling Kindersley; (c,d1) Peter Anderson © Dorling Kindersley.)*

(a)

(c)

(b)

(d)

Growing container plants: (a) In this container garden, foliage color, form and texture are the dominating elements of design. The bold, fuzzy textured *Salvia argentea* grabs attention to develop focus in the center of the composition. Lotus 'Amazon Sunset' adds color echo for rhythm and a fine texture for contrast to the coarse, gray foliage of the salvia. Coleus 'Compact Red', coleus 'Stormy Weather' and ipomoea 'Blackie' (clockwise) complete the container garden. Designed by Lori Osburn, Photographed by Lori Osburn.

(b) This Flower Color Wheel is similar to an artist's color wheel but uses names that florists commonly use to describe color. This color wheel divides the primary color of violet into three additional segments to include indigo (bluish violet) and fuchsia (reddish violet) because there are so many variations of violet in flower colors. Designed by Terri Starman, Photographed by Kristen Eixmann.

(c) The maroon (a shade of red) coleus 'Compact Red' adds depth and draws the eye deep into the otherwise pink (a tint of red) monochromatic (one color) container garden. Different flower forms (daisy, cluster, and star-shaped) and foliage forms (upright, bushy, and trailing) are design elements that make this container garden interesting. Agastache and dracena back each other with their vertical forms to establish the height of the container garden. Argyranthemum 'Comet Pink' serves as a filler plant; verbena 'Babylon Pink' takes the corner position, and bacopa 'Penny Candy Pink' fills the edge position. Designed by Terri Starman, Photographed by Lori Osburn.

(d) This container gardens uses several bulbous species with annuals. The mixture of flower forms, sizes, statures and textures make the container garden stimulating. Gladiolus 'Muriel' (star-shaped), lily 'Salmon Classic' (cupped), calla 'Captain Romance' (unusual), streptocarpella 'Conord Blue' (nodding), begonia 'Fimbriata Yellow' (solid), and begonia 'Sinbad' (variegated foliage) (clockwise) fill this 11" tall X 14" wide container. Designed by Lauren Edwards, Photographed by Kristen Eixmann.

(a)

(b)

(c)

(d)

(a) This container garden emphasizes foliage forms and textures and uses an all neutral color scheme (black, white, and gray). Calla 'Schwazwalder', Gypsophila paniculata 'Festive Star', Trifolium repens 'Dark Dancer', Eranthemum nigrum 'Ebony', Japanese painted fern, Calochortus 'Cupido' and Carex flagellifera 'Toffee Twist', (clockwise) enhance each other in a 10" tall X 15" wide container garden. Designed by Terri Starman, Photographed by Kristen Eixmann.

(b) The focal point lies deep in the center of this container garden and is established by the radiating leaves and emerging flower of eucomis 'Bicolor'. Its unusual plant form and hefty leaves also help to grab attention. A microclimate is formed underneath the canopy of eucomis and coleus 'Sedona' to filter light for the shade-loving plants below which include tatting fern, huechera 'Amber Waves', ajuga 'Black Scallop', hosta 'Fragrant Bouquet', impatiens 'Infinity Salmon' and streptocarpella 'Conord Blue' (clockwise). The terra cotta color of the 14" tall X 11.5" wide decorative container contributes to the blue and orange complementary color harmony. Designed by Terri Starman, Photographed by Kristen Eixmann.

(c) *Curcuma petiolata* 'Emperor' (Siam Tulip) forms the center, while Breynia, Japanese forest grass 'Aurora', and Japanese painted fern serve as fillers. Caladium 'Florida Sweetheart' is the focal plant in the corner position and *Lysimachia nummularia* is in two edge positions. The various plant species are compatible for a shady location on the patio. Designed by Phil Campbell, Photographed by Terri Starman.

(d) The analogous color harmony and various plant forms are what make this container garden attractive. The terra cotta container repeats the color of the salmon arctotis 'Flame' daisy flowers and ipomoea 'Sweet Caroline Bronze' leaves. The red-orange fuchsia 'Koralle' flowers add accent and their nodding flower form help give the container garden rhythm. Maroon leaves of purple fountain grass and *Alternanthera dentata* complete the analogous color harmony. The gray foliage of artotis 'Flame' helps to brighten the container garden. Designed by Terri Starman, Photographed by Terri Starman.

Houseplants: (a) Aluminum plant (*Pilea cadierei*), (b) Peacock plant (*Calathea roseopicta*), (c) Variegated Swiss cheese plant (*Monstrera delicisiosa*), (d) Umbrella plant (*Cyperus albostratus*), (e) Prayer plant (*Maranta leuconeura*), (f) Zebra plant (*Aphelandra squarrosa*), (g) Blushing bromeliad (*Neoregelia carolinae*), (h) Chinese evergreen (*Aglaonema* sp.), (i) Bird of paradise (*Strelitza reginae*). *(Source:* (a–i) Matthew Ward © Dorling Kindersley.)

Houseplants: (a) Madagascar dragon tree (*Dracaena marginata*), (b) Jade plant (*Crassula ovata*), (c) *Dracaena fragrans* 'Compacta', (d) Rubber plant (*Ficus elastica* 'Robusta', (e) Asparagus fern (*Asparagus umbellatus*), (f) *Chrysanthemum indicum*, (g) *Aloe*, (h) Peace lily (*Spathiphyllum wallisii*), (i) Snake plant (*Sansevieria trifasciata*). *(Source:* (a–i) Matthew Ward © Dorling Kindersley.)

Houseplants: (a) *Monstera oblique*, (b) Friendship plant (*Pilea involucrate*), (c) Poinsettia (*Euphorbia pulcherima*), (d) Easter lily, (e) Boston fern (*Nephrolepsis exaltata* 'Bostoniensis'), (f) *Shefflera arboricola* 'Luciana', (g) *Cyclamen persicum* 'Sylvia', (h) Cactus (*Notocactus leninghausii*), (i) African violet (*Saintpaulia* sp). *(Source:* (a–i) Matthew Ward © Dorling Kindersley.)

Houseplants: (a) Flamingo flower (*Anthurium scherzerianum*), (b) Common lily (*Hedera helix*), (c) Hyacinth, (d) Arrowleaf (*Syngonium* sp), (e) *Kalanchoe blossfeldianer*), (f) Dumbcane (*Dieffenbachia seguine*), (g) Elephant foot (*Beaucarnea recurvata*), (h) Peperomia obtusifolia, (i) Coleus (*Solenostemon* sp). *(Sources:* (a–d, f–i) Matthew Ward © Dorling Kindersley; (e) Tom Dobbie © Dorling Kindersley.)

Certain plants are adapted to dry environments. These plants (called *xerophytes*) have special anatomical and physiological modifications that make them able to reduce transpiration losses. These species, which include a large number of succulents, are able to store and retain large amounts of water. Physiologically, the plants photosynthesize by the CAM pathway and close their stomata at night.

5.3.4 HOW WATER MOVES IN PLANTS

Water moves in plants via the conducting elements of the xylem. It moves along a water potential gradient from soil to root, root to stem, stem to leaf, and leaf to air forming a continuum of water movement. The trend is for water to move from the region of highest water potential to the region of lowest water potential, which is how water moves from the soil to the air. Transpiration is implicated in this water movement, because it causes a water gradient to form between the leaves and the soil solution on the root surface. This gradient may also form as a result of the use of water in the leaves. Loss of moisture in the leaves causes water to move out of the xylem and into the mesophyll area, where it is depleted. The loss of water at the top of the xylem vessels causes water to be pulled up. This movement is possible because of the strong cohesive bond among water molecules. The movement of water up the xylem according to this mechanism is explained by the *cohesion-tension theory*. It is the cohesiveness of water molecules that allows water to withstand tension. Water is withheld against gravity by capillarity. The rise is aided by the strong adhesion of water molecules to the walls of the capillary vessel.

Capillary flow is obstructed when air bubbles interrupt the continuity of the water column, called *embolism*. This event is preceded by *cavitation,* the rupture of the water column. Once the tracheary elements have become embolized, they are unable to conduct water. In the cut flower industry, the stems of flowers are cut under water to prevent embolism.

Water enters the plant from the soil via the root hairs, which provide a large surface area for absorption. Once inside the root hairs, water moves through the cortex and into the tracheary elements. There are three possible pathways by which this movement occurs, depending on the differentiation that has occurred in the root (e.g., presence of endodermis, exodermis, or a transcellular pathway suberin). Water may move from cell to cell, passing from vacuole to vacuole. Sometimes water may move via the *apoplastic pathway,* through the cell wall, or the *symplastic pathway,* from protoplast to protoplast through the pores in the plasmodesmata (minute cytoplasmic threads that extend through openings in the cell wall and connect the protoplast of adjacent living cells).

Root pressure plays a role in water movement, especially at night when transpiration occurs to a negligible degree or not at all. Ions build up in the xylem to a high concentration and initiate osmosis, so that water enters the vascular tissue through the neighboring cells. This pressure is called root pressure and is implicated in another event, *guttation,* whereby droplets of water form at the tips of the leaves of certain species (e.g., lady's mantle [*Achemilla vulgaris*]) in the early morning. These drops do not result from condensation of water vapor in the surrounding air but rather are formed as a result of root pressure forcing water out of hydathodes. Root pressure as a water movement mechanism is least significant during the daytime when water moves through plants at peak rates. Further, some plants such as pine (conifers) do not develop root pressure.

The absorption and movement of water in plants occurs via the xylem vessels. Inorganic nutrients are also transported through these vessels. Solutes are moved against a concentration gradient and require an *active transport* mechanism that is energy dependent and mediated by carrier protein. Some amount of exchange between xylem and phloem fluids occurs such that inorganic salts are transported along with sucrose and some photosynthetic products are transferred to the xylem and recirculated in the transpiration stream.

Root Pressure
The development of positive hydrostatic pressure in the xylem followed by osmotic uptake of water.

5.3.5 TRANSLOCATION

Translocation is the long-distance transport of organic solutes through the plant. Photosynthetic products are moved out of the leaves and into the assimilate stream from the *sources* (especially leaves but also storage tissue) to where they are used or stored *(sinks)*. The primary translocation source (leaves) is located above the primary sink (root). However, the movement of organic solutes is not unidirectional or fixed.

During vegetative growth, assimilates are distributed from leaves to growing parts in upward and downward directions. However, when the plant enters the reproductive phase of growth, developing fruits require large amounts of assimilates and hence there is redistribution so that most of the flow from neighboring sources and even from distant ones are redirected to the fruits. Movement in the assimilate stream occurs via the phloem vessels as *sap*, a fluid consisting mainly of sugar and nitrogenous substances (Figure 5–11).

Phloem transport is believed to occur by the mechanism of *pressure flow*. This hypothesis suggests that assimilates are moved from translocation sources to sinks along a gradient of hydrostatic pressure (turgor pressure) of osmotic origin. Sugar is asserted to be transported in the phloem from adjacent cells in the leaf by an energy-dependent active process called *phloem loading*. The effect of this process is a decrease in water potential in the phloem sieve tube, which in turn causes water entering the leaf in the transportation stream to move into the sieve tube under osmotic pressure. The water then acts as a vehicle for the passive transport of the sugars to sinks, where they are unloaded, or removed, for use or storage. The water is recirculated in the transpiration stream because of the increased water potential or the sink resulting from the phloem unloading.

5.4 DEVELOPMENTAL STAGES OF GROWTH

A growing plant seedling goes through a number of developmental changes:

$$\text{embryonic} \rightarrow \text{juvenile} \rightarrow \text{transitional} \rightarrow \text{maturity} \rightarrow \text{senescence}$$

5.4.1 EMBRYONIC STAGE

The seed consists of an embryo or miniature plant. Until the conditions for germination are right, the embryo remains dormant. *Seed dormancy* is said to occur when a viable seed fails to germinate under favorable environmental conditions. This biological mechanism is especially advantageous when plants are growing in the wild. It ensures that seeds will germinate only when adequate moisture and other necessary environmental

FIGURE 5–11 Accumulation of carbohydrates and sugars above the position of girdling or stem that interrupts the continuity of the phloem.

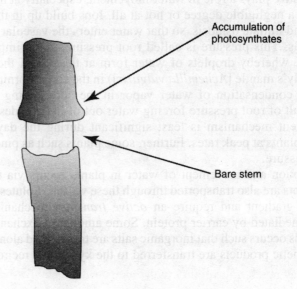

Accumulation of photosynthates

Bare stem

conditions exist to sustain growth after germination. The condition may be physical (*physical* **dormancy**) or physiological (*physiological dormancy*) in origin. A frequent source of physical dormancy is the presence of an impervious seed coat that does not permit water imbibition for germination. In modern cultivation, such seeds may be mechanically scratched (a process called scarification) to make the seed coat permeable to water. Persistence of seed dormancy may cause undesirable delay in germination, resulting in nonuniform seed germination and consequently an incomplete stand and irregular maturity in the field that leads to unnecessary delays in harvesting. Leguminous species are most plagued by mechanical seed dormancy because of an impervious seed coat.

Dormancy may be caused by physiological causes stemming from chemicals in various parts of the seed or the fruit that inhibit germination. Certain desert species require a good soaking rain in order to leach away a germination inhibitor before seeds will germinate. Consequently, adequate moisture is ensured for the young seedlings to become established and be able to fend for themselves before a dry spell occurs. Seeds seldom germinate while they are in the fruit. However, once excised and washed, the mature seeds promptly germinate. In tomato, the chemical *coumarin* is implicated in this inhibitory condition. Abscisic acid is another chemical known to impose seed dormancy in plants.

In some species, seed maturity lags behind fruit ripening. In the American holly (*Ilex opaca*), an *after-ripening* process is required to bring the embryo in the seed to maturity, without which it will not be able to germinate. Seed dormancy in certain situations can be broken through a cold temperature treatment (*cold* **stratification**). In these species, seeds germinate after a brief storage at temperatures above freezing (e.g., 5°C [41°F]).

Buds can also become dormant under certain environmental conditions. *Bud dormancy* is a period of quiescence during which growth is temporarily suspended. Bermuda grass becomes dormant and changes color to a dull brown with the onset of cold temperature. It resumes active growth in spring. Both flower and vegetative buds may experience dormancy. Buds on the same plant have different dormancy characteristics. Just as seed dormancy protects seeds from damage due to adverse weather, woody plants in temperate climates are protected by internally imposed dormancy. Such dormancy ensures that new growth does not occur until the danger of damage from adverse temperatures is minimized. However, the requirements for breaking dormancy vary between the two structures (vegetative and reproductive). In plants such as peach and cherry, the period of cold treatment required to break dormancy is shorter for flower buds than for vegetative buds. If a peach cultivar with a long *low chill requirement* is grown, insufficient chilling can cause some fruiting to occur in the absence of vegetative growth.

5.4.2 JUVENILE STAGE

Juvenility starts after germination and is the stage during which the plant undergoes vegetative growth without any reproductive activities. The period of juvenility is variable among species, being several weeks in some and several years in others. Certain species display telltale characteristics of this stage. For example, in the English ivy (*Hedera helix*), immature (juvenile) plants trail or climb and have three to five deeply lobed palmate alternative leaves. When mature, the plants produce upright shoots with nonlobed ovate opposite leaves. In fruit trees, juvenile branches appear on older ones as vertical shoots (Figure 5–12). These shoots, called *suckers*, or **water sprouts**, may occur at the base of mature tree trunks. Another trait of juvenility is the retention of leaves or juvenile plant parts through the winter, as occurs in oak trees. In *Acacia melnoxylon*, juvenile leaves have compound bipinnate forms, but mature plants have simple leaves.

5.4.3 TRANSITIONAL STAGE

The stage of transition occurs between juvenility and maturity. Plants at this stage may display characteristic features of both stages simultaneously. In the transitional stage, mature plants may revert to juvenility with changes in the environment.

Dormancy
The failure of seeds, bulbs, buds, or tubers to grow due to internal factors or unfavorable environment.

Stratification
The practice of exposing imbibed seed usually to cold temperatures for a period of time prior to germination in order to break dormancy.

Water Sprouts
A vigorous and vertical-growing shoot produced on the trunk or branches of a tree.

5.4.4 MATURITY OR REPRODUCTIVE STAGE

The stage of maturity is characterized by reproductive activities (flowering and fruiting). As mentioned previously, plants such as English ivy have a specific adult (or mature) leaf form that is different from the juvenile form. It should be mentioned that the attainment of maturity does not mean activities (such as flowering) occur automatically. The appropriate conditions for flowering and fruiting must prevail for such activities to take place. Though the plant in this phase is relatively stable, the application of growth regulators can induce juvenility in mature tissue. Other activities in mature plants are aging and senescence.

Physiological maturity is the stage at which the plant has attained maximum dry weight. At this stage, it will not benefit from additional growth inputs. To realize the potential yield of a crop that has been well cultivated, it should be harvested at the right time, using the appropriate methods, and then stored under optimal conditions. Since some horticultural crop products are highly perishable (such as fresh fruits, vegetables, and cut flowers), if they are to be harvested for sale at a distant location from the farm, temporary storage is a critical consideration. If crops are not harvested at the right time, their quality may not be acceptable to consumers. A fresh produce may be too fibrous or not succulent enough or it may taste bitter if not harvested at the proper time. In some crops, such as green beans, consumers prefer a tender product and hence growers harvest beans before they are fully mature.

Physiological Maturity
The stage of development at which a plant or, in grain crops, the seed reaches maximum dry weight.

5.5 PHASES IN THE PLANT LIFE CYCLE

The pattern of growth takes a flowering plant through two distinct phases in its life cycle: (1) *vegetative growth* and (2) *reproductive growth*. Plants do not grow continuously but have periods in which they are dormant or in a resting phase.

5.5.1 VEGETATIVE PLANT GROWTH AND DEVELOPMENT

The vegetative phase of growth is characterized by an increase in the number and size of leaves, branches, and other characteristics of the shoot. Shoot growth follows certain patterns that may be used as a basis for classifying plants.

Shoot Elongation

In certain plants, most shoot elongation ceases after a period of time, and the terminal part is capped by a flower bud or a cluster of flower buds. Plants with this habit of growth are said to be **determinate**. These plants are also described as bush types and are usually able to stand erect in cultivation. They flower and set seed within a limited period. The pods mature and can all be harvested at the same time. In other plant types, shoot elongation continues indefinitely, such that flower buds arise laterally on the stem and continue to do so for as long as the shoot elongates. Plants with this growth habit are said to be *indeterminate*. Mature pods and flowers occur simultaneously on such plants. Trees behave in this way, as do vines. Some indeterminate vegetables require support (staking) in cultivation. Certain species have growth habits between these two extremes. Breeders sometimes breed for bush or erect plant types in certain crops to adapt them for mechanized culture.

Determinate
The concept of restricted potential whereby a plant or organ has a genetically limited size and cannot grow indefinitely.

Duration of Plant Life

A complete life cycle in flowering plants is the period it takes from seed to seed (i.e., germination to seed maturity). On the basis of life cycle, there are four classes of flowering plants. These classes are discussed in detail in Chapter 2.

1. *Annuals.* Annual plants complete their life cycles in one growing season. They are herbaceous and have no dormancy during the growing season (the dormant stage being the seed). Garden crops are mostly annuals, and so are many bedding plants (e.g., lettuce and petunia). Climatic factors may cause species such as impatiens and tomato to behave like annuals, although they are not true annuals.
2. *Biennials.* Biennial is a less common plant growth pattern found in plants such as evening primrose (*Primula* spp.), sugar beet, carrot, cabbage, and celery (*Apium graveolens*). These herbaceous plants complete their life cycles in two growing seasons. They grow vegetatively in the first season, remain dormant through the winter months, resume active vegetative and reproductive activities in the second season, and finally die. Plants such as carrot and sugar beet are grown for their roots (the storage organs), which are harvested at the end of the first growing season. These plants are often grown as annuals.
3. *Perennials.* Perennial plants live for more than two seasons and may be herbaceous or woody. In climatic zones where frost occurs, herbaceous perennials may lose their vegetative shoots, leaving only the underground structures to go through the winter. Woody perennials, on the other hand, maintain both above- and belowground parts indefinitely. In flowering perennials, the flowering cycles are repeated over and over, year after year. Examples include rhubarb, asparagus, bulbs, tomato, eggplant, fruit trees, and ornamental trees and shrubs. As indicated previously, tomato and eggplant are frequently cultivated as annuals in temperate zones.
4. *Monocarp.* Monocarpic plants are a kind of perennial in the sense that they live for many years. However, they flower only once in a lifetime, after which they die. An example is the century plant.

5.5.2 REPRODUCTIVE GROWTH AND DEVELOPMENT

Reproductive activities occur in phases.

Flower Induction

Most agricultural plants are self-inductive for flowering. However, some need a cold temperature treatment to overcome the resting period, or dormancy. The chemical reaction of flower induction is the first indication that the plant has attained maturity. In certain species, the process is known to be dependent on environmental factors, the most common being temperature and light.

Vernalization   **Vernalization** is the cold temperature induction of flowering required in a wide variety of plants. The necessary degree of coldness and duration of exposure to induce flowering vary from species to species, but the required temperature is usually between 0 and 10°C (32 and 50°F). Although some plants such as sugar beet and kohlrabi can be cold sensitized as seed, most plants respond to the cold treatment after attaining a certain amount of vegetative growth. Some plants that need it are not treated because they are cultivated not for flower or seed but for other parts such as roots (in carrot and sugar beet), buds (brussels sprout), stems (celery), and leaves (cabbage). Apple, cherry, and pear *(Pyrus communis)* require vernalization, as do winter annuals such as wheat, barley, oat, and rye. Flowers such as foxglove *(Digitalis* spp.), tulip, crocus *(Crocus* spp.), narcissus *(Narcissus* spp.), and hyacinth *(Hyacinthus* spp.) need cold treatment, which may be administered to the bulbs, making them flower in warmer climates (at least for that growing season). However, they must be vernalized again to flower in subsequent years. In some of these bulbs, the cold treatment is needed to promote flower development after induction but not for induction itself. Sometimes vernalization helps plants such as pea and spinach to flower early, but it is not a requirement for flowering.

In onion, the bulbs are the commercial products harvested. Cold storage (near freezing) is used to preserve onion sets during the winter. This condition vernalizes the sets, which will flower and produce seed if planted in the spring. To obtain bulbs (no flowering), the sets should not be vernalized. Fortunately for growers, a phenomenon of *devernalization* occurs, in which exposure to warm temperatures above 27°C (80°F) for two to three weeks before planting will reverse the effect of vernalization. Onion producers are therefore able to store their sets and devernalize them for bulb production during the planting season.

Flowering in certain species is affected by a phenomenon called *thermal periodicity,* in which the degree of flowering is affected by alternating warm and cool temperatures during production. For example, tomato plants in the greenhouse can be manipulated for higher productivity by providing a certain cycle of temperature. Plants are exposed to a warm temperature of 27°C (80°F) during the day and cooler night temperatures of about 17 to 20°C (63 to 68°F). This treatment causes increased fruit production over and above what occurs at either temperature alone.

Photoperiodism   The effect of *photoperiodism* is discussed in detail in Chapter 4. As explained there, photoperiod is a phenomenon whereby day length controls certain plant processes. Further, it is actually the length of darkness, rather than light, that controls flowering, making the terminology a misnomer. Plants such as *Xanthium* require only one long-night (short-day) treatment to induce flowering, whereas others such as poinsettia *(Euphorbia pulcherrima),* chrysanthemum *(Chrysanthemum* spp.), and kalanchoe *(Kalanchoe* spp.) require several days (three to four). Although photoperiodism and vernalization both influence flowering, they seem to do so by different mechanisms and are not interchangeable. That is, a plant that needs both treatments will not flower if only one is provided.

Other Factors   Apart from duration of light, its intensity also affects flowering. Under the controlled environment of a greenhouse, light is provided in adequate amounts regarding intensity and duration. When potted flowering plants are purchased for the home, flowering may be poor or lacking because of the low light intensity in most homes. Flowering has been known to be stimulated under conditions of stress from drought or crowding. On the other hand, excessive moisture during the period of flower initiation in philodendrons causes a disproportionate number of seeds to be vegetative. Generally, woody plants tend to flower more copiously in spring if the preceding summer and fall were dry than if these seasons were wet.

Flower Initiation and Development

After being appropriately induced to flower, flowers are initiated from vegetative meristems that change into flowering meristems. This change is an irreversible process. The meristems differentiate into the flower parts. Proper temperature conditions are required for success, since high temperatures can cause flower abortion. The duration of the developmental process varies from one species to another. Time of flower initiation is important in horticulture. Flower primordia are laid down for a few to many months before flowering in many perennial species. For example, in the crocus, flowers in spring are produced from buds initiated in the previous summer. Flower primordia are initiated under a short photoperiod of August to September in plants such as June-bearing cultivars of strawberry.

Flowers can be chemically induced by externally applying certain growth regulators such as auxins. Commercial production of certain crops such as pineapple is aided by artificial flower induction. Other growth regulators are used to control the number of flowers set on a plant.

Pollination

Pollination is the transfer of pollen grains (male gametes) from the anther to the stigma of the flower. If the pollen deposited is from the anther of the recipient flower, or from another flower on the same plant, the pollination process is called *self-pollination*. Nut trees are mostly self-pollinated. Sometimes pollen from different sources is transferred to a flower, as is the case in most fruit trees. This type of pollination mechanism is called *cross-pollination*. Some species may be self-pollinated but have a fair capacity for outcrossing. When different cultivars are planted close together, there is a good chance for outcrossing. Wind and insects are agents of cross-pollination. Wind is particularly important for pollinating plants with tiny flowers such as grasses. Many fruit crops and vegetables are pollinated by insects that are attracted to the bright colors and nectaries of the flowers. In commercial production, growers of certain crops (such as orchard crops and strawberry) deliberately introduce hives of domestically raised bees to aid pollination for a good harvest. Without pollination, flowers will drop off, thus reducing crop yield.

Flowers that are specifically adapted to pollination by bees, wasps, and flies have showy and brightly colored petals. These flowers are usually blue or yellow in color. The nectary is located at the base of the corolla tube and has special structures that provide for convenient landing by bees. Bee flowers include rosemary (*Rosemary officinalis*), larkspur, lupines, cactus (*Echinocereus*), foxglove (*Digitalis purpurea*), California poppy (*Eschscholzia californica*), and orchids of the genus *Ophys*.

Flowers specifically adapted to pollination by moths and butterflies are typically white or pale in color so that they are visible to nocturnal moths. These flowers also have strong fragrance and a sweet, penetrating odor that is emitted after sunset. The nectary of such flowers is located at the base of a long and slender corolla tube. Such nectaries can be reached only by the long sucking mouth parts found in moths and butterflies. Examples of flowers associated with moths and butterflies include the yellow-flowered species of evening primrose (*Oenothera*), pink-flowered *Amarylis belladonna*, and tobacco (*Nicotiana* spp.).

Birds are associated with flowers that produce copious, thick nectar and have very colorful petals (especially red and yellow). These flowers are generally odorless. Examples are bird-of-paradise (*Strelitzia reginae*), columbine (*Aquilegia canadensis*), poinsettia (*Euphorbia pulcherima*), banana, fuchsia, passion flower, eucalyptus, and hibiscus.

Bats pollinate certain flowering species. Similar to "bird flowers," "bat flowers" are generally large and strong, with dull colors. Most of these flowers open at night, when nocturnal bats operate. Some flowers hang down on long stalks below the foliage of the plant. Bat flowers have strong fruitlike or musty scents. Examples are banana, mango, and organ-pipe cactus (*Stenocereus thurberi*).

Fertilization

Fertilization is the union of a sperm from the pollen with the egg of the ovary to form a *zygote*. For this union to occur, the pollen must grow rapidly down the style to unite with the egg in the ovary. In some plants, pollen from a flower is unable to fertilize the eggs

Fertilization
The union of two gametes to form a zygote.

of the same flower, a condition called *self-incompatibility*. These plants, of necessity, must then be cross-pollinated. Most fruit trees are self-incompatible (and thus self-sterile), which may be due to the inability of pollen to germinate on the stigma or unsynchronized maturity of male and female parts of the flower such that the pollen is shed after the stigma has ceased to be receptive or before it becomes receptive (*protandry* and *protogyny,* respectively). Some incompatibility mechanisms are genetic in origin. Plants such as date palms and willows are compelled to cross-pollinate because of a condition called *dioecy,* in which plants are either male or female. This condition arises because staminate and carpellate flowers occur on different plants. In monoecious plants such as corn and oak, both staminate and carpellate flowers are found on the same plant. The stigma should be mature and ready physically and chemically in terms of the presence of fluids in the right concentration and nutrient content, especially certain trace elements such as calcium and cobalt, to stimulate pollen germination.

Fruit Formation and Development

Fertilization normally precedes fruit formation. However, under certain conditions, the unfertilized egg develops into a fruit, the result being a seedless fruit. This event is called **parthenocarpy**. Since seedlessness is desired in certain fruits, horticulturalists sometimes deliberately apply certain growth regulators to plants to induce parthenocarpic fruits. In tomato, high temperatures have been known to induce seedlessness. Seeds appear to play a significant role in the growth and development of certain fruits. As such, if the embryo dies or pollination is not complete, some eggs will not be fertilized. Fruits formed as a result of this event are malformed, as is observed in cucumber and apple. In the case of stone fruits (e.g., cherry, peach, and apricot), the death of an embryo results in fruit drop. Each plant has an optimal number of fruits it can support in relation to vegetative matter (leaves). In commercial production, growers of orchard crops undertake what is called *fruit thinning,* whereby the number of fruits set is reduced artificially. Fruit set is adversely affected by improper temperature (high or low), low light intensity, and inadequate moisture and nutrition. As fruits develop, they enlarge and become filled with soluble solids.

Parthenocarpy
The development of fruit in the absence of fertilization.

Fruit Ripening

There are two basic patterns of fruit ripening—*nonclimacteric* and *climacteric*. Nonclimateric fruit ripening patterns occur in species in which fruits ripen only when they are attached to the parent plant (i.e., vine-ripen only). In these plants, (e.g., cherry, grape, cucumber) it is imperative that fruits are harvested only vine- or tree-ripened for the highest taste and flavor. The process of maturation and ripening is a gradual process that tapers off. Respiration rate in fruits occurs at a gradual rate. On the other hand, climateric fruit ripening is characterized by a rapid rise in respiration rate at the onset of ripening (called respiratory climacteric), followed by a gradual rate as ripening progresses. The fruits of such species (e.g., apple, banana, tomato) can be harvested prematurely and forced to ripen in the warehouse or allowed to vine- or tree-ripen.

Fruit ripening starts after enlargement ceases. The results of ripening are usually a change in color from the breakdown of chlorophyll to reveal other pigments, softening of the fruits (caused by breakdown of pectic substances that strengthen cell walls), and change in flavor (sour to sweet) (Figure 5–13). Ripening is a physiological event that signifies the end of fruit maturation and the onset of senescence. This event is associated with a sudden and marked increase in the rate of respiration of a fruit and the concomitant evolution of carbon dioxide. Levels of enzymes such as hydrolases, synthetases, and oxidases increase. Color change of the fruit exocarp is one event that is visible to the grower in many crops. The color change depends on the crop and cultivar. In banana, raw (unripe) fruit is green and while ripening goes through shades of color changes to yellow. The green chlorophyll is broken down to reveal the hitherto masked yellow color of carotenoids. The acceptable degree of ripening depends on the crop, the consumer (or use), and the marketing system. As ripening progresses, fruits become more

FIGURE 5–13 Ripening of plantain shows a gradual change in color from green to yellow. *(Source: George Acquaah)*

susceptible to fungal attack and rot due to the activities of enzymes. Fruits become softer. Ethylene is associated with ripening; it initiates and also accelerates the process.

Ethylene gas can be biosynthesized in the plant from methionine, an amino acid, with the aid of indoleacetic acid (IAA). In fact, high amounts of endogenous IAA can trigger the production of ethylene in large quantities. Wounding of a plant can stimulate the production of ethylene. Ethylene gas is used in the banana production industry to hasten ripening. Bananas are harvested and shipped green from production centers and are induced to ripen at their destination.

By volume, the CO_2 content of the atmosphere is only about 0.035 percent. To reduce the rate of fruit ripening, the carbon dioxide content of the storage room atmosphere is increased to about 2 to 5 percent, and the oxygen percentage is reduced from 20 percent to between 5 and 10 percent. This environment results in a reduced rate of respiration. Respiration rate can also be slowed by reducing the storage room temperature to about 5°C (41°F). Ripening fruits respire at a higher rate.

Senescence

Senescence precedes death, the final stage in the life cycle of a plant. This phase may occur naturally or be accelerated by environmental conditions including pathogenic attack. During senescence, cells and tissues deteriorate. The effect of senescence is physically visible. In this state of decline, yield progressively decreases and the plant becomes weak. The whole plant eventually dies, as in annuals; however, in deciduous perennials, the leaves drop in the fall season and the rest of the plant remains alive.

Senescence is a complex process that is not clearly understood. It occurs in patterns that appear to be associated with the life cycle of plants (annual, biennial, and perennial). In terms of the ultimate end of living organisms, plants may experience *partial senescence* (in which certain plant organs age and eventually die) or *complete senescence* (in which the whole plant ages and eventually dies). In annual plants, death occurs swiftly and suddenly, and senescence is complete. It occurs after maturity in fruits; dramatically, a whole field of annuals can deteriorate and die in concert in a short period. In biennials, the top portions of the plants wither after the first season and the bottom part remains dormant in the winter. Deciduous perennial plants shed their leaves in fall and resume active growth with a new flush of leaves in spring. Whereas senescence in animals is terminal, growers can employ the horticultural method of pruning (Chapter 19) and nutritional supplementation to revitalize an aged plant.

Plant *hormones* are organic molecules produced in small amounts in one (or several) parts of the plant and then transported to other parts called *target sites,* where they regulate plant growth and development (Figure 5–14). Because of this physiological role, plant hormones are also called *plant* **growth regulators,** a broad term that includes and is often associated with synthetic chemicals that have effects similar to hormones. Plant hormones are classified on the basis of their origin, *natural* or *synthetic.* Unlike animal hormones, which have specificity in site of production and target site, plant hormones tend to be more general with respect to both source and target. There are five basic groups of natural plant hormones: auxins, gibberellins, cytokinins, ethylene, and abscisic acid.

Growth Regulator
A natural or synthetic compound that in low concentrations controls growth responses in plants.

5.6.1   AUXINS

Auxins are produced in meristematic tissue such as root tips, shoot tips, apical buds, young leaves, and flowers. Their major functions include regulation of cell division and expansion, stem elongation, leaf expansion and abscission, fruit development, and branching of the stem. Auxins move very slowly and in a polar (unidirectional) fashion in plants. In shoots, the polarity is *basipetal* (toward the base of the stem and leaves), whereas it is *acropetal* (toward the tip) in roots. Auxin movement is not through defined channels such as sieve tubes (phloem) and vessels (xylem) but through phloem parenchyma cells and those bordering vascular tissues. This hormone is believed to move by an energy-dependent diffusion mechanism. The only known naturally occurring auxin is indole-3-acetic acid (IAA). Synthetic hormones that are auxins include 2,4-dichlorophenoxyacetic acid (2,4-D), which is actually an herbicide for controlling broadleaf weeds such as dandelion in lawns, α-naphthaleneacetic acid (NAA), and indole-3-butyric acid (IBA). Other uses of auxins in horticulture are as follows:

1. As rooting hormones to induce rooting (adventitious) in cuttings, especially when propagating woody plants.
2. To prevent fruit drop (control of abscission) in fruits trees (e.g., citrus) shortly before harvest.
3. To increase blossom and fruit set in tomato.
4. For fruit thinning to reduce excessive fruiting and thus produce larger fruits.
5. For defoliation before harvesting.
6. To prevent sprouting of stored produce, for example, in potato; when applied to certain tree trunks, basal sprouts are suppressed.

The concentration of auxin can be manipulated in horticultural plants in cultivation. Auxins are produced in relatively higher concentrations in the terminal buds than in other parts. This localized high concentration suppresses the growth of lateral buds located below the terminal bud. When terminal buds are removed (e.g., by a horticultural operation such as pruning or pinching), lateral buds are induced to grow because of the abolition of **apical dominance.** This technique makes a plant fuller in shape and more attractive (Figure 5–15). *Phototropism,* the bending of the growing point of a plant toward light, is attributed to the effect of auxins. Light causes auxin to be redistributed from the lit area to the dark side, where it causes cell elongation, leading to curvature (Figure 5–16).

Apical Dominance
The regulatory control of the terminal bud of a shoot in suppressing the development of lateral buds below it.

FIGURE 5–14 Selected synthetic hormones.

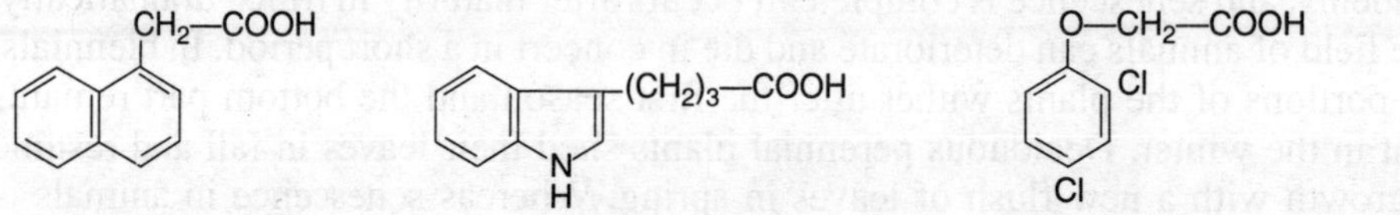

α-Naphthaleneacetic acid (NAA)

Indole-3-butyric acid (IBA)

2,4-Dichlorophenoxyacetic acid (2,4-D)

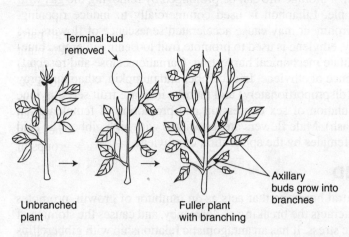

FIGURE 5–15 The effect of abolishing apical dominance in plants.

Terminal bud removed

Axillary buds grow into branches

Unbranched plant

Fuller plant with branching

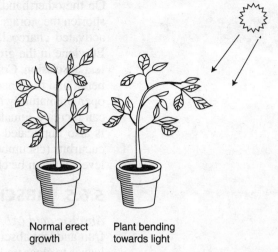

FIGURE 5–16 Phototropism displayed by a plant located near a window.

Normal erect growth

Plant bending towards light

5.6.2 GIBBERELLINS

Gibberellins are produced in the shoot apex and occur also in embryos and cotyledons of immature seeds and roots. They occur in seed, flowers, germinating seed, and developing flowers. The highest concentration occurs in immature seeds. This class of hormones promotes cell division, stem elongation, seed germination (by breaking dormancy), flowering, and fruit development. In carrot (*Daucus carota*) and cabbage (*Brassica oleracea* var. *Capitata*), among others, exposure to long days or cold is required to induce flowering (*bolting*). Application of gibberellic acid eliminates the need for these environmental treatments. Gibberellins are noted for their ability to overcome dwarfism in plants, allowing compact plants to develop to normal heights. Gibberellic acid is used to induce seedlessness in grapes; the size of seedless grapes is also increased through the application of this hormone. An example is gibberellic acid (GA_1), one of the numerous (more than seventy) closely related terpenoid compounds that occur naturally.

5.6.3 CYTOKININS

Cytokinins are hormones that stimulate cell division and lateral bud development. They have been isolated mainly from actively dividing tissue. Cytokinins occur in embryonic or meristematic organs. Examples of natural cytokinins are isopentenyl adenine (IPA) and zeatin (Z). Zeatin, isolated from the kernels of corn, is the most active naturally occurring cytokinin. Kinetin was first isolated from yeast. Benzyl adenine (BA) is also a commonly used cytokinin. Cytokinins interact with auxins to affect various plant functions. A high cytokinin-auxin ratio (i.e., low amounts of auxin, especially IAA) promotes lateral bud development because of reduced apical dominance. Relatively high amounts of auxin induce root formation in callus. The principal role of cytokinins in plant physiology is the promotion of cell division. They are important in tissue culture work and are more effective when IAA is also added. The effect of cytokinins when used this way is to cause cells to remain meristematic (undifferentiated) in culture, producing large amounts of callus tissue.

5.6.4 ETHYLENE

Ethylene is a gas found in the tissues of ripening fruits and stem nodes. It promotes fruit ripening and leaf abscission. In the horticultural industry, ethylene is used to aid in uniform ripening of apple, pineapple, and banana, and in changing the rind color of fruits (as in orange and grapefruit from green to yellow and tomato from green to uniform red).

On the other hand, ripening apples produce this gas in large quantities, which tends to shorten the storage life of fruits. Storage life can be prolonged by removing the gas with activated charcoal, for example. Ethaphon is used commercially to induce ripening. Ethylene in the growing environment may cause accelerated senescence of flowers and leaf abscission. Commercially, ethylene is used to promote fruit loosening in grape, blueberry, and blackberry to facilitate mechanical harvesting. Carnations close and rosebuds open prematurely in the presence of ethylene. In cucumber and pumpkin, ethaphon spray can increase female flowers (disproportionately) and thereby increase fruit set. Ethylene is also implicated in the regulation of sex expression and promotion of femaleness in cucurbits (cucumber and squash). Male flowers are associated with high gibberellic acid levels but can be changed to females by the application of ethylene.

5.6.5 ABSCISIC ACID

Abscisic acid (ABA) is a natural hormone that acts as an inhibitor of growth, promotes fruit and leaf abscission, counteracts the breaking of dormancy, and causes the stomata of leaves to close under moisture stress. It has an antagonistic relationship with gibberellins and other growth-stimulating hormones; for example, ABA-induced seed dormancy may be reversed by applying gibberellins. Commercial application of ABA is limited partly by its high cost and unavailability.

Plant hormones may also be classified based on their effect on plant growth as *stimulants* or *retardants*. Cytokinins and gibberellins have a stimulating effect on growth and development, whereas ABA inhibits growth. Alfalfa is known to produce the alcohol *triacontanol,* which stimulates growth. Naturally occurring inhibitors include benzoic acid, coumarin, and cinnamic acid. A number of synthetic growth retardants are used in producing certain horticultural plants. Their effect is mainly a slowing down of cell division and elongation. As such, instead of a plant growing tall, with long internodes, it becomes short (dwarf), compact, fuller, and aesthetically more pleasing. Examples of these commercial growth retardants include the following:

1. Daminozide (marketed under trade names such as Alar and B-nine): plants that respond to it include poinsettia, azalea, petunia, and chrysanthemum.
2. Chlormequat (CCC, cycocel): retards plant height in poinsettia, azalea, and geraniums.
3. Ancymidol (A-Rest): effective in reducing height in bulbs, such as Easter lily and tulip, as well as chrysanthemum and poinsettia.
4. Paclobutrazol (Bonzi): used to reduce plant height in bedding plants including impatiens, pansy, petunia, and snapdragon.
5. Maleic hydrazide: used to prevent sprouting of onions and potatoes.

5.7 NONPATHOGENIC (PHYSIOLOGICAL) PLANT DISORDERS

Horticultural plants are plagued by numerous diseases and pests, some of which can completely kill the affected plants. Generally, if a grower observes certain precautions and adopts sound cultural practices, the chance of experiencing a disease problem in plants is reduced drastically. Some diseases are endemic in certain areas. As such, plants that are susceptible to such diseases should not be grown there. If they must be grown in such areas, resistant cultivars should be used; otherwise, disease control measures such as spraying with pesticides will be required for successful production. Other cultural observances such as using high-quality, clean seeds; weed control; right timing of planting; phytosanitation; and preplanting seed treatment will minimize the occurrence of diseases in a production enterprise.

However, many other disorders are *nonpathogenic* (not caused by pathogens) in origin. They are caused by improper or inadequate plant growth environmental conditions—pertaining to light, moisture, temperature, nutrients, and air—as well as improper cultural operation, involving compaction of soil and pesticide application, for example. Since these disorders are nonpathogenic, their effect is localized and usually within complete control of the grower. Further, since plant production under uncontrolled environmental conditions is subject to the uncertainties of the weather, certain disorders are unpredictable and sometimes difficult to prevent.

This section is devoted to nonpathogenic disorders, many of which are weather related. Chapter 4 contains related information. Plants are not affected equally by adverse weather conditions. An important caution to observe when inspecting plants for disorders is not to hastily attribute every disorder to parasitic or pathogenic causes and exercise caution before initiating pest-control measures.

5.7.1 WEATHER-RELATED PLANT DISORDERS

The following are different categories of weather factors and how they inflict damage on horticultural plants when they prevail in adverse levels. It should be emphasized that these factors often interact or interplay in producing an effect. The role of these factors in plant growth has been discussed previously.

Temperature

Extreme Cold Plants in temperate zones may suffer one of two kinds of injury from extremely cold temperatures. Similar to frostbite in humans, plants may suffer from *frost damage* when temperatures suddenly drop below seasonable levels. Affected plants may show signs of wilting overnight. When this cold strikes during the blooming period, the plant may lose most or all of its flowers. Frost damage occurs more frequently in younger tissues, and herbaceous species are more susceptible than woody ones.

A much more severe cold damage called *winter kill* occurs when plants are subjected to prolonged periods of freezing temperatures. Under such conditions, branches may die back (tips wilt); when roots are severely impaired, however, the plant may die. In evergreens, such as pine, extreme cold may cause the foliage to "burn" (turn brown).

Extreme Heat Microclimates, both natural and human-made, occur in the landscape in places such as underneath trees and the eaves of homes. Brick structures absorb heat during the day and radiate it at night. This property is advantageous during the cold months, because radiated heat protects plants in the vicinity from frost. However, in hot months, these same walls, especially those that face south, can create extremely hot microclimates, thereby injuring plants within their spheres of influence. Similarly, the hot asphalt of parking lots, concrete, and some pavements can radiate intense heat that damages plants. Heat-sensitive plants may show marginal scorching of leaves.

Moisture

Excess Moisture Excess moisture overwhelms the pore spaces in the soil leading to waterlogged conditions. Poorly drained soils create anaerobic conditions that lead to root death (root rot), if they persist for an extended period. Plants vary in their response to poor drainage. Root rot eventually results in plant death through stages, starting with stunted growth and yellowing and wilting. Excess moisture received after a period of drought might cause tubers and roots of root crops, as well as the walls of fruits such as tomato, to crack.

Excess Dryness (Drought) Lack of moisture usually is expressed as wilting of plant leaves.

Low Humidity The tips and margins of leaves of tropical plants brown (tip burn) under conditions of low humidity. This browning is caused by rapid transpiration, which overwhelms the rate at which water is moved through the leaf to the ends. As a result, water fails to reach the edges of the leaf, leading to drying and browning.

Light

Intense Light Strong and direct sunlight may scorch certain plants. Potted plants placed in south-facing windows receive direct sunlight unless the presence of a tree in the direction of the sun's rays filters the light. Intense light also causes the foliage of certain plants to bleach and look pale and sickly.

Low Light Inadequate sunlight induces etiolated growth (spindly) and yellowing of leaves. Plant vigor is reduced, and leaves drop prematurely.

Nutrients

Nutrient Deficiency Generally, an inadequate supply of any of the major plant nutrients, especially nitrogen, causes plants to be stunted in growth and leaves to yellow (chlorosis). Deciduous plant leaves may prematurely senesce and defoliate. In addition to yellowing, lack of potassium shows up later as marginal leaf burns of leaves; young and expanding leaves show purple discoloration when phosphorus is lacking in the soil. Calcium deficiency in tomato shows up as *blossom end rot*.

Nutrient Excess Excess acidic soils may cause excess availability of trace elements (e.g., iron and aluminum), which can lead to toxicity in certain plants.

5.7.2 HUMAN-RELATED ACTIVITIES

Industrial Production

Industrialized and heavily populated areas often experience excessive amounts of chemical pollutants in the air. These toxic gases damage horticultural plants. Acute amounts of sulfur dioxide cause chlorosis and browning of leaves and sometimes necrosis (cell destruction and death). Fluoride injury has been recorded in sensitive plants such as ponderosa pine as reddish-brown bands that appear between necrotic and green tissue. Ozone is a major pollutant that is produced primarily from the photochemical action of sunlight on automobile emission. It can cause chlorosis and necrosis in a wide variety of plants.

Pesticide Application

Improper application of pesticides may cause collateral damage to cultivated plants. Applying sprays on a windy day may cause the chemicals to drift onto desirable plants, resulting in deformed leaves, discoloration, and in some cases death of tissue and possibly the entire plant. Herbicide damage appears suddenly and may last through the cropping season. Often, the symptom is bleaching; in severe cases, it may be followed by leaf drop. Unlike the effect of herbicides, collateral damage from insecticides shows up as browning of the foliage.

Fertilizer Application

Chemical fertilizers are frequently applied to houseplants or outdoor plants in production. Eagerness for good yield may lead some growers to overfertilize their plants, resulting in a buildup of excessive fertilizer in the soil. High amounts of salts create *sodic* soil conditions. A higher salt-soil concentration than root fluids can cause dehydration of roots. Instead of the roots absorbing soil moisture, they become depleted of moisture. Plant growth is inhibited under such conditions, and plants wilt (as they would under drought conditions) and eventually die.

SUMMARY

The variety of activities that have been described to occur at various phases in plant growth and development are the results of certain growth processes. These processes provide the raw materials and the energy required for building new tissues and nurturing them to maturity. The major processes include photosynthesis, respiration, transpiration, and translocation. Photosynthesis is the process by which green plants manufacture food from water and nutrients absorbed from the soil and light energy. Photosynthates are translocated to other parts of the plant where, through the process of respiration, the energy locked up in the food is released for use by the plants. Gaseous exchange between the plant and its environment occurs through pores in the leaves called stomata. Plants lose moisture by the process of transpiration. Plant development and growth occur in phases described by a sigmoid curve—a rapid logarithmic growth phase, followed by a decreasing growth phase, and then a steady growth phase. Plants have two general phases in their life cycles—a vegetative phase and a reproductive phase. Based on the duration of the life cycle, plants can be categorized into annuals, biennials, perennials, and monocarps. In flowering plants, a reproductive phase follows a vegetative phase. Flowers are produced and eventually become pollinated and fertilized to produce seed and fruit. When plants are subject to adverse conditions in the environment, they develop a variety of physiological disorders such as wilting, drying, cracking, and abnormal growth.

REFERENCES AND SUGGESTED READING

Galston, A. W. 1980. *Life of the green plant,* 3d ed. Englewood Cliffs, N.J.: Prentice Hall.

Nicklel, L. G. 1982. *Plant growth regulators: Agricultural uses.* New York: Springer-Verlag.

Noggle, G., and G. F. Fritz. 1983. *Introductory plant physiology,* 2d ed. Englewood Cliffs, N.J.: Prentice Hall.

Wareing, P. F., and I. D. J. Phillips. 1985. *Growth and differentiation in plants.* New York: Pergamon Press.

More, R., and W. D. Clark. 1995. *Botany: Form and function.* Dubuque, Iowa: Wm. C. Brown Publishers.

Raven, P. H., R. F. Evert, and S. E. Eichhorn. 1992. *Biology of plants,* 5th ed. New York: Worth Publishers.

Photosynthesis
http://www.emc.maricopa.edu/faculty/farabee/BIOBK/BioBookPS.html

Photosynthesis
http://www.biology.arizona.edu/biochemistry/problem_sets/photosynthesis_l/ photosynthesis_l.html

PRACTICAL EXPERIENCE

1. *Translocation.* Obtain a young tree (about a year old) and girdle the midsection by carefully removing the bark and making sure to scrape away the phloem layer completely. Maintain the plant under proper growth conditions in which it will be able to photosynthesize adequately. After some time, the upper edge of the girdle should begin to swell from accumulation of photosynthates being translocated down to other parts of the plant from the leaf.

2. *Growth regulators.* Cytokinins and gibberellins stimulate plant growth, and abscisic acid is an inhibitor. Commercial growth regulators are available. Plant geraniums in pots and divide the pots into two groups, each containing plants of equal size. To one set apply a growth regulator (e.g., Cycocel) and leave the other as a control. You may also apply various concentrations of the hormone. Observe the changes in growth after a period by comparing hormone-treated plants with controls.

3. *Apical dominance (pinching).* Obtain young poinsettia plants. Pinch off the apical buds in some plants and leave others unpinched. After a period, observe the changes in the plants' branching.
4. *Fruit ripening.* Obtain two bunches of green bananas. Place one bunch in the open air in the laboratory and tie up another bunch in an airtight plastic bag. The latter will trap the ethylene gas in the bag and accelerate ripening.

OUTCOMES ASSESSMENT

1. Discuss how a horticulturalist may apply the sigmoid growth curve in managing crop production.
2. What crop production management practices may be adopted to optimize photosynthesis?
3. Distinguish between, giving examples plants that use the C_3 and C_4 carbon dioxide fixation in food manufacture.
4. Discuss the roles and importance of aerobic respiration and anaerobic respiration in plant growth and development.
5. Define the following terms, giving their importance in horticultural industry:
    a. Physiological dormancy
    b. Physiological maturity
    c. Vernalization
    d. Transpiration
6. Discuss the occurrence of physiological plant disorders in crop production and their economic importance.
7. Discuss the physiological role of ethylene in plant growth and development, and its application in the horticultural industry.
8. Describe the characteristic features of the embryonic stage of plant development, pointing out how they impact management of plant production.

6

Breeding Horticultural Plants

PURPOSE AND EXPECTED OUTCOMES

This chapter is designed to review basic genetic principles and concepts and how they are applied in the breeding of new horticultural plants.

After studying this chapter, the student should be able to

1. Discuss the importance of genetics in horticultural plant improvement.
2. Explain the genetic basis of biological variation.
3. Describe and discuss the steps in a simple plant breeding program.
4. Discuss the use of molecular biotechnological tools in plant improvement.
5. Discuss specific practical applications of classical genetics and molecular biology in plant improvement.

OVERVIEW

Plant breeding or improvement is a science and an art. Genetics is the underlying science of plant breeding. In fact, breeders are sometimes referred to as applied geneticists. They try to nudge nature to the advantage of humans by manipulating plants to perform according to their schedule and needs. They manipulate the nature (heredity) of plants and thereby create new types that are adapted to new environments (nurture) and produce higher-quality products that are disease resistant. Every year, new and improved flower and vegetable garden cultivars are released by plant breeders for use by growers. These are products of calculated and deliberate manipulation of plants by scientists who understand the genetics and environment of those plants.

As agents of heritable change, plant breeders are sometimes also described as applied evolutionists. This chapter is devoted to describing how these scientists operate, highlighting the role genetics plays in their endeavors. This is not to say that plant breeding is an exact science; it is also an art, as already stated. Experience (breeder's eye) is a valuable asset in breeding. Conventional or classical methods of breeding depend more on this artistic component. However, thanks to advances in science and technology, new and more effective methods of plant improvement are now available to breeders. Instead of

185

manipulating plants at the whole-plant level, breeders are able to manipulate plants directly at the DNA level (*molecular biotechnology*), thereby expanding the degree to which they are able to affect the course of nature. It should be emphasized that conventional and modern tools are used side by side for best results. As such, discussions in this chapter include both types of techniques.

6.1 WHAT IS PLANT BREEDING?

Plant breeding (plant improvement) is the science and art of manipulating plant heredity to develop new and improved plant types for use by society. It is a deliberate effort by humans to nudge nature, with respect to the heredity of plants, to an advantage. Plant breeders manipulate plants to address specific needs of society.

1. *Address world food, feed, and nutritional needs.* Breeders develop new fruits, vegetables, and food crops that have higher nutritional value. Cereals are low in amino acids lysine and threonine, while rice lacks pro-vitamin A. Nutritional deficiency disorders such as blindness and rickets abound in regions where foods are staples. Breeders work to enhance the nutritional value of such foods, an example being the high-lysine corn.
2. *Address the food needs of a growing population.* As the world population continues to explode, the world food supplies must be expanded to meet the needs of society. Plant breeders develop new varieties that are higher yielding to increase agricultural productivity. For example, the yield of corn rose from about 2,000 kg/ha in the 1940s to 6,000 kg/ha in the 1990s.
3. *The need to adapt plants to environmental stresses.* Environmental stresses may be biotic or abiotic. Plant breeders develop new varieties that are adapted to abiotic environmental stresses like drought, cold, acid soils and salty soils, and biotic ones like diseases and insect pests. This action expands the production areas of plants.
4. *The need to adapt crops to specific production systems.* Different varieties are needed for different production systems. For example, a different variety of tomato is needed for hand harvesting, and another for mechanized production.
5. *Satisfying industrial and other end-use requirements.* The quality requirements for fresh produce meant for the table are different from the requirements for the food-processing industry. Potato for chipping should have low sugar content to avoid the browning from the caramelization of sugar upon heating that is undesirable. Different varieties are bred for baking, cooking, and fries.
6. *Developing new horticultural plants.* Apart from fruit and vegetables, horticulture is identified with ornamentals for beautifying the indoors and outdoors. Plant breeders develop new varieties of flowers each year.

6.2 THE ART AND SCIENCE OF PLANT BREEDING

Plant breeding is firmly rooted in science, depending on principles of genetics especially, as well as biology, botany, statistics, biochemistry, agronomy, to name other major disciplines. Plant breeding is like evolution, the theory proposed by Charles Darwin to explain biological variation. The three principles of evolution are variation, heredity, and selection. Without variation, there can be no evolution! Natural variation arises through mutations. Some variations are more useful for survival than others. Natural selection will discriminate among variability to advance the ones that most fit the prevailing environment. Through heredity, the offspring of the selected individuals will resemble the parents more than other unrelated individuals.

Similarly, there can be no plant breeding without variation. If the breeder intends to develop a new variety of tomato that is short, there must be a source of the genes for shortness to access. Otherwise, such a desire cannot be fulfilled. Whereas evolution depends on random mutations to create variability, plant breeders can assemble and create variability through the use of specific techniques. Then, they impose artificial selection to pick out individuals that exhibit the traits of interest to advance and eventually develop a new variety for use by producers.

The significant differences between evolution and plant breeding include the duration of the processes. Evolution takes millions of years to bring about change in a direction; plant breeders take about ten years (or more or less), depending on the species, to develop a new variety. Evolution is driven by nature, following the path of chance. Plant breeders have a definite plan and objective in their breeding program, not leaving anything to chance. Selection is artificial (by humans–breeders) not by nature. The product of evolution is determined primarily by survivability as dictated by the environment. In plant breeding, the goal is first the value of the product or outcome to society. The variety may not survive on its own in nature, but modern advances in crop production allow us to provide supplemental inputs to overcome natural environmental factors, or to design plants to adapt to specific natural environments to produce desired products.

Plant breeding is not an exact science. Whereas genetic principles are depended upon in modern plant breeding, skill, intuition, good judgment, and keen observation are desirable qualities for successful plant breeding. Together, these qualities are called the "breeder's eye." Visual selection is the primary method of discriminating among variation in plant breeding.

There are two basic approaches to breeding—conventional and nonconventional. Conventional plant breeding entails using the sexual process to transfer and assemble genes of interest in a new plant individual. Traditionally, this occurs via crossing selected parents. Nonconventional plant breeding can circumvent the sexual process as a means of gene transfer. Genes of interest can be obtained from their sources and physically incorporated into the genetic system of another plant. Such genetic feats are accomplished in the often-controversial plant genetic manipulation called **genetic engineering.**

Genetic Engineering
The manipulation of genes, composed of DNA, to create heritable changes in biological organisms and products that are useful to people, living things, or the environment.

6.3 THE CONCEPT OF GENETIC MANIPULATION

The underlying principle of plant genetic manipulation by breeders can be summarized by the following simplified genetic relationship:

$$Phenotype = Genotype + Environment\ (P = G + E)$$

This means that what you see (phenotype or trait) is the product of the interaction of the genes that condition or control the trait (genotype), and the environment in which the genes are being expressed.

If you do not like what you see, you can change the genotype, the environment, or both. Changing the genotype amounts to developing a new variety by manipulating plant genetics to assemble genes in a new genetic matrix. Such a change is permanent and heritable. One can also change the environment. This is largely what agronomists do. Changing the environment includes providing production inputs like fertilizers, irrigation, and pesticides. Such changes are temporary, for if you desire to retain the level of expression of the trait (e.g., if you want to maintain the yield level), you must resupply the environmental factors. Their effects are not heritable and cannot be passed on from one generation to the next.

Plant breeders are interested in heritable changes, but, a new and improved variety is only as good as its environment. If you invest money to purchase a new and high-yielding hybrid seed, you will get the potential high yield inherent in the variety by virtue of the genes assembled by breeding methods, only if you provide an environment that supports high performance.

Application Of Tissue Culture In Modern Genetic Improvement Of Daylily (Hemerocallis sp).

Kanyand Matand[1], George Acquaah[2], Caula A. Beyl[3], Khairy M. Soliman[4], Stephen Garton[5]

Center for Biotechnology Research and Education[1], Department of Agriculture and Natural Resources[2], Langston University, Langston, OK; College of Agriculture and Natural Resources[3], Department of Plant Sciences[5], University of Tennessee, Knoxville, TN; Department of Plant and Soil Science[4], Alabama A & M University, Normal, AL.

[1]Corresponding author: Kmatand@luresext. edu.

Importance Of Daylily And Classical Breeding Challenges

Daylily (Hemerocallis sp) is a popular perennial monocot valued for the beauty of the colors and shapes of its flowers. It is also used as a vegetable in China. As in most crops, the improvement of daylily is usually achieved through classical breeding. This method has been used to produce many new cultivars with a wide range of colors (Stout, 1986). However, the time required to produce and introduce a new cultivar is very long, because only few new plants are produced annually under natural conditions (Apps and Heuser, 1975; Meyer, 1976). Even with the use of improved horticultural techniques whereby daylily is propagated per crown cottage, only 20 to 30 or a little more new plants could be obtained from hybrids per year in the greenhouse environment (Traub, 1936). There are also other limitations that have not been successfully and speedily resolved through classical breeding alone. For instance, after blooming, daylily flowers last only one day (Panavas et al., 1999) despite the fact that its beauty, thus its value, is based upon this organ. The approach of classical breeding to address this problem was to lengthen the flowering season. It has also been established that an increase in ubiquitin protein content speeds up the wilting of daylily flowers (Courtney et al., 1994). Thus the lack of longer flower life remains an unsolved challenge that might be tackled through modern techniques.

Ideal Daylily Tissue Culture Method For The Crop Improvement

Tissue culture is not required for genetic transfer in crops (Bent, 2000). However, efficient and large scale transformations of crops have been achieved via tissue culture (Vain, 2007). Unlike other tissue culture-free methods, transformation methods via tissue culture are generally reliable, reproducible, and can involve large scale plant materials for transformation with subsequent regeneration, thus, are very efficient. An efficient and reproducible tissue culture method in daylily should produce a high frequency of new shoots in a short period of time, preferably involving a few steps. It should induce repetitive or multiple shoots or embryos with a minimum amount of variationS. The method should also offer a wide choice of explant tissues such that the availability of tissues should not be restricted to the reproductive cycle of the crop.

APPLICATION, CHALLENGES, AND PROSPECTS OF DAYLILY TISSUE CULTURE FOR GENETIC IMPROVEMENT

The cloning and subsequent transfer into plants of ubiquitin inhibitor gene(s) and perhaps other genes including those influencing flower color and forms, might prolong the life and diversity of the color and shape of the flowers. In addition, the use of modern techniques might also avoid the incorporation of unwanted genes into the crop, which could occur during conventional plant breeding.

MERISTEM AND INFLORESCENCE EXPLANTS AND RELATED CHALLENGES

In daylily, methods for *in vitro* organogenesis have been established (Aziz *et al.*, 2003; Krikorian and Kann, 1981; Meyer, 1976). The vegetative meristem can be used as explant of choice for *in vitro* plant regeneration (Smith and Krekorian, 1991). However, since it is located underground, meristematic tissues are difficult to obtain in a sterile condition and excision destroys the mother plant (Meyer, 1976). Of all the floral tissues investigated, the use of the whole inflorescence has become common in part because it is available en masse and less difficult to obtain in sterile condition. Also, it is relatively easier to manipulate the whole inflorescence than petals or sepals. However, limitations with the use of floral tissues are obvious. For instance, those tissues are not available all year-round and, further, they are reproductive cycle dependent. Thus, this limits the freedom of scientists working with daylily to plan and effectively carry out experiments when needed.

LEAF EXPLANT POTENTIAL

Leaf tissue may be the key to overcome such problems because: (1) with some exceptions, it is the only daylily organ above-ground that is available year-round; (2) it might be easier to obtain such tissues in sterile condition; (3) the use of the leaf as an explant might not affect the survival of the mother plant; and (4) the fact that leaf is flat and flexible might make it a more suitable target for particle bombardment and gene transfer, than the round and tough inflorescence. Further, it might be much easier to produce leaf discs providing an efficient wound area for *Agrobacterium* infection than the inflorescence for gene transformation. Despite all these advantages, the use of leaf tissue in daylily tissue culture is limited. This tissue is flexible and has successfully been used to produce protoplasts for subsequent production of callus and shoots (Ling and Sauve, 1995). However, the induction of shoots (Matand, 1999) or callus directly from leaf tissue has not been widely investigated (Matand, 1999).

MORPHOGENIC POTENCY OF SELECTED GROWTH REGULATORS

Morphogenesis in daylily has been manipulated using mostly common types of growth regulators such as NAA (naphthaleneacetic acid), 2, 4-D (2, 4-dichlorophenylacetic acid), BA (6-benzyl aminopurine), and KIN (kinetin), (Aziz *et al.*, 2003; Griesbach, 1989; Meyer, 1976). Thidiazuron (TDZ) has been proven to be a very powerful cytokinin. It is up to 10,000 times more active than DPU (N, N'-diphenylurea), and 10 times more active than zeatin (Pierik, 1987). In general, thidiazuron is 1000 times more active than other standard growth regulators (Huettman and Preece, 1993). The use of TDZ in daylily is also limited (Matand, 1999, Aziz *et al.*, 2003) but has several advantages. TDZ is characterized by a unique rapid induction of repetitive multiple shoots across explants and plant species, which needs to be fully explored also in daylily. This chemical has consistently induced shoots faster in higher frequencies than other cytokinins commonly used. TDZ is successfully used across species to induce direct as well as indirect adventitious shoots (Matand and Prakash, 2007). It is used for shoot regeneration even at lower concentrations. The lowest TDZ recommended concentrations (established after investigation) in plant propagation is 10^{-8}M (Huetteman and Preece, 1993). TDZ concentrations lower than the preceding proposed is also applicable. Reports also suggest that when TDZ is being used for the first time in a new species, the initial experiment should be designed using 10^{-7} M as a middle concentration and evaluating two orders of magnitude above and below that concentration. The normally recommended concentration range of TDZ activity is 10^{-9} to 10^{-5} M (Huetteman and Preece, 1993). However, depending on the species, this range might proliferate more calli than shoots. Thus to reduce callus proliferation in favor of shoot growth, it is recommended to use concentrations up to 10^{-4}M (Huetteman and Preece, 1993).

PHYSICAL STATE OF THE MEDIUM

In some plant species, the success or failure of tissue culture might depend upon whether a liquid or an agar medium is employed (Murashige, 1974). For, instance, most bromeliads studied in laboratories could be started in cultures only in a liquid nutrient (Murashige, 1974). This has been true also with the cattleman orchid (Murashige, 1974). In contrast, shoot tip cultures of *Asparagus* (the closest relative of daylily) and *Gerbera* required initiation on agar gel medium (Chen and Galston, 1967). It has also been reported that the same species may require a different physical form of medium during each of the three growth stages *in vitro*. This change of the physical state of the nutrient medium in progressive stages of culture has been illustrated with *Asparagus officinalis* and *Daucus carota* (Murashige, 1974). In daylily, Krihorian and Kann (1981) demonstrated that besides semi-solid, liquid medium could be used to produce plants. Their studies suggested that the cultural conditions might be cultivar specific. They reported also that it is possible to use both solid and liquid medium to induce new shoots in daylily. Liquid medium was preferred over solid medium because of its more efficient use of space and the enhancement in shoot production (Krihorian and Kann, 1981). Also liquid medium has the capacity of diluting plant cell-excreted chemical toxic waste compared to solid medium. In liquid, explant cells are fully exposed to nutrients than on solid medium. However, their report failed to determine a shoot production ratio of liquid to solid medium in daylily. A rationale in the use of either physical medium needs further investigation in crop.

THE INFLUENCE OF TRANSFORMATION METHOD
IN REGENERATION EXPLANT SELECTION

As indicated earlier, the selection of tissue culture method one should utilize for modern gene transfer into daylily should be dictated by the transformation technique. For instance, callus cells are more suitable for particle bombardment because a large number of cells that might be susceptible to subsequent plant regeneration can be efficiently arranged on the target plate for efficient gene blasts. This is also true for leaf tissue, except that in most cases plant regeneration is more likely to occur at leaf wound sites than non-wound areas. However, practically leaf wound cells are less likely to be hit with target DNA. Therefore, it is recommended that leaf discs be lightly wounded across lamina to enhance chances of regenerating transgenic plants. The latter might not be necessary when the regeneration protocol involves complete de-differentiation of explant tissue. When callus is used for *Agrobacterium,* although some success might be possible, it should be remembered that (1) such bacteria are less infectious of monocots, (2) callus cells especially those that have lasted longer in *in vitro* culture produce very limited phenolic compounds, as those from wound response. The possibilities become even more restricted when cell suspension cultures are proposed for *Agrobacterium* infection; because limited phenolic compounds produced by cells are instantly diluted in the liquid medium. Phenolic compounds from fresh plant tissue wounds have been reported to be essential in carrying out special molecular signals that are thought to activate *Vir* genes in *Agrobacterium* for subsequent T-DNA excision and transfer into plant cells (Anand *et al.*, 2007). Huge amounts of phenolic compounds are usually associated with fresh tissues. Thus, fresh tissues such as leaf, stem, or inflorescence are generally recommended as explants for *Agrobacterium* infection.

DAYLILY EXPERIMENTAL APPROACHES

This report also focuses on the investigation of eight-month-old callus potential for shoot regeneration, using kinetin or TDZ with or without NAA (see treatment layout Table 1). **Plant material:** Initial callus was developed from inflorescence tissues of daylily cultivar 'Incredible Charm' using Meyer (1976)'s protocol. This cultivar was selected from the Alabama A & M University's daylily germplasm (Normal, Alabama), which comprised a dozen of cultivars. Most of them were obtained as gifts from local growers in North Alabama. This crop had been maintained *in vitro* for eight months on Murashige and Skoog (MS) medium (1962). During the first seven months and half callus and very lmited shoots were induced and maintained on MS medium containing 2.68 μM NAA+0.46 μM KIN (Meyer, 1976), and then callus was subcultured onto basal MS medium for maintenance for the two weeks preceding this study. It was such callus that was used to initiate cultures for the present report. **Culture media:** Murashige and Skoog (1962) medium with the addition of myo-inositol (100 mg/l), sugar (30 mg/l), and agar (4 g/l) was used. The pH of the medium was adjusted to 5.8 prior to autoclaving. Three growth regulators including NAA, kinetin, and TDZ at various combinations, as shown in Table 1, were included in the media. Morphogenesis in daylily is commonly achieved using two types of media with respect to the kinds and concentrations of growth regulators that include (1) MS medium including 2.68 μM NAA+0.46 μM KIN, generally used to induce cell organization and differentiation (Meyer, 1976); (2) MS medium including 50 μM NAA+0.46 μM KIN, generally used for cell growth and division (Meyer, 1976). Those media are usually used to induce plants through callus phase. **Cultural conditions:** All cultures were conditioned similarly. 400 mg of callus was placed into a baby jar and used as a single experimental unit. Twenty mls of agar medium were assigned to each jar prior to culturing callus. Twenty experimental units were randomly assigned to each growth regulator treatment. Cultures were incubated in growth chamber at $25 \pm 30°C$ under 16h/8h photoperiod and subcultured on similar medium every three weeks. Data were collected at two months of culture for each experimental unit.

TABLE 1 Treatments layout

NAA(M)	Kinetin(M)		Thidiazuron (M)	
	0	46×10^{-8}	10^{-7}	10^{-8}
0	*	*	*	*
2.68×10^{-8}	*	*	*	*

However, regular observations of the experiment were made as needed. During the visual inspection, the physical growth and development of each explant were assessed. Assessment criteria included callus cell division, and/or organ formation, color development from callus, contamination of some tissue or media, development of vitrification, and the intensity of phenolic compounds waste accumulation.

THE INFLUENCE OF TDZ ON DAYLILY CALLUS ORGAN FORMATION

Route 3 on the flow chart for daylily plant regeneration shown in Figure 1,was the approach applied in this investigation. A unique aspect of this investigation was to assess the potential of older callus (eight-month old) for shoot induction. This has a special meaning as older callus cells are known for losing their morphogenic potential and inducing more variations compared to fresh younger callus. The study showed that large callus multiplication was observed primarily from treatments that included at least one growth hormone as shown in Table 2. However, average or limited callus growth was observed from control samples.

FIGURE 1 Daylily morphogenic flow-chart

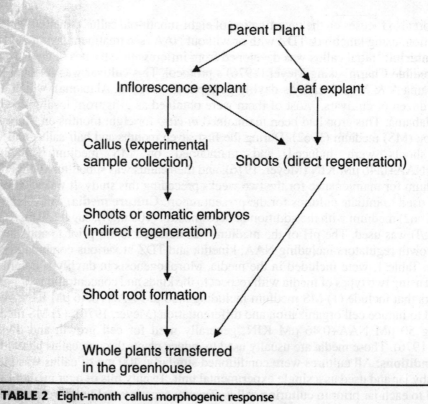

TABLE 2 Eight-month callus morphogenic response

NAA	NAA/KIN	KIN	NAA/TDZ[7]	NAA/TDZ[8]	TDZ	TDZ[8]	Control
Callus multiplication							
++	++	++	++	++	++	++	++
Shoot formation							
4.9±3	6.3±5	3.7± 4	9.3±1	15±2	7.6±5	9.3±4	1.8±5
Root formation							
0	3.4±3	5.5± 3	5.6±3	0	0	0	0

Legends: −: no callus multiplication; +: limited average callus multiplication; ++: large callus multiplication; NAA: 2.68×10⁻⁸M; KIN; 46×10⁻⁸M; TDZ⁸: 10⁻⁸M; TDZ⁷: 10⁻⁷M; Control: MS basal medium; Shoot and root formation averages with standard errors were observed per callus unit.

Generally, within ten days of experimental culture organ primordia were observed. Shoot primordia particularly were identified by the development of localized greenish cells from callus, as shown in Figure 2. The development of greenish cells was the precursor for callus shoot meristem. All shoots reported in this investigation were observed from a single treatment and are only those that were initially formed after the experimental initiation. Repetitive shoots and those that formed after two months were not included in this study. Shoots were observed on all the treatments including the control, and the shoot averages ranged from 1.8 to 15 per callus unit (Table 2). The greatest shoot average of 15 per callus unit was observed from calli treated with 2.68 μM NAA and 10^{-8} μM TDZ, followed by 9.3 from those cultured on MS medium containing 10^{-8} μM TDZ or 2.68 μM NAA and 10^{-8} μM TDZ. All treatment media containing TDZ formed greater shoot averages than those containing NAA, NAA and KIN, KIN, or the control. The greatest shoot average influenced by KIN was 6.3, and was observed when KIN was combined with NAA. KIN alone induced relatively fewer shoots than NAA used alone. Almost two shoots per callus were observed from the control. Although there are not other obvious reasons, we believe that shoot formation on control media was influenced by residual effect of 2.68 μM NAA+0.46 μM KIN that were previously included into the initial medium, prior to transferring experimental sample callus onto the MS basal medium for two weeks maintenance. It was callus from the latter maintenance medium that was used for this study. During the study, some calli formed first roots then shoots (Figure 3) while some others formed only roots (Figure 4). Except Kinetin, most of the rooting calli were observed from samples cultured on treatments that included both auxin and cytokinin (Table 2). No roots were observed on control. No variations were observed from either callus or adventitious shoots. Shoot rooting was achieved on similar shoot inducing media or by transferring shoots onto MS basal medium (Figure 5). All plants that were transferred into the greenhouse recovered without much difficulty.

FIGURE 2 Callus tissues showing localized meristemoids, prerequisite for shoot formation *(Source: George Acquaah)*

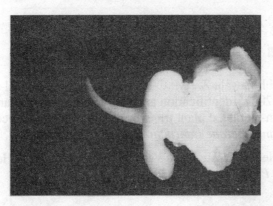

FIGURE 3 Picture showing root formation prior to shoot development *(Source: George Acquaah)*

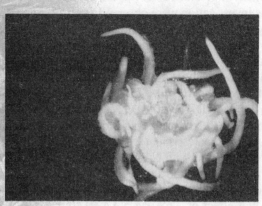

FIGURE 4 Picture showing only root development from callus *(Source: George Acquaah)*

FIGURE 5 Picture showing roots forming on shootlet kept on shoot-inducing medium *(Source: George Acquaah)*

By experience plant regeneration in daylily can be achieved directly or indirectly (Matand, 1999) as outlined in daylily plant regeneration flow chart (Figure 1). Indirect regeneration is the most common approach in daylily (Smith and Krikorian, 1991). However, direct shoot regeneration has also been demonstrated and proven to occur much faster than the indirect regeneration (Matand, 1999), In that report, shoots were directly observed from both florescence and leaf explants. Those shoots formed within two weeks when TDZ treatments, as described in this report, were applied.

Overall, this report has presented select key challenges and considerations that have to be taken into account when one considers culturing daylily *in vitro* for either standard commercial or research micropropagation, or the crop genetic improvement using modern techniques. The report also succinctly addressed some considerations for the selection of plant regeneration method based upon its compatibility with the corresponding gene transfer method, while ensuring the availability of plant materials year-round. One of the highlights of this report is that daylily callus as old as eight months still has the potential to respond exogenous inducing hormones for organ formation. Although there is no clear explanation, it should be noted also that, under the conditions of the present study, daylily callus, which had been pre-cultured on hormone-inducing medium and then maintained on MS basal medium for two weeks retained the potential to form shoots without additional shoot-inducing hormones. TDZ as in many other species has proved to possess higher potency for shoot formation in daylily than KIN. It even induces shoots directly adn faster in both leaf and inflorescence tissues.

References

Anand A., Vighchhipawala Z. Ryu C-M, Kang L., Wang K, Del-Pozo O., Martin G.B., Mysore K.S., 2007. Identification and characterization of plant genes involved in Agrobacterium-mediated plant transformation by virus-induced gene silencing. *Molecular Plant-Microbe Interactions* 20(1): 41–52.

Apps D.A. and Heuser C.W., 1975. Vegetative propagation of Hemerocallis including tissue culture. *Proc. Inter. Plant Prop. Soc.*: 362–367.

Aziz A.N., Sauve R.J., Zhou S., 2003. Genetic transformation of Stella De Oro daylily by particle bombardment. *Can. J. Plant Sci.* 83: 873–876.

Bent A.F., 2000. Arabidopsis in Planta transformation. Uses, mechanisms, and prospects for transformation of other species. *Plant Physiology* 124: 1540–1547.

Chen H. and Galston A.W., 1967. Growth and development of Pelar geranium pith cells *in virto Physiol. Plant* 20:533–539.

Courtney S.E., Rider C.C., Stead A.D., 1994. Changes in protein ubiquitination and the expression of ubiquitin-encoding transcripts in daylily petals during floral development and senescence. *Physiol. Plant 90*: 196–204.

Griesbach R.J., 1989. Selection of dwarf Hemerocallis through tissue culture *HortScience* 24:1037–1028.

Huettman C.A., and Preece J.E. Thidiazuron: a potent cytokinin for woody plant tissue culture. *Plant Cell Tissue and Organ Culture* 33:105–119.

Krikorian A.D. and Kann R.P., 1981. Plantlet production form morphogenetically competent cell suspensions of daylily. *Ann. Bot* 47: 679–636.

Ling J. and Sauve R.J., 1995. Isolation of daylily mesophyll protoplasts. *Plant Cell Reports* 15: 293–296.

Matand K., 1999. Tissue and Histological Studies in Daylily. Ph. D. Thesis. Dept. of Plant and Soil Science, Alabama A & M University, Normal, AL., U.S.A.

Matand K. and Prakash C.S., 2007. Evaluation of Peanut Genotypes for *In Virto* Plant Regeneration Using Thidiazuron *Journal of Biotechnology* (Online Publication ht://www.sciencedirect.com/science?_ob=articleURL&_udi=B6T3C-4N4J2VP-37_user=7517; doi:10.1016/jbiotec.2007.02.014)

Meyer Jr.,M.M., 1976. Propagation of daylily by tissue culture. *Horscience* 11:485–487.

Murashige T., 1974. Plant propagation through tissue cultures. *Ann. Rev. Plant Physiol.* 25:135–166.

Murashige T., and Skoog F., 1962. A revised suitable medium for rapid growth and bioassays with tobacco tissue cultures. *Physiol. Plant.* 15:473–497.

Panavas T., Pikula A., Reid P.D., Rubinstein B., Walker E.L., 1999. Identification of senescence-associated genes from daylily petals. *Plant Mol. Biol.* 40:237–248.

Pierik R.L.M., 1987. *In vitro* culture of higher plants Eds Martinus Nijhoff Publishers. pp344.

Smith D.L. and Krikorian A.D., 1991. Growth and maintenance of an embryogenic cell culture of daylily (Hemerocallis) on hormone-free medium. *Ann. of Bot.* 67:591–597.

Stout A.B., 1986. Daylilies. Ed. Saga Press. N. Y. pp145.

Traub H., 1936. Propagation of Hemericallis (dayliles) by crown cuttage. *Herbertia* 3:123.

Vain P., 2007. Thirty years of plant transformation technology development. *Plant Biotechnology Journal 5* (2): 221–229.

6.4 REVIEW OF GENERAL GENETIC PRINCIPLES

The dominant scientific discipline in plant breeding is genetics, since breeding is all about manipulating the genetics of the organism in a predetermined way. The *cell* is the unit of organization of living things. Some organisms, like bacteria, are entirely one cell (unicellular) while others comprise numerous cells (multicellular). In one group of organisms, prokaryotes, the cellular components coexist without barriers, while in eukaryotes, the components are compartmentalized into discrete units called *organelles*, with membranous walls. The organelles include the nucleus, mitochondria, and chloroplasts, which are the three parts of a plant cell that contain DNA, the hereditary material.

Each nucleus contains a set of chromosomes (or genes) that is characteristic of the species, called the *genome*. A sexually reproducing plant has two basic types of cells, the gametes (pollen, ovules) of the sex cell have half the number (haploid, n) of the chromosomes of the somatic (body) cells (diploid, $2n$). The nuclear chromosomes are subject to the laws of genetics as described by Mendel and are transmitted through the hereditary process in a predictable fashion (Mendelian inheritance). The genes in the mitochondria and chloroplast (extranuclear) are not subject to Mendel's laws (cytoplasmic or extranuclear inheritance).

The totality of all the genes an individual possesses constitutes its genotype. However, this total number is hard to determine. The term is more commonly used to represent the specific combinations of alleles present at a locus or loci of interest. That is, if the alleles of height are *H* and *h*, the genotype of an individual with respect to height, could be *HH*, *Hh*, or *hh*. What is observed is called the **phenotype**.

Phenotype
A biological characteristic or a trait possessed by an organism that results from the expression of a specific gene.

The cells in a sexually reproducing organism may undergo one of two basic kinds of cell division. Mitosis is the process in which the nucleus divides to create two identical daughter nuclei that contain the same number of chromosomes as the mother cell. It occurs only in the somatic tissue. Meiosis, the other division process, occurs only in the gametes and results in four cells with the haploid number of chromosomes as well as being nonidentical. This is because of the critical genetic phenomenon called *crossing over* in which certain chromosomes physically exchange parts. There is a shuffling of chromosomes in a new genetic matrix (recombination) to create new cells that are unlike the mother cell. Recombination is the primary source of variation in sexually reproducing organisms. It is the reason why no two individuals are genetically alike (except identical twins).

6.5 BRIEF REVIEW OF MENDELIAN GENETICS

The fundamental unit of heredity is called a *gene*, a segment of DNA that codes for a specific trait. There are alternate forms of a gene, called *alleles*. A diploid organism has two of these forms at a specific site on the chromosome (locus). Alleles control the same trait (e.g., height) but with different effects (e.g., short, tall). A diploid has only two alleles at one time at each locus, and may have identical or different effects (Figure 6–1). If different, one of the alleles (dominant) may mask the expression of the other (recessive). The locus with identical alleles is said to be homozygous, while one with different alleles is said to be heterozygous.

An individual that is heterozygous for the locus of interest will produce two distinct types of alleles because the alleles segregate into different gametes during meiosis (Mendel's law of segregation). Consequently, when two heterozygous individuals are crossed, random combinations will allow the two alleles to form new combinations, including one in which two recessive alleles will occupy the same locus. By being homozygous, the recessive allele whose effect was suppressed previously by the dominant allele in the heterozygous state, is now able to fully express its effect. When more than one locus of interest is simultaneously considered, the same principle operates. The genes for the different traits are inherited independently of each other. This is called *Mendel's law of independent assortment*. Plant breeders, knowing these laws, can select parents for use in crosses to produce predictable outcomes.

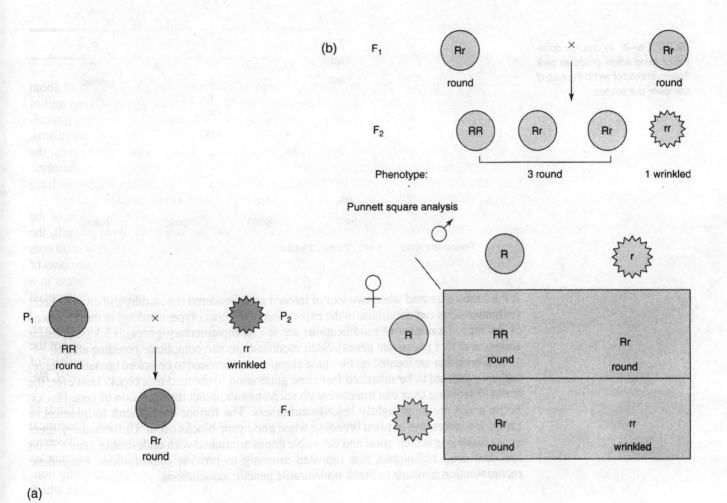

FIGURE 6–1 (a) Homozygous loci (RR,rr) interact to produce heterozygous locus (Rr); (b) heterozygous loci interact to reveal homozygous locus (rr).

6.6 COMPLEX INHERITANCE

Mendel's work focused on traits that were controlled by one or a few genes. Such traits are called *simply inherited* or *Mendelian traits*. The genetics are straightforward and easy to breed. Unfortunately, many traits are controlled by many genes and hence have complex inheritance that is not readily amenable to Mendelian treatment. At the simpler end of the complex inheritance spectrum is incomplete dominance (or partial dominance), whereby the effect of the dominant allele over the recessive allele is not decisive, resulting in an average or blending of the two effects (Figure 6–2). In another situation, the two contrasting alleles are equally expressed (codominance). There are situations in nature whereby one gene has more than two alternative forms (multiple alleles), one being the ABO blood groups in humans.

On the other end of the inheritance spectrum are traits that are governed by numerous genes whose individual effects are difficult to distinguish (polygenes, quantitative genes). The trait they control is called **quantitative traits.** Each gene contributes little effect to the overall phenotype. Such traits are best measured (metrical traits) rather than counted as in Mendelian traits because they are difficult to breed.

Mendelian traits can be neatly categorized into distinct classes (ratios) by counting. Sometimes the expected ratios do not manifest because of various interferences. The phenomenon of epistasis, whereby alleles at different loci (nonallelic genes) interact, can modify genetic outcomes and consequently the expected ratios. For example, instead of the

Quantitative Traits
Traits that are controlled by many genes, each contributing a small effect to the overall phenotypic expressions of the trait.

FIGURE 6–2 Incomplete dominance gene action produces pink flowers instead of red in the case of complete dominance.

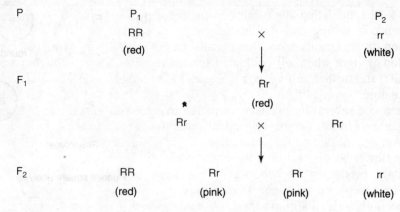

Phenotypic ratio: 1 red : 2 pink : 1 white

9:3:3:1 ratio expected when two loci of interest are considered (i.e., a dihybrid cross), alleles at another locus can contribute to the expression of the phenotype, resulting in modifications of the ratio. Examples of modifications are 9:7 (complementary genes), 13:1 (suppressor genes), and 15:1 (duplicate genes). Such modifications can complicate breeding efforts.

Genes that are located on the same chromosome are said to be linked (genetic linkage) and are expected to be inherited from one generation to the next as a block. However, the event of crossing over can interfere with such smooth, intact transmission of gene blocks. Some genes are more tightly linked than others. The former are difficult to interrupt or break. It is a blessing to plant breeding when good gene blocks occur. Unfortunately, there are occasions in which good and desirable genes are linked with undesirable genes! Plant breeders used techniques like repeated crossing to provide opportunities for genetic recombination to occur to break undesirable genetic associations.

6.7 THE IMPORTANCE OF REPRODUCTIVE SYSTEMS

Plant breeders must be familiar with the reproductive systems of the plants they seek to manipulate. The genetic structure of plants depends on their mode of reproduction. Plants may be sexually reproducing or asexually reproducing, the latter not involving the sexual process or crossing. Asexually reproducing species remain "pure" or genetically identical from one generation to the next (clones) because the sexual process involves meiosis, the process that creates natural genetic variability.

To breed sexually reproducing species, the breeder must understand the floral biology and other factors associated with their flowering. To cross plants, you must know when the flowers open, how long the pollen stays viable, when the stigma is receptive, and other factors. Some sexually reproducing species are called self-pollinating because they receive pollen grains from their own flowers or from like plants. This habit makes them have a narrow genetic base. They are homozygous at most loci and produce relatively uniform products. Other species are cross-pollinating, receiving pollen from an available source. Cross-pollinated species are heterozygous at most loci and have a broad genetic base. These two basic reproductive behaviors dictate how the species are genetically manipulated. If you treat a cross-pollinated species as self-pollinated, once you remove the artificial restriction, it would revert back to its old ways!

In addition to the state genetic differences, there is a critical factor that plant breeders exploit in breeding plants. It is known that the farther apart genetically parents in a cross are, the more vigorous the product of their mating. Because cross-pollinated species are heterozygous, they can maintain a high genetic load without consequences. Lethal recessive alleles can enjoy a heterozygous advantage, remain innocuous while being suppressed by a dominant allele. However, when selfed (crossed with itself, e.g., $Aa \times Aa$), the lethal allele can become homozygous (aa) and be expressed! The consequence of selfing cross-pollinated species is a reduction in vigor because of the expression of deleterious gene. This event is called *inbreeding depression*. There is no depression of vigor when self-pollinated species are selfed, because that is their natural way of life, and further, selfing over the years has eliminated the deleterious genes from the population.

There are several mechanisms in nature that promote one mode of reproduction over the other. *Monoecy* is the anatomical condition in which the male and female parts of a flower are located on the same plant but on different parts. For example, in corn, the male flower occurs on top of the plant, while the female flower occurs on the side of the stalk, producing the cob. Such a condition promotes cross-pollination. Some species have separate male and female plants (dioecy; dioecious plants). Similarly, some species have a condition called self-incompatibility, whereby a plant is unable to fertilize itself with its own pollen. Self-incompatibility occurs in some nut trees and other species like broccoli. Yet, some species have a genetic problem, male sterility that renders pollen grains infertile. All these natural conditions are exploited by plant breeders in their breeding work, as will be discussed shortly. Further, it is always advisable in fruit and nut production to be certain you have provided adequate pollen sources for optimal yield.

6.8 ROLE OF VARIATION IN PLANT BREEDING

As previously indicated, there can be no plant breeding without variability! Genetic recombination produces variability in sexually reproducing species. But, the ultimate source of biological variation is mutation. Plant breeders start by assembling variability for their breeding program according to their state objectives. The recommendation is to always start looking for suitable parents from commercial cultivars, having gone through the rigorous testing and adaptation processes that are part of plant breeding. Germplasm banks are repositories of variability in plant species. Some banks hold thousands of different genotypes of a particular species. A breeder, if need be, can consult these centers for materials to use in a project.

6.9 THE PLANT BREEDER AS A DECISION MAKER

Modern plant breeding is a carefully planned and executed activity. Breeding is tedious and time consuming, often taking over ten years to produce a variety for use by producers. It is imperative that sound decisions be made to avoid waste and prolonging the process. Some of the specific decisions that are made are in the following areas:

1. *Organization design.*   The breeder plans the entire operation, regarding personnel, equipment, field and nurseries needed, and so on.
2. *Planning and control.*   The breeder must set clear objectives and define the strategies for achieving them.
3. *Behavioral process.*   The team engaged in the breeding program should work and relate well to each other.

Breeding objectives drive the project. Not all plant problems are amenable to plant breeding. Some are better resolved by changing the plant cultural environment. Objectives may be decided upon following consultation with consumers and producers. Do not spend ten years to develop a new variety and then look for customers. Specific objectives could be higher yield, disease resistance, augmenting nutritional quality, early maturity, and adaptation to abiotic stress (cold tolerance, drought resistance, etc.).

6.10 General Steps in a Breeding Program

Regardless of the breeding approach, plant breeders follow certain general steps.

1. *Objectives.* Set clearly defined and attainable objectives.
2. *Germplasm.* Assemble appropriate germplasm to use to initiate the project. That is, if you desire to breed for resistance to a disease, you must have a source of resistance to this disease.
3. *Selection.* When you assemble variability and you make crosses to create more of it, you have to discriminate among the variability to find which individual plant has accumulated all the desirable gene combinations, according to the breeding objectives.
4. *Evaluation.* Breeders evaluate germplasm in the field to determine which ones to release for use by producers.
5. *Certification and cultivar release.* Once satisfied with the "winner," the next step is to pursue certification to demonstrate compliance with existing **seed laws,** as well as to obtain some protection from unauthorized use of your invention, if so desired.

Seed law
Seed law is a legislation that regulates the labeling, possessing for sale, sale and offering or exposing for sale or otherwise providing for planting purposes of agricultural seeds, vegetable seeds and screenings; to prevent misrepresentation thereof; and for other purposes

6.11 Selection in Breeding

As previously indicated, plant breeding is like evolution. In evolution, the arbiter of what survives (makes the cut, so to speak) is natural selection. In plant breeding, plant breeders are the ultimate decision makers, deciding which genotype becomes a commercial variety of cultivar. A *cultivar* is the term for the product of plant breeding. Variety (botanical variety) occurs in nature. However, the term *variety* is used in society to refer to the products of plant breeding.

Selection is a discriminating force. In plant breeding, breeders have a state objective and hence seek to bias the choices they make at every stage of the process toward achieving their objective. This focused approach to discriminating among variation is called *directional selection.* When two plants are crossed, their genes are mixed up and reorganized into new genetic matrices. As previously stated, some traits are controlled by one or a few genes, while others are controlled by numerous genes. The chance of finding the individual that combines all the desirable genes increases as the number of genes that control the traits increases. For example, if the trait is controlled by one gene, only four combinations are possible in the F_2. To find that ideal plant, the breeder needs to plant only four plants. If three genes are involved, sixty-four plants are needed. If *n* genes are involved, the formula for calculating the F_2 population size is $(1/4)^n$. For quantitative traits, breeders routinely produce, grow, and evaluate hundreds of thousands and even millions of plants! To find the proverbial needle in a haystack requires an excellent breeder's eye. Modern breeders use various scientific techniques to reduce the guess-work to make the selection process more efficient (e.g., genetic markers for selection).

From the thousands of plants generated in the F_2, only a fraction is selected for more careful evaluation in the F_3. The numbers decrease progressively with each generation. The goal is that progress (genetic gain) is made with every cycle of selection; that is, the breeding objective is continuously advanced, each step moving the breeder closer to attaining it. The progress from one generation to the next is called the *response to selection (R)* or the *genetic gain.* A mathematical relationship will make this clearer:

$$R = ih^2\sigma$$

where R = the advance in one generation of selection, h^2 = heritability, i = intensity of selection, and σ = phenotypic standard deviation. Heritability measures the proportion of the observed variation in a progeny that is inherited. This is sometimes called the *breeder's* equation. Simply stated, the higher the heritability estimate, the higher the success one can have by using plant breeding approaches to solving the breeding problem. If heritability is low, the impact of the environmental effect would be so strong that what you observe would not always be an accurate reflection of the genes the plant has. Selection intensity reflects the proportion of the plants that you select to advance to the next generation. Obviously, the smaller the better because of cost and the labor involved. But, ultimately, you want to be sure the plant with all the desired combinations is always included in the sample. If you advance only a few plants, you have a higher chance of leaving it behind. Plant breeders are always looking for ways of enhancing the selection process to make it more efficient and effective.

6.12 HYBRIDIZATION IN PLANT BREEDING

Hybridization (crossing) is the principal tool or technique used to achieve gene transfer in conventional breeding; it can occur naturally. Artificial crossing entails exercising control over the parents used and how they are crossed (controlled pollination). Parents to be crossed should be reproductively compatible. Once the parents are chosen, the breeder decides how to cross them. A critical decision is what parent to use as male or female. As previously pointed out, DNA (genes) occurs in both the nucleus and the cytoplasm (in mitochondria and chloroplasts). During gamete formation, the male gametes (pollen) are produced from only the nucleus without the cytoplasm. The egg or ovule has both parts. If there is a gene of interest on the mitochondrion, pollen grains will not have it. Using a parent with such a gene means you cannot pass the gene on to the offspring. In this instance, the parent should be the female. Some male sterility genes reside on the mitochondria.

Pollen transfer is often by physical or mechanical means (hand pollination). However, in a large-scale program, hand pollination may not always be practical. Once a female parent has been identified, the next thing is to prevent self-pollination. This is achieved in species whose flowers are hermaphrodites (have both sexes) by the tedious technique called *emasculation*. This entails removing the anthers from the flower to leave only the exposed pistil. Emasculating a large field of plants is feasible in places like India where labor is cheap. Alternatively, breeders resort to techniques like male sterility and self-incompatibility to render one sex infertile. If a parent is made sterile by incorporating a male sterility gene, this effectively genetically emasculates the plant, leaving no need for the tedious mechanical emasculation that usually has a low success rate.

6.13 METHODS OF BREEDING

The methods of breeding differ according to the reproductive biology of the species. Breeding methods are essentially methods of selection after creating an initial population. The initial population sets the tone for the selection program. It can be as simple as a landrace (farmer-developed variety). Often, it is generated by planned crosses following the judicious selection of parents.

Plant breeders develop six basic types of cultivars: pure line, open pollinated, hybrid, clonal, apomictic, and multilines.

1. *Pure-line cultivars.* These are developed for self-pollinated species. They are homogeneous and homozygous in genetic structure and have a narrow genetic base. They are preferred for markets and products where uniformity has a premium.
2. *Open-pollinated cultivars.* As the name implies, these cultivars are developed for cross-pollinated species. They are heterogeneous and heterozygous and have a broad genetic base.

3. *Hybrid cultivars.* Hybrids are known for their high yield. Most of the highly successful ones are developed for cross-pollinated species like corn that are easy to pollinate.
4. *Clonal cultivars.* These are cultivars that are propagated by asexual (vegetative) methods. Some species have the capacity to bear viable seed, so they are improved through crossing. However, they are propagated asexually so that the vigor created through hybridization will be kept intact. Remember, genes are reshuffled anytime we cross parents.
5. *Apomictic cultivars.* Seed is normally produced after pollination and fertilization. However, the phenomenon of apomixis is the production of seed without fertilization. This behavior is common in perennial forage grasses. In effect, apomictic seeds are clones of the parent plant, and are equivalent to vegetative propagation through seed.
6. *Multilines.* This cultivar is developed for self-pollinated species. A multiline cultivar consists of a mixture of specially developed genotypes called *isolines* (or *near isogenic lines*) because they differ only in a single gene or a defined set of genes. They are developed primarily for disease control. Instead of incorporating one gene for protection, breeders insert multiple genes for protection against the same disease. Should one succumb while in use in production, there are several "backup" genes that can provide some protection.

6.14 Breeding Hybrids

Heterosis (hybrid vigor)
The increase in size, vigor, fertility, and overall productivity of a hybrid plant over the average performance of the two parents.

Inbreeding depression
Opposite and complementary to heterosis, this is the reduction in fitness of an individual as a result of inbreeding.

Hybrids are very intriguing cultivars. They are developed based on the phenomenon called **heterosis** or **hybrid vigor.** This is the phenomenon whereby the hybrid (the F_1; product of the cross of two parents) exceeds both parents in the expression of the trait of interest. Commercially, the parents for a hybrid in a cross-pollinated species are developed by first selfing them repeatedly to make them pure or homozygous (called *inbred lines*). Such repeated selfing exposes the deleterious alleles by making them homozygous. These parents experience **inbreeding depression** and look very weak and unproductive. However, when these inbred lines are crossed, the hybrid becomes invigorated (hybrid vigor) and excels in productivity. A suggested scientific explanation is that crossing the two inbred lines results in a highly heterozygous hybrid. Heterozygosity per se, is thought to cause this dramatic vigor.

Hybrid vigor is most pronounced in the F_1 generation. Seed companies sell the F_1 seed to farmers to grow to experience the benefit of heterosis. However, if seed is saved from the F_1 or hybrid for planting the next season, this beneficial heterotic effect is reduced by 50 percent! This compels farmers to go back and purchase fresh hybrid seed each season. That is why companies make money, to recoup their investment in developing inbred lines and other activities associated with hybrid development.

6.15 Cultivar Release and Certification

Once genotypes with potential have been identified, the breeder proceeds to conduct performance evaluation trials, often at various locations including where the new cultivar will be released for use by farmers. This evaluation is conducted over seasons and years. After this activity, one of the potential genotypes is released as a cultivar. It is often given a name that can be readily identified by customers. Sometimes the name reflects the breeding process and includes some codes for tracking by the breeder or company.

Before the seed or product becomes available for sale, it goes through a certification process. Certification is conducted by certifying agencies according to prescribed guidelines for the crop or species. For seed products, the breeder retains the most authentic version of the cultivar called the *breeder seed*. Some of the seed is increased by a contracted producer to obtain the *foundation seed*. This seed is further increased by farmers under contract to yield the *registered seed*. Registered is further increased to obtain *certified seed* for sale to farmers. These are called *seed classes*.

For certification, the agency inspects the variety in the field according to the guidelines for the crop. The breeder is also required to furnish specific product information including the history and origin of the cultivar and documentation of the processes of evaluation and plans for maintenance of the various seed classes.

The seed has to be submitted for testing (seed testing) to determine viability or germination percentage, purity, vigor, seed health, and noxious weed seed. Before being offered for sale, the bags are tagged, as described in Chapter 9.

6.16 BREEDING ASEXUALLY PROPAGATED SPECIES

As previously indicated, variation is the lifeblood of plant breeding. Recombination is the primary source of variation for species that reproduce sexually. For species that do not reproduce sexually, variation can be generated through other means such as inducing artificial mutations. Mutations have been used, not only in asexually reproducing species but also in sexually producing species, to develop numerous commercial species of fruit trees, ornamentals, and other species. Tissue culture and other biotechnological techniques that can be used are discussed next.

6.17 BREEDING SEEDLESS FRUITS

Seedlessness in fruits is a desirable trait in horticulture breeding. Seedless fruits are more convenient to eat because there are not seeds to spit out. Seedless cultivars are commercially available for fruits such as watermelon, grape, orange, and strawberry. The conventional method of breeding seedless fruits is the use of triploid hybrids. To obtain a triploid, a tetraploid ($4x$) parent is crossed with a diploid ($2x$) line. In watermelon, for example, the tetraploid is always the female parent ($4x = 44$; $2x = 22$). The reciprocal cross, with the female as male parent, does not produce seed (Figure 6–3). The triploid resulting from this cross ($3x = 33$) is female-sterile and hence the fruit is seedless.

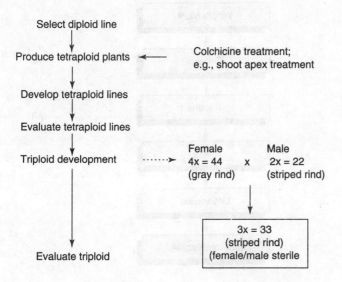

FIGURE 6–3 Breeding seedless watermelon.

Because the triploid is also male-sterile, growers of seedless watermelon must plant rows of diploid lines as pollinators for stimulation of fruit formation.

6.18 Biotechnology in Plant Breeding

So far, we have discussed the concepts and methods of conventional plant breeding. This section is devoted to discussing the principles and concepts of nonconventional breeding at an introductory level.

6.18.1 WHAT IS BIOTECHNOLOGY?

Biotechnology may be broadly defined as the use of techniques based on living systems to make products or improve other species. This definition would include the use of microbes to make products by the age-old process of fermentation. However, a narrower definition would restrict the term to the genetic manipulation of organisms for specific purposes. Again, this definition would include classic plant breeding by crossing. Another term is used to distinguish between the levels of genetic manipulation—indirect manipulation of plant genetics by conventional methods at the whole organism level using methods like crossing, and direct genetic manipulation at the molecular level (Figure 6–4). The term *genetic engineering* is used to describe the genetic manipulation of organisms at the molecular level, directly involving the DNA. Scientists, using the revolutionary technology of **recombinant DNA** (rDNA), are able to transfer genes from any organism to another.

Recombinant DNA
A hybrid DNA molecule produced in the laboratory by joining pieces of DNA from different sources.

What makes this radical gene transfer possible is the fact that DNA is "universal." Regardless of source, all DNAs obey the same rules and are chemically identical. So, it is possible to transfer DNA from an animal and insert it into a plant! This, theoretically, removes all biological barriers, reducing all life into just one humongous gene pool. The controversy with genetic engineering primarily stems from this radical approach to genetic manipulation.

The term *molecular breeding* is used to describe the application of a variety of tools for manipulating the DNA of plants, which may or may not involve rDNA, to improve them for specific purposes. Even though crossing two different parents produces new recombinants in the segregating population, the term *recombinant DNA* is reserved for the union of DNA segments of different biological origins.

A cultivar developed by genetic engineering protocols is called a *transgenic cultivar* or a *genetically modified (GM) cultivar*. Generally, an organism developed by rDNA procedures is called a *genetically modified organism (GMO)*.

FIGURE 6–4 Levels of eukaryotic organization.

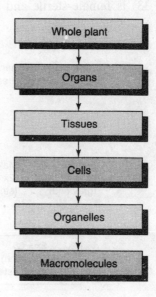

6.18.2 THE GENERAL STEPS OF RDNA TECHNOLOGY

General steps in rDNA manipulations are as follows:

1. The DNA segment or gene of interest is identified. This is called the *transgene*. It is extracted and snipped out of the source using restriction enzymes.
2. The transgene is inserted into a special DNA molecule called a *cloning vector* and joined to create a new rDNA molecule.
3. The rDNA molecule is transferred into and maintained in a host cell (bacterium) by the process of genetic transformation. The vector replicates to produce identical copies (clones) of the insert DNA.
4. The host cells with the cloned transgene are identified and isolated from untransformed cells.
5. The cloned transgene can be manipulated such that the protein product it encodes is expressed by a host cell.

There is modification to these general steps, according to the purpose of the research.

6.19 BREEDING GENETICALLY MODIFIED CULTIVARS

Breeding genetically modified (GM) cultivars is a very lengthy process and involved process, compared to conventional breeding. Researchers need to establish the appropriate facilities and receive clearance from a local biosafety committee in order to conduct rDNA research. One may discover and isolate the gene of interest or procure it from another source. Either way, it can be very expensive. Recombinant DNA technology may sound like a simple event, but it involves numerous patented subprotocols. To be able to produce and market new products, one must be untangled from the web of patents, something that adds to the cost of product development.

Once an appropriate transgene has been obtained and incorporated into a plant, the breeder conducts a controlled environment (greenhouse) evaluation. After that, an application must be made to the appropriate federal agency (APHIS—Animal and Plant Health Inspection Service) to conduct a field test. After the agency is satisfied that the product is stable, nonpathogenic to animals or humans, and meets safety stipulations according to the nature of the GM product, approval is given for commercialization.

The convergence of conventional and molecular approaches to plant breeding should be pointed out. The critical difference between the two approaches is the method of gene transfer, one method within normal biological reproductive modes, and the other by outside biological boundaries. However, before the GM cultivar is released for use by producers, it undergoes the same field evaluation process as a conventional cultivar.

6.20 USE OF MARKERS IN PLANT BREEDING

Whereas rDNA research incorporates foreign DNA into plants, there are other applications of molecular genetics that do not incorporate transgenes. Molecular techniques are used to identify parents for hybridization. This method in plant breeding is called *marker assisted selection (MAS)*. As previously pointed out, plant breeders face the daunting task of finding that ideal plant with all the gene combinations from a sea of segregating plants. They employ various techniques to help them effectively and efficiently do their work. One such strategy is to use genetic markers.

Genetic markers are simply landmarks on chromosomes that serve as reference points to the location of other genes of interest. The rationale of markers is that an easy-to-observe trait (marker) is tightly linked or associated with a more difficult-to-observe trait of interest to the breeder. By knowing the presence of such an association, breeders can select plants directly on the basis of the marker, and indirectly select them for the traits of interest. This greatly facilitates the selection process.

There are morphological markers that manifest outside the organism as adult phenotypes, and molecular markers that are identified at the subcellular level. Molecular markers can be assayed before the adult stage in the life cycle of the organism and hence are more advantageous, allowing breeders to make early decisions, saving time and money. Molecular makers may be proteins (isozymes) or DNA. DNA markers are more versatile, including RFLPs (restriction fragment length polymorphisms), AFLPs (amplified fragment length polymorphisms), SSRs (single sequence repeats), SCARs (sequence characterized amplified regions), STSs (sequence tagged sites), and SNPs (single nucleotide polymorphisms).

One application of markers is the authentication of hybridity. When a cross is made, breeders may run simple tests to ensure that the F_1 is a true hybrid, not a self. It is a tragedy and a waste of resources to advance a self-pollinated product as if it were a cross. When morphological markers are available, these are easiest to use. For example, it is known that a purple flower is dominant to a white flower color. If one is crossing two parents that happen to differ in flower color, the dominance test could be used. By using the white parent as female, you would expect the F_1 seed to be purple-flowered if it is truly a hybrid.

6.21 SUCCESS OF GENETIC ENGINEERING OF PLANTS

The first bioengineered food crop, *FlavrSavr* tomato, was introduced in 1985. It was designed to have reduced levels of the enzyme polygalacturonase that is associated with fruit ripening. By so doing, tomato could be harvested as vine-ripened and hence tastier than the green-harvested and forced-ripened tomato. The GM tomato also had an extended shelf life. This product literally ignited the GM food wars that continue today. Another feat that has been attempted is the development of the Golden Rice, a GM product that represents the first rice known to man to have the capacity to produce pro-vitamin A. No natural rice has this capacity, making blindness very common in societies that depend on rice as a staple food.

Pest resistance is an area where GM cultivars abound. Most notable are the Bt products, short for *Bacillus thuringiensis*, the bacterium from which the gene for resistance to the lepidopteran pest was derived. Bt products are resistant to the devastating attacks of the European corn borer. Other common products include the herbicide-tolerant transgenic such as Roundup Ready® products. These plants allow producers the additional flexibility in weed control by being able to apply the herbicides while the crop of interest is still growing in the field. There are several other achievements that have been commercialized, with many in the pipeline.

6.22 THE BIOTECHNOLOGY DEBATE

There are many issues associated with the development and application of biotechnology in plant breeding. The issues of patents are more technical and can often be resolved. However, the issue of ethics continues to be debated on three main fronts:

1. *Scientific disagreements.* Society is concerned about the potential risk that the development and application of biotechnology poses to humans, animals, and the environment health. Even though resolvable empirically by scientific methods, some value judgment is in play, for example, regarding the level of risk deemed acceptable.

2. *Political disagreement.* There are political positions on the social and economic impacts of biotechnology on society, the pendulum swinging in favor of the dominant political ideology of the day.

3. *Religious, ethical, and philosophical disagreements.* These are faith-based issues about morality and whether scientists are playing God, or whether biotechnology is natural. In a pluralistic society, consensus is often difficult to achieve, leading some to pursue extremist acts of vigilantism (e.g., destroying biotech research labs). There are perceptions and fears about biotechnology in society. Some think the technology is alien, unnatural, and too radical. The normal direction of genetic information transfer (central dogma) is from DNA to RNA to proteins; genetic engineering can reverse this process, synthesizing DNA from protein. The transfer of DNA across natural biological boundaries is deemed playing God, as well. It should be pointed out that such a transfer occurs in nature whereby the bacterium *Agrobacterium tumifaciens* causes tumors in plants by transferring bacterial DNA into cells upon infection. In fact, this bacterium is widely used in genetic engineering in this natural role. There is the concern of the unknown, the possibility of creating monsters and superweeds. These and many other concerns prevail, keeping the debate alive.

Biotechnology is a very highly regulated industry. In the United States, the USDA (United States Department of Agriculture), EPA (Environmental Protection Agency), and the FDA (Food and Drug Administration) are all engaged. The USDA focuses on plant pests, plants, and veterinary biologics; the EPA on microbial/plant pesticides, novel microorganisms, and existing pesticide; and the FDA on food, feed, food additives, veterinary drugs, human drugs, and medical devices. GM products are evaluated and labeled as such before commercialization.

6.23 TISSUE CULTURE IN PLANT BREEDING

Tissue culture or micropropagation, as it is sometimes called, is a technology that is useful to plant breeders. The premise of this technology is that the cell is the fundamental unit of organization of the organism, and contains all the requisite genetic information to make the entire organism (totipotent). It is possible, and routinely done, to raise a whole plant from a single cell! This is critical to genetic engineering, for the transgene is inserted into a single cell that is nurtured and regenerated into a full blown plant in vitro (in the test tube).

Micropropagation is useful for multiplying a limited amount of plant material very rapidly. Pieces of the plant part (leaf, stem, roots, flower, etc.) can be obtained and nurtured into full plants. Plants so produced are clones (genetically identical). The plant part used to start tissue culture is called the *explant*. By manipulating the cultural environment using growth regulators, the researcher can induce a variety of morphological structures, including roots and shoots. The induction of organs from explants is called *organogenesis*. In genetic engineering applications, often the explant used is the callus, an amorphous mass of meristematic cells that are equivalent to human stem cells in that they can be manipulated to produce various organs. Pieces of DNA or genes can be inserted into single cells in the callus by direct bombardment in a special device called a *gene gun* (Figure 6–5). Another common approach is to use specially modified bacteria (*Agrobacterium*) to transfer the gene of interest into the cell.

Another application of tissue culture in breeding is embryo rescue. When plants that are genetically distant are crossed, there is often a number of problems, including lethality, failure of fertilization, or failure of the embryo to develop. Just like premature birth in humans, plant breeders may extract the immature embryo from the flower and culture on appropriate media to produce a full plant.

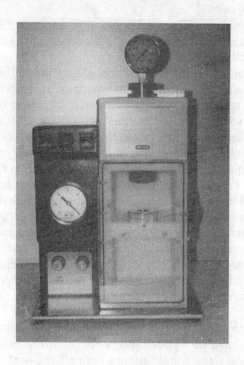

FIGURE 6–5 A gene gun. This tabletop model uses compressed helium gas to propel the DNA. *(Source: George Acquaah)*

SUMMARY

Plant improvement involves the manipulation of the genome of the plant with a specific goal in mind. A good understanding of genetics helps breeders to be effective and efficient in their endeavors. DNA, hereditary material, is located mostly in the nuclei of plants in linear structures called chromosomes. Genes, the factors that condition traits, are pieces of DNA arranged in a linear order in chromosomes. Gene—not traits—are inherited by the offspring from their parents. The transmission of genes in this fashion is governed by certain laws that were discovered by Mendel: gene pairs segregate during cell division so that only one from each pair ends up in each gamete, and genes assort independently during meiosis. Some genes (dominant) mask the expression of others (recessive) when they occur at the same locus.

Meiosis is the major source of biological variation. However, the ultimate source of variation is mutation. The expression of genes is subject to the environment in which they occur. Certain traits are governed by one or a few genes (simply inherited), whereas others are governed by many genes with small effects (quantitative traits).

The underlying principle in plant breeding is that the phenotype (what is observed) is a product of the interaction between the genotype (genetic makeup) of the individual and its environment. Phenotype can therefore be changed by manipulating either the genotype (plant breeding) or its environment (agronomy). Before starting a breeding program, breeders should first ascertain whether adequate heritable variation is available. Then they should have clear goals or objectives. The specific methods used depend on the mating system of the plant. Genetic changes may be made in flowering plants through crossing (hybridization).

Molecular biotechnological procedures are being utilized by plant breeders to accelerate their breeding programs through the use of molecular markers for effective selection. Further, breeders are able to import genes from outside of the genus with which they are working and thereby develop transgenic plants. Problems that once were impossible to solve with conventional breeding are being tackled with amazing success using molecular biotechnological tools.

It should be emphasized that conventional and molecular biotechnological methods of breeding are complementary tools. Geneticists and breeders work together to improve horticultural plants.

208 *Chapter 6 Breeding Horticultural Plants*

REFERENCES AND SUGGESTED READING

Acquaah, G. 2004. *Understanding biotechnology: An integrated and cyber-based approach*. Upper Saddle River, N.J.: Prentice Hall.

Campbell, N., L. Mitchell, and J. Reece. 1997. *Biology: Concepts and connections*, 2d ed. New York: Benjamin/Cummings.

Klug, W. S., and M. R. Cummings. 1996. *Essentials of genetics*. Englewood Cliffs, N.J.: Prentice Hall.

Wallace, R. A. 1997. *Biology: The world of life*, 7th ed. New York: Benjamin/Cummings.

Breeding watermelon
http://cuke.hort.ncsu.edu/cucurbit/wmelon/wmelonmain.html

Mendelian genetics
http://www.cliffsnotes.com/WileyCDA/CliffsReviewTopic/Mendelian-Genetics. topicArticleId-23791,articleId-23725.html

Rose breeding
http://aggie-horticulture.tamu.edu/rose/rosebreeding/index.html

PRACTICAL EXPERIENCE

LABORATORY

1. Select one (or more) vegetable and one ornamental flowering crop and assemble seeds of as many variant types as possible. For this activity, sources of seed include the market, farms, research stations, other universities, and germplasm banks. Place the collection in test tubes in a rack and label clearly.
2. Plant samples of selected specimens from activity 1 and describe the differences in morphology.

FIELD WORK

Attempt to cross two different cultivars of tomato, pepper, or an ornamental flowering plant.

OUTCOMES ASSESSMENT

1. Why is plant breeding important to society?
2. In what way is plant breeding a science and an art?
3. Compare and contrast conventional and nonconventional approaches to plant breeding.
4. Discuss the importance of plant genetics in plant breeding.
5. Why is it more challenging to improve traits that are controlled by many genes?
6. Discuss the plant breeder as a decision maker.
7. Discuss the underlying genetic principles of hybrid breeding.
8. Why do growers have to purchase fresh hybrid seed each growing season, rather than save seed from the previous season for planting?
9. What is biotechnology?
10. Discuss the underlying genetic principle in genetic engineering.
11. Discuss specific achievements of genetic engineering of plants.
12. Discuss, giving specific examples, the biotechnology debate in society.

PART 2

PROTECTING HORTICULTURAL PLANTS

7

Biological Enemies of Horticultural Plants

PURPOSE AND EXPECTED OUTCOMES

The purpose of this chapter is to present and discuss the various classes of pathogens and parasitic factors that cause disorders in horticultural plants.

After studying this chapter, the student should be able to

1. Discuss the economic effects of pests in horticulture.
2. List the categories of organisms that are pests to plants.
3. Distinguish among insect pests on the basis of life cycle.
4. Distinguish among insect pests on the basis of feeding habits.

[COLOR PLATES—*see color plates 4 and 5* for additional chapter photos]

OVERVIEW

Pests are organisms that are harmful to plants. They include organisms ranging from tiny microorganisms (or microbes) to large animals and other plants. They damage above-ground plant parts and belowground parts, the latter kind of damage being more difficult to detect. The activities of pests may cause physical injury to plants. They may also cause disorders in plants, making them unable to grow and develop properly. In some cases, pests do not come into contact with desirable plants but, just by being in close vicinity, compete for growth factors and deprive the desirable plants of adequate nutrition. Certain pests only cause blemishes on plants, making them unsightly and unattractive without physically damaging or upsetting the physiology of the plant. Whatever the form of pests associated with cultivated plants, they need to be controlled when their presence threatens to cause economic loss to the grower.

Pests of cultivated plants include weeds (other plants), insects, nematodes, and mites. Those that cause diseases are bacteria, fungi, and mycoplasma-like organisms. These organisms can be divided into two broad classes: plant pests and animal pests. The life cycles of these organisms are important in their control. Control measures are usually targeted at the stages in their life cycles when they are most vulnerable. In terms of plant diseases, fungal problems predominate.

MODULE 1

PLANTS AS PESTS

7.1 WEEDS

Weed
A plant that is growing where it is not wanted.

A **weed** may be broadly defined as a plant out of place. A corn plant in a bed of roses is as much a weed as a rose plant in a cornfield, no matter how attractive it may look. In theory, any plant can be considered a weed at some point. However, the term is commonly used to refer to certain undesirable plants, often with no economic use to growers. Such plants vary widely in characteristics and include algae, mosses, ferns, and flowering plants. Weeds tend to be more aggressive than cultivated plants and have characteristics that enable them to survive under very harsh conditions. They can thrive on marginal soils and have seeds that have longevity, dormancy, and other allied survival characteristics associated with life in the wild.

7.1.1 ECONOMIC IMPORTANCE

Weeds are undesirable in cultivated fields or the landscape—or for that matter anywhere. They should be controlled because they usually result in economic losses. The following are some of the significant ways in which weeds show their undesirable characteristics.

1. They compete with cultivated plants for growth factors (light, moisture, air, and nutrients [Chapter 4]), thus diminishing the performance of crop plants. Weeds often are better competitors than cultivated plants. They are more vigorous in growth and produce many seeds for effective dispersal. They have long viability and efficient dormancy mechanisms.
2. Weeds may harbor pests of cultivated plants and other dangerous animals. For example, chickweed harbors whitefly, red spider mites, and cucumber mosaic virus. Charlock may harbor clubroot organisms, which attack brassica crops. Groundsel may harbor nematodes. Snakes and rodents hide among weeds.
3. They are an eyesore in the landscape, diminishing the aesthetic value of lawns and other ornamental displays.
4. When they arise, weeds are removed at a cost. Mechanical removal of weeds by using a hoe or uprooting is tedious. Herbicides are commonly used in large operations to control weeds—at a tremendous cost, not to mention the adverse environmental impact.
5. Weeds increase the costs of crop production. Additional equipment and machinery are needed to control weeds. When weed infestation is high and weeds are allowed to flower, the harvested grain may be infested with weeds. These unwanted weeds are cleaned at additional cost to the operation.
6. They reduce the quality and market value of horticultural products. Weeds compete with crops for nutrients and cause desired crops to grow and develop improperly. Yield is decreased, and along with it, income. Seeds infested with weeds command a low market price. Impurities may be eliminated, adding to production costs.
7. They may be poisonous plants that can harm people. Pollen from weeds causes allergies in humans. Plant species such as ragwort and buttercup are toxic to animals. If the fruits of weeds such as black nightshade contaminate the desired crop seed and are eaten by accident, humans may be poisoned.

8. Weeds may clog drains, waterways, and other water bodies such as ponds. A pond or lake infested with weeds soon becomes shallow, thus reducing its effective use (e.g., for irrigation). Waterways choked with weeds encourage flooding.

7.1.2 BIOLOGY, CLASSIFICATION, AND DISTRIBUTION

Weed species have wild characteristics for adapting to marginal conditions and have effective mechanisms for self-perpetuation in the environment. Many weed seeds can persist in the soil for long periods of time in a dormant state until appropriate conditions for germination and growth occur. Many weeds such as groundsel establish rapidly and thereby can suppress crop seeds that germinate later. Some weeds germinate during particular seasons (e.g., orache in spring), whereas others, such as annual meadow grass, germinate throughout the year.

Soil moisture, pH, and nutritional status affect the distribution of weeds. Some weed species adapt to acidic soils, and others prefer poorly drained soils. Weeds, like other plants, are adapted to various environments. Some are tropical, whereas others prefer temperate conditions. Within the same environment, certain weeds are more of a problem in fields of cultivated crops than others. Weeds also differ in growth pattern and means of propagation.

Some weed species have underground vegetative structures (e.g., swollen roots and rhizomes) used for propagation. These weeds include bindweed, dandelion, bracken, and plantain. Unfortunately, some cultural practices designed to control weeds in actuality help them to establish more rapidly. Cultivation cuts these underground structures into pieces and spreads them around. Grasses and other species with rhizomes are among the most difficult weeds to control.

Types of Weeds Based on Life Cycle

Weeds may be classified into three groups based upon their life cycles:

1. *Annuals.* Annual weeds complete their life cycles in one year. *Summer annuals* germinate in spring and grow through summer. They produce seed and then die in fall or winter. Examples of summer annual weeds are lamb's-quarter, cocklebur, foxtail, and crabgrass, which infest lawns and vegetable fields. *Winter annuals* germinate in fall, live through winter, and produce seed in spring. The seeds remain dormant in summer, germinating in fall. Examples include chickweed, shepherd's purse, and hairy chess, which appear in plots of winter vegetables and fall nursery plants. Annual weeds are relatively easy to control, in spite of the fact that their short life cycle means they produce seeds more often.
2. *Biennials.* A few biennial weeds occur in crop cultivation and the landscape. Biennial weeds germinate in the spring of one year and remain vegetative until the next spring, when they flower. Weeds with biennial habits include hogweed and ragwort.
3. *Perennials.* Perennial weeds are very difficult to eradicate once established. They may be started from seed initially, but once mature, they also propagate by vegetative means. Many noxious perennial weeds are grasses (e.g., Bermuda grass, nutgrass, and quackgrass). Nongrass perennial weeds include plantain and dandelion. In fact, Bermuda grass, guineagrass, barnyardgrass, johnsongrass, goosegrass, and purple nutsedge are among the most difficult weeds to control.

7.1.3 CONTROLLING WEEDS

Since weeds may cause economic loss, they should be controlled when they occur. When weeds appear after the crop is mature or ripened, controlling them may not be economical. However, one of the preventive measures against weeds is to exclude weed seeds from crop seeds at harvest. Planting impure seeds is a means of spreading weeds. Poor-quality compost and unsterilized soil are ways by which weed seeds can be introduced into the greenhouse or garden. Poor-quality sod often contains weed seedlings. Further, improperly laid sod with gaps between strips creates opportunities for weeds to rapidly infest a lawn.

A plant's life cycle or growth pattern influences the control strategy employed in weed control. Winter annuals are best controlled while still in the seedling stage during the fall and early spring. Similarly, summer annuals should be controlled soon after germination. Biennials are vegetative in the first year of growth; they should be controlled in that year. Perennials are very difficult to control and hence should not be allowed to become established. Once established, they have a persistent root system, making them difficult to control. Perennials can be controlled effectively during the period of rapid growth before flowering or during the regrowth period after cutting. Flowering species should be prevented from setting seed.

Biological, chemical, and cultural control of weeds and other pests is discussed in Chapter 8. Annual weeds may be effectively controlled by mulching. However, mulching is ineffective in controlling perennial weeds. Controlling any type of weed is easier when the plants are in the seedling stages. Application of herbicides during the seedling stage is often effective in controlling weeds; however, it is ineffective when weeds are mature. Annuals and biennials also respond less favorably to chemical control when plants are entering the reproductive phase. In perennials, chemical control is effective at the bud stage, just before flowering.

7.1.4 WEEDS AS INDICATORS OF SOIL FERTILITY

Weeds may be plants out of place, but they arise where conditions are most favorable for their existence. The type of weed species found on a piece of land is often a fairly good indicator of the soil characteristics (especially fertility, pH, and type). Examples of such telltale signs are as follows:

1. An area of land on which a good population of, for example, goosegrass, thistles, chickweed, and yarrow are found usually indicates that the soil is fertile and nutritionally balanced.
2. When dandelion, poppy, bramble, shepherd's purse, bulbous buttercup, and stinging nettle occur in dense populations, the soil is likely to be light and dry.
3. Sedge, buttercup, primrose, thistle, dock, comfrey, and cuckooflower are found in wet soils.
4. Acidic soils support acid-loving plants such as cinquefoil, cornflower, pansy, daisy, foxglove, and black bindweed.
5. White mustard, bellflower, wild carrot, goat's beard, pennycress, and horseshoe vetch are found in alkaline soils.
6. Clay and heavy soils hold moisture and favor crops such as plantain, goosegrass, annual meadowgrass, and creeping buttercup.

It should be emphasized that large populations of mixtures of several of the associated species listed must occur for the diagnosis to be reliable.

7.2 PARASITIC PLANTS

Parasitic Organism
An organism that lives on or in another species and derives part or all of its nourishment from the living host.

There are more than 3,000 species of parasitic angiosperms. These plants have little or no chlorophyll and thus are incapable of photosynthesizing to meet their nutritional needs. **Parasitic** plants connect themselves to their host plants' water- and food-conducting tissues through specialized rootlike projections called *haustoria* (singular: *haustorium*). The dodder *(Cuscuta salina),* a parasite with bright-yellow or orange-colored strands, is a member of the family Convolvulaceae (morning glory family). It is a stem parasite. Others in this category are *Loranthes* and *Arienthobium.* Root parasites include the broomrapes (family Orobanchaceae). The Indian pipe *(Monotropa uniflora)* is also a root parasite that obtains its food from the host through the fungal hyphae it inserts into the host. Similarly, the world's largest flower, *Rafflesia arnoldii*, and others in the genus are root parasites in the grape family (Vitaceae).

Plants in five families have the capacity to trap and use insects to supplement their nutritional needs. These plants are described as carnivorous and include Venus-flytrap, pitcher plant, and sundew. Plants that live on the surfaces of other plants (not symbiotically but parasitically) are classifiable into three types:

1. *Epiphytes.* **Epiphytes** are plants that are *autotrophic* (photosynthesizing) but depend on others for support and some of their water and nutrient needs. These plants absorb water and minerals from the surfaces of their host plants and from the atmosphere. They are particularly adapted to the humid tropical forest; an example is Spanish moss.
2. *Hemiparasites.* Hemiparasites are equipped to photosynthesize but depend on the host species for water and nutrients. For example, mistletoe (*Phoradendron* spp.) is parasitic to many broadleaf trees including oak, birch, and huckleberry. Certain cultivars of these species are resistant to the parasite. Like mistletoe, the Indian warrior plant also produces haustoria. These plants are green plants and can therefore photosynthesize to some degree.
3. *True parasites.* Plants that are true parasites lack photosynthetic structures and are completely dependent on the host for all nutritional needs. An example is the dodder (*Cuscuta* spp.), which is parasitic to some vegetables and woody perennials.

Epiphyte
A plant that grows on another plant without deriving nutrition from the host.

7.3 SELECTED COMMON WEEDS

The following are examples of common weeds that occur in the vegetable garden or landscape. A weed may be more of a problem in one part of the country than another because of adaptation.

1. *Canada thistle (Cirsium arvense).* Canada thistle is more of a problem in the northern states of the United States. It has well-branched, deep roots. A perennial that reproduces both sexually and asexually (by rhizomes), has disk flowers that may be white, lavender, or rose-purple.
2. *Hedge bindweed (Convolvulus sepium).* Bindweed, a perennial weed that reproduces by seed or rhizomes, is a twining weed with white or pinkish flowers. It occurs in different places, including cultivated fields, especially in the eastern half of the United States.
3. *Field bindweed (Convolvulus arvensis).* Field bindweed differs from the hedge variety by being more widespread and having extensive and deep root systems. It is also a perennial and reproduces by seed and rhizomes. It has twining habits and may also spread on the ground; its white or pink flowers are bell shaped.
4. *Dandelion (Taraxacum officinale).* Dandelion is widespread, occurring nearly everywhere in the United States. It is a perennial with a deep taproot system, and the crown is branched. Dandelion produces flower heads that are golden yellow and easily dispersed by the wind. This weed is particularly common in lawns.
5. *Common milkweed (Asclepias syriaca).* Common milkweed is a broadleaf weed with milky sap. It has sweet-smelling, pink-white flowers. This perennial has a well-branched root system with long rhizomes and reproduces by seed or rhizomes. It is more of a problem in fields in the eastern half of the United States.
6. *Common lamb's-quarter (Chenopodium album).* Lamb's-quarter is an annual weed that reproduces by seed. It has a taproot system and green flowers that are borne in spikes in a clustered panicle at the end of the branch and leaf axil. This weed is problematic, especially in the eastern half of the United States.

THE CURRENT APPROACH TO WEED CONTROL

Department of Agriculture and Natural Resources
Langston University

RAYMOND FAUCETTE

For the sake of clarity we will begin with the following three definitions from Webster's Online Dictionary.

Weed is the generic word for a plant growing in a spot where it is not wanted. The most prominent use of the word is in connection with farming, where weeds may damage crops when growing in fields and poison domesticated animals when growing on pasture land. Many weeds are short-lived annual plants, that normally take advantage of temporarily bare soil to produce another generation of seeds before the soil is covered over again by slower growth; with the advent of agriculture, with extensive areas of ploughed soil exposed every year, the opportunities for such plants have been greatly expanded.

Pest is any animal or plant that is directly or indirectly detrimental to human interests, causing harm or reducing the quality and value of a harvestable crop or other resource. Weeds, termites, rats, and mildew are examples of pests.

Integrated pest control is a pest control strategy based on the determination of an economic threshold that indicates when a pest population is approaching the level at which control measures are necessary to prevent a decline in net returns. In principle, IPM is an ecologically based strategy that relies on natural mortality factors, such as natural enemies, weather, and crop management, and seeks control tactics that disrupt these factors as little as possible. Also, a USDA/Environmental Protection Agency program aims to decrease pesticide applications by teaching farmers to use a variety of alternative control techniques to minimize pesticide use. These techniques include biological controls, genetic resistance, tillage, pruning, and others. (IPM)

The current approach to pest control is Integrated Pest Management (IPM). As stated earlier IPM is an interdisciplinary approach that does not focus on eradication, but managing the pest population to keep it below a threshold that would cause economic loss to a crop. IPM combines legislative, cultural, biological, chemical, and physical methods of pest management. None of these methods are new, however they are used symbiotically to reduce our impact on the environment (Figure 1).

FIGURE 1 Crop consultant scouting for both weed and insect pests. *(Source: USDA)*

LEGISLATIVE

Both state and federal directives have been emplaced over the last ten years that both identify and make provisions for the management of noxious and invasive weeds and also regulating agricultural chemicals both acceptable and unacceptable.

CULTURAL

Crop rotations, varying planting dates, crop spacing, traps, cover and buffer crops are a few of the cultural methods employed to reduce the impact of weeds on crops (Figure 2, and 3).

BIOLOGICAL

Research is ongoing at several locations to identify and evaluate the effectiveness of both insects and pathogens that may be used in weed suppression. Crop breeding is also used to create new varieties with enhanced competitiveness to weeds.

FIGURE 2 Planting no-till corn into barley cover crop. *(Source: USDA)*

FIGURE 3 Cover crop in an orchard. *(Source: USDA)*

CHEMICAL

Research also continues in an effort to identify weed management compounds that function well in precision and conservation agriculture, but that will not have such a negative effect on neighboring crops, or downstream/downwind environments. Precision Farming includes Precision Weed Management that utilizes GPS technology to apply herbicides in variable rates, and only to untreated areas. The benefits are reduced pesticide usage, and a reduction in the associated costs. (Figure 4 and 5)

PHYSICAL

To date, no new physical methods of weed control are mentioned, however, tillage, mowing, cutting, and burning are considered by some as the only effective methods of controlling certain noxious plants. Seed purity, sanitation, and host eradication along with tillage may fit just as appropriately in the "Cultural" category of weed management.

BIOCHEMICAL

Research continues in an effort to incorporate natural resistance and immunities to current pesticides into crops so pesticide usage will not affect the desired crops.

FIGURE 4 Contact herbicide applied to weeds growing above soybean canopy. *(Source: USDA)*

FIGURE 5 GPS utilization in precision pesticide application. *(Source: USDA)*

Example

Integrated cultural, physical, and chemical weed control methods are utilized at the cropping system level by many Oklahoma farmers. Weed control methods on WillCrest Farms in Payne County Oklahoma have been changed from conventional weed control to an integrated pest management scheme in the last five years as a part of converting their entire farming venture from conventional tillage to no-till. Their cropping system has transitioned from a monoculture based system to a rotational system that produces three crops in two years that allows the land to lay fallow for one growing season. The crops in the rotation are Milo, Wheat and Corn. A broadleaf crop was been added to the rotation in 2007 to enhance the control of grass type weeds. A pre-planting burn-down is done with Roundup™ before drilling in the new crop. A crop consultant has also been retained who makes recommendations based on weekly surveys.

Sources

Agricultural resource service

University of Florida Extension

Burnside, O.C., Orf, J.H., and Pester, T.A., 1999. *Journal of Crop Production: agricultural management in global context* Volume: 2 Issue: 1 ISSN: 1092-678X

Shaner, D.L., 2004. Precision Weed Management: The wave of the future or just a passing fad? Phytoparasitica. 32:107-110

Personal communication: Clark Williams. 2007

Additional information

http://www.websters-online-dictionary.org/
http://www.nal.usda.gov/
http://edis.ifas.ufl.edu/WG041
http://www.oznet.ksu.edu/weedmanagement/
http://www.weeds.iastate.edu/
http://plants.usda.gov/

7. *Common cocklebur (Xanthium pensylvanicum).* Cocklebur is a monoecious annual weed. Its stem is hairy and the taproot system strong and branched. It may attain 90 centimeters in height under certain conditions and reproduces by seed.
8. *Redroot pigweed (Amaranthus retroflexus).* Redroot pigweed has a shallow taproot system and green flowers borne in dense panicles at the end of the stem and branches. Under certain conditions, it may grow as tall as 200 centimeters.
9. *Large crabgrass (Digitaria sanguinalis).* An annual grassy weed, large crabgrass is a problem in most parts of the United States. It is found in lawns and cultivated areas and has a dense, fibrous root system.
10. *Smooth crabgrass (Digitaria ischaemum).* Crabgrass is an annual and a common lawn weed in most parts of the United States.

11. *Barnyardgrass (Echnochloa crus-galli).* An annual grassy weed, barnyardgrass has a bunch form, as opposed to crabgrass, which has a spreading form. It prefers a relatively moist growing environment.
12. *Quackgrass (Agropyron repens).* Quackgrass is a perennial weed that reproduces by seed and rhizomes. It has an extensive, fibrous root system. It is not a problem in many of the southern states.
13. *Johnsongrass (Sorghum halepense).* Johnsongrass is a perennial weed that reproduces by seed and rhizomes. It is a greater problem in the southern states.

SUMMARY

Weeds are plants out of place. They may be annual, biennial, or perennial in life cycle. They compete with garden and landscape plants for growth factors. They may also harbor diseases and pests. Weeds are more adapted than cultivated plants and hence more competitive. The preponderance of certain weed species in a location often indicates soil fertility status. Weeds are spread through use of impure seeds, lack of phytosanitation, and other factors. Grass weeds are especially difficult to eradicate. Certain plants live parasitically on others.

MODULE 2

ANIMAL PESTS OF PLANTS

7.4 INSECTS

Insects are classified under the phylum Arthropoda (characterized by jointed legs, exoskeleton, segmentation, and bilateral symmetry). They belong to the class Insecta (true insects) and along with species in the class Arachnida (spiders and mites) are the sources of most plant pests.

7.4.1 ECONOMIC IMPORTANCE

An estimated 80 percent of known animal life consists of insects. There are more than 800,000 species of insects known to humans, out of which less than 1 percent are classified as pests. Insects are not only abundant in numbers and diversity but also are widely distributed and adapted. Horticultural plants are attacked by a wide variety of insect pests. Some of them cause gradual and progressive damage, whereas others, such as swarms of locusts, can strip a vast acreage of green plants of every leaf in a matter of only a few days. Many modern plant species are grown from improved seeds and are able to resist a number of insect pests. However, modern cultivation often depends on the use of *insecticides* to obtain economic yields. Insects inflict damage on plants, and some are carriers (vectors) of disease-causing organisms that are harmful to animals including humans.

Fortunately, certain insects are beneficial to the economic production of certain horticultural plants. For example, orchard crops depend on insects for pollination. In fact, in the production of crops such as strawberry, growers often deliberately introduce hives of bees into their fields for effective pollination and good yield.

7.4.2 IMPORTANT INSECT ORDERS

Insects are distinguished from other insectlike animals such as mites and spiders by having three pairs of jointed legs (the others have four pairs). Insects also have wings and antennae. Taxonomically, there are four major insect orders of economic importance in horticultural production:

1. *Lepidoptera.* Only the larva stage of Lepidoptera causes economic damage to plants. Adults feed mainly on plant fruits. Of this order, several important families cause severe damage to plants. The family Gelechiidae includes stem borers, which are larvae that bore through shoots, stems, and fruits. The family Pyralidae includes stem borers and leaf rollers, whereas Noctuidae (owls and moths) consists of a large variety of leaf eaters, stem and fruit borers, armyworms, and cutworms.
2. *Coleoptera.* Coleoptera is the order for beetles, which are biting and chewing insects. Important families are Curculionidae (weevil proper), Chrysomalidae (leaf beetles), and Bruchidae (pulse beetles), which attack pods of legumes. The family Coccinellidae includes the beneficial lady bird beetle. The family Scarabaeidae includes white grubs, which inhabit the soil and feed on roots and tubers.
3. *Hymenoptera.* The family Formicidae (ants) of the Hymenoptera order consist of leaf-cutting ants. Bees belong to this order but are considered beneficial insects rather than pests.
4. *Diptera.* The adults of the order Diptera (flies) are not pests. The larvae are the pests of this order. The family Tephritidae (fruit flies) includes important pests of ripening fruits.

Other important orders are Thysanoptera (thrips) and Orthoptera (grasshoppers and crickets). The order Homoptera, which includes families such as Cicadellidae (leaf hoppers), Aphididae (aphids), and Pseudococcidae (mealybugs), is also important.

7.4.3 CLASSIFICATION OF INSECT PESTS

Classification Based on Life Cycle

Like all living things, insects have a life cycle that consists of various stages of growth and development (starting from egg to adult). At one or more of these stages, insects may be capable of causing damage to plants. The processes of change that insects pass through is called **metamorphosis,** which is a basis for classifying insects into one of four classes.

1. *No metamorphosis.* Insects that do not metamorphose are hatched as miniature adults, meaning they look like small versions of their adult forms (Figure 7–1). Insect orders such as Thysanura and Collembola exhibit this type of metamorphosis.
2. *Gradual metamorphosis.* In gradual metamorphosis, eggs hatch into young insects called *nymphs* that do not have all of the adult characteristics. As they mature, nymphs exhibit adult characteristics (Figure 7–2). Common orders of insects in this class are Homoptera, Hemiptera, Orthoptera, and Isoptera.
3. *Incomplete metamorphosis.* Insects exhibiting incomplete metamorphosis change shape gradually through the maturation process (Figure 7–3). Insects in the equivalent of the nymph stage are described as *naiads.* An example of this order is Odonata (which includes, for example, dragonfly).

Metamorphosis
Transformation of larva into an adult.

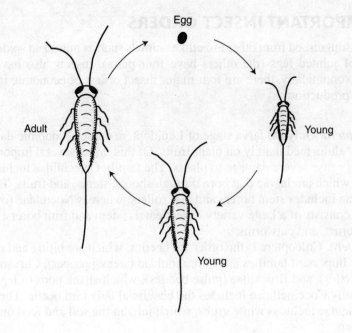

FIGURE 7–1 Life cycle of an insect with no metamorphosis.

Egg

Adult

Young

Young

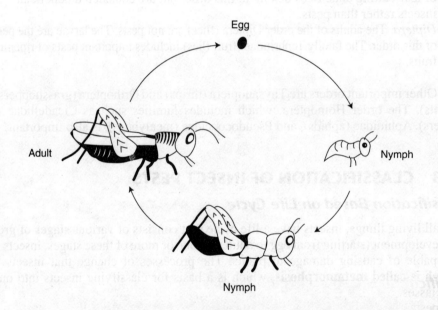

FIGURE 7–2 Life cycle of an insect with gradual metamorphosis.

Egg

Adult

Nymph

Nymph

4. *Complete metamorphosis.* A complete metamorphosis consists of four distinct stages, in none of which the insect looks like the adult (Figure 7–4). The egg hatches into a *larva* that feeds on plant foliage and other parts. The larva passes through a dormant stage called *pupa*. The mature adult emerges from the pupa as a beautiful butterfly, which is harmless to plants. Examples of insects in this class are Lepidoptera (butterflies) and Hymenoptera (bees). Bees and butterflies are important in aiding crop pollination. The larvae differ from one order to another. In Diptera (flies), the larva is called a *maggot*. The larvae of Lepidoptera (butterflies and moths) are called *caterpillars* (Figure 7–5). Certain larvae tunnel through leaves, as occurs in the Diptera orders; they are called *miners*. Larvae of moths and beetles are able to tunnel through stems and other tissue and are called *borers.*

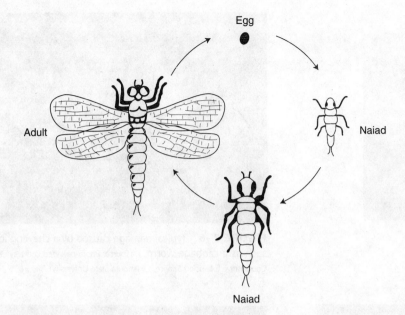

FIGURE 7–3 Life cycle of an insect with incomplete metamorphosis.

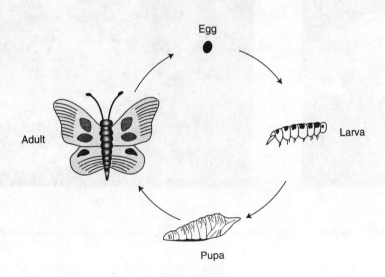

FIGURE 7–4 Life cycle of an insect with complete metamorphosis.

Classification Based on Feeding Habit

Insect pests can also be classified based on how they inflict damage on the plant through their eating habits. On this basis, there are two categories of insects: chewing insects and sucking and piercing insects.

Chewing Insects   Chewing insects, as their name implies, chew plant parts (e.g., petals, leaves, stems, fruits, and flowers) during feeding. They have chewing mouthparts. Their damage is not limited to the aboveground parts of plants but also includes roots. This group includes larvae such as caterpillars and grubs, as well as adults such as grasshoppers, beetles, and boring insects. The tissue of the plant is destroyed in the process of feeding, the damage caused being more serious as the insect matures. Damage from chewing insects is easy to identify (Figure 7–6). Symptoms include the following:

Defoliating. Insects such as leaf beetles, caterpillars, cutworms, and grasshoppers devastate the foliage of plants by chewing portions of leaves and, in severe cases, stripping the plant completely of leaves. Defoliation causes a reduction in photosynthetic area, thereby reducing plant vigor and productivity.

FIGURE 7–5 Caterpillar of cotton bollworm.
(*Source:* USDA)

FIGURE 7–6 Typical damage caused by a chewing insect pest such as a cabbage worm. (*Source:* Photo provided courtesy of Oklahoma Cooperative Extension Service, Oklahoma State University)

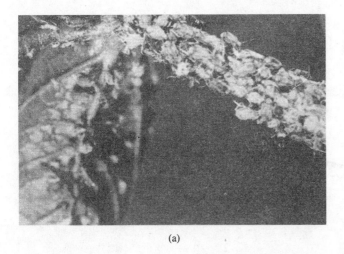

(a)

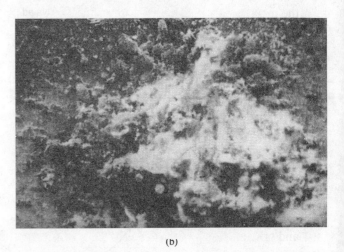

(b)

FIGURE 7–7 Sucking insects: (a) aphids and (b) mealybugs. (*Source:* Photos provided courtesy of Oklahoma Cooperative Extension Service, Oklahoma State University)

Boring. The chewing mouthparts of borers are used to bore channels into succulent tissue—stems, fruits, tubers, and seeds. Examples of pests that bore into plant parts are corn borers and white grubs.

Leaf mining. Unlike borers, which bore directly into the tissue, leaf miners only tunnel between epidermal layers.

Root feeding. Root feeders damage plants from below in the soil by chewing roots and other underground structures. Examples are white grubs and wireworms.

Sucking and Piercing Insects Sucking and piercing insects puncture the plant part on which they feed in order to suck out plant fluids. Examples of such insects include aphids, scales, mealybugs, thrips, and leaf hoppers. Insects in this group are often small in size (Figure 7–7). Even in their adult stage, they can be microscopic, making them difficult to readily detect and control.

Their effect is often recognized as curling up or puckering of leaves (leaf distortion) or bleaching of leaves. Sucking and piercing insects also damage fruits. They are often found on the undersides of leaves. Certain sucking insects may inject toxins into the plant in the feeding process. Another characteristic of damage caused by sucking insects (also found with some chewing insects) is an abnormal growth called a *gall* (Figure 7–8).

Identifying the kind of insect is a critical first step in their control. Insects, like other living things, have a preference for feeding time. Some avoid the bright daylight, feeding only when it is dark. As such, some insect pests hide on the undersides of leaves or even retreat and hide in the soil at the base of the plant during the day. Being aware of such habits not only helps identify insect pests but also aids in their control. Mealybugs and scales often dwell in colonies and at some stage may secrete a waxy layer over themselves for additional protection; that layer is difficult to penetrate by many insecticides.

7.4.4 CLOSE RELATIVES OF INSECTS

Mites

Mites are insectlike organisms. They belong to the order Acrina, of which the family Tetranychidae (spiders and mites) is very important in horticultural plant production. They have four pairs of legs (not three) and have no antennae or wings. They are among the most widely distributed of pests, affecting a variety of plant species including ornamentals, fruits, vegetables, and field crops. They occur in the field and greenhouse. Mites are sucking insects that reproduce rapidly and frequently. Where infestation is high, they form fine webs on plant parts (Figure 7–9). Spider mites (*Bryobia praetiosa, Tetranychus urticae,* and *Panomychus ulmi*) are economically important horticultural pests.

Spiders

Spiders are closely related to true insects. They belong to the class of arthropods (jointed legs) called Arachnida, which also includes mites.

Millipedes and Centipedes

Millipedes (Diplopoda) and *centipedes* (Chilopoda) occur most commonly in damp areas such as beneath stones, piles of leaves, and logs. They rarely damage plants directly and prey on small insects and spiders.

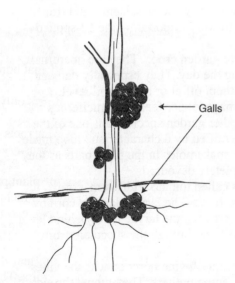

FIGURE 7–8 Galls can develop on both the above- and belowground parts of plants.

FIGURE 7–9 Typical spider mite damage. (*Source:* Photo provided courtesy of Oklahoma Cooperative Extension Service, Oklahoma State University)

FIGURE 7–10   A Colorado potato beetle.   (*Source:* Photo provided courtesy of Oklahoma Cooperative Extension Service, Oklahoma State University)

FIGURE 7–11   Cucumber beetle.   (*Source:* USDA)

7.4.5   STORAGE PESTS

Insects inflict considerable damage on stored food. A variety of weevils, moths, beetles, and flies are known postharvest pests that damage stored products. Examples include the sawtoothed grain beetle, dried fruit beetle, raisin moth, and *Drosophila*.

7.4.6   SOME IMPORTANT GENERAL INSECTS AND MITES

Horticultural plants are plagued by numerous insects and mites. The following are some of the important types:

1. *Colorado potato beetle (Leptinotarsa decimilneata)*. Commonly called the potato beetle, this insect also feeds on tomato, eggplant, and others. Both the larvae and adults are pests. They occur throughout the country, wherever the host plants are found (Figure 7–10).
2. *Cucumber beetles (Diabrotica undecimpunctata [12-spotted beetle]; Acalymma trivittata [striped beetle])*. Cucumber beetles feed on leaves, stems, and fruits. The larvae attack plant roots. Two species are very important—the 12-spotted and striped beetles (Figure 7–11).
3. *Cutworms*. Cutworms are pests of vegetable garden crops. They are nocturnal and thus hide under rocks and debris during the day. They especially damage recently transplanted seedlings by cutting them off at or below soil level.
4. *Cabbage looper (Trichoplusia ni)*. The cabbage looper feeds on cruciferous garden plants (cabbage family) and many other garden species. It is one of the most common garden caterpillars and is identified by a characteristic loop made by its body as it moves forward. The larvae make holes in the plant parts as they feed, but sometimes the plant may be completely devoured.
5. *Corn earworm (Heliothus zea)*. Sometimes called tomato fruitworm, corn earworm prefers to feed on corn and tomato fruits. The larvae damage corn by eating the succulent kernels. In the feeding process, the larvae leave behind large quantities of feces. In tomato, the earworms bore through the succulent fruits (Figure 7–12).
6. *Squash vine borer (Melittia calabaza)*. The squash vine borer attacks the vines of pumpkin, squash, cucumber, and melon, among others. They tunnel through the vines of these plants, resulting in wilting and eventual death.

FIGURE 7–12 Corn earworm damage. (*Source:* Photo provided courtesy of Oklahoma Cooperative Extension Service, Oklahoma State University)

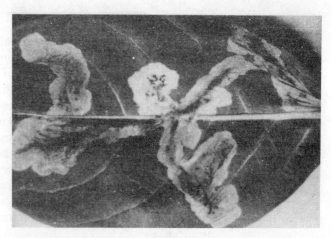

FIGURE 7–13 Leaf miner damage on spinach. (*Source:* Photo provided courtesy of Oklahoma Cooperative Extension Service, Oklahoma State University)

7. *Leaf miners.* Leaf miner damage is visible as tunnels between leaf surfaces (Figure 7–13). These tunnels are caused by larvae of flies such as the serpentine leaf miner (*Liriomyza* spp.). When a leaf is heavily infested, it yellows and eventually drops. Leaf miners attack a variety of garden plants such as tomato, pepper, eggplant, and especially lettuce and melon.

8. *Spider mites (Tetranychus spp.).* Mites are piercing or sucking insects that live on the undersides of leaves. They vary in color from reddish-yellow to light green. They attack a variety of garden crops, especially tomato and cucurbit. After feeding, the leaves appear bronzed or discolored. Severely attacked plants whither and drop. Spider mites have the capacity to produce six to ten generations each year. They devastate ornamentals, fruits, nuts, vegetables, and numerous other species.

9. *Thrips.* Sucking insects, thrips are very common in the garden. Plants attacked have distorted leaves. Onion thrips *(Thrips tabaci)* and western flower thrips *(Frankliniella occidentalis)* are two of the most common thrips in the garden and landscape.

10. *Aphids.* Also called plant lice, aphids are common on young leaves and growing tips of stems. One of the most common of the aphid species is the green peach aphid *(Myzus persicae),* which attacks many garden crops. Aphid populations are effectively held in check where natural enemies such as lacewings occur. This sucking insect affects many ornamentals, orchard crops, and vegetables. They are important because they are able to transmit a number of viruses that cause devastation to horticultural crops, examples being cucumber mosaic, bean mosaic, and lettuce mosaic. Aphids cause plants to grow with less vigor.

11. *Ants.* Ants are common in the garden and the landscape. One of the most common is the Argentine ant *(Iridomyrmex humilis).* It feeds on honeydew secreted by aphids. The leaf cutter ant *(Acromyrmex* spp.) cuts pieces of leaves for food.

7.4.7 CONTROL

Insects are commonly controlled by the use of chemicals. However, they may be controlled by cultural, legislative, and biological methods. Control methods are discussed in detail in Chapter 8.

Cultivated plants are usually more susceptible than their wild relatives to diseases. This susceptibility is due in part to the fact that many different cultivars have uniform genetic backgrounds as a result of the activities of plant breeders using the same breeding stock in developing new cultivars. Further, modern cultural practices allow plants to be grown in dense populations (as in monoculture), which facilitates the spread of disease.

Horticultural plants are attacked not only by insects but also by a large number of microorganisms that cause infectious diseases. These parasitic **pathogens** (disease-causing organisms) can be placed into four categories—*fungi, bacteria, viruses,* and *mycoplasma-like organisms.* Like all living things, these organisms have their own life cycles. Since they are parasitic, they need a susceptible host on which to survive.

Plant diseases may be classified on the basis of the causal organism, such as fungi, bacteria, viruses, and microplasma-like organisms.

Pathogen
An organism that causes disease.

7.5.1 FUNGI

An estimated 75 percent of all seed plant species live in some form of association with fungi in their roots, which is known as *mychorrizae.* This association is called *mutualism,* where both host and fungus benefit, and is similar to *symbiosis,* a mutually beneficial plant-bacteria association found in legumes only. Mychorrhizal fungi are known to be more efficient than plant roots in absorbing phosphorus. They are also essential for the growth and development of forest trees and herbaceous species. Acid rain destroys michorrhizae.

The reproductive structures from which fungi develop are called *spores.* Spores occur in a tremendous variety of shapes, sizes, and colors. A few fungi have no spore stage. When spores germinate, they produce *hyphae,* which grow and branch to form the fungus body called *mycelium.* Certain spores are visible as mold growth on the leaf surface. Fungal diseases such as *Helminthosporium* leaf spots, rusts, powdery mildew, and cercospora leaf spots are examples of this mold growth form. Other fungi occur as tiny dark fruiting bodies that are embedded in the tissue of the diseased plant. Examples of fungi are *Septoria* and *Ascochyta.*

Fungal spores are transported in a variety of ways—by wind, water, birds, insects, spiders, slugs, and mites. Some of them have a protective covering that enables them to survive adverse environmental conditions. In order to infect, hyphae of fungi gain access to the host through wounds (caused by equipment, pests, hail, ice, and so forth) or natural openings such as stomata. Sometimes the pathogen penetrates the epidermal layer by direct action on that layer.

Most of the infectious plant diseases are attributed to fungi. Fungi are either unicellular or multicellular (mostly) plants that lack chlorophyll. More than 250,000 species of fungi have been described, of which about 22,000 are known to cause plant disease. Some of them can live only on dead tissue **(saprophytic),** such as organic matter, while others live on living tissue *(parasitic).* Some of them are restricted *(obligatory)* to one host type (dead or living), while others have flexibility *(facultative).* Those that feed on dead and decaying matter are beneficial to plants because they aid in the decomposition of organic matter or compost to release nutrients for plant use. In the lawn, they aid in the decomposition of thatch (accumulated dead grass on the surface of the soil).

Saprophyte
An organism that derives its nutrients from the dead body or the nonliving products of another plant or animal.

All fungi are not pathogenic. Many are useful to humans and plants. *Penicillin* (from *Penicillium*) is one of the most important antibacterial drugs. Mushrooms used for food are fungi; fermented beverages and foods (e.g., bread, wine, cheese, and beer) depend on fungi (yeast) in their production.

Even though most plant diseases are caused by fungi, they are usually relatively easy to control. Methods of disease control are described later in this chapter. Table 7–1 shows some important plant fungal diseases, their symptoms, causal organisms, hosts, and methods of control.

TABLE 7–1 Selected Fungal Diseases of Horticultural Plants

Common Name	Pathogen	Example of Plant (Host)
Damping-off	*Pythium* spp.	Common problem of seedlings
	Rhizoctonia spp.	in the nursery
Downy mildew	*Plasmopara viticola*	Grape
Rust	*Puccinia striiformis*	Turfgrasses
	P. graminis	
Late blight	*Pythium infestans*	Tomato and potato
Powdery mildew	*Erysiphe polygoni*	Many different plants
	E. graminis	Cereal
	E. cicoracearum	Cucurbits
Brown rot	*Monilinia fructicola*	Peach, plum, almond, and
		other stone fruits
Dutch elm	*Ceratocystis ulmi*	Elm tree
Fusarium wilt	*Fusarium oxysporum*	Pea, tomato, and watermelon

7.5.2 BACTERIA

Bacteria are unicellular organisms that may occur in one of three basic shapes—spherical, rodlike, or spiral. They are ubiquitous in the environment. Bacteria are also classified according to *Gram reaction* (positive or negative for violet or pink-red reaction to Gram's stain).

Bacteria cause very few known economically important diseases in horticultural plants. However, the diseases they cause are difficult to control. Pathogenic bacteria have rodlike shapes and prefer a pH of about 6.5 to 7.5. Most of them are intolerant of high temperatures and will die if exposed to temperatures of 51.7°C (125°F) for about ten minutes. The pathogenic bacteria that attack plants are mostly facultative parasites. They enter the host through wounds or natural pores. These unicellular organisms are not always pathogenic; some, like fungi, being beneficial to humans and plants. The bacterium *Escherichia coli* (commonly called *E. coli*) occurs in the intestinal tract of humans. Bacteria are involved in the decomposition processes in septic tanks and other sewage systems and compost heaps. Bacteria-plant associations (symbioses) involving legumes and *Rhizobia* species result in the fixation of nitrogen in the host plant's roots. Bacteria multiply rapidly by simple fission (mother cell divides in half).

Pathogenic bacteria and their hosts, symptoms, and control measures of diseases are described in Table 7–2. Bacteria cause rots, cankers, spots, wilts, and blights. Bacterial diseases can be reduced through the observance of phytosanitation, but chemicals are not very effective against them. Bacterial disease-resistant cultivars are available for many species. Bacteria can overwinter in or on plant materials.

7.5.3 VIRUSES

Technically, *viruses* cannot be described as animals. They generally consist of a core of RNA or DNA encased in protein or lipoprotein. They cannot be cultured in vitro. They act like living organisms only when found inside of a living cell of a plant or animal. Viruses are not like bacteria and fungi in that they are not capable of digestion and respiration. They are obligate parasites and operate by infecting a host cell and taking over its hereditary machinery for the production of viral DNA (or RNA). The consequence is an altered host metabolism. Viruses are microscopic and can be transmitted from infected plants to healthy ones through the feeding action of insects *(vectors)* such as aphids, leaf hoppers, and mites.

Viral diseases plague horticultural plants but to a lesser extent than fungi (Table 7–3). However, once infested, viral diseases are virtually impossible to treat. The disease may not kill the plant but instead stunt growth. The vectors may be controlled to curtail the spread of the disease. Exposure of infested plants to high temperatures (38°C or 100.4°F) for twenty

TABLE 7–2 Selected Bacterial Diseases of Horticultural Plants

Common Name	Pathogen	Plant (Host) Attacked
Bacterial wilt	*Erwinia tracheiphila*	Cucumber and other cucurbits
Bacterial soft rot	*Erwinia carotovora*	Vegetables, fruits, and tubers
Crown gall	*Agrobacterium tumifasciens*	Tree fruits and woody ornamentals
Bacterial canker	*Pseudomonas syringae*	Pitted fruits: cherry, peach, and plum
Common blight	*Xathomonas phaseoli*	Field bean, lima bean, and snap bean

TABLE 7–3 Selected Viral Diseases of Horticultural Plants; Viruses Are Given Descriptive Names Based on the Diseases They Cause

Tobacco mosaic virus (TMV)
Tomato ring spot virus (TomRSV)
Tomato spotted wilt virus (TSWV)
Potato leaf roll virus (PLRV)
Potato virus Y (PVY)
Cucumber mosaic virus (CMV)
Bean common mosaic virus (BCMV)
Curly top virus of sugar beet (CTV)
Prunus necrotic ring spot virus (PNRV) (affects most stone fruits)

to thirty days *(heat therapy)* has been used to inactivate certain viruses. Actively growing tips of plants are virus free and provide another effective means of producing disease-free plants from infected plants (see propagation of plants by *tissue culture*). Viruses are often described according to the species they infect (host specificity) (e.g., lettuce mosaic virus, maize dwarf mosaic virus, and sugar beet curly top virus). They are also described according to serological properties, particle morphology, mode or modes of transmission, morphology, and nucleic acid type (DNA or RNA).

Common symptoms of viral infection are yellowing of leaves, loss of vigor, poor growth, and stunting. Viruses are primarily systemic in the host plant's vascular fluids and hence transmitted readily by sucking insects. They commonly remain indefinitely in biennial or perennial hosts for as long as the host remains alive (except tobacco mosaic virus [TMV], which can thrive on dead plant tissue). To control viruses, one may use resistant cultivars, control the vectors, or limit their transmission in vegetative plants or their parts. Some viruses are transmitted by seed. Sometimes infected plants may show no symptoms (symptomless).

7.5.4 MYCOPLASMA-LIKE ORGANISMS

Mycoplasmas, which occur in the phloem of plants, are parasites that are intermediate in size between viruses and bacteria. Like viruses, mycoplasmas are technically not animals. Some of the symptoms associated with mycoplasma-like infections include yellowing, stunting, wilting, and distortions, as in viral infections. Aster yellows have been identified in, for example, carrot, strawberry, lettuce, phlox, and tomato.

7.6 OTHER PESTS OF HORTICULTURAL PLANTS

Apart from insects, fungi, bacteria, viruses, and mycoplasma-like organisms, horticultural plants are plagued by other animal species. They may not cause diseases but can nonetheless cause economic loss to growers. The major ones include small animals, birds, nematodes, and snails and slugs.

7.6.1 SMALL ANIMALS

Rabbits, mice, gophers, bats, and moles are among the rodents and other small animals that plague cultivated plants. They may attack plants from above or below the ground. Moles, for example, damage lawns from underground. They may eat seeds when planted, causing incomplete plant stand in the field, or they may eat mature fruits and seeds. These mammals, especially the ones that bore holes in the ground, may improve drainage.

7.6.2 BIRDS

Birds cause damage similar to that effected by small animals. Fruits and cereal crops are particularly prone to bird damage. On the other hand, birds feed on insects at all stages in their life cycles, thereby playing a beneficial role in controlling some insect pests.

7.6.3 NEMATODES

Nematodes are unsegmented roundworms. They are microscopic plant parasites that attack above- and belowground parts of plants, including vegetables, fruit trees, ornamentals, and foliage plants. However, most that are parasitic on plants are soilborne. The most common nematodes include root knot (*Meloidogyne* spp.) and cyst (*Heterodera* spp.). They are spread by equipment, water, shoes, and other means. On the roots, they cause irregularly shaped knots that interrupt nutrient flow in the plant. This amorphous growth is distinguishable from the well-defined and usually round shape of *root nodules* produced in legume-*Rhizobia* symbiosis (Figure 7–14). The plant may be discolored (abnormal yellowing) and stunted in growth. Tuber crops may have disfigured and unsightly skin.

Many nematodes are inactive at temperatures below 10°C (50°F). A field infested with nematodes can be managed by cultural operations to lower the population of the parasites. When the populations are high, fumigation is most effective, even though it is not possible to irradicate the pest from the soil. Nematodes are especially difficult to control in dormant form (cysts or eggs).

7.6.4 SNAILS AND SLUGS

Nocturnal creatures, snails and slugs are similar in many respects, one distinguishing feature being the lack of a shell in slugs (Figure 7–15). The presence of these mollusks is betrayed by the slimy trail they leave behind as they move on the soil surface. They feed on leaves and young plant stems. Because of their nocturnal habits, they hide during the daytime in cool and moist places such as under rocks, debris, and mulch. Slugs cause more damage than snails to horticultural plants. The most common garden snails are the brown garden snail (*Helix aspersa*) and the decollate snail (*Rumina decollata*). The former has a globular spiral shell and the latter a cone-shaped spiral shell. The most common slugs in the home garden are the spotted garden slug (*Limax maximus*) and the tawny garden slug (*Limax flavus*). The tawny slug leaves a trail of yellow slime. The gray garden slug (*Agricolimax reticulatus*) is small and leaves a clear slime trail.

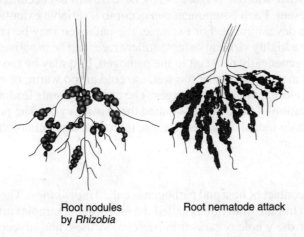

FIGURE 7–14 Nematode damage as distinguished from root nodules formed as a result of *Rhizobia* infection.

Root nodules
by *Rhizobia*

Root nematode attack

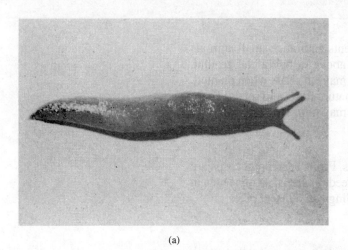

(a)   (b)

FIGURE 7–15   (a) Slug and (b) snail.   *(Source:* Photos provided courtesy of Oklahoma Cooperative Extension Service, Oklahoma State University)

7.7 HOW DISEASE OCCURS

7.7.1   DISEASE FACTORS

Every organism has a life cycle during which it reproduces, develops, grows, and dies. Disease conditions involve the interaction between the life cycles of the host and the pathogen. To understand the nature of disease, it is important to distinguish between *parasitism* and *pathogenicity*. An organism that lives in or on another for the purpose of deriving food is called a parasite, and the relationship between the two individuals (parasite and host) is called parasitism. A parasite deprives its host of food, making the latter less vigorous and less productive. This one-sided relationship may not go beyond depriving the host of nutrients. In certain cases, the relationship is mutually beneficial (symbiotic), as occurs in the root nodules of legumes where *Rhizobia* reside. The bacteria derive nutrients from the legumes and in return fix atmospheric nitrogen into usable form for the plant. Sometimes the activities of the parasites coupled with the reaction of the host result in abnormal physiological activities in the host and physical degeneration of cells and tissue. This condition describes the state of **pathogenicity,** and the organism associated with it is called a *pathogen*.

Pathogenicity
The capability of a pathogen to cause disease.

Pathogens differ in the plant types, parts, tissues, and organs they can successfully attack and grow on. Obligate parasites tend to be *host specific* (limited to one species), whereas nonobligate parasites can produce disease symptoms on a variety of plants. The variety of plants a pathogen can grow on is called its *host range*. For disease to develop, three ingredients must be present: (1) a pathogen (causal agent), (2) a susceptible host (plant on which the pathogen can grow), and (3) a favorable environment. This grouping constitutes the *disease triangle* (Figure 7–16). Disease will not occur if one of these components is not present. Each component can occur to a variable extent, which affects the degree of disease development. For example, the pathogen may be present in small or large numbers, be a highly virulent or less virulent race, and be in active or dormant stage. The host may be genetically resistant to the pathogen, or it may be too young or too old. The environment may be too dry or too wet, too cold or too warm, or very favorable.

Disease development occurs in stages. The chain of events leading to the development and perpetuation of the disease is called the *disease cycle*. The primary events in a disease cycle include inoculation, penetration, infection, dissemination, and overwintering or oversummering.

Inoculation

The coming into contact of host and pathogen is called *inoculation*. The pathogen (or any part of it) that can initiate infection is called the *inoculum*. Examples are spores and sclerotia (in fungi) or the whole organism in bacteria, viruses, and mycoplasmas. Since an

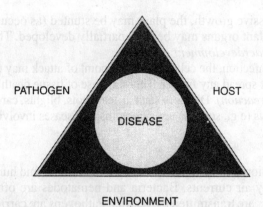

FIGURE 7–16 The disease triangle.

inoculum may consist of one or more individual pathogens, the unit of inoculum of any pathogen is called a *propagule.* The inoculum that causes the original infection is called the *primary inoculum,* and the subsequent infection is called the *primary infection.* Primary inoculum produces secondary inoculum, which produces secondary infection. The inoculum may be harbored by plant debris, soil, or planting material (e.g., seeds and tubers). It is transmitted to the host either passively, by wind, water, or insects, or actively, by *vectors* (e.g., insects and mites).

Penetration

Whereas all pathogens in their vegetative state are capable of initiating infection immediately, fungal spores and seeds of parasitic higher organisms must first germinate. Germination requires good conditions. Before penetration, recognition between the host and the pathogen must occur. The recognition process may trigger a defense reaction in the host to resist penetration. If successful, disease development will be curtailed.

Penetration may occur through natural openings (e.g., stomata), wounds, or intact membrane boundaries. Fungi frequently penetrate the host directly. Bacteria and viruses require existing wounds or those caused by vectors to gain entry into the host.

Infection

The **infection** stage in disease development involves contact, growth, and multiplication of pathogens in host tissues. The symptoms of successful infection may include necrosis and discoloration of tissue. Symptoms may not always develop immediately; certain infections remain *latent* until conditions are more favorable. The time interval between inoculation and the onset of disease symptoms is called the *incubation period.* During infection, the tissue of the host may or may not be killed. The success of infection depends on favorable environmental conditions.

Infection
The establishment of a parasite within a host.

After penetration, pathogens invade the host cells or tissue. Invasion relates to the spread of infection. Many infections caused by fungi, bacteria, and nematodes are *local* (limited to one or a few cells and involving small areas on the plant). On the other hand, infections caused by mycoplasmas and all natural viral infections are *systemic* (spreads to or invades all susceptible cells and tissue throughout the plant). Certain fungal diseases (e.g., downy mildew, rusts, and smuts) are systemic in the way they invade the host. Part of the infection process is growth and reproduction, which leads to colonization of the host cells or tissue. With reproduction, new cells are invaded by the pathogen.

Responses to Invasion by Pathogens When plants respond to an invasion by a pathogen, a disease is said to have developed. There are three general responses to invasion:

1. The affected host may experience excessive abnormal growth such as galls (as in crown gall) or curling (e.g., peach leaf curl). This growth is called *overdevelopment of tissue.*

2. Instead of excessive growth, the plant may be stunted (as occurs with most viral infections) or plant organs may be only partially developed. This response is described as *underdevelopment of tissue*.

3. To contain the infection, the cells around the point of attack may die so that the organism cannot spread any further. This response of tissue death is called *necrosis (hypersensitive reaction)*. Diseases such as leaf spots, blights, cankers (e.g., anthracnose), and decays (e.g., soft rot) are symptoms of diseases involving tissue death.

Dissemination

Agents of dissemination are air, water, insects, other animals, and humans. Fungal spores are usually spread by air currents. Bacteria and nematodes are often disseminated by water. Viral infections are transmitted by vectors. Pathogens are carried on farm tools and equipment and on the feet or bodies of animals.

Overwintering or Oversummering

Annual plants die after a season, infection or no infection. The pathogen must therefore be able to survive in the absence of its host. Similarly, pathogens of perennial plants must survive during the period of dormancy while adverse weather prevails. For example, nematodes overwinter as eggs in plant debris. Some fungi inhabit the soil.

7.7.2 DEFENSE AGAINST PATHOGENS BY PLANTS

Plants have structural and biochemical means of combating an invasion by pathogens. Structural and biochemical defense mechanisms involve the use of physical barriers or the secretion of chemicals to block entry of pathogens into plant hosts. Plants differ in the types of mechanisms they possess.

Structural Defense

Preexisting Defense Mechanisms   When a pathogen lands on the surface of the plant and attempts to penetrate the tissue, the plant's first means of defense is its epidermis. Some plants have deposits of wax in the epidermal cells or a thick cuticle over the epidermal layer, either of which is impenetrable to pathogens. Some leaves have a waxy, water-repellent surface or a pubescent surface that makes it difficult for water to settle to provide the moisture certain pathogens such as fungi and bacteria require to grow or multiply. The presence of such a tough material severely limits direct penetration of pathogens, thus reducing infection because the remaining avenues for entry are the natural openings (stomata).

Induced Defense Structures   If the pathogen gains entrance into the tissue, the presence of the alien matter may induce the formation of a cork layer for containment of the invasion. In some cases, especially in stone fruits, an abscission layer may be induced to form in active leaves. This layer causes a permanent break between the site of infection and the rest of the leaf, consequently forestalling the advancement of the infection. In some plants, an injury (e.g., resulting from penetration) induces gums to be formed around the point of infection, thus limiting its spread. Another induced structure is tissue necrosis, a hypersensitive reaction to invasion. A cell that is penetrated by the hyphae of fungi, for example, soon experiences degeneration of the nucleus, followed ultimately by death. Death of tissue means the fungus has no access to nutrients, leading to the eventual death of an obligate parasite.

Biochemical Defense

Plants under attack by pathogens may secrete certain metabolites to ward off attack.

Preexisting Mechanisms   Certain plants under normal conditions exude chemicals onto the plant surface (stem, root, or leaves). Tomato, for example, is known to release *fungitoxic exudates* in its leaves, which in high enough concentrations inhibit the germination of the fungus *Botrytis*. The scales of red onions are known to exude red pigments (protocatechaic acid and catechol) that make this variety resistant to onion smudge fungus; the white-scaled variety remains susceptible.

In another scenario, a pathogen may fail to attach to and infect a plant if it is unable to recognize the plant as one of its hosts. For example, in a viral attack, no infection may occur if the viral nucleic acid is not compatible with the host nucleic acid. Some pathogens require certain essential nutrients for proper growth and development that, when absent, make the host less susceptible, or more resistant, to the pathogen. In bacteria soft rot (*Erwinia carotovora* var. *atroseptica*), the disease is less pronounced in potato cultivars that are low in reducing sugars than in cultivars that are high in reducing sugars.

Induced Mechanisms   When a plant is injured, the cells in the area secrete certain chemicals to initiate healing. These chemicals include a variety of phenolic compounds and others such as chlorogenic acids and caffeic acids. These chemicals are already present in the plant. However, an injured plant may secrete a special group of compounds called *phytoalexins,* which do not occur naturally in healthy plants. Phytoalexins are produced in large amounts when a plant is stimulated by injury. Most of the known phytoalexins are induced by fungal infections. Examples are *phaseolin* (from bean), *pisatin* (from pea), *capsidol* (from pepper), and *rishitin* (from potato). In certain plants, detoxification of toxins from pathogens (e.g., pyricularin) is known to occur.

Resistance to certain pathogens, including fungi, bacteria, viruses, and insects, has been induced *(induced resistance)* in many plants by treatment with biotic agents. In tobacco, an infection of a hypersensitive cultivar with TMV induces a nonspecific resistance to TMV, fungi *(Phytophthora),* and aphids, among others.

7.7.3   GENETICS OF DISEASE RESISTANCE

True resistance is disease resistance genetically controlled by one, a few, or many genes. There are two kinds of true **resistance**—horizontal and vertical.

Horizontal Resistance

Horizontal resistance is also called *polygenic* or *multigenic resistance* because it is controlled by numerous genes. Each gene contributes toward total resistance and hence is said to have *minor gene resistance. Horizontal* resistance is controlled largely by environment and thus may vary under different environmental conditions. Generally, it does not protect plants from becoming infected. Instead, it slows down the spread of disease and the development of epidemics in the field. Every plant has some degree of horizontal resistance.

Vertical Resistance

Vertical resistance, also called *qualitative, specific,* or *differential resistance,* is usually controlled by one or a few genes *(monogenic* or *oligogenic resistance).* Plants with this kind of resistance may be resistant to certain races of a pathogen while remaining susceptible to others. Because the resistance gene plays a major role in the expression of resistance (instead of contributing in small amounts toward the overall resistance), this kind of resistance is also called *major gene resistance.* When a pathogen attacks a plant with vertical resistance to the disease, the plant usually reacts in a hypersensitive way, thus preventing the pathogen from becoming established.

Plants with vertical resistance usually show complete resistance to a particular pathogen under a wide variety of environmental conditions. However, it takes only one or a few mutations in the pathogen (new race) to make the previously resistant plant susceptible to the disease. Thus, this kind of resistance is not *durable* (horizontal resistance is *durable resistance*). The ideal genetic system for disease resistance is both horizontal and vertical resistance in one cultivar.

Resistance
The ability of an organism to exclude or overcome, partially or completely, the effect of a pathogen or other damaging factors.

7.7.4 APPARENT RESISTANCE

Certain plants known to be susceptible may not be adversely affected by pathogens under certain conditions. Two kinds of apparent resistance are known—escape and tolerance.

Escape

Plants may not show symptoms of disease because one of the three critical ingredients in the disease triangle may be missing (e.g., required temperature may not be present or moisture may be inadequate). In some plants, the young tissue may be susceptible to pathogens and an older one may not. For example, powdery mildew (caused by *Phytium*), bacterial, and viral infections affect younger tissue more severely than older tissue. By manipulating the cultural environment (e.g., spacing, planting date, pH, fertility, and moisture), susceptible plants may escape diseases.

Tolerance

Plants are said to be tolerant when they are able to grow, develop, and be fairly productive even when infected with a pathogen. Most plant viral infections produce this kind of resistance, in which the pathogen (virus) does not kill the host but causes reduced productivity or performance.

7.7.5 GENETIC BASIS OF DISEASE INCIDENCE

Virulence
The degree of pathogenicity of a pathogen.

As previously discussed, a virulent pathogen, a susceptible host, and an appropriate environment are all required for disease to occur. The **virulence** of a pathogen and the resistance of a host have genetic bases. For each gene that confers resistance in the host, there is a corresponding gene in the pathogen that confers virulence to the pathogen and vice versa, called the *gene-for-gene concept* of genetics of disease resistance and susceptibility. Generally (exceptions occur) in the host (e.g., plants), the genes for resistance are dominant *(R)* and the genes for susceptibility or lack of resistance are recessive *(r)*. However, in the pathogen, the genes for avirulence (inability to infect) are usually dominant *(A)* and those for virulence are recessive *(a)*. Therefore, when two cultivars, one carrying the gene *R* (for resistance to a certain pathogen) and the other carrying the gene *r* (for susceptibility) are inoculated with two races of the pathogen of interest, one of which carries the gene *A* (for avirulence against *R*) and the other race carrying the gene *r* (for virulence against *R*), the progeny will have the genotypes summarized in Table 7–4.

TABLE 7–4 The Genetics of Disease Resistance in Plants

Virulent or Avirulent Genes in the Pathogen	Resistance or Susceptibility Genes in the Plant	
	R (resistant) dominant	*r (susceptible) recessive*
A (avirulent) dominant	AR (−)	Ar (+)
a (virulent) recessive	aR (+)	ar (+)

Where − is incompatible (resistant) reaction (no infection) and + is compatible (susceptible) reaction (infection develops).
AR is resistant because the plant (host) has a certain gene for resistance (R) against which the pathogen has no specific virulence (A) gene. This does not mean other virulence genes do not occur.
Ar is susceptible due to lack of genes for resistance in the host and hence susceptible to other virulence genes from the pathogen. aR host has the resistance gene, but the pathogen has a virulence gene that can attack it.
ar is susceptible because the plant is susceptible and the pathogen is virulent.

Summary

Insects are a major class of horticultural pests both indoors and outdoors. The economically important insect orders that affect plants are Lepidoptera, Coleoptera, Hymenoptera, and Diptera. Some insects chew, whereas others suck, during feeding. Some insects attack stored products. Important insect pests include aphids, fruit flies, and corn earworms. Spider mites (not true insects) are common pests of horticultural importance. Plant diseases are caused by fungi, bacteria, viruses, and mycoplasma-like organisms. Most infectious plant diseases are caused by fungi. Bacterial diseases of horticultural plants are few. Other animal pests include birds, rodents, and nematodes.

References and Suggested Reading

Agnos, G. N. 1988. *Plant pathology.* New York: Academic Press.

Bohmont, B. L. 1997. *The standard pesticide user's guide.* Englewood Cliffs, N.J.: Prentice Hall.

Brooklyn Botanical Garden. 2000. *Natural disease control: A common-sense approach to plant first aid.* Handbook #164. Brooklyn Botanic Garden, Inc., 1000 Washington Avenue, Brooklyn, NY.

Cravens, R. H. 1977. *Pests and diseases.* Alexandria, Va.: Time-Life.

Dixon, G. R. 1981. *Vegetable crop diseases.* Westport, Conn.: AVI Publishing.

Ellis, B., and F. Bradley. 1996. *The organic gardener's handbook of natural insect and disease control.* Emmaus, Pa.: Rodale Press.

Gilberg, L. (ed.). 1993. *Garden pests and diseases.* Sunset Books. Sunset Publishing Corporation, CA.

Klingman, G. C., F. M. Ashton, and L. J. Noordhoff. 1982. *Weed science: Principles and practices,* 2d ed. New York: John Wiley & Sons.

Olkowski, W., S. Daar, and H. Olkowski. 1995. *The gardener' guide to common-sense pest control.* The Tauton Press, USA.

Prone, P. 1978. *Diseases and pests of ornamental plants,* 5th ed. New York: John Wiley & Sons.

Ware, G. W. 1988. *Complete guide to pest control,* 2d ed. Fresno, Calif.: Thomson Publications.

Horticultural pests
http://www.uky.edu/Ag/Entomology/entfacts/efveg.htm

Houseplant pests
http://www.ext.colostate.edu/PUBS/insect/05595.html

Viral diseases of plants with photos
http://plantpathology.tamu.edu/Texlab/Multicrop/virus.html

Outcomes Assessment

1. What is a weed?
2. Why is it important to control weeds in horticultural production?
3. Prior to implementing a pest control plan, it is important to know the life-cycle of the pest. Why is this so?
4. Give a specific reason why viral infections commonly do not kill infected plants.
5. Discuss the concept of the disease triangle.
6. Explain the gene-for-gene concept in the understanding of disease incidence in pants.
7. Distinguish between vertical and horizontal disease resistance.
8. The mere presence of a pathogen does not warrant the implementation of pest control. Explain.

8

Principles and Methods of Disease and Pest Control

PURPOSE AND EXPECTED OUTCOMES

This chapter is designed to classify the methods of disease and pest control and discuss the rationale behind their use, their effectiveness, and the environmental consequences of their use.

After studying this chapter, the student should be able to

1. Discuss the general principles of pest control.
2. Discuss the rationale behind each of the four control strategies.
3. Classify pesticides.
4. Classify insecticides.
5. Classify herbicides.
6. Discuss the strategies for the safe and effective use of herbicides.
7. Describe the equipment used in the application of pesticides.
8. Describe the pros and cons of each pest-control strategy.

OVERVIEW

In Chapter 6, we learned that the expressed phenotype depends on the genotype (the kinds of genes) and the environment in which the genes are expressed ($P = G + E$). The environment (E) should not be limited to the growth factors (light, moisture, temperature, and nutrients), even though these are the essential components. *Biological competitors* in the general environment may compete with useful plants for these growth substances to the detriment of the latter or destroy tissues and interrupt physical and developmental functions of cultivated plants. In terms of the environment, some of these competitors are native, or endemic, to particular areas. Others are imported by a variety of modes.

Diseases and pests must be controlled because they cause economic loss to a horticultural operation. The loss may come as a result of

1. Increased cost of production (additional inputs)
2. Decreased yield
3. Decreased quality

240

For the home growers or those who cultivate plants as a hobby and not for sale, losses to horticultural plants may come in more subtle ways. There may be emotional drain from the disappointment of a ruined crop or blemishes on plants in the landscape that reduce their aesthetic value.

Diseases and pests must be controlled safely and economically. A cost-effective control calls for a good understanding of the nature of the disease (pathogen), the environment, and the plant species (host).

From the formula $P = G + E$, the effective control of pests can be handled by either changing the crop growing environment or improving on the nature of the plant (genetic constitution) to include disease resistance genes.

MODULE 1

PRINCIPLES OF PEST CONTROL

The purpose of pest control is to minimize or completely eliminate the economic loss to a horticultural operation through reduced productivity, reduced product quality, or reduced aesthetics.

8.1 CONTROL STRATEGIES

8.1.1 PRINCIPLES OF CONTROL

Four basic principles are involved in pest control—exclusion, eradication, protection, and resistance.

Exclusion

Exclusion involves activities that prevent the pathogen from being introduced into a given area in the first place. If introduced, the conditions should prevent a pathogen from becoming established. Excluding the pathogen on a large scale often involves enacting government policies that make it illegal to import or export certain plant materials. This legislative control (or quarantine) is discussed in detail in Module 2 of this chapter.

Eradication

If a pathogen succeeds in entering and becoming established in an area to some extent, measures may be undertaken to curtail its spread while reducing the current population until the pathogen is eventually eliminated completely from the area.

Protection

Protection entails the isolation of the host from the pathogen. Such isolation is usually accomplished by applying a chemical to the host. Physical methods of protection are also used.

Resistance

A form of protection of genetic origin is resistance, whereby a plant or host is equipped with disease-resisting genes. Resistance breeding is undertaken by breeders to incorporate these genes into new cultivars through planned crosses and the use of other plant improvement strategies. The result of resistance breeding is a plant armed with natural means of defense, thus eliminating the need to use chemicals.

8.1.2 PREVENTING PEST ATTACK

Pest control is an additional production cost that can be eliminated or reduced by adopting certain preventive strategies. Some of these strategies are described as follows and include the observance of good cultural practices.

1. *Certain environmental conditions predispose plants to diseases.* Chapter 7 stated that one of the three factors that must be present for disease to develop is the proper environment. This environment includes proper temperature, light, and humidity. Warm and humid conditions often invite diseases; aeration is needed to reduce the creation of this kind of microclimate around plants. Plants should be properly spaced and humidity controlled (e.g., by watering at the right time of day to allow excess moisture to evaporate).

2. *Select and use adapted cultivars.* Plants have climatic conditions under which they grow and perform best. When grown in the wrong regions, plants are unable to develop properly and are more likely to succumb to diseases.

3. *Use pest-resistant cultivars.* If certain pests are prevalent in the production area, it is best to use resistant cultivars, if available, in any production enterprise. For soilborne diseases, tree seedlings grafted onto an appropriate stock may be desired.

4. *Plant at the best time.* Seasonal planting may prevent exposure to unfavorable climatic conditions. This approach applies mostly to annuals, which complete their life cycles in one growing season. Sometimes short-duration cultivars may be selected to successfully grow a crop in a short window of opportunity where conditions reduce pest incidence.

5. *Provide adequate nutrition.* Strong and healthy plants resist diseases better than malnourished ones. Soil testing reveals the nutritional status of the soil so that fertilizer amounts can be amended for adequate plant nutrition.

6. *Observe good sanitation.* Because plant remains left on the soil surface can harbor pathogens, debris should be removed or buried in the soil. Diseased plant parts can spread the problem to healthy plant parts. Similarly, wounds provide easy entry to disease organisms. As such, the horticultural operation of pruning should be undertaken as needed to remove diseased plant parts, following up with proper wound dressing. Tools should be cleaned and disinfected periodically.

7. *Remove weeds.* Weeds compete for nutrients and also harbor diseases and other pests. Since weeds are volunteer plants in a cultivated plot, they are usually found in areas in which they are capable of performing under the prevailing conditions. They are thus more competitive than the cultivated crops, which require the grower's care.

8. *Use quality seeds or seedlings (or appropriate planting material).* Poor-quality seeds may have a high proportion of weed seeds and may also carry seedborne diseases. Obtain all planting materials from reputable nurseries or growers.

9. *Prepare the soil or growing medium properly for planting.* Depending on the tillage operation desired, weeds must be controlled by either killing them with chemicals or plowing them under the soil. In greenhouse culture, the growing medium should be sterilized to eliminate pests. Garden soils can also be sterilized by the method of solarization. A well-prepared soil or growing medium should drain freely to avoid waterlogged conditions, which prevent good plant development.

These general strategies of disease prevention are applicable to all production types. In addition, some production enterprises may use unique strategies that help to reduce pest incidence.

8.1.3 DESIGNING CONTROL STRATEGIES

Effective control of diseases and pests should take into account the pathogen (e.g., bacterium), the host (species), and the environment. A good strategy should be effective, inexpensive, and safe (in terms of both application and residual consequences for consumers and the environment). From the perspective of the pathogen, the strategy should exploit the vulnerability of the pathogen by administering the control at the stage in the life cycle at which it is most vulnerable. The strategy should also consider the stage in the life cycle at which the organism is destructive to horticultural plants. Control measures should be effected *before* the destructive stage. Certain organisms are destructive at more than one phase in their life cycles. For example, an insect may lay unsightly eggs on the flowers or leaves of ornamental plants or fruits. When the eggs hatch, the larvae may be destructive and the adult harmless. What may be a problem or undesirable in one case may have no economic consequence in another. Eggs on flowers may be unsightly and undesirable, but for a plant whose economic part is the seed, blemishes on the pods may not affect the quality of the seeds they carry. A control strategy should also consider the feeding habits of the organism, since insects may either suck or chew plant parts.

From the perspective of the host plant, control strategies should consider inherent genetic capacity. Some diseases affect young plants and others older plants. Certain cultivars have disease resistance genes and are able to resist infection. To be effective, a control strategy should consider the environment in several ways. Weather factors such as temperature, precipitation, and winds limit the effectiveness of the control measure. Rainfall after pesticide application may wash away the chemicals. In this age of environmental awareness, there is a call for reduction in pesticide use, since residues end up in groundwater as pollutants.

Cultural practices should be considered in adopting a strategy for disease control. For example, by changing crop spacing, pruning, adopting crop rotation, weeding, and taking other cultural measures, disease incidence can be effectively controlled. Finally, the cost of the control measure should be considered.

8.1.4 PRINCIPLES AND METHODS OF CONTROL

Controlling Insect Pests

Based on the nature of the agents employed, there are six general methods of control.

1. *Biological control.* The principles involved in the biological control of pests are geared toward favoring organisms (natural enemies) that are antagonistic to the pest or pathogen, and improving the resistance of the host.
2. *Cultural control.* Cultural control employs the principles of protection and eradication by helping plants avoid contact with the pest or pathogen and reducing the population of or eradicating the causal organism in the area. Cultural methods depend on certain actions of the grower.
3. *Regulatory or legislative control.* Regulatory control involves the intervention of government with laws aimed at excluding the pathogen or pest from a given geographic area.
4. *Chemical control.* The chemical control of pests involves protecting plants from the pathogen or pest, curing an infection when it occurs, and destroying the pest if the attack is in progress.
5. *Mechanical control.* Insects can be controlled by mechanical methods that employ devices to prevent them from making contact with the plants or lure and entrap the insects.
6. *Integrated pest management (IPM).* The method of integrated pest management, as its name suggests, entails the use of a combination of the other general methods of pest control in a comprehensive approach to disease and pest control. However, efforts are made to minimize the use of chemicals.

The preceding methods are discussed in detail in the various modules in this chapter.

Controlling Diseases

The principles of disease control are exclusion, eradication, protection, and resistance.

1. *Exclusion.* The principle of exclusion entails the use of a method such as regulation to prevent the introduction of the pathogen into an area where it does not currently exist.
2. *Eradication.* When disease incidence occurs to a limited extent or is restricted in distribution, it is feasible to completely eliminate the pathogen from the area.
3. *Protection.* Plants can usually be protected from pathogens by applying a chemical that prevents the pathogen from infecting the host.
4. *Resistance.* Plant breeding programs aim at providing a level of resistance (not total immunity) to a disease in plants. Whereas certain plants may be susceptible to a disease, others may be able to resist it, depending on a variety of factors such as the age of the plant, the environment, and the aggressiveness of the pathogen.

These four basic principles apply to controlling insects. Similarly, some methods of insect control (e.g., cultural, regulatory, and chemical) are applicable to diseases. In controlling diseases and insect pests, four general strategies may be adopted, depending on whether the attack is yet to occur or is already in progress. A single strategy may involve the use of one or more principles and methods of pest control. These strategies are summarized in Table 8–1.

TABLE 8–1 Strategies and Methods of Pest Control

Strategy 1: **Exclude Pathogen from Host**

Methods:		Quarantine
		Crop inspection
		Crop isolation
		Use of pathogen-free planting materials

Strategy 2: **Reduce or Eliminate Pathogen's Inoculum**

Methods:	Cultural	Crop rotation
		Host eradication
		Improved sanitation
		Improved crop growth environment
		Soil drainage
		Aeration of soil
		Proper soil pH
		Proper soil nutrition
		Remove weeds
Methods:	Physical	Heat treatment
		Solarization
		Sterilization
		Traps—polyethylene sticky sheets
		Mulches
	Chemical	Seed treatment
		Soil fumigation
	Biological	Trap crops
		Antagonistic plants (repellants)

Strategy 3: **Improve Host Resistance**

Methods:	Cultural	Improved crop growth environment
		Nutrition, moisture, drainage
	Biological	Genetic resistance (plant breeding)
		Resistant cultivars

TABLE 8–1 Strategies and Methods of Pest Control (continued)

Strategy 4: Protect Host Directly

Biological	Use natural antagonists
Chemical	Use pesticides
	Seed treatment
	Spray plants
Physical	Use protective aids (e.g., tree guard)

8.2 CLASSIFICATION OF PESTICIDES

Pesticides are chemicals designed to kill pests. They are frequently very toxic to humans and thus should be used judiciously and with care. Pesticides differ not only in chemical composition but also in killing action, toxicity, residual effect, specificity, species destroyed, cost, and effectiveness, among others.

Based on the type of organisms on which they are used, there are two broad categories of pesticides in horticulture:

1. *Pesticides used to control unwanted plants.* **Pesticides** used to control unwanted plants are called *herbicides*. Plants that are pests are generally called *weeds*. Weeds may be defined as plants out of place. The different types of herbicides are based on killing action, specificity, active ingredient, and other characteristics as described in detail in Module 4 of this chapter.
2. *Pesticides used to control nonplant pests of plants.* Horticultural plants are attacked by a wide variety of pests that may be grouped on the basis of animal class. The major pesticide groups are described in the following sections. They are readily identified because the prefix denotes the class of animals (the suffix *-cide* is common to all).

Pesticide
A substance or mixture of substances used to control undesirable plants and animals.

8.2.1 INSECTICIDES

Insecticides are pesticides designed to control insects. They are the most widely used pesticide for killing animal pests. Module 3 of this chapter is devoted to a detailed discussion of insecticides.

Insecticide
Pesticide used to control unwanted insects.

8.2.2 FUNGICIDES

Fungicides are pesticides designed to control fungal pathogens. There are two basic kinds:

1. *Protective fungicides.* Unlike the protection offered by other kinds of pesticides, protective fungicides offer protection only to the part of the plant surface that is covered by the chemical. It is critical therefore to apply fungicides in a uniform and even manner over the entire surface to be protected. One of the oldest and still widely used nonsystemic fungicides is Captan, which is applied as a protective spray or dust in vegetables, fruits, seed treatments, and ornamentals.
2. *Systemic fungicides.* Systemic fungicides penetrate the plant tissue and circulate through all parts of the plant to combat infection. This relatively new group of fungicides is more efficient in controlling pests. An example is the benzimidazole (e.g., benomyl), which is effective against *Botrytis, Sclerotinia*, and others.

In terms of chemistry, fungicides may be classified as *organic* or *inorganic*.

Phytotoxicity
The immediate (acute) or continuous low (chronic) impact of a chemical on a plant or its part.

1. *Organic fungicides.* Organic fungicides are more selective and pose less environmental danger. The newer types are especially readily biodegradable and less **phytotoxic** (damaging to plant tissue). The most widely known class of organic fungicides is the dithiocarbamates, which include old and still useful fungicides such as thiram, maneb, zineb, and mancozeb. Thiram is used in apple and peach orchards, turf, and vegetable gardens. Other classes of organic fungicides are the substituted aromatics, thiazoles, triazines, and dicarboximides.

2. *Inorganic fungicides.* The core elements in inorganic fungicides are sulfur, copper, and mercury. Sulfur is available in one of several formulations: powder, colloidal sulfur, or wettable powder. When applied, it may kill by direct contact at high environmental temperatures (21°C [above 70°F]) by fumigant action. Sulfur is used in controlling powdery mildew. One of the most popular copper formulations is *Bordeaux mixture,* the oldest fungicide (consisting of $CuSO_4$ and hydrated lime), which is effective against downy mildew. It also repels insects such as flea beetles and leaf hoppers. Inorganic copper fungicides are not water soluble.

8.2.3 NEMATICIDES

Nematicides are chemicals designed to penetrate the relatively impermeable cuticle of nematodes. They are generally applied by professionals by injecting fumigants of halogenated hydrocarbons under pressure into the soil.

8.2.4 RODENTICIDES

Rodenticides are pesticides designed to kill rodents. Rodents are most effectively controlled by poisoning. The most widely used class of rodenticides are the coumarins. They must be ingested repeatedly to kill the pest. Thus, they are safe in case of accidental ingestion. An example is Warfam, which was developed by the University of Wisconsin. Coumarins are anticoagulants.

8.2.5 MOLLUSCIDES

Chemicals that are designed to kill mollusks are called *molluscides*. These chemicals are usually formulated as baits; an example is methiocarb, which is very effective against snails and slugs in ornamental plantings. Metaldehydes are one of the oldest and most successful molluscides.

8.2.6 MITICIDES

Miticides are pesticides designed to kill mites.

8.2.7 AVIACIDES

Aviacides are pesticides designed to kill birds. They are commonly included in grain and used as bait. Strychnine is an aviacide.

8.3 GROWTH REGULATORS IN PEST CONTROL

Plant growth regulators are used to manipulate plant height, promote rooting, and reduce fruiting, among other uses. A high concentration of certain plant hormones can reduce infection by some pathogens. This effect has been observed in tomato with respect to *Fusarium* and in potato with respect to *Phytophthora*. Viral and mycoplasma infections are known to cause reduced vigor and stunting in plants. However, an application of gibberellic acid spray overcomes stunting and axillary bud suppression. Sour cherry yellows is a common viral infection of cherries that is commercially controlled by the application of gibberellic acid on a significant scale.

8.4 CHOOSING A PESTICIDE

8.4.1 STEPS IN THE DECISION-MAKING PROCESS OF PEST CONTROL

The following are general steps that may be followed in the development and implementation of a pest-control strategy (Figure 8–1). Depending on whether the pest problem is new, as well as the experience of the person making the decisions, some of the steps may be skipped.

1. *Detection.* A pest-control program always starts with a problem. The pest must first be detected. The presence of a pest may be detected by visual observation of the organism or the damage it causes. While certain pests can be identified from a distance, some pests have hiding places (e.g., the underside of the leaf, under stones, or under debris) and require the grower to make an effort to search at close quarters. The key to successful pest control is early detection. It is advisable, therefore, that the grower routinely inspect the plants and look for pests and disease organisms known to be associated with the production operation and those prevalent in the area.

2. *Identification.* When a problem has been observed, it is important to make a positive identification of the insect or pathogen. Without knowing the organism involved, no sound control measure can be developed. Trial and error is wasteful. If the grower does not have the expertise to positively identify an insect or disease organism, a sample of an infected plant or the organism itself should be collected and sent to an appropriate identification center, such as the department of agriculture at a land grant institution or the U.S. Department of Agriculture (USDA) Extension Office. County extension agents should be consulted before contacting the national office.

3. *Biology and habits.* An organism has a life cycle. In insects that undergo a complete metamorphosis, there is a dramatic change from one stage of

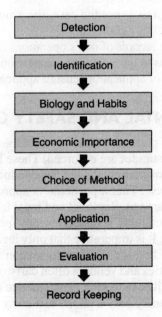

FIGURE 8–1 Steps in the decision-making process for pesticide application.

development to another. Each of these stages has its unique characteristics and habits. One stage may be more vulnerable than another to a particular control measure. The most vulnerable stage should be targeted for controlling the organism. It is important to know the habits of the organism in order to plan a control strategy. Certain insects hide on the undersides of leaves. Others inhabit the soil, and still others live on plant materials. Some insects are nocturnal in feeding habit, and others feed during the daytime. It has already been stated that certain insects have chewing mouthparts and others have piercing mouthparts. Some organisms have or secrete a protective covering, whereas others do not. These and other biological characteristics and habits are important in designing effective pest-control strategies.

4. *Economic importance.* It is economically wasteful of resources and time if it costs more to control a pest than the returns expected from the enterprise without protection. In other words, if the pest incidence does not pose an economic threat, the grower should ignore the pest. Certain pests can completely wipe out a production operation and must therefore be controlled immediately at the sign of their presence.

5. *Choice of method of control.* The most effective, economic, safe, and environmentally sound method of control should be selected after identifying the pest and assessing the potential damage. It may be found that a combination of methods rather than one particular method may be most effective. Some methods are easier to apply than others. Further, some methods may require the use of special equipment or the hiring of professional applicators.

6. *Application.* If chemicals are to be used, they must be applied at the correct rate. Premixed chemicals are available for purchase in certain cases. Otherwise, the user must follow the instructions provided with the chemical to mix the correct rate. Timeliness of application is critical to the success of a pest-control method.
To eradicate a pest, it is important to know its life cycle. Certain applications may destroy the adults without damaging the eggs. By knowing when eggs hatch, an appropriate schedule can be developed to implement repeated application of the pesticide for more complete control. The environmental conditions under which application of a pesticide occurs is critical to its effectiveness. Pesticides should not be applied if rainfall is expected soon after the application. Further, a calm day is required to contain chemicals applied as sprays and dusts within the area of intended use.

7. *Evaluation.* The effectiveness of an application should be evaluated within a reasonable period after application to determine whether a repeat application is necessary. Evaluating the impact of pest control on the total operation is important. Controlling pests is expected to significantly increase productivity and returns on investment. If this is not the case, the grower should review the operation and make necessary changes.

8. *Record keeping.* Keeping records of one's operations is critical. The only way to make alternative choices is to have data for comparison. Such a record should include the type of pesticide, rate of application, cost of application, yield, and net returns.

8.4.2 ENVIRONMENTAL AND SAFETY CONCERNS

To avoid indiscriminate use of pesticides and to protect the environment, laws and guidelines that govern the use of pesticides are enforced. These laws vary from place to place. Pesticide manufacturers and governmental agencies conduct extensive tests on pesticides before they are approved for use. That a pesticide is approved for use does not mean it may be used in any situation desired. Regional and local factors such as climatic factors, soil characteristics, and agricultural production may preclude the use of approved chemicals in certain situations. It is imperative that only legally approved chemicals (with respect to the particular area) be used. Such information is available through the local extension service. Local nurseries and vendors often carry only state-approved pesticides. For the inexperienced grower, it pays to seek expert advice on the correct pesticide to use. This kind of information is usually only a phone call away and free of charge.

In a competitive industry, a variety of pesticides abound for the same problem. Some are more effective than others; some are safer than others. Pesticides also vary in their ease of use and *formulation*. Some pesticide formulations are suited for outdoor use only. In fact, the utmost care should be taken when using pesticides in the home. When you purchase a pesticide, be sure—at the very least—to read the label and understand the recommendations for its safe use. You may also let the seller know whether the problem is indoors or outdoors.

In sum, the chemical selected should be

1. Legally approved for use in the area.
2. Effective against the pest.
3. Appropriate for the conditions under which it will be used.
4. Accompanied by detailed instructions about its proper use.
5. Relatively safe (to humans, the environment, and the economic parts of the plant). Certain chemicals can be applied only by certified personnel.
6. One that the grower can apply safely (based on available equipment, location of a problem, and other factors).

8.4.3   IMPORTANCE OF PESTICIDE LABELS

A *label,* the piece of paper (or other suitable material) affixed by the manufacturer to the container of a product, provides certain specific information about the product (Figure 8–2). The information is not arbitrary and must meet specific governmental guidelines. A label is much more than an advertisement. Several categories of information are provided on a label, including the following:

1. Name of the product, which may include a trademark name and chemical name
2. Company name, address, and logo (where applicable)
3. Type of pesticide (e.g., fungicide or insecticide)
4. Product chemical analysis and characteristics: active ingredients and proportions (common and/or chemical names of ingredients) and formulation of substances (e.g., dust, emulsion, and wettable powder)
5. Pests it controls
6. Directions for proper use and any restrictions
7. Hazard statements (appearing as *caution, warning, danger,* or *poison*)
8. Storage and disposal directions
9. Governmental administrative stipulations (e.g., Environmental Protection Agency [EPA] approval and EPA number)
10. Net content

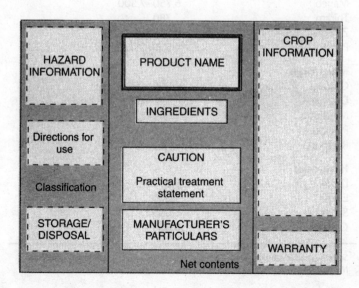

FIGURE 8–2   A typical pesticide label.

Typically, the trade name of the chemical, the type of chemical, and the company name are most visible. The hazard term is also quite conspicuous. Much of the other information is often in fine print. However, the user must endeavor to *read and follow all directions* very carefully. Understanding the warning signs of toxicity should be a high priority, since pesticides are generally very toxic to humans. As more research information becomes available on various aspects of the chemical product and also its impact on the environment, the governmental regulatory agencies may require additional information to be included on the product label.

8.4.4 PESTICIDE TOXICITY

It is wise to treat all chemicals and especially pesticides (designed to kill) as poisonous until information to the contrary is clearly available. A measure of the danger associated with pesticides is the *hazard* rating, which is a function of **toxicity** and *exposure*. Toxicity is a measure of the degree to which a chemical is poisonous to the organism. A pesticide that is very toxic as a concentrate may not be hazardous when formulated as a granule. On the other hand, a pesticide of low toxicity may become very hazardous when used at high concentrations. Apart from formulation, the frequency of use and the experience of the operator may increase or decrease the hazard level.

The standard way of measuring toxicity is by determining the **lethal dose (LD_{50})** of the chemical. LD_{50} represents the dose sufficient to kill 50 percent of laboratory test animals, usually rats. Since the test is performed on mammals, the LD_{50} is sometimes described as *mammalian toxicity*. The higher the LD_{50} value, the less poisonous the chemical. LD_{50} is measured in units of milligrams of substance per kilogram of animal body weight. It follows, therefore, that children (low total body weight) could be killed by a dose that would only make an adult very sick. The LD_{50} values for selected garden chemicals are presented in Table 8–2. Since a pesticide may be ingested, inhaled, or absorbed through the skin, toxicity is sometimes broken down into three kinds—*oral toxicity, toxicity on inhalation,* and *dermal toxicity.*

Toxicity
The relative capacity of a substance to be poisonous to a living organism.

Lethal Dose (LD_{50})
The milligrams of toxicant per kilogram body weight of an organism that is capable of killing 50 percent of the organisms under the test conditions.

TABLE 8–2 LD$_{50}$ Values (Oral) of Selected Pesticides

Pesticide	LD_{50}
Fungicides	
Captan	9,000–15,000
Maneb	6,750–7,500
Thiram	780
Zineb	8,000
PCNB	1,550–2,000
Insecticides	
Carbaryl	500–850
Dursban	97–279
Malathion	1,000–1,375
Pyrethrum	820–1,870
Rotenone	50–75
Herbicides	
DCPA	3,000
EPCT	1,600
Simazine	5,000
Oxyzalin	10,000

Source: Extracted (and modified) from extension bulletin B-751, Farm Science Series, Michigan State University, University Cooperative Extension Service.

Chemicals gain access to humans through ingestion, touching, or inhaling. Some chemicals are highly corrosive and burn the skin upon contact. Chemicals that produce fumes or are formulated as dusts or powders are easily inhaled. Certain chemicals have strong odors that alert the user to their potential danger if inhaled.

8.4.5 USING PESTICIDES SAFELY

A first rule to using pesticides safely is to treat them as health hazards. After all, they are designed to *kill* pests. Use them as the last resort for controlling pests. If pesticides are necessary, the user should

1. Choose the correct one. Look for safer or less toxic alternatives of pesticides.
2. Purchase or mix only the quantities needed. Do not store excess chemicals, since it poses a serious health hazard, especially in homes where children live. Leftover chemicals also create disposal problems.
3. Read the label and act accordingly. Be very familiar with the manufacturer's directions for safe use. Note and observe all warnings. Use *only* in the way prescribed by the manufacturer. Follow directions for use. Be sure to use the correct concentration.
4. Wear protective clothing and avoid contact with the skin. Wear gloves or at least wash your hands thoroughly and immediately after using any chemical. Protect your eyes and cover your nose and mouth with a mask to prevent inhalation or ingestion of chemicals.
5. Do not eat food, drink, or chew anything while handling chemicals, and do not eat afterward until you have washed your hands with soap.
6. Apply chemicals under the best conditions possible. Do not spray on a windy day. If a light wind prevails, do not spray into it, proceeding such that the wind is behind you as you move along. If rain (or irrigation) occurs after application, much of the chemical will be lost to the ground. When applying chemicals outdoors, it pays to listen to the weather report to know the best time for application. When applying chemicals indoors, avoid spraying onto cooking utensils and food. All such items should be covered before spraying. Children, especially, should leave the house for a period of time if extensive spraying is to be done. Moving a diseased plant outside of the house rather than spraying it indoors is recommended. Chemicals should be applied in conditions of adequate ventilation. A closed area such as a greenhouse should be adequately ventilated before people return to work in the area.
7. Apply with extreme care. Certain pesticides are injurious to both pests and humans and will kill indiscriminately. Plants can be damaged through accidental splashing or drifting during a spraying operation. The operator can be injured through carelessness. Premixed chemicals are less concentrated and safer to handle. Concentrated chemicals should be handled with extra care.
8. Know what to do in case of an accident. The label should indicate proper actions in case of a spill, ingestion, or inhalation. Water and a detergent should be readily available to wash any body part that comes in direct contact with the chemical. Cleaning certain spills requires more than water.
9. Clean all applicators thoroughly after use and store them in a safe place.
10. Store chemicals as directed by the manufacturer. A cool, dry place is often required for chemical storage. Keep *all* chemicals out of the reach of children and pets. It is best to store unused chemicals in their original containers for ease in recognizing the chemicals and avoiding accidents through misidentification.
11. Be very careful of using pesticides near the time of produce harvest. Pesticide poisoning may occur if produce is harvested before the pesticide effect wears off. Where applicable, produce grown with pesticides should be washed before being eaten or fed to animals.

8.4.6 METHODS OF PESTICIDE APPLICATION

Pesticides may be applied to plants, products, or the growing medium, according to need. The general ways in which pesticides are used are as follows:

1. *Foliar application.* Pesticides may be applied to plant foliage in the form of a liquid or dust (powder).
2. *Soil treatment.* A soil may be fumigated (by treating with volatile chemicals) to control nematodes and other soilborne diseases. Sometimes various formulations including drenches, granules, and dusts may be applied.
3. *Seed treatment.* Planting materials (e.g., seeds, bulbs, corms, and tubers) may be treated with a pesticide to control soilborne diseases that cause seed decay or damping-off of young seedlings.
4. *Control of postharvest pests.* Fruits may be dipped in dilute solutions of fungitoxic chemicals to protect them from rotting in storage.

8.5 INTEGRATED PEST MANAGEMENT

Integrated Pest Management (IPM)
An approach to pest control that attempts to use all the best management methods available to keep pest populations below the economic and/or aesthetic injury level, with least damage to life and the environment.

Integrated pest management (IPM) is a pest-control strategy whose goal is not to eradicate but to manage a pest such that its population is maintained below that which can cause economic loss to a production enterprise or aesthetic injury. In this strategy, human health and the general environment are paramount considerations. By nature, IPM depends on a broad and interdisciplinary approach to pest control, incorporating various aspects of the basic control methods (cultural, biological, legislative, and chemical) (Figure 8–3).

8.5.1 GOALS OF IPM

The goals of IPM may be summarized as follows:

1. *Improved control of pests.* Methods of pest control should be reviewed regularly so that the best strategy is always used. As scientific knowledge abounds and technology advances, new and improved alternative measures will become available. Strategies should draw on the strengths of all of the basic control methods in a truly interdisciplinary fashion to develop the best control package. Improvements in control should consider the fact that nature has built-in means of controlling population growth by the presence of natural enemies of organisms in the environment. Preference should be given to natural methods of control over the use of chemicals.

FIGURE 8–3 The components of an integrated pest management (IPM) system. *(Source: G. Acquaah, Principles of Crop Production)*

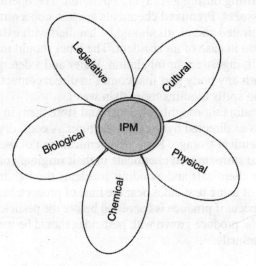

2. *Pesticide management.* Controlling pests should be a planned activity such that pesticides are used judiciously. Pesticides should be used so that natural enemies of plant pests are not destroyed in the process. Further, pesticides should be contained and applied only when absolutely necessary. Care must be taken to minimize the side effects of chemical application.

3. *Economic protection of plants.* As previously stated in this module, the mere sight of a pest does not necessarily mean that it constitutes a threat to economic production. A control measure should be enforced only when its necessity has been determined. When needed, IPM ensures that a control package includes the bare minimum for effectiveness. By using minimal quantities of pesticides (through reduced rate of application and reduced frequency of application), the cost of protection can be reduced significantly.

4. *Reduction of potential hazards.* A paramount objective of IPM is the responsible use of pesticides. When pesticides are deemed necessary, they should be used at the lowest effective level to prevent adverse environmental impact. IPM strategies are aimed at maintaining ecological stability and protecting the health of the grower (or user), the consumer, and the general environment. Hazardous chemicals should be prevented from entering the *food chain* (the sequence of transfer of food from producers through several levels of consumers in the biological community). Excess pesticides and other agricultural chemicals seep into the groundwater and also pollute the general environment, posing serious health problems to humans and wildlife.

8.5.2 DECISION-MAKING PROCESS IN DEVELOPING AN IPM PROGRAM

An IPM program is developed by following the basic principles for a conventional pest-control program, but with certain modifications. It is important to remember that an IPM program is broad based and interdisciplinary, including strategies involved with the basic methods of control. The general decision-making steps are as follows:

1. Identify the pest and the beneficial organisms in the area of interest. IPM uses natural enemies to control pests. By knowing these two groups of organisms, one can make the appropriate choices of control method that will selectively kill the pest while protecting the beneficial insects.

2. Know the biology of the organisms involved and how the environment influences them.

3. Select an appropriate cultural practice that will be detrimental to the pest while favoring the desirable organisms. Cultural control is usually considered first because the method of plant production plays a role in the pest problems encountered in cultivation. Cultural practices include selecting cultivars that are resistant to pests in the production area, preparing the soil properly, planting at the right time, providing adequate nutrition and water, and so forth.

4. Develop a pest-monitoring schedule for the production enterprise to record the kinds and populations of various organisms. This step requires some expertise to be successful.

5. Determine tolerable threshold levels of pest populations. Since one of the goals of IPM is economic pest control, it is important to know what level of pest population constitutes an economic threat. When this threshold is reached, an appropriate control strategy should be implemented. The strategy should take into account the pest plant species, the stage of plant development, the economic product, and the general environment. Whereas a threshold may be deemed an economic threat when it occurs in the early stages of plant growth, the same threshold may not be economically threatening when the plant is approaching maturity.

6. If an economic threat is deemed eminent, decide on a definite course of action to forestall the danger. Sometimes the best decision is to wait a while.

If intervention is delayed, the grower must increase monitoring of the population dynamics of the pest to avoid any surprise disaster.

7. Evaluate and follow up on the IPM program to make appropriate strategic adjustments for increased effectiveness and efficiency of control.

8.5.3 TOOLS FOR AN IPM PROGRAM

Tools used to implement an IPM program reflect the basic methods of pest control. Using these tools in an informed and responsible manner results in a successful pest-control program with minimal adverse environmental impact.

1. *Cultural tools.* Cultural tools include proper soil preparation, proper time of planting, and use of resistant cultivars.
2. *Biological tools.* Biological tools include use of natural enemies of the pests and pheromones as sex traps.
3. *Chemical tools.* Chemical tools include the use of pesticides and improved methods of application.
4. *Legislative tools.* Legislative tools include the use of laws to restrict the transport of plant materials that may be contaminated.

SUMMARY

Diseases and pests can be controlled by implementing certain preventive measures such as observing phytosanitation, using quality disease-resistant seeds, and planting adapted cultivars. If diseases and pests become a problem, they may be controlled by one of four strategies: biological, cultural, chemical, or governmental controls. A fifth strategy, integrated pest management, uses a combination of all four strategies. Pesticides that control weeds are called herbicides. Nonplant pests may be controlled by one of several specifically designed pesticides including insecticides, fungicides, nematicides, miticides, rodenticides, and molluscides. Pesticides are toxic to humans and should be handled with care. Pesticide labels should be read very carefully and the directions followed meticulously. In pest control, the first step is to identify the specific pest and determine its potential for damage as well as the damage already caused.

MODULE 2

BIOLOGICAL, CULTURAL, LEGISLATIVE, PHYSICAL, AND MECHANICAL CONTROL OF PLANT PESTS

8.6 RATIONALE OF BIOLOGICAL CONTROL

Nature has built into its dynamics a variety of mechanisms whereby it maintains a state of equilibrium. Whenever a destabilizing force comes into effect, this natural balance shifts in the direction of the force. Unaided by humans, nature effectively maintains this desirable state of balance, or equilibrium. Unfortunately, when humans interface with nature, they tend to nudge it to their advantage and in the process often wind up destroying the delicate balance, which may lead to serious environmental consequences.

Every organism has its natural enemies. Unless a disaster or a drastic change occurs in their living conditions, the danger of extinction of organisms is minimized, in part because one organism does not dominate nature through overpopulation. This natural means of mutual control makes **biological control** the oldest method of pest control. Biological control is the control of diseases and pests by the direct activities of living organisms or the indirect activities of their products.

Industrialization and technical advancement have been major contributors to the destabilization of natural balance. Such advancements changed the lifestyles of people and caused consumers to be more demanding in terms of product quality. Subsistent agriculture was gradually replaced by mechanized farming of large tracts of land. Instead of allowing the farmland to lay idle (fallow) for a period of time to rejuvenate, the same tract of land was repeatedly farmed, predisposing it to depletion of plant growth nutrients. This practice ushered in the era of artificial soil amendments with fertilizers (Chapter 4). Instead of *mixed cropping,* which is closer to what occurs in nature, *monocropping,* which encourages the buildup of pests associated with one particular species, is common today. To curb this disproportionate increase in the population of one pest, farmers use more chemicals (pesticides) to control pests. As previously indicated, an unfortunate aspect of chemical use is that these toxins often kill indiscriminately, depleting the population of both pests and desirable organisms.

Biological Control
The use of other organisms to control populations of pathogens.

8.7 STRATEGIES OF BIOLOGICAL CONTROL

A variety of strategies may be adopted to control diseases and pests biologically. In fact, biological control involves the exploitation of natural defense mechanisms and managing and controlling them to increase their effectiveness. The natural systems exploited in biological control are discussed in the following sections.

1. *Structural.* Some species have characteristics that condition resistance to certain pests and disease-causing organisms. Certain species, for example, have hairs (pubesence) on their leaf surfaces and other parts that interfere with oviposition in insects. In this way, the multiplication of insects is impeded, thus hindering their spread and devastation to the plant. Other plants have genetically conditioned structural features such as a thick cuticle that sucking and chewing insects have difficulty penetrating.
2. *Chemicals.* Certain chemicals extracted from plants have insecticidal action. Common ones include the widely known *pyrethrum* extracted from plants in the chrysanthemum family, *rotenone,* and *nicotine* (rotenone being more common). Other species, including the neem tree, mamey, and basil, contain a chemical that repels insect pests or hinders their growth and development into adults.
3. *Phytoallexins.* In nature, certain plants exude toxins from their roots into the soil. These toxins prevent the growth of other species in the immediate vicinity. The species hence maintains a kind of territorial boundary similar to that which occurs in the animal kingdom.
4. *Parasitism.* The Japanese beetle *(Tiphia),* for example, is attacked by the larvae of a beetle, while the adult alfalfa weevil is a host for the eggs of the stingless wasp *(Microstomus aethipoides),* which hatches inside the weevil, eventually destroying it. Cyst nematodes *(Heterodera* and *Globodera)* are parasitized by certain fungi (e.g., *Catenaria auxilianis*), and the root-knot nematode *(Meloidogyne* spp.) is parasitized by the fungus *Dactylella oviparasitica.* Similarly, bacteriophages are viruses that destroy bacteria. These viral parasites occur in the environment.
5. *Prey-predator relationships.* Birds may prey on insects and rodents. Snakes also prey on rodents that destroy horticultural plants. Carabid beetles (ground beetles)

Antagonism
The phenomenon of one organism producing toxic metabolic products that kill, injure, or inhibit the growth of some other organism in close proximity.

prey on aphids, caterpillars, slugs, and others. Lacewings *(Chrysopa)* prey on aphids, spiders prey on flying insects, and social wasps prey on caterpillars.

6. *Antagonism.* As described previously in this chapter, nature has built-in mechanisms for maintaining balance so that no single organism dominates. If an organism is introduced into a new environment where its antagonizing organism is not present, the organism can multiply rapidly and pose a great economic threat to vulnerable cultivated crops in the area. In olive orchards, for example, the olive parlatoria scale, an economic pest, can be controlled effectively by biological means if its antagonistic organism, the parasitic wasp, is introduced into the environment. Antagonistic plants that exude toxins against nematodes are known to occur in nature.

7. *Repellents.* Some plant species exude strong scents that are repulsive to certain insects. Onion, garlic, and leek have been known to repel aphids, and mint repels cabbage butterflies and flea beetles. Horseradish repels potato bugs, and sage repels cabbage pests and carrot flies. Marigolds repel root nematodes. By planting the appropriate combinations of plants in a particular area, the grower can gain some degree of crop protection from a specific pest.

8. *Alternative host (trap plants).* Pests have preference for the plant species they attack. If two hosts are available, one may be preferentially attacked. Slugs prefer lettuce to chrysanthemums, and, as such, a good crop of the latter can be produced in the field by planting lettuce among them as "decoy" plants, or trap plants. Similarly, nematodes may be controlled by planting certain species that prevent the development of larvae into adults. This practice has the effect of decreasing the population of nematodes in the soil. *Clotalaria* plants are used to trap the larvae of root-knot nematodes *(Meloidegyne* spp.).

9. *Biocontrol.* In the storage of horticultural produce, *biocontrol* is employed in the postharvest control of diseases in stone fruits such as peach and plum. This control is effected by treating fruits with a suspension of the bacterium *Bacillus subtilis,* which is found to delay brown rot caused by the fungus *Monilinia fruticola.* Biocontrol measures involving other bacteria and fungi exist. Bacteria damage certain frost-sensitive plants by aiding in the formation of ice (called *ice nucleation*). Ice-nucleated active bacteria (e.g., *Pseudomonas syringae*) are replaced by applying non-ice-nucleated bacteria, which reduces bacteria-mediated frost injury.

10. *Microbial sprays (biopesticides).* Scientists have identified and cultured natural enemies of certain horticultural plants. An infected field is sprayed with large populations of laboratory-cultured microbes. For example, aerial application of spores of the fungus *Collectotrichum gloesporiodes* has been successfully used to control the northern jointvetch in rice fields. Also, the fungus *Talaromyces flavius,* when applied to the soil, is effective in controlling soilborne diseases such as wilts of potato (potato wilt) and eggplant (verticilium wilt). Through breeding efforts, more aggressive and effective strains of these microbes are being developed, as in the case of plant cultivars. Another commercially available microbial spray is the *Bacillus thuringiensis* spray, which is effective against caterpillars or cutworms, corn borers, cabbage worms, and others. The effect on caterpillars starts upon ingestion of the bacteria.

8.7.1 ADVANTAGES AND DISADVANTAGES OF BIOLOGICAL CONTROL

Advantages

The advantages of biological control include the following:

1. Pesticides are harmful to the environment and are hazardous to humans and wildlife. Biological control uses organisms already present in the environment.

2. Seeds of improved cultivars (resistant cultivars) are cheaper to use than spraying against pests with chemicals.

3. Biological control is safer to apply than chemicals.

TABLE 8-3 Selected Examples of Biological Control of Horticultural Pests

Biological Agent	Some Pests Controlled
Ladybug	Aphid
Bacillus thuringiensis	Colorado potato beetle and caterpillar
Bacillus popillise	Japanese beetle
Green lacewing	Aphid and mealybug
Parasitic wasp	Tomato hornworm and cabbage looper
Nedalia beetle	Citrus cottony scale
Tilleteopars	Powdery mildew
Talaromyces flavius	Potato wilt and verticillium wilt

In addition to these organisms, the use of resistant cultivars, plants with repellent scents, and crop rotation are other nonchemical methods of pest control.

Disadvantages

The major disadvantages of biological control include the following:

1. Availability and application are limited to relatively few crop species.
2. Handling of organisms is less convenient than chemicals, often requiring special care.

8.7.2 OTHER EXAMPLES OF BIOLOGICAL CONTROL

A variety of beetles have been identified as predators of pests of cultivated crops:

1. The European seven-spotted lady beetle *(Coccinella septempunctata)* preys on aphids.
2. The ladybug *(Crystalaemus montrocizieri)* destroys mealybugs.
3. The larvae of the Japanese beetle feed on the larvae of other beetles.

In addition to beetles, the bacterium *Bacillus thuringiensis* is known to infest and kill a variety of insects, including the larvae of butterflies, moths, and corn borers, while being harmless to plants. Other examples are presented in Table 8–3. Figure 8–4 presents examples of various organisms in effecting biological control. These exhibits represent only a select few examples.

8.8 CULTURAL CONTROL

A variety of strategies are employed to implement cultural control of diseases and pests in plants.

8.8.1 CROP ROTATION

As indicated in the introduction to this chapter, monoculture and repeated cultivation of one species on the same area of land encourages the buildup of the diseases and pests that plague the cultivated species. Crop rotation is a strategy whereby no one species is perpetually planted on the same plot of land (Figure 8–5). Additionally, a species is not followed by its relative. Instead, species with different soil requirements or use are rotated in a definite cycle (e.g., corn to tomato to bean to corn, or a four-year rotation). Note that the rotation has a cereal, a solanaceous species, and a legume. A rotation consisting of, for example, potato, tomato, and eggplant (all solanaceous species) certainly violates the rule of not following a species with its relative. Similarly, cruciferous plants (e.g., cabbage, broccoli, mustard), leguminous plants (e.g., beans, peas), onions (e.g., garlic, leek), and Curcubitaceous plants (watermelon, squash) are groups of plants affected by similar diseases. Rotation of crops is effective in reducing the populations of

FIGURE 8–4 Selected examples of biological control. (a) A lacewing attacking prey. (b) *Tetrastichus gallerucae* attacking elm leaf beetle eggs. (c) Female *Aphytis* piercing scale insect with ovipositor. (d) Predaceous midge larva eating aphid. (e) Yellow jacket attacking a caterpillar. (f) Flower fly larva eating aphids. (*Source:* Photos provided courtesy of Oklahoma Cooperative Extension Service, Oklahoma State University)

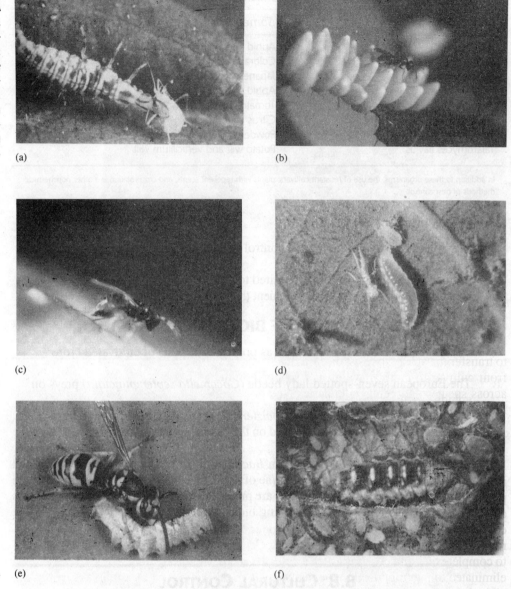

(a)

(b)

(c)

(d)

(e)

(f)

certain soilborne diseases such as tomato wilts. The causal organisms of such diseases need the host plant in order to thrive and consequently cannot persist in the soil if the host is absent for about two to three years. Rotations are particularly effective in controlling diseases and pests whose causal organisms do not travel long distances (such as nematodes, weevils, certain wilts, and phytophthora).

8.8.2 SANITATION

Disease-causing organisms and insects remain in the field if infected plant debris is left on the ground. Sometimes infected plant remains have to be incinerated to kill the pathogens. Uninfected plant remains may harbor insects and disease organisms.

8.8.3 USE OF RESISTANT CULTIVARS

Plant breeders genetically manipulate the genotypes of plants to the advantage of humans. Through scientific inquiry, some of the protective strategies of plants in the wild have been discovered and studied. Some species resist certain diseases and pests because they have genes that condition such characteristics. Through breeding, scientists are able

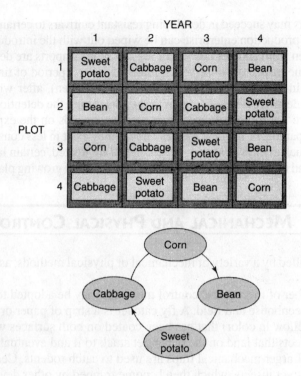

FIGURE 8–5 A crop rotation cycle.

to transfer the ability to resist diseases and pests from the wild into cultivated species and from cultivar to cultivar within the species. Sometimes resistance is even transferred across species and genus boundaries (see biotechnology). Resistant cultivars exist for most of the major pests of horticultural plants.

8.8.4 HOST ERADICATION

Host eradication is often a drastic preemptive method of pest control that involves the elimination of all susceptible hosts when a pathogen is known to have been introduced into the production area. This tactic is used to forestall an eminent disease epidemic. For example, all citrus trees in a production area where a pathogen has been introduced may be completely eradicated. On a small scale, host eradication is conducted in nurseries and greenhouses by rouging (removing off types) infected plants. Certain pathogens require two alternative hosts to complete their life cycles. In such a case, the less economically important host should be eliminated to interrupt the developmental cycle of the pathogen. For example, *Cronartium ribicola* requires pine and currant plants to complete its life cycle.

8.8.5 MULCHING

Plastic mulching has the capacity to trap heat, which causes the soil temperature to increase. The high temperature destroys some soil pathogens, including *Verticilium*.

8.9 LEGISLATIVE CONTROL

Various regulatory or legislative restrictions are placed on the movement of live plants and produce from one place to another. Controlling the spread of plant pests through laws is called **plant quarantine.** The purpose of such laws is to prevent the importation and spread of pathogens and insect pests into areas where they do not already occur. In the United States, the Plant Quarantine Act of 1912 established the laws that govern such restricted movement of materials. International and local (with and between states) restrictions are designed to curb the spread of diseases and pests that are associated with specific plants. Enforcement is especially strict with regard to plants that are of high economic importance.

Plant Quarantine
The use of legislation to control the import and export of plants or plant materials to prevent the spread of plant pests and diseases.

Plant breeding efforts may succeed in developing resistant cultivars to certain pests and diseases. However, the production enterprise can be wiped out with the introduction of a new strain of the pathogen from another country or region. When imports are detained in quarantine procedures, the inspectors observe the materials over a period of time (at least for the duration of the incubation period of the insect or pathogen), after which plants are released, treated, or destroyed, depending on the results during the detention.

Quarantines are not foolproof since their success depends on the experience of the inspectors. Further, pathogens may escape detection if they exist in less conspicuous stages in their life cycles, such as eggs or spores. Where plants are treated, certain latent infections may exist in seeds and other plant materials even after a period of growing plants in the field.

8.10 MECHANICAL AND PHYSICAL CONTROL

Pests may be controlled by a variety of mechanical or physical methods, as outlined here:

1. *Traps.* A number of mechanical control measures may be adopted to control pests in the greenhouse and field. A fly catcher is a strip of paper or polyethylene (commonly yellow in color) that has been coated on both surfaces with a sticky substance. Insects that land on the paper get stuck to it and eventually die (Figure 8–6). Larger mechanical traps are used to catch rodents. Certain lights are designed to attract insects, which then become trapped by other devices installed for that purpose.

2. *Handpicking.* In a small garden, caterpillars and other large bugs may be hand-picked (not necessarily with bare hands) and destroyed.

3. *Barriers.* Rodents can be kept out of a garden by fencing it. A band of sticky paper (similar to a fly catcher) wrapped around the base of a tree prevents crawling insects on the ground from climbing up the tree.

4. *Tillage.* As a pest-control measure, tillage (cultivation) is used to remove weeds from the area.

5. *Mulching.* Mulching can be a method of mechanical control because a material such as plastic prevents weeds from growing through the material.

FIGURE 8–6 Polyethylene trap. *(Source: George Acquaah)*

6. *Heat treatment.* In the greenhouse, soil and other growing media are routinely sterilized before use. Depending on the temperature, sterilization may kill nematodes and water mold (at 50°C [122°F]). To kill bacteria, fungi, and worms, the temperature should be about 72°C (162°F). Weed seeds and some bacteria and viruses are killed at temperatures of about 82°C (180°F). When soil is oven sterilized, beneficial microbes (e.g., bacteria involved in the nitrogen cycle) may be killed, and toxic levels of salts (e.g., that of magnesium) may occur.

   Hot water is used in the greenhouse to clean certain dormant planting materials (e.g., seeds and bulbs) to remove pathogens. Heat treatment by hot air is used to dry cut surfaces of vegetative plant materials such as tubers to accelerate healing and thus prevent rot. For example, sweet potato may be air dried at 28 to 32°C (82 to 90°F) for about two weeks. Drying of grains and nuts is required before long-term storage. Fruits such as grapes and plums can be dried to produce raisins and prunes, respectively. The latter products can be stored for long periods without decay.

7. *Cold treatment.* Most postharvest protection of fresh produce is achieved through cold storage to maintain quality. Cold storage does not kill pathogens but slows their activity.

8. *Radiation.* Exposure of harvested products to the appropriate dose of radiation (e.g., gamma radiation) is known to prolong shelf life. Similarly, it is known that certain pathogenic fungi (e.g., *Botrytis* and *Alternaria*) produce spores only under conditions in which the light received contains ultraviolet (UV) radiation. Some greenhouses are glazed with UV-absorbing material so that radiation with a wavelength below 390 nanometers is not received within the greenhouse. Vegetables may be produced without infection by these pathogens.

SUMMARY

Every organism has natural enemies. Biological control exploits natural defense mechanisms, managing and controlling them to increase their efficiency. Some plants have structural features that confer upon them resistance to particular pests. Certain plants contain chemicals such as pyrethrums that repel pests. Parasitism and prey-predator relationships occur in nature. Plant breeders are able to breed resistance to pests and diseases into cultivars. Diseases and pests can be controlled by adopting crop rotation practices. Some microbial sprays are available for use against a number of pests. Governments enact legislation to restrict the movement of live biological material from one place to another to limit the spread of contagious diseases. Such quarantine laws differ from place to place. Sometimes pests have to be physically or mechanically removed by, for example, trapping or handpicking.

MODULE 3

CHEMICAL CONTROL OF PLANT PESTS: INSECTICIDES

8.11 INSECTICIDES AND THEIR USE

Insecticides are chemicals used to control insect pests. They are classified in several standard ways.

8.11.1 CLASSIFICATION BASED ON KILLING ACTION

Chemicals used to control insect pests vary in the way they kill, which thus provides a basis for classifying insecticides. This method of classification is outmoded. Since insects differ in morphology and feeding habits, for example, it is critical that the insecticide attack the pest where it is most vulnerable. The various action modes under which insecticides may be classified are as follows:

1. *Contact action.* Insecticides that kill by contact action are also called *contact poisons.* They are effective when sprayed directly onto the pests or when the pests come into contact with poisons as they move on plant parts that have been sprayed. Once in contact with the pest, contact poisons attack the respiratory and nervous systems, with lethal consequences. Most insects succumb to contact poisons (e.g., malathion). Insects that hide on the undersides of leaves are hard to hit directly by contact poisons.
2. *Stomach action.* *Stomach poisons* must be ingested by the pest to be effective. As such, chewing insects (e.g., grasshoppers, beetles, and caterpillars) are effectively controlled by this class of poisons. Once ingested, the poison (e.g., rotenone) is absorbed through the digestive tract.
3. *Systemic action.* *Systemic insecticides* permeate the entire plant so that any insects that suck or chew are exposed to the poisons. They may be applied as foliar sprays or directly to the soil to be absorbed by roots. Insects cannot hide from this chemical since once they feed (whether by sucking or chewing) they ingest the toxin. The caution to observe with systemic poisons is that when applied to food crops, the produce must not be eaten until the toxin (e.g., orthene) has broken down to a safe level.
4. *Fumigation.* *Fumigants* are volatile chemicals that enter the target pest through its respiratory system. They are effective when used in closed systems such as storage houses and greenhouses. The soil can also be fumigated to control soilborne diseases such as root-knot nematodes. Though gaseous, fumigants have contact action. The fine particles settle on the body of the insect before entering through the pores.
5. *Repellent action.* Most insecticides are designed to kill pests. However, some chemicals, called *repellants* (e.g., Bordeaux mixture), repel insects (e.g., leaf hopper and potato flea beetle) from plants without any killing action.
6. *Attractant action.* Females of many insect species secrete certain chemicals called *pheromones* that attract male partners. Scientists have successfully synthesized these chemicals for use in luring male insects to traps, where they are caught and destroyed. The Japanese beetle moth and gypsy moth are easily baited by the use of pheromones. By baiting males and destroying them, most females are left unfertilized, thus reducing the population of the insects.
7. *Suffocation.* Scale insects are widely controlled by spraying oils that plug the breathing holes in their bodies and suffocate them.

8.11.2 CLASSIFICATION BASED ON CHEMISTRY OF ACTIVE INGREDIENT

Active Ingredient (A.I.) *The amount of actual pesticide in a formulation that is toxic or inhibiting to the pest.*

Modern classification of insecticides is based on chemical composition, since many modern insecticides have both contact and stomach actions. The two broad classes of insecticides are based on the chemistry of the **active ingredient** (the compound responsible for the killing action).

Inorganic Compounds (Inorganics)

Insecticides made up of inorganic compounds or minerals are becoming increasingly less common. They are usually designed to kill by stomach action and include compounds such as arsenic (lead arsenate or calcium arsenate), sulfur, and fluorine.

Organic Compounds (Organics)

Organic insecticides may be *natural* or *synthetic*.

Natural (Botanicals)   Botanicals are products from plants that have insecticidal effects. Many plant species produce organic compounds that are toxic to insect pests that feed on them. Plant organic substances are usually safe and nontoxic to humans. An example of a botanical is *pyrethrum,* which is obtained from chrysanthemum. Another organic substance is *nicotine,* which is obtained from tobacco plants and is an addictive substance found in cigarettes. Other botanicals are rotenone, ryania, and sabadilla. Many organic compounds act as stomach or contact poisons.

Synthetic Organic Compounds   Synthetic organic chemicals are artificially compounded and are effective against a wide variety of insects and pests. On the basis of the active ingredients in chemicals, several classes of synthetic organic insecticides are identified:

1. *Organochlorines (chlorinated hydrocarbons).* Organochlorines are most readily associated with dicarbo-, dihydrotetrachloride (DDT), which is one of the earliest and most successful to be developed. It has wide application, being effective against horticultural field pests, mosquitoes, fleas, and flies. It has a long residual effect, working long after initial application. Organochlorines are not readily biodegradable, which contributes to their rapid buildup in the environment in the soil and water, as well as in the tissues of plants and animals and their products. They are thus not only toxic to humans through their action on direct contact but also through the ingestion of food that has been contaminated, such as dairy and meat products (i.e., through a cow eating contaminated feed) and fish from contaminated waters. Consequently, DDT (as well as its close relatives) has been banned in many parts of the world. Other organochlorines are chlordane, lindane, methoxychlor, heptachlor, and aldin.
2. *Organophosphates.* Unlike chlorinated hydrocarbons, organophosphates (or organic phosphates) have shorter residual action (breakdown within thirty days) and are more readily biodegradable. As such, they do not build up in the environment. However, certain types (e.g., parathion) are extremely toxic to humans. Organophosphates are generally effective insecticides. Malathion is less toxic and widely used as a horticultural spray. Other organophosphates include diazinon, phorate, dameton, and chlorpyrifos.
3. *Carbamates.* Carbamates are relatively safer to use than those previously described. They have somewhat low mammalian toxicity and short residual action (breakdown within seven days). They are effective against sucking and chewing insects. One of the earliest and most successful was carbaryl (trade named Sevin). Others are carbofuran, aldicarb, and propoxur.
4. *Pyrethroids.* Pyrethroids are synthetic equivalents of natural pyrethrins found in species such as chrysanthemum. They are less toxic to humans and effective against a broad spectrum of insects.

Fumigants   Fumigants act in the gaseous state and are best used in closed environments (e.g., as storage pesticides) or injected into the soil. One of the most common types is methyl bromide, an odorless and colorless gas that is highly toxic to humans but is used widely to fumigate stored vegetables, seeds, fruits, and grains. It is also used to chemically sterilize soil mixes for use in greenhouses. Malathion is one of the most widely used fumigants of stored grain.

Spray Oils   Spray oils are obtained by specially distilling and refining crude oils. They are used to combat scale insects and mites in orchard plants and ornamentals. A common form is called dormant spray.

Biologicals (Microbial Insecticides) Biologicals are commercially produced pathogens (e.g., bacteria, fungi, and viruses) that are applied to the foliage of plants to prey on specific insect pests. For example, commercial preparations of the bacterium *Bacillus thuringiensis* are applied to foliage to control several species of *Lepidoptera* (caterpillars).

8.11.3 FORMULATIONS OF INSECTICIDES

The chemical that actually controls the target pest *(active ingredient)* is not marketed or utilized directly but mixed with an inert ingredient to create what is called a **formulation.** Although some formulations are ready to use, others require diluting with a solvent or water before use. The two general types of formulations are dry and liquid.

Dry Formulations

Dusts Dusts are chemicals formulated as powders and applied as such without mixing or diluting. They usually contain low concentrations of the active ingredient or ingredients (about 1 to 10 percent) mixed with fine-powdered inert material (e.g., chalk, clay, or talc). Dusts are applied by using simple equipment called *dusters.* They are easy to apply but leave unsightly residue on foliage. Further, when applied in even the slightest wind condition, **drift** (blowing away in the wind) may be a problem. Drifting of a pesticide onto plants not intended to be sprayed may result in collateral damage.

Wettable Powders Wettable powders are concentrated chemicals formulated as dusts or powders that require dilution before use. Wettable powders are usually formulated to a high concentration of active ingredient (about 50 percent or greater). The addition of water decreases drift, but since the powders, even in solution, tend to settle, care should be taken to stir the mixture frequently so that the chemical is applied uniformly and at the desired rate. To increase the effectiveness of pesticides that require mixing with water before use, they are mixed with surfactants (agents that help pesticides to stick or spread better by lowering surface tension). This mixing is necessary because the plant surface naturally repels water to a varying extent. Wettable powders require constant agitation during use.

Granules Sometimes insecticides are formulated as coarse particles called granules. Granules are applied to the soil in the same way as granular fertilizer formulations are applied. They may require dissolution in water before roots can absorb the chemicals. Some may have to be incorporated into the soil. Systemic herbicides may be formulated this way. Other granules are designed to act like fumigants and thus need no water to initiate their effects. Granules are ready to use and pose little danger to the user. There is no danger of drift, and application requires only simple equipment such as a spreader.

Pellets Pellets differ from granules in that the former consists of particles that are uniform in size and of specific weight. Unlike granules, pellets can be applied by precision applicators.

Baits When an active ingredient is mixed with food or some other substance that attracts pests, the formulation is called a bait. Pests are attracted to baits and die when they ingest the poisons. Baits are usually low in active ingredient (less than 5 percent). They are commonly used to control indoor pests including mice and cockroaches.

Liquid Formulations

Aerosols Aerosols contain one or more active ingredients in a solvent. Household chemicals are frequently formulated as aerosols. These insecticides are contained in pressurized cans and are ready for use. They are very convenient to use but still require adherence to the safety measures that apply to all insecticides. The insecticides are propelled by special gases (propellants) including fluorocarbons (e.g., freon), isobutane, and isopropane. Aerosols may be formulated for use as smoke or fog in special generators under enclosed conditions (e.g., warehouses or greenhouses). The advantage of this formulation is that the entire space is filled with the pesticide. However, because aerosols are difficult to confine to the target, everything in the area is exposed to the pesticide. Injury due to inhalation is possible if aerosols are used without proper protection.

Emulsifiable Concentrates   Emulsifiable concentrates consist of an active ingredient mixed in a petroleum solvent and an **emulsifier.** The emulsifier is an *adjuvant* that allows the formulation to be mixed with water. Emulsifiable concentrates are used widely in horticultural applications. They are adaptable to a variety of methods of application and equipment, including mist blowers, aerial applicators, and portable sprayers. Emulsifiable concentrates are desirable for several reasons, including the fact that, unlike wettable powders, they do not separate out in solution and hence do not require frequent stirring in the tank as dusts. They are mixed with water to the required concentration and leave very little residue on plants and fruits. However, mixing errors may occur, leading to a high potential for *phytotoxicity* (plant damage from chemicals).

Emulsifier
A surface-active agent that facilitates the suspension of minute droplets of one liquid in another to form a stable emulsion.

Flowables   Flowables are suspensions of active ingredients. They are easy to use but may leave some residue on plants.

Fumigants   Fumigants are formulations that produce gases during application. They may be liquids or solids. Fumigants are best applied in closed environments such as granaries, warehouses, and greenhouses. They are used in controlling some soilborne pests. A major advantage of fumigants is their ability to invade any space in the areas of application (such as cracks and crevices). A single application is usually effective in controlling the pest. The disadvantages include the need for special equipment, limitation to use in enclosed areas, and a high potential for human respiratory injury.

Solutions   Sometimes, by including special additives in the formulation, the active ingredient may become soluble in water. Solutions have the advantage of leaving no residue on surfaces and requiring no agitation during use.

8.11.4   APPLICATION EQUIPMENT

The type of equipment used in insecticide application depends on several factors, including the area to be treated, the kinds of plants to be treated, and the formulation. Some equipment is mechanically operated, and others are motorized. Although some are handheld, others require the use of tractors and other means of transportation. Common insecticide applicators are described in the following sections.

Small-Scale Applicators

Pressurized Cans   Aerosols come ready to use in pressurized cans (Figure 8–7). Special equipment is not needed. The pesticide is released by simply pressing down on the nozzle to deliver a fine, misty spray.

Compressed-Air Tank Spray   A compressed-air tank is a much larger version of the handheld aerosol can, but the principle of operation is the same (Figure 8–8). The tank is partially filled with the correctly prepared chemical solution. The remainder of the space is occupied by air, which is compressed in a variety of ways depending on the design of the equipment. A handle may be used to mechanically pump air into the tank. The tank is attached with a flexible tube fitted at the tip with a nozzle for delivering fine sprays in patterns according to its design. The flexible tube enables the operator to spray hard-to-reach places. The design of the compressed-air tank sprayer may allow the equipment to be carried as a knapsack on the back or hung on the shoulder in a sling.

Atomizer Sprayer   An atomizer sprayer is a simple handheld implement with a plunger that is pushed to draw air into the tube for dispersing the chemical solution in a fine spray at each stroke.

FIGURE 8–7 Pressurized can used for spraying aerosols.

FIGURE 8–8 Compressed-air tank sprayer. *(Source: George Acquaah)*

Dusters   Pesticides formulated as dust are applied with the aid of dusters that may have plungers similar to those of atomizers. Some dusters have a squeezable bulb.

Large-Scale Applicators

Motorized Ground Applicators   Motorized ground applicators work on the same principle as those for small-scale applications, except that certain functions that are manually performed in small applicators are automated in large applicators. The designs and sizes of the equipment vary:

1.   *Portable (usually on the back of the operator)*. Some compressed tanks are small enough to be carried around. They are fitted with small motors so that the operator needs only control the delivery tube and direct the spray at desired targets.
2.   *Tractor-mounted*. The power take-off of the tractor may be used to provide the source of power for operating large sprayers, which are drawn or attached to the rear of tractors (Figure 8–9).
3.   *Truck-mounted*. Some trucks are equipped with tanks and other devices for spraying or spreading (granular) pesticides, such as the fan jet applicator for orchards.

Aerial Applicators   Where very large acreages must be treated, using airplanes or helicopters equipped with sprayers may be most economical. Some commercial companies specialize in aerial applications (Figure 8–10).

8.11.5   EQUIPMENT CALIBRATION

Chemicals used to control insects are very toxic to both pests and humans and as such should be used very carefully, only if needed, and also in the minimum strength or concentration needed to be effective. Overapplication is not only wasteful but may damage the plants and produce being protected and may be injurious to operators and consumers of the produce.

FIGURE 8–9 A tractor-mounted sprayer for trees. *(Source: USDA)*

FIGURE 8–10 Aerial application of pesticides. *(Source: USDA)*

Insecticide manufacturers provide adequate instructions with their products for their correct and safe use. The recommended rate of application should be adopted. Premixed insecticides are available for easy and ready application and are especially recommended for the novice.

Small applicators are usually not calibrated beyond that for which the manufacturer designed them, and as such the operator should be careful to deliver just the right quantity of the correctly mixed chemical. When liquid chemicals are used, a good application is one that covers the leaf surface to a point where dripping is about to occur. Dusts should similarly cover the leaf surface uniformly in one round of application. The amount applied depends on the distance between the leaf and the applicator.

Large applicators need calibration beyond the manufacturer's settings. Factors to take into account in calibration include the rate of application; the speed of the tractor, truck, or airplane; the nozzle type at the end of the sprayer; and the distance of the nozzle from the plants.

8.11.6 STRATEGIES FOR EFFECTIVE AND SAFE APPLICATION

Identify Pest

Treatment is most successful if the disease is identified in its early stages. In horticulture, then, the grower should visit the field or inspect the plants regularly. Certain insects are known to be perpetual pests at certain times in the growing season and should be anticipated. In insect control, the grower should determine whether the problem is caused by chewing or sucking insects. Chewing insects chew away the leaves especially, leaving holes, a network of veins, whitish patches, or partly eaten leaves. Stomach and contact poisons are effective for their control. It is more difficult to detect the presence of sucking insects. Plants are deprived of nutrients and may appear weak, grow less vigorously, or show rolled leaf edges. Sometimes, as in the case of aphids, these sucking pests can be found by turning over the leaf to examine the underside. Systemic and contact insecticides are effective against sucking insects.

Determine Economic Damage Potential

Certain insects are unable to inflict enough damage to cause the grower any significant economic loss. Since chemicals are not only expensive but hazardous to health, they should be applied only when the grower has determined that the potential loss is significant enough to warrant their use.

Insect Biology

Knowing the biology of the insect enables the timely application of insecticides for effectiveness. Insects must be controlled before they reach the stage where they cause devastation to the crop and before they have a chance to multiply. Insect pests are more susceptible when they are active than when they are in the egg or pupa stages. If, upon examination of the field or garden, only dormant stages are observed, chemical control should be delayed until the eggs hatch or adults emerge. Immediate control measures are required when mixed stages occur. In such a situation, a follow-up application should be made as appropriate (with respect to the life cycle of the insect) to coincide with the hatching of eggs.

8.11.7 HOUSEPLANT PESTS AND THEIR CONTROL

Common houseplant pests and their means of control are presented in Table 8–4.

8.11.8 VEGETABLE PESTS AND THEIR CONTROL

A selected number of vegetable pests and their means of control are summarized in Table 8–5.

TABLE 8–4 Suggestions for Control of Selected Houseplant Pests

Pest	Plants Attacked	Control
Mite	African violet, begonia, cyclamen, gloxinia, palm, geranium, and English ivy	Spray with dicofol
Mealybug	Begonia, African violet, gardenia, palm, dracaena, and gloxinia	Use malathion, diazinon, or orthene or remove by hand
Aphid	Gloxinia and begonia	Use malathion or remove by hand
Whitefly	Geranium, coleus, and begonia	Use malathion, rotenone, or orthene
Scale	Philodendron, azalea, citrus, fern, and palm	Remove by hand or use nicotine sulfate
Fungus gnat	Philodendron, fuchsia, and fern	Use nicotine sulfate

It is recommended, whenever possible, to use pesticides on plants on which they are registered and to follow the manufacturer's directions.

TABLE 8–5 Suggestions for Control of Selected Vegetable Pests

Pest	Plants Attacked	Control
Aphid	Cole crops (cabbage, broccoli, cauliflower, and brussels sprout)	Use diazinon or malathion
Mite	Bean (dry, lima, and snap) and tomato	Use malathion, diazinon, or kelthane
Caterpillar	Cole crops	Use Sevin, malathion, or thiodan
Cutworm or white grub	Cole crops	Use Sevin or diazinon
Earworm or fruitworm	Corn and tomato	Use Sevin or diazinon
Damping-off	Eggplant, pepper, cucumber, muskmelon, pumpkin, and tomato	Use captan or thiram
Downy mildew	Cole crops and beans	Use zineb or maneb
Powdery mildew	Bean, pumpkin, and squash	Use sulfur or benomyl
Wilt	Tomato, eggplant, and pepper	No chemical control
Cercospora leaf spot	Beet and carrot	Use zineb or maneb

It is recommended, whenever possible, to use pesticides on plants on which they are registered and to follow the manufacturer's directions.

8.11.9 LANDSCAPE PESTS AND THEIR CONTROL

A selected number of landscape pests and their means of control are presented in Table 8–6.

TABLE 8–6 Common Landscape Pests and Control

Pest	Description and Suggested Control
Lawn Pests	
Ants	Inhabit the soil in nests and destroy vegetation, leaving denuded spots in the lawn; their mounds are unsightly Control: Drench nests with pesticides (e.g., diazinon, Sevin, and malathion)
Chigger	Also called red bug, it is the larval stage of a small mite; it sucks sap from stems and causes stunted growth Control: Apply insecticide dusts and sprays (e.g., durban, Sevin, and diazinon)
Billbug	Also called a snout beetle, it damages the roots and crowns of grasses Control: Apply diazinon or carbaryl
Armyworm	Feeds on stems and leaves Control: Apply diazinon or carbaryl
Sod webworm	Also called a grass moth; as it feeds, it spins threads that bind soil and leaves into tubelike structures on the soil surface Control: Spray carbaryl, aspon, or diazinon
Japanese beetle	Destructive in both larval and adult stages; destructive also to trees, fruits, and other ornamentals Control: Apply diazinon
Leaf bug	Damaged leaf shows yellow dots initially and eventually yellows and dies Control: Apply malathion or diazinon
General Landscape Pests (Annuals, Perennials, Trees, and Shrubs)	
Aphid	Sucking insect found on the underside of leaves; causes puckering or curling of leaves; it secretes honeydew that attracts other pests (e.g., flies, mites, and ants) Control: Apply orthene, diazinon, or malathion
Caterpillar	Larva of many insect pests (e.g., cankerworm, gypsy moth, eastern tent caterpillar, webworm, California orange dog, and sawfly) feed on the foliage of landscape plants Control: Use diazinon, Sevin, or orthene
Borer	Larvae of certain insects (e.g., peach twig borer and other wood borers) damage flowering fruit trees and other ornamental trees Control: Apply dimethoate, bendiocarb, or lindane
Beetle	Adult and larva may inflict damage to plant foliage Control: Apply methoxychlor or carbaryl
Mite	Presence characterized by discolored patches on leaf as a result of feeding (sucking) from underneath the leaf; affected plants are less vigorous and may eventually brown and die Control: Apply dicofol, malathion, or kelthane
Gall	May occur on stems, branches, twigs, or leaves; leaf galls usually cause less damage, being primarily unsightly and reducing aesthetic value Control: Apply carbaryl, diazinon, or malathion
Scale	Scale insects overwinter as eggs or young. They may be armored or unarmored according to scale characteristics. They suck plant juice by using their piercing mouthparts. Control: Apply dormant oil, acephate, or carbaryl

Summary

Chemicals used to control insect pests are called insecticides. On the basis of killing action, they are classified as contact poisons, stomach poisons, systemic insecticides, fumigants, repellents, attractants, and those that kill by suffocation. Active ingredients of insecticides may be organic or inorganic. Organic insecticides may be created from natural or synthetic compounds. Synthetic organic compounds have several classes: chlorinated hydrocarbons (e.g., DDT), organophosphates (e.g., malathion), carbamates (e.g., Sevin), pyrethroids (synthetic pyrethrins), and others. Insecticides may be formulated as dusts, wettable powders, emulsifiable concentrates, granules, or aerosols. Insecticide applicators vary in size from handheld to aerial sprayers.

Module 4

Chemical Control of Plant Pests: Herbicides

Overview

Herbicides are chemicals used to control weeds. Chemicals are the method of choice in killing weeds in large-scale plant production operations. Although their use facilitates plant production, the collateral damage to the environment and health hazard they pose to humans often detract from their role in agricultural production. Herbicides are also convenient for controlling weeds in the landscape and along railroads and highways. They work by interfering with the metabolic processes of the plant. The challenge in their design and application is to minimize damage to cultivated plants while killing unwanted plants. Indiscriminate use of herbicides should be avoided. Certain chemicals are restricted for use by professionals (licensed or certified applicators). As with all toxic chemicals, strict adherence to the directions for their safe use minimizes the danger to the health of humans and cultivated plants.

8.12 Classification of Herbicides

Herbicides may be grouped in one of several ways—by selectivity, how they kill (mode of action—by contact or systemic [translocation]), timing of application, and chemistry.

8.12.1 SELECTIVITY

On the basis of selectivity, there are two types of herbicides: selective and nonselective.

Selective Herbicides

Selectivity
The ability of a pesticide to kill some pests and not others without injuring related plants or animals.

True **selectivity** is achieved when an herbicide applied at the proper dose and timing is effective against only certain species of plants but not against others. *Selective herbicides* are designed to kill only certain plants without harming others. Generally, they are designed to discriminate between broadleaf and narrowleaf (grasses) morphologies. Selective herbicides are the most widely used because most situations require only certain plants to be killed but not others. For example, in lawn (grass), broadleaves of any kind are not desired. Broadleaf weeds such as dandelions and wild mustards can be safely eliminated by spraying the lawn with a selective herbicide such as (2,4-dichlorophenoxy acetic acid), which kills only broadleaf plants. Certain chemicals can be manipulated to be selective by changing the concentration at which they are applied. At a high rate of application, a particular herbicide may kill a certain species but fail to do so at a lower concentration. However, even at lower concentrations, these chemicals remain toxic and should be handled with care. As such, by spraying older cultivated plants with low application rates, younger weeds may be controlled without harming the desired crop plants.

Nonselective Herbicides

Nonselective herbicides literally kill all plants exposed to them—weeds and crops alike. These nondiscriminating herbicides are used to control weeds in areas where no plant growth is desired, such as driveways, parking lots, and along railroad tracks. Examples of nonselective herbicides are Roundup and atrazine. Nonselective herbicides may be made selective through manipulation of the concentration or rate of application. For example, using atrazine at low concentrations decreases its killing action to certain plant types.

8.12.2 CONTACT VERSUS TRANSLOCATED

Some chemicals use two modes of action. *Contact herbicides* kill by direct contact with plants and are very effective against annual weeds. To be most effective, the application must completely cover the plant parts. **Systemic (translocated) pesticides** are absorbed through either roots or leaves. Those applied to the soil have residual action and thus are most suitable for controlling perennial weeds. Complete coverage is not necessary when using these chemicals.

Systemic Pesticide (translocated)
One that is absorbed and moved from the site of uptake to other parts of the plant.

8.12.3 TIMING OF APPLICATION

Regarding crop (or weed) growth cycle, three stages are important for herbicide application.

Preplant

Preplant herbicides are applied to the soil before planting the crop. Depending on the kind, it may or may not require incorporation into the soil to be effective. Preplant applications are made at low rates or concentrations and have the advantage of damaging weeds when they are in the most vulnerable seedling stage.

Preemergence

Like preplant herbicides, preemergence herbicides are applied after planting the crop, either before crops or weeds emerge or after crop emergence but before weed emergence. These herbicides kill only germinating seedlings and not established plants. Whenever soil is disturbed, weeds arise. A newly planted ground cover may be sprayed with a preemergence herbicide to suppress weeds that may have been stirred up.

Postemergence

Herbicide application after cultivated plants have emerged is described as postemergence treatment. In several situations, such as occurs in orchards, the grower has no choice but to adopt postemergence application. However, the grower may choose to apply a herbicide before weeds emerge (preemergence). It is important, therefore, that emergence always be in reference to either the weed or the crop plant.

8.12.4 CHEMISTRY

Herbicides may be classified according to their chemical nature as either organic or inorganic.

Organic Herbicides

The various classes of organic herbicides include organic arsenicals and phenoxy herbicides.

Organic Arsenicals   Organic arsenicals are translocated herbicides and thus are effective against plant species with underground structures (e.g., rhizomes and tubers), as occurs in nutsedges and johnsongrass. They are relatively less toxic than inorganic chemicals and are salts of arsenic and arsenic acid derivatives.

Phenoxy Herbicides Phenoxy herbicides are also referred to as hormone weed killers. One of the most common phenoxy herbicides is 2,4-D. Another is 2,4,5-trichlorophenoxy acetic acid, which is used in the control of woody perennials and is associated with the Agent Orange episode in Vietnam, where it was used to defoliate large forest areas. The latter has been banned by the EPA.

Diphenyl Ethers An example is Fusilade.

Substituted Amide These herbicides are readily biodegradable by plants and in the soil. An example is Diphenamid.

Substituted Ureas Selective preemergence herbicides, substituted ureas have strong residual effects in the soil. An example is Siduron.

Carbamates This class of herbicides is formulated generally for preemergence application. An example is EPTC.

Triazines An example of this class of herbicides is Simazine. It is used in driveways and around patios.

Aliphatic Acids An example is Dalapon, used to control grasses.

Arylaliphatic Acid An example is DCPA.

Substituted Nitriles These herbicides are fast acting and also have broad action. An example is Dichlobenial.

Bipyridyliums Examples are diquat and paraquat, called contact herbicides.

Inorganic Herbicides

Inorganic herbicides have great residual effects and thus are strictly regulated by the EPA. They are not recommended for use around the house.

8.13 FORMULATIONS

Herbicides are formulated to be applied as either *liquids* or *granules*.

8.13.1 LIQUIDS

Liquid formulations are applied as either wettable powders or water-dispersible granules in water. Most herbicides are applied as sprays, making the sprayer the most important implement in herbicide application. Sprayers come in a variety of designs and may be hand or power operated. Sprayers may be mounted on trucks or tractors. Sprayer application may also be at low volume (high herbicide concentration delivered in small amounts per unit area) or high volume (low concentration of a herbicide applied in large amounts per unit area).

8.13.2 GRANULES

When granules are used, they may be applied at low or high rates. When applying at low rates (small amounts of granules), a carrier material such as sand may be mixed with the granules to increase the bulk for more effective and uniform application. Granular formulations are more expensive than others because of the bulk and shipping costs.

Further, they do not provide uniform application. However, the equipment for application is less expensive and there is no need to haul large amounts of water to the field during application.

8.14 METHODS OF APPLICATION

Depending on the areas to be treated and the distribution of vegetation, herbicides may be applied in several ways, including broadcast, band, and spot application.

1. *Broadcast application.* When the entire area is to be treated, the herbicide may be broadcast without fear of damaging other plants. Liquids and granules may be broadcast. Aerial application by aircraft is a form of broadcasting.
2. *Band application.* In orchards and vineyards, the paths between rows may be readily cultivated, but the plant canopy may not permit the equipment to get close enough to clear all of the weeds from around the stem. Herbicides may be applied by band application to control the narrow strips of weeds around plants.
3. *Spot application.* Weeds that break through gaps in the driveway or walkway and masses of weeds concentrated in a small or hard-to-reach area are often spot treated.

8.15 FACTORS INFLUENCING HERBICIDE EFFECTIVENESS

Herbicides are applied directly to plants or the soil. As such, plant and soil conditions, coupled with the conditions in the general environment in which application occurs, influence the effectiveness of herbicides. Although some of these factors are environmental, the effectiveness of herbicide application depends largely on the operator. Some sources of error in application are discussed in the following paragraphs.

1. *Weed identification and assessment of infestation.* Since a weed is simply a plant out of place, a volunteer corn plant in an orchard is a weed. The presence of a few plants of corn in a tomato field does not warrant chemical control. The corn (the weed) may be cut down or uprooted by hand. The weeds to be controlled must be correctly identified for the correct treatment to be prescribed.
2. *Herbicide selection.* Since most herbicides are selective, it is important that the correct plant species be identified so that the appropriate chemical is used.
3. *Time of application.* Certain weeds are extremely difficult to eradicate. However, their spread may be slowed if the weeds are controlled before they flower so that they do not bear seed. Also, since herbicides may be applied as preplant, preemergence, or postemergence herbicides, it is important that they be applied at the correct time in relation to the emergence of the crop or weed. If one is depending on rainfall to wash the herbicide into the soil, the operator should follow the weather forecast to ensure that rain will fall within about a week after application or make provisions for irrigation. Not all herbicides require rainfall (water) after application to be effective.
4. *Correct rate of application (equipment calibration).* The recommended rate of application should be adopted in a weed-control program. The equipment used should be properly calibrated to deliver the desired rate. If the chemical is overdiluted, the application will be a waste of time and money since the weed will not be controlled. On the other hand, too high a rate of application may injure desired crops and also waste money.
5. *Good ground coverage.* If the ground is not completely covered during an application, weeds may germinate and survive at untreated spots. This result may necessitate an additional spot application or manual removal of weeds, increasing production costs.

6. *Weather factors.* Although little rainfall may be unsatisfactory in some situations, excessive rain may wash granules away. Spraying in windy conditions causes excessive drift that may damage crop plants.

7. *Age of weeds.* Herbicides are more effective on younger plants than older ones. Weed-control measures should be effected before weeds are mature.

8. *Soil characteristics.* Herbicides such as Dacthal are readily absorbed by the soil organic matter, making them less effective on soils that are high in organic matter. Clay soils also absorb certain herbicides. In such situations, a higher rate of application may be necessary for better results.

8.16 INDOOR WEED CONTROL

Weeds should not become a problem indoors, especially in the home. Most houseplants are planted in pots or suitable containers. Weeds may occasionally arise because of the source of the growing medium. Such unwanted plants should be uprooted by hand. There is absolutely no need to use chemicals to control weeds in the home. In greenhouses without concrete floors, weeds could become a problem if neglected. Weeds could also arise through cracks in the concrete. Such weeds may be spot treated with chemicals. Certain herbicides are approved for use in greenhouses.

8.17 SUGGESTED HERBICIDES FOR THE LANDSCAPE

Common herbicides used in ornamental plant culture are presented in Table 8–7.

8.18 SUGGESTED HERBICIDES FOR THE HOME GARDEN

Weed control in the home garden can be accomplished without chemicals. Annual weeds (e.g., purselane, pigweed, and crabgrass) and perennial weeds (e.g., bindweed and quackgrass) can be controlled by hoeing, mulching, cultivating, or pulling by hand. Chemicals such as Dacthal may be used if necessary.

TABLE 8–7 Suggested Herbicides for the Landscape

Problem Weeds	Suggested Herbicides
Lawn	
Annual grass weeds	Trifluralin
	Dacthal (DCPA)—apply as preemergent
Annual broadleaf weeds	Bromoxynil
Perennial and other weeds	Glyphosate—as spot treatment; use for nonselective control or as preemergent for new lawns
General control of broadleaf weeds	2,4-D amine
Flower beds	
Annual weeds	Dacthal
Perennial weeds	Eptam (EPTC)
Around shrubs and trees	
Annual weeds	Dacthal, Bensulide
Perennial grass weeds	Eptham, Glyphosate

SUMMARY

Herbicides are chemicals used to control weeds. They may be classified according to selectivity (as selective herbicides, which kill only certain plants, or nonselective herbicides), timing of application (as preplant, preemergence, or postemergence herbicides), mode of action (as either contact or translocated), and chemistry (as either organic or inorganic herbicides). Herbicides may be formulated as liquids or granules. They are applied by either broadcast, or band application. Sometimes they are applied as a spot application to control highly localized weed infestation. The effectiveness of herbicide application depends on several factors, including plant species, type of herbicide, time of application, weather factors, age of weeds, and soil factors.

MODULE 5

GREENHOUSE PEST CONTROL

Greenhouses are enclosed structures and hence have environmental conditions that are different from the general open environment. Further, the greenhouse environment can be controlled, and thus the pest incidence can be controlled to some extent. However, even with best efforts, certain pests occur in greenhouses.

8.19 COMMON GREENHOUSE INSECT PESTS

Some of the most common and economically important greenhouse pests are described in the following list.

1. *Aphids.* The most common aphid found in greenhouses is the green peach aphid *(Myzus persicae)*. They may be winged or wingless. Whereas the winged green peach aphids are brown in color, the wingless ones are yellowish-green or pink. Aphids attack a wide variety of greenhouse plants. Younger leaves that are attacked become distorted, and older leaves show chlorotic patches.
2. *Fungus gnats.* Important species of the fungus gnat are *Bradysia* spp. and *Seiara* spp. Gnats are gray-colored, long-legged flies. They live on the soil. The stage in their life cycle that constitutes a pest problem is the larva stage. Gnat larvae are white worms with black heads. They prefer soils that are rich in organic matter, feeding on soil fungi and decaying organic matter. However, they can also feed on underground storage organs and the roots of young seedlings.
3. *Leaf miners.* Leaf miners are insects that in the larval stage tunnel between the outer layers of leaves. Their activity blemishes leaves severely. Chrysanthemums are particularly susceptible to leaf miner attack; the chrysanthemum leaf miner is called *Phytomyza atriconis*. Other species exist.
4. *Mealybugs.* Mealybugs *(Pseudococcus* spp.) are oval-shaped piercing insects that secrete a waxy covering over their bodies, causing them to appear white. This waxy layer forms a protective covering that makes pesticidal control of bugs difficult. To be most effective, mealybugs are controlled by spraying the nymphs. The economic damage they cause to plants is similar to aphid attack. Mealybugs also secrete honeydew, which attracts black mold to grow on the plant.
5. *Mites.* Mites belong to the spider or scorpion family (Arachnida). They are very tiny in size and develop well under conditions of high humidity and low temperatures of about 16°C (60°F). A common species is the *Steneotarsonemus pallidus* (Cyclamen

mite). However, the most important mite in greenhouse production is the two-spotted mite (or red spider) *(Tetranychus urticae)*. Mites usually hide on the undersides of leaves. The red spiders may spin unsightly webs over leaves and flowers.

6. *Scale insects.* Scale insects are similar to mealybugs. Some of them also secrete honeydew and thus cause black mold growth to appear, as in mealybug attack. They may be armored and have rubbery outer coatings or be without such a coating and armor.

7. *Slugs and snails.* Slugs and snails are mollusks (which include shell animals such as oysters). These pests chew tender seedlings and leaves. They are nocturnal in feeding habit and thus hide during the day under stones, leaves, and other objects; they prefer very damp environments. Slugs and snails gain access to the greenhouse area through growing media and attachment to plants and containers.

8. *Thrips.* Thrips are very tiny insects. They feed on a wide variety of greenhouse plants, usually congregating on buds, petals, or leaf axils. A gentle tap on the hiding place causes aphids to become dislodged. During feeding, aphids scrape the surface of the leaf, resulting in whitish streaks that may eventually turn brown. They excrete brown droplets that eventually turn black.

9. *Whiteflies.* Whiteflies are also tiny insects. The greenhouse whitefly *(Trialeurodes vaporariorum)* is covered with a white, waxy powder. Greenhouse plants most affected by whiteflies include petunia, poinsettia, ageratum, chrysanthemum, and tomato. Since they are attracted to the color yellow, sticky strips are usually suspended over benches to trap these flies. Whiteflies also secrete honeydew.

10. *Caterpillars.* Caterpillars, or the worm stage of some moths, are a menace to greenhouse production. Examples are corn earworms (which attack buds and succulent parts of plants such as chrysanthemum), European corn borers (bore through stems), cutworms (attack shoots), and beet armyworms (attack plants such as geranium, chrysanthemum, and carnation).

8.20 COMMON GREENHOUSE DISEASES

8.20.1 VIRUSES

Viruses, as previously indicated, cause stunting of affected plants and discoloration of leaves in the form of streaks, rings, or blocks. They are seldom transmitted by seed, exceptions including tomato ring spot and tobacco ring spot, which affect geraniums. Other greenhouse viruses include carnation mottle, carnation mosaic, chrysanthemum stunt, and chrysanthemum mosaic.

8.20.2 BACTERIA

Few greenhouse bacterial diseases exist. Major diseases include bacterial blight of geranium *(Xanthomonas pelargonium);* bacterial leaf spot of geranium and English ivy *(Xanthomonas hederae);* bacterial wilt of carnation *(Pseudomonas caryophylli);* and crown gall of rose, chrysanthemum, and geranium *(Agrobacterium tumifasciens)*.

8.20.3 FUNGI

Major greenhouse fungal diseases include the following:

1. *Powdery mildew.* Mildew occurs under conditions of high humidity. Plants affected by powdery mildew have a whitish, powdery growth on plant parts. Some plants (e.g., rose) are susceptible at an early stage and thus become very distorted. In other species, such as zinnia and dahlia, powdery mildew occurs on older plant parts. In the latter scenario, the economic damage is blemishing, which makes plants less aesthetically desirable and thus not usable as cut flowers.

Sulfur may be applied for both prevention and control, along with monitoring the humidity and temperature of the greenhouse to prevent high humidity levels.

2. *Botrytis blight. Botrytis* blight is known to affect numerous species of plants. The species *Botrytis cinerea* (common gray mold) causes rots and blights of many greenhouse plants, including carnation, chrysanthemum, rose, azalea, and geranium. Depending on the species, the stem, leaf, flower, or other tissue may be affected. Observing greenhouse sanitation reduces the incidence of *Botrytis*. Ample ventilation is required, as is preventing irrigation water from splashing on plants.

3. *Root rot.* Three important causal agents of root and basal rots are *Rhizoctonia, Phythium,* and *Thielaviopsis.* These fungi are soilborne and transmitted by mechanical means such as splashing of water during irrigation and contamination of tillage tools and containers. They are controlled by soil pasteurization and sterilization of tools, containers, and greenhouse bench tops. Root media should be well drained. Observance of good sanitation is necessary to control this pest.

4. *Damping-off.* When damping-off occurs before germination of seeds, the seeds tend to rot in the soil. Postemergence infection causes young seedlings to topple and eventually die. Preemergence damping-off is caused by *Phythium,* and *Rhizoctonia* causes damping-off of seedlings. Since the fungi are soilborne, damping-off is controlled largely by planting seeds in a pasteurized soil or medium that is well drained. Also, care should be taken when watering to prevent splashing.

5. *Verticillium wilt. Verticillium* wilt is caused by a fungus that inhabits the soil. It affects a wide variety of plants including rose, geranium, begonia, and chrysanthemum. The symptoms vary from one species to another and depend also on the stage of plant development. Some plants may not show any symptoms until they reach the reproductive stage, at which time the flower buds wilt. Generally, affected plants show wilting and yellowing of leaf margins, starting from the lower and older leaves. Once infected through the soil, the fungus grows upward in the plant through the xylem tissue. Thus, cuttings from infected plants also spread the disease. Soil pasteurization is effective in controlling the disease.

8.20.4 NEMATODES

Nematodes (eelworms) are soilborne organisms, one of the widely known species being the root-knot nematode (*Meloidogyne* spp.). Infected plants have knotted roots and amorphous growth of the roots. The knots in the roots interrupt vascular flow, and affected plants soon experience stunted growth. Soil pasteurization and general aeration help to control this pest.

Certain nematodes cause leaf spots and eventually leaf drop. The spots start on the lower sides of leaves as light-colored brown spots that eventually turn black. Leaf nematodes require plant materials to survive in the soil. Thus good sanitation, including removal of plant debris, helps to control these organisms. Spraying the affected plant foliage with appropriate pesticides (e.g., parathion or diazinon) is an effective control measure.

8.21 CONTROL METHODS

The common methods of pest control in the greenhouse include:

1. *Pesticide spray.* Most greenhouse pest problems are controlled by spraying appropriate chemicals. The pesticides may be emulsifiable concentrates or wettable powders. Certain pesticide formulations are approved for use in greenhouses.

2. *Aerosol.* Aerosols are usually applied in the greenhouse when immediate killing of pests is desired, since very little residue is left on the plant, and, even then, only the upper surfaces of leaves show residue. Aerosols should be applied to dry

leaves on a calm day to prevent the material from being drawn out of the greenhouse through openings. The greenhouse must usually be kept closed overnight after an aerosol application.

3. *Dust.* Dusts are not commonly used to control pests in the greenhouse.
4. *Fog.* Fogs are applied by using fogging equipment. Fogs are oil based and usually prepared to 10 percent strength of the regular insecticide or fungicide. The fogging equipment heats up the pesticide, which breaks down into a white fog that spreads throughout the facility. However, leaks in the greenhouse may cause uneven distribution of the gas.
5. *Smoke.* Unlike fogs, dusts, and sprays, smokes do not require special equipment for application. Instead, a combustible formulation of the pesticide packaged in containers is placed in the center isle of the greenhouse and ignited. Smokes are generally not as phytotoxic to foliage as other gas applications. When in use, all vents and doors must be closed.
6. *Application to root media.* Soilborne diseases and pests may be controlled by drenching the soil with pesticides. Granules or powder formulations may be applied to the soil surface and washed down in irrigation water.

8.22 CONTROL STRATEGIES

To be effective, the timing of application of the pesticide is critical. Three factors should be considered regarding the intervals between pesticide applications:

1. The residual life of the pesticide
2. The life cycle of the pest
3. The killing action of the pesticide

It is important to know the life cycle of the insect to be controlled and the developmental stage at which it is most susceptible to the pesticide. For example, if the insect has a seven-day life cycle and the pesticide to be applied (e.g., smokes and aerosols) is not effective against eggs, the pesticide should be applied at six-day intervals. The rationale is that the first application will kill most of the adults. Since aerosols and smoke leave no residue, the eggs will hatch on schedule. However, before they develop to adult stage, when they can lay a new batch of eggs, the next round of treatment kills that population, along with any that survived the first treatment. The survivors of the first round of treatment have a chance to lay eggs, which will be missed by the second application. However, the eggs will hatch within six days, in time for the third application. This third application is usually adequate in completely eradicating the pest within twelve days. Usually, as temperatures increase, the life cycle of the pest increases in length. Spraying intervals of between five and seven days are generally effective in controlling many greenhouse insect and mite attacks.

When controlling mites, keep in mind that mites are known to develop resistance to pesticides rapidly. They are also known to occur as a heterogeneous mixture in a given population. A three-miticide cycle of control is recommended. First, one miticide should be selected for use at one time until the mites develop resistance to it. A second miticide should then be selected and used repeatedly until resistance against it has also been developed, followed by use of the third pesticide. When resistance to the third pesticide has been developed, the first should be reintroduced, since by this time the population would have lost its resistance to the first pesticide. The three-miticide cycle is then repeated.

Certain pesticides are specially formulated or approved for greenhouse application. Pesticides are also registered for use on certain plants. States may have preferred chemicals for use under various circumstances. It is important to check with appropriate local authorities such as the cooperative extension service to find out which pesticide is best for use on a particular occasion.

8.23 PREVENTING GREENHOUSE DISEASES

The greenhouse is an enclosure in which plant growth factors are under artificial control. The conditions are often ideal for plant production and similarly favor greenhouse pests associated with the specific production. Diseases can be prevented by adopting several cultural practices: environmental control; strict observance of sanitation; use of clean, healthy plant materials; and use of sterilized soil.

8.23.1 ENVIRONMENTAL CONTROL

One problem associated with environmental control that is a frequent source of diseases is condensation. This problem is caused by the combination of temperature and moisture content of the greenhouse atmosphere. During the daytime, the sun causes air inside of the greenhouse to warm. Warm air holds more moisture than cold air. Thus, during the night when it is cooler, the warm air is progressively cooled until it reaches the dew point. At this stage, water starts to condense on the surfaces of plants and greenhouse structures. Drops of water on plant leaf surfaces provide the condition needed for spores of pathogens to germinate and thus promote the incidence of diseases such as *Botrytis* blight caused by the gray mold fungus.

To reduce condensation, the greenhouse should be equipped with exhaust fans and ventilation that will circulate air by bringing in fresh, cooler air periodically. If the vents are closed, still air can be avoided by using a horizontal airflow system to move the air through the greenhouse and reduce the incidence of cold spots, which cause condensation of moisture.

Greenhouse structures, including floors, have surfaces that can retain water over a period of time. High humidity levels favor diseases such as mildews. When plants are watered in the morning, the moisture on solid surfaces has enough time to evaporate. With appropriate ventilation, excessive humidity is eliminated. Excessive moisture in rooting media can be avoided by using well-drained media and also watering only when needed.

8.23.2 SANITATION

Weeds are known to harbor insects and disease-causing organisms, apart from being unsightly. They may be mechanically removed or controlled by using approved herbicides.

Debris remaining after a crop harvest should be promptly removed and disposed of. Plant material from horticultural practices such as pinching and disbudding should be gathered during the operation and discarded outside of the greenhouse. Decaying plant materials provide a fertile medium in which disease organisms thrive.

Greenhouse containers—flats, pans, and pots—should be sterilized before reuse. Clay pots may be steam sterilized. Pots can be chemically sterilized by soaking containers in a formaldehyde solution (1 part formalin [40 percent formaldehyde] to 100 parts water) for thirty minutes, followed by rinsing and air drying. Apart from containers, all greenhouse tools should be cleaned and sterilized after use. First, the dirt should be scraped off and the tools washed with water; the tools should then be dipped in household bleach (sodium hypochlorite) at 1 part bleach (5.25 percent sodium hypochlorite) to 9 parts water. Watering hoses should not be left on the greenhouse floor such that the ends touch the floor; they should be hung with the ends turned upward.

Greenhouse benches should be sterilized periodically. All workstations should be cleaned and wiped with disinfectant or bleach after use. Wooden benches and flats may be painted or dipped in a 2 percent solution of copper naphthenate. Soil and growing media used in the greenhouse should be sterilized. If bulk root media are purchased, they should be stored such that they will not become contaminated by unsterilized soil or water.

Restricted access to parts of the greenhouse where preparation takes place (e.g., media and seeds) should be enforced to prohibit the general public from entering those areas. Visitors and customers come from a variety of places and may carry infected soil on the soles of their shoes. It is important to routinely clean and disinfect the floor at frequent intervals.

SUMMARY

Because of their enclosed nature, greenhouses have specific pest problems. The most common insect pests include aphids, fungus gnats, leaf miners, mealybugs, mites, scale insects, slugs, snails, thrips, whiteflies, and caterpillars. Common diseases include a variety of viral and bacterial problems and fungal diseases (e.g., powdery mildew, *Botrytis* blight, root rot, damping-off, *Verticillium* wilt, and nematodes). Because of the enclosed condition, pesticide formulations for greenhouses such as smokes, fogs, and aerosols are suitable for use.

When controlling pests, it is important to know the life cycle of the organism, the residual life of the chemical to be used, and the pesticide's mode of action. The environment in the greenhouse can be controlled and monitored to reduce pest incidence. Further, observance of good sanitation and hygiene, as well as sterilizing growing media, tools, and other greenhouse structures, reduces the incidence of disease.

REFERENCES AND SUGGESTED READING

Bohmont, B. L. 1997. *The standard pesticide user's guide,* 4th ed. Englewood Cliffs, N.J.: Prentice Hall.

Boodley, J. W. 1996. *The commercial greenhouse,* 2d ed. Albany, N.Y.: Delmar.

Cravens, R. H. 1977. *Pests and diseases.* Alexandria, Va.: Time-Life.

Dixon, G. R. 1981. *Vegetable crop diseases.* Westport, Conn.: AVI Publishing.

Klingman, G. C., F. M. Ashton, and L. J. Noordhoff. 1982. *Weed science: Principles and practices,* 2d ed. New York: John Wiley & Sons.

Nelson, P. V. 1985. *Greenhouse operation and management,* 2d ed. Retson: Retson Publishing.

Prone, P. 1978. *Diseases and pests of ornamental plants,* 5th ed. New York: John Wiley & Sons.

OUTCOMES ASSESSMENT

1. In disease control, prevention is better than cure. Discuss, giving specific examples, how diseases may be prevented in horticultural production.
2. Discuss specific methods that may be used to reduce or eliminate the presence of a pathogen's inoculum during horticultural production.
3. Discuss the concept of integrated pest management as a pest-control strategy.
4. Discuss the pros and cons of the use of pesticides in crop production. What can a producer do to minimize the adverse effects of the use of pesticides?
5. Describe the information one can obtain from a pesticide label.
6. If a producer does not want to use pesticides in crop production, suggest an alternative approach that may be adopted to control pests.

PART 3

PROPAGATING HORTICULTURAL PLANTS

9

Sexual Propagation

PURPOSE AND EXPECTED OUTCOMES

This chapter discusses the principles of plant propagation and describes the various methods of propagation, including the advantages of each and their best time of use.

After studying this chapter, the student should be able to

1. Describe how seeds are commercially produced.
2. List and discuss the factors that affect the use of seeds in plant propagation.
3. Describe how seed germination can be improved.
4. List and discuss the environmental conditions for seed germination.

[COLOR PLATES—*see color plate 6* for additional chapter photos]

OVERVIEW

Plant propagation is simply the reproduction or duplication of a plant from a source (mother plant). The ultimate objective of propagation is to produce more plants exactly like the parent. Flowering plants produce seeds that can be used for propagation. Seeds vary in size and other characteristics, which influence how they can be used for propagation. Certain plants do not produce seed and hence can be propagated by using parts of the plant other than seed. In some species, either seed or vegetative parts can be used for propagation. There are advantages and disadvantages to either method of propagation. This chapter explores the wide variety of methods of propagating horticultural plants by seed.

There are three major purposes of propagation:

1. *Preservation of germplasm.* Scientists on a crop expedition collect samples of plant materials intended for use in research endeavors. Such materials are often present in only small quantities and must be increased. Sometimes scientists discover novelties that arise spontaneously in nature or in a research project. These rare finds must be preserved, and, to utilize them in any research, they must be increased. In developing

a new cultivar, plant breeders create the new genotype through a variety of breeding methodologies. The prototype must first be preserved and then multiplied for use by growers. The ultimate goal of preservation, therefore, is to ensure that the original characteristics of the plant are maintained.

2. *Crop production.* Growing crops or plants involves propagation using an appropriate material (e.g., seed, cutting, and others). The goal in propagation in commercial production is to increase or replicate the source material. In this instance, the product of propagation could be thousands of plants or seeds.

3. *Landscaping.* Plants are increased for use in the landscape to fulfill aesthetic and functional purposes.

The success of propagation, whether to produce a small or large quantity, is judged by how closely the daughter plants resemble the parent. In some cases, such as in research, exact copies are required. In other cases, as long as the products express the major desirable traits of the parent or source material, the propagation is deemed successful.

The outcome of propagation depends on the genetics of the plant (genotype) as well as the mating system. Some parent plants have identical alleles at each locus and are said to be homozygous. If they reproduce by means of seed, employing the self-fertilization mating system, these plants will reproduce true to type by seed. On the other hand, the strength of some plants lies in the fact that they are heterozygous, as is the case in hybrids. Such plants do not reproduce true to type from seed. Many horticultural plants, including fruits and ornamentals, are heterozygous. The only way of perpetuating the desirable qualities in the progeny is to use means of propagation other than use of the seed. Using seed always requires that the genotype be subjected to reorganization in a new genetic matrix through the process of meiosis (except in the case of apomixis). Since meiotic products are not alike, the resulting plants are different from each other. To circumvent meiosis, some plants may be regenerated from vegetative tissue (e.g., leaf, stem, or root). When this route is followed, the products of propagation are genetically identical (*clones*).

Flowering plants are capable of producing seed that can be used for their propagation. A seed houses a miniature plant that is nurtured to life when appropriate conditions are provided. Growing plants from seed is more convenient than using vegetative methods. Seed planting is easier to mechanize, and seeds are also less bulky and easier to store than other plant parts. The seed industry has played a significant role in the growth of the horticultural industry.

9.1 SEED FORMATION

Pollination
The transfer of pollen from an anther to a stigma.

Sexual propagation starts with seed formation. The process of seed formation follows *fertilization,* the union of gametes (formed by the process of meiosis), which occurs after **pollination** (deposition of pollen on the stigma of the flower). The processes involved in the reproduction of seed plants are described in Figure 9–1. The two processes were introduced in Chapter 3.

Anthers contain pollen grains. When anthers dehisce (shed their contents), pollen grains are released and ready to be transported to the stigma by various vectors or agents of pollination. The pollen grain germinates on the stigma and produces a tube (*pollen tube*) that carries two *sperm nuclei (n)* down the style into the *embryo sac.* The sperm nuclei are produced by the mitotic division of the *generative cell.* In the embryo sac, one sperm fertilizes the egg to form a *zygote* (2*n*). Fertilization thus restores the diploid number of the cell. The other sperm fuses with the large *central cell* of the embryo sac to produce a *triploid* (3*n*) cell, a process called *triple fusion.* The process whereby both a zygote and a cell with 3*n* nuclei are formed within the embryo sac is called *double* **fertilization**.

Fertilization
The union of gametes, an egg and a sperm, to form a zygote.

The next step after fertilization is the development of the ovule (containing the zygote and the 3*n* central cell) into a seed. The 3*n* cell divides repeatedly and develops into the *endosperm,* a nutrient-rich mass of cells that provides nourishment to the embryo until it develops to a stage where it becomes self-supporting (seedling stage).

The mature ovule is the *seed.* The outer tissue of the ovules (the inner and outer *integuments*) fuse and lose their water to become the **seed** *coat,* or *testa.* The endosperm contains large amounts of starch that serve as food reserves to be broken down into glucose for use during seed germination. In monocots, the outermost layer of the endosperm is called the *aleurone layer* and is the site of protein storage. In seeds such as sunflower, mustard, pine, and fir, the endosperm stores a large amount of fats and oils.

Seed
The mature ovule of a flowering plant.

The embryo is variable in size in terms of the volume of the seed it occupies. It occupies a large volume in species such as pea and oak, but occupies a relatively small volume in cereals. In species such as holly and orchid, the embryo remains relatively undifferentiated. However, in grass, the embryo is highly differentiated into structures including the *shoot apex, scutellum* (single cotyledon), and *coleoptile* (a cylindrical protective leaf). The *root apex* is protected by the *coleorrhiza.*

9.2 SEED PRODUCTION AND CERTIFICATION PROCESS

Plant breeders are engaged in plant improvement. Old cultivars are changed by importing new genes that condition improved characteristics, making new cultivars more disease resistant, higher yielding, more beautiful, and better in other ways according to breeding objectives. Once the breeder has completed the breeding program and tested the new material extensively, the seed is then released by the researchers to special producers for propagation.

Before the seed becomes available to the ordinary grower, it goes through stages of increase and certification. According to the stages, there are four classes of seed (Figure 9–2):

1. *Breeder seed.* A small amount of seed is developed and released by a breeder as the source of foundation seed.
2. *Foundation seed.* Breeder seed is increased under supervision of agricultural research stations and monitored for genetic purity and identity.

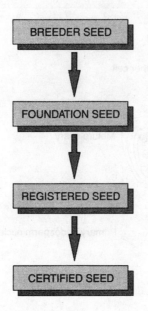

BREEDER SEED — Small quantity of original seed produced by plant breeders through a carefully designed and conducted breeding program and according to specific objectives. Controlled by breeder/institution or company.

FOUNDATION SEED — An increase of the breeder seed by Agricultural Experimental Stations or reputable growers under supervision of researchers.

REGISTERED SEED — An increase of foundation seed by registered growers.

CERTIFIED SEED — An increase of registered seed (or foundation seed) that is inspected and approved by certifying agency for sale to farmers and other growers.

3. *Registered seed.* Foundation seed is distributed to certified seed growers to be further increased for distribution.

4. *Certified seed.* The progeny of registered seed is sold to farmers. During the process of increase, certifying agencies in the state or region of production monitor the activity to ensure that the product meets standards set for the crop. Before sale, the certified seed grower is required to perform certain basic analyses (*seed quality analyses*) of the seed as described in the following section.

Certified Seed
The progeny of registered seed that is maintained at a satisfactory genetic identity and purity, and approved and certified by an official certifying agency.

9.3 SEED LAW

The **seed law** is an act intended to regulate the labeling, coloring, sale, offering, exposing, or transporting for sale of agricultural, vegetable, flower, and tree and shrub seeds, to prevent those in the industry from misrepresenting their products to customers. It is important to assure that seed offered for sale to growers of agricultural crops, landscapers, and private homeowners meets quality standards set by the state in which the products are used or produced.

The Association of American Seed Control Officials (AASCO), comprising officials from the United States and Canada, developed the Recommended Uniform State Seed Law (RUSSL) as a model law for states and federal programs. The RUSSL is to be enforced only after a state has enacted it into its own seed law by its legislature. The organization meets annually to be updated on new developments in the seed industry and to update the RUSSL as needed.

Among other things, a seed law describes the issue of seed tags and what specific information goes on them, brand registration, seed permits, arbitration of seed complaints, and the enforcement of the law.

9.4 SEED QUALITY ANALYSIS

Certified seed producers are required to declare their *seed analysis* on the seed packet or tag. The interpretation of the tag is provided in Table 9–1. To do so, a seed test must be conducted. The common seed tests available in the seed industry include the germination test, cold test, tetrazolium test, and purity test.

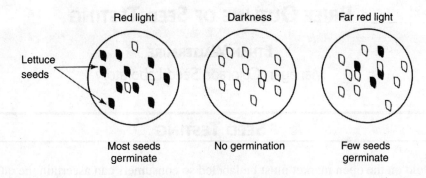

Red light   Darkness   Far red light

Lettuce seeds

Most seeds germinate   No germination   Few seeds germinate

FIGURE 9–3 The role of phytochrome in seed germination. Red light stimulates germination while darkness inhibits it. Far red light is only mildly stimulatory of germination of lettuce seed.

TABLE 9–1 Information on seed tags

Item	What It Means
Kind and variety	Sates variety name; term "mixture" is used to refer to seed with more than one component.
Lot identification	Identifies a specific amount of seed of uniform quality associated with a specific seed test.
Pure seed	Indicates percent purity as it relates to the kind and variety of crop species indicated.
Other crop seed	Percent by weight of other crop seed as contamination.
Weed seed	Percent by weight of weed seed present.
Inert material	Percent by weight of foreign material such as chaff, stones, cracked seed, soil, etc.
Prohibited noxious weeds	Weed seeds prohibited in the variety to be sold (e.g., field bindweed, Canada thistle).
Restricted noxious weeds	Weed seeds that may be present up to an allowable limit (90 seeds per pound of pure seed), e.g., quackgrass, dodder, and hedge bindweed.
Germination	Percent of seed that germinates to produce normal seedlings during a standard seed analysis.
Date of test	Year and month in which seed test was conducted
Origin	Source of seed—where seed was produced
Name and address	Name of seed company or seller of the seed

9.4.1 GERMINATION TEST

A germination test involves growing a number of seeds under moist and warm conditions. The number of seeds that germinate to produce healthy, normal seedlings is recorded, along with the number of ungerminated seeds.

9.4.2 COLD TEST

A cold test is conducted by subjecting seeds to a period of cold temperature (10°C or 50°F) before germination under warm conditions. The goal of this test is to find out how seeds will germinate and grow under the cold, wet conditions often found in the field.

9.4.3 TETRAZOLIUM TEST

The tetrazolium test depends on the use of a chemical called *tetrazolium chloride* (2,3,5-triphenyltetrazolium chloride). It is a rapid test in which seeds are soaked in water and then dissected longitudinally. One set of halves is placed in petri dishes containing

Brief Outline of Seed Testing

Ethan Waltermire
Manager, Colorado Seed Laboratory

Seed Testing

Seed sold on the open market must be labeled so consumers can ascertain the quality of the seed they are purchasing. Information that appears on seed labels is determined by having the seed tested by a seed laboratory or an independent seed analyst. The Colorado Seed Laboratory is the official state lab for Colorado, and is a member of the Association of Official Seed Analysts (AOSA). The lab performs seed tests for commercial, certification, regulatory, and research applications (Figure 1).

The Colorado Seed Laboratory began testing seed in 1912. Located in Fort Collins, Colorado, on the campus of Colorado State University, the lab has been on the forefront of seed testing for over 95 years. Many seed testing procedures were researched and developed in Colorado. Depending on the location of a seed lab they will specialize in testing certain species. Labs in the northwest specialize in turf grasses, while those in the southeast specialize in cotton, peanuts, and soybeans. In Colorado native seed testing is prominent, but the lab also tests a variety of agricultural and horticultural crops grown in the western region.

As seed production and trade becomes internationalized, industry and governments have made issues surrounding seed quality a top priority. Assuring a quality product, stopping the spread of noxious weeds, and accurate labeling are top concerns. Growers and companies must adhere to the highest standards if they want to represent their product well in a highly competitive market.

AOSA Rules For Testing Seed

The Colorado Seed Laboratory is an official AOSA laboratory, and the majority of our tests conform to the AOSA rules. The AOSA rules give labs a uniform set of procedures to follow when testing seed. The primary reason for having rules regarding seed testing is consistency; it should be possible to replicate the results of a Colorado seed test in other states.

FIGURE 1 Logo of Colorado Seed. (*Source:* Annette Miller, USDA-ARS National Center for Genetic Resources Preservation. Fort Collins, Colorado).

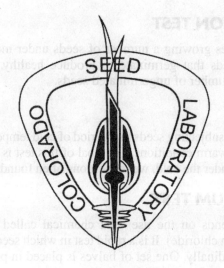

FEDERAL AND STATE SEED LAWS

Federal and State laws regulate the sale and labeling of seed. Seed producers must adhere to the seed acts of each state they sell seed in, and if seed is sold in interstate commerce then it is subject to the Federal Seed Act. Seed act requirements stipulate that purity and viability information be present on all seed labels. Labs help companies and growers determine this information so they can label their seed properly.

COMMON SEED TESTS

Purity Exam

A purity exam determines the percentage (by weight) of pure seed, other crop, weed, and inert material in a seed lot (Figure 2). The pure seed component is the desired species in the seed lot, and the other three components are essentially unwanted material. Weeds and other crop may appear in a sample if the field was contaminated, or if the harvesting equipment was not properly cleaned before use. Inert material usually consists of dust, stones, plant parts, and the like.

Performing the purity exam can be a tedious, difficult task. The sample (sent by the seed producer) is divided into a sub-sample consisting of roughly 2,500 seeds. A seed divider is used to indiscriminately select the seeds that the lab will test. There are many types of seed dividers, but the most widely used is an electric Gamet divider (Figure 3). The sample is mixed and split in half until the desired weight is obtained.

The analyst, using a microscope or a magnifying lamp (depending on the seed size), then separates the sample into the four components (Figure 4). Each component is

FIGURE 2 This is a typical purity station. Tools include a microscope, seed blower, and purity bench. (*Source:* Annette Miller, USDA-ARS National Center for Genetic Resources Preservation. Fort Collins, Colorado).

FIGURE 3 This electric Gamet divider is routinely used to obtain a sub-sample for laboratory testing. (*Source:* Annette Miller, USDA-ARS National Center for Genetic Resources Preservation. Fort Collins, Colorado).

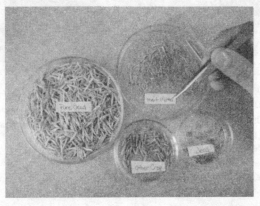

FIGURE 4 These are the four components of a purity test. (*Source:* Annette Miller, USDA-ARS National Center for Genetic Resources Preservation. Fort Collins, Colorado).

weighed and a percentage is derived. Other crop and weed seeds are identified so they can be listed on the lab report. The lab uses a variety of texts and seed herbariums to identify contaminants. Virtual herbariums are becoming popular for seed identification because of their fast search mechanisms and ease of use. http://www.seedimages.com is a good example of a virtual seed herbarium.

In addition to tweezers and magnification, a purity analyst may use an array of other tools to help separate the components. Screens (to separate seed according to size and shape) (Figures 5 and 6) and seed blowers (separates according to density) are valuable tools that speed the process up (Figures 7, and 8).

Viability Testing

There are two common types of viability testing: germination and tetrazolium (TZ). Only a handful of states allow TZ test results to be used for labeling, so the industry relies heavily on the germination test as the benchmark for viability.

FIGURE 5 Round screens used for small seed can separate seed based on size and shape. *(Source: Annette Miller, USDA-ARS National Center for Genetic Resources Preservation. Fort Collins, Colorado).*

FIGURE 6 Square screens are used to separate larger seeds based on size and shape. *(Source: Annette Miller, USDA-ARS National Center for Genetic Resources Preservation. Fort Collins, Colorado).*

FIGURE 7 A seed blower separates based on density, and is used for removing chaff, empty seeds, or other contaminants. *(Source: Annette Miller, USDA-ARS National Center for Genetic Resources Preservation. Fort Collins, Colorado).*

FIGURE 8 Magnifying lamps make it easier to see weeds. *(Source: Annette Miller, USDA-ARS National Center for Genetic Resources Preservation. Fort Collins, Colorado).*

Germination Test

In laboratory practice (according to the AOSA Rules for Testing Seed), seed germination is defined as "the emergence from the seed embryo of those essential structures which, for the kind in question, are indicative of the ability to produce a normal plant under favorable conditions." It is important to note that a germination test is not designed to predict how seed will perform in the field. Favorable conditions are used so the test can be easily reproduced between labs (Figure 9). Vigor testing (tests that subject the seed to types of stress) are designed to mimic field conditions and are a better indicator of field performance.

400 seeds are always planted in a standard germination test. The seed is taken from the pure seed component of the purity test. Depending on seed size, four to sixteen replicates may be used. Seed is either counted and planted by hand or a vacuum planter is used (Figure 10).

Many different types of substrate are used for germination tests. Blotters, towels, and filter paper are the most common, but creped cellulose paper and sand are also widely used (Figure 11). Water is the commonly used as the moisture, but in dormant species potassium nitrate (KNO_3) is also used.

FIGURE 9 Typical germination workroom with growth chambers and workbench. (*Source:* Annette Miller, USDA-ARS National Center for Genetic Resources Preservation. Fort Collins, Colorado).

FIGURE 10 A vacuum planter aids in planting by selecting a set number of seeds in a uniform pattern. (*Source:* Annette Miller, USDA-ARS National Center for Genetic Resources Preservation. Fort Collins, Colorado).

FIGURE 11 Germination Rolled Towels Small. Safflower planted in special seed germination towels. (*Source:* Annette Miller, USDA-ARS National Center for Genetic Resources Preservation. Fort Collins, Colorado).

Once planted, the seed is placed into a growth chamber. Chambers are set at various temperatures, and some even alternate temperature between night and day to simulate natural conditions (Figure 12). Crops that were developed closer the equator usually have a single temperature, such as wheat (20 degrees C). Native species in north America usually require alternating temperatures, such as blue grama (20C at night, 30C during the day).

As soon as the seeds develop discernable structures they can be evaluated. Just because a seed sprouts does not mean it is counted as viable. All the structures must be present and in working order for the seed to be considered normal (Figures 13 and 14). When evaluating, the analyst separates the seed into five categories: normal, abnormal, dead, hard, and dormant (a TZ test is used to determine dormancy). Only normal, hard, and dormant seeds are counted as viable.

Tetrazolium Testing (TZ)

A TZ test is a quick way to determine total viability. The test usually takes 24 hours to complete, and is the primary method for determining dormancy. The steps

FIGURE 12 Typical growth chamber. (*Source:* Annette Miller, USDA-ARS National Center for Genetic Resources Preservation. Fort Collins, Colorado).

FIGURE 13 Triticale is grown on towels. This sample is ready to be evaluated. (*Source:* Annette Miller, USDA-ARS National Center for Genetic Resources Preservation. Fort Collins, Colorado).

FIGURE 14 The three beans on the left have sprouted, but are missing primary leaves—thus they are considered abnormal. (*Source:* Annette Miller, USDA-ARS National Center for Genetic Resources Preservation. Fort Collins, Colorado).

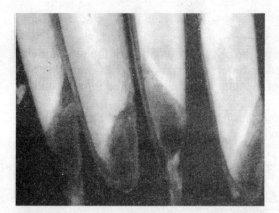

FIGURE 15 The essential structures of these embryos have all stained, indicating that this seed is viable. *(Source:* Annette Miller, USDA-ARS National Center for Genetic Resources Preservation. Fort Collins, Colorado).

FIGURE 16 These lupine seeds have varying degrees of stain. The root tips on three of the seeds have not stained, and the cotyledons of the lower middle seed are also void of stain: this indicates that the seed is dead or abnormal. *(Source:* Annette Miller, USDA-ARS National Center for Genetic Resources Preservation. Fort Collins, Colorado).

FIGURE 17 Pigweed (Amaranthus spp.) has a peripheral embryo that must be extracted from the seed to stain. The embryo on the left is viable. *(Source:* Annette Miller, USDA-ARS National Center for Genetic Resources Preservation. Fort Collins, Colorado).

are relatively simple, but it takes a good analyst to evaluate a TZ test correctly. The seeds are imbibed in water overnight, and then the embryo is bisected (or pierced) with a razor blade the next day. Then bisected seed is placed into TZ solution to stain, and as the embryo respirates it soaks up the solution. The parts of the embryo that do not respirate are dead, and they will not soak up the solution. A chemical reaction takes place, and the live structures of the embryo stain red. Once the seed has stained (this can take 2-48 hours, depending on the species) the analyst 'reads' the TZ. Under a microscope the analyst can see all the essential structures of the plant, and if they all have an appropriate amount of stain then the analyst considers them viable (Figures 15, 16, and 17).

0.1 percent tetrazolium solution; the other set is left untreated. Living tissue in the seed is stained, whereas the dead tissue remains the same color. Percentage germination is given by the proportion of stained seeds. This test only indicates that seeds are respiring and does not equate the respiring seed with germination.

9.4.4 PURITY TEST

Seed purity analysis provides information on the physical condition of the seed and the presence of unwanted material (weed seed and inert material other than desired seed). It provides information on the proportion of the total seeds being offered for sale that are the desired seeds.

The various tests provide specific information, which is listed on the seed envelope or tag. The information includes the following:

1. *Percent germination.* Percent germination is determined using a simple ratio:

$$\frac{\text{number of healthy normal seedlings}}{\text{total number of seeds tested}} \times 100$$

The higher the percentage, the better.

2. *Percent pure seed.* Percent pure seed measures the proportion of desired seed in the lot.

3. *Percent of other crop seed.* When harvesting equipment is not cleaned properly after harvesting one kind of seed and before harvesting another, remnant seed from the previous harvest may contaminate the latter harvest. This contamination may also arise as a result of crop weeds (unwanted plants) being allowed to mature and being harvested along with the desired crop without rouging. Contamination of this kind is common in situations in which impure seed is used to establish a crop.

4. *Percent inert material.* Inert materials such as stones, pieces of wood, and the like may be present in seed packaged for sale because of improper cleaning of seed before packaging. Sometimes the harvester blades may be set too low such that they not only cut plant material but also scoop up some soil and rocks. Inert material may also come from seed processing. For example, if corn seed is being produced, pieces of the cob may be included if the corn is shelled improperly or is not dried to the proper moisture content before shelling. In seed purity tests, weeds may be classified as *common, restricted* (allowed in minimal amounts), or *noxious* (most undesirable and hardest to control).

5. *Percent weed seed.* Weed species are associated with certain crops. Seeds offered for sale should be free from noxious weed seeds. Weed seed contamination occurs when the seed producer does not implement proper weed control during production.

6. *Percent pure live seed.* From the preceding information, one can calculate percent pure live seed (the percentage of desired cultivar seed that will germinate) by the formula

$$\text{percent live seed (PLS)} = (\%\ \text{germination} \times \%\ \text{purity})/100$$

Seed should be purchased from a reputable grower or shop to ensure the highest quality. Further, the grower should purchase fresh seed each season if possible and purchase only as much as is needed to avoid the need to store remnant seed. If seed is to be stored for planting the next season, cold storage is often required. Even when high-quality seeds are purchased for planting in the current season, they can deteriorate before harvesting if there is a delay in planting, unless the seed is stored properly.

Mechanical Seed Damage

Seed suffers mechanical damage during harvesting, threshing, and handling. It is critical to harvest seed crops when they have dried to the right moisture content. If too dry, seeds are prone to splitting or cracking. Also, if the mechanical harvester is not set properly, excessive force may be delivered to the plant during harvesting, which contributes to physical damage. Cracked seeds may not be a critical problem for some markets (e.g., for processing into flour or meal). However, cracked seeds can significantly reduce the market value of the produce in other markets.

Mechanical damage may be determined by a simple laboratory procedure as follows:

1. Obtain twenty to fifty seeds (randomly selected) from the lot.
2. Place a sample in a petri dish containing a 1 percent sodium hypochlorite solution. (If household bleach is used, it should be noted that it contains 5.25 percent sodium hypochlorite.)
3. Soak seeds for fifteen minutes.
4. Count the number of swollen seeds.
5. Count the number of swollen seeds after soaking for thirty minutes.
6. Calculate percent cracked seed as follows:

$$\frac{\text{number of swollen seeds}}{\text{total number of seeds}} \times 100$$

9.5 SEED VIABILITY AND LONGEVITY

Seeds may look healthy but fail to germinate when planted. Two other seed qualities that are essential but not displayed on the seed envelope are viability and longevity. **Viability** is a measure of the proportion of seeds in a lot that are capable of germinating. **Longevity** is a measure of how long seeds remain viable. Viability is measured using germination and tetrazolium tests. Species in the pumpkin family (Cucurbitaceae) (e.g., cucumber, squash, and cantaloupe) remain viable for a long time (sometimes for several years), whereas species in the lily family (Liliaceae), including onion and leek, lose viability only about two to three months after harvesting. Seeds of pine, hemlock, and spruce remain viable with proper storage for several years. On the contrary, seeds of maple, elm, and willow have a very short period of viability, lasting only a few weeks. Apart from longevity inherent in the plant species, viability of seed during storage depends on the storage environment as pertains to seed moisture content temperature, and relative humidity.

Seed longevity depends on the species and the conditions at harvest and during storage. Seeds should be stored only when they have attained the appropriate moisture content (usually less than 15 percent). Seed dried to about 7 percent moisture and under low relative humidity can be stored for a long time in a refrigerator (0 to 4°C or 32 to 39°F). Very low relative humidity of about 5 percent allows seeds to be stored for a long time while retaining the highest level of viability. However, a relative humidity of 50 to 65 percent maintains the viability of most seeds for about one year. To increase longevity, seeds may be stored *cryogenically* in liquid nitrogen at −192°C (−313.6°F) for years. For ordinary storage, ziplock plastic bags, or bottles are adequate containers.

Seed Viability
The proportion of seed in a lot that is capable of germinating.

Seed Longevity
A measure of how long seed remains viable.

9.6 TAGGING COMMERCIAL SEED

Before certified seed can be released for sale to customers, it must be identified with an appropriate tag. Tags are color-coded. A white tag identifies breeder or foundation seed, a purple tag for registered seed, and blue tag for certified seed. Sometimes, a breeder may have seed that meets certification standards and yet opt not to have it certified. Such seed is identified with a green tag. Apart from these color codes, a seed tag displays some basic information about seed quality and source. The interpretation of the information on the tag is presented in Table 9–1.

9.7 PURCHASING SEED

Select seed cultivars that are adapted to your locality. Extension agents can assist you in making the right choice. Select fresh seeds if possible, and have them ready to plant on time. Seeds should be purchased from a reputable grower or store. The date of harvest is usually printed on the seed packet. Mail-order purchases are available through a variety of outlets. Seed companies produce seed catalogs on an annual basis. Some small seed companies may provide seed at a lower cost to growers. However, more established companies provide a variety of information on the seed packet to guide the grower with limited knowledge about growing plants.

9.8 SEED COMPANIES

The seed industry was introduced in Chapter 1. The seed market is very lucrative worldwide. There are numerous small seed producers, some specializing in vegetables, specialty crops, and ornamentals. Being a lucrative area, mergers and acquisitions have characterized the seed industry in the past two decades, some of the recent shuffling including the acquisition of Novartis by Monsanto in 2005, and prior to that Syngenta (formerly Novartis/Astra Zeneca), Pioneer incorporating Dupont, and the merger of Monsanto and Pharmacia. These behind-the-scene corporate maneuverings notwithstanding, growers of horticultural crops deal with the smaller seed companies that specialize in their crop or plant species of interest.

9.9 SEED DORMANCY

Seed Dormancy
The failure of viable seed to germinate under adequate environmental conditions.

All seeds do not germinate, even when optimal conditions are provided. A physiological or structural adaptive mechanism called **dormancy** imposes further restrictions on the requirements for germination. Seeds germinate only after the dormancy is overcome or broken. Dormancy is desired in the wild, where plants depend entirely on nature for survival. It prevents germination in the face of adverse weather, which will kill the vulnerable seedlings after emergence. *Structural dormancy* is imposed via the seed coat (*seed coat dormancy*) (e.g., Camellia and redbud). Hard seed coats are impermeable to the much needed moisture that is critical for germination. The seed coat may be softened before planting by one of several methods, such as *scarification,* a method of mechanically scratching the seed coat (by, for example, tumbling seeds in a drum containing coarse material). Seeds may also be scarified by soaking them in concentrated sulfuric acid or household bleach for a period.

Physiological dormancy (embryo dormancy) occurs when the embryo requires a special treatment to induce it to start active growth. A cold temperature application (called *stratification*) of about 1 to 7°C (34 to 45°F) is commonly required to break the dormancy. Woody species like holly (*Ilex* spp.) and magnolia (*Magnolia grandiflora*) require this treatment. Seed to be stratified is soaked in water for about twelve to twenty-four hours prior to placement in a sterile medium container such as a polyethylene bag to hold in moisture. The medium should permit good aeration to occur. Effective media include coarse vermiculite, sphagnum moss, coarse sand, or a mixture of equal volumes of peat and perlite. Seed may be wrapped in cheese cloth prior to placement in the medium to eliminate the need for cleaning the seed after the treatment. Stratification in the fridge takes about three to four months to complete.

A number of chemicals in plants inhibit germination of seeds while they are still embedded in the pulp of the fruit (e.g., in tomato and strawberry). In some species, such as *Pinus* and *Ranunculus,* the fruits are shed before the embryo fully matures. Such *physiologically immature* seeds must undergo certain enzymatic and biochemical changes to attain maturity. These changes are collectively called **after ripening**. Immature embryos cannot germinate. Of necessity, such fruits are stored for a period of time to allow embryos to mature completely.

Seeds of ancient origins have been reported to germinate after the hard seed coat was weakened. The sacred lotus (*Nelumbo nucifera*) is reported to have germinated after 2,000 years, and the arctic lupine (*Lupinus articus*) germinated in forty-eight hours after being dormant for 10,000 years.

9.10 IMPROVING GERMINATION CAPACITY OF SEEDS

Ideally, seeds should germinate within the reasonably expected period that is characteristic of the species, provided the right conditions for germination are present. Germination of seeds should be quite predictable by the grower, especially in commercial operations where timing of harvest is essential to obtain premium prices for horticultural produce. Furthermore, in commercial operations, uniformity of germination and maturity are critical, especially where any aspect of production is mechanized. When machines are used to harvest a crop, they are unable to distinguish between ripe and unripe fruits. Additional labor costs are incurred to manually sort out the harvest to remove immature fruits before marketing.

Some horticultural practices initiate germination processes in a seed to a safe stage and then discontinue it (see *primed* seed in). These seeds germinate quickly. Because of dormancy, seeds extracted from mature pods or fruits fail to germinate if planted immediately without a rest period. Through breeding activities, dormancy has been bred out of some cultivated species, since after a species becomes domesticated, the responsibility of caring for and protecting plants is transferred from nature to humans. In some plants, such as legumes, seeds germinate in the pod while still on the plant. At the other extreme, some seeds need special treatment to germinate.

Structural dormancy is imposed by seed testa or other protective covering, which prohibits the entry of moisture and air to start the physiological process of germination. Species with hard, impervious seed coverings occur in trees such as pine and in some legumes. To help such seeds germinate, certain methods (mechanical and chemical) may be employed to loosen the seed covering or initiate physiological processes for germination. These processes are described in the following sections. To address the situation of double dormancy from multiple causes, one may combine two or more of these treatments.

9.10.1 PHYSICAL

Mechanical

Mechanical processes include a variety of methods adopted to scratch the surface of the seed to loosen the covering, which is called scarification. Seeds may be mechanically rubbed between sheets of abrasive tissue (such as sand paper). They may also be scratched by tumbling them in a rotating drum lined with a coarse material (such as emery cloth). Some people also mix abrasive material such as gravel with seeds in the drum. Mechanical bruising of seed must be done carefully to avoid damaging the embryo.

Temperature

Scientists have observed that forests that have experienced a fire produce new seedling growth soon after a rainfall, whereas forests that have not burned do not have such new growth. The inference is that the heat (high temperature) weakens the seed covering enough to enable it to imbibe moisture. In horticultural applications, some seeds may be placed in boiling water (with heat turned off) for about twenty-four hours. Some seeds require cold temperature treatment (stratification) to germinate.

Light

Light is required by many weed species and some small seeds such as lettuce (*Lactuca sativa*) before germination can occur. Soil tillage exposes buried seeds to light. Small seeds should be sown in loose soil and to a shallow depth to expose them to light.

The light requirement to stimulate germination must be of a certain quality (wavelength). Exposure of lettuce to red light (about 660 nanometers) induces germination, but far red light (730 nanometers) inhibits it. It was discovered that if seed received red light after exposure to far red light, germination occurred. In fact, germination occurred as long as the last treatment before sowing was red light.

9.10.2 CHEMICAL

Acid Treatment

Seed dormancy due to a hard seed covering may be overcome by soaking the seed in concentrated sulfuric acid for a period ranging from a few minutes to several hours. Soaking in acid is done in a nonmetallic container. Periodic stirring helps to uniformly expose the seed to the acid. Concentrated acid is very injurious and must be handled with great caution: gloves should be worn. It is best to test a small sample first to find the best duration of soaking before treating the whole lot. Acid-treated seed should be washed thoroughly under running water for about ten to fifteen minutes before sowing. Sowing should occur without delay.

Leaching with Water

Leaching may be used where dormancy is due to chemical factors (such as coumarin). Hot-water leaching is done at 67–88°C. It is more effective than cold-water leaching. However, if the water is too hot, the seed may be injured. As previously mentioned, the seed of some fleshy fruits, such as strawberry and tomato, will not germinate in the fruit because of the presence of chemical germination inhibitors. Some desert plant seeds germinate only after a heavy downpour of rain that is able to wash away the inhibitors. By germinating only after a heavy rain, the seedlings are assured adequate moisture for survival and development until their roots are developed enough to absorb moisture.

Okra seed may be soaked in water for twelve to twenty-four hours to leach away a water-soluble inhibitor. Soaked seed should be planted immediately after the treatment without allowing it to dry. If prolonged soaking is needed, periodically refreshing the water is necessary.

Primed Seeds

Primed Seed
Seed soaked in a specific solution to initiate physiological processes for quicker germination.

Primed or enhanced seeds are seeds that have been soaked in a solution (e.g., ethyl alcohol or potassium chloride [KCl]) to give the germination process a head start by activating the enzymes and hormones. Seeds must be primed carefully to ensure success. Primed seeds germinate early and uniformly.

9.11 SEED TREATMENT

Unlike soilless mixes that are sterile, field soil harbors a wide variety of pathogens that are harmful to seeds. Some seeds benefit from seed treatment in which appropriate pesticides are applied to seeds to protect against soilborne diseases prevalent in that soil. Seeds may be coated with a fungicide such as calcium hypochlorite or cuprous oxide before planting. Also, seeds may be dipped in 10 percent household bleach or sodium hypochlorite for five minutes for the same effect. The soil may be sterilized or treated against pathogens that cause damping-off in seedlings. Greenhouse soil and soilless mixes are easier to sterilize than field soil.

Direct seeding is extremely difficult when seeds are very tiny. To overcome this problem, tiny seeds may be *pelleted,* by coating with clay, for example. Bedding plant seeds may be treated in this way before planting. Pelleting makes planting easier and spacing more precise. New methods of preparing seeds for planting are being investigated. For uniform germination and establishment of a crop, planting of pregerminated seeds is being investigated. Recently, sprouted seeds have been suspended in a protective gel or drilled with some water, a method called *fluid drilling*.

9.12 ENVIRONMENTAL CONDITIONS FOR SEED GERMINATION

Germination involves physiological and biochemical processes. The belowground environmental conditions (Chapter 4) must be adequate for seeds to germinate. The critical factors are as follows:

1. *Moisture.* Seeds must imbibe moisture to a certain degree for the germination process to be initiated. Moisture is needed to initiate the enzymatic breakdown of food reserves. The critical degree of imbibition differs among species. For example, whereas soybean needs to imbibe about 50 percent of its weight before germination, sorghum requires only about one-third of its weight. Horticultural plants that germinate best under conditions of high moisture include beet, celery, and lettuce. When raising seedlings in flats, a glass plate may be used to cover the flat to prevent moisture loss through evaporation (Figure 9–4). Similarly, the flat may be placed in a plastic bag to accomplish the same purpose (Figure 9–5). Although moisture is critical to germination, excessive moisture encourages rotting and other diseases.

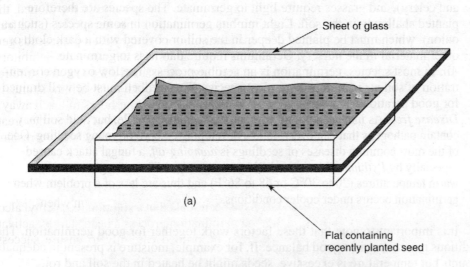

Sheet of glass

(a)

Flat containing recently planted seed

(b)

FIGURE 9–4 Seed germination: (a) using a flat covered with a sheet of glass to retain humidity; (b) using a plastic cover over a flat. *(Source: For (b) George Acquaah)*

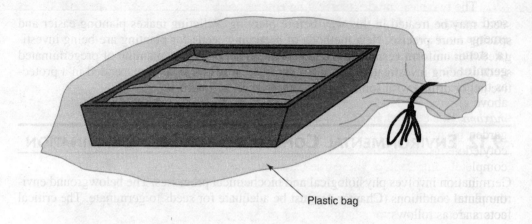

Plastic bag

2. *Temperature.* Temperature regulates seed germination. In seeds that require cold temperature treatment to break dormancy, abscisic acid or other inhibitors are broken down under low temperatures (as obtained in winter). When warm spring temperatures arise, levels of endogenous gibberellins increase, resulting in germination. The rates of biochemical reactions are controlled by temperature. When soils are too cold, growth processes slow down or cease altogether. Generally, a warm seedbed is desirable for seed germination, but warm-season crops (such as bean and squash) do better at warmer temperatures (15 to 25°C or 59 to 77°F) and cool-season crops (such as cole crops) do well at cooler temperatures (less than 10°C or 50°F).

3. *Light.* Most seeds do not need light to germinate. A number of horticultural species including some herbaceous garden flowers, some vegetables (e.g., lettuce and celery), and grasses require light to germinate. The species are therefore planted shallowly in the soil. Light inhibits germination in some species (such as onion), which must be planted deeper in the soil or covered with a dark cloth or other material in the nursery. Geraniums require darkness to germinate.

4. *Air.* In most species, germination is an aerobic process. The low oxygen concentration of soil air is inhibitory to most species. The seedbed must be well drained for good aeration.

5. *Disease free.* As indicated previously, soilless media are sterile, but field soil may contain pathogens that can overwhelm a developing embryo or young seedling. One of the most common diseases of seedlings is *damping-off,* a fungal attack caused especially by *Pythium ultimum* and *Rhizoctonia solani.* These fungi are active at warm temperatures (20 to 30°C or 68 to 86°F) and thus are less of a problem when germination occurs under cooler conditions.

It is important to note that these factors work together for good germination. The conditions must occur in a good balance. If, for example, moisture is present in adequate amounts but temperature is excessive, seeds might be heated in the soil and rot.

9.13 SEED GERMINATION AND EMERGENCE

Seed Germination
A sequence of events in a viable seed starting with water imbibition and leading to embryo growth and development.

Seed germination is a complex process involving metabolic, respiratory, and hormonal activities. The dry seed first imbibes water to initiate enzymatic breakdown of stored metabolites. These metabolites provide the source of nutrition for the developing embryo and are located in the cotyledons of dicots and endosperms of monocots. As these stored foods (proteins, fats, and oils) are metabolized, respiration occurs to synthesize chemical energy, or ATP. Also DNA and RNA are synthesized, the RNA being required for the production of certain hydrolytic enzymes such as amylases, proteases, and lipases. The net result of these biochemical and enzymatic processes is the production of new cells and formation of new tissue, leading to growth and development of the embryo into a seedling.

The two basic modes of seedling emergence are associated with what parts of the seed emerge first from underground. In certain species, the cotyledons (seed leaves) emerge above the ground, preceded by a characteristic arching (hook) of the *hypocotyl* (a stemlike axis). This mode of shoot emergence is called **epigeous** (*epigeal*) **germination** (Figure 9–6) and is associated with dicots. However, in certain dicots such as the pea (*Pisum sativum*), the cotyledons remain underground. The cotyledons, once above ground, gradually change from a creamish color to green. In squash (*Cucurbita maxima*), the cotyledons are important in photosynthesis. However, in castor bean and garden bean, these seed leaves do not contribute significantly to photosynthesis. The cotyledons gradually shrivel in size and eventually drop when the seedling becomes completely autotrophic. These true leaves are called *seed leaves*.

In other species such as the grasses, the endosperm remains underground so that the plumule emerges first. This mode of seedling emergence is associated with monocots and is called **hypogeous** (*hypogeal*) **germination** (Figure 9–7). The cotyledon remains underground and eventually decomposes. In this mode of germination, the *epicotyl* (rather than the hypocotyl) elongates.

Epigeous Germination
A type of seed germination in which the cotyledons rise above the soil surface.

Hypogeous Germination
A type of seed germination in which the cotyledons remain below the soil surface.

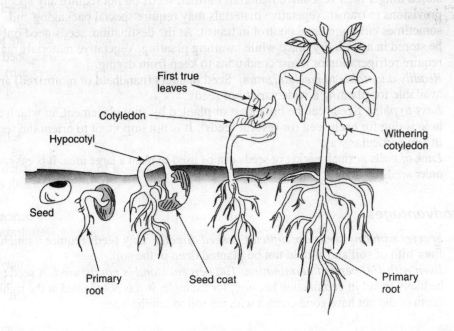

FIGURE 9–6 Epigeous or epigeal germination of bean seed. Cotyledons emerge above the ground.

First true leaves

Cotyledon

Hypocotyl

Withering cotyledon

Seed

Primary root

Seed coat

Primary root

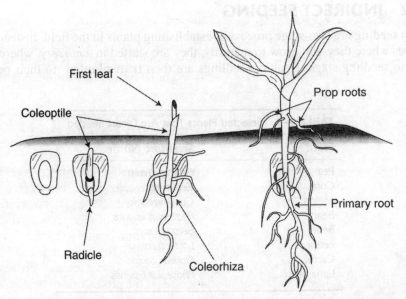

FIGURE 9–7 Hypogeous or hypogeal germination of corn seed. Cotyledons remain underground.

First leaf

Coleoptile

Prop roots

Radicle

Coleorhiza

Primary root

There are two methods of establishing or propagating a plant by seed—direct and indirect seeding.

9.14.1 DIRECT SEEDING

Direct seeding is a one-step planting method in which seeds are placed permanently in the spots in the field where they will germinate, grow, and go through the entire reproductive cycle. Table 9–2 provides a selected listing of crops and ornamentals that can be seeded directly. Direct seeding entails certain advantages and disadvantages.

Advantages

1. *Convenient to use.* Seeds are easy to handle, transport, and store. They can be stored longer than vegetative material. Further, seeds do not require any special provisions in transit. Vegetative materials may require special packaging and sometimes environmental control in transit. At the destination, seeds need only be stored in a cool, dry place while awaiting planting. Vegetative materials may require refrigeration or moist conditions to keep from drying.
2. *Readily adaptable to mechanization.* Seed planters (handheld or motorized) are available for planting a wide variety of seeds.
3. *Easy to plant.* Seeds can be broadcast or planted by spot placement, in which a hole is dug for each seed (or several seeds). It is not important to orient the seed in any particular way.
4. *Lack of bulk.* A small packet of seeds can be used to plant a large area. It is easy to order seeds by mail.

Disadvantages

1. *Species with tiny seeds are difficult to seed directly.* Tiny seeds require a much finer tilth of soil and should not be planted deep in the soil.
2. *Even with 100 percent germination, 100 percent stand is not assured.* A seed may be likely to fail in germination because, for example, it was not planted at the right depth or did not have good contact with the soil to imbibe water.

9.14.2 INDIRECT SEEDING

Transplanting
The process of relocating plants usually from a nursery to the field.

Indirect seeding is a two-stage process of establishing plants in the field. Instead of placing seeds where they will grow to maturity, they are started in a *nursery,* where they are grown to seedling stage. Healthy seedlings are then **transplanted** to their permanent

TABLE 9–2 Selected Plants That Are Direct Seeded

Plant	Scientific Name
Pea	*Pisum sativum*
Corn	*Zea mays*
Melon	*Cucumis melo*
Bean	*Phaseolus vugaris*
Beet	*Beta vulgaris*
Lettuce	*Lactuca sativa*
Carrot	*Daucus carota*
Lima bean	*Phaseolus limensis*

locations in the field. Home gardeners may produce their own seedlings. However, the horticultural industry offers professionally grown seedlings for variety of crops. Table 9–3 presents a list of some of the crops and ornamental plants that are commonly seeded indirectly (Figure 9–8).

Advantages

1. *Good establishment.* Only healthy seedlings are transplanted, ensuring a 100 percent initial establishment. With direct seeding, some seeds may not germinate, even if the highest quality of seed is used.
2. *Early maturity.* Establishing a crop by seedlings has been known to hasten maturity.
3. *Shortened field growing period.* By using a greenhouse (or other facility) to raise seedlings, the grower can have a head start on the season. During adverse conditions (e.g., cold temperature), seedlings may be raised indoors for several weeks while the ground conditions remain too cold for seeds to germinate. When good weather arrives, these seedlings are transplanted into the field for an early crop.

TABLE 9–3 Selected Plants That Are Not Direct Seeded

Plant	Scientific Name
Ageratum	*Ageratum houstonianum*
Alyssum, sweet	*Lobularia maritima*
Begonia	*Begonia x semperflorens-cultorum*
Coleus	*Coleus blumei*
Dusty miller	*Centaurea gymnocarpa*
Geranium	*Pelargonium x hortorum*
Impatiens	*Impatiens* spp.
Marigold	*Tagetes* spp.
Pansy	*Viola tricolor*
Phlox	*Phlox drummondii*
Snapdragon	*Antirrhinum majus*
Verbena	*Verbena x hybrida*
Zinnia	*Zinnia elegans*
Tomato	*Lycopersicon esculentum*
Cabbage	*Brassica oleracea*
Eggplant	*Solanum melongena*
Pepper	*Capsicum annuum*
Parsley	*Petroselinum crispum*
Cucumber	*Cucumis sativus*
Onion	*Allium cepa*

FIGURE 9–8 Transplanting seedlings in the field. Often, workers feed the seedlings into units attached to a moving tractor. *(Source: USDA)*

Disadvantages

1. *Nursery care is an additional production activity that increases production costs.* Nursery care requires the provision of artificial sources of heat (in some cases), light, and space.
2. *Seedlings are not as readily amenable as seeds to mechanized planting.* Mechanized planters for seedlings have been developed for some crops, but vegetative planting materials are more delicate than seeds. In some cases, semimechanized planting operations, in which people feed seedlings into the planter manually as the tractor moves along, are used.
3. *Seedlings are bulky to handle.* Seedlings are raised in containers that need to be transported to the field.
4. *Seedlings should be planted promptly.* Seedlings must be transplanted before they are too old. Seedlings may become too big for their containers and develop root problems (pot-bound).
5. *More immediate postplanting care is needed.* Transplanting shock is a problem when indirect seeding is used. If seedlings are not properly prepared for transplanting, they will take a longer time to become established. Transplanting must be done at a certain time of day and may require a starter application of fertilizer for good and rapid establishment. Newly transplanted seedlings must be watered immediately and more frequently until well established.

9.15 SEED NURSERY ACTIVITIES

When raising seedlings at home, a section of the garden may be reserved for this purpose. A raised bed should have a very fine tilth. Seedlings may be grown in beds or in a variety of containers as described in the following section. Seedlings may be raised indoors in the basement of a home or some other convenient place. Special units may be purchased for this purpose. These units vary in size, design, and versatility; some are equipped to control temperature, humidity, and light.

9.15.1 CONTAINERS

Containers are discussed more fully in Chapter 11.

Flats

Flat
A shallow, rectangular container used to start seedlings.

A horticultural **flat** was originally a wooden box measuring, for example, $24 \times 18 \times 3$ inches ($61 \times 45.7 \times 7.6$ centimeters) ($L \times W \times H$) (Figure 9–9). Plastic flats are more durable and easier to manage and thus more popular today. Styrofoam flats are also used. Provision must be made for drainage by either drilling holes in the bottom boards or by leaving spaces between the pieces of wood. To prevent losing the soil through the openings in the bottom of the box, a sheet of paper (e.g., newsprint) may be used to line the bottom before filling with the appropriate mix of planting media. The flat should be filled and leveled off to about 1 inch (2.54 centimeters) below the top of the box.

Cavity Seeding Trays

Cavity seeding trays are plastic containers that may be obtained as individual cells (cells vary in size) but often come in sets (2, 4, 6, and so on) (Figure 9–10). Each cell has a drainage hole in the bottom. The advantage of this container system is that it facilitates transplanting because the roots of individual plants are confined to a cell. Commercial producers of bedding plants employ a large-scale mechanized system called *plug production*, which entails the sowing of individual seeds into individual plastic cells by specially designed machines. The sown seeds are automatically

FIGURE 9–9   A plastic flat.   *(Source: George Acquaah)*

FIGURE 9–10   A cavity seeding tray.   *(Source: George Acquaah)*

covered with the appropriate soil mix and then transferred to a nursery where, under conditions of appropriate moisture, temperature, and light, the seeds are nursed to the size ready for sale.

Seedlings are sold in units called *packs*. Homeowners and other growers who do not wish to raise their own seedlings find these packs a very convenient source of planting materials. Since seedlings have individual cells in the pack, they are easier to transplant.

Peat Pots and Discs

Peat pots are made of compressed sphagnum peat moss and newspaper fiber. They are biodegradable, and, as such, when used as material for containers for seed germination, the containers are planted directly along with the seedling. Peat pots are usually treated with a fungicide and nitrogen fertilizer to aid in germination (Figure 9–11).

A grower may also find it convenient to use a compressed **peat moss disk** for starting certain seeds (Figure 9–11). The advantage of this method of raising seedlings is that the seedling can be directly transplanted without removing it from the moss medium. If desired, a grower can purchase a simple mechanical unit for making home-made seedling blocks for raising seedlings. These blocks work similarly to peat moss disks. Seedlings raised in this way can be easily transplanted with a ball of soil, which increases transplanting success. Sometimes, peat pots may be used for raising seedlings.

Peat Moss Disks
Compressed peat moss disks used to start seeds or root cuttings and planted with the seedlings.

9.15.2   TIMING OF SEEDING

Horticulture, as previously indicated, is a science, art, and business. Timeliness of operation is crucial for success, especially if production is geared toward a seasonal or holiday market. If you want to produce pumpkins for Halloween, you must know the date for the event, the duration of growth for pumpkins, and when you should sell for maximum profit (definitely before the event); you can then decide when to plant the crop. Some horticultural products have year-round markets.

9.15.3   SEED TREATMENT

Most ornamental seeds are not pretreated by the seed production company. If properly produced, no pretreatment may be necessary for seeds. However, pretreatment with a fungicide is helpful in protecting against soilborne diseases.

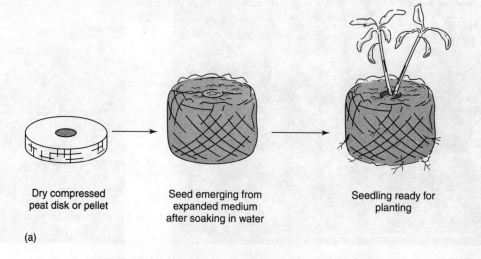

Dry compressed peat disk or pellet

Seed emerging from expanded medium after soaking in water

Seedling ready for planting

(a)

(b)

9.15.4 SOWING SEEDS

The seed packet displays a variety of information, including the name of the cultivars and directions for production (sowing, spacing, care, and maturity). When in doubt, always consult the instructions on seed packets.

The soil surface should be of fine tilth. Instead of broadcasting over the entire soil surface, seeds should be planted in rows. This strategy helps in transplanting the seedlings. A number of shallow grooves should be made by placing a straightedge on top of the soil and drawing a line with a finger or stick. If the seeds are not too small, they can be evenly distributed in the grooves. With care, the seeds can also be distributed fairly evenly in the grooves by tilting the opened packet and gently tapping it as it is moved along the groove. A simple handheld seed planter, a folded paper, or even the seed envelope itself may be used to drill seeds (Figure 9–12).

Most seeds must be covered lightly after sowing (Figure 9–13). This covering may be part of the germination medium or other material such as shredded sphagnum moss. Fine seeds (e.g., petunia and begonia) are best left uncovered to be washed down with water during watering. Since a flat may contain rows of different plant species or cultivars, it is a good practice to always label each different item with a plastic label that indicates the plant name, cultivar, and date of planting. Some seed companies enclose labels in their packages. Some growers simply invert the empty packet over a stake that marks the rows sown to a particular cultivar. However, sometimes the paper rots under repeated watering or may be blown away by wind. Use indelible or water-insoluble ink in writing the label.

(a)

(b)

FIGURE 9–12 (a) Sowing seed in flat. (b) Covering seed in flat. *(Source: For (a) Dave King © Dorling Kindersley, (b) Paul Goff © Dorling Kindersley)*

FIGURE 9–13 Sowing seed in cavity tray. *(Source: Peter Anderson © Dorling Kindersley)*

9.15.5 AFTER-SOWING CARE

Mechanized sowing by mechanical seeders (plug seed production) has revolutionized the bedding plant industry. However, sowing certain popular seeds such as zinnia and marigold is problematic because of anatomical features that interfere with the process.

Moisture

Seeds should be watered immediately after sowing, using a fine mist of a fine-spray nozzle to apply water to avoid washing seeds away or burying them too deeply. Excessive moisture is undesirable. Where possible, the container may be watered from the bottom (*subirrigation*) by placing the flat in water. If cavity seeding trays are used, the water may be added to the bottom of the holding tray. The flat may be covered with a pane of glass or plastic sheet to retain moisture in the soil. It is important to keep the soil surface moist throughout the germination period until seedlings emerge. A seed will die if allowed to dry after imbibing water or initiating sprouting.

Temperature

The soil should be kept warm for good germination by most seeds. Place the flat in a warm place at 20 to 26°C (68 to 79°F), depending on the species. Even though 21°C (70°F) may be adequate, a warmer temperature of about 24°C (75°F) will cause germination to occur more rapidly. Certain seeds such as pansy and snapdragon prefer a relatively cooler germination temperature of about 18°C (65°F).

Temperature fluctuations in the seedbed are caused by evaporation and irrigation water. Evaporation of moisture may cool the soil surface water by about 1 to 3°C (2 to 5°F). When cold water 7 to 10°C (45 to 50°F) is used in watering, it can cause the soil temperature to drop. A cold soil takes a long time to regain its heat. To stabilize soil temperature, some growers use *hotbed cables*. Some of the small-scale propagation boxes have heating coils. In commercial greenhouses, *biotherm*, or *bioenergy, systems* or hot water tubes are used to provide plants growing in containers with heat from the bottom.

Fertilizing

Fertilizers are not required until the seeds germinate. The stored food in the cotyledon is usually adequate for the period of germination. High fertility in the germination medium results in weak seedlings. The soil medium should have a good pH (6.0 to 6.8). Phosphorus is required for strong root development; consequently, the element should be available as soon as possible to ensure seedling survival.

9.15.6 AFTER-GERMINATION CARE

Fertilizing

Once the seeds germinate, the seedlings should be provided with a low-level application of a complete fertilizer analysis such as 20-20-20 at the rate of 1 ounce (28.35 grams) per 3 gallons (11.4 liters) of water. Fertilizer should be applied weekly to avoid the development of weak seedlings. Weak seedlings are difficult to transplant and less likely to survive the operation.

Hardening Off

Hardening Off
The process of preparing seedlings for transplanting by gradually withholding water, nutrients, and decreasing temperature.

Transplanting Shock
A temporary setback in growth suffered by fresh transplants due to adverse conditions.

Hardening off is a horticultural practice whereby seedlings are prepared for transplanting to the field. The danger transplants face in the field is the drastic change in the growing environment from a more controlled one to a harsh one. If unprepared, transplants are prone to **transplanting shock** (stress that may be suffered by transplanted seedlings). This preparative process is called hardening off and is usually accomplished by manipulating the temperature and moisture levels. Seedlings are gradually exposed to slightly cooler temperatures (13 to 15°C or 55 to 59°F) and/or reduced moisture.

9.16 TRANSPLANTING

9.16.1 TRANSPLANTING FROM FLATS

If seedlings cannot be transplanted when they are ready, they should be stored at a cool temperature to slow their growth (e.g., in a refrigerated environment at about 5.5°C [40°F]). They should be brought into the open for at least a day before transplanting.

Seedlings may be transplanted from the nursery bed directly to the field. If the grower is raising seedlings for sale, the seedlings are transplanted into containers such as peat pots or cavity seedling trays and nursed to marketable size. In the second case, seedlings are transplanted at a younger age and then must be transplanted a second time by the gardener or grower. Whatever the situation, seedlings should be transplanted after at least the first true leaves have developed (Figure 9–14).

Seedlings are fragile and must be handled with care. Leaves may be damaged without great repercussion; new ones form in a short while, unless the terminal bud is damaged. An injured stem is a much more serious situation, and, as such, seedlings should be handled by their leaves (not stem). Instead of pulling seedlings from the soil, a trowel or hand fork may be used to dig them up. Watering plants before transplanting makes the operation easier. Seedlings should have some soil around the roots to aid in reestablishment. For transplanting, a tool called a *dibble* may be used (Figure 9–15). However, a trowel is just as effective.

Seedlings are placed in holes in the receiving medium to a depth of at least that used in the nursery. Once in place, soil is added and gently patted down around the base of the stem. After transplanting, the plants should be watered.

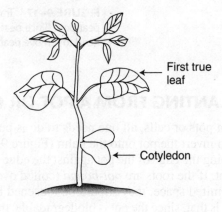

First true leaf

Cotyledon

FIGURE 9–14 Seedlings should be transplanted after true leaves have developed.

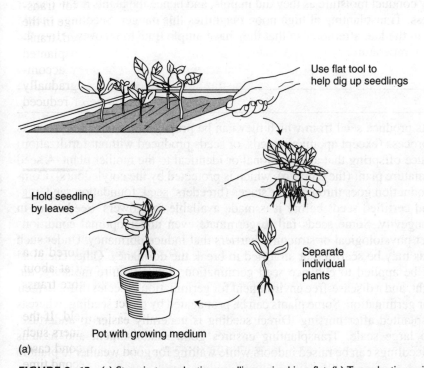

Use flat tool to help dig up seedlings

Hold seedling by leaves

Separate individual plants

Pot with growing medium

(a)

(b)

FIGURE 9–15 (a) Steps in transplanting seedlings raised in a flat. (b) Transplanting using a dibble. *(Source: For (b) Peter Anderson © Dorling Kindersley)*

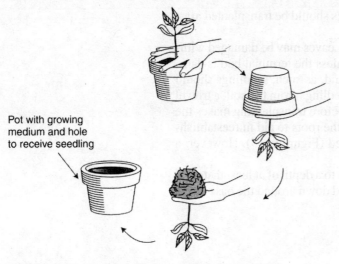

Pot with growing medium and hole to receive seedling

FIGURE 9–16 Removing larger seedlings from pots for transplanting or repotting.

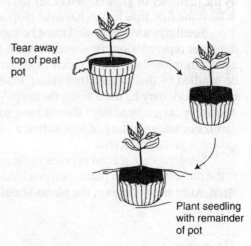

Tear away top of peat pot

Plant seedling with remainder of pot

FIGURE 9–17 Transplanting seedlings raised in peat pots. Since peat is biodegradable, there is no need to remove peat pots before transplanting.

9.16.2 TRANSPLANTING FROM A POT OR CAVITY TRAY

When transplanting from pots or cells, all one needs to do is position the stem between a pair of fingers and then invert the pot onto the palm (Figure 9–16). A gentle tap at the bottom of the pot or tapping the edge of the pot against the edge of a table aids in removing the plant from the pot. If the roots are *pot-bound* (coiled over themselves at the bottom of the pot) due to limited space, they should be loosened before transplanting. An advantage with peat pots is that, since the pot is biodegradable, there is no need to remove the seedlings from the pot before transplanting (Figure 9–17).

Transplanting into the field should be undertaken at a good time of day. Freshly transplanted seedlings need time to establish and resume normal activities. The roots will not immediately conduct moisture as they did in pots, and hence the plants are in danger of moisture stress. Transplanting at high noon magnifies this danger. Seedlings should be transplanted in the late afternoon so that they have ample time to recover before the next day's noon temperature.

SUMMARY

Flowering plants produce seed from which they can be propagated. Seeds are products of the meiotic process (except apomictic seeds, or seeds produced without fertilization) and hence produce offspring that are not clonal or identical to the mother plant. A seed contains the miniature plant (the embryo), which is protected by the cotyledon(s). Commercial seed production goes through four stages (breeders' seed, foundation seed, registered seed, and certified seed) before it is made available to growers. Seeds vary in viability and longevity. Some seeds fail to germinate even under optimal conditions because of either physiological or structural barriers that induce dormancy. Under such conditions, seeds may be scarified or stratified to break the dormancy. Other chemical treatments may be applied to enhance seed germination. Seeds require moisture, air, temperature, light, and a disease-free environment for germination. Species differ in their requirements for germination. Some plants can be propagated by direct seeding, whereas others are transplanted after nursing. Direct seeding is generally easier to undertake, especially on a large scale. Transplanting ensures good establishment and hastens crop maturity. Seedlings can be raised indoors while waiting for good weather to plant in the field.

REFERENCES AND SUGGESTED READING

Copeland, L. O. 1976. *Principles of seed science and technology*. Minneapolis: Burgess.

Hartmann, H. T., and D. E. Kester. 1983. *Plant propagation: Principles and practices,* 4th ed. Englewood Cliffs, N.J.: Prentice Hall.

Mayer, A. M., and A. Poliakoff-Mayber. 1975. *The germination of seeds,* 2d ed. Oxford: Pergamon Press.

Sexual reproduction in angiosperms
http://users.rcn.com/jkimball.ma.ultranet/BiologyPages/A/Angiosperm.html

Stefferud, A., ed. 1961. *Seeds: USDA yearbook of agriculture*. Washington, D.C.: U.S. Department of Agriculture.

PRACTICAL EXPERIENCE

1. Plant seeds of a legume and a grass in a soilless medium.
   a. Observe the pattern of germination between the two plant types.
   b. Wash away the potting medium and compare the anatomical differences between the legume and the grass.
2. Test the germination percentage of a seed
   a. Purchased from various sources (e.g., grocery, nursery, and supermarket)
   b. Produced in different seasons (1, 2, 3 years)
   c. Stored under different conditions (e.g., cold storage, freezer, and room temperature)

OUTCOMES ASSESSMENT

1. Distinguish breeder seed and certified seed.
2. What is seed law and why is it important in the seed industry?
3. Describe, giving examples, the techniques growers may use to enhance the germination capacity of seeds.
4. Discuss the importance of seed analysis to horticultural crop production.
5. Discuss how seed emergence and seed size are considered in crop production.
6. What is hardening off and what is its importance in crop production?
7. Give the major purposes of plant propagation.

10

Asexual Propagation

PURPOSE AND EXPECTED OUTCOMES

This chapter discusses the methods of propagating horticultural plants by using materials other than seed.

After studying this chapter, the student should be able to

1. Distinguish between sexual and asexual methods of propagation.
2. Discuss the advantages and disadvantages of asexual propagation.
3. Describe propagation by cutting.
4. Describe propagation by budding.
5. Describe propagation by grafting.
6. Describe propagation by layering.
7. Describe propagation by underground plant parts.
8. Describe and discuss micropropagation.

[COLOR PLATES—*see color plate 7* for additional chapter photos]

OVERVIEW

When plants are propagated by any material other than seed, they are said to be *asexually,* or *vegetatively, propagated.* Since the sexual mode of reproduction is the principal means by which biological variation is generated (through recombination), propagation that circumvents the sexual mechanism (asexual, or vegetative, propagation) results in no genetic changes. The progeny, or offspring, are genetically identical (**clones**). Therefore, instead of meiosis, mitosis is the mechanism governing asexual propagation. Species that are heterozygous and hence fail to reproduce true to type may be propagated vegetatively or clonally to preserve the genotype. Trees or woody perennials benefit from this method of propagation, since it drastically shortens the time of breeding of such plants.

The vegetative tissues commonly used in asexual propagation are the stem, leaf, and root. Modern technology allows full-fledged plants to be regenerated from tissues and even single cells (*micropropagation*). A common phenomenon that occurs in some

Clone
An individual or a group of individuals that develop asexually from cells or tissues of a single parent individual.

312

species enables vegetative propagation to be conducted using seeds. These seeds are different in that they are produced without a sexual union between male and female gametes. Instead, certain elements in the sexual apparatus (such as the nucellar tissue that has not undergone meiotic division) spontaneously develop into seed. Plants that are capable of this kind of reproduction are said to be apomictic, and the phenomenon that produces such seeds in these plants is called *apomixis*. In citrus, a sexual embryo and nucellar embryo can be produced side by side. It should be mentioned that since an individual's appearance (phenotype) is determined by its genes (genotype) but influenced by the environment, differences in the environment can cause clones to perform differently.

Asexual propagation has certain advantages and disadvantages.

10.1 ADVANTAGES

1. *Plants are uniform.* The offspring are genetically identical (clones) and are the same in appearance as the parental source (true offspring). Uniformity (homogeneity) of produce quality is critical to the success of certain production enterprises where the market demands uniform products.
2. *Quick establishment of plants.* Only strong and healthy seedlings are transplanted, and thus a good stand is always obtainable. Asexual propagation is generally known to hasten crop maturity. In geranium, for example, asexual propagation causes plants to flower about three weeks sooner than if propagated from seed.
3. *Only means of propagation in certain species.* Certain plant species such as banana and grape produce seedless or nonviable fruits. Other species including foliage plants do not produce seed at all. On such occasions, the grower has no choice but to use asexual means of propagation to produce these crops.
4. *Seedborne diseases avoided.* Seedborne diseases are not a problem when plants are asexually propagated.
5. *Less expensive.* For certain species, asexual propagation is less expensive than propagation by seed.
6. *Heterozygous material may be propagated without genetic alteration.* Certain plants can be propagated either sexually or asexually. If through plant breeding activities a hybrid is developed with high heterosis (hybrid vigor or hybrid superiority over parents), this heterozygous advantage is "locked up" and can be expressed indefinitely (until further genetic alteration occurs). In seed propagation, the hybrid must be reconstituted each time for planting because each sexual cycle changes the genetic constitution of the offspring.

10.2 DISADVANTAGES

1. *Systemic viral infection can spread to all plants, making planting material taken from infected plants a carrier of the infection.* This viral infection may be eliminated by
   a. Starting with a new, disease-free seedling
   b. Using heat treatment (where an infected clone is held at 37 to 38°C [98.6 to 100.4°F] for about three to four weeks)
   c. Using tissue culture of terminal growing points that, even in infected plants, are usually disease free
2. *Planting materials are bulky.* Unlike seed, which can be stored in a small seed envelope, products of cuttings and seedlings in containers are bulky to handle and transport.
3. *Storage of asexual material is cumbersome and usually short term.* Seeds are dormant propagating materials, whereas asexual materials such as seedlings are actively

growing and thus need special care to sustain growth processes until transplanted. If they are not transplanted on time, they need to be held under certain conditions to slow growth. Overgrown seedlings have a lower success rate in the field.

4. *All plants are genetically identical and thus subject to the same hazards to the same degree.* Because of extreme uniformity among plants, a disease infection can wipe out entire populations of plants.
5. *Mechanized propagation in some cases is not practical.* Automation of asexual propagation methods is often problematic.

10.3 ADVENTITIOUS ROOTING IN ASEXUAL PROPAGATION

True roots *(seminal roots)* are produced only by seed. When vegetative parts of the plant are used for propagation, it is critical that roots be induced on these materials. The roots are nonseminal and called *adventitious roots*. They originate from root initials that are formed adjacent to vascular tissue. Some plants are easier to root than others. Rooting ability is a function of plant characteristics and the environment.

10.4 APOMIXIS

Apomixis is a form of asexual reproduction through which seeds are produced without fertilization (i.e., no fusion of gametes). The common dandelion, a known weed in lawns, is capable of reproducing by sexual and ordinary vegetative means, as well as apomictically. Wild blackberry can also reproduce apomictically. This phenomenon should be distinguished from parthenocarpy, which is the development of fruits from unfertilized eggs. These fruits (parthenocarpic fruits) are seedless (e.g., navel orange, banana, certain grapes, and fig). However, all seedless fruits are not parthenocarpic; for example, seedlessness may be artificially induced in tomato by spraying flowers with a dilute hormone.

Apomixis, however, involves normal structures such as ovaries. For example, an embryo of a seed may develop from a $2n$ nutritive cell or other diploid cell in an ovule. Because usually the embryo of a seed develops from a zygote, plants raised from apomictic seeds are genetically identical to the parent plant (clones).

MODULE 1

CUTTINGS

10.5 TYPES OF CUTTINGS

Cuttings are pieces of vegetative material obtained from any of the three primary plant organs—stem, leaf, or root. These tissues are nursed under appropriate conditions of temperature, humidity, light, moisture, and nutrients to develop into full-fledged plants. Cuttings are by far the most commonly used asexual propagation method in the horticultural industry. A variety of cuttings may be grouped on the basis of several factors, including parts of the plant used, age of the plant part, and succulence of the tissues. It is possible to obtain more than one kind of cutting from a single plant. However, certain materials are more successful or easier to use for establishing certain species than others. Stock plants from which cuttings are obtained should be grown under optimal conditions for rapid rooting. There are two basic types of cutting—terminal or tip cutting and basal or subterminal cutting.

10.5.1 STEM-TIP (TERMINAL) CUTTINGS

In *stem-tip cutting* the tip of the stem is cut (or in some cases snapped with the fingers) and used to produce a seedling. The piece cut is about 3 inches long and has leaves (Figure 10–1). The leaves on cuttings may be reduced $1/2$ to $2/3$ to allow closer spacing in the propagation bed, more effective misting, and reduce water loss. However, cuttings with full leaves produce stronger roots more quickly. Terminal cuttings may be obtained from herbaceous, softwood, semisoftwood, and hardwood plants. The cut may be made at either the node or internode of the stem. Stem-tip cuttings produce seedlings much more rapidly than stem-section cuttings.

10.5.2 STEM-SECTION CUTTINGS

Stem-section cutting (or simply *stem cutting*) is the asexual method of propagation whereby pieces of stem material containing at least one bud are used for planting. The difference lies in the type of wood from which the cuttings are made.

Softwood Cuttings

Softwood cuttings are made from soft tissues (nonlignified) of shrubs or deciduous trees. They are taken from the new growth of the current season (spring growth). The parent source should be actively growing and have leaves (Figure 10–2). The age of the cutting material is critical. A suitable material is flexible but can snap when sharply bent. Examples of plants that can be propagated by this method are rose, forsythia, plum, dogwood, lilac, jasmine, boxwood, and azalea. Because of the presence of leaves, these cuttings must be maintained under high humidity during root induction to avoid desiccation. Softwood cuttings usually root more easily and faster than other types of stem cuttings.

FIGURE 10–1 Stem tip cutting. *(Source: George Acquaah)*

FIGURE 10–2 Softwood cuttings are made from young leafy shoots from spring growth. *(Source: Peter Anderson © Dorling Kindersley)*

Semihardwood Cuttings

As the name implies, semihardwood cuttings are derived from tissues that are more woody than softwood cuttings. Semihardwood cuttings are made from the spring growth of trees and shrubs, are more mature than softwood, but will snap when bent. This material may be obtained around midsummer. The cuttings should have some leaves on the top parts and be handled in the same manner as softwood cuttings (Figure 10–3). Plants such as azalea, rhododendron, holly, and other broadleaf evergreen ornamentals are propagated by this method.

Hardwood Cuttings

Deciduous Wood   Deciduous **hardwood cuttings** are made from plant parts that are more hardened, woody, and mature enough to spring back when bent and released. They are taken before the plants produce a flush of spring growth, in early spring or late winter. The materials are thus obtained from the previous summer's growth. These cuttings do not have leaves and are about 6 to 12 inches (15 to 30 centimeters) long (Figure 10–4). They are best rooted in a well-drained, sandy medium. The cuttings are inserted vertically into the rooting medium. Some fruits (e.g., grape, fig, and currant), deciduous shrubs (e.g., rose, forsythia, and honeysuckle), and deciduous trees (e.g., willow) yield hardwood that is used in their propagation.

Narrow-Leaved Evergreens   Conifers, narrowleaf evergreens, are commonly propagated by hardwood cuttings obtained from plants in early winter. These cuttings should have needles on the upper part (Figure 10–5). Conifer cuttings root slowly, sometimes requiring months to produce adequate rooting. The preferable rooting environment is cool and humid. Sometimes a cold frame with high light intensity can be used to accelerate the rooting process. Examples of plants in this category are juniper, spruce, hemlock, yew, and pine.

Herbaceous Cuttings

Herbaceous stem cuttings are also considered softwood cuttings. Numerous potted succulent greenhouse plants are propagated by herbaceous cuttings (Figure 10–6). Geranium, carnation, chrysanthemum, coleus, ivy, spider plant, and lanta are

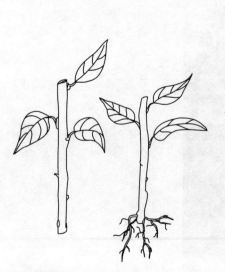

FIGURE 10–3 Semihardwood cuttings. Broadleaf evergreens are commonly propagated in this way.

FIGURE 10–4 Deciduous hardwood cuttings are obtained from leafless plants in late winter or early spring.   *(Source: Peter Anderson © Dorling Kindersley)*

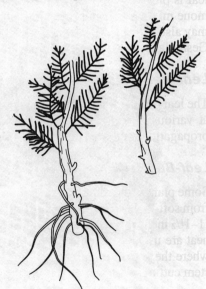

FIGURE 10–5 Narrowleaf evergreen or conifer cuttings.

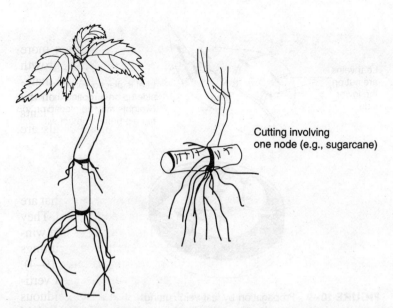

Cutting involving
one node (e.g., sugarcane)

FIGURE 10–6 Herbaceous stem cuttings may be rooted vertically or horizontally.

FIGURE 10–7 Propagation by leaf cutting. The petiole may be dipped in a rooting hormone to aid rooting.
(Source: Peter Anderson © Dorling Kindersley)

propagated by herbaceous stem cuttings. Many of these species root easily from cuttings. In species that are intolerant of high moisture levels, cuttings can be rooted in a flat covered with a wire frame with a sheet of white polyethylene. The cuttings are watered lightly once or twice daily. The covering maintains adequate humidity.

10.5.3 LEAF CUTTINGS

Full or Partial Leaf Cuttings

Leaf cuttings are herbaceous cuttings that involve the use of either a piece of or an entire leaf. Popular species propagated in this way include begonia, gloxinia, peperomia, echeveria, crassula, sansivieria, and African violet. In plants such as African violet, the leaf is picked with a leaf stalk attached. The leaf stalk may be dipped in a rooting hormone mixture before inserting it into a rooting medium in a pot (Figure 10–7). The leaf may also be rooted in a container of water before transplanting it into soil (Figure 10–8). Gesneriads are commonly propagated by leaf cuttings.

Leaf Cuttings
A whole leaf or part of one that is detached and used to raise a new plant.

Leaf-Vein Cuttings

The leaf-vein cuttings method may be used to raise plantlets by cutting through the veins at various points. The leaf is then placed face down so that the cut parts touch the propagation medium (Figure 10–9). Plantlets grow from these cut points.

Leaf-Bud Cuttings

Some plants, including rhododendron, may be propagated from leaf-bud cuttings obtained from soft- or hardwood (Figure 10–10). A leaf-bud cutting consists of a short piece of stem (1–1½ inches) with an attached leaf and a bud in the leaf axil. High humidity and bottom heat are usually required for rooting to occur. This method of leaf propagation is useful where the source of cuttings is limited. Instead of using a long piece of stem as a single stem cutting, each bud on the stem can be removed and nursed to become a single plant.

10.5.4 ROOT CUTTING

Roots are cut into short pieces (2–6 inches) in late winter to early spring from young stocks (2–3 years old). The tip of the root farthest from the stem is inserted into the

FIGURE 10–8 Rooting in water. *(Source: Peter Anderson © Dorling Kindersley)*

FIGURE 10–10 Propagation by leaf-bud cutting.

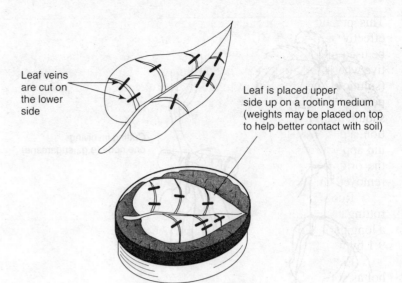

Leaf veins are cut on the lower side

Leaf is placed upper side up on a rooting medium (weights may be placed on top to help better contact with soil)

FIGURE 10–9 Propagation by leaf-vein cutting.

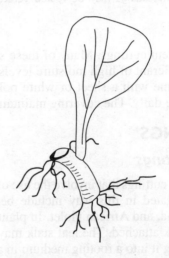

rooting medium. Species that are propagated by this method include wisteria; bayberry; yucca; oak-leaf; hydrangea; hibiscus; and species from *Rhus, Carya,* and *Malus* genera.

10.6 FACTORS AFFECTING ROOTING OF CUTTINGS

These factors should be optimized at all stages in the production of rooted cuttings.

10.6.1 PLANT FACTORS

Nutritional Status of the Plant

Cuttings obtained from healthy, well-nourished plants and that have accumulated carbohydrates are more successful in rooting than those obtained from malnourished plants. Plants low in nitrogen make better cuttings. The leaves on cuttings act as sources of carbohydrates, and the buds are sources of auxins.

Hormone Level

The auxin level in the plant affects the rooting capacity of the cutting. Nursery growers routinely dip cuttings in commercially prepared rooting hormones to stimulate rooting.

This practice is especially important when handling hard-to-root species. The most effective and widely used root-promoting hormone is indolebutyric acid (IBA). IBA may be used in combination with naphthalene acetic acid (NAA), but the latter is less effective when used alone. Rooting hormones may be formulated as a powder (dust) or liquid (solution) and available as ready-to-use, or can be prepared to the desired strength from powders or salts. To avoid contamination in case any of the cuttings are diseased, they should not be dipped into the same container of powder or solution. For powder application, a puffer duster (squeezable bottle) may be used; a spray bottle may be used for liquid applications to spray the ends of the cuttings. Cuttings should never be dipped into the original container of the hormone. The amount needed should be poured out or removed and any leftover amount discarded.

Rooting hormones may be mixed with fungicides to protect the cut surface from rotting under humid conditions. Fungicides are especially helpful in species that require a long period of time to root. A suggested ratio of hormone to fungicide (e.g., captan) is 9:1 by weight.

Reagent grades of these hormones are not water soluble, requiring the use of alcohol as solvents. Salts of IBA and NAA, though more expensive, are water soluble, but require more of the substance to be effective. Prepared solutions store well for a long time at 40–45°F in darkness (wrap bottle with aluminum foil and place in a fridge.)

Juvenility

The physiological age of the cutting significantly affects its rooting success. Cuttings from mature woody and fruiting stock plants are less successful than those from newer shoot growths. The juvenile stage is thus more conducive to rooting. Cuttings are commonly made from one-year-old plant parts. Some propagators prune stock plants to obtain fresh growth as needed.

Position of Plant Part

The position of plant parts used as cuttings plays a role in their capacity to root. Lateral shoot cuttings root better than terminal shoot cuttings.

10.6.2 ENVIRONMENTAL FACTORS

Time of Year Cutting Is Made

Whereas cuttings may be taken any time of the year for herbaceous and perennial plants, hardwood cuttings root better when the materials are obtained in late winter when plants are dormant. Similarly, softwood cuttings from deciduous woody plants are best taken in spring; semihardwood cuttings root best when obtained in midsummer.

Darkness

Darkness promotes etiolation in plants. Although this condition indicates improper development, materials obtained from etiolated plants root better than plants exposed to full light. A practical application of this condition is the keeping of basal plant parts of shoots to be used for cuttings in darkness for a period of time. This technique may be applied in species that are very difficult to root.

Light

Even though etiolated plant materials root better than normal ones, rooting cuttings in full light under a mist makes them root more quickly. Optimal conditions for photosynthesis are needed for producing healthy liners. However, when light intensity is excessive, plants may be in jeopardy of moisture stress. Producing short and stubby products. During such periods, shading is required. Similarly, in winter, supplemental lighting is required.

Temperature

Bottom heat in cutting beds warms the soil to induce quicker rooting. It is important to have adequate rooting before the shoot starts to grow vigorously. The bottom heat is usually about 6°C (10°F) higher than the air temperature, which should be maintained between 18 and 27°C (65 and 75°F). Supplement heating is critical during cold periods to avoid injury.

Moisture and Humidity

Intermittent mist and fog system, controlled by a timing device, are commonly used for propagation. The misting frequency and duration depend on light, radiation, and air temperature. Cuttings do not have roots and hence are unable to absorb moisture. However, the exposed plant parts are subject to evaporation. To reduce moisture loss, cuttings are generally maintained under conditions of high moisture by misting them. Initially, misting may be required almost continuously. As time goes by, the misting schedule is modified, being less frequent and less intense. In some greenhouses, a mist is replaced by a *fog*.

Nutrition

No fertilization is needed for unrooted cuttings since they can take up very little of it. Light fertilization may be applied through the mist. Once rooted, a complete fertilizer application of 20:20:20, for example, at a rate of 1 pound (0.45 kilogram) per 100 gallons (378.5 liters) of water may be applied.

Rooting Medium

Certain species, including coleus, African violet, and *Philodendron scandens,* can root in water alone. Most cuttings are rooted in solid media that must be sterilized, freely draining, and of good moisture-holding capacity. Sand is well drained but poor in moisture-holding capacity. If sand is used, the rooting should be conducted under shady conditions and should be hand watered. Vermiculite and perlite make good propagation media, especially when combined with peat most. The medium for propagation must be very loose to enable rooted cuttings to be readily removed from the rooting medium and planted with little loss of roots. Propagation may also be conducted in outdoor conditions, provided the medium is well drained and aerated to avoid saturated water conditions.

In place of the conventional rooting media, a variety of preformed, lightweight materials are widely used. These media include rockwool media, compressed peat pellets, and other artificial materials marketed under various brand names such as Oasis root cube, Oasis wedge, and Horticubes. Sometimes cuttings are rooted directly in the finish pots. Species such as geranium and poinsettia are propagated in this way.

Sanitation

Cuttings have exposed surfaces and hence are prone to disease attack. The propagating medium must be sterilized before use. Steam sterilization is effective in controlling most soilborne diseases.

10.6.3 TAKING AND PREPARING CUTTINGS

Select the material according to age and size. Cuttings from plant parts that receive optimal sunlight are most desirable. If cuttings are obtained from stocks in the field, they should be wrapped in moist burlap or other suitable material to reduce water stress, and be kept out of sunlight as well. If cuttings will not be prepared right away, the material should be stored in a fridge or a cool place, or misted.

10.6.4 STICKING THE CUTTING

Cuttings may be rooted in a variety of media. Placing cuttings in a medium for rooting is called "sticking." It is important to stick the base end of the cutting into the medium. Rooting hormone is applied just before sticking. Sticking depth is about $1/2$ to 1 inch.

10.6.5 CARE OF CUTTINGS AFTER ROOTING

Once rooting starts, liners (rooted cuttings) should be moderately fertilized, as previously indicated. Some pruning for uniform growth may be required or uniformity of the products or to develop the desired branching habit. Prior to transplanting in the field, liners are hardened by transplanting them into larger containers and gradually moderating the environmental condition (light, fertilizer, water temperature) to reflect field conditions.

10.7 TRANSPLANTING

Cuttings are ready to be transplanted when a mass of roots has formed. The rooted cutting should be lifted gently with little pulling. It should be planted no deeper than it was in the propagating medium. These materials are transplanted like any other seedling.

SUMMARY

Cuttings may be obtained from the stem, leaf, or root for propagating certain plants. Once taken, the pieces may be directly planted in some cases, but in other cases must be rooted before transplanting into pots or the field. Cuttings may be obtained from softwood or hardwood. The application of a rooting hormone may be required in certain cases for rooting to occur or to hasten rooting.

MODULE 2

GRAFTING

10.8 NATURE OF GRAFTING

Grafting is an asexual propagation method in which parts of two different plants are joined so that they continue their growth as one plant. To accomplish this, one of the two plants serves as the bottom part, which is in contact with the soil and is called the **rootstock** (or simply *stock*), and the other as the top part, or **scion.** In this plant union, the plant material used as the scion is being propagated and is usually the only one allowed to grow. In effect, the scion becomes the new shoot of the plant union, and the stock serves as the root, conducting nutrients across the graft junction and into the shoot. There are two basic methods for bringing about the union between the two plant parts in a graft:

1. *Detached-scion grafting.* Detached-scion grafting is the method in which the scion is detached; only the stock remains rooted (Figure 10–11). This technique is the most commonly used for grafting.
2. *Approach grafting.* In this method, two plants are united at a predetermined and prepared site (Figure 10–12). That is, the scion and the stock both remain an integral part of the respective parent plant. This procedure is used when detached scion

Grafting
A technique of uniting two plants so they grow as one.

Rootstock
The bottom part of a graft that is in contact with the soil and not allowed to produce side shoots.

Scion
The plant part that is the top part of a graft and grows to become the desired shoot.

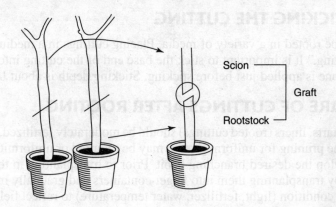

FIGURE 10–12 Methods for making an approach graft.

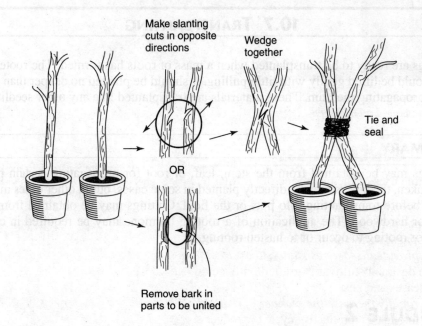

grafting is not feasible. The produce harvested from the plant reflects only the characteristics of the scion parent and not both stock and scion. The scion serves only as ground support.

10.8.1 HEALING OF A GRAFT JUNCTION

A graft is successful if healing is complete and vascular transport restored between the scion and stock. It is critical that the tissues in the two parts be correctly aligned—xylem for xylem and phloem for phloem. Healing starts with the production of call (undifferentiated cells) by mitosis and occurs in the cambium region of the two part Next, some of the cells differentiate to form new cambium tissue to join the old in t two parts (Figure 10–13). This stage is followed by further differentiation of cells to fo vascular tissue, which completes the repair of the cuts and allows for uninterrup vascular transport.

10.9 WHEN TO USE GRAFTING

Grafting may be used for relatively simpler and more routine propagation of plants for more complicated and specialized repair of damaged plants.

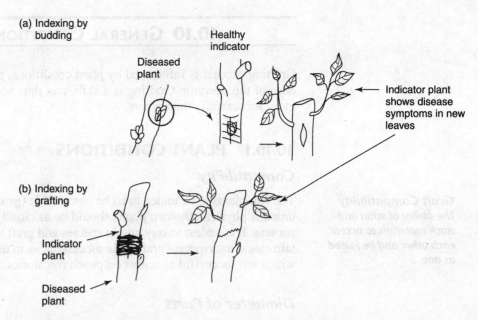

FIGURE 10–13 A healed graft junction. *(Source: © Dorling Kindersley)*

FIGURE 10–14 Virus indexing using (a) budding and (b) grafting.

10.9.1 GENERAL USES

The routine uses of the technique of grafting include the following:

1. *To propagate plants whose cuttings are difficult to root.* Grafting provides an opportunity for clones to be produced without rooting the cuttings in a propagating medium. The cutting is "rooted" on another plant.
2. *To provide disease resistance to a susceptible but desirable cultivar.* In this case, the desirable cultivar is grafted onto a cultivar that is able to resist soilborne diseases and pests.
3. *To rapidly increase the number of a desirable cultivar.* The plant does not have to go through a reproductive cycle to produce seed to propagation. Plant parts can be taken and rooted to produce new plants.

10.9.2 SPECIALIZED USES

Grafting may be used to repair damaged plants, invigorate them, or change their form.

1. *To change plant size and vigor.* Special rootstocks with the capacity to dwarf scion cultivars exist. Called *malling rootstocks,* they have a dwarfing effect on the plant.
2. *To repair damaged plant (established tree) parts.* Grafting may be used to repair a damaged trunk, for example, from girdling caused by rodent attacks. A damaged root may also be repaired by grafting.
3. *To change plant form.* One or several cultivars may be grafted onto several limbs of a single plant. Such grafting may be done to change the plant form and improve aesthetics.
4. *Virus indexing.* Plant pathologists may use grafting (or budding, discussed in Module 3) in a special technique to find out whether a plant is free of virus. This technique is called virus indexing. Any of the grafting or budding methods may be used in this evaluation. In a simple budding procedure, a bud is obtained from a diseased plant and budded onto susceptible or sensitive species called *indicators*. The indicator plant is decapitated above the budding site so that the remaining stem of the indicator plant has about two to three buds (Figure 10–14). As these sensitive buds grow, they exhibit symptoms characteristic of whatever virus (or mycoplasma) has infected the plant from which the bud was obtained.

Virus Indexing
A procedure used to determine whether a given plant is infected by a virus.

Grafting success is influenced by plant conditions, prevailing environment, and experience of the operator. Grafting is a skill, and thus some operators are able to perform it more successfully than others.

10.10.1 PLANT CONDITIONS

Compatibility

Graft Compatibility
The ability of scion and stock materials to accept each other and be joined as one.

The two plants to be united must be compatible (**graft compatibility**). Even though this union is physical, the two plants should be as closely related genetically as possible for success. It is easiest to stay within species and graft apples onto apples. However, in certain cases, interspecies grafting is successful, as in the case of some almonds and plums, which are successful as scions on peach rootstocks.

Diameter of Parts

The stock diameter must be equal to or larger than the scion diameter. The scion is usually no larger than the size of a regular pencil, but some methods of grafting use larger stocks so that several scions can be grafted onto one stock. Scions are usually derived from healthy one-year-old plants.

Physiological State

Grafting is done primarily in wood species and usually done using dormant plants. These plants have no leaves (except in the case of evergreens). In some cases, the rootstock may be actively growing, but the scion should not be growing.

Alignment of Tissues

Since grafting is a physical union that depends on healing of the cut surfaces (wounds) through mitotic division, the cambium tissues of both parts must be properly aligned. They must make contact over as wide an area as possible. If the tissues are not aligned properly, the graft will fail. The graft junction may be tied to keep the alignment in place throughout the healing period.

10.10.2 ENVIRONMENT

Grafting Wax
A pliable, sticky, water repellant material made of beeswax, resin, and tallow, and applied to waterproof a graft junction.

The worst environmental enemy of a new graft is desiccation. Therefore, a newly made graft should be waterproofed. After tying, **grafting wax** may be applied over the entire surface. Some operators use plastic or rubber ties instead of wax. Either way, the purpose is to prevent desiccation from occurring at the graft junction and also to prevent entrance of disease and decay-causing organisms. There are three types of waxes—hot, cold, and hyard—the first two being most widely used in commercial grafting. A hot wax may be prepared by combining the following ingredients: a-lb resin + 1-lb beeswax + 1-pint raw linseed oil + 1-oz lamp black, and heating together. Cold waxes are best purchased ready-made.

10.10.3 THE OPERATOR

In addition to all of the mentioned factors, the operator should always use a sharp knife and make sharp, clean cuts to ensure good contact of tissue. A more experienced operator is likely to have greater success than a novice at grafting.

Grafting may be accomplished by one of several methods, depending on the species, the age and size of the plant, the problem to be corrected, and the purpose. These methods also differ in difficulty and the skill required for success. Although some methods are for general purpose use, others are used to solve specific and specialized problems. Notwithstanding the method, the principles are the same. There are two basic methods—one in which the scion is removed from its source and transferred onto another plant and a second in which no detaching is done before the formation of the graft union.

10.11.1 GENERAL PURPOSE METHODS

Detached-Scion Grafting

Common methods of detached-scion grafting are described in the following sections.

Whip or Tongue Grafting The steps involved in the **whip** or tongue method of grafting are illustrated in Figure 10–15. This method is suited for plant materials that are about 1/4 to 1/2 inch (0.64 to 1.3 centimeters) in diameter. The scion and stock should be as close in diameter as possible to provide maximum contact between the cambia of both parts. This method is best employed in the winter. The cuts in both scion and stock are made in the internode region. All cuts should be sharp and clean and the angles as close as possible in shape in both parts. The first cut is a long, smooth, sloping cut, followed by a cleft cut across the surface to form the tongue. The scion and stock should fit as tightly as possible. It is critical that the buds on the scion point upward. After properly aligning the two parts, the graft junction is tied or taped. A wax coating may be applied over the tie. Fruit trees are grafted by this root grafting method. After the graft is tied and waxed, the plants are stored under conditions that encourage callus formation

Whip
A young tree seedling (about one year old) with a slender single stem (less than 1/2 inch wide).

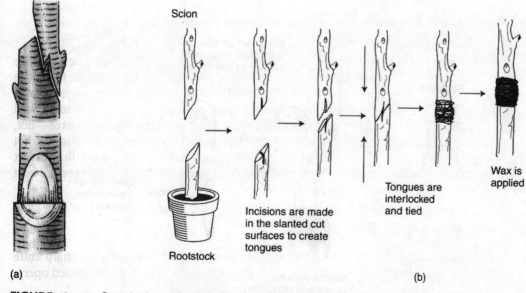

(a)   (b)

FIGURE 10–15 Steps in the method of whip or tongue grafting. *(Source: For (a) © Dorling Kindersley)*

(7.2 to 10°C or 45 to 50°F) for about three to four weeks. Top growth should not be allowed to occur before healing of the graft. Storing the grafted plants at 0 to 4.4°C (32 to 40°F) discourages top growth. Remove the tying material when the graft has united. New growth occurs in spring as the temperature begins to rise. *Grafting machines* are available and used widely in grafting grapes.

Cleft Grafting

As the name indicates, in cleft grafting the scions are inserted into a cleft in the stock (Figure 10–16). Unlike the whip or tongue method in which both plant parts are usually of the same diameter, the stock is considerably wider in cleft grafting, thus allowing multiple grafts to be made on one stock. After cutting the stock at right angles, a meat cleaver or a special grafting tool is hammered into the center to produce a wedge cut. A wedge is inserted into the shallow split to keep it open for the scions to be inserted. Care should be taken to avoid tearing the bark away. This method is particularly suited for **topgrafting,** or *topworking,* the grafting strategy in which several scions are grafted onto one large scion to change fruiting cultivars in a fruiting tree. It is one of the oldest and most widely used types of grafting and used primarily to convert old cultivars into newer and more desirable cultivars. No tying is necessary in this method since the split in the stock has enough pressure from both sides to hold the scions together. Care must be exercised to ensure that the two cambial layers make effective contact. Leaning the scion toward the outside of the stock improves the chance of good contact. A wax coating is essential, especially when the parts are not tied after grafting. Cleft grafting is done in late winter or early spring.

Bark Grafting

Grafting is applicable to species whose bark separates easily from the wood. Since the bark must be separated, this method is employed during the early to middle spring, when the rootstocks are actively growing. The scion should be dormant. This method is also used for topgrafting or topworking trees such as broadleaf evergreens, including citrus and olive. One unique characteristic is that instead of tying, the scion is nailed to the stock (Figure 10–17).

Approach Grafting

Approach grafting may be tried when other general detached-scion methods have failed. At least one of the two plants involved should be in a container (although both can be in containers). Smooth cuts in opposite directions but identical in size, shape, and depth and occurring at the same height are made on the plants. Sometimes a tongue cut may be used in this method. The prepared parts are appropriately united, after which the graft junction

Topgrafting
A method of grafting in which the cultivar of a tree is changed by grafting the main scaffold branches or the stem using a new cultivar.

FIGURE 10–16 Steps in the method of cleft grafting.

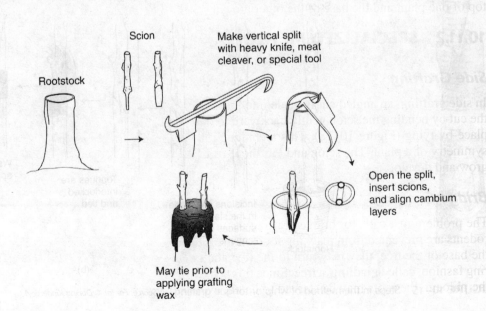

Rootstock

Scion

Make vertical split with heavy knife, meat cleaver, or special tool

Open the split, insert scions, and align cambium layers

May tie prior to applying grafting wax

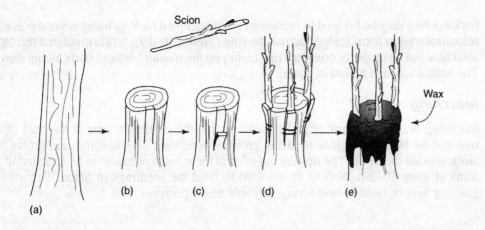

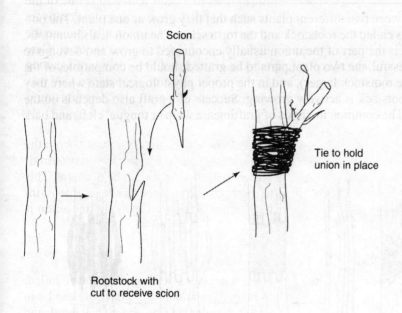
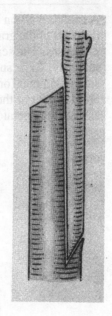

FIGURE 10-18 Steps in side grafting. *(Source: For (b) © Dorling Kindersley)*

is tied and sealed to keep the union in place for healing. After healing is complete, the top of one plant and the base of the other are cut so that only one stem remains.

10.11.2 SPECIALIZED METHODS

Side Grafting

In side grafting, an angled cut is made into the stock. A scion is prepared and fitted into the cut by bending the scion gently backward to open up the cut. The scion is secured in place by tying (Figure 10–18). This technique may be used to improve the shape and symmetry of a plant. The scion and the shoot from the stock parent are both allowed to grow and develop.

Bridge Grafting

The problem that calls for bridge grafting occurs in temperate or colder regions. When rodents are prevented from reaching food on the ground by the presence of snow around the base of the tree, they may turn to the tree and gnaw away a portion of the bark in a ring fashion, called **girdling** a tree. Since this activity interrupts the transport of food via the phloem, the roots may be starved to death, eventually affecting the whole tree. The

Girdling
The interruption of phloem transport by removing a ring of bark from the stem.

10.11 Methods of Grafting **327**

barkless ring may be bridged to reconnect the interrupted bark by using several pieces of scion material to form bridges across the ring (Figure 10–19). It is critical that the twigs used as scion be properly oriented (tips facing up the tree and bottom parts facing down). The scions are then nailed in place.

Inarching

Inarching is similar to bridge grafting except that the girdling occurs at the base of the tree and the bridging is done by using growing seedlings. The seedlings are grown in a circle around the trunk. The tips are cut off and the stumps prepared to be attached to the trunk (Figure 10–20). Nailing is required to hold the seedlings in place. This radical grafting may be used to save a very valuable tree (specimen tree).

SUMMARY

A graft is a union between two different plants such that they grow as one plant. The bottom part of the graft is called the rootstock and the top a scion. The union heals by mitotic processes. The scion is the part of the union usually encouraged to grow and develop to maturity. To be successful, the two plant parts to be grafted should be compatible, of the same diameter (or the rootstock larger), and in the proper physiological state where they are dormant or the rootstock is actively growing. Success of a graft also depends on the skill of the operator. The common methods of grafting are whip or tongue, cleft, and bark grafting.

FIGURE 10–19 Steps in bridge grafting. This method is similar to bark grafting except that it requires both ends of the scion to be grafted.

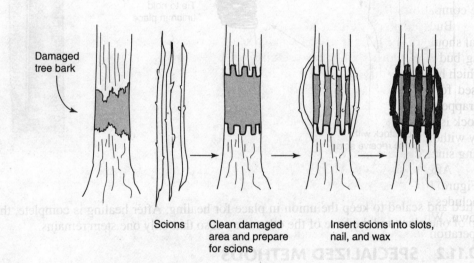

Damaged tree bark

Scions | Clean damaged area and prepare for scions | Insert scions into slots, nail, and wax

FIGURE 10–20 Steps in inarching. This method is similar to bark grafting except that undetached scions are used and the scions are inserted from below the graft junction.

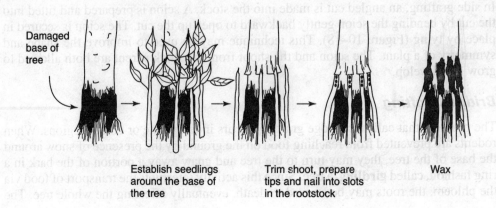

Damaged base of tree

Establish seedlings around the base of the tree | Trim shoot, prepare tips and nail into slots in the rootstock | Wax

MODULE 3
BUDDING

10.12 TYPES OF BUDDING

Budding may be described as psuedografting and is sometimes called *bud grafting.*
A major difference between budding and grafting is that budding uses a single bud as the
scion, whereas grafting uses a piece of plant material consisting of several buds. Budding is less involved and much easier to accomplish than grafting. Since a bud is inserted
into an opening in the bark of a stem or branch, it is important that budding be done when
the rootstock is actively growing (i.e., in spring, late summer, or fall).

10.12.1 T-BUDDING

T-budding or shield budding, gets its name from the shape of the cut made in the bark
of the stock in which the bud (scion) is inserted. It is the most commonly used budding
method in plant propagation. The stock should be actively growing and young (one to
two years old) so that the bark can be easily separated from the stem. T-budding is
widely used to propagate fruit trees (e.g., apple, pear, peach, and citrus) and roses.
Both the bud and the stock are encouraged to grow, but after the bud has attained a
good size, the stock is cut off above the site of budding. The scion and rootstock must
be compatible.

Buds are obtained from *bud sticks,* which are small pieces of shoot. The shoot material should be the current season's shoot and also be vigorously growing. When collecting bud sticks, one should be careful to collect only vegetative (not fruiting) shoots,
which have buds that are slender in shape and are more pointed. Vegetative shoots to be
used for bud sticks are collected on the same day budding is to be done. They are
wrapped in waterproof paper or placed in plastic bags to prevent desiccation. A good
stock is about one to two years old and is considered ready when its bark peels off easily without tearing. Buds on the middle section of the bud stick are usually best for budding since they are mature.

After making the T-shaped cut, the bark is opened up with the end of a knife
(Figure 10–21). A bud is extracted from the budwood in the shape of a shield and
includes a small piece of wood. The bud shield is inserted into the opening and pushed
down. When in place, it is tied with budding tape, raffia, or plastic tape. A successful
operation shows a take in about three weeks, at which time the wrapping is removed.

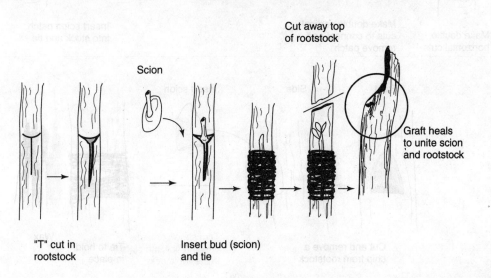

Cut away top
of rootstock

Scion

Graft heals
to unite scion
and rootstock

"T" cut in
rootstock

Insert bud (scion)
and tie

FIGURE 10–21 The method
of T-budding.

10.12.2 PATCH BUDDING

Plants that are difficult to bud by the T-method (e.g., pecan and walnut) because of a thick bark may be patch budded. *Patch budding* involves removing a piece of bark (Figure 10–22). A patch of equal size containing a bud is obtained and fitted into the stock plant. The patch is tied in place, ensuring that the bud is exposed. It is also important that the plants be actively growing to ensure that the bud can be more readily extracted from the parent. The best time for patch budding is mid to late summer. As in other methods, it is necessary to remove all sprouts occurring below the budded area.

10.12.3 CHIP BUDDING

Chip budding differs from T-budding in several ways. Chip budding uses a cut that includes a larger chip of wood—in fact, more wood than bark. The method is applicable to a dormant stock since the bark does not need to be separated from the wood as in T-budding. Therefore, chip budding can be done in summer or fall. The removed chip is replaced by a bud that is cut to fit the hole in the stock (Figure 10–23). It is important, as always, to align the cambia in both bud (scion) and stock. After inserting the bud, it is taped with rubber tape or other similar waterproof material. When the bud takes and grows, the stock is cut above the bud.

SUMMARY

Budding is similar to grafting in that part of two different plants are united. The difference is that in budding the scion is a single bud rather than a piece of twig with several buds as in grafting. Budding is a relatively easier procedure than grafting. It is done while the plant that is designated as stock is still actively growing, since the bark needs to be opened up for the bud to be inserted. Vegetative (not fruiting) bud sticks are used and are collected on the same day the operation is to be performed. The method of T-budding is commonly used to propagate fruit trees. Other methods include patch and chip budding. Chip budding can be done in summer or fall when the plant is not actively growing since it does not require the bark to be opened up but only a chip to be cut from the wood.

FIGURE 10–22 Steps in the patch budding method of propagation.

FIGURE 10–23 The method of chip budding.

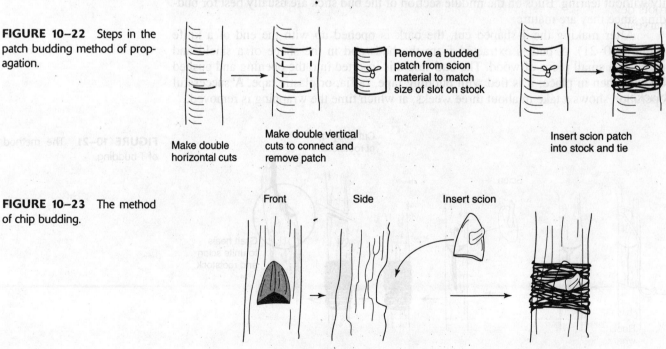

Make double horizontal cuts

Make double vertical cuts to connect and remove patch

Remove a budded patch from scion material to match size of slot on stock

Insert scion patch into stock and tie

Front   Side   Insert scion

Cut and remove a chip from rootstock

Tie to hold in place

Module 4

LAYERING

10.13 TYPES OF LAYERING

Layering may be described as modified cutting. The plant part to be cut is rooted before it is completely cut away from the parent plant. Roots or stems may be propagated by layering. The part of the plant that is eventually cut off to be grown independently is called the *layer*. Layering is accomplished in a variety of ways that may occur naturally or with the help of humans.

10.13.1 NATURAL LAYERING

Layering occurs naturally in certain species because their anatomy permits portions of the plant to come into contact with soil at some point.

Tip Layering

Species such as boysenberry and black raspberry (cane fruits) have been known to propagate naturally by *tip layering*. When the tips of the current season's long canes bend down and touch the soil, they turn around to grow upward once again. At the point of contact with the soil, roots start to develop, provided the portion is adequately covered with soil (Figure 10–24). The layer may then be severed from the parent and dug up for replanting as an independent plant.

Runners

Natural layering involving roots occurs in horticultural species such as the strawberry. As the plant grows, it produces *runners,* or *stolons* (aboveground creeping stems), in various directions. When the nodes on these structures come into contact with the soil, roots develop, and eventually new plants arise at these nodes; these new plants may be harvested by cutting and digging out for replanting (Figure 10–25).

Suckers

Suckers are adventitious shoots produced by species including spirea, red raspberry, and blackberry. These shoots arise from the horizontal roots produced by these plants

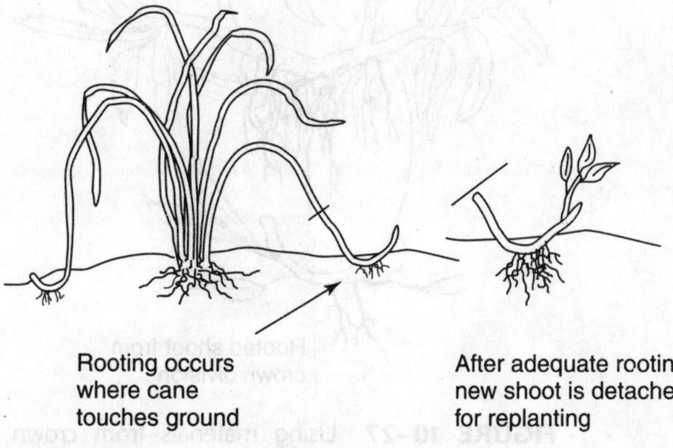

> **Layering**
> *A method of vegetative propagation of plants usually with flexible limbs (shrubs, vines) in which roots are generated on the limb before being severed for planting as an independent plant.*

Rooting occurs where cane touches ground

After adequate rooting new shoot is detached for replanting

FIGURE 10–24 Propagation by tip layering.

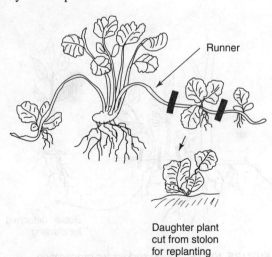

Runner

Daughter plant cut from stolon for replanting

FIGURE 10–25 Propagation by using runners.

(Figure 10–26). The result of this habit is that a single original plant may produce several new plants clustered together. Each of these adventitious shoots may be harvested for replanting.

Crowns

The *crown* is the root-shoot junction. In species such as shasta daisy and African violet, the crown grows larger with time and produces lateral shoots from the underground parts of older stems and roots. These new shoots may be harvested by *crown division*, which entails cutting the crowns into pieces such that each piece has roots and a shoot (Figure 10–27). These new shoots may then be replanted.

10.13.2 HUMAN-AIDED LAYERING

Simple Layering

The *simple layering* method of propagation is easier to employ in species that produce long, flexible shoots that arise from the plant at ground level because it requires the part to be layered to bend to touch the ground (Figure 10–28). The selected stem (one-year-old stem preferred) is girdled or nicked about halfway through the portion that will be in contact with the soil. Nicking or girdling the stem causes auxins and carbohydrates to accumulate in the area of the stem for quick rooting. A shallow hole (4 to 6 inches or 10.2 to 15.2 centimeters) is dug at an appropriate spot. The stem is gently curved such that the nicked part of the stem is positioned erectly, aided by another peg. The hole is then filled with soil, mulched, and watered regularly. In some cases, an additional weight (e.g., a large stone) may be placed on top of the mulch. When adequately rooted, the layer is cut from the parent and dug up for replanting. Foliage plants including *Philodendron* and *Dieffenbachia* and other species such as climbing roses are propagated by simple layering.

Serpentine Layering

Serpentine layering is sometimes called *compound layering* because several layers can be obtained from one shoot that is anchored to the ground. The flexible shoot is anchored to the soil at various sites rather than buried along the entire length (Figure 10–29).

Trench Layering

In *trench layering*, the midsection of the flexible stem is buried in the soil after nicking in several places (Figure 10–30). This type of layering causes several seedlings to develop. Species including rose and rhododendron can be propagated by trench layering.

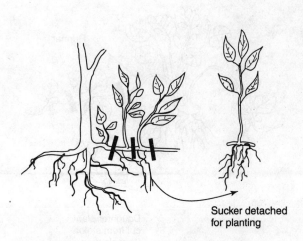

Sucker detached
for planting

FIGURE 10–26 Using suckers for propagation.

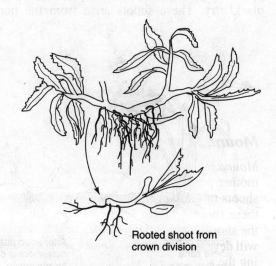

Rooted shoot from
crown division

FIGURE 10–27 Using materials from crown division for propagation.

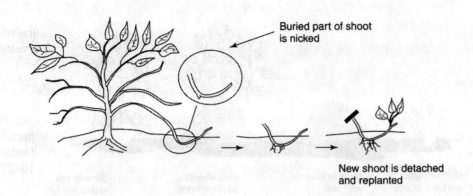

FIGURE 10–28 Simple layering.

Buried part of shoot
is nicked

New shoot is detached
and replanted

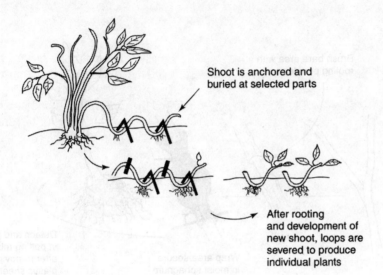

FIGURE 10–29 Serpentine layering.

Shoot is anchored and
buried at selected parts

After rooting
and development of
new shoot, loops are
severed to produce
individual plants

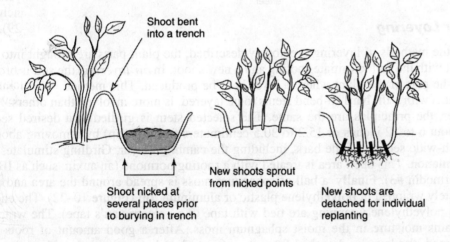

FIGURE 10–30 Trench layering.

Shoot bent
into a trench

New shoots sprout
from nicked points

Shoot nicked at
several places prior
to burying in trench

New shoots are
detached for individual
replanting

Mound Layering

Mound layering is also called *stool layering*. It is accomplished by first cutting back the mother plant close to the ground, most often in late winter. This pruning causes new shoots to grow in spring. At the onset of new growth, soil is heaped around the base of these shoots to form a stool bed (Figure 10–31). The size of the mound is increased as the shoots grow bigger. It is critical to keep the mound of soil moist continually. Roots will develop from the base of these shoots. The individual shoots are harvested by removing the soil and cutting them off from the mother stump for replanting. Species such as rose, apple, and currant are commonly propagated by this method.

FIGURE 10–31 Mound layering.

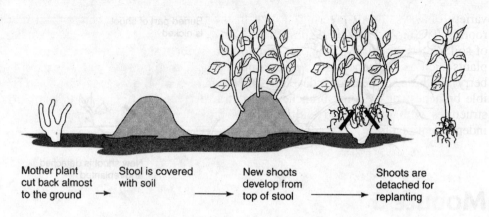

Mother plant cut back almost to the ground → Stool is covered with soil → New shoots develop from top of stool → Shoots are detached for replanting

FIGURE 10–32 Air layering.

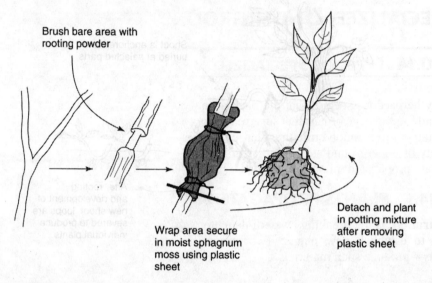

Brush bare area with rooting powder

Wrap area secure in moist sphagnum moss using plastic sheet

Detach and plant in potting mixture after removing plastic sheet

Air Layering

In the methods of layering previously described, the plant parts are brought into contact with the soil to initiate rooting and a new shoot. In *air layering,* the soil is brought to the part of the plant where a layer is to be produced. This method, which enables plants with stiff, hard-to-bend stems to be layered, is more involved than others. However, the principles are the same. The selected stem is girdled at a desired section (about 6 to 12 inches or 15.2 to 30.5 centimeters from the tip) by removing about an inch-wide section of the bark, including the cambium layer. Girdling stimulates root formation. This open area is treated with a rooting hormone (an auxin, such as IBA or Hormodin #3). Finally, a ball of sphagnum moss is spread around the area and completely wrapped in polyethylene plastic or aluminum foil (Figure 10–32). The ends of the polyethylene wrapping are tied with tape (e.g., electrician's tape). The wrapping retains moisture in the moist sphagnum moss. After a good amount of roots have formed, the layer is detached from the parent plant by cutting below the wrap. The layer is then replanted. Species including *Dieffenbachia,* litchi *(Litchi chinensis),* and the Indian rubber plant *(Ficus elastica)* may be propagated by this method.

SUMMARY

In effect, layering is a modified form of cutting in which the plant part is cut after it has been either naturally or artificially induced to root while still attached to the mother plant. When ample rooting has occurred, the part (the layer) is cut away from the parent and planted as an independent plant. This procedure may be accomplished in a variety of ways. In air layering, a nick in the branch is wrapped in soil to induce rooting. The nicked part of the branch may be arched down and buried under a mound of soil, called mound layering. Layering occurs without the aid of humans in certain plants such as the cane fruits (e.g., raspberry) and rhizomatous plants (e.g., strawberry). In these species, roots develop at the point of contact between the soil and flexible branches (or creeping branches as in strawberry). The tips or portions of these structures with the new adventitious roots may be detached and planted as new, independent plants.

MODULE 5

SPECIALIZED UNDERGROUND STRUCTURES

10.14 TYPES OF SPECIALIZED UNDERGROUND STRUCTURES

Many herbaceous species that die back at the end of the growing season have underground food storage organs that survive the dormant winter period. These organs are also vegetative propagation structures that produce new shoots in the growing season. The variety of underground storage organs may be grouped into two classes based on how they are propagated: plants propagated by *separation* and plants propagated by *division*.

10.14.1 PLANTS PROPAGATED BY SEPARATION

Separation is the breaking away of daughter structures from the parent structure to be used to establish new plants. Two specialized underground structures—*bulbs* and *corms*—produce such materials.

Separation
A method of propagation in which underground structures of plants are divided not by cutting but by breaking along natural lines between segments.

Bulbs

Structurally, a bulb is an underground organ that consists predominantly of fleshy leaf scales growing on a stem tissue (basal plate). The scales wrap around a growing point or primordium to form a tight ball. Lateral *bulblets,* or miniature bulbs, originate in the axils of some of these scales and when developed *(offsets)* may be separated from the mother bulb to be planted independently as new plants (Figure 10–33). Offsets first grow vegetatively in the first few years and may take several more years for the bulb to attain sufficient size to produce a flower. The two types of bulbs are tunicate and scaly bulbs.

FIGURE 10–33 Propagation by using bulblets.

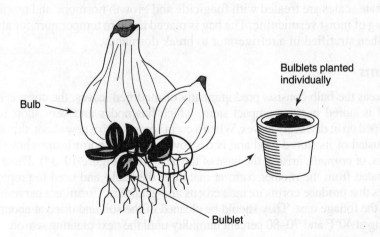

Bulblets planted individually

Bulb

Bulblet

Tunicate Bulbs   The onion is an example of a *tunicate bulb* (also called *laminate bulb*). This type of bulb consists of concentric layers of tightly arranged scales, the outermost layer being a dry, membranous protective layer (tunic). Other examples are daffodil, tulip, and hyacinth.

Hyacinths and several other bulbs do not readily produce offsets. Several techniques are used for propagating these species.

1. *Scooping*. The entire basal plate is cut out to remove the shoot and flower bud. The exposed surface should be treated with a fungicide and placed in darkness at 21°C for two weeks to dry to form a wound tissue. After that, the temperature should be increased to 30°C with a level of humidity of 85 percent The exposed fleshy bases will produce twenty-five to thirty bulblets with this treatment. It might take several years before the bulblets reach flowering stage.

2. *Scoring*. Three to four pie-type deep cuts are made to produce six to eight sections through the basal plate. The bulb is placed in a warm dark place with high humidity. This treatment takes several months. If done in summer, the bulb should be ready for planting in fall. It produces about twenty bulbs that need an additional three to four years to grow to flowering stage.

3. *Coring*. Like scooping, coring entails removing the basal plate, only this time, the center portion is removed to a deeper extent, extracting the primary growing point. The treatment is the same as for scoring. It yields a fewer number of bulbs than scoring and scooping.

4. *Sectioning*. Sectioning is like scoring, only the cuts are made completely through to produce 6–8 separate sections. The sections are treated like scoring. Bulblets form at the basal plate of each of the sections.

5. *Cuttage*. Cuttage is like sectioning. The segments are further trimmed to leave one to four scales attached to the basal plate. These materials are treated with fungicide. New bulblets will develop after several weeks of propagating in a well-drained medium, like vermiculite.

Scaly Bulbs   *Scaly*, or *nontunicate*, bulbs lack an outer dry protective membrane. They are more delicate and require special handling to prevent drying and damage. The scales are not tight but loose and can be removed individually from the bulb. The lily is a nontunicate bulb. The daughter bulb or bulblets develop at the base of the scales of the mother bulb.

When the foliage of the plant dies back, the bulb resumes a dormant state. Bulbs may be dug up, separated, cleaned of soil, and then stored at a cool temperature to keep them dormant. The ability of a bulb to flower depends on its size. If it is too small, it may have to be grown for as long as several years before it will reach flowering size. Small bulb size may be due to premature removal of the foliage of the plant. The bulb should be harvested after the top has turned brown by natural processes.

The scales of nontunicate bulbs may be separated by cutting at the basal plate. The separate scales are treated with fungicide and growth hormone and propagated in a plastic bag of moist vermiculite. The bag is placed at room temperature for about two months and then stratified in a refrigerator to break dormancy.

Corms

Whereas the bulb consists predominantly of modified leaves, the corm is a modified stem. Food is stored in this compact stem, which has nodes and very short internodes and is wrapped up in dry, scaly leaves. When a corm sprouts into a new shoot, the old corm becomes exhausted of its stored food and is destroyed as a new corm forms above it. Several small corms, or *cormels*, arise at the base of the new corm (Figure 10–34). These cormels may be separated from the mother corm at maturity (die back) and used to propagate new plants. Plants that produce corms include crocus and gladiolus. Corms are harvested by digging up after the foliage dies. They should be cleaned of the soil and dried at about 90–92°F before storing at 40°F and 70–80 percent humidity until the next planting season.

FIGURE 10–34 Propagation by using cormels.

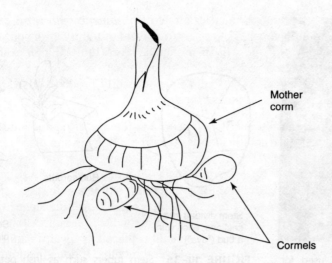

Mother corm

Cormels

Disease Problems

Having fleshy and soft tissue, bulbs are prone to infection by fungi during propagation, especially when some of the techniques that require cutting are used. Common infections include *Fusarium* bulb rot that starts as a white mold growing on the tunic of the bulb. This infection could be carried over from the field during harvesting. *Penicillium* blue-gray mold may be a problem when techniques like scoring and cutting are used. Treating freshly cut surfaces with fungicides (e.g., Captan, Banrot, PCNB) protects against rot.

10.14.2 PLANTS PROPAGATED BY DIVISION

In plants propagated by separation, complete and individual miniature plants are naturally produced and attached to the mother plants. These plants can be separated by simply breaking the bunch apart or cutting along natural boundaries. In **division,** no such clearly defined and individually packaged miniature plants exist. Rather, the large mass of mother plants is strategically divided by cutting into pieces so that each piece consists of certain basic structures to permit development into a new plant. When using the division method for propagation, it is advisable to treat the cut surfaces of materials with fungicides to prevent rotting when planted. Various underground storage structures found in plants may be used for propagation.

Division
A method of propagation in which underground stems are cut into pieces and replanted.

Rhizomes and Stolons

Rhizomes are underground stems that grow horizontally. These features vary in diameter from one species to another, some being slender and others thick. Similar to *stolons* (aboveground horizontally growing stems) in strawberry, these rhizomes have nodes that produce adventitious roots that support shoots at these junctions. Rhizomes are also used for propagation by cutting dormant ones into pieces at the internodes (Figure 10–35). Examples of plants propagated by rhizomes are ginger, banana, Kentucky bluegrass, and iris. Like rhizomes, stolons may be divided into sections that must each contain a vegetative bud. Lateral branches may be removed and used for planting.

Stem Tubers

Certain plants store food underground in modified stems. These swollen ends of stems do not have nodes but rather buds (or eyes), each of which can be nurtured to produce a new plant. To produce a new plant, the tuber is divided into sections so that each section has a good amount of flesh (1–2 oz at least), or stored food and buds. Once divided, the cut surface should be allowed to dry for up to three days before planting. An example of a stem tuber is found in the edible Irish potato.

FIGURE 10–35 Rhizomes may be divided and used for propagation. *(Source: George Acquaah)*

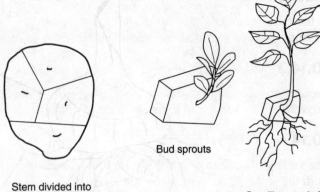

Bud sprouts

Stem divided into sections, each with a bud ("eye")

Seedling ready for planting

FIGURE 10–36 Stem tubers such as Irish potato may be divided into sections for propagation.

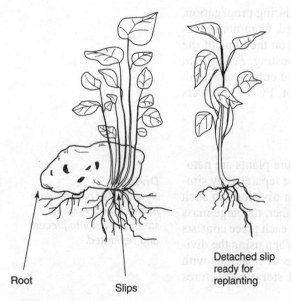

Root

Slips

Detached slip ready for replanting

FIGURE 10–37 Slips of sweet potato may be used for propagation.

FIGURE 10–38 Propagation by dividing clumps. *(Source: © Dorling Kindersley)*

Tuberous Roots

Whereas the Irish potato produces a swollen stem, the sweet potato produces a swollen root. When a tuberous root is buried in the soil, it produces a number of adventitious shoots called *slips* (Figure 10–37). These slips can be detached and planted individually to produce new plants. In most tuberous roots, propagation is accomplished by dividing the crown *(crown division)* or cluster of roots of dominant plants, or more often by stem, leaf, or leaf-bud cutting. Another example of a tuberous root is the dahlia.

Clumping Species

Herbaceous perennials (e.g., daylily, zamia, liriope) often produce multiple stems and clump growth. To propagate, the clump is separated into smaller pieces such that each piece has sufficient amount of roots and shoots (Figure 10–38). In some cases, a tool (e.g., axe, saw) may be needed to cut the wood material. It is important to plant the divided pieces at the same depth as the parent plant.

Psuedobulbs

In the *Dendrobium* orchid, for example, roots form at the base of the offshoots. These offshoots may be removed and transplanted.

10.14.3 SUCKERS

Suckers are adventitious shoots that arise from roots. In raspberry, the shoots are harvested from horizontal roots and used to propagate the plant.

10.14.4 OFFSHOOTS

The variety of adventitious shoots (suckers, crown division, slips, and offsets) that arise from the stems or roots of plants are called **offshoots**. The pineapple plant is quite versatile in terms of parts that may be used to propagate the plant. The crown on top of the fruit, slips arising from axillary buds at the base, and suckers that originate from the lower part of the stem may all be used for propagation.

Offshoot
The generic term for adventitious shoots that arise from various parts of the plant.

10.14.5 PLANT PATENT ACT

A patent is a tool used by the government to provide incentive for discovery and invention of products. A plant patent may be awarded to an applicant who has "invented" or discovered and asexually reproduced a distinct and new variety of plant (other than a tuber propagated or a plant found in an uncultivated state). A plant patent holder is given the right to exclude others from asexually reproducing the plant and from using, offering for sale, or selling the plant so reproduced, or any of its parts, throughout the United States, or from importing the plant so reproduced, or any parts thereof, into the United States. Such rights are enforceable for a period of twenty years.

Asexual (clonal) reproduction is specifically mentioned in the act because it is a means of preserving the genetic integrity of the product from one generation to the next. The owner of the patent is encouraged to reproduce it asexually and make adequate amounts of such materials available to the public.

Plant produces that qualify for patenting are sports, mutants, and hybrids. A *sport* is a new and distinct variety that originates from a bud. Such spontaneous variations are distinguishable from the appearance or characteristic of a normal plant. Seedling variation by self-pollination may give rise to mutants, while a *hybrid* is a product of the cross-pollination of two unidentical plants (e g., two species, varieties). Plant seedlings discovered, asexually reproduced, and proved to be stable, uniform, and to have new characteristics distinct from other known plants, are patentable. The law, however, specifically excludes plants found in an uncultivated state. The plant must not have been introduced to the public, sold, or offered for sale, more than one year prior to the patent application.

To file for a plant patent, the patentee is required to clearly document his or her claim in writing, describing and defining the new plant, showing its unique and distinguishing features from known varieties, supplementing with drawings and or photographs, and making an oath or declaration. The applicant must declare that the plant has been reproduced asexually, or found in a cultivated area. Descriptions of the plant should be made in standard botanical terms and include the origin or parentage of the plant, geographic location, and the method of asexual reproduction (e.g., budding, cutting). If color is a distinguishing feature, it must be described using a color atlas or dictionary, preferably, The Royal Horticulture Society Color Chart.

SUMMARY

Apart from roots, certain species develop a variety of underground swollen structures that are, in some cases, the economic, edible, or usable part of the plant. These modifications may be in the roots or stem. Bulbs such as onion, daffodil, and tulip have modified leaves that are scaly; corms such as gladiolus and crocus have modified stems that have assumed a globelike shape. In some plants, including ginger and banana, modified underground stems grow horizontally and are called rhizomes; in the Irish potato, the underground stem is swollen. However, in the sweet potato, the root is swollen into a tuberous root that is edible. The modified underground structures are used in propagating the respective plants.

MODULE 6

MICROPROPAGATION (TISSUE CULTURE)

10.15 THE TECHNIQUE

Micropropagation
The technique of producing new plants from single cells, tissue, or small pieces of vegetative material.

Callus
A mass of undifferentiated cells that can be induced or arise naturally as a result of wounding.

Explant
Generic term for the living vegetative plant material extracted for tissue culturing on an appropriate medium.

Somaclonal Variation
Heritable variation that arises spontaneously as callus forms on a tissue culture medium.

Micropropagation (or *tissue culture*) is a technique by which tissue obtained from a plant is cultured in an artificial medium. This tissue first changes into a mass of undifferentiated cells called **callus,** from which differentiation into shoot and roots or embryos may later occur (Figure 10–39). Molecular biotechnological procedures often incorporate tissue culture as one of their critical methods. Micropropagation may be used in herbaceous (e.g., strawberry, gladiolus, tobacco, carnation, and gloxinia) and woody plants (e.g., apple, rose, kalmia, and rhododendron).

Tissue culture requires a completely sterile environment to be successful. Propagation can be initiated with any part of the plant: leaf, stem, root, pollen grain, embryo, and others. These excised plant parts used to initiate propagation by tissue culture are called **explants.** Both immature and mature plant tissue may be used. Explants are aseptically prepared by *surface sterilization* before being placed in a sterile medium. The medium is fortified with all of the nutrients required for plant growth and development, including mineral salts (major and minor elements), sugar, vitamins, and growth regulators (auxins and cytokinins). One of the most commonly used tissue culture media is the Murashige and Skoog medium. By modifying the composition of the medium, with respect to growth regulators, one can cause it to sustain normal plant growth or induce the explant to develop callus tissue, the result of repeated mitotic cell division.

Sometimes scientists are able to manipulate callus tissue through the introduction of chemicals into the growth medium that induce heritable variations (mutations). Such variations occasionally arise spontaneously even in normal media culture and are called **somaclonal variations.** Some of these variants have agronomic value and are utilized in crop improvement by plant breeders.

FIGURE 10–39 Callus formation in tissue culture.
(Source: George Acquaah)

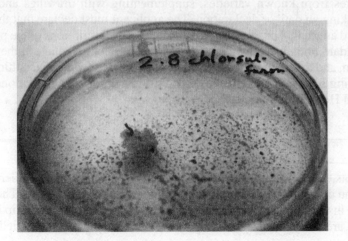

The technique is used widely in crop improvement and other biotechnological procedures. It can be used to replicate asexual plant materials clonally to produce numerous plantlets for planting the crop. This practice is undertaken in the laboratory and is space saving. Viral infections are noted for crippling plants without killing them. Further, it is known that new tissue that develops in an infected plant is usually virus free. This healthy tissue may be extracted and tissue cultured to produce numerous virus-free plants, an effective way of purifying an infected parental stock.

10.16 APPLICATIONS

10.16.1 ARTIFICIAL SEEDS

The concept of *artificial seeds* is being pursued by several biotechnology companies. It entails the mass production of clones of embryos through tissue culture. These embryos are then coated with growth nutrients in a biodegradable carrier as a protective layer. This covering may also carry pesticides, fertilizers, and even nitrogen-fixing bacteria. Once packaged, the artificial seeds may be planted like natural ones. The technology is currently in its infancy, and hence artificial seeds are more expensive than natural ones.

10.16.2 SHOOT MERISTEM CULTURE

Shoot meristem culture, or *mericloning,* is another innovative micropropagation technique. It is used to facilitate improvement in certain crops such as orchard crops, which require about seven years from planting to first blooming. In orchards, it appears that a certain seed-fungi association is a normal prerequisite for germination to occur. A quick way of obtaining planting material is through tissue culture of shoot meristems in a medium fortified with certain hormones and other substances to perform the role of fungi. After about a month of tissue culture, adventitious roots begin to develop. Before this stage, the tissue is separated into small pieces, each of which is capable of developing into a new plant. By this process, numerous genetically identical plants are produced in a short time.

10.16.3 EMBRYO RESCUE

Sometimes in plant improvement programs, crosses are made between genetically divergent plants. Crossing plants within the same species usually has no genetic consequences. The cross is able to develop normally to produce seed and subsequently a plant upon planting the seed. On certain occasions, the breeder would have to import desirable genes from a source different from the species of the plant being improved. Such gene transfers, when performed by the conventional method of crossing, usually have genetic consequences. The embryo may fail to develop normally. When this happens, it is possible to remove the developing embryo and nurture it in an artificial medium under tissue culture conditions.

10.16.4 APPLICATIONS IN SELECTED CROPS

Practical applications of tissue culture in horticulture have been widely reported. In garlic, in vitro cultivation has been used to produce quality planting material that is free from viral and bacterial diseases. In leek, explants from the stem, leaves, flower head, and basal plate have been micropropagated. Onion meristem tip culture was used to rid vegetatively propagated shallots of viral infection. Similarly, meristem culture has been used to develop clones of self-incompatible inbreds for use in F_1 hybrid seed production in broccoli. Anther culture is used to develop instant homozygous inbred lines for hybridization. Following an interspecific cross between broccoli and cauliflower to transfer clubroot resistance for *Brassica napus* to *B. calabrese,* embryo rescue was used to regenerate surviving interspecific embryo cabbage.

Protoplast Fusion
The techniques of in vitro union of two protoplasts into somatic hybrids.

Mass production in vitro of virus-free and disease-resistant *Brassica* plants occurs. *Embryo* and *ovary rescue* techniques are frequently employed in the rescue of nonviable interspecific hybrids. **Protoplast fusion** was successfully employed in creating hybrid plants of red cabbage and radish. The somatic hybrids were male sterile but female fertile. Carrot is easy to manipulate in cell culture. A very creative use of biotechnology is exemplified by work done with carrots whereby scientists have produced synthetic seed by encapsulating asexual somatic embryos with polyethylene oxide or sodium oxide. Somaclonal variants with resistance to downy mildew and lettuce mosaic virus have been reported in lettuce.

Tissue culture techniques can be utilized to create what may be described as in vitro hybrids. Cells obtained from different plants are prepared by removing their cell walls using enzymatic procedures to leave the protoplasts. These naked protoplasts are induced to fuse through the use of chemicals such as diluted polyethylene glycol (antifreeze used in automobiles). This technology is called *protoplast fusion,* and the resulting plants are called *somatic hybrids.* Through further manipulation, the nucleus of one of the two protoplasts may be destroyed so that only one of the two cytoplasms fuse. The product then is called a *cybrid.*

REFERENCES AND SUGGESTED READING

Boodley, J. W. 1998. *The commercial greenhouse.* Albany, N.Y.: Delmar.

Hartmann, H. T., and D. E. Kester. 1983. *Plant propagation,* 4th ed. Englewood Cliffs, N.J.: Prentice Hall.

Kyte, L. 1983. *Plants from test tubes: An introduction to micropropagation.* Portland, Oreg: Timber Press.

McMillan, B. P. 1979. *Plant propagation.* New York: Simon & Schuster.

Thorpe, T. A., ed. 1981. *Plant tissue culture: Methods and applications in agriculture.* New York: Academic Press.

Excellent notes with illustrations
http://users.rcn.com/jkimball.ma.ultranet/BiologyPages/A/AsexualReproduction.html

General plant propagation
http:aggie-horticulture.tamu.edu/propagation/propagation.html

Grafting and budding
http://www.ces.ncsu.edu/depts/hort/hil/ag396.html

OUTCOMES ASSESSMENT

1. Under what conditions is it more advantageous to propagate plants by vegetative methods?
2. Distinguish between softwood cuttings and hardwood cuttings.
3. Discuss the factors that enhance the success of vegetative propagation.
4. Discuss the importance and application of grafting horticultural production.
5. Give two critical factors to the success of grafting.
6. How does budding differ from grafting?
7. What is layering? Describe how airlayering is done.
8. Describe how plant propagation by division is done.
9. Give two examples each of plants that are propagated by separation and rhizomes.

PART 4

GROWING PLANTS INDOORS

Growing Houseplants

PURPOSE AND EXPECTED OUTCOMES

This chapter discusses the environmental factors required for growing plants indoors and how to choose, grow, care for, and use houseplants.

After studying this chapter, the student should be able to

1. Distinguish between the practices involved in growing plants in the house and under controlled environments (greenhouses).
2. List and discuss the factors that one should consider in growing houseplants.
3. List ten common houseplants.
4. Discuss the correct ways of watering plants.
5. Discuss the correct ways of feeding plants.
6. Describe how plants are repotted.

[COLOR PLATES—*see color plate 8–16* for additional chapter photos]

OVERVIEW

Plants can be successfully grown indoors in a *controlled environment* in which all of the required plant growth factors are supplied in appropriate amounts. Growing plants indoors at home is an activity that enables homeowners to enjoy plants year-round. However, the home environment is not as controlled as a greenhouse environment because the home is shared by humans, and sometimes pets, whose needs take precedence over the needs of plants. Home conditions are generally less than ideal for general plant growth, especially with respect to light. For this reason, not all plants can be successfully grown indoors.

Growing plants indoors necessitates that plants be grown in containers, which restricts the growing environment for plant roots. Choice of proper growth medium is critical to the success of growing potted plants. Also, proper choice of plants is essential in growing indoor plants. After choosing the right plants and the appropriate medium, the grower must employ good management practices to maintain the plants in good health. A green thumb is not hereditary but is an acquired trait obtained through experience and knowledge of basic horticultural principles.

In this chapter, a list of indoor plants is provided, along with the principles of indoor plant culture. The reader will learn how to constitute a good growth medium and is provided with guidelines for caring for houseplants. Further, use of plants indoors either for purely decorative purposes or to serve certain functions is discussed.

11.1 FACTORS THAT INFLUENCE THE CHOICE OF HOUSEPLANTS

The variety in outdoor horticultural plants is tremendous. Similarly, many ornamentals are adapted to indoor environments, although they are fewer in number than field plants. The choice of which plants to grow depends on several factors.

11.1.1 PERSONAL PREFERENCE

Some people are cactus enthusiasts, and others love roses. For some people, it is love at first sight—they decide what to grow when they see a plant growing somewhere. Such people often visit a nursery, ask to be shown some possibilities, and then buy what most appeals to them. People are more likely to invest time and resources in growing and caring for plants that they like, rather than in plants with less appeal. If one decides to be a collector of a certain kind of plants, variety and diversity occur in some species such as *Peperomia* and *Ficus.* Peperomias vary in shape, size, texture, and color. In *Ficus,* one can find trees, shrubs, and creeping and trailing plants.

11.1.2 GROWING CONDITIONS

Some houseplants can do well in nearly any part of the room. Others may require special conditions that only an avid flower enthusiast can afford the time and patience to provide. Many people just want a plant that will grow without intensive care (Table 11–1). As will be discussed, houseplants need good care to grow properly.

11.1.3 ROOM DECOR

Interiorscaping
The use of ornamental plants for functional and aesthetic purposes.

Plants are used to enhance the room decor. They come in different shapes, sizes, colors, and textures. For best results, when different kinds of plants are used in interior decoration (**interiorscaping** or *plantscaping*), they should not only complement the room furnishings, but also relate well to each other and blend to create a pleasant environment.

11.1.4 PLANT CHARACTERISTICS

Plant characteristics include the following:

1. *General attractiveness.* The plant should be aesthetically pleasing to behold. The foliage and/or flowers should be attractive.
2. *Appearance at maturity.* People seldom purchase fully grown plants for the home. Instead, indoor plants grow and change (e.g., in shape, size, and height). A young plant may not be as appealing as when it is much older.
3. *Growth cycle.* Some plants are only attractive when they flower and may be unattractive in the vegetative state. Some foliage plants are attractive as such and become even more so when they flower.
4. *Growth (maturity) rate.* Houseplants do not grow or attain maturity at the same rate. Although some plants, such as annuals, grow rapidly, others, such as palms, take several years to attain a good size that is aesthetically pleasing.

11.1.5 COST

Houseplants vary in cost. The choice of plants to purchase is influenced by how much the homeowner is willing to pay for the new plant. Some plants (e.g., pothos) are easy to grow and propagate easily, producing vegetative material that can be clipped and shared with other people.

TABLE 11−1   Common houseplants

Common name	Scientific name
a. Easy to grow	
Cast iron plant	*Aspidistra elatior*
Christmas cactus	*Zygocactus* or *Schlumbergera*
Dragon tree	*Dracaena marginata*
Lucky bamboo	*Dracaena sanderian*
Mother-in-law's tongue (snake plant)	*Sansevieria*
Pothos	*Epipremnum*
Spider plant	*Chlorphytum comosum*
b. Somewhat easy to grow	
African violet	*Saintpaulia*
Aloe	*Aloe*
Chinese evergreen	*Aglaonema commutatum*
Croton	*Codiaeum variegatum*
Dumb cane	*Dieffenbachia*
Jade plant	*Crassula argentea*
Parlor plant	*Chamaedorea elegans*
Peace lily (white flag)	*Spathiphyllum*
Prayer plant	*Maranta*
Rubber plant	*Ficus elastica*
c. Other popular houseplants	
Anthurium	*Anthurium* sp.
Asparagus fern	*Asparagus densiflora*
Baby tears	*Helxine soleirolii*
Begonia	*Begonia* sp.
Bird's nest fern	*Asplenium nidus*
Boston fern	*Nephrolepsis exaltata*
Crown of thorns	*Euphorbia millii*
English ivy	*Hedera helix*
False aralia	*Dizygotheca elegantissima*
Fiddle leaf	*Fiscus lyrata*
Gardenia	*Gardenia augusta*
Grape ivy	*Cissus rhombifolia*
Hawaiian schefflera	*Schefflera arboricola*
Heart leaf philodendron	*Philodendron scandens*
Neanthe bella palm	*Chamaedorea elegans*
Nephthytis	*Syngonium podophyllum*
Norfolk island pine	*Araucaria heterophylla*
Peperomia	*Peperomia obtusifolia*
Piggyback plant	*Tolmiea menziesii*
Pittosporum	*Pittosporum tobira*
Pleomele	*Pleomele reflexa*
Podocarpus	*Podocarpus macrophyllus*
Pony tail palm	*Beaucarnea recurvata*
Purple passion plant	*Gynura aurantiaca*
Sago palm	*Cycas revolute*
Staghorn fern	*Platycerium bifurcatum*
Ti plant	*Cordyline terminalis*
Umbrella plant	*Schefflera* (or *Brassaia*) *actinophylla*
Wax plant	*Hoya carnosa*
Weeping fig	*Ficus benjamina*
Zebra plant	*Aphelandra squarrosa*

11.1.6 SAFETY

Some houseplants contain toxins that can be harmful upon contact to the skin or if ingested. Further, some plants produce flowers and hence some pollen grain that can trigger allergies in humans. If children are going to be in the home, homeowners should not only concerned about toxic plants, but also about those with anatomic features that can cause physical harm (e.g., pointed tips, thorns).

11.1.7 TOXIC PLANTS

Generally, plants that exude a milky liquid when snapped or bruised (the *Euphorbia* species) contain some toxic substances. Many of the species with underground modified structures (roots, corms, bulbs) contain toxic substances. The toxins vary in potency and most are glycosides or oxalates. While these toxic houseplants may not cause death, they can cause gastrointestinal inflammation and dermatitis. Glycosides like those found in oleander and lily of the valley can stimulate the heart in addition to being irritants to the mouth and intestinal tract. Pothos and saddle leaf contain oxalates that irritate the mouth, lips, tongue, and stomach. Those plants with solanine can cause diarrhea and vomiting.

Houseplants that are relatively more toxic than others, sometimes dubbed the "dirty dozen" are aloe vera, Boston ivy, caladium, dumbcane, English ivy, German ivy, Indian rubber plant, mistletoe, philodendron, potted chrysanthemum, weeping fig, and yew. Other toxic plants are listed in Table 11–2.

TABLE 11–2 Toxic houseplants

Other toxic plants		*Comments on toxin*
Amaryllis	*Amaryllis*	Alkaloid lycorine in bulbs,
Arrowhead plant ; Nephthytis	*Syngonium podophyllum*	*Toxic oxalates*
Asparagus fern	*Asparagus setaceus*	Toxic dermatitis
Azalea	*Rhododendrum occidentale*	*Variable toxins*
Bird of paradise	*Poinciana gilliesii*	Variable toxins
Bittersweet	*Solanum dulcamara*	*Toxic solanine*
Boston ivy	*Parthenocissus quinguefolia*	Toxic oxalates
Caladium	*Caladium* sp.	*Toxic oxalates*
Chenille plant	*Acalypha hispida*	Causes skin and gastrointestinal inflammation
Christmas rose	*Helleborus niger*	*Toxic glycosides*
Chrysanthemum	*Chrysanthemum* sp.	May cause dermatitis
Creeping Charlie; ground ivy	*Glechoma hederacea*	*Variable toxins*
Creeping fig	*Ficus*	Possible dermatitis
Croton	*Codiaeum variegatum*	*Croton oil, strong purgative causes gastroenteritis*
Crown of thorns	*Euphorbia millii*	Variable toxins
Dumbcane	*Dieffenbachia seguine*	*Toxic oxalates*
English ivy	*Hedera helix*	Variable toxins
God toothed aloe	*Aloe nobilis*	*Possible dermatitis*
Heartleaf philodendron	*Philodendron cordatum*	Toxic oxalates
Hydrangea	*Hydrangea* sp.	*Cyanogenetic glycoside*
Jerusalem cherry	*Solanum pseudocapsicum*	Contains solanine
Lily of the valley	*Convallaria majalis*	*Toxic glycosides*
Marble queen	*Scindapus aureus*	Toxic oxalates
Majesty	*Philodendron hastatum*	*Toxic oxalates*
Narcissus	*Narcisuss* sp.	Toxic alkaloid lycorin
Needlepoint ivy	*Hedera helix*	*Variable toxins*
Oleander	*Nerium oleander*	*Toxic glycosides*
Poinsettia	*Euphorbia pulcherima*	Irritant
Pothos	*Scindapus aureus*	Toxic oxalates
Rhubarb	*Rheum rhaponticum*	*Toxic oxalates*

Saddle leaf	Philodendron selloum	Toxic oxalates
Split leaf philodendron	Monstera deliciosa	Toxic oxalates
Umbrella plant	Cyperus alternifolius	Variable toxins
Weeping fig	Ficus benjamina	Possible dermatitis

11.2 Using Plants in the Home

The key to the successful use of plants in the home is creativity and experimentation. Plants are living things and, like people, need regular (in some cases daily) attention. Ornamentals in the home are meant to be enjoyed, so the use of horticultural plants should not be on a scale such that it becomes a chore instead of a joy. Indoor use of plants may involve one, a few, or even a whole room full of plants (*garden room*).

11.2.1 LOCATING PLANTS

Locating plants in the room depends on several factors, described in the following sections.

Architecture of the Room

Some homes have high ceilings and can accommodate tall plants including larger tropical plants such as *Dracaenas*. Some homes are designed with skylights, which can provide the additional lighting needed by some plants. Leaf form and plant shape should complement the architectural style of the room. If the architecture is big and bold, big and bold plants should be selected. Traditional interiors usually require plants with delicate foliage, such as ferns and grape ivy *(Cissus rhombifolia)*. Existing features such as fireplaces and mantlepieces should be utilized in the design of plant displays. Plants with distinctive foliage such as the rubber plant *(Ficus elastica)* and Swiss cheese plant *(Monstera deliciosa)* fit in well with the straight lines of contemporary architecture.

Space

Large plants do better in large rooms. Large plants make small rooms appear too crowded. For example, a fully grown weeping fig *(Ficus benjamina)* is out of place in a cottage drawing room. Similarly, a small plant in a large room has virtually no impact.

Level

Plants may be placed on the floor or on pieces of furniture (such as on tabletops or bookshelves). Elevated positions are suited to small plants (Figure 11–1). The top shelves of bookshelves or other high levels are suitable for plants that have trails or long vines. Small plants should be placed on tabletops.

FIGURE 11–1 A potted plant displayed on top of a piece of furniture. *(Source: George Acquaah)*

Color of Walls and Upholstery

Plants should be placed against a background that will bring out their colors. Plants with strong foliage forms are effective against walls with patterns, provided the motifs in the pattern and leaf size contrast sufficiently. The leaves of the umbrella plant (*Schefflera phylla*) are effective against a background of small-patterned wallpaper. Where the background consists of bold, abstract designs, it can be balanced with a display of plants with delicate foliage such as asparagus fern.

11.2.2 SPECIFIC USES OF INDOOR PLANTS

Plants may be used to perform certain functional roles in the room.

Fill in Gaps

Plants are often placed in areas too awkward for a piece of furniture, such as a corner.

Brighten Up an Area

Flowering plants in bloom can brighten up the room. A variety of dull spots occur in a room (e.g., empty walls, unused fireplace, stairwell, and corners). Plants with distinct leaves, such as the silhouette plant *(Dracaena marginata),* climbers (e.g., trained on poles), or other trailing and cascading plants mounted on wall brackets may be displayed against an empty wall. Because some dull spots such as corners usually have poor conditions for plant growth, plants adapted to such conditions (e.g., *Aspidisaenas, Sansevieria,* and *Philodendrons*) should be chosen.

Cover Up Sharp Edges

Potted plants can be positioned to cover the edges of walls or architectural features. For example, climbers such as *Fatshedera lizei* can be used in the stairwell.

Create Room Dividers

Instead of using wooden structures, for example, appropriate plants may be arranged to form a wall (Figure 11–2). Where dividers are used, plants such as *Philodendron* or *Hedera* may be trained to grow over these physical structures. Trailing or climbing plants need to be monitored and pruned or trained to keep them within desired boundaries. Plants may be positioned to climb up structures or cascade down them. Sometimes smaller displays such as a *terrarium*, bottle garden, or a small group of plants may serve the purpose of separating one area of the room from another.

FIGURE 11–2 Room dividers created with living plants. *(Source: George Acquaah)*

Window Displays

Plants in windows enhance the room decor. Since light enters the house primarily through windows, the selection of plants to use should consider the position of the windows, the plant sensitivity to light, and the plant size. While south-facing windows receive sunlight year-round, north-facing windows receive the least amount of light, especially during the winter. North-facing windows favor foliage plants such as aspidistra and sansevieria. Desert cacti do well in unshaded south-facing windows.

Fragrance

Certain plants exude sweet scents that freshen the indoor atmosphere. For example, scented pelargonium has a pleasant fragrance.

Direct Traffic

Plants can be strategically arranged to steer people away from certain parts of the room and to prevent people from using certain spaces as pathways.

Cover Up Undesirable View

A *window garden* may be planted to block the view to unattractive areas on the outside. Plants may be arranged to hide unsightly parts of a room.

Environmental Quality (Air Quality Control)

Certain plants are known to improve the air quality of indoor areas by absorbing contaminants in the air (Table 11–3). Contaminants include fumes from cleaning solvents, radon, secondhand smoke, furniture, carpeting, and ozone from copying machines. Some of the most effective plants for this purpose are gerbera daisy, chrysanthemum, golden pothos, and *Spathiphyllum*.

11.2.3 IMPROVING THE DISPLAY OF HOUSEPLANTS

Apart from selecting appropriate plants and arranging them effectively in the room, there are several specific ways in which the display can be enhanced:

1. Use a spotlight to draw attention to conversation pieces or specimen plants (unique plants that invite conversation). Backlighting enhances the display of some species such as Boston fern *(Nephrolepsis)*. Certain plants may be displayed in less-than-ideal conditions with appropriate lighting.

TABLE 11–3 Houseplants that clean the air

Pollutant	Sources	Plants
Benzene	Detergents, gasoline, oils, tobacco smoke, printing inks, synthetic fibers	English ivy, dracaena, chrysanthemum gerbera daisy
Formaldehyde	Carpeting, clothing, furniture, foam insulation, household cleaners, paper goods, particle board	Azalea, palms, chrysanthemum, diffenbachia, golden pothos, mother-in-laws tongue, poinsettia, spider plant
Trichloroethylene	Adhesives, dry-cleaning fluids, lacquers, paints, varnishes	Chrysanthemums, gerbera daisy, dracaena

FIGURE 11–3 (a) Displaying a plant potted in a plastic pot in a more attractive decorated pot. (b) Examples of decorative containers. *(Source: For (b) George Acquaah)*

Plastic inner pot

Decorative outer pot

(a)

(b)

Double Potting
A method of enhancing the display of potted plants by placing the potted plant in a more decorative pot.

2. Use decorative containers to hold the plants (**double potting**). The plastic pot from the nursery may be placed in a very attractive container to enhance the display (Figure 11–3). Other containers include wicker baskets, brass saucepans, and in some cases patterned containers. When using patterned pots, the color of the foliage and flowers should blend well with the pot color and pattern. Growers do not often plant directly into decorative containers. Instead, they are used as outer coverings to hide the ordinary flowerpot. Containers may be clay or china.

3. Group plants. Instead of scattering plants throughout a room, a number of plants of the same type can be grouped together (massed). Compact plants may be grouped on a stand, on a pebble tray, or on a table as a centerpiece. Small specimens may also be effectively displayed in tiny, unusual containers (e.g., egg cup). Colorful seasonal plants such as tulip, hyacinth, azalea, and geranium can be massed on a windowsill.

4. Use hanging baskets. By themselves, hanging baskets can have very attractive holders. Plants grown in hanging baskets offer some of the most attractive displays.

5. Use ornamental paper. Wallpaper and plants can be used together to provide an effective display, with the paper as the background.

6. Use plant support. Plants may be displayed on pedestals, wooden tables, glass-topped, wrought-iron tables, and other such specially designed supports (wooden or metal jardinieres, tiered plant stands, and aspidistra stands). Other pieces of furniture in the house can be adapted as flower stands (e.g., corner cupboards and washstands). Plants may be grown and displayed on a plant trolley.

11.2.4 GROUPING PLANTS

A large plant can be effectively displayed alone. Smaller specimens do better when grouped. Grouping can be accomplished by arranging individual potted plants together (e.g., on a gravel tray) or by planting a mixture of plants in large troughs (Figure 11–4). A wide variety of containers are available for use. They vary in type of material (e.g., plastic, wrought iron, wood, and clay), shape, size, and decorative appearance.

CONTAINER GARDENS

DR. TERRI W. STARMAN
Dept. of Horticultural Sciences
Texas A&M University

Container gardens are a condensed and mobile form of gardening. Many plants are packed into a small space for an instant effect that can be easily changed each season. Container gardens offer gardeners an opportunity to be bold, dramatic and to experiment with plants in a non-committal way. Container gardens can now be purchased ready-made also called do-it-for-me (DIFM) for instant color on the patio. If preferred, an assortment of plants can be purchased for do-it-yourself (DIY) container gardens.

One should always select top quality plants, but otherwise, just about any type of plant can be used in container gardens. Possible exceptions would be extremely slow-growing plants, plants lacking attractive foliage that only flower for about two weeks out of the year, very large plants, or plants with deep tap roots. Plants commonly used in container gardens today are seed or vegetatively propagated annuals, herbaceous perennials, herbs, vegetables, grasses, bulbs, tropical foliage plants, succulents, and woody shrubs.

How many plants to put in a container garden depends on the size of the container. The rule of thumb is to use bigger and/or more plants with larger containers and to use less and/or smaller plants with smaller containers. It is best to use odd numbers of each type (i.e., species or cultivar) of plant to achieve a natural and rounded look. One to three plants of each type should be adequate to make a visual impact in the container garden.

A fun and inexpensive way to learn plants and their cultivars that are adapted to a specific location is to visit close-by public or university trial gardens. One should purchase and grow a few new cultivars/species each year to experiment and learn their appeal and adaptability. The more one knows about plant materials that are available and adaptable in a specific climate the more unique the container gardens will be.

The container for a container garden can be just as important as the plants. Make sure the container has a drainage hole. If a perspective container does not have a drainage hole initially, one can be drilled with a masonry bit. It may be necessary to elevate the container slightly off the ground so that water can move freely from the drainage hole. Attractive "feet" or stands can be purchased for this purpose. Do not add coarse gravel to the bottom of the container as it causes a perched water table rather than improving drainage. A few pieces of shale or broken pieces of pots can be

FIGURE 1 In this container garden, foliage color, form and texture are the dominating elements of design. The bold, fuzzy textured *Salvia argentea* grabs attention to develop focus in the center of the composition. Lotus 'Amazon Sunset' adds color echo for rhythm and a fine texture for contrast to the coarse, gray foliage of the salvia. Coleus 'Compact Red', coleus 'Stormy Weather' and ipomoea 'Blackie' (clockwise) complete the container garden.
Designed by Lori Osburn   Photographed by Lori Osburn

placed inside the container directly over the drainage hole to help keep the media from washing out, but usually are not necessary. Polystyrene peanuts can be placed in the bottom half of the container below the media to reduce the weight of really large container gardens.

One criterion for a container purchase would be weather resistance. No one wants to spend a lot of money on a container they love just to have it get wet, freeze, and crack the first winter in the garden. Italian and Asian terra cotta containers vary widely in cost. They are porous and therefore dry out fast and need more watering. Being porous, they could break in winter. Their color goes well with plants and many landscape settings, but they are heavy to move around. Plastic and poly-resin containers look good and are less expensive. They are non-porous and light weight but sometimes have thin walls that can break. Asian glazed containers come in many colors. They are affordable but heavy, and they are non-porous and therefore freeze tolerant. Concrete containers are affordable, very heavy, stainable, and long-lasting but they are porous. Fiberglass containers are light weight, affordable and look authentic. Metal is a newer look and attractive, but can get very hot when placed in the sun.

The container can be any shape or size; however fourteen inch and larger containers hold more media. The increase in soil volume in a large container is beneficial for reducing frequency of watering. A large container holds more plants having the potential to be more colorful and textural, thus pleasing to the eye. Hanging baskets and rectangular troughs are vessels that will hold mixed plantings to hang from arbors, light poles, and window sills.

Container gardens can be filled with plants from early spring using cool season annuals and spring blooming perennials and bulbs, for example. In the summer, they can house heat-tolerant annuals, tropical foliage plants, summer blooming perennials, herbs, succulents, etc. Fall and southern winter container gardens can be made using frost tolerant

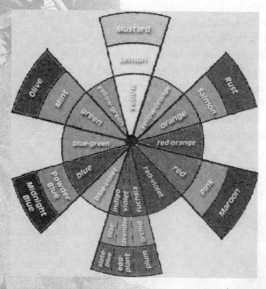

FIGURE 2 This Flower Color Wheel is similar to an artist's color wheel but uses names that florists commonly use to describe color. This color wheel divides the primary color of violet into three additional segments to include indigo (bluish violet) and fuchsia (reddish violet) because there are so many variations of violet in flower colors. Designed by Terri Starman Photographed by Kristen Eixmann

FIGURE 3 The maroon (a shade of red) coleus 'Compact Red' adds depth and draws the eye deep into the otherwise pink (a tint of red) monochromatic (one color) container garden. Different flower forms (daisy, cluster, and star-shaped) and foliage forms (upright, bushy, and trailing) are design elements that make this container garden interesting. Agastache and dracaena back each other with their vertical forms to establish the height of the container garden. Argyranthemum 'Comet Pink' serves as a filler plant; verbena 'Babylon Pink' takes the corner position and bacopa 'Penny Candy Pink' fills the edge position. Designed by Terri Starman Photographed by Lori Osburn

annuals and hardy perennial species. Fall and winter container gardens can be brought inside under incandescent or fluorescent lights or left outside and covered with cloth in inclement weather. Further north, attractive, tasteful, non-living plant materials can be used in outdoor containers for decoration in winter.

Container gardens are small gardens that will need to be cared for throughout the season. Container gardens are dynamic and constantly changing. Individual flowers will bloom and die and plants will intertwine and grow together. Some plants may go dormant or die out and can be replaced with other interesting plants. Dead-heading flowers and pruning back aggressive plants is healthy for the plants and it can be enjoyable to touch and smell container gardens while tending to them.

The species of plants put in the same container should be compatible as to temperature, light and water preferences. Use plants that tolerate low light for shady locations. Since microclimates can exist within containers, some shade-loving plants can actually thrive underneath sun-loving plants that grow up and provide shade to them. In addition, patio light levels vary throughout the day, so the container may be in direct sunlight for part of the day and in shade the other part. Also, because container gardens are mobile, they can be moved around the patio to provide the optimum sun and wind exposure throughout the different seasons.

It's best not to mix drought-tolerant species with those that need lots of water. Container gardens will dry out more quickly and need to be watered more often than plants in the ground. It is not unusual to water them everyday in the heat of summer. Mixing sterilized field soil into the soil-less potting media when planting will help the

FIGURE 4   This container garden uses several bulbous species with annuals. The mixture of flower forms, sizes, statures and textures are what make the container garden stimulating. Gladiolus 'Muriel' (star-shaped), lily 'Salmon Classic' (cupped), calla 'Captain Romance' (unusual), streptocarpella 'Conord Blue' (nodding), begonia 'Fimbriata Yellow' (solid), and begonia 'Sinbad' (variegated foliage) (clockwise) fill this 11" tall X 14" wide container.   Designed by Lauren Edwards   Photographed by Kristen Eixmann

FIGURE 5   This container garden emphasizes foliage forms and textures and uses an all neutral color scheme (black, white, and gray). Calla 'Schwazwalder', Gypsophila paniculata 'Festive Star', Trifolium repens 'Dark Dancer', Eranthemum nigrum 'Ebony', Japanese painted fern, Calochortus 'Cupido' and Carex flagellifera 'Toffee Twist', (clockwise) enhance each other in a 10" tall X 15" wide container garden.   Designed by Terri Starman   Photographed by Kristen Eixmann

media hold water and make it available to the plants. Because of its physical structure, rockwool will also improve water holding capacity when added to a soil-less media. Saucers placed under the containers are also good for reducing watering frequency. On the other hand, amendments such as coarse bark or perlite can be added to improve drainage.

Homeowners will need to fertilize their container gardens. One teaspoon of a water soluble 20–20–20 dissolved in one gallon of water applied every two weeks will supply about 300 ppm N which is enough to keep the plants healthy. Or, an encapsulated, slow release fertilizer can be sprinkled on the potting media surface. Slow release fertilizers are sold at garden centers and one can follow the directions on the package. The fertility is released from this type of fertilizer when the potting media is watered. When watering with plain water or when applying soluble fertilizer, hold the watering can spout or hose nozzle at the rim of the container and add water until some water leaks from the drainage hole in the bottom. This should take a few minutes, so make certain that the water is being soaked up by the entire root area and not just dripping down the inside wall of the container and out. One way to check for this is to lift or tilt the container enough to feel if it is getting heavier as it is being watered.

It is best to grow or purchase plant material for a container garden that is already starting to flower or otherwise maturing in 4 to 6–inch size pots and then plant them together in the final large container. Keep the plants in their pots and arrange them on top

FIGURE 6 The focal point lies deep in the center of this container garden and is established by the radiating leaves and emerging flower of eucomis 'Bicolor'. Its unusual plant form and hefty leaves also help to grab attention. A microclimate is formed underneath the canopy of eucomis and coleus 'Sedona' to filter light for the shade-loving plants below which include tatting fern, huechera 'Amber Waves', ajuga 'Black Scallop', hosta 'Fragrant Bouquet', impatiens 'Infinity Salmon' and streptocarpella 'Conord Blue' (clockwise). The terra cotta color of the 14" tall X 11.5" wide decorative container contributes to the blue and orange complementary color harmony. Designed by Terri Starman Photographed by Kristen Eixmann

FIGURE 7 *Curcuma petiolata* 'Emperor' (Siam Tulip) forms the center, while Breynia, Japanese forest grass 'Aurora', and Japanese painted fern serve as fillers. Caladium 'Florida Sweetheart' is the focal plant in the corner position and *Lysimachia nummularia* is in two edge positions. The various plant species are compatible for a shady location on the patio. Designed by Phil Campbell Photographed by Terri Starman

of the large container filled with potting media before actually planting them. This will allow for easy, quick modifications in the planting design. When all plants are in the desired positions, remove them from their individual pots and plant them in the potting media, working from the center to the outside edge.

Variety in moderation is the key when choosing flowers for container gardens. Include plants with different flower forms to add interest and avoid monotony in container gardens. For example, use one plant in a container garden that has a daisy-type flower form like osteospermum, one with tubular flowers like nicotiana, and one with cluster flowers like heliotrope. Look for a variety of flower sizes too because it is good to have a large flower that adds a focal point or thrill factor, mid-size flowers to add mass and small flowers to transition or fill in between other flowers and foliage.

Achieve balance and proportion with plant size and plant positioning in the container. Within the container, the plants will fit into one of four positions. The center position should be filled a plant that is sturdy and upright in growth habit like phormium for example, to add height to the container garden. In order to create massive height and fullness in a very large container, and when aiming for a full-bodied look, plant three plants of upright stature together in the center of the pot. Around or next to the center of the container garden should be filled with filler plants which typically have upright but compact, yet bushy growth to add stability around the center plant(s) and round out the top of the container. Coleus makes a very good filler plant, as one example.

Next to the filler plant goes corner plants that grow up, out and then down over the edge of the container. Corner plants, like petunias, add bulk at the bottom of the container so the media is covered and the center and filler plants' stems are not overly exposed. The fourth position to fill in the container is the edge. Edge plants that drape over the rim of the container will soften it and fill in spaces between corner plants. Edge plants are horizontal-growing, trailing, or creeping plants like English ivy. Not only the habit of the plant, but the size of the container, will determine where a plant works best within that container. For example, a plant may be a center plant in a smaller container and a filler plant in a larger container.

When planting container gardens, some plants are selected for the appeal of their foliage rather than their flowers. Species having at least three textures of foliage (fine, medium, and coarse) mixed in a container garden will make it more appealing. Foliage with large leaves will provide a bold background to stage the flowers of a plant that has good flower power but fine foliage of its own. This principle keeps a container garden from looking messy and weedy. If a good flowering plant also has bold foliage, another plant with fine foliage placed next to it in the container garden will add textural contrast. When selecting foliage for container gardens, look for interesting colors such as gray

FIGURE 8 The analogous color harmony and various plant forms are what make this container garden attractive. The terra cotta container repeats the color of the salmon arctotis 'Flame' daisy flowers and ipomoea 'Sweet Caroline Bronze' leaves. The red-orange fuchsia 'Koralle' flowers add accent and their nodding flower form help give the container garden rhythm. Maroon leaves of purple fountain grass and *Alternanthera dentata* complete the analogous color harmony. The gray foliage of artotis 'Flame' helps to brighten the container garden. Designed by Terri Starman   Photographed by Terri Starman

(*helichrysum*), silver (*dichondra*), maroon (*coleus*), black (*huechera*), brown (*carex*), and chartreuse (*ipomoea*). Plants with spots (*hypoestes*) and stripes (*canna*) or other patterns on the foliage will add surprise and uniqueness to a container garden.

A color wheel can be used as a tool to develop a color harmony for a container garden. The most subtle color harmony to use is one color (monochromatic) with all flowers and foliage being tints and shade of that one color or neutral shades of white, black or gray. An example would be using all plants with some flowers that are violet, some that are a tint of violet (*lavender*) and some that are a shade (*eggplant*) of violet.

One may choose colors next to each other on the color wheel to make an analogous color harmony. An analogous color harmony is still subtle but more invigorating than monochromatic. An example would be using plants with flower colors in the red, red-violet, violet, and blue-violet area of the color wheel. Or, one may choose colors across from each other on the color wheel, called complementary, to get more contrast and a more exciting color harmony. An example would be using yellow and violet flowered plants. Colored containers can be used to provide hues that are hard to find in flowers and foliage and will become an integral part of the overall container garden color harmony.

A grower can start sowing seeds and/or receiving seedling plugs and rooted liners in January for a spring container garden crop and continue receiving plugs and liners through March. Plants should not arrive at or be started in the greenhouse too early or they will become overgrown. Timing and scheduling are critical. The goal is to try to get all the plants to be compact and full and keep them in proportion to each other for planting in the final container. Vegetative annuals, for example, will take only six to eight weeks to flower and be ready to transplant to the final large container. Early arrivals would be perennials and other plants that take longer to grow than annuals.

The rooted seedlings and plugs should be transplanted upon arrival into 4 or 6-inch pots using a general purpose soil-less substrate. Plants will need to be watered in after transplanting During production in the greenhouse, fertilizer can be applied with every watering using 15–5–15 or 20–10–20 at 200 to 300 ppm N. Check electrical conductivity and pH of the media periodically and adjust fertility level as needed. Use insecticides and fungicides when necessary to maintain plant health and quality.

Pinch any plants that tend to grow as a single stem to make them branch. Prune plants back and round their growth when they start getting too large. However, limit pruning because it is labor intensive thus expensive and plants will start to get distorted. The height of some really fast or large plants can be controlled with plant growth regulators. Plant growth regulators should be used sparingly and not on all plants because plants for container gardens need to grow naturally and hold their flowers up high above the leaf canopy. Keeping the various cultivars and species of plants in proportion to each other on the bench will give a consistent, uniform group of plants when it comes time to put the container gardens together.

By mid March and through mid May start planting the container gardens for Easter through Mother's Day sales. Utility type nursery liners of 14, 17 or 23–inch diameter can be used and slipped down into decorative containers later or at the retail outlet. The containers can be filled half-way full with media the day before, so planting is mostly placing the plants in the proper order into the final container and filling in around them with a small amount of additional media. When doing a mass planting of several container gardens of the same type all at once, it would be wise to make a prototype first, to determine if the planting design needs adjustment before starting a planting assembly line. Design container gardens by placing the chosen plants together on top of the pot before any actual planting is done. Changes can be made by mixing and matching plants. Then begin to plant from the center to the outside edge.

When planting the container garden, space plants closely so the root balls of individual plants are touching for instant beauty. Plants of different growth habits may be placed closer together than those of the same habit. This way all of the container gardens will look salable as soon as they are planted. Most of the container gardens get more attractive as they become established in the container and begin peaking in bloom and perfection about four to six weeks after planting. When leaving the greenhouse in spring, container gardens may need to be acclimated. Acclimatize container gardens by putting them outside under shade cloth for a couple of weeks to get them used to the higher light intensity and cooler temperatures outdoors.

A retailer can set up Container Garden Boutique within the garden center. Do-it-for-me (DIFM) i.e. ready-made container gardens can be arranged in their own kiosks within the boutique. These ready-made container gardens should have price tags for sale but also serve as mannequins for those customers who would rather buy the plants for Do-it-yourself (DIY) container gardens. In close proximity, customers should be able to find everything they need for building and maintaining their container gardens. The boutique area should have plants, containers, media, slow-release fertilizer, tools and accessories for containers gardens and for decorating patios. A potting bench for customers could be provided for those who don't have the room or desire to do potting at home. Employees should be on hand for consulting with consumers. It is a good idea to group plants by color for use in container gardens. This helps customers to choose the colors they need and it makes an attention-grabbing display. Plants can also be sub-grouped by their light needs.

Container gardens are heavy and delivery is a service that will set an independent garden center apart from the mass merchants and will help sell container gardens. Container gardens can also be rented for special occasions. Customers are happy to pay the price necessary to make their homes beautiful and to amaze their friends. Maintenance of container gardens must be done, so it's up to the industry to either educate consumers on how to do it or offer it as a service. Well-groomed container gardens are going to need weekly inspection and be cleaned and dead-headed to remove any dead foliage or spent flowers. Summer container gardens may need to be replanted once over the summer in warmer climates. It is a good idea to offer "replacement packs" for purchase to replant container gardens. The pack should have a handle for carrying home easily. A service for seasonal replanting could also be offered.

Container gardens should not be priced solely on indirect plus direct costs as other floriculture products. Some compensation should be recouped on the training and expertise of employees for designing and building pleasing, high quality container gardens. It is wise to have three or four price points ranging from $29.99 to $200. These might be $49.99, 79.99 and $149.99 depending on the cost of the container and the market. If the container gardens are beautiful, the plants are high quality, the designs are awesome, and the consumer wants them, they will sell. It is important to track sales to determine the profitability of a Container Garden Boutique or program. If they are not selling at these price points, then adjustments will need to be made. But growers and retailers should not sell themselves short and should make a good profit on this specialty, high value and desirable product.

BOOKS

Tips on Designing, Growing and Marketing Mixed Baskets and Containers, Peter S. Konjoian, Terri W. Starman and Kathy Pufahl, published by OFA Services Inc., Columbus, OH.

Vegetative Annuals: Guide to Crops and Container Gardens, Terri W. Starman, published by Meister Media Worldwide, Willoughby, OH.

Container Garden Websites on Aggie-Horticulture at Texas A&M University
"http://aggie-horticulture.tamu.edu/floriculture/container-garden/index.html"
"http://aggie-horticulture.tamu.edu/floriculture/containertrials/index.html"

FIGURE 11–4 Planting different species of plants in one container. *(Source: George Acquaah)*

FIGURE 11–5 When different species or types of plants are grown in a single container they may be selected and arranged to create an overall shape. *(Source: George Acquaah)*

After choosing a container, the next task is to choose the right combination of plants. Plants should be grouped according to their need (e.g., sun loving, partial light loving, and moisture loving). Certain plants such as sansevieria are adapted to less-than-ideal conditions and hence can be utilized in a variety of groups. The combination of plants should also consider the plant size, color, form, and texture. Plants can be grouped to create an overall shape (Figure 11–5). Further, one may include a flowering plant in an arrangement to give it some color. It may be necessary to prune periodically to maintain a good balance in the display. Plants should be repotted, or replanted, when the container becomes too small for them. During replanting, the original set of plants may be retained or new ones included.

11.2.5 GROWING PLANTS IN THE WINDOW

Displaying plants in windows is very popular because windows (especially south-facing windows) are the source of most of the natural light entering the house. Although plants in south-facing windows are prone to scorching due to excessive light, those in north-facing windows may not receive enough light. Windows experience temperature fluctuation, some of which is due to either cold or warm drafts from air conditioners or radiators located beneath windows. Nonetheless, with good care, one can raise healthy, attractive plants on a windowsill or near a window. They can range from single-potted plants to an elaborate plant display (Figure 11–6). They can be displayed inside or outside the window (Figure 11–7). Plants in the window display do not have to be displayed on the sill and can instead be hung in hanging baskets. Shelves may also be constructed in windows so that tiers of potted plants may be arranged. A window may be modified to create a container (such as a terrarium) in which plants can be grown. After arranging the pots, the base of the container may be filled with moss to hide the pots. Lighting may be installed, as well as automatic mist spraying and temperature control units. Plants for display in well-lit windows are presented in Table 11–4.

FIGURE 11–6 Flowers displayed on the windowsill. *(Source: Peter Anderson © Dorling Kindersley)*

FIGURE 11–7 A window garden—Flowers growing in a container outside the window. *(Source: © Dorling Kindersley)*

TABLE 11–4 Plants That Grow Well under Well-Lit (Window or Full-Sun) Conditions

Plant	Scientific Name
Bougainvillea	*Bougainvillea spectablis*
Medicine plant	*Aloe vera*
Amaryllis	*Hippeastrum* spp.
Bird-of-paradise	*Strelitzia reginae*
Lipstick vine	*Aeschynanthus lobbianus*
Rubber plant	*Ficus elastica*
Coleus	*Coleus blumei*
Hen and chickens	*Escheveria peacockii*
Fuchsia	*Fuchsia × hybrida*
Gardenia	*Gardenia jasminoides*

11.2.6 GARDEN ROOMS

Garden rooms are usually extensions of the main part of the house designed to be sunny. A large variety and number of plants are housed in the room, but some space is reserved for large furniture. Ideally, the garden room is adjacent to the living room. The structure may consist of panes of glass or some other durable and transparent material. Designs vary widely, with some homeowners installing pools in their garden rooms. The floor of the room may be made of wood, ceramic tile, or some other kind of material.

Plants may be grown in pots or ground beds or hung in baskets. A large variety of plants are grown successfully by strategically placing plants in the locations where they receive the best available conditions. For example, sunlight-loving (or light-loving) plants should be located near windows. It should be remembered that a garden room is meant to provide a comfortable environment for people before plants. As such, plants that prefer high humidity should be avoided, since such an environment will make it uncomfortable for humans to use the garden room. Plant species suitable for greenhouse production, including *Acacias, Musa enseta* (dwarf banana), *Eucalyptus,* dwarf conifers, potted roses, garden annuals, cacti, and some *bonsai* can be raised in a garden room.

Garden Room
Usually a casually furnished extension of the living room that is sunny, has room for lounging, and houses a large collection of plants.

11.2.7 HANGING BASKETS

Hanging baskets provide another avenue for displaying houseplants (Figure 11–8). An advantage of using hanging baskets is that it allows plants to be displayed in very awkward places such as over doorways and suspended from ceilings, patios, and walls. In this way, plants can be grown at eye level. Hanging basket containers can be made of wood, wire, ceramic, or plastic. For wall attachments, the container is halved (i.e., flat on one side) so that it can be fixed to the wall. Suspended baskets are usually round. The container may also be solid sided or made of wire. In the latter case, a lining of plastic (less attractive) or moss is needed before the planting medium is placed. The advantage of wire baskets is that plants can be planted on both the inside and outside of the container to cover it up completely (Figure 11–9).

FIGURE 11–8 Plants with vines and other hanging structures can be effectively displayed in hanging baskets. *(Source: George Acquaah)*

FIGURE 11–9 (a) Creating a hanging basket. (b) A completely planted hanging basket. *(Source: For (a) Peter Anderson © Dorling Kindersley, (b) © Dorling Kindersley)*

TABLE 11–5 Selected Plants for Hanging Baskets

Plant	Scientific Name
Begonia	*Begonia* spp.
Spider plant	*Chlorophytum* spp.
Aparagus fern	*Asparagus* spp.
English ivy	*Hedera helix*
Boston fern	*Nephrolepis exaltata*
Coleus	*Coleus blumei*
Wandering Jew	*Zebrina pendula*
Lipstick vine	*Aeschynanthus* spp.
Swedish ivy	*Plectranthus australis*
Pothos	*Scindapus aureus* (or *Epipremnum aureum*)
Heat leaf philodendron	*Philodendron scandens*
Christmas cactus	*Zygocactus truncatus; Schulmbegergia* hybrids

Like potted plants, it is critical that hanging basket containers drain properly. However, hanging baskets dry out much more quickly than potted plants on the floor or tabletop because they are exposed to warmer temperatures (since warm air rises) at the level at which they are suspended (about 3°C or 5°F warmer) and airflow around them is much greater. Hanging baskets should be watered more frequently than regular potted plants. Wire basket designs dry out more quickly than solid-sided container designs. To add to the decor, some homeowners replace the wires attached to the pots for suspension with decorative chains or fabric support. Hanging baskets need attention similar to that for potted plants. Some species prefer sunny conditions, whereas others prefer shade (Table 11–5). Plants should be fertilized as needed.

11.3 CARING FOR HOUSEPLANTS

Houseplants need all of the growth factors that are obtained in the outside environment—good *soil, air, water, light,* and *nutrients.* Houseplants, however, differ in the quality and quantity of each factor required for optimal growth.

Caring for houseplants starts with bringing home healthy plants. Commercial nurseries grow plants under controlled conditions year-round. These conditions are adjusted to suit the needs of plants. However, at home, even though homeowners adjust the house temperature as the seasons change, these adjustments are designed for the comfort of people, not plants. Rooms are often evenly heated or cooled. It is very easy for the homeowner who is not a houseplant enthusiast to forget about the special needs of plants in the home.

11.3.1 BRINGING PLANTS HOME SAFELY

In spring or summer, temperatures in nurseries and homes are not likely to be significantly different. More significant differences are likely to occur between the home and the nursery during the cold period (early fall to early spring). Buying plants for use in the home requires the most attention and care during this period to reduce shock to plants. Plants purchased in the cold season should be transported with some insulation. The car should be heated before plants are moved into it from the nursery. For long-distance transportation, plants may be placed in cardboard boxes and wrapped in several layers of paper. Some plants are more delicate than others.

11.3.2 MONITORING LIGHT

A photographic light meter is used to determine light intensity. Light is a critical requirement for plant growth and development. The average light intensity in a house is about 55 **lux**, compared with more than 130,000 lux outside on a bright sunny day. A room is

Lux
The metric unit expressing the illumination falling on all points on a surface measuring one meter square, each point being one meter away from a standard light source of one candle; 1 lux = 0.093 foot-candles.

not uniformly lit. While plants are in the care of commercial nurseries, light conditions are maintained at optimal or near-optimal conditions, which usually means at higher intensities than would be found at home. For example, tropical foliage plants generally prefer high light intensities (above 10,000 lux and in some cases even above 30,000 lux).

Chloroplasts in leaves are known to orient themselves differently to suit high- and low-intensity light conditions. The problem with houseplants arises when they are transferred from the greenhouse (high intensity) to the home (low intensity). This change is drastic for many plants, which immediately begin to readjust to adapt to the home environment. Plants readjust differently, with variable consequences in terms of their aesthetic value. Some plant species such as *Ficus benjamina* and *Coleus hybridus* adjust to low light levels by losing chlorophyll and subsequently dropping their leaves. These plants develop new leaves that are much thinner and have chloroplasts that are uniformly distributed throughout the lamina, obviously for better interception of light. Other species including palms and lilies respond to low light levels by changing color from green to yellowish, but without abscission. By remaining attached to the plant, these sickly leaves reduce the aesthetic value of the plant. Some nursery owners, anticipating the eventual transfer of plants to homes by customers, may put plants through a weaning period to acclimatize and prepare them for the home environment.

A variety of sunlight intensities are experienced in the home, depending on the season, architectural design of the house, and other landscape activities around the house or even nearby houses (Figure 11–10):

1. *Direct sunlight (full light).* A house that has no large trees in its immediate vicinity or structures that may block sunlight can receive 100 percent sunlight for parts of the day through windows that face east, west, southeast, and southwest.
2. *Indirect sunlight (filtered bright light).* When trees obstruct the direct sunlight, it enters the house after going through the leaves. Some windows have decorative curtains and blinds that also filter direct sunlight, making only a portion of its intensity (about 50 to 75 percent) available indoors.
3. *Bright light.* Bright light occurs near the areas where sunlight directly or indirectly enters the house. Such areas are less bright (about 25 percent) than the primary source.
4. *Medium light.* North-facing windows do not receive direct sunlight. Even windows facing east or west do not receive direct sunlight if heavily obstructed.

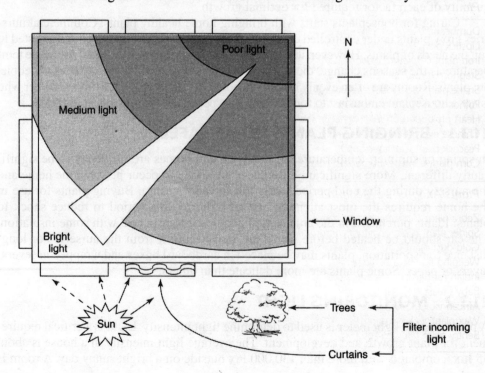

FIGURE 11–10 Natural light received in a room is influenced by factors such as the number and kinds of windows, the window treatment, the presence of trees near the windows, and the orientation of the house.

The lighting condition near these windows is of medium intensity (about 10 percent).

5. *Poor light.* As one moves away from windows into the center of the room, natural light intensity diminishes drastically (to about 5 percent). Room corners that are not near light sources are usually dimly lit. Poor lighting conditions can be contributed to by the interior design of the room. Dark colors absorb light, whereas lighter colors reflect it. A white wall reflects light to a plant placed in front of it. Furniture arrangement can create dark sections in the room.

Fortunately for home gardeners, most indoor foliage plants do not require high light intensities. However, when growing flowering plants such as azalea, chrysanthemum, geranium, and poinsettia indoors, high light intensity is desired for flower initiation. Plants such as cacti prefer higher light intensities to compensate for reduced photosynthetic surface from thickened leaves. Also fortunate for home gardeners is that many plants are quite tolerant of imperfect lighting conditions, at least for a period. Therefore, plants can be shifted around in a room without adverse consequences, as long as efforts are made to periodically provide the proper lighting conditions. The best approach, however, is to purchase plants that suit the lighting conditions one has or can provide, because shade-loving plants such as fern and aglaonema are less tolerant of improper lighting conditions (Table 11–6).

TABLE 11–6   Selected Plants Adapted to Various Light Conditions Indoors

Plants Adapted to Direct Natural Light (Place in South-Facing Window)

Norfolk Island pine (*Araucaria heterophylla*)
Croton (*Codiaeum* spp.)
Florist's chrysanthemum (*Chrysanthemum x morifolium*)
Florist's cyclamen (*Cyclamen persicum*)
Poinsettia (*Euphorbia pulcherrima*)
Dutch hyacinth (*Hyacinthus orientalis*)
English ivy (*Hedera helix*)
Christmas cactus (*Schulmbergia hybrids. Zygocactus truncatus*)
Azalea (*Rhododendron* spp.)

Plants Adapted to Low Light (Place in North-Facing Windows)

Dumbcane (*Dieffenbachia* spp.)
Lipstick plant (*Aeschynanthus* spp.)
Iron plant (*Aspidistra elatior*)
Staghorn fern (*Platycerium* spp.)
Snake plant (*Sansevieria trifasciata*)
Pothos (*Scindapsus aureum*) or (*Epipremnum aureum*)
Heart philodendron (*Philodendron scandens*)
Chinese evergreen (*Aglaonema commutatum*)
Peacock plant (*Calathea* spp.)
Corn plant (*Dracaena fragrans* 'Massangeana')

Plants Adapted to Medium Light (Place in East-Facing Windows)

Zebra plant (*Aphelandra squarrosa*)
Spider plant (*Chlorophytum comosum*)
Gold-dust plant (*Dracaena surculosa*)
Weeping fig (*Ficus benjamina*)
Indian rubber tree (*Ficus elastica*)
Baby's tears (*Helxine soleirolii*)
African violet (*Saintpaulia ionantha*)
Wax plant (*Hoya carnosa*)
Sentry palm (*Howea* spp.)

Phototropism
The response of a plant to nonuniform illumination, usually resulting in bending toward the strongest light.

When plants at home experience improper lighting conditions, they may grow spindly, have poor coloration (look pale) and small leaves, and exhibit **phototropism.** The shape and aesthetic value of plants can be drastically diminished when, in search of more light, plants turn their leaves in the direction of the source.

In split leaf philodendron (*Monstera deliciosa*), plants grown under dim light have unsplit leaves, whereas those grown under bright light have split leaves. Generally, plants with colored leaves (such as the red color of coleus) require more intense light to reach the chloroplasts masked by the red pigment. Similarly, variegated plants require more light to compensate for the lack of chlorophyll in certain parts. When grown in dim light, they do not variegate but show solid green color.

11.3.3 SUPPLEMENTARY LIGHTING (ARTIFICIAL LIGHTING)

Plants generally need twelve to sixteen hours of light per day for proper growth and development. Plants in the house receive a varying duration of light depending on how long people stay at home. Lights are turned on and off as people come into and leave the house. As such, plants may receive long periods of exposure to light on some days and little on others. Artificial lighting may be used in large houses for several reasons.

Decorative

A homeowner may desire to draw attention to specimen plants. These showcase plants may have unique and very attractive features and may be placed under a spotlight to emphasize their beauty. Lights and plants can be placed strategically to enhance the decor of a room.

Physiological

Plants need light to grow and develop. No plant can survive in darkness. As such, in dimly lit parts of the room, as well as in winter when natural light is least available, artificial light may be used to supplement natural light for plants to grow properly.

11.3.4 SOURCES OF ARTIFICIAL LIGHT

When additional lighting is required in a room, the type used is influenced by how it fits into the general decor of the room. When needed in a garden room, the styling may be compromised, but in the living room, styling of the light source is an important consideration for most people. There are three general sources of artificial light for indoor use—incandescent, mercury vapor, and fluorescent lights.

Incandescent Lights

Incandescent lights are commonly used in homes. The light they emit is high in orange-red and low in blue-violet wavelengths (Chapter 4). Even though they produce adequate light, the major disadvantage of this source of light is the tremendous amount of heat generated in the process of providing light. Only about 30 percent of the energy from an incandescent bulb is in the form of light, the remainder being given off as heat. When used for supplemental lighting, incandescent bulbs should be placed at a safe distance (depending on the power rating) to prevent scorching the plant. However, when placed too far away, incandescent light does little to help the plant, since most of its energy is heat and not light. This light source is hence largely decorative (e.g., spotlights). Flood-light models of incandescent lights are available and are more efficient. They also come in a variety of appealing styles.

Fluorescent Lights

Fluorescent lights are the most efficient of all sources and most recommended for houseplants. They are very energy efficient, cost less than the other types to operate, emit little heat, and can be placed close to plants without scorching them. They are available in a variety of colors, which adds to their decorative use at home.

Fluorescent tubes are also designed to emit different qualities of light. The spectrum of light usable by plants includes the violet-blue and red wavelength. Thus, it is important to take note of the spectrum on the label. Daylight fluorescent tubes provide mostly blue light and little red light. They are suitable for foliage plants. The best fluorescent tube lights for plants are those that provide a reddish hue, especially if flowering species are being grown. For extra light, the wide-spectrum light may be used. Extra light is desired by plants such as orchids, cacti, and pelargoniums. This requirement may be satisfied by using the very high output (VHO) fluorescent tubes. Cool white light, though poor in orange-red quality, provides excellent conditions for foliage plants to develop rich colors, branch more, and have a slow rate of stem elongation, resulting in fuller and more attractive plants. Unlike incandescent lights, which burn out suddenly, fluorescent lights age and lose intensity slowly. They have to be replaced after about four months of use.

Skylight

A skylight is not a light fixture but an architectural design strategy to allow more natural light to reach the interior of a room through the roof. For best results, the shell covering the opening in the roof should be constructed out of a material with *translucent* (not transparent) glazing. Translucent material allows the incoming solar radiation to be better distributed over a larger area without hot spots.

Caution: Even though light is very important for plant growth, it is better to provide too little than too much light. The danger of overexposure to light is greatest in summer. Note that when you place a plant in a window, only one-half of it, at best, receives full sunlight. Intense light may bleach or scorch the foliage of plants. Glass in a window is a filter of light preventing most of the ultraviolet rays from reaching the plant. When growing sensitive plants, one should be aware of their needs. As already indicated, variegated plants (e.g., *Hedera helix*) cease to variegate but instead produce dark-green leaves under light intensity lower than optimum. Other light-related disorders are discussed in Chapter 4.

11.3.5 TEMPERATURE

Houseplants generally prefer temperatures of between 18 and 24°C (64.4 and 75.2°F) for good growth and development. This condition often prevails in the average home in temperate climates. For most foliage ornamentals, a room night temperature of 21°C (70°F) is satisfactory, whereas growth is stalled at temperatures of 15°C (59°F). Flowering houseplants do well at 15°C (59°F) night temperatures. Even though plants may tolerate less-than-optimum temperatures above or below (10 to 30°C [50 to 86°F]), the danger to houseplants lies in the fluctuations in temperature. Night outdoor temperature may drop below freezing (0°C or 32°F), whereas indoor temperature may be 28°C (82°F) or higher. A change in temperature of more than 20°C (36°F) is detrimental to houseplants. As such, plants that are positioned close to windows or on windowsills run the risk of exposure to drastic temperature changes (warm inside and freezing outside) and may die as a result. Summer temperatures of 26 to 32°C (78.8 to 89.6°F) are tolerable for most indoor plants, provided the humidity is maintained at a high level. It is advisable to invest in a thermometer, preferably a maximum-minimum type, which helps determine the temperature fluctuations in the room.

Some caution in the care of houseplants can reduce the risk of loss to adverse temperature:

1. Keep humidity high in winter by periodically spraying plants with mist sprayers to keep microclimates humid.
2. Do not place plants in the path of drafts (from air conditioners or heaters). Some plants may benefit from the additional warmth from a radiator as long as it is not direct and the humidity level is high.
3. Windows and doors close to plants should be airtight to prevent unsuspected cold drafts in winter.
4. If plants must be placed close to windows, they should be protected by having a storm window installed to prevent cold chills at night.
5. When curtains are drawn at night during winter, be sure that the plant on the windowsill is inside of the curtain.
6. If you have flowers in the kitchen, avoid placing them near sources of heat (e.g., stoves and refrigerator tops).
7. Plants directly facing doorways are subject to crosscurrent air.

11.3.6 HUMIDITY

Humidity and temperature work together. Humidity, the relative amount of water vapor in the air, is measured by using a *hygrometer,* an instrument recommended for homes with plants. A high humidity level is uncomfortable for humans. Generally, a relative humidity (RH) of 60 percent is satisfactory for most houseplants. Many plants experience stress when RH is below 40 percent. Under such conditions, drying of leaf tips occurs in plants such as palms. Indoor RH is seasonal, being lower in winter than at other times. Plants with thick leaves are often able to tolerate low levels of humidity in the air, unlike those with thinner leaves.

11.3.7 PROVIDING SUPPLEMENTARY HUMIDITY FOR PLANTS

In winter, the use of heaters tends to cause indoor air to be dry. Dry air encourages excessive evaporation from surfaces. Humidity indoors can be increased by several methods:

1. *General humidification.* Provide additional humidity for the whole room by using a domestic humidifier.
2. *Localized humidification*
   a. *Mist spraying.* Periodically, plants can be misted with water, but this practice provides only short-term effects.
   b. *Pebble tray.* Potted plants can be placed on pebbles in a tray (Figure 11–11) and the tray watered (but not above the pebbles). This approach provides a more continuous humid microclimate. Pebble trays

FIGURE 11–11 A pebble tray may be used to keep the plants' microenvironment humid.

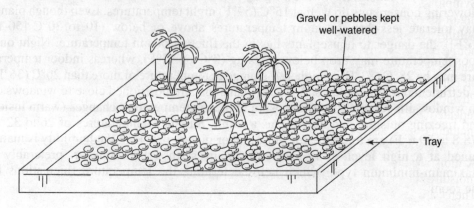

Gravel or pebbles kept well-watered

Tray

may be used for one pot or a group of several pots. Alternatively, a pot may be set on a wooden block placed in a saucer and treated like the pebble tray setup.

3. *Enclosed chamber.* For plants that are very sensitive to low humidity, enclosed glass or plastic chambers or bottles may be used to hold potted plants or grow such plants (as is done in a terrarium).

4. *Move plants.* Certain parts of the home have higher humidity levels than others (e.g., bathroom and kitchen). Plants may be moved close to these humid sections during the winter months.

Caution: Relative humidity and temperature work together. If the temperature is high, RH will be low. On the contrary, when RH is high and the temperature in the house drops, water will bead on the leaves. These droplets of water provide a humid environment for maintenance of disease organisms.

11.3.8 WATER

Water plays a very important role in plant nutrition. One of the most common problems in houseplant culture is overwatering. Plant species differ in their moisture requirements. Several factors determine the water needs of houseplants:

1. The room condition, which varies with the season, determines how plants must be watered. Warm or hot environments cause plants to lose more water than cooler environments.

2. Actively growing plants use more water than dormant plants.

3. Plants with thin leaves and larger leaf surfaces transpire more and thus need more water than other types of plants.

4. The container material plays a role in the moisture needs of plants. Plastic, styrofoam, and glazed containers retain more moisture in the growing medium than clay pots or unglazed containers. Plants grown in unglazed pots require frequent watering.

5. Plant growth media differ in their water-holding capacity. Sandy soils or those containing perlite drain more freely than those containing organic materials such as peat. Freely draining soils require more frequent watering than those with good water-holding capacity.

6. The size of the container in relation to plant size is also critical. When a large plant is grown in a small pot that can hold only a small amount of water at a time, more frequent watering is required. In addition, the roots of large plants in small pots become pot-bound, requiring repotting of the plant.

The greatest danger of overwatering is from watering according to a set schedule. It is safest to always determine that a plant needs water before providing it. If, a week after watering, the soil is still reasonably moist, further watering should be delayed. Symptoms of overwatering are wilting (in the presence of abundant moisture), yellowing of leaves, and rotting; symptoms of lack of moisture include drooping of leaves and wilting. Although these symptoms are stress alerts, it is best to avoid them. Plants cannot be revived after a certain stage of wilting, especially in the case of plants with thick leaves. Sometimes, when the plants are revived, portions of the leaves (the edges) may be permanently scorched, leading to disfigured leaves and decreased aesthetic appeal. Physiologically, alternating between drought and adequate moisture conditions (just like repeated freezing and thawing of food) offsets developmental processes in the plant including reproductive processes and may cause tissue death.

Many different types of equipment are available for measuring soil moisture. A moisture meter may be purchased by the avid gardener. For most people, a simple moisture indicator that changes color based on the dryness of the soil is satisfactory. There are other ways in which soil moisture can be determined without using instruments, although one of them is not soil surface dryness. Most plants are overwatered because growers look at the soil surface without knowing what is going on beneath it and decide that watering is required. It is best to stick a finger into the potting medium to a depth of about 1 inch or more (or use a piece of stick) to determine the stickiness or moisture level of the soil.

11.3.9 HOW MUCH WATER TO PROVIDE

Plants have different water needs. It is a waste of resources and a danger to plants to supply more water than is needed. For a particular plant, the amounts applied may be varied depending on the growth phase. In terms of quantity applied, plants may be watered in these general ways:

1. *Plentifully (or liberally).* In watering liberally or plentifully, the potting medium is kept constantly moist. When water is needed, plants may be drenched with water until the medium can hold no more. At this stage, excess water collects in the drip tray or saucer. This excess water should be discarded. Drenching can be done from the top or by placing the pot in a container of water and allowing it to soak up water until it can take in no more. The pot is then removed from the water.
2. *Moderately.* When water is applied in moderate amounts, only a small amount of excess water drains into the saucer. If a grower is using the soaking method, only a little water should be added to the container at a time. Water is added continually until the surface of the soil is moist. The plant is watered again when the soil feels slightly dry.
3. *Sparingly.* Watering sparingly keeps the growing medium only partially moist. Water never drains out of the pot. The plant is rewatered when most of the soil is dry.

Caution: These three general watering regimes are not alternatives. The method chosen for a situation depends on the specific needs of the plant, the conditions under which it is growing, and its growth phase.

11.3.10 ROLE OF PLANT GROWTH CYCLE IN WATER NEEDS

The plant growth cycle is often overlooked in the management of houseplants. Deciduous plants have a visible and predictable alteration between active growth (spring to fall) and rest period (winter), because they shed their leaves in the cold season. Without leaves, it is not difficult to guess that the plant does not need as much nutrition (water and minerals) as it does when it has leaves. Many bulbs and corms also have periods of rest during which their aboveground portions die back. However, many plants also have rest periods in their biological clocks that are less obvious. These species do not exhibit any dramatic signals to prompt the grower to make the necessary adjustments in management practices. These evergreen species, like most foliage houseplants, retain their foliage year-round. Some horticulturalists recommend that many indoor plants be forced to rest in winter when daylight is reduced. Induced resting may be accomplished by reducing the amount of water supplied and discontinuing fertilizer application. The best approach, however, is to consult the growing instructions supplied with plants or seeds purchased from a nursery.

11.3.11 METHODS OF APPLYING WATER

Water may be applied to plants by using any convenient container such as a cup. However, it is advisable and most convenient to use a watering can to water houseplants. Very inexpensive, lightweight plastic watering cans with long and thin spouts may be purchased from supermarkets. A long spout enables watering without spilling and splashing onto leaves. It also increases the maneuverability of the operator so that plants positioned in hard-to-reach places are readily watered. For homes with glasshouses, garden rooms, atriums, or a large collection of plants, a watering hose with an on/off control switch at the nozzle may be more convenient. There are two basic methods of watering houseplants:

1. *Water soil directly from above.* In this method, care is taken not to splash water on the leaves (Figure 11–12). The soil level in the pot should permit a good amount of water to collect on top without spilling over.
2. *Water soil from below.* Potted plants may be placed in a saucer or container into which water is poured (Figure 11–13). Water is then slowly absorbed through the drainage holes in the bottom of the pot.

As much as possible, plants should be watered carefully to avoid wetting the plant leaves. If the water is hard, it leaves unsightly marks on the leaves. Also, if fertilizers are applied through the irrigation water, marks from the salts are left on leaves if splashing occurs. Water on leaves may also create humid conditions in which disease-causing organisms thrive. Some plants, such as bromeliads, can tolerate water on the foliage. When watering plants, lukewarm water should be used. Tap water in some places can be very cold. The water should also be soft, since plants such as camellias are sensitive to salts in water.

When plants are going to be left unattended for extended periods, such as while a homeowner is on vacation, creative methods of watering should be devised to avoid wilting of plants. For example, plants may be enclosed in a plastic bag to retain moisture (Figure 11–14). A wick system may also be used (Figure 11–15).

FIGURE 11–12 Watering a potted plant from above.

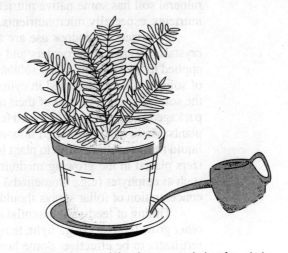

FIGURE 11–13 Watering a potted plant from below.

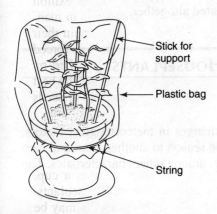

FIGURE 11–14 A potted plant enclosed in a plastic bag to maintain high humidity.

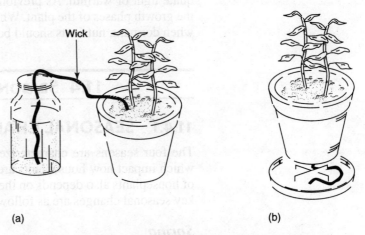

(a)   (b)

FIGURE 11–15 Watering potted plants by using a wick (a) inserted into the pot from above from a feeder bottle and (b) inserted through the drainage hole in the bottom of the pot.

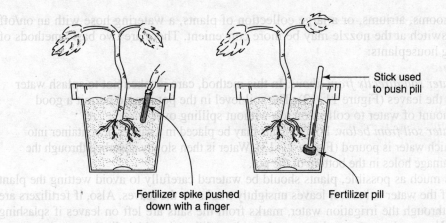

Stick used to push pill

Fertilizer spike pushed down with a finger

Fertilizer pill

11.3.12 FERTILIZING HOUSEPLANTS

All plants need balanced nutrition to grow, develop properly, and produce well. The nutrients in the potting soil are gradually depleted as the plant grows and develops. Unlike field plants, whose fertilizer needs usually consist of only macronutrient elements (nitrogen, phosphorus, and potassium), potted plants need both macro- and micronutrients as part of a fertilizer program. Both types of nutrients are required because whereas mineral soil has some native nutrients, greenhouse soilless mixes are often deficient in nutrients, especially micronutrients.

Fertilizers for indoor use are available in several forms—solids, liquids, powders, crystals, or granules. Powders and crystals, which are dissolved in water before being applied to the soil, are called *soluble fertilizers*. Fertilizer sticks and spikes are examples of solid fertilizers packaged in cylindrical shapes similar to pencils that are inserted into the soil for gradual release of their nutrients (Figure 11–16). Such fertilizers may also be packaged as pills. Specially coated fertilizer granules are commonly used in feeding houseplants. These solids are called slow-release fertilizers. Finally, fertilizers may be applied in liquid form as foliar sprays to plant leaves. While all plants grown in soil respond to fertilizers placed in the growing medium, foliar application is especially beneficial to plants such as epiphytes (e.g., bromeliads), which absorb little nutrition through their roots. The concentration of foliar sprays should be carefully selected to avoid scorching the leaves.

Timing of feeding is essential in houseplant nutrition. It should be remembered that other growth factors (e.g., light, temperature, and water) must be adequately supplied for fertilizers to be effective. Some home growers misdiagnose plant problems, thinking a poorly growing plant is starving when it actually is overwatered or not receiving adequate light or warmth. As previously mentioned, fertilization should take into account the growth phases of the plant. When a plant is growing actively, it needs more nutrition; when dormant, nutrients should be reduced or eliminated altogether.

11.4 SEASONAL CARE OF HOUSEPLANTS

11.4.1 SEASONAL CHANGES

The four seasons are characterized by certain key changes in meteorological factors, which impact how houseplants are cared for from one season to another. Seasonal care of houseplants also depends on the plant growth cycle, among other characteristics. The key seasonal changes are as follows:

Spring

The key changes in weather during the spring season that have a significant bearing on how houseplants are cared for are increasing day length and gradual rise in temperature.

The photoperiod affects when the house light is turned on. The air can be relatively humid because of the rainfall.

Summer

During the summer season, light intensity increases to a peak, while temperature also rises to maximum levels. The air can be dry and hot. Homeowners maintain comfortable room ambience by turning on the air conditioner. Some people make use of the bright outside light by parting the curtains or opening the window blinds. The danger to plants may be the intense light from the sun.

Fall

During the fall season, day length shortens while temperature decreases. Homeowners begin to turn on the heating system to keep warm.

Winter

Day length is at its minimal value during winter. Similarly, room temperature drops to its lowest during the year. Indoor heating is at its maximum. Danger to plants comes in a variety of ways. Plants in window sills may be exposed to temperature extremes, very cold on the outside of the window and very warm temperature inside the home. If the curtain is pulled over such that the plant is between the window and the curtain, it might suffer severe winter damage. Further, winter plant damage may come to plants placed in the way of a draft when the door is opened or when placed on/near heating vents or space heaters.

11.4.2 SEASONAL WATERING AND FERTILIZATION OF INDOOR PLANTS

Evergreen Plants

Evergreen plants retain their leaves year-round. Evergreen plants need normal watering in spring, summer, and fall. Watering should be reduced during the winter months. Similarly, evergreen plants should be fertilized at regular rates in spring, summer, and winter, reducing the rates in winter.

Deciduous Plants

Deciduous plants shed their leaves at some point in their growth cycle, starting in fall and losing them all in winter. Fresh leaves appear in spring. During this time, plants should be moderately watered and fertilized. As vegetative growth peaks in summer, watering and feeding should be increased. Fertilizing should be stopped in fall, while watering is reduced in fall and winter. As the plant rests in winter, the soil should be kept just moist enough to keep the plant from dying.

Annual Plants

Annual plants complete their life cycle in one growing season. If the plants are started in spring, the young plants should be moderately watered and sparingly fertilized. As the plants grow, watering should be plentiful while fertilizer rates are increased for optimum vegetative growth and flowering, where applicable. Annual plants will begin to die as fall begins. As the leaves begin to drop, watering and fertilizing should cease.

Bulbs and Tuberous Species

Bulbs and tuberous species are characterized by a growth cycle in which there is a distinct dormant period. These plants grow actively in spring and need to be well watered and fertilized during this period. However, the aboveground parts cease to grow and die during summer as plants enter into a period of dormancy. Active growth resumes in fall when the underground structures begin to sprout. Sprouting tubers should be watered sparingly but not fertilized yet. As winter arrives, vegetative growth increases, reproductive growth starting where applicable. Watering and fertilizing should be increased to a moderate level during this time.

11.5 POTTING MEDIA

Potting media are discussed more fully in Chapter 4. Potting mixtures differ widely in constitution. Some commercial mixes are designed for specific purposes (e.g., mixes for use in the terrarium or for seed germination) and others for general purposes. It is critical that a potting medium be sterilized to kill pathogens. The mixes may be soil based (i.e., they include natural soil) or soilless (containing no natural soil ingredients). The grower can sterilize his or her own homemade medium by placing an aluminum-covered tray of the mix in a conventional oven and baking at 82°C (179.6°F) for about an hour. Such an undertaking can be very messy. Soilless mixes are lighter in weight and easier to handle than soil-based mixes, but they lack nutrients. When used for potting top-heavy plants, the plants can be toppled easily. A simple homemade recipe for a mix may consist of the following:

1. One part sterilized soil plus one part medium-grade peat moss plus one part fine perlite
2. One part coarse peat moss plus one part medium-grade vermiculite plus one part medium-grade perlite

These mixes should be supplemented with balanced fertilizer.

11.6 POTTING PLANTS

After the appropriate potting mixture has been determined and purchased or prepared, and the right container chosen, the next step is to pot the plant. The drainage hole or holes in the bottom of the pot should be partially covered with pieces of broken pot (crock) or small stones. Care should be taken not to plug the hole (Figure 11–17). Potting mix is then added to the container. A hole is made in the soil to receive the plant roots and then

FIGURE 11–17 Steps in potting plants.

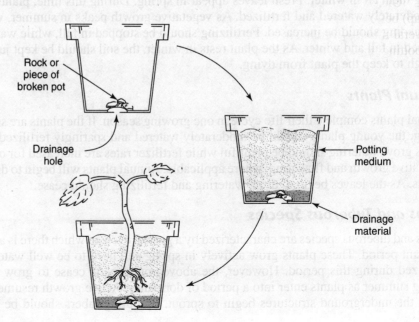

Rock or piece of broken pot

Drainage hole

Potting medium

Drainage material

patted firm to keep the plant erect. Additional soil, if needed, should be added, but at least 1/2 to 1 inch (1.3 to 2.54 centimeters) of space should be left at the top of the soil to hold water during watering (sometimes called the *headspace* of the container). It should also be noted that the soil will settle with deep watering.

11.7 REPOTTING

11.7.1 WHEN NEEDED

Repotting is actually transplanting from one pot to another. Sometimes plants are repotted because a grower desires to change containers for cosmetic or aesthetic reasons. However, there are certain times during the growth of a plant when it needs to be repotted for better growth and development. One such occasion and perhaps the chief reason for repotting is when a plant grows too large for its container. When this happens, the roots become **pot-bound** (roots grow over each other and around the bottom of the pot, forming a ball) (Figure 11–18). Many roots at this stage are not in contact with soil and thus not aiding in nutrient or water absorption. Pot-bound plants grow slowly even with good nutrition and watering. Roots often grow through the drainage holes in the bottom of the container. To find out whether a plant is pot-bound, it should be removed, along with the soil, by positioning its stem between two fingers of one hand and turning the pot over into the palm. Gently tapping on the bottom of the pot or tapping the pot against the edge of a table can help to dislodge the soil. In the case of larger plants, a small block of wood may be used to tap the side of the pot while it is lying on its side. A sharp edge (e.g., the blade of a knife) may be run around the inside wall of the pot to break loose any attachment to the walls. Watering plants before repotting is recommended to aid in their removal from the pot.

Pot-bound
Growth of roots over each other and around the bottom of the pot as a result of limited space.

11.7.2 CHOOSING A POT OR CONTAINER

The plant height (size) in relation to pot size is important for aesthetic reasons. The grown plant height should be about two times the pot height. An oversized pot not only wastes soil mix but also increases the risk of overwatering to the detriment of the small plant. Pots come in different shapes, sizes, and materials. The strategy of repotting involves changing to a bigger pot size in a stepwise fashion.

Old pots should be cleaned and disinfected (use household bleach or germicidal soap) before reuse. When cleaning glazed clay pots, they should be soaked in water for several minutes to remove all air bubbles in the clay. When dry clay pots are used for repotting, the clay tends to absorb moisture rapidly from the soil.

FIGURE 11–18 An extreme case of pot-bounding. *(Source: Peter Anderson © Dorling Kindersley)*

Containers come in all shapes and sizes. In effect, any receptacle may be used to grow plants, provided adequate provision is made for drainage and the container is convenient to use. Pots are also chosen to complement the design of the room.

Container Materials

There are two basic materials used in making horticultural pots. Each has advantages and disadvantages.

Clay *Clay* (or earthenware) used to be the industry standard for pots but has been replaced with newly developed material. Clay, being a natural material, "breathes," or is porous, allowing water to evaporate from its surface. As such, it reduces the danger of waterlogging from overwatering. Clay pots are heavier, more sturdy, and able to support large plants without toppling over (Figure 11–19). However, clay pots are also bulky to handle and breakable, requiring care in handling. Because it is capable of absorbing mineral salts and water from the medium, the surfaces of clay pots often show unsightly whitish marks from salt deposits. During repotting or topdressing, these marks should be scrubbed off by using household bleach and then rinsed in vinegar. Such marks are not associated with glazed clay pots.

Pot-bound root growth occurs more rapidly in plants grown in clay pots than those in plastic pots because the porosity of clay allows air to reach plant roots more readily than those in plastic (where air is obtained from the open top only). Roots thus tend to grow rapidly toward the wall of the pot where, upon meeting the obstacle, they begin to circle around on the surface of the wall.

Plastic *Plastic pots* are very popular today and are available in a wide range of colors, thickness, durability, shapes, and sizes (Figure 11–20). Plastic pots are generally less breakable than clay pots. Even though molded polystyrene pots are used in some situations, hard plastics are most common because they are lightweight and easy to handle. Plant roots grow more evenly in a plastic container. One problem with this synthetic material is that it is not porous and thus plants grown in plastic pots are prone to waterlogging because they lack the ability to absorb moisture and lose it through evaporation. Although overwatering plastic-potted plants may be a problem in winter when drying is slow, plastic pots are advantageous in summer when water stress is most common.

Plastic pots are intolerant of the high temperatures needed for sterilization and thus are best sterilized by using chemicals. Pots may be soaked for about ten minutes in a commercial disinfectant solution (e.g., Floralife or Green-Shield), rinsed in water, and then air dried. This chemical sterilization is not as effective as steam sterilization. For better results, plastic pots should be washed to remove all dirt before being treated with chemicals. Plastic pots are also readily toppled when plants grow larger.

FIGURE 11–19 Clay pots. *(Source: George Acquaah)*

FIGURE 11–20 Plastic pots. *(Source: George Acquaah)*

Other Materials Apart from clay and plastic, another synthetic material called *styrofoam* is used in the horticultural industry for plant culture. This material is known for its insulation quality and hence is used especially when keeping the soil warm is a priority.

Shapes and Sizes

The shape of a pot is largely a matter of personal preference. Most pots have a circular lateral cross section, but other shapes occur (Figure 11–21). Sometimes rectangular pots are used to grow mass displays of plants that hang from places such as the balconies of apartments.

In terms of size, there are four general types of pots:

1. *Standard pots.* Standard pots vary in size but are characterized by having a height that equals the pot width. This shape is not suitable for growing tall plants since such pots are then prone to tipping over.
2. *Azalea pots.* Many flowering plants are grown in azalea pots. They are more stable than standard pots because they stand three-fourths as high as they are wide.
3. *Bulb pots.* Bulb pots are also called *half pots* because they stand half as high as they are wide. They are widely used in the propagation of plants. They may be used to grow plants with shallow roots to maturity or plants that may be displayed in mass form (e.g., zebrina, tradescantia, daffodil, hyacinth, and tulip).
4. *Rose pots.* Rose pots are one and a half times as tall as they are wide and are used for growing deeply rooted plants.

Within each type, pots are referred to by their height (e.g., 6- or 9-inch [15.2- or 22.9- centimeter] pots). Nurseries that produce bedding plants and vegetable seedlings for sale often grow these in small peat pots or plastic containers in packs of six or twelve plants *(community packs)* (Figure 11–22).

Some plants may be repotted or shifted several times before they are settled in a more permanent container. When plants grow too large for the standard sizes of pots, they may be transplanted to larger containers called *tubs* that may be made out of wood or plastic (Figure 11–23). Even though changing pot sizes as plants grow may be an unpleasant chore, it is safer to "pot up," progressively increasing the pot size as the plant increases in size, than to grow plants in pots that are too small. A small plant in a large pot not only looks awkward but also is prone to overwatering and possibly death. Further, it is a waste of the potting medium.

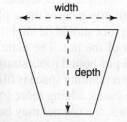

Typical pot: depth = width
Range = 1 1/2 – 15 inches (3.81–38.1 cm)

Azalea pot   Standard pot   Square pot

FIGURE 11–21 Pot shapes and sizes.

FIGURE 11–22 A community pack of seedlings. *(Source: George Acquaah)*

FIGURE 11–23 Large container. *(Source: George Acquaah)*

FIGURE 11–24 Steps in repotting large plants.

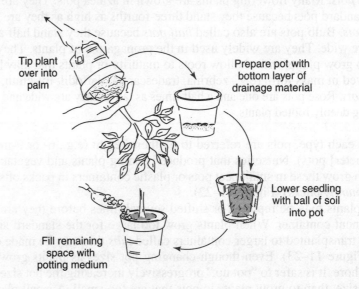

Tip plant over into palm

Prepare pot with bottom layer of drainage material

Lower seedling with ball of soil into pot

Fill remaining space with potting medium

11.7.3 REPOTTING PROCESS

In repotting, the drainage hole in the container should be covered, as described earlier. As insurance against overwatering, the bottoms of pots with drip pans or those placed in saucers should be lined with gravel or pebbles. The potting mix should be slightly moistened before use. First, some soil is placed at the bottom of the pot. The plant is then removed, along with a ball of soil from the old pot, and all pot-bound roots straightened out before setting on the moist soil in the receiving pot. The remaining space is filled with more of the fresh potting medium (Figure 11–24). In some cases, adding more soil to fill up the empty spaces may be cumbersome. In such situations, the old pot may be placed in the new one and the space around it filled to create a mold into which the ball of soil from the transplant will fit. The plant should be placed no deeper than the depth used in the previous pot.

11.7.4 TOPDRESSING

Topdressing
Applying fertilizer to the surface of the soil while the plants are growing.

The practice of **topdressing** in potted horticultural plants involves providing plants with fresh growing media without transplanting when the biggest pot size desired or available has been used. It entails scraping off about 1 to 2 inches (2.54 to 5.1 centimeters) of topsoil and replacing with a fresh soil mix. Where it has been determined that roots are pot-bound, they should be pruned to remove the excess roots before topping with fresh soil. Pruning and topdressing should be done with care to avoid damaging the plant.

(a)   (b)

FIGURE 11–25   Support for plants. (a) Wooden stake, (b) wire cage. (*Source:* USDA)

11.8 PROVIDING SUPPORT

Many flowering houseplants are freestanding and self-supporting. However, plants sometimes need additional support when they produce heavy flower heads that cause the stem to bend (e.g., cineraria and tomato). Other plants (e.g., fatshedera) may have slender stems that need additional support. Another instance where houseplants may need reinforcement in their support system is when they grow large but have brittle stems (e.g., impatiens).

In all of these instances, additional support may be provided by tying the weak stem to a stake with a string. Bamboo provides strong stakes. It may be split into smaller pieces and remain capable of providing good support. Whenever necessary, several stakes may be used to support a single plant in a pot. To keep the aesthetic value, stakes and twine used for tying should be positioned strategically and all loose ends neatly removed. Knots should not be tied too tightly around the stem. The idea is to provide additional support, not to bunch branches together.

Climbing plants (e.g., ivy, depladenia, and hoya) are known to produce vines. The grower should decide whether the vines will be allowed to hang freely or whether the plant will be encouraged to climb on some support (e.g., a wall or pole). The grower may purchase wire frames designed in a wide variety of shapes for *training vine plants* (e.g., philodendron and cissus) or create his or her own support frame (Figure 11–25). When plants are trained on supports, they must be tied, as when using stakes.

11.9 DISEASES AND PESTS OF HOUSEPLANTS

When it comes to houseplant diseases and pests, the key is to prevent their occurrence in the first place. Since plants cohabit with humans in small, enclosed spaces, diseases and insect pests should not be allowed to infest the environment. It is most undesirable to be confronted with a situation in which pesticides, which are toxic to humans as well as the pests they control, must be used in the house.

Diseases and pests of houseplants are often traceable to improper growing conditions (e.g., poor lighting, improper temperature, insufficient or excessive moisture, poor nutrition, still air, and high humidity). As such, before a homeowner scrambles to implement disease-control measures, it is best to first check whether plants are receiving proper care. Maintenance of strict phytosanitary conditions in the home is important.

Where possible, leaves should be cleaned to remove dust, grease, and environmental pollutants that settle on them. Plants may be cleaned with plain or soapy water, and care should be taken not to leave drops of water on parts of the plant after washing. Diseases and pests of houseplants are discussed more fully in Chapter 8.

11.10 COMMON SYMPTOMS OF ILL HEALTH
IN HOUSEPLANTS

Houseplants under stress from inadequate or improper levels of nutrition and other growth factors may exhibit one or more of the following common symptoms associated with ill health in plants:

1. *Yellowing of leaves (chlorosis).* Yellowing of leaves is usually a sign that plants are in distress. When older leaves yellow, it could be due to nitrogen deficiency. However, any disease that interrupts the flow of nutrients may cause leaves to yellow. When young leaves yellow, the plants may be under stress from poor drainage. When both young and old leaves yellow, the cause could be poor lighting or drought (underwatering). Chlorosis occurring with leaf drop could signal cold temperatures or poor aeration due to waterlogging.
2. *Stunted growth.* Whenever plants show stunted growth with small leaves and poor color, the condition could be due to one or a combination of the following: moisture stress, improper temperature, roots that are pot-bound, and restricted growth.
3. *Foliar burns.* Burns on leaves—when they occur as patches without any definite pattern—could be caused by fungal pathogens or could be the result of burns from foliar application of an insecticide. When plants have experienced severe drought, they may recover but the tissues at the edge may die, especially in young leaves. When the edge burn occurs in older leaves, it could be caused by excessive fertilization, leading to accumulation of salts in the soil. Other symptoms and possible causes are described in Table 11–7.

TABLE 11–7 Common Problems of Houseplants and Their Management

Water-Related Problems

Symptom:	Plant wilting; wilting is intensified with continued irrigation
Possible cause:	Medium is saturated or drainage is poor
Suggested action:	Repot properly for improved drainage; reduce frequency of watering
Symptom:	Plant wilting but recovers with watering
Possible cause:	Medium was left to dry for too long; plant may be pot-bound
Suggested action:	Increase watering frequency; repot into a larger pot
Symptom:	Leaf edges or tips appear scorched
Possible cause:	Insufficient or infrequent watering; medium left dry for a long period
Suggested action:	Water more frequently and more thoroughly each time
Symptom:	Plant is stunted in growth; leaves are of reduced size
Possible cause:	Insufficient watering frequency and quantity of water applied
Suggested action:	Water plant at proper frequency and apply adequate water each time

Light-Related Problems

Symptom:	Etiolated plant growth
Possible cause:	Insufficient light intensity
Suggested action:	Relocate plant into brighter area of room or provide artificial supplemental lighting
Symptom:	Chlorosis (especially in older plants)
Possible cause:	Insufficient lighting

(Continued)

Light-Related Problems

Suggested action:	Relocate to brighter part of room
Symptom:	Bleaching or discoloration of leaves
Possible cause:	Plant is intolerant of direct sunlight
Suggested action:	Relocate to part of room with lower light condition
Symptom:	Flowering is poor or drastically reduced
Possible cause:	Low light intensity
Suggested action:	Relocate to area with proper light condition
Symptom:	Leaf abscission accompanied by chlorosis
Possible cause:	High light intensity
Suggested action:	Relocate plant to lower light area

Nutrition-Related Problems

Symptom:	Uniform chlorosis of leaves on the whole plant
Possible cause:	Nitrogen deficiency
Suggested action:	Apply or increase rate of application of nitrogen fertilizer
Symptom:	Stunted growth of plant
Possible cause:	Inadequate fertilization
Suggested action:	Apply fertilizers
Symptom:	Leaf tips and edges brown or scorched
Possible cause:	Excessive fertilization
Suggested action:	Flush excess salts with large quantities of water; adjust fertilizer rate

Temperature-Related Problems

Symptom:	Slow growth
Possible cause:	Low temperature
Suggested action:	Place in warmer area of room
Symptom:	Leaf abscission
Possible cause:	Drop in temperature
Suggested action:	Protect plant from cold, chilling temperature
Symptom:	Chlorosis with abscission
Possible cause:	High temperature
Suggested action:	Lower temperature; do not locate near heating system

Pathogenic Problems

Symptom:	Gray, fluffy mold
Possible cause:	Gray mold attack due to high humidity
Suggested action:	Reduce residual moisture on leaf; mist spray only lightly; aerate; remove affected parts
Symptom:	Leaf spot
Possible cause:	Fungal or bacterial infection due to high humidity or residual moisture on foliage
Suggested action:	Do not mist spray foliage; keep leaves dry by watering media without wetting foliage; remove affected leaves
Symptom:	Blackening and rotting at the base of the stem
Possible cause:	Blackstem rot from gray mold attack; results from overwatering or poor drainage of potting medium
Suggested action:	Remove plant and examine root; if rot is extensive, discard; otherwise treat with fungicide and repot in well-draining medium
Symptom:	Stunted growth; mottling of leaves; distortion of leaves
Possible cause:	Viral infection; due to attack of sucking insects (e.g., aphids)
Suggested action:	Destroy infected plant
Symptom:	Healthy-looking plant starts to wilt in spite of watering and fertilizing; roots are knotted
Possible cause:	Root-knot nematode attack
Suggested action:	Destroy plant and discard potting medium; use sterilized medium for potting plants

Symptom:	A fine web coating on leaf undersides
Possible cause:	Attack of spider mites; favored under hot, dry air conditions
Suggested action:	Mist plant; cut affected part and discard
Symptom:	Holes in leaves
Possible cause:	Attack of chewing insects (e.g., caterpillar and earwig)
Suggested action:	Remove pest and destroy
Symptom:	Rolling of leaves
Possible cause:	Leaf roller attack
Suggested action:	Locate and destroy moths

11.11 COMMON HOUSEPLANTS AND THEIR CARE

[COLOR PLATES—*see color plate* 13–16 for photos]

The care of selected houseplants is briefly summarized in this section. The color photos corresponding to these plants are found in color plates 13 to 16.

1. Aluminum plant (*Pilea cadierei*)
    - Prefers medium light; place in east of west window
    - Water frequently and thoroughly
    - Keep in cool temperature

2. Peacock plant (*Calathea roseopicta*)
    - High light
    - Moist soil and high humidity
    - High temperature
    - Repot annually and clean leaves frequently

3. Umbrella plant (*Cyperus albostratus*)
    - High light (direct sunlight), keep moist (place in saucer with water), high humidity
    - Maintain average temperature and cool night temperature
    - Cut plant to base if it appears rugged
    - Propagate by leaf bud cuttings, suckers, or seed

4. Variegated Swiss cheese plant (*Monstera deliciosa*)
    - Medium light (bright indirect)
    - Dry out soil between watering
    - High temperature (in 80s) during the day
    - If light is dim characteristic holes and slashes develop poorly
    - Needs support, hence plant in a large pot

5. Zebra plant (*Aphelandra squarrosa*)
    - Place in full light, or filtered in south window
    - Water frequently and thoroughly
    - Prefers high temperatures
    - Fertilize every two months

6. Blushing bromeliad (*Neoregelia carolinae*)
    - Place in bright light
    - Water regularly
    - Keep temperatures cool

7. Chinese evergreen (*Aglaonema*)
    - Place in medium light in west or east window
    - Variegated forms lose their color under low light

- Keep soil moist all the time
- Place on pebble tray for high humidity
- Keep temperature around the 80s
- Tolerates pot-bounding
- Propagate by rooting leaf in water, by stem cutting, or air layering

8. Bird-of-paradise (*Strelitza reginae*)
   - Bright light (full sun) in fall and winter; medium (indirect) light in spring
   - Let soil dry between watering
   - Prefers moderate temperatures
   - May take up to ten years before flowering

9. Madagascar dragon tree (*Dracaena marginata*)
   - Prefers bright light (full sun) in winter; tolerates low light
   - High humidity for good leaf growth
   - Mist often
   - Keep daytime temperatures high
   - Propagate by layering or stem cutting

10. Jade plant (*Crassula ovata*)
    - Place in high light (south window)
    - Let dry between watering; excess moisture causes rot; soil should be well drained
    - High temperatures preferred
    - Pot-bounding stimulates flowering
    - Pinch growing tips to produces branching

11. Corn plant (Dracaena fragrans 'Compacta')
    - Place in bright, indirect light away from direct sun
    - Keep soil moist and mist often to keep humid
    - Tolerates cool and warm temperatures
    - Pinch tips for a bushy growth
    - Clean leaves with tepid water
    - Propagate by stem cutting or air layering

12. Rubber plant (*Ficus elastica* 'Robusta')
    - Medium bright light (indirect sunlight)
    - Tolerates low light
    - Mist frequently to maintain high humidity
    - Let soil dry between waterings
    - Water thoroughly and then drain and let dry
    - Clean leaves with moist cloth

13. Asparagus fern (*Asparagus umbellatus*)
    - Prefers high light (full sun)
    - Soil should be kept moist
    - Keep temperature above 50°F
    - Prune often to keep it in shape.
    - Propagate by division; black seeds produced may also be used

14. Chrysanthemum (*Chrysanthemum indicum*) Mums (*Dendranthema grandiflora*)
    - Prefers high light in vegetative growth and medium light in blooms
    - Water moderately; keep soil moist
    - Day temperature is about 50–60°F
    - Cut stems back after blooms to about four inches
    - Pinch stem tips to produce a fuller bushy plant
    - Propagate by stem cuttings

15. Aloe (*Aloe Vera*)
    - Prefers high light (place in south window)
    - Can bloom if light is intense
    - Do not overwater
    - High daytime temperatures needed
    - Fertilize moderately on a monthly basis
    - Propagate by offsets, cuttings, or division

16. Peace lily (*Spathiphyllum wallisii*)
    - Prefers medium light (bright indirect); intolerant of full sun
    - Maintain high humidity and moist soil
    - Temperature should be kept around 80°F during the day
    - Yellowing leaves should be removed
    - Propagate by dividing or seed

17. Snake plant (*Sansevieria trifasciala*)
    - Grows well in medium light (bright, indirect sunlight); tolerant of dim light
    - Drench and drain and let dry between watering; drought tolerant
    - Prefers high room temperature
    - Clean leaves with moist cloth periodically
    - Propagate by cuttings, offset, or rhizome division

18. Swiss cheese plant (*Monstera oblique*)
    - Bright light promotes characteristic windowed leaves
    - Can grow on totem poles or in baskets
    - Low water requirements; keep dry between waterings
    - Prefers moderate temperatures

19. Friendship plant (*Pilea involucrata*)
    - Prefers light shade or medium light
    - Keep soil moist
    - Keep temperatures moderate

20. Poinsettia (*Euphorbia pulcherima*)
    - Place in south window for high light when color is developed
    - Water well but keep dry between waterings
    - Keep temperature moderate during the daytime
    - Cut plant back to about eight inches
    - To have color during next season, place plant in darkness (short photoperiod) from 5 P.M.–8 A.M. for about thirty days starting on October 1

21. Easter lily (*Lilium longiforum*)
    - When in bloom, keep in medium light (bright, indirect sunlight)
    - Water well but keep dry between waterings
    - Prefers cool temperature during bloom
    - Cut the stalk after plant dies, dig bulb, clean and store in cool dry place for planting in early fall
    - Propagate by scales

22. Boston fern (*Nephrolepis exaltata* 'Bostoriensis')
    - Place in east window for medium light
    - Water well but let soil dry between waterings; mist especially during the summer
    - Temperature should be no more than 75°F for best growth
    - Supply fertilizers sparingly
    - Propagate by division or runners; mature spores may also be used

23. Umbrella tree (*Schefflera arboricola* 'Luciana')
    - Place in medium light (bright, indirect sunlight); dim light produces reduced foliage
    - Keep soil dry between watering and mist frequently

- Prefers high temperatures
- Prune as necessary to keep in shape

24. Cyclamen (*Cyclamen persicum* 'Sylvia')
    - Place in east window for medium light
    - Avoid watering leaves directly (promotes crown rot)
    - Prefer cool temperatures
    - Repot when foliage dies
    - Propagate by corm division
    - Plant gets leggy under dim light; cut back to base
    - Propagate stem or tip cutting, air layering, or suckers

25. African violet (*Saintapaulia ionantha*)
    - Keep under medium light (avoid direct sunlight)
    - Keep soil moist, watering with tepid water (cold water can spot leaves)
    - Grows best in high temperatures
    - Fertilize frequently with low analysis fertilizer
    - Remove withered flowers
    - Propagate by leaf cutting, seed or by division

26. Flamingo flower (*Anthurium scherzerianum*)
    - Keep in partial light
    - Keep soil moist
    - Keep in warm place

27. English ivy (*Hedera helix*)
    - Display in bright, indirect light
    - Water well and keep humid
    - Prefers cool temperature
    - Prune to keep shape and control vine length
    - Propagate by stem cutting or division
    - Plant is suitable for training into topiary shapes

28. Hyacinth (*Hyacinthus orientalis*)
    - Display blooming plants in medium light
    - Water often during bloom
    - Keep temperature cool during blooming
    - Fertilize moderately
    - Remove and store bulb in cool place after the stem dies
    - Bulbs need to be precooled before flowering (place bulb in fridge for twelve weeks)

29. Kalanchoe (*Kalanchoe blossfeldianer*)
    - Place in southern window for high light
    - Drench and drain; keep dry between waterings
    - Prefers cool temperatures

30. Dumbcane (*Dieffenbachia seguine*)
    - Grows best in medium light (avoid direct light); can tolerate low light
    - Mist often and keep dry between waterings
    - Prefers high temperatures
    - Cut plant back to base when it becomes leggy
    - Propagate by stem cutting, suckers, or air layering

31. Peperomia (*Peperomia obtusifolia*)
    - Place in medium light; if variegated, the leaves might lose color in low light
    - Do not overwater

- Tolerates cool to warm temperatures
- Prune as necessary to keep shape

32. Flame nettles (*Coleus* spp.)
   - Display in bright or full light for best color development
   - Keep soil moist and mist often
   - Grows best under cool temperatures
   - Pinching helps to shape plant and produce a bushy appearance
   - Propagate by cutting

33. Elephant's ears (*Caladium* spp.)
   - Keep out of direct full light
   - Keep soil moist
   - Grows best under high temperatures

34. Spider plant (*Chlorophytum comosum*)
   - Keep away from direct sunlight; prefers medium light
   - Keep temperatures at moderate level
   - Mist frequently
   - Fertilize moderately
   - Propagate by aerial runners or plantlets
   - Display as hanging basket

35. Croton (*Codiaeum variegatum*)
   - Prefers high light intensity (south window) for full color development
   - Keep temperature moderate
   - Leaves drop under drought stress of improper temperature (drafts)
   - Pinching can be used to create a bushy plant instead of a tall, single-stemmed plant
   - Propagate by air layering, or cuttings

36. Christmas cactus (*Schlumbergera bridgesii*)
   - Keep in south window for high light intensity
   - Keep soil dry between waterings and maintain high humidity
   - Keep temperatures moderate
   - When plant blooms, do not rotate the plant (flowers will drop)
   - Propagate by stem cuttings or seed

Plants that require low light should be placed at least five feet away from the window. Placed closer to the source of light, such plants can suffer severe foliage burn. They may be placed in room corners, hallways, and on shelves. To provide moderate light to plants, they should be placed five to eight feet from the window. Plants that require moderate to bright light should be placed three to five feet near the east and west windows. To receive bright light, plants should be kept two to three feet near the south-facing windows.

SUMMARY

Many plants can be grown indoors, provided the conditions for plant growth are adequately provided. Plants can be grown indoors to enhance the appearances of rooms. They can be strategically positioned to perform other functions such as dividing a room, directing traffic, and hiding unsightly areas. Indoor plant displays can be greatly enhanced by using ornate containers and placing them under a spotlight, for example. It is important that plants be brought indoors from the nursery in good condition. In winter and under severe weather conditions, plants need protection during transport from the nursery to the home. Various parts of the room in a house receive different amounts of light. As such, plants should be located carefully so that they receive the appropriate amount and quality of light. If supplemental lighting is required, artificial light can be provided by using a variety of light source types, such as incandescent light, florescent light, or mercury vapor light. Florescent light sources are most efficient and recommended for home use. Incandescent light generates too much heat in the process of providing light. A room temperature of between 18 and 24°C (64.4 and 75.2°F) is adequate for most plants.

Many houseplants die as a result of excessive watering. The containers and media used should permit free drainage. Plants should be watered only when they need it. They may be watered from below by placing the pot in water or from above by using a watering can. As much as possible, water should not be left on the leaves, because this condition invites disease organisms. Since nurseries frequently use soilless media, plants need to be fertilized at periodic intervals to ensure good growth; either solid or liquid fertilizer preparations may be used. Potted plants outgrow their containers with time and need to be repotted into larger containers. As plants grow larger, some may require artificial support to stand erect. With good care and management, indoor plants seldom become diseased.

REFERENCES AND SUGGESTED READING

Briggs, G. B., and C. L. Calvin. 1987. *Indoor plants*. New York: John Wiley & Sons.

Crockett, J. U. 1972. *Foliage houseplants*. New York: Time-Life.

Perkins, H. O., ed. 1975. *Houseplants: A handbook*. Brooklyn, N.Y.: Brooklyn Botanical Gardens.

Reader's Digest. 1990. *Success with houseplants*. New York: Reader's Digest Association.

Wright, M., ed. 1979. *The complete indoor gardener*. New York: Random House.

Common houseplants
http://www.urbanext.uiuc.edu/houseplants/

Common houseplants
http://www.urbanext.uiuc.edu/houseplants/types_common.html

Examples of poisonous houseplants
ttp://www.blankees.com/house/plants/poisonous.htm

Houseplants problems
http://www.ces.purdue.edu/extmedia/BP/BP-55.html

PRACTICAL EXPERIENCE

Purpose: To study the effect of varying the levels of plant environmental growth factors on the growth of plants.

Materials and methods: Raise tomato seedlings and transplant individual plants into 6-inch (15.2-centimeter) pots (or smaller). Select twelve pots with plants of equal size and group into sets of three pots. Place the pots in an area in the greenhouse where they will be equally exposed to the environmental conditions. Apply four levels of a growth factor (fertilizer, moisture, light, and temperature) to the twelve pots, each set of three pots receiving only one of the levels. One of the levels should be "zero level"—that is, it should have only the normal conditions of the environment (e.g., no fertilizer at room temperature). This is called the control. Suggested levels are 0, $1x$, $2x$, and $3x$ (where x is a unit of the factor being applied). Your instructor will guide you to make the right choices.

Measure (nondestructively) plant characteristics of interest (e.g., height) at weekly intervals. Your instructor will assist you in applying appropriate statistical procedures to summarize the data and plot them graphically. Interpret your results.

OUTCOMES ASSESSMENT

1. Compare and contrast the environmental conditions required for growing plants outdoors and indoors, pointing out how they are managed for optimum plant growth.
2. Discuss, giving examples, how plants are used in the home.
3. Discuss the basis for locating plants in the home on the basis of light requirements.
4. Explain why plants often exhibit some degree of abnormal growth or changes in plant characteristics shortly after being brought home from the commercial greenhouse.
5. Discuss how moisture may be applied safely and effectively to potted plants.
6. Discuss how the materials used in making containers feature in the management of potted plants.
7. Give three major signs that a potted plant needs repotting.
8. Discuss the role of plant growth cycle and seasons in the water and nutrient management of houseplants.
9. Tap water may be injurious to some potted plants. Explain.
10. Discuss the properties of a desirable potting mix.

Controlled-Environment Horticulture

PURPOSE AND EXPECTED OUTCOMES

This chapter is designed to show that plants may be grown outside of their natural environments by providing all of the growth requirements needed and to describe the facilities required for such a plant cultivation practice.

After studying this chapter, the student should be able to

1. Discuss different designs, construction materials, and locations of greenhouses.
2. Describe the methods of controlling indoor plant growth factors (light, temperature, moisture, nutrients, and air) for the benefit of crops.
3. Describe how greenhouses are used in the production of horticultural plants.
4. Compare and contrast greenhouse and field production of crops.

[COLOR PLATES—*see color plates 17 and 18* for additional chapter photos]

SECTION 1

CONTROLLED-ENVIRONMENT FACILITIES AND THEIR OPERATION

OVERVIEW

Plants, like other living organisms, have certain requirements for growth. Climatic conditions are not uniform throughout the world. As such, certain plants are grown or found in nature only in certain regions (i.e., plants are adapted to certain environments). Some plants are more restricted in their range of adaptation. The general principle in choosing plants is that if you desire to grow a plant outside of its region of natural adaptation, you must provide all of the necessary growth requirements (above- and belowground conditions [Chapter 4]) in the new growing environment. Sometimes supplementation of natural conditions such as the provision of additional light is necessary.

In tropical regions of the world where growing seasons are longer, growing flowers indoors is not as popular as growing them outdoors. Outdoor flower gardens can be enjoyed for longer periods of time. On the contrary, the growing season in temperate climates is much shorter. Flowers do not grow outdoors in the cold winter months, which may last more than six months in some areas. In such regions, people desire to grow plants indoors under artificial conditions.

To enjoy flowers or horticultural products out of season, plants must be grown in a *controlled environment*, meaning that humans, not nature, determine how the conditions change. Growers can create stable microclimates that are ideal for specific plants. Otherwise, flowers or crops can be produced elsewhere in due season and imported into an area where the plant is out of season. Although some of this import-export trade in flowers and other horticultural products occurs, the ready availability of controlled-environment structures or facilities called *greenhouses* has spawned an industry that produces off-season ornamentals and vegetables for local and distant markets. This chapter is devoted to the greenhouse industry and discusses its advantages, limitations, design, operation, and maintenance. The culture of plants in liquid media *(hydroponics)*, perhaps the ultimate in controlled-environment production, is also discussed.

12.1 WHAT IS A GREENHOUSE?

Greenhouse
A structure with transparent covering that is used for growing plants under controllable conditions.

A **greenhouse** is a specially constructed building for growing plants under controlled conditions. It is covered with a transparent material and as such permits entry of natural light. The building has no green color but perhaps gets its name from the fact that (green) plants are grown in it. Greenhouses differ in design, size, and the extent of environmental control. Some of the simplest ones are capable of controlling temperature and light. Others are fitted with state-of-the-art computer-based equipment for controlling humidity, light, temperature, nutrients, and soil moisture. In Europe, a greenhouse is called a *glasshouse*.

Small-scale and simply equipped greenhouses are used for the domestic culture of houseplants. Greenhouses are a necessary feature of the horticultural nursery operation, even when plants are grown in season. Commercial greenhouses are widely utilized to produce premium-quality fruits, vegetables, and ornamentals by providing optimal growth conditions for these plants.

12.2 GREENHOUSE DESIGN AND CONSTRUCTION

The most prominent feature of a greenhouse is how it is designed to take advantage of sunlight. As such, except for the foundation, a short wall (called a *curtain wall*) erected above it, and the metallic frame, a greenhouse consists of a transparent material (e.g., glass, plastic film, or fiberglass-reinforced plastic) that freely admits natural light.

12.2.1 TYPES OF GREENHOUSES

There are three basic types of greenhouses: attached, detached (freestanding), and connected. These types of greenhouses are constructed according to one of several styles. The older styles include the following:

1. Even-span
2. Uneven-span
3. Lean-to
4. Quonset
5. Gothic arch

6. Curvilinear
7. Curved eave
8. Dome

Quonset is the most common detached greenhouse design for commercial production. Though suitable for most crops, the growing area and hence productivity is reduced because of the arching of the side walls.

Modern greenhouses are highly sophisticated with a significant amount of automation of operations for increased efficiency. In addition to the modifications and modernizations of older styles of greenhouses, there are newer greenhouse designs concepts, such as the open roof design (Figure 12–1).

Attached Greenhouses

A greenhouse is attached if part of it is connected to a building. *Attached greenhouse* designs and construction are usually simple. They are less expensive to construct because one side is preexisting, which cuts down on the amount of materials needed. However, because they are connected to existing structures, their sizes and uses are affected by the characteristics of the buildings to which they are attached. The buildings may shade the greenhouse at some time of day. Further, light control and ventilation may be problematic. Attached greenhouses are not used for commercial production but are found in homes, commercial buildings, garden centers, and where plant displaying is needed.

A style of greenhouse that is specifically designed to be attached is the *lean-to greenhouse* (Figure 12–2). The ridge of the roof is attached to the preexisting wall such that the roof slopes away from the wall. Lean-to greenhouses are small in size and best

FIGURE 12–1 An open-roof greenhouse used for research at Rutgers University. (*Source:* Dr. AJ Both, Bioresource Engineering, Department of Plant Biology and Pathology, Rutgers University, New Brunswick, NJ 08901)

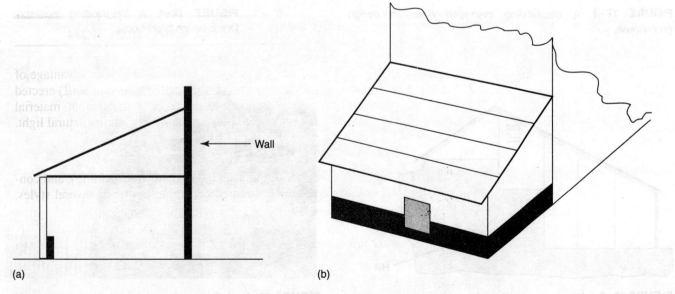

Wall

(a)

(b)

FIGURE 12–2 A lean-to greenhouse:(a) side view and (b) front view.

located on the south side of the building to take advantage of sunlight. Where more space exists, the even-span style (see later section) may be adopted. A lean-to greenhouse may also be window mounted.

Detached Greenhouses

As the name implies, *detached greenhouses* are designed to be freestanding and thus are sometimes called by that name. None of the walls or the roof are attached to a preexisting structure. A detached greenhouse can thus be located such that it takes maximum advantage of environmental factors such as light and wind. Environmental regulation is easier in detached than in lean-to styles. The most common style of greenhouse is the *freestanding even-span greenhouse.* Also called the *A-frame,* this style consists of a symmetrical roof. The even-span, or A-frame design, is the most common design for a glass greenhouse. An even-span design has a symmetrical roof whose slopes have equal pitch and width. The American-style A-frame design has a larger roof surface area (Figure 12–3), and the Dutch design has small gables and a smaller roof surface area (Figure 12–4).

Another detached greenhouse style is the *uneven-span* design (Figure 12–5). This design has asymmetrical roof slopes of unequal pitch and width. While it is adaptable to hillsides or slopes, it does not readily lend itself to modern greenhouse automation and as such is not commonly used.

Greenhouse roofs may be arched, as in the *Quonset* design (Figure 12–6) or the *Gothic arch* design (Figure 12–7). The former design is quite commonly used, while the latter is not.

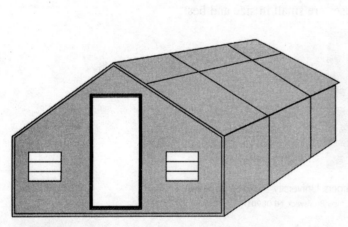

FIGURE 12–3 A freestanding even-span American design greenhouse.

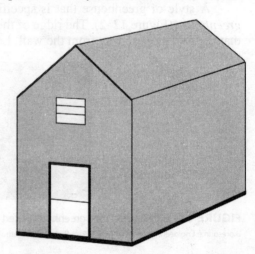

FIGURE 12–4 A freestanding even-span Dutch design greenhouse.

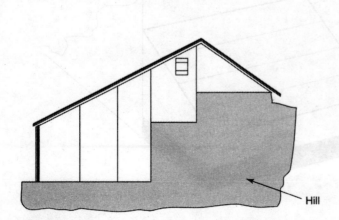

FIGURE 12–5 An uneven-span greenhouse design.

FIGURE 12–6 A Quonset greenhouse design. *(Source: George Acquaah)*

Detached greenhouses have several advantages. Environmental control is easier and can be programmed to meet the needs of a specific production operation. Ventilation is easy to implement, thus limiting carbon dioxide buildup, which can be a limiting factor in plant growth during winter. General operation and maintenance is relatively easier in detached greenhouse designs than attached designs. However, because of their generally vaulted ceilings, they are less energy efficient, increasing operating costs in winter.

Gutter-Connected Greenhouses

Greenhouses of one style can stand alone and are called *Single Span*. Several greenhouses of one style may be joined together to form a *connected greenhouse or Multi span (gutter-connected)*. These greenhouse units are joined along the eaves to create a large, undivided space for a large operation. This arrangement makes the buildings more economical to heat on a per-unit-area basis. Since the junction between two adjacent eaves creates a gutter, *ridge-and-furrow* designs (Figure 12–8) may be in danger of stress from accumulation of snow where this weather pattern exists. Their design takes this potential problem into account by the installation of heating pipes in these depressions to melt away any accumulation of snow when it occurs. Ridge-and-furrow designs are suited to greenhouse production enterprises that require similar environments. When used for smaller projects requiring unique environmental conditions, this type of greenhouse must be partitioned. When Quonset greenhouse units are connected, they form a *barrel-vault greenhouse* (Figure 12–9). Similarly, several lean-to greenhouse units

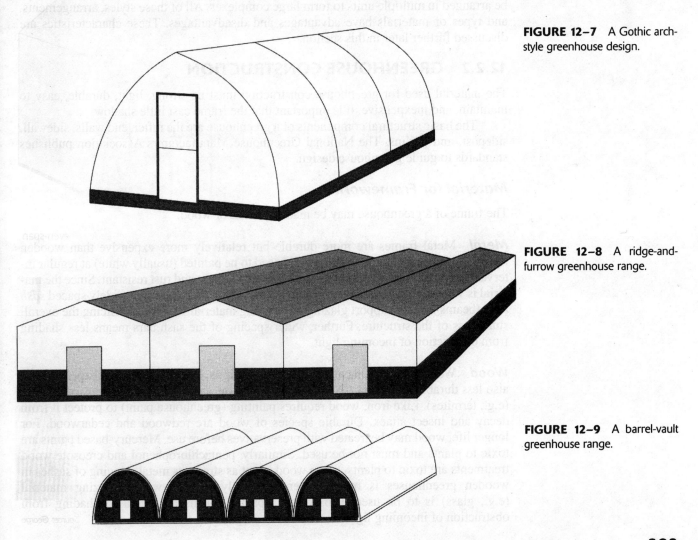

FIGURE 12–7 A Gothic arch-style greenhouse design.

FIGURE 12–8 A ridge-and-furrow greenhouse range.

FIGURE 12–9 A barrel-vault greenhouse range.

FIGURE 12–10 A saw-tooth
greenhouse range.

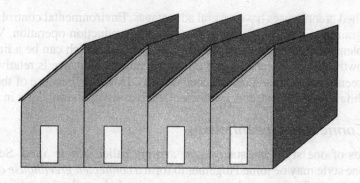

Greenhouse Range
*A collective term for two or
more greenhouses at a
single location belonging
to the same owner.*

may be connected to form a saw-tooth greenhouse (Figure 12–10). *Saw-tooth green-houses* are used in places such as Texas, Florida, and California, where the climate is mild. Large nurseries, for example, may construct a number of greenhouses on one site to form what is collectively called a **greenhouse range.**

The construction costs of connected greenhouses are higher than freestanding designs. The roofs are longer and thus require more structural strength in the framework to support the building. They are also lower, and hence the volume of air space is less, decreasing the amount of carbon dioxide available for plants in winter.

Greenhouses may also be categorized based on the material used in their construction. These materials may further be grouped according to those used in the framework of the structure and those used for framing or covering the structure. Greenhouses may be arranged in multiple units to form large complexes. All of these styles, arrangements, and types of materials have advantages and disadvantages. These characteristics are discussed further later in this section.

12.2.2 GREENHOUSE CONSTRUCTION

The material used for greenhouse construction must be strong, light, durable, easy to maintain, and inexpensive. It is important that the frame cast little shadow.

The basic structural components of a greenhouse are the rafter, end walls, sidewall, sidepost, and purlins. The National Greenhouse Manufacturers Association publishes standards to guide greenhouse design.

Material for Framework

The frame of a greenhouse may be made of metal or wood.

Metal Metal frames are more durable but relatively more expensive than wooden frames. Iron frames are prone to rust and need to be painted (usually white) at regular intervals to prevent rust. Aluminum frames are lightweight and rust resistant. Since the material is very strong, greenhouse designs incorporate fewer and more widely spaced *sash bars* (beams used to support glazing or covering material without sacrificing the overall sturdiness of the structure. Further, wider spacing of the sash bars means less shading from obstruction of incoming light.

Wood Wood was used in early greenhouse designs. It is relatively less expensive but also less durable than metal. Wood decays over time and is susceptible to insect attacks (e.g., termites). Like iron, wood requires painting (greenhouse paint) to protect it from decay and insect attack. Durable species of wood are redwood and cedarwood. For longer life, wood may be treated with preservatives before use. Mercury-based paints are toxic to plants and must not be used. Similarly, pentachlorophenol and creosote wood treatments are toxic to plants. Since wood is not as strong as metal, spacing of sashes in wooden greenhouses is much closer, especially if heavyweight glazing material (e.g., glass) is to be used. Closer sash spacing means an increased shading from obstruction of incoming light.

12.2.3 FRAME DESIGN

There are two basic frame designs: A-frame (gabled) and arched-frame greenhouses (curved arch). The gabled types are more expensive to construct.

A-Frame Greenhouses

In A-frame design, most of the weight of the greenhouse rests on the *side posts,* which are often encased in concrete. These erect posts support the *truss* (consisting of *rafter, strut,* and *chords*). The trusses on either side meet at the peak (ridge) of the roof. Series of trusses are connected by long bars *(purlins)* that run the length of the greenhouse. The end view presents an A-shaped structure called a *gable* (Figure 12–11). The bottom 2 to 3 feet (0.6 to 0.93 meters) of the greenhouse above the ground consists of a wall called the curtain wall, which is made out of materials such as cement or concrete blocks. The curtain wall is the structure to which heating pipes are usually attached. Sash bars are attached to purlins as anchors for panes.

Arched-Frame Greenhouses

In arched-frame greenhouse designs, the trusses are pipes that are bent into an arch and connected by purlins (Figure 12–12). This design is called a Quonset.

12.2.4 GLAZING (COVERING) MATERIAL

The most important role of **glazing** or covering material is transmittance of light. No material can transmit 100 percent of all of the light that strikes its surface. It is hoped that most of the light will be transmitted through the material, but some of it will be absorbed or reflected back into the atmosphere. The materials used for glazing are described in the

Glazing
A transparent material used to cover a greenhouse frame.

FIGURE 12–11 A-frame greenhouse structure: (a) end view and (b) general view.

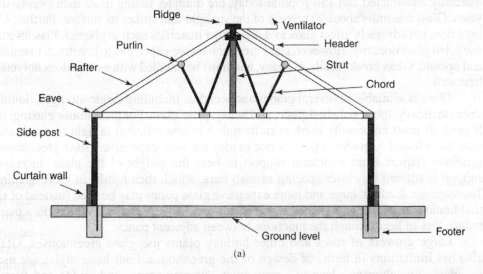

(a)

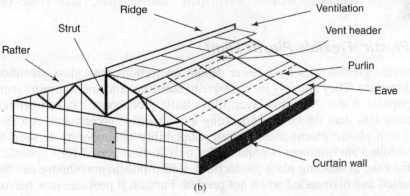

(b)

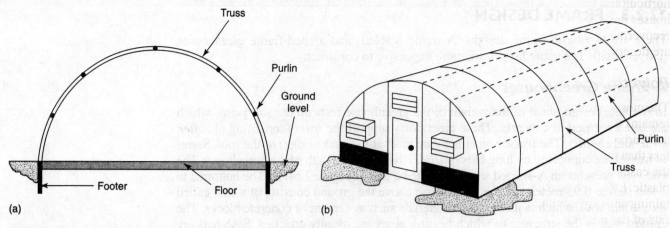

FIGURE 12–12 Arched-frame greenhouse structure: (a) end view and (b) general view.

following sections. The dominant material used varies among the states. In most cases, the single most important glazing used is film plastic.

Glass

Glass is about 70 percent silica dioxide (SiO_2). However, it contains other oxides, including iron trioxide (Fe_2O_3), which may be present at a level between 0 and 1.15 percent. The amount of light glass transmits depends on the iron content; the higher the iron content, the lower the transmittance. Glass used to glaze greenhouses does not transmit light in the ultraviolet (UV) range of the light spectrum. Glass greenhouses, the first to be commercially constructed and still popular today, are durable, lasting more than twenty-five years. Glass transmits about 90 percent of the sunlight that strikes its surface. Further, UV light does not adversely affect glass as it does other materials such as plastics. Plastics may warp, but glass does not. However, glass greenhouses are expensive to construct, maintain, and operate. Glass breaks easily, is heavy, and must be handled with care. It does not retain heat well.

Glass is available in several grades and weights, including single-strength, double-strength, heavy-sheet, polished-plate, and heavy-plate glass. For greenhouse glazing, the B grade is most commonly used, even though it is less efficient in light transmittance than the AA and A grades. The superior grades are very expensive. Glass greenhouses generally require extra structural support to bear the weight of the glass. Increased support is offered by closer spacing of sash bars, which then results in more shading. To overcome shading, large and more expensive glass panes may be used (instead of the traditional size of 16 × 18 inches, some panes are 32 × 36 inches). Wider glass panes reduce loss of heat through the junctions between adjacent panes.

Large growers of roses and other holiday plants use glass greenhouses. Glass also has limitations in terms of design of the greenhouse. Four basic styles are used in glass greenhouses—lean-to, even-span, uneven-span, and ridge-and-furrow designs.

Film Plastic (Flexible Plastic Film)

Film-plastic greenhouses have fewer design restrictions than glass greenhouses and are lightweight. They are very inexpensive to construct and are becoming increasingly more popular in use. A double-layer, film-plastic greenhouse can be operated at over 30 percent less than the cost of operating a comparable greenhouse. Another advantage of film-plastic greenhouses is their adaptability to temporary or short-term use. If a controlled environment is required for only a short period for a specific purpose (as is the case in bedding plant production), a film-plastic greenhouse can be quickly constructed and dismantled when not needed. Further, it provides new persons in the horticultural business a less-expensive means of entering the field. Film-plastic green-houses have disadvantages. They are less durable than glass and may require periodic recovering (e.g., once every three years). The common types of flexible plastic films are described in the following sections.

Polyethylene

The most common but least durable plastic film material is *polyethylene*. This material remains flexible at low temperatures. Polyethylene is permeable to gases such as oxygen and carbon dioxide. Light transmittance through this material is about 5 to 10 percent less than through glass. Ultraviolet light makes plastic material brittle over time, even in the case of the highest-quality, light-resistant, 0.15-millimeter-thick (0.006-inch-thick) plastic. Life expectancy is generally increased by using thicker plastic films or those containing antioxidants and UV inhibitors. These chemical additives reduce the weathering rate of the material. Double sheets of polyethylene inflated with air are widely used for commercial production in places like Texas.

Woven Polyethylene

Woven *polyethylene* is found in greenhouses equipped with retractable roofs (Figure 12–13). This type of roof is made of woven polyethylene, a UV-resistant material capable of preventing water condensation on the inner surface of the roof. It transmits light at the rate of 80 percent of light reaching its surface. High-quality crops are produced under this roof, and the amount of light is closely monitored. The material is quite durable, lasting about five to seven years.

Polyvinyl Fluoride

Another film material, made out of *polyvinyl fluoride,* (Tedlar) is also available. This material is very durable (lasts over ten years), has excellent light transmission properties, and is resistant to UV radiation. It transmits light at a level equivalent to that of glass.

Polyvinyl Chloride

Polyvinyl chloride (pvc) films are more durable than polyethylene films. Unfortunately, vinyl films hold an electrical charge that attracts and holds dust particles over time, thereby reducing light transmittance. Further, it becomes soft on warm days and brittle when temperatures are low. The material transmits long-wavelength infrared radiation at a greatly reduced level, thus reducing heat loss at night.

FIGURE 12–13 Retractable roof greenhouse used for overwintering of nursery crops. The covering material is a woven fabric that is retracted as soon as outdoor conditions allow. The design is strong enough to support some snow and wind load when closed. (*Source:* Dr. AJ Both, Bioresource Engineering, Department of Plant Biology and Pathology, Rutgers University, New Brunswick, NJ 08901)

Ethylene–Vinyl Acetate Copolymers

Ethylene–vinyl acetate copolymers are very expensive and thus not widely used as glazing materials. They are durable, of high light diffusion, and less susceptible to weathering than other materials.

Polymethyl Methacrylate (Acrylic)

Acrylic (plexiglass) is an excellent glazing material. It is weather resistant, lighter than glass, and of comparable light transmission with other materials. Structurally, this material consists of plastic to which acrylic has been chemically bonded. It is more expensive than glass. As a glazing material, it has a tendency to turn yellowish after a period.

Earlier greenhouse designs adapted to plastic films included the A-frame and scissor truss film-plastic types. These designs were temporary structures and built on wooden frames. They had to be protected and preserved through regular painting and wood treatments. Some of the chemicals used (e.g., creosote and pentachlorophenol) were discovered to be toxic to plants. A safer wood treatment is copper naphthenate. More durable and modern designs are made of trusses constructed from metal pipes. A popular one is the Quonset greenhouse. It is very durable, inexpensive, and adaptable to *double-layer covering* with film plastic. A dead-air space is created between the two layers by inflating with a squirrel cage fan. The dead-air space has insulating properties and also prolongs the life of the greenhouse.

Since greenhouses are constructed to be as airtight as possible, condensation of moisture occurs in the internal environment. When plastic coverings are used, droplets of moisture often form on their water-repellent surfaces. Although this condensation poses no immediate danger, when the droplets fall on leaves, a disease-promoting condition is created. The water repellency can be eliminated by spraying detergents on the film surface.

Fiberglass-Reinforced Plastic

Fiberglass-reinforced plastic is a semirigid glazing material and can be bent. It is used in constructing Quonset and even-span greenhouses. The light transmission of this material when newly installed is near the quality of glass. However, with time, the light transmittance reduces as a result of etching and accumulation of dust. Fiberglass-reinforced plastic lasts about ten to fifteen years. The fiberglass content disperses light such that its intensity in the greenhouse is more uniform. Greenhouses constructed from this material are also easier to cool than glass greenhouses. They are available in different colors. However, the clear type permits the greatest light transmission, at a level equivalent to that of glass. They are available in flat or corrugated forms. Greenhouses constructed from fiberglass-reinforced plastic and other plastics are more expensive to insure because they are prone to extreme heat or fire damage. These materials are said to be *thermosetting,* or heat setting. However, fire-retardant fiberglass-reinforced material is available.

Rigid Sheet Plastics

Rigid plastics, when cut into panes (resembling glass panes), may be used as glazing materials for greenhouses. The most popular rigid plastic materials are acrylic and polycarbonates and are available as single- and double-layered rolls. Double-layered types are more durable and increase the energy efficiency of greenhouses by about 50 percent over glass greenhouses. Rigid plastic and glass are the most expensive glazing materials in use. Acrylic may last up to twenty-five years, and polycarbonate may last between ten and fifteen years. Because they are relatively less heavy than glass, they require less support and hence are adaptable to wider sash bar spacing. Using fewer sash bars reduces the amount of shading.

Saran Plastic Mesh

Saran-glazed greenhouses are used where the intensity of sunlight is very high. This mesh plastic film is used to provide shade, and hence the greenhouses glazed with this material are sometimes described as saran shade houses. They are used in areas such as Florida,

Texas, Hawaii, and California. The material is available in a range of colors, thicknesses, and closeness of weave. These factors affect the degree of shading provided by the material.

12.2.5 SEALING THE GREENHOUSE

A greenhouse is a controlled environment and should be constructed with an "airlock" entrance design. This design incorporates an entrance porch that prevents direct ingress of undesirable wind, soil, insects, and spores into the facility. Greenhouses with this design make it easier to open and close doors when the fans are operating.

12.2.6 GROUND COVER

Greenhouses with bare grounds that expose the native soil are prone to weeds and soil borne pathogens. Some producers line the grounds with gravel. Plastic may be used as flooring material, but concrete flooring is most durable, improving sanitation as well as facilitating the movement of materials in the structure.

12.2.7 COLD FRAMES AND HOTBEDS

Cold frames and **hotbeds** are simple climate-controlling structures for growing plants on a limited scale. The difference between a cold frame and a hotbed is that the latter is simply a cold frame fitted with a heating system. Heat may be supplied by electrical cables beneath the soil or steam run through pipes along the wall. Environmental control is limited to opening and closing the structure or rolling away the covering for aeration and temperature modification (Figure 12–14). The designs are variable. They may either be attached to a regular greenhouse or erected separately. The glazing may be clear plastic or glass. Cold frames are heated by sunlight, which makes their operation very inexpensive. However, their use is limited since environment cannot be controlled. Cold frames may be used for hardening purposes, rooting of hardwood cuttings, raising vegetable seedlings, and limited production of crops such as lettuce, radish, cucumber, and sweet potato. Placing a thermometer inside of a cold frame to monitor the environmental temperature is recommended. For cool-season crops, the structure should be ventilated whenever the temperature reaches 21°C (70°F). Warm-season crops can tolerate a higher temperature, and ventilation is thus needed only when the temperature rises to about 30°C (86°F). Cold frames are not as popular as they once were, largely because greenhouses that provide a broader range of environmental control are used widely.

Cold Frame
An enclosed, unheated covered frame used for growing and protecting young plants in early spring, and for hardening off seedlings.

Hotbed
A bed of soil enclosed in transparent material and heated to provide a warm medium for germination of seeds or rooting of cutting.

12.2.8 CROP TUNNELS

Crop tunnels or high tunnels are structures designed to provides early- and late-season protection of crops for high product quality (see Chapter 20). These structures are about sixteen to twenty-five feet wide and about four to eight feet high. Production of crop like blueberry, strawberry, vegetables, cut flowers, and perennials all experience higher

FIGURE 12–14 A cold frame. *(Source: Peter Anderson © Dorling Kindersley)*

quality of the harvested product when protected from the elements (wind, frost, rain, cold) during production. Strawberries grown under crop tunnels arrive early as well as late on the market for producers to obtain higher prices during these times when demand exceeds supply. Also, the shelf life of fruits is extended by the production.

12.2.9 LOCATING A GREENHOUSE

Greenhouse production is initially capital intensive and hence must be embarked upon only after good planning. The following are important factors for consideration in locating a greenhouse.

Market

The grower must first identify the potential market in terms of its size and distance from the production site.

Accessibility

Greenhouse accessibility is closely related to its potential market. The production site should be readily accessible to the primary customers. If a retail operation is intended, the greenhouse should be located where the general public can readily reach the facility. Certain production operations require that products be delivered promptly to sales outlets. Transportation between greenhouse site and markets should be reliable and convenient. Cut flowers may be able to survive several days of refrigeration with little loss in quality. It is important that supplies for production be delivered on schedule even in inclement weather.

Greenhouses should be readily accessible by a reliable means of transportation because production inputs (including soil mixes, fertilizers, pesticides, and seed) and the harvested produce must be hauled to and from the greenhouse. Locating a greenhouse enterprise near markets significantly reduces operational costs. *Bedding* and *potted plants* are expensive to transport; consequently, these enterprises should be located near primary market outlets, if possible.

Climatic Conditions

The patterns of weather factors including light, rainfall distribution and other precipitation (e.g., snow, ice, and sleet), and winds affect production costs (e.g., heating, cooling, and lighting). High elevations may provide cleaner air but are colder, requiring more heating in the cold season. Establishing a production enterprise for a crop that requires warm conditions in an area that is mostly cold will increase heating costs (unless the area has a great potential market to offset the additional costs).

Topography

Topography affects the drainage of the area. Greenhouses use large amounts of water and must be located on soils that drain freely. Further, it is easier to mechanize operations if the site is flat. It is more difficult to maneuver on slopes than on flat land. Construction costs may not vary, but it is easier to automate a greenhouse built on level ground than one built on a hill.

Utilities

Another factor to consider in locating a greenhouse is the source of water. Greenhouses use large amounts of water for a variety of activities such as watering plants, washing, and maintaining high humidity inside of the facility. If an urban-treated water supply is not accessible, an alternate source of water must be found (e.g., a well). It is critical that the source of water be reliable to provide water year-round. The success of certain production practices depends on the availability of water. The quality of water is also critical, since certain plants are adversely affected by specific pollutants (e.g., fertilizers and pesticides). Pollutants can make water acidic or alkaline. Supplemental light is also required, as is a source of heat for times when the temperature drops below a desirable level. Providing artificial light and heat requires a source of energy. The greenhouse should be located where there is ready access to a reliable and economic energy (fuel) supply.

Labor Supply

The location of a greenhouse should also take into account the kind and availability of labor. Certain chores in the greenhouse are not automated but require some level of skill. Not all greenhouse operations are readily amenable to automation.

Types of Production Enterprises

The type of production enterprise is related to the accessibility factors. Bulky products (e.g., potted plants) are expensive to transport over long distances.

Zoning Laws

Various localities have zoning regulations regarding location of an agricultural enterprise and building codes.

Future Expansion

For a commercial venture, it is advisable to acquire more land than needed immediately. This extra land will allow future expansion to be undertaken as needed.

12.2.10   GREENHOUSE ORIENTATION

The location of a greenhouse is critical to its efficiency. The orientation of the structure has a bearing on the temperature variations experienced within a greenhouse. It is important that tall structures (such as tall trees and buildings) that might cast shade (especially on the south side of the greenhouse) not be in the vicinity. This natural light advantage is diminished when greenhouses are located in areas of intense fog or highly cloudy areas. Shadows are also cast by the frames used for construction. To reduce this occurrence, the ridge of greenhouses in regions above 40 degrees north latitude should be oriented in an east-west direction so that the low angle of winter light has a wider area to enter the house from the side rather than from the end.

12.2.11   GREENHOUSE BENCHES AND BEDS

Greenhouse production occurs either in *ground beds* (in the ground) or on *benches* (raised platforms). The design and layout of these structures should facilitate greenhouse operations and make the most efficient use of space.

Beds and benches in a greenhouse are located so as to allow personnel to freely move around and work and also to move greenhouse equipment such as carts and trolleys. To accommodate equipment, the principal aisles should be about 3 to 4 feet (0.93 to 1.24 meters) wide. Some arrangements are more efficient than others in terms of the efficient use of space. The more usable space, the greater the profits from a greenhouse operation.

In terms of where the planting media and containers are located, three strategies may be adopted in a greenhouse production enterprise.

No Bench

No bench, or floor benching, is the practice in which production takes place directly on the floor of the greenhouse. The floor may be covered with gravel or concrete and should be well draining. It is best to have a gentle slope in the floor so that excess irrigation water drains into a gutter and is carried out of the facility. Gravel covers and porous concrete are prone to weed infestation. Bedding and seasonal plants such as poinsettia are commonly grown on floor benches. Aisle space is created by the way flats or containers are arranged on the floor (Figure 12–15). If done properly, up to about 90 percent of the floor space can be utilized for production.

FIGURE 12–15 A no-bench greenhouse production system showing plants placed directly on the floor. *(Source: George Acquaah)*

FIGURE 12–16 Raised bench. *(Source: George Acquaah)*

Raised Benches

Raised benches are suited to potted plant production. Most greenhouses have raised benches of a wide variety of designs and constructions. Some of them are makeshift and temporary, consisting of brick legs and movable bench tops. The top may be of wood, concrete, or wire mesh and may or may not have side boards (Figure 12–16). Metal benches are most common. Molded plastic is sometimes used to make troughs in which potted plants are grown. This material is also used in the construction of benches for ebb-and-flow irrigation. Notwithstanding the material used, the bench must have a system for draining properly. If wood is used, cedar, redwood, and cypress make good bench materials because they resist decay. Wooden benches may be painted with copper naphthenate preservative to prevent decay. Redwood has natural preservatives that are corrosive to iron and steel; as such, nails and other construction materials that come into contact with this wood should be of different materials such as aluminum or zinc.

The height of the bench above the floor should be such that cultural operations (e.g., pinching, spraying, harvesting, and staking) are facilitated. Width of the bench is also important. It should be narrow (3 to 6 feet or 0.93 to 1.86 meters) enough to permit pots located in the middle rows to be easily reached. Air should be able to move freely around and under the bench, as well as around the pots on the bench.

Ground Benches or Beds

Plants to be grown for several years that will grow tall in the process (e.g., cut flower plants such as roses) are planted in ground beds (Figure 12–17). Ground beds vary in design and construction. Using ground beds can be problematic from the standpoint of disease control. If the ground bed has no real bottom in terms of depth, diseases such as bacterial wilt are hard to control because of the impracticality of thorough pasteurization of the soil to a reasonable depth. To correct this problem, concrete bins may be constructed in the ground to hold the soil and to facilitate periodic pasteurization to control soilborne diseases. These concrete bins have V-shaped bottoms and drain holes for good drainage. They should be about 6 to 12 inches (12.2 to 30.5 centimeters) deep, depending on the plant to be grown. When drainage is poor, drainage tiles may be installed and overlaid with gravel before topping with the root medium. Walkways should be strategically located between beds to allow gardeners easy access to the beds to prepare them, plant the crop, care for it, and harvest the produce. These spaces should be graded so that water flows away from the beds to reduce

FIGURE 12–17 Greenhouse production of lettuce in soil. (*Source:* Dr. AJ Both, Bioresource Engineering, Department of Plant Biology and Pathology, Rutgers University, New Brunswick, NJ 08901)

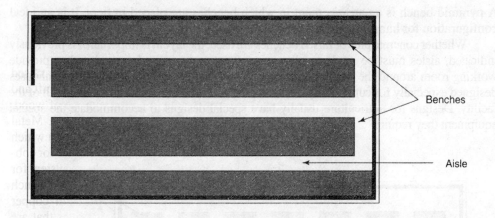

Benches

Aisle

FIGURE 12–18 Longitudinal layout of greenhouse benches.

contamination from pathogens carried on the wheels of carts and wheelbarrows and the shoes of gardeners.

12.2.12 LAYOUT (ARRANGEMENT)

The five types of bench arrangements commonly used in greenhouses are described in the following sections. The layout depends on the crop and the nature of the production enterprise, taking into account row spacing, irrigation type, and structural support systems (e.g., trellises).

Longitudinal Arrangement

In a longitudinal arrangement, beds or benches are constructed to run the full length of the greenhouse in several rows (Figure 12–18). This arrangement is associated with cut flower production. It is easier to conduct mechanized operations with this type of arrangement, which provides for long, uninterrupted production areas. However, moving across the facility is hampered and requires workers to go all of the way to one end of one row to make a turn to the next row.

Cross-Benching

Cross-benching is like the longitudinal arrangement except that the orientation of the benches are not lengthwise with respect to the greenhouse but are arranged crosswise (Figure 12–19). The benches are shorter and aisles numerous. Although the aisle space significantly reduces the usable area of the greenhouse, movement around the greenhouse is easier with this arrangement.

Peninsula Arrangement

The difference between the peninsula arrangement and cross-benching is the presence of a primary central aisle in the former that runs the entire length of the greenhouse. The primary aisle in cross-benching runs along the wall (Figure 12–20).

Movable Benches

Movable benches are especially popular container production enterprises. To maximize the use of space, some greenhouse designs include movable benches and one aisle. When work on one bench is completed, the bench is mechanically moved so that work can be completed on the next bench (Figure 12–21).

Pyramid Bench

A pyramid bench is an arrangement in which benches are placed in tiers. It is an ideal configuration for hanging basket production.

Whether concrete bins or raised benches are used, the layout is important. As previously indicated, aisles must be made to allow equipment to be moved around and to provide working room around the bench while maximizing the use of floor space. In greenhouses designed especially for cut flower production, the ground bed may run the full length of the facility. Designs for nutriculture usually have special designs to accommodate the special equipment they require.

FIGURE 12–19 Cross benching layout of greenhouse benches.

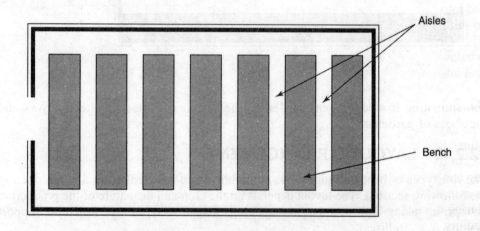

FIGURE 12–20 Peninsula arrangement of greenhouse benches.

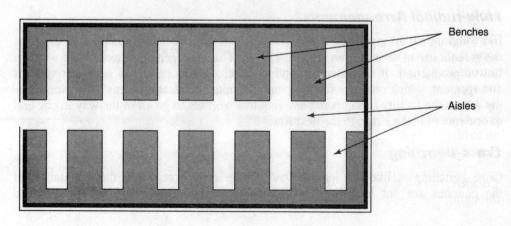

FIGURE 12–21 Moving tables allowing for maximized space efficiency of the greenhouse growing area. Note the heating pipes used to provide "bottom heat" to the seedlings grown on the tables. (*Source:* Dr. AJ Both, Bioresource Engineering, Department of Plant Biology and Pathology, Rutgers University, New Brunswick, NJ 08901)

12.3 INTERNAL ENVIRONMENTAL CONTROL

Greenhouses are controlled-environment facilities because the user is able to adjust at least some of the plant environmental growth factors to meet specific needs. The factors and their control are discussed in the following sections. Modern greenhouse climate control is highly automated. Sensors are installed for measuring factors including temperatures (of the air, water, and growth media), humidity, wind speed, wind direction, solar radiation, carbon dioxide concentration, and rainy conditions. The information is fed into computers with climate control software to regulate the greenhouse conditions to suit the crop or plant cultural activity.

Greenhouse climate is controlled primarily through devices as open motorized windows or vents, ventilations fans, circulations fans, heaters, heating circles cooling pads and misters, thermal shades, sprayers and evaporators, and carbon dioxide generations.

12.3.1 TEMPERATURE

The daytime temperature in greenhouses is usually higher than the nighttime temperature. Room temperature in most greenhouses is maintained at about 13 to 18.5°C (55 to 65°F) (at night) and 18.5 to 27°C (65 to 80°F) higher during the day. Maintaining temperature is the next most expensive operational cost after labor. The greenhouse is essentially a giant solar collector. The sunlight energy that enters the greenhouse during the day is trapped (*greenhouse effect*) and used in heating up the contents of the facility.

How Heat Is Lost

Temperature control is perhaps the major reason for greenhouse use. Greenhouse temperature depends on the heat balance or net energy between the greenhouse system and its surrounding environment. The goals of heating a greenhouse are to provide heat at the appropriate time and in the appropriate amount, distribute it effectively through the facility, and conserve it. The ideal situation is to maintain a stable air temperature in the greenhouse by adding heat at the same rate at which it is lost. Fuel cost is a big contributor to high overhead in greenhouse enterprises. Therefore, heat loss should be minimized. Heat is lost from greenhouses by three ways: *conduction, infiltration,* and *radiation.*

Conduction **Conduction heat loss** is the principal mode of heat loss and occurs through the material used in framing and glazing the greenhouse. Metals conduct heat

Conducting Heat Loss
Heat loss by transmission through a barrier such as a greenhouse glazing material.

BUILDING AND MAINTAINING GREENHOUSES FOR ENERGY SAVINGS

A.J. BOTH AND D.R. MEARS

Rutgers University

BACKGROUND

Historically the energy consumption of a commercial greenhouse was not necessarily a very high priority item in either facility design or subsequent management. One significant exception was the energy crisis of the 1970's brought on by the oil embargo of 1973, which resulted in shortages of supply and rapidly escalating costs. With the shortages causing significant disruptions there was general consensus that fossil fuels represent a finite supply that must eventually be replaced with sustainable energy resources and that it was prudent for the country to take steps to free itself of dependence on Middle East oil. This stimulated government and industry support of a significant research program on energy conservation and alternative energy sources for commercial greenhouses at several land grant universities. The application of the results of these efforts enabled many greenhouse operations to substantially reduce energy consumption and costs. For those who implemented the most effective steps to reduce fossil fuel use for energy, further significant improvements are much more difficult to discover and implement.

More recently as energy prices climbed past $30 per barrel in the summer of 2004 and later past $60, the cost of energy again renewed concerns of most greenhouse growers. There are some significant differences between the two situations. After the embargo ceased and subsequent price increases moderated there was a long period of relative price stability and net decrease in real energy costs for greenhouse operations that implemented key conservation strategies that were developed. The response of government and industry to substantially fund energy conservation and alternative energy supply research specifically for the greenhouse industry led to significant savings possibilities, but similar responses are not redeveloping recently. The issues that drive recent concerns for energy supply are more complex than earlier. There seems little likelihood of a near term sustained period of price reduction or even price stability. Society in general is now more aware that fossil fuel resources, especially natural gas and oil, are finite and that while some new resources will no doubt be discovered rising global consumption is likely to outstrip the rate of new discoveries. The environmental impact of burning fossil fuels is now much more widely understood than 30 years ago. Political instability in key production regions combined with international terrorism activities substantially compromise supply security regardless of price.

CONSERVATION DEVELOPMENTS

The design of the greenhouse structure and the environmental control equipment selected has major impact on the energy consumption of the facility. Beyond that, for any given system there are many factors, beyond alteration of the facility and equipment that the greenhouse manager can implement to optimize energy use for the best management of the crop. There are many good sources of information on energy conservation measures that for any production greenhouse and on the factors to consider in building new facilities or upgrading existing structures or equipment. A comprehensive and extremely useful publication is "Energy Conservation for Commercial Greenhouses," compiled from information developed through an integrated collaborative Northeast Regional

Research program on greenhouse engineering, Bartok, 2001. This publication is available from NRAES, Ithaca, NY, http://www. nraes.org/. There is a website devoted to greenhouse engineering issues maintained by Michigan State University: http://www.hrt.msu.edu/ Energy/ Notebook.htm . There are additional links to information as well as a number of energy related publications posted on the Rutgers Horticultural Engineering website: http://aesop.rutgers.edu/~horteng/.

There are several greenhouse design developments that have significant energy conserving features even if this was not the primary reason for the development. One such is the use of multi-span greenhouses for large facilities rather than a number of single-span units. In exercises 1 and 2 the heat requirements for single and multi-span units can be compared. While the major advantages of the larger unit are the ease of conducting cultural operations and the economy of construction, there is also an energy advantage as the common sidewalls are eliminated reducing the structural area for heat loss. A good rule of thumb is that when the total greenhouse space needed will equal or exceed three single span structures a multi-span unit should be seriously considered.

Another is the development of low-cost plastic film greenhouse structures. The first plastic film covered greenhouses consisted of single layer plastic films fastened with nailers on wooden frames. A significant problem when growing small seedlings was the dripping of condensation, which accumulated on the cold film. To alleviate this problem, a second plastic film layer was added. One early method of construction involved putting on the first layer with a wooden nailer on the rafters that was then also the spacer between the layers. The outer layer was then added with additional nailers to hold this second layer. When recovering, both sets of nailers needed to be removed and then reapplied.

While the initial motivation for double layer covering was to alleviate condensation dripping, it was also noted that the insulating property of the airspace reduced energy consumption by about a third. The breakthrough that made double-layer plastic-film covering practical on a wide scale was the use of a small inflation blower to lightly pressurize air to separate the layers. With this technique it is no longer necessary to add multiple nailers and the glazing need only be fastened around the perimeter of each pair of sheets. The development of this concept and its impact has been recognized by the ASAE Historic Landmark designation given the first structure of this type located on the Rutgers campus. A full discussion of this development and its impact can be found under the ASAE Historic Landmark Dedication link on the home page of the Rutgers University Horticultural Engineering website, http:// aesop.rutgers. edu/~horteng/.

Another effort originally undertaken to solve one problem that evolved into a major energy conservation tool was an undertaking to develop a simple, low-cost, mechanical drive system for black cloth photoperiod control that could be installed by a grower. After installing a system in a glass greenhouse the idea of utilizing the closed curtain for energy savings at night was tried and the first experiment indicated about a fifty percent heat savings. This effort also prepared a good basis for later work on movable curtain systems with materials selected for energy conservation and/or shading. Greenhouse shade and heat retention materials and systems are available for a wide range of solar shading and significant energy savings for night heating are also realized. When a movable curtain system is to be selected for both shading and heat retention the material should be selected for its shading property first. In some cases it is desirable to install more than one curtain for finer control of shading and cumulative heat savings. Exercise 5 can be done for several choices of commercially available curtain materials and the relative energy savings compared.

To further understand the potential of moving curtain systems for energy conservation, a series of experiments were carried out in a small research greenhouse and an environmental control chamber (Simpkins et al., 1976). The energy savings of a curtain system in a greenhouse are due both to the insulating value of a trapped airspace between the curtain and the glazing and the ability of the curtain to block outgoing thermal radiation.

Since glass is essentially opaque to thermal radiation, the major contribution to energy savings of a curtain in a single glazed glass greenhouse is the reduction of conductive and convective heat loss by the creation of a dead air space. Radiative heat loss from a glass greenhouse is a two-step process, from the crop to the glazing and then from the glazing to the external environment.

Double-layer plastic-film covering already has the advantage of an enclosed air space with additional energy savings achieved by adding a second dead air space by installing the curtain. Pure polyethylene is highly transparent to thermal radiation so most radiative heat loss is directly from the crop canopy through the covering to the external environment. For this reason the thermal emmisivity of a curtain material used for energy savings in a polyethylene covered greenhouse is very important. It was found that aluminized materials with a very low thermal emmisivity are preferable for reducing the radiative component of the heat loss. For all curtain materials it was found important to achieve good closure at the edges and ends to prevent air circulation around the curtain, which would reduce the insulating value of the trapped air space.

The energy conserving potential of a number of different curtain materials were evaluated during the 1970's at several universities and other institutions. When employed in glass greenhouses a major benefit of the curtain is the creation of a dead air space between the curtain and the glazing. Curtain materials with relatively low thermal emissivity, such as aluminized materials, will transmit less energy to the glass by radiation. Glass itself absorbs thermal radiation contributing significantly to reduction in thermal radiation heat loss relative to pure polyethylene, which has a high transmission of thermal radiation. In the case of double layer polyethylene greenhouses there is already a dead air space so the savings due to adding another such space with the curtain is less significant than in a single glazed greenhouse. However, as pure polyethylene is highly transmisive of thermal radiation the radiative properties of the curtain are more significant than for curtain materials installed under glass. Aluminized materials with low thermal emissivity are particularly effective at reducing heat loss from the crop to the sky by radiation.

Initially there were no materials available that had been specifically designed for greenhouse energy conservation so trials were based primarily on materials developed for other uses and adapted to this application. Radiation heat loss is significantly greater under clear skies than cloudy or rainy conditions so the actual heat savings will vary with weather conditions. The average savings for the best of the materials tested was over half for both types of glazing systems, with the major benefit being the first dead air space for single glazed structures and the major benefit the radiative property of the curtain material for double polyethylene structures. While almost none of these early materials tested are in current use, in later years other materials have been specifically designed for greenhouse applications.

In the early 1980's research was undertaken at Rutgers University on the energy conserving potential of adding an infrared (IR) absorbing material to polyethylene greenhouse covering to overcome the problem of high radiation loss through such covers. Earlier research had shown the increased significance of radiation loss in polyethylene-covered greenhouses relative to glass. The purpose of this research program was first to document and confirm the energy savings potential of and IR additive, second to determine what significant changes in plant growth could be expected, and finally to better understand the details of heat loss through double layer polyethylene covering with and without the IR inhibition feature, (Simpkins et al., 1984).

Four experimental greenhouses were constructed and fully instrumented so that glazing systems of IR film, non-IR film and combinations could be compared. Instrumentation included a full weather station and instruments to measure total energy transmission, PAR transmission, net heat radiation both from the plant canopy to the glazing and from the glazing to the sky as well as infrared thermometry to measure plant surface temperature and numerous thermocouple temperature sensors. An important aspect of this complete instrumentation system was the ability to constantly evaluate heat loss from the greenhouses both in terms of total heat loss and the component of heat loss that was radiation under all weather conditions. Earlier work on measuring heat loss from greenhouses equipped with a variety of curtain insulation systems had demonstrated the significant variation in transfer rates under different weather conditions. From this work it was possible to develop a quantitative relationship between the heat loss coefficient of each covering system and the weather conditions as defined by wind speed and sky clearness index. It was found that the sky clearness index has a strong influence on radiative heat loss from the greenhouse that is substantially reduced by the IR inhibitor.

In addition to determining the heat loss characteristics of the different films and their combinations, light transmission and changes in transmission were evaluated. PAR light transmission of both types of film were generally comparable with the non-IR film having slightly greater transmission initially and both films loosing some transmission over time due to a combination of dirt build up and film darkening. Both film darkening and reduction in light transmission due to dirt accumulation were measured at the end of the test period. As the IR film did not darken as much or accumulate as much dirt over time it had slightly greater light transmission in the second year of use. Another effect of the IR inhibitor, which is generally accepted as significant for improved plant production, is that the transmitted light is much more diffuse than is the case for the non-IR film. The heat savings in the series of tests varied from about 25% to 40% depending upon weather conditions. While the specific film developed and tested in the early 1980's is no longer commercially available, IR inhibited films are in widespread use with similar energy savings characteristics according to manufacturers. An important aspect of both IR inhibited plastic films and internal curtain systems is that in addition to the energy savings, the reduction in heat loss by radiation results in significant increases in plant tissue temperatures relative to the greenhouse air which can result in slightly lower thermostat settings for air temperature resulting in additional energy savings.

Another research activity of the late 1960's, not initially regarded has having energy savings consequences, was focused on improving the watering systems for tomato production in trough culture. While doing this work, several attempts were made to also increase the temperature of the root zone by watering with warm water but it was found that within less than an hour, with evaporation and other heat loss, soil temperature had returned to its initial condition. Therefore several techniques were tried to keep the soil warm, including circulating water in plastic tubes under the beds, which served to keep the soil warmer and did improve growth. This observation led to an increasing interest in using floor-heating systems to augment traditional overhead heating systems and to reduce the difference between colder root zone and warmer overhead air temperatures for crops grown on the floor. Without soil heating, it is often necessary to overheat the greenhouse air to achieve target soil temperatures. An independently controlled soil heating system has the potential to reduce the total energy requirement by reducing the air temperature and thus the heat loss from the greenhouse. More importantly, the ability to have somewhat independent control of soil and air temperature enables the grower to find the right combination of soil and air temperatures for a given crop and at a given stage of development. In general, the aim of the environmental control engineer should be to provide environmental control tools to the grower, and clearly independent control of soil and air temperature give more management opportunities to the grower.

A number of techniques have been developed for root zone heating in greenhouses and during research at Rutgers University heat transfer coefficients for many have been measured and used to guide system design (Roberts and Mears, 1980). More detailed information on the research and guidance on system design is available on the Horticultural Engineering web site and in the publication NRAES-3. Early research focused on designs incorporating plastic or rubber tubing in porous concrete floors. Porous concrete, produced with aggregate and cement but no sand, provides a solid working surface and good drainage for pots and flats placed directly on the floor. Both small diameter tubing and 3/4 inch plastic pipe were initially studied to determine the uniformity of floor surface temperature and heat transfer rate as determined by the spacing of the pipes within the floor and the arrangement and moisture condition of the pots or flats on the floor.

Through the extension program, a large number of commercial installations of floor heating systems were designed for growers to install on their own throughout the world. In addition some bench top systems were designed utilizing 1/2 or 3/4 inch plastic tubing, and smaller diameter tubing systems provided by commercial suppliers have come into widespread use. In all cases it is important to design the system so that the floor or bench surface is heated uniformly so the crop will be uniform. An important characteristic of root zone heating systems is the large heat storage capacity. Soil temperature will only change slowly in response to changes in the aerial environment or changes in the temperature of the circulating water that is the heat source. This means that, unlike air temperature, root zone temperatures cannot be programmed to change significantly except over long time periods.

To consider the implications of the energy conservation aspects of the various greenhouse design choices discussed above consider the energy requirements representative designs of commercial greenhouses. In Table 1 below the annual heat requirement for an acre of growing space at temperatures ranging from 50 to 70°F have been calculated based on a 10 year composite hourly weather data base for the Philadelphia International Airport. Similar calculations could be prepared for locations with different weather patterns and compared with commercial experience. The heat transfer coefficients for glass, polyethylene and IR inhibited polyethylene used in this table are based on values presented in NRAES-3 and the glass plus curtain figures are based on tests done in The Netherlands for modern curtain materials. The coefficients for plain and IR inhibited polyethylene with modern curtain materials are estimated from the others. These figures are useful for comparative purposes but it is important to note that specific building design, location and exposure to wind, installation of glazing and curtain systems, heating system design and other factors all affect actual fuel consumption.

Single span greenhouses would require more fuel than multi-span gutter-connected units for all temperatures as seen by comparing the first two rows. For example, for greenhouses in reasonably good repair running at 65°F, an acre of single span glass houses could require about 123,000 Therms while a gutter-connected block of the same size would need about 80,000 Therms. For the calculations in Table 1 the wall heights were all assumed at 12 feet, though even higher wall and gutter heights are becoming increasingly popular. Reducing wall height would have some significant savings for the single span units but not for the gutter connected designs. A significant advantage of a gutter connected greenhouse for large areas is that with the elimination of many side walls the heat loss from the walls is minimized relative to that through the roof and relative to the floor growing area. Increased height is advantageous in that space is available for mechanical systems, curtain systems, lighting and automation. Also research and experience has shown that height promotes uniformity of environmental conditions, particularly in cooling.

Continuing with the comparison at 65°F, an acre block of gutter-connected double-layer polyethylene would only need 50,000 Therms and adding a good energy conserving curtain system could reduce this requirement to 37,000 Therms. The development of IR

TABLE 1   Annual per acre heat requirement in Therms

Greenhouse Temperature °F →	50	55	60	65	70
Small single span glass units	48,582	69,074	93,330	123,041	161,823
Large gutter connected glass	30,393	42,662	59,014	80,490	107,342
Gutter con. plain polyethylene	18,089	25,949	36,529	49,949	66,097
Gutter con. IR poly	11,701	16,946	24,025	32,915	43,683
Gutter con. poly + curtain	13,204	19,216	27,231	37,353	49,484
Gutter con. IR poly + curtain	8,995	12,993	18,252	24,897	33,027
Gutter con. Glass + curtain	13,037	18,980	26,911	36,884	48,928

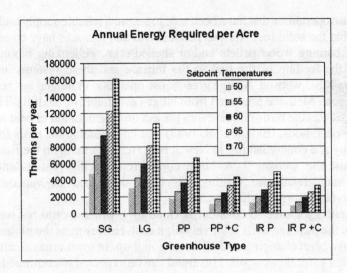

FIGURE 1 Annual energy required per acre by greenhouse type. *(Source: A.J. Both and D.R. Mears)*

inhibited film reduces heat requirements significantly relative to uninhibited film and the IR additive reduces the 50,000 Therm heat requirement to about 33,000. Combining the IR feature with the curtain system provides a further reduction to 25,000 Therms. Thus the grower with an acre under IR inhibited poly with a modern curtain system has almost a 5:1 advantage on his heat bill relative to a competitor in single span glass units with no curtain.

Of course operating temperature has a significant impact on all greenhouse designs, particularly in the milder months of spring and fall. Those greenhouses kept at warmer temperatures would need more heat than those running cooler as shown by comparing columns in Table 1 for all designs. Any management strategy that allows for temperature reduction some or all of the time is helpful. It is possible and even beneficial for many crops to lower air temperatures, providing the soil can be kept warm. Thus with a soil heating system significant energy savings can be achieved. For example, if a floor heating system were added that would enable the air temperature in the IR polyethylene with curtain greenhouse to be reduced 5°F to 60°F the heat requirement would be further reduced to 18,000 Therms per acre per year and if the same crop could do well with warm soil and only 55°F air that drops to only 13,000 Therms. These approximate estimations of annual energy consumption for a range of structural designs, glazing options, use of curtains and floor heating demonstrate the tremendous differences that there can be in fuel bills from one situation to the next.

The results for the first six greenhouse types tabulated above are plotted in the bar graph in Figure 1 for easy comparison. In a survey of greenhouse energy use conducted by Ohio State University in 1979, it was found that the fuel consumption of glass greenhouses in Ohio averaged the equivalent of about 100,000 gallons of fuel oil per acre of greenhouse, (Short et al., 1979), indicated by the line on the bar chart at 100,000 therms. With typical heating system efficiencies at the time, a gallon of fuel oil consumed would result in about 100,000 BTU, (1 Therm), delivered to the greenhouse. It should be noted that many of those greenhouses were single span glass greenhouses and the figures would include the energy consumption of such houses that were not in good repair and would have higher fuel consumption than any of the illustrations. It should be noted that even as of the writing of this section one can tour significant numbers of commercial greenhouses where the state of repair and maintenance will be such that actual fuel consumption will be much greater than this 1970's average.

ENERGY SUPPLY ALTERNATIVES TO FOSSIL FUELS

One alternative to fossil fuels for greenhouse heating is non-fossil fuel, primarily biomass of one form or another. Wood in various forms has provided an alternative fuel source for some greenhouse operations that have been able to secure a reliable supply and develop systems for handling the solid fuel. Various pellet stoves and furnaces have come on the market capable of burning wood pellets and/or shelled corn. Pelletizing biomass facilitates automation of the feeding of the fuel to the furnace and these systems are more fully described on the MSU website. A large greenhouse operation in Ireland has been heated for a long time on peat. Methane produced from biogas generators or landfills. The concept of using landfill gas was the basis of a research project on cogeneration of heat and electricity for greenhouse operations, (Ekholt et al, 1983) that later became the basis for design of a prototype facility at a county landfill in New Jersey, (ref something on the Burlington facility, perhaps just the website?). A large commercial facility using landfill gas for cogeneration and greenhouse heating has been developed in Vancouver, Canada, (http://www.cityfarmer.org/LandfillGas.html).

Another energy source to consider is electricity, which would not have been considered at all in the past due to its relatively high cost. However, as the global energy supply markets have been changing and all costs going up, in most areas electric rates have risen far less than natural gas or oil. This trend can be expected to continue for some time and as a result there are areas where electric rates are competitive or below gas or oil on the basis of energy delivered. A major factor in this shifting of relative costs is the variety of energy sources used for electricity generation including nuclear, hydro, relatively low cost coal and hopefully increasing reliance on renewable resources. Electrical generation depends on oil for only about 3% of capacity, (Woolsey, 2006).

ALTERNATIVE ENERGY STRATEGIES

At the time of the 1973 oil embargo, a paper was written to advance the idea of using power plant waste heat as an energy source for greenhouse operations, (Mears et al., 1974). The major ideas presented included the concept of somehow establishing a floating greenhouse floor over a pond of warm water to warm both the soil and the greenhouse air. Another idea presented was that of spraying the warm water between the double layers of polyethylene glazing creating a warm barrier between the internal and external environments. Some work was done on this latter concept including running the water during the day when it was found to intercept about 15% of the incoming energy without significantly reducing visible light. This is because water does absorb infrared radiation to a high degree and a significant portion of incoming solar radiation is in the infrared region. Of the two concepts presented, the floor heating idea seemed the most promising and became the focus of attention. Another idea considered in this paper was that of using solar energy for commercial greenhouse.

In response to the energy crisis resulting from the 1973 oil embargo, the USDA funded a research program to utilize solar energy for the heating of greenhouses and this was followed by a DOE funded commercial demonstration program. Utilizing these resources, a full system was developed incorporating the movable shade/heat retention curtains in double-layer plastic-film covered greenhouses with a system to store warm water heated by low-cost plastic-film solar collectors under the greenhouse floor. The floor heating system developed for solar energy heating systems and later adapted for cogeneration and power plant reject heat applications is the storage floor. A plastic liner is put down, usually over a thin layer of closed cell insulation to protect the liner from punctures. The liner is filled with approximately 9 inches of gravel that can be flooded with water and capped with a concrete floor. In solar systems, the water is pumped through the collectors in daytime and the heat is released during the night. Since the heat storage capacity of the gravel/water combination is so large, the temperature rise during the day and drop at night is modest. As the entire floor surface is the heat delivery system the water in the floor is only warm and the floor does not significantly contribute heat to the greenhouse during the day. When used with either a cogeneration unit or industrial waste heat source, the heat can be added to the floor storage whenever available.

This system was demonstrated in a 58,000 square foot section of greenhouse at Kube Pak Garden Plants, Inc. in Allentown NJ. Experience with this complete system quickly showed that the major benefits, on a commercial scale, to both energy conservation and improved plant growth, were the curtain system and the floor heating. While the solar collectors did make a significant contribution to the savings of fossil fuel, the major energy savings were derived from the curtains and floor heating for those crops grown on warm floors with reduced air temperatures. As noted earlier, curtain insulation systems and root zone heating are widely applied in commercial greenhouses but use of solar collectors as a source of warm water for root zone heating has not been widely adopted. As the cost of gas and oil continue to escalate the economics of utilizing solar collectors for this type of application are likely to improve. A portion of the 58,000 square feet of the first crop of fall Poinsettias grown on the warm floor under the energy saving curtain are shown in Figure 2. Figure 3 illustrates the low cost solar collectors used to warm the water in the floor. The energy savings due to the greenhouse construction, warm floor, energy saving curtain and solar collectors are documented in Figure 4.

Partly as a result of the technical success of the large commercial solar energy demonstration project, interest in the use of industrial waste heat led to the design and construction of a 3-acre commercial greenhouse facility in 1980. The performance of this first block is fully described by Manning et al., (1983). Like the solar demonstration project, the first and most important aspects were to design an energy efficient multi-span greenhouse with insulating curtains and a floor heating system. The first floor heating system incorporated the flooded floor for heat storage capacity as well as maximum heat transfer capability with warm water from the power station circulating through plastic pipes on one foot centers embedded in the under floor gravel. Waste heat could also be circulated through finned pipe in the greenhouse and there was a coal fired back-up system that could be used to provide additional heat in the coldest weather. During the first years of operation there was only connection to one of two cooling towers at the power plant seen in Figure 5, so the back-up system had to be used when that unit was

FIGURE 2   First crop of fall Poinsettias. *(Source: A.J. Both and D.R. Mears)*

FIGURE 3   Low cost solar collectors. *(Source: A.J. Both and D.R. Mears)*

Energy for Fall Poinsettia Crop

Category	Thousands of Gallons of Oil Equivalent
Calc. Single Glazing	34.8
Double Poly Control	22.8
Calc. Floor Heat	15.6
Calc. Curtain	9.4
Actual Total Input	6.4
Oil Used for Backup	3.0

FIGURE 5   Cooling towers at
power plant.   *(Source: A.J. Both and
D.R. Mears)*

not operating. When operating, the power plant provided about 95% of the greenhouse heat requirements.

In subsequent years additional acreage was built, some with the storage floor concept, some with plastic pipe circulating the warm water in porous concrete floors and some utilizing solid concrete floors with ebb and flood irrigation. Later units were able to utilize newly developed forced air heat exchangers specifically designed for larger volumes of lower temperature water to replace the finned pipe for air heating. By 1993 the greenhouse range at this site had grown to over 15 acres and in that winter an unusual snowstorm caused significant structural damage. The reconstruction provided the opportunity for significant redesign of some of the waste heat delivery systems utilizing knowledge gained in evaluating system performance over the years. The redesign significantly improved the effectiveness of utilizing the waste heat resource and the performance of the heating system (Mears and Manning, 1996).

The principles of utilizing both solar energy and industrial waste heat have been demonstrated on large commercial facilities and the technology can be applied at additional facilities. For solar thermal collectors to achieve greater utilization the key issues are the economics of the application, the availability of space for the collectors and the smooth integration of the management of the solar aspects with the greenhouse operating systems and management. For the utilization of industrial waste heat site specific issues include the match between the characteristics of the available heat in terms of temperature and quantity and the needs of the greenhouse as well as the logistical and business aspects of tapping into the resource. It has been recognized that greenhouse operations and industrial activities such as electric power generation are significantly different businesses and the importance of establishing good communications and relationships for a specific project cannot be overlooked.

While the use of solar energy and industrial waste heat has been demonstrated as practical on a commercial scale there are a number of other opportunities yet to be tried on such a scale. Several of these have been modeled in computer simulations to analyze

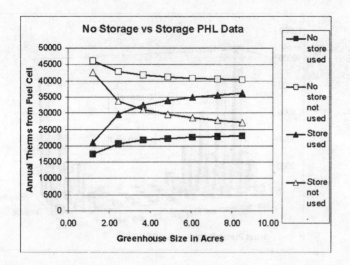

FIGURE 6 Amounts of waste energy utilized in various size greenhouses. *(Source: A.J. Both and D.R. Mears)*

technical feasibility and identify key design relationships, (Ekholt et al, 1983 and Both et al, 2007). Using performance data from a small cogeneration unit designed to operate on landfill gas the first study was done to compare the relative effectiveness of floors with and without the flooded storage. It was found that the larger storage capacity provided more management options for both the sizing of the cogeneration unit relative to the electrical load of the greenhouse and the periods of operation of the unit to realize optimum economics. The later study investigated alternative warm water storage systems and capacities for more flexibility in matching specific greenhouse operations.

Additional concepts modeled include the use of an industrial scale fuel cell designed to operate on natural gas. With sufficient storage it was found that matching such a unit to an appropriately sized greenhouse will enable a half or more of the total waste heat put out by the unit over a year to be utilized in the greenhouse. In addition there is the opportunity to capture the carbon dioxide that is produced by the unit as it first converts methane to pure hydrogen for the fuel cell exhausting the carbon component as carbon dioxide. The key barrier to economic application of such a unit remains high initial cost. Figure 6 illustrates the amounts of the waste energy generated by a 200 kW fuel cell that can be utilized in various size greenhouses. Having significant capacity to store heat enables the greenhouse to use the full daily output when heat is only needed at night. The weather database used for the calculations in the figure is a composite constructed from ten years of records at the Philadelphia International Airport.

Another concept investigated is the use of a heat pump for environmental control in a greenhouse. With the continuing rise in the cost of gas and oil relative to electricity noted previously the use of a heat pump, which may generate three to six times the output relative to electricity input, would become economically competitive as the operating cost savings amortize the initial investment. An efficient system can incorporate a water-to-water heat pump using groundwater as a source for heating and/or a sink for cooling. As the equipment is relatively expensive there is significant economic advantage in using energy thermal storage so a smaller unit can run day and night with the heat generated during the day available for night heating. Such a system should be designed to meet only base load heat requirements with a lower cost backup system on gas or oil utilized for peak requirements.

As heat pumps provide cooling capacity as well as heating another mode of operation can be considered in which the heat pump provides early stage cooling to the greenhouse. With storage for cool and warm water the heat pump can cool the greenhouse during the day in fall, winter and spring storing the heat for use at night. A significant advantage of such an approach is that the greenhouse may be kept closed longer during periods when only early stage ventilation is needed and ventilation can be reduced under hotter conditions thereby extending the time that carbon dioxide enrichment can be economically employed. Figure 7 illustrates the contributions to the heat requirements that are predicted for various months for a proposed system cooling the greenhouse when needed but drawing on a well at other times to maximize its utilization. The large, energy efficient greenhouse was projected to

FIGURE 7 Contributions to the heat requirements predicted for various months. *(Source: A.J. Both and D.R. Mears)*

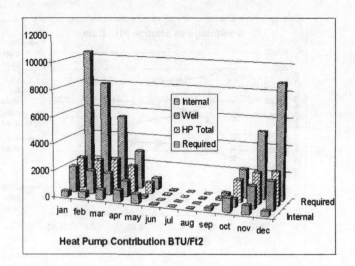

Heat Pump Contribution BTU/Ft2

require 43,580 BTU/ft^2 per year and the heat pump with a heating capacity of 3.4 BTU/(hr*ft^2) would collect 5,509 BTU/ft^2 per year when doing internal cooling and another 11,221 BTU/ft^2 per year from a well for a total contribution of 38% of the annual requirement. The cooling capacity corresponds to the requirement for first stage cooling.

SUMMARY

There are substantial differences in the energy requirements of commercial greenhouses determined in large part by the design of the facility but also influenced by the maintenance and management strategies. These differences are so significant that examples can be found in commercial practice where energy consumption per unit growing area will be at least ten times as great as could be achieved. There are excellent sources of information with specific application to various types of greenhouse operations and increasingly this information can be found on websites and some of these will be periodically updated as new information becomes available.

Beyond the application of the best design and management practices and the consistent following of maintenance procedures there are also alternatives to fossil fuel consumption that can be pursued and it can be expected that practical examples will increase as new ideas are further refined and developed and the relative price of natural gas and oil continue to escalate. There have been many practical demonstrations of systems burning alternative fuels whose economics depend on the facility designed to take advantage of the fuel and its availability and cost. Beyond that further development of alternative energy systems can be expected. Several potential systems mentioned above have been analyzed well enough to show progress and hopefully will be evaluated on a commercial scale.

REFERENCES

_____ Rutgers University Horticultural Engineering Website: http://aesop.rutgers.edu/~horteng/

Bartok, J.W. Jr., 2001. Energy Conservation for Commercial Greenhouses. NRAES-3. NRAES, Ithaca, NY.

Both, A.J., D.R. Mears, T.O. Manning, E. Reiss and P.P. Ling. 2007. Evaluating energy savings strategies using heat pumps and energy storage for greenhouses. ASABE Paper No. 074011. ASABE, 2950 Niles Road, St. Joseph, MI 49085-9659.

Ekholt, B.A., D.R. Mears, M.S. Giniger and T.O. Manning. 1983. Simulation of Greenhouse Floor Heating with a Cogeneration Unit. ASAE Paper No. 83-4018, ASAE, St. Joseph, Michigan 49085.

Manning, T.O., D.R. Mears and M. Buganski. 1983. Engineering Performance of a 1.1 Hectare Waste Heated Greenhouse. ASAE Paper No. 83-4020, ASAE, St. Joseph, Michigan 49085.

Mears, D.R. and T.O. Manning. 1996. Redesign of a Greenhouse Waste Heat System. ASAE Paper No. NABEC-9642, ASAE, St. Joseph, Michigan 49085.

Mears, D.R., W.J. Roberts and J.C. Simpkins. 1974. New Concepts in Greenhouse Heating. ASAE Paper No. NA 74-112, ASAE, St. Joseph, Michigan 49085.

Roberts, W.J., and D.R. Mears. 1980. Floor Heating of Greenhouses. ASAE Paper No. 80-4027, ASAE, St. Joseph, Michigan 49085.

Simpkins, J.C., D.R. Mears and W.J. Roberts. 1976. Reducing Heat Losses in Polyethylene Covered Greenhouses. Transactions of the ASAE (4): pp. 714–719.

Simpkins, J.C., D.R. Mears, W.J. Roberts and H. Janes. 1984. Evaluation of an Experimental Greenhouse Film with Improved Energy Performance. ASAE Paper No. 84-4033, ASAE, St. Joseph, Michigan 49085.

Short, T.H., M.F. Brugger and W.L. Bauerle. 1979. Energy Conservation Ideas for New and Existing Greenhouses. Transactions ASHRAE, 86(2): pp. 449–454.

Woolsey, J.R. 2006. Energy Independence. Testimony for U.S. Senate Committee on Energy. March 7, 2006.

faster than glass, and glass conducts heat faster than plastic. Heat loss is related to surface area. Thus, a corrugated (corrugation gives it more surface area) fiberglass-reinforced plastic greenhouse loses more heat than a flat-plate plastic one. If a glazing material loses heat rapidly, it is more expensive to heat a greenhouse constructed out of it. An estimated 40 percent of savings on heating costs may be realized with a properly constructed double-layered plastic covering because of the insulating property of dead-air space.

Infiltration Greenhouse heat is lost through cracks and holes that occur in the structure. This mode of heat loss is called *infiltration*. Cracks occur in places such as the area around closed doors and improperly closed vents. Anytime doors are opened, fresh cool air enters the greenhouse. This influx of air increases heating costs. Older and poorly maintained greenhouses often have air leakage problems.

Radiation Heat can also be lost from a greenhouse through radiation. **Radiant heat loss** is minimal and occurs as heat energy is lost from warmer objects to colder objects. Polyethylene covering can lose large amounts of heat through radiation, whereas glass and fiberglass-reinforced plastic lose virtually no energy to radiation. Water on the plastic covering can reduce this energy loss in polyethylene greenhouses.

Radiant Heat Loss
The radiations of heat from a warm body, such as a plant, to a cooler body, such as the glazing material of a greenhouse.

Heating a Greenhouse

Types of Fuel Three types of fuels are commonly used to heat greenhouses. The most popular is *natural gas*. It is relatively inexpensive, burns clean, and is delivered to the facility directly via pipes in most cases, thus eliminating storage and delivery costs. Its heat value is about 1,000 Btu per cubic foot. (One Btu is the amount of heat required to raise the temperature of one pound of water by 1°F.) *Fuel oil* is second in popularity to natural gas. It is often used as a backup fuel where natural gas is used. A grade 2 oil has about 140,000 Btu per gallon. Apart from the storage required when fuel oil is used, its viscosity is affected by temperature. As such, oil does not flow properly at low temperatures, the time when heat is needed the most. Further, it has undesirable ash as a product of combustion. The third and least preferred heating fuel is *coal*. It produces considerable pollution when

FIGURE 12–22 Dual-fuel boiler system. This boiler can be operated on fuel oil or natural gas depending on availability and pricing of the different fuels. (*Source: Dr. AJ Both, Bioresource Engineering, Department of Plant Biology and Pathology, Rutgers University, New Brunswick, NJ 08901*)

burned. The ash produced from burning coal poses a disposal problem. If the coal has a high sulfur content, pollution is an even greater problem, requiring additional equipment to be installed in some cases to reduce air pollution. Because exhaust fumes are toxic to greenhouse plants, it is critical that during greenhouse construction the exhaust stack be located downstream of the wind. Such a location ensures that fumes have little chance of polluting the greenhouse environment.

In choosing a fuel type, one should consider the following:

1. *Availability.* The source should be readily available year-round.
2. *Delivery or transportation.* The cost for delivery of the fuel is important. If gas is used, will it be delivered by truck or piped to the site?
3. *Storage.* If gas or fossil fuel is selected, there must be a storage facility to hold it while in use.
4. *Special equipment needs.* Gas must be stored under pressure in a container.

Heating Systems

Greenhouse heat is circulated through several different kinds of media.

Hot Water Heating Systems   The fuels described earlier are used to heat water, in a boiler (Figure 12–22) which becomes the medium through which heat is circulated throughout the greenhouse. Hot water systems are adapted for use in small greenhouses. The temperature of water may be varied as needed. The disadvantage of this system is that an elaborate network of pipes is usually needed to carry the hot water from a boiler throughout the facility. Further, if a gravity flow return system is installed, gravity causes cold water to flow back into the boiler, thus reducing its efficiency. Modern systems utilize forced-water circulation. Apart from being more expensive to heat and maintain a desired temperature, its heat value is lower than that of steam. Further, hot water is not amenable to use in pasteurization. The system is adapted to small greenhouses because it is difficult to transfer water over long distances without losing heat (temperature drops over long distances).

Steam Heating Systems   Steam can be heated to a higher temperature (100 to 101.7°C or 212 to 215°F) than hot water. Smaller pipes are needed to transport steam over long distances and hence can be efficiently used in large greenhouses. In large greenhouses, the steam pressure at the boiler may be as high as 120 psi (pounds per square inch). Even though steam can be transported over long distances, it condenses in the pipes; thus, provision must be made to drain and recirculate the water for reheating. Steam is very efficient for pasteurization.

Radiant Energy Heating System

INFRARED RADIANT HEATER   Heating a greenhouse by infrared radiation is very economical. Reductions in fuel bills of about 30 to 50 percent have been reported. Heat is not conducted through any medium but transmitted directly to plants (or other objects) without even warming the surrounding air. As such, while plants receive the desired temperature, the general greenhouse atmosphere may be several degrees colder than would be the case if hot water or steam were used. Even though infrared heaters are highly efficient, the equipment or sources of the radiation must be located directly above the plant or object to be warmed. Failure to provide for such placement will result in **cold spots** (pockets of low temperature) in the facility. Further, as plants grow bigger, they tend to block the radiation from reaching the soil, leaving it cold.

SOLAR RADIATION SYSTEM Like infrared radiation, solar heaters are nonpolluting. The initial cost of solar collectors is high, but they are cost effective once installed. A major disadvantage with solar heating is its weather dependency. Clouds limit the effectiveness of this system.

COAL The third and least preferred heating fuel is coal. It produces considerable pollution when burned. The ash produced from burning poses a disposal problem. If coal has a high sulfur content, pollution is even greater, and laws may require that additional equipment be installed to reduce air pollution. Since exhaust fumes are toxic to greenhouse plants, it is critical that the smoke stack be located downstream of the wind, preventing the fumes from polluting the greenhouse environment.

Design of Heat Distribution System

Heat is provided in a greenhouse by using a *heater*. In terms of the nature of the source of heat, a heater may be *localized* or *centralized*.

Localized Heaters
The various designs of localized heating systems are described in the following sections.

UNIT HEATERS Unit heaters are also called *forced-air heaters*. They burn fuel or circulate hot water or steam in a chamber and then depend on a fan to blow on the hot surface to spread the warm air either vertically or horizontally through the greenhouse (Figure 12–23). The more popular models expel heated air horizontally and are called *horizontal units* (as opposed to *vertical units,* which are suspended from above). Because such heaters use oxygen for combustion, there is a potential danger in their use in airtight greenhouses. All of the available oxygen could be used up such that if the burner has been on for a long time (e.g., overnight), carbon monoxide could accumulate in the greenhouse to dangerous levels and be life threatening to anyone entering the building. Further, in more airtight greenhouses such as those with plastic covering, oxygen shortage has been blamed

FIGURE 12–23 A forced-air unit heating system. *(Source: George Acquaah)*

for burners going out during the night. To avoid these situations, greenhouses that use unit heaters are designed to have a 1 square inch (6.5 square centimeter) opening in the structure to let fresh air in at all times. Unit heaters are readily amenable to automation. All heaters that use open flames to burn fuel require adequate ventilation through a chimney pipe vented outside of the greenhouse. These units are also called *venting heaters.*

CONVECTION HEATERS Convection heaters are another class of localized heaters that, like unit heaters, burn a variety of fuels in a fire box. Heat is distributed by convection current, a natural process. The pattern of airflow depends on the location and arrangement of heaters. Generally, in convection current flow, warm air rises and cold air drops. These heaters are suitable for small-scale use and not readily amenable to automation; however, they are relatively inexpensive. Whenever fuel is burned, it is critical that the exhaust system be effective and efficient in removing all products of combustion from the greenhouse. Such materials include products of incomplete combustion such as ethylene gas, which is harmful to plants. Other exhaust products include sulfur dioxide gas, which when dissolved in water forms corrosive sulfuric acid that scorches plants on contact.

RADIANT HEATERS Radiant heaters do not burn fuel. They do not warm greenhouse air directly but depend on radiant energy (infrared) to warm objects in their path, which in turn warm the air in their vicinity. Radiant heaters, which are low-energy heaters, are reported to be over 30 percent more efficient than other sources of greenhouse heat. Since air is not heated directly as in conventional systems, the air temperature in a greenhouse heated by this source may be as much as 4°C (7°F) cooler than that in conventionally heated environments. Problems with condensation on surfaces, a common occurrence under warm air conditions, are reduced and subsequently the incidence of diseases associated with condensation is also lowered when using radiant heaters. Further, the greenhouse environment is heated uniformly with little heat stratification. When using radiant heaters, the fans often installed to aid in air circulation under conventional heating systems should not be used. These fans tend to cool the plants and other surfaces and move the heated air around them away. Since the air temperature is lower, the temperature differential between the outside and inside air is lower, resulting in less heat loss. Radiant heaters consume about 75 percent less energy than conventional heaters.

When heaters that combust fuels are used, the potential for injury to people and plants from the pollutants they release into the air is real and must be monitored. In addition to carbon monoxide, products of incomplete combustion such as ethylene can injure sensitive plants such as chrysanthemum. Fuel impurities such as sulfur are burned and converted to sulfur dioxide, which, when dissolved in moisture, produces the corrosive sulfuric acid that burns leaves.

Centralized Heaters Centralized heating systems require a greater investment than localized heaters and are economical for large operations. A boiler produces the heat source, which boils the water that is pumped through pipes and other accessories laid through the greenhouse (e.g., mounted on curtain walls). Pipes may also be located under benches or hung over the plants from the roof. Heat is lost through the plumbing and other parts of the boiler. To increase the surface area for heating, square metal fins may be attached to the pipes in series. Centralized heaters are more efficient than localized heaters. The boiler should be located in the service building, where it is dryer, to prolong the life of the unit. Centralized heating may be accomplished by circulating steam instead of boiled water. A steam system is more common in large ranges since it takes a large boiler and large amounts of water to supply adequate amounts of boiled water to heat a large range.

Certain boilers are classified as those that permit the grower to reduce the level of water to generate steam for pasteurization purposes. This process is called *trimming for steam* and is used when the greenhouse operation has no demand for hot water (e.g., in late spring or summer), since the heating system must be shut off during the process.

Solar Heaters A greenhouse by nature is a giant solar converter, only less efficient. Sunlight enters the facility through all of the transparent parts and is intercepted by objects in its path (e.g., the floor, soil, plants, and benches). These "collectors" store the energy for a short period and then release it into the atmosphere. Some modern greenhouses depend on solar heat collectors for heating. The initial investment for a solar heating system is high. As such, low-temperature solar systems are often preferred and used in conjunction with a conventional heating system for additional heating, especially in the winter season. A complete system consists of a collector, heat storage unit, heat exchanger, and control panel.

Biotherm Heating   The floor of the greenhouse can be heated by laying down rows of flexible tubes (Figure 12–24). This strategy of heating a greenhouse, in which the soil is the primary target, favors enterprises in which pots and trays are placed directly on the floor (as often occurs in bedding plant production). The floor of the bench can also be heated by a similar method. This method of heating the greenhouse is called *biotherm heating*. Propagation benches benefit from heating from below.

Improving Heat Distribution

Notwithstanding the system of heating, it is crucial that heat generated be uniformly distributed throughout the greenhouse to prevent cold spots from occurring. Heat distribution is a more significant problem in large greenhouses than in small ones. When central heaters are used, heating pipes should be strategically located throughout the facility to effect uniform heating. Where cold spots occur, nearby plants grow slowly. The heating system should provide adequate heat not only for the aboveground plant parts but also for the root zone. In the case of unit heaters, attachments such as perforated polyethylene tubing located above the plants are used to aid in the distribution of warm air (Figure 12–25). The other important factor is that heaters should supply heat at a rate to offset what is lost by conduction, infiltration, and radiation.

FIGURE 12–24 Greenhouse floor heating. Hot water (90–120°F) is circulated through plastic pipes embedded in the (porous) concrete floor of this greenhouse. This heating system uniformly distributes heat ensuring uniform crop production. By providing heat where needed (i.e., close to the plants), the greenhouse aerial temperature can in some cases be lowered and, thus, reducing greenhouse heating costs. (*Source:* Dr. AJ Both, Bioresource Engineering, Department of Plant Biology and Pathology, Rutgers University, New Brunswick, NJ 08901)

FIGURE 12–25 Perforated polyethylene tubing used for heat distribution in a greenhouse. (*Source: George Acquaah*)

Regulation of Heat

Thermostat
A device used to regulate temperature.

The regulation of heat is as important as its distribution. Heat cannot be continuously generated unless the conditions are such that it is lost as rapidly as it is produced. **Thermostats** are used to regulate heat in the greenhouse (Figure 12–26). In commercial greenhouses, aspirated thermostats provide effective control. This unit monitors the temperature of a continuous airflow caused by a tiny electrical fan. The greenhouse air is thus sampled continuously for more uniform control. Thermostats should be located at the height of growing plants so as to monitor the actual conditions of the plants. When the right temperature is attained, the heat should be turned off. To be on the safe side, emergency units should be provided as standby heaters in case the primary heat source fails during a crop production cycle. Large greenhouses are divided into sections that are monitored separately. These sections enable the greenhouse to be used for different enterprises simultaneously.

Conserving Heat

Heating a greenhouse is very expensive, and as such, every possible measure should be taken to conserve heat. The greenhouse should be inspected regularly to replace broken glasses, seal leaks, and clean boilers and heaters. As previously described, when polyethylene is used to glaze the frame of a greenhouse, a second sheet (i.e., double layer) creates a dead-air space between the layers for additional insulation.

Since most of the heat lost from a greenhouse is dispersed through the roof, the installation of an interior ceiling that can be drawn at night and opened during the day can conserve up to 30 percent of heat. For much greater heat conservation, *thermal screens* or sheets may be installed in the facility. These screens are installed on the ceilings and walls. Double thermal sheets are known to reduce fuel costs by more than 50 percent. Heat can be conserved by using fans installed in the ceiling to distribute the heat that would have been lost through the roof.

Ventilating and Cooling a Greenhouse

Greenhouse Ventilation Systems   Ventilation is required to reduce excessive heat and humidity buildup in a greenhouse and aerate the environment with fresh air and fresh supplies of carbon dioxide for plant use. Since plants release oxygen and take in carbon dioxide, the carbon dioxide concentration in a closed system such as a greenhouse declines with time. The location of vents depends on the design and construction of the greenhouse. In an A-frame greenhouse, vents may be located in the ridge section of a side wall (Figure 12–27). Vents may be operated manually or be automated. Quonset greenhouses use forced-air ventilation (horizontal air flow) systems or side vents. There are two basic systems used in greenhouse air circulation—the **fan tube system** and the **high-volume, low-velocity fan system**. The former draws and distributes fresh air through perforated polyethylene tubes laid through the crop. The latter moves air through the entire length of

FIGURE 12–26 Aspirated box containing temperature and humidity sensors connected to the computerized environmental control system. Note that the box is located at a representative location and close to the crop canopy. (*Source:* Dr. AJ Both, Bioresource Engineering, Department of Plant Biology and Pathology, Rutgers University, New Brunswick, NJ 08901).

FIGURE 12–27 Motorized ventilation inlet opening using the rack-and-pinion system. The opening area selected should ensure proper mixing of the incoming air with the greenhouse air. (*Source:* Dr. AJ Both, Bioresource Engineering, Department of Plant Biology and Pathology, Rutgers University, New Brunswick, NJ 08901).

the greenhouse. Exhaust fans installed at one end of the greenhouse draw in fresh air through louvers installed at the opposite end (Figure 12–28). It should be pointed out that ventilation not only refreshes the greenhouse environment but also cools it.

Greenhouse Cooling Systems   Although heat is required in winter and cool periods of the growing season, greenhouses need cooling in summer and warm periods. On the average, the ambient temperature in a greenhouse is about 11°C (20°F) higher than the outside temperature. Plants are damaged by both excessive heat and cold. Excessive heat can cause low crop yield through high flower abortion and drop. Greenhouses have vents that help circulate fresh air and provide cooling. However, in certain situations venting is not sufficient to reduce temperatures and cooling systems must be installed.

The most common way of cooling a greenhouse is by using an *evaporative cooling system* (Figure 12–29). This system involves drawing air through pads soaked with water, and hence is also called a *fan-and-pad cooling system*. The cooling pads are soaked with water dripping from above. These cross-fluted cellulose materials retain moisture quite well. Excelsior pads may also be used. The excess water is drained into a lower trough (sump) and recirculated by a pump. Warm air from outside is forced through the pads by the drawing action of fans at opposite ends of the greenhouse. In the process, some of the trickling water evaporates. Water evaporation removes heat from the air. The fan-and-pad cooling system uses the principle of evaporative cooling. To be effective, all incoming air should be drawn through the cooling pad. Cross-fluted cellulose pads, which look like corrugated cardboard, last longer than excelsior pads and are more popular.

Controlling Temperature

Controlling temperature should be distinguished from heating the greenhouse. Under conditions in which no heat is required, the temperature of the greenhouse should be maintained at an optimal level. The rule of thumb is to operate a greenhouse at a daytime temperature of 3 to 6°C (5 to 10°F) higher than the nighttime temperature on cloudy days and even higher (8°C or 15°F) on clear days. Since increasing the temperature accelerates growth, it must be done with care so as not to compromise the quality of the produce. Fast growth can cause spindly or thin stems and small flowers. Raising the temperature on a clear, bright day is necessary because light is not a limiting factor for photosynthesis under such conditions. Failure to raise the temperature may cause heat to become a limiting factor.

12.3.2 LIGHT

Light is required for photosynthesis and other growth activities. As previously explained, the light required by plants is described in terms of intensity, quality, and duration (Chapter 4).

FIGURE 12–28 Electric-driven ventilation fans used in stages to provide the required ventilation rate necessary to maintain set point temperatures. *(Source: Dr. AJ Both, Bioresource Engineering, Department of Plant Biology and Pathology, Rutgers University, New Brunswick, NJ 08901)*

FIGURE 12–29 Evaporative cooling pads used to cool the greenhouse when (mechanical) ventilation alone is not sufficient to maintain the desired set point temperature. The (wetted) pads are installed inside the ventilation inlet opening and outside air is drawn through them by ventilation fans installed in the opposite sidewall (not visible). Evaporative cooling is only successful when the relative humidity of the outside air is below saturation (100%). The drier the incoming air, the larger the temperature drop accomplished. Note that evaporative cooling increases the humidity of the greenhouse air. *(Source: Dr. AJ Both, Bioresource Engineering, Department of Plant Biology and Pathology, Rutgers University, New Brunswick, NJ 08901).*

Intensity

On a clear summer day, plants in a greenhouse may receive as many as 12,000 foot-candles (or 129 kilolux) of light, an excessive amount for most crops, since by 3,000 foot-candles (32.3 kilolux), most plant leaves in the direct path of incoming light are light saturated and cannot increase their photosynthetic rate. Whole plants can utilize about 10,000 foot-candles (108 kilolux). Sunlight intensity is also seasonal, being less in winter and more in summer. Crops have different preferences and tolerances for light intensity. For example, foliage (nonflowering) plants are scorched and fade in light intensities above 2,000 to 3,000 foot-candles (21.5 to 32.3 kilolux). African violets lose green color at an even lower light intensity (1,500 foot-candles). Poinsettia plants are a darker shade of green when light is reduced. Also, plants such as geranium and chrysanthemum require shading in cultivation to prevent petal burn. Shading to reduce light by about 40 percent from midspring to midfall is helpful to prevent chloroplast suppression in most greenhouse plants. Greenhouse light intensity can be manipulated in several ways.

Shading In addition to fans and evaporative cooling systems, there are certain times during the year (early fall planting season and late spring harvesting period) when excessive heat buildup in detrimental to plant growth, fruit development, and ripening. Some modern greenhouses have retractable shade cloths that automatically deploy when radiation load on the greenhouse exceeds what the cooling systems can handle (Figure 12–30). In some designs the shade system is fixed (Figure 12–31). Shading the greenhouse to reduce excessive light is accomplished in several ways. Glass greenhouses may be sprayed with paint (whitewash) in summer to reflect light and reduce its intensity. Commercial shading paints may be purchased. A screen made from fabric may be more convenient to use if only a section of the greenhouse requires shading. Durable fabrics include polyester and polypropylene; they are available in different densities of

FIGURE 12–30 Movable internal shade curtain. Note that curtains can be mounted in a variety of greenhouse designs, including designs with a fair amount of overhead installations (heating and irrigation pipes, supplemental lighting, etc.). The curtain fabric is selected based on the two functions it is to perform: reflect sunlight (during the summer and particularly the middle of the day) and heat (at night and during the winter months). (*Source:* Dr. AJ Both, Bioresource Engineering, Department of Plant Biology and Pathology, Rutgers University, New Brunswick, NJ 08901)

FIGURE 12–31 Fixed external shade curtain. Compared to internal shade curtains, these systems reduce the amount of heat entering the greenhouse (requiring removal by the ventilation and/or cooling system). External shade curtains are particularly practical for crops requiring low light levels. (*Source: Dr. AJ Both, Bioresource Engineering, Department of Plant Biology and Pathology, Rutgers University, New Brunswick, NJ 08901)*

weave for providing degrees of shading from 20 to 90 percent, 50 percent being the most common. Some modern greenhouses have retractable shades that are used as needed. Saran may be used to cover plants in sections of a greenhouse or bench. Also, aluminized strips may be used to create an interior ceiling that can be drawn on sunny days.

Undesirable shading may be inherent in the design of the greenhouse. Materials for construction and design of the frame, cooling systems, and plumbing and light fixtures that are located overhead intercept incoming light. The narrower the frame material, the better. Overall, these obstructions may reduce greenhouse light intensity by 30 percent or more. Further, seasonal and daily light intensity reductions may be caused by the orientation of the greenhouse and the characteristics of the location.

Plant Density Plants may also be spaced to utilize incoming light. In summer, closer spacing should be used, whereas wider spacing is recommended in winter. Spacing–light intensity interaction can be manipulated to control the size of plants, since the same amount of dry matter will be produced under an available light intensity. Therefore, to obtain larger plants, space widely; to obtain smaller plants, space closely.

Washing To increase light intensity, the glass covering of the greenhouse should be cleaned (Figure 12–32). Dust particles on the glass plates reduce intensity by up to about 20 percent. Washing by running water through a hose may not be sufficient. A cleaning solution should be used (e.g., 11 pounds [5.0 kilograms] of oxalic acid dissolved in 33 gallons [150.2 liters] of water may be sprayed onto a damp, dirty greenhouse and hosed down with water after three days). Other greenhouse types also need periodic cleaning.

Supplemental Lighting

In winter or darker periods (middle of fall to early spring season), supplemental lighting may be required by certain plants for good growth and quality. When needed, it may be supplied by using a variety of sources, categorized as follows.

FIGURE 12–32 A machine used to clean the roof glass of a Venlo-type greenhouse. Over time, dust and dirt accumulation can significantly reduce light transmission into the greenhouse. (*Source:* Dr. AJ Both, Bioresource Engineering, Department of Plant Biology and Pathology, Rutgers University, New Brunswick, NJ 08901)

Incandescent Lamp   Incandescent lamps have tungsten filaments. They are not desirable for greenhouse use because, in addition to light, they generate excessive heat. Incandescent lamps characteristically emit a high proportion of red and far red light, which produces abnormal growth in some plants (e.g., soft growth or induced tallness). They are very inefficient, converting less than 10 percent of the electrical energy consumed into light.

Fluorescent Lamps   Fluorescent lamps are energy efficient (20 percent electrical energy converted to light) and produce little heat. However, because they are low-power sources, many of them are often required to produce the desired intensity. Consequently, a large number of fixtures must be installed. These installations end up blocking incoming natural light. They are commonly used in growth rooms where seeds are germinated or in small greenhouses. The cool white model, which provides light of predominantly blue wavelength, is commonly used. However, fluorescent tubes with capacities to emit a superior quality of light for photosynthesis are available. One class, called *plant growth A*, produces light in the red region of the light spectrum; another class of tubes, *plant growth B*, has capabilities for emitting radiation beyond the 700-nanometer wavelength.

High-Intensity-Discharge Lamps   As their name indicates, high-intensity-discharge lamps can generate intense light (Figure 12–33). There are several types and designs available: high-pressure mercury discharge, high-pressure metal halide, and high-pressure sodium light. In certain types, power ratings may be as high as 2,000 watts. The high-pressure sodium lamps are less expensive than the others to install and operate and can generate up to 1,000 watts of power for 24,000 hours. The light quality emitted is in the 700- to 800-nanometer spectral range. Low-pressure versions of the high-pressure sodium lamps are available. Considered the most efficient lamps for supplemental greenhouse lighting (27 percent electrical energy converted to light), they are available in power ratings of up to the popular 180-watt size. However, these lamps are deficient in quality of light produced and do not emit enough light in the 700- to 850-nanometer range. Therefore, when used alone, plants often develop abnormally (e.g., pale foliage in lettuce and petunia). When used in combination with daylight or

FIGURE 12–33 A high pressure sodium (HPS) lamp consisting of a bulb, a reflector, and housing containing a current-regulating ballast and related electrical components. (*Source:* Dr. AJ Both, Bioresource Engineering, Department of Plant Biology and Pathology, Rutgers University, New Brunswick, NJ 08901).

another appropriate source, plant growth problems are eliminated. Supplemental lights in growth rooms can double up as heat sources, except in very cold seasons.

Height of Light

The various types of lamps emit light at different intensities, ranging from about 2,000 to 11,000 lux (185 to 1,000 foot-candles), or even higher in some cases, as in growth rooms. The effect of each source depends not only on the power rating of the unit but also on the arrangement and height above the plants. For example, if a 4-foot-wide (1.2-meter-wide) bed of plants is to be illuminated using one row of 60-watt bulbs spaced 4 feet (1.2 meters) apart, the arrangement should be hung no more than 5 feet (1.5 meters) above the soil. Fluorescent tubes are used widely in growth rooms because they provide uniform light intensity over a wide area. Using cool white lamps (at 125 watts), seven tubes mounted 1.5 to 2 feet (0.45 to 0.62 meters) above the soil provide low-intensity light for a 3.5-foot-wide (1.1-meter-wide) bench.

Incandescent light installed at about 2 to 3 feet above the plants to generate 10 foot-candles of light intensity is referred to as *standard mum lighting.* At this intensity, flower formation is prevented so that plant growth is stimulated during the short nights of summer. Poinsettia plants can be kept vegetatively by using this treatment. It is important that light intensity be monitored periodically to ensure that the crop receives at least 10 foot-candles of light. Sometimes reflectors (e.g., aluminum foil) may be installed above the lightbulbs to direct more light to plants. High-density lamps are usually encased in reflectors. They have a higher output and are hence hung higher above the plants.

Duration

Duration of light *(photoperiod)* is a precise time-tracking mechanism (Chapter 4). Even changes between duration of light and darkness that deviate minutely could spell disaster in certain situations. Plants are traditionally categorized as *long day, short day,* or *day because neutral* As already indicated, this is a misnomer, the tracking mechanism actually relates to the duration of darkness rather than daylight.

The importance of controlling photoperiod lies in the consequences of not doing so. In poinsettia, the red (or other color) pigmentation in the bracts depends on photoperiod, similar to flowering in chrysanthemum. Short nights are required for asters and lettuce to bolt (form stems and flower). Under short-night conditions, dahlias are prevented from producing tubers and thus produce flowers instead.

On the other hand, plants such as kalanchoe, azalea, and chrysanthemum flower when nights are long. When nights are long, dahlias form tubers instead of flowers; bryophyllum leaves produce plantlets along the margin when nights are long. For some

Facultative Long- and Short-night Plants
Plants that do not require a specific duration of dark period for a response to occur, but will respond faster if the dark period is extended or shortened, respectively.

Cyclic Lighting
A method of light application where the total duration of light is reduced by approximately 80 percent by replacing continuous lighting with intermittent lighting of about 6 cycles of 5 minutes of light and 25 minutes of darkness.

plants, the duration of night length is not inhibitory to flowering, but the process occurs much more quickly under ideal conditions. These plants are called **facultative short-night** (e.g., carnations) or **facultative long-night** (e.g., Rieger begonias) plants. As indicated previously, photoperiod is influenced by other factors such as temperature, species, and maturity. Plants such as roses are day neutral.

Extending Day Length   To control photoperiod, incandescent lamps are best for extending the day length in short-night treatments because they emit light in the red wavelength of the light spectrum. The Pr *phytochrome* (red phytochrome) responds to this light. To reduce the cost of short-night treatment, intermittent lighting (called **cyclic lighting,** or *flash lighting* is sometimes used instead of continuous lighting over the prescribed duration of light interruption. The duration of short-night treatment depends on whether the crop is planted in winter or summer. Nights are naturally short in summer, and therefore no interruption may be necessary then. Short-night treatment involving turning lights on for two to eight weeks is necessary during the winter. The treatment may be administered by turning lights on during the late afternoon to extend the day or interrupting the dark period during the middle of the night (for a shorter duration). The number of hours of supplemental light also increases toward December. The latitude plays a significant role in the duration of light interruption, since northern latitudes experience shorter summer nights and longer winter nights.

Decreasing Day Length   Plants that require decreasing day length treatment flower only when they are exposed to extended periods of darkness. In commercial greenhouses, black cloth is used to block out light at the desired time and removed after the required period (usually from 7 P.M. to 7 A.M.). Light blocking may be done mechanically (very laborious) or automatically. Care must be taken to provide complete darkness since leaks that let in light can cause aberrant developments such as hollow flower buds (crown buds).

12.3.3   WATER

Water is critical to the quality of plant products produced under greenhouse conditions. Plants are adversely affected by both excessive and inadequate moisture supplies. Overwatering can injure plant roots by creating anaerobic conditions in the root zone. Because air pores are occupied by water, plants may wilt and die or become stunted in growth. Too-frequent watering may produce excessive tissue succulence, making plants weak. Moisture stress from infrequent watering may cause plants to wilt or grow at a slow rate. Plant leaves may become small and the general plant stature stunted, with short internodes.

A successful watering regime depends on a well-constituted growing medium. The medium must drain freely while holding adequate moisture for plant growth. The purpose of watering is not to wet the soil surface but to move water into the root zone. The growing medium should be watered thoroughly at each application, requiring that excess water be drained out of the pot. This practice also prevents the buildup of excessive amounts of salts from fertilizer application. Excessive watering is not due to one application but rather is the result of watering repeatedly when it is not needed. When watering frequency is too high, the soil is prone to waterlogging and poor aeration. Roots need to breathe and thus must not be constantly under water. A good watering regime is one that applies water in a timely fashion, just before plants go into moisture stress. This stage must be ascertained through keen observation and experience. It is recommended that about 10 percent of water applied to a pot drain out of the bottom of the container. This amount ensures that the soil is thoroughly wet, and aids in flushing out excessive salts that may have accumulated as a result of fertilizer applied over a period. A 6-inch (12.2-centimeter) azalea pot should receive 10 to 20 ounces (283.5 to 567 grams) of water, an amount that must be adjusted according to the kind of soil (soilless or real soil mix).

Source of Water

The quality of local water depends on its source because of groundwater pollution problems and water treatment programs. Even where domestic water is used for irrigation, it should be noted that cities treat their water differently. Some add fluoride (called *fluoridation*) to reduce tooth decay in humans. Unfortunately, many plants, including the spider plant *(Chlorophytum)*, corn plant *(Drocaena fragrans)*, and spineless yucca *(Yucca elephantipes)*, are sensitive to and injured by fluoride. Most of these plants belong to the families Liliaceae and Marantaceae. Chlorine is less of a problem but nonetheless injurious to some plants, such as roses, when the concentration reaches about 0.4 parts per million (ppm). When the source of water is a well, the level of soluble salts (sodium and boron) is often high. Many arid coastal regions have high boron toxicity; liming of soil reduces the potential for this problem. Bicarbonate is another water pollutant that affects plant growth.

Water Application Methods

Hand Watering The age-old method of hand watering by using a watering container or water hose is appropriate for small-scale watering. When a large area is involved, commercial companies often use automated systems. Even then, hand watering may be best and is thus used on certain occasions. The devices used are equipped with nozzles designed for a variety of situations. Some provide fine, misty sprays and others coarser sprays. Watering seedlings and newly sown seeds requires a fine spray. Applying water uniformly is difficult when hand watering. One of the advantages of hand watering is the instant judgment of the operator as to whether a plant needs water. Also, a keen operator can observe any problems (e.g., diseases and insect pests) during hand watering.

Automatic Watering Systems Automatic watering systems differ in cost, efficiency, and flexibility. Some are semiautomatic and must be switched on and off. In a truly automatic system, the operation is controlled by a programmable timer, which allows watering to occur for a specified period.

TUBE WATERING Growers use sophisticated methods of water application for premium-quality produce. The tube watering system is the most widely used system of watering for potted plants. When flowers are grown for the fresh flower market, they must be clean. Water is administered only to the soil in the bed without splashing on the plants, which reduces the chance for disease spread. By using microtubes, individual pots can be automatically watered to provide water in the right amounts and at the right frequency for high quality. Two commonly used tube watering systems are the Chapin and Stuppy® systems. The difference between the two lies in the weights at the end of each tube. The Chapin system uses a lead weight, and the Stuppy uses plastic (Figure 12–34). Tube watering is also amenable to the application of water-soluble chemicals (e.g., growth hormones and fertilizers). The system is expensive to install and not flexible. Pots on the bench have to be uniform in size, and the tubes must be inspected periodically to ensure that no blockage exists.

CAPILLARY MAT The capillary mat is a subirrigation system in which potted plants are placed on a water-absorbing fiber mat covered with a perforated plastic sheet (Figure 12–35). Water is absorbed by capillary action through the drainage holes in the bottoms of the pots. The mat is kept moist by tubes installed on the bench. Potted plants such as African violets are watered by this method. A capillary mat is flexible and easy to install. Different pot sizes can be accommodated simultaneously. Further, it is easy to rearrange plants as required by growth. For the system to work properly, the mat must be placed on a level surface. One problem with using a capillary mat is the growth of algae.

OVERHEAD SPRINKLERS When used on ground beds, nozzles are mounted on risers whose height depends on the mature height of the crop (Figure 12–36). For plants on benches, the sprinkler nozzles may be suspended above the plants. Overhead sprinklers wet the foliage and predispose it to diseases (Figure 12–37). Watering should be done

FIGURE 12–34 Microirrigation system. Also called the tube, or "spaghetti," watering system.

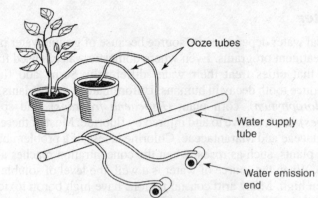

Ooze tubes

Water supply tube

Water emission end

FIGURE 12–35 A capillary mat watering system.

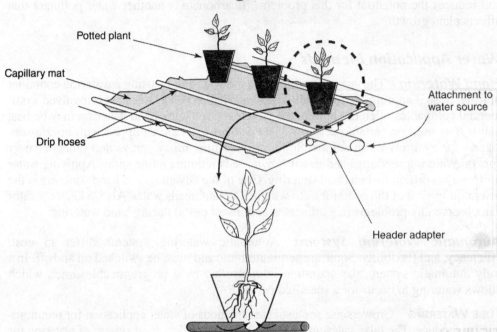

Potted plant

Capillary mat

Drip hoses

Attachment to water source

Header adapter

FIGURE 12–36 An overhead irrigation system for watering plants on greenhouse benches. *(Source: George Acquaah)*

FIGURE 12–37 Overhead sprinkler irrigation system. Such a system is relatively simple to install and operate, but results in significant leaf wetting during irrigation. (*Source:* Dr. AJ Both, Bioresource Engineering, Department of Plant Biology and Pathology, Rutgers University, New Brunswick, NJ 08901).

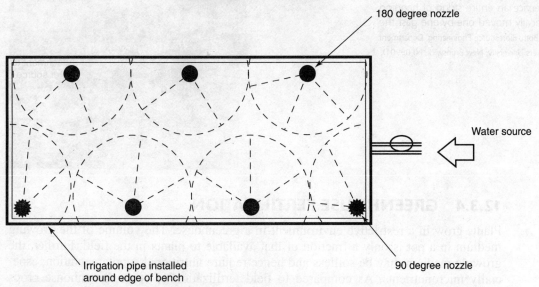

180 degree nozzle

Water source

90 degree nozzle

Irrigation pipe installed
around edge of bench

FIGURE 12–38 Perimeter watering of a greenhouse bench.

in the morning to give plant foliage a chance to dry during the day. This system is used widely for watering bedding plants.

PERIMETER WATERING The cut flower industry cannot afford to have blemishes on foliage and flowers. The perimeter watering system is a method of greenhouse irrigation in which water is provided without wetting the foliage of the plants (Figure 12–38). Sprinkler nozzles are installed along the perimeter of the bench. These nozzles deliver a flat spray, and thus the foliage and the part of the plant stem to be included in cut flowers are not wet. The water must be sprinkled at a high enough pressure to reach plants in the center of the bench.

ISRAELI DRIP SYSTEM (FOR HANGING BASKETS) The Israeli drip system of watering hanging baskets involves hanging plants on a support pipe at intervals that coincide with drip points on a plastic pipe located under the support pipe (Figure 12–39). The disadvantage of this system is that water drips on foliage, predisposing it to disease. To minimize this problem, plants should be watered early in the morning so that they have a long time to dry before nightfall. A modern and efficient way of watering hanging baskets is the use of carousels (Figure 12–40).

MISTING Misting systems provide very fine sprays of water. They are used on plant propagation benches or beds. Mists are produced from sprinklers fitted with nozzles for very fine sprays.

POLYETHYLENE TUBING Perforated plastic pipes may be used to water cut flowers. Pipes are laid between rows of plants in the bed.

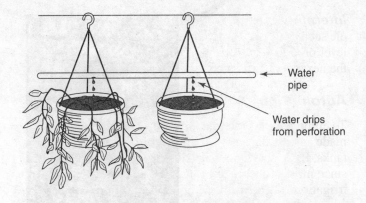

FIGURE 12–39 An Israeli drip irrigation system for hanging baskets.

→ Water pipe

→ Water drips from perforation

FIGURE 12–40 Irrigation carousel for hanging baskets. A single irrigation point can service an entire string of hanging baskets as they are automatically moved one-by-one past the irrigation point. (*Source:* Dr. AJ Both, Bioresource Engineering, Department of Plant Biology and Pathology, Rutgers University, New Brunswick, NJ 08901).

12.3.4 GREENHOUSE FERTILIZATION

Plants grow in a restrictive environment in a greenhouse. The volume of the growing medium in a pot is only a fraction of that available to plants in the field. Further, the growing medium may be soilless and hence require nutritional supplementation, especially micronutrients. As compared to field fertilization of crops, greenhouse crops sometimes receive a hundredfold of the fertilizer applied in the field. Organic fertilizers are not commonly used in greenhouse plant production because they do not lend themselves to automation (e.g., application through irrigation water). They tend to have odors that make their use under enclosed conditions unpleasant. Further, it is difficult to apply exact concentrations of nutrient elements when using organic fertilizers. Fertilizers are discussed in detail in Chapter 4.

Inorganic Fertilizers

Inorganic fertilizers are convenient to apply and amenable to a variety of methods of application, including through irrigation water. Inorganic fertilizers can be applied in exact amounts as needed. Dry and liquid fertilizers are used in the greenhouse, the more common being liquid fertilizers, which are applied through the irrigation water. Another form of fertilizer used in greenhouses is slow-release fertilizer it is highly desirable because nutrients are released over a period of time and thus better utilized.

Methods of Application of Liquid Fertilizer

Liquid fertilizers may be applied to plants in the greenhouse in several ways.

Constant Feed Constant-feed application entails administering low concentrations of fertilizer each time the plant is irrigated. It mimics the slow-release fertilizer action and is the most popular method of greenhouse fertilization. This method is desirable because plants receive a fairly constant supply of nutrients in the soil for sustained growth and development.

Intermittent Feed Greenhouse plants may be fertilized according to a periodic schedule such as weekly, biweekly, or monthly. The disadvantage of this method is that the high level of nutrition available at the time of application gradually decreases over time until the next application. Plant growth is thus not sustained at one level but fluctuates.

Automation

To eliminate the tedium in preparing fertilizer solutions each time an application is to be made, growers usually prepare concentrated stock solutions that are stored in stock tanks. By using devices called fertilizer injectors (also commonly called **proportioners,** since most of them are of this type), the desired rate of fertilizer is applied through the irrigation water, a process called **fertigation** (Figure 12–41).

Measuring Fertilizer Concentrations

Nutrients may be applied as solids or liquids. When in solid form, they are either mixed in with the medium or applied in the form of slow-release fertilizer. Fertilizer is often applied through the irrigation water; these fertilizers must thus be water soluble. They are formulated as high concentrations of the elements they contain and must be diluted before use. The most common greenhouse fertilizer grade is 20-20-20.

Liquid fertilizer concentrations used in greenhouses are measured in parts per million. To prepare a stock solution to a desired concentration, the grower needs to know the proportioner ratio, stock tank volume, rate of application intended, and fertilizer analysis of the fertilizer source.

The formula for calculating stock concentrations is as follows:

1. ounces/100 gallons of water = ppm desired/% element $\times$ correction factor $\times$ 0.75

    where correction factors are % P = % P_2O_5 $\times$ 0.44

    % K = % K_2O $\times$ 0.83

    (No correction is needed for nitrogen.)

    Example: A nursery grower would like to fertilize his plants at the rate of 275 ppm of nitrogen. He purchases a complete fertilizer of analysis 20:10:20 and intends to use a 1:200 proportioner for the application. His stock tank can hold 50 gallons (227 liters) of liquid. How many pounds of the fertilizer should be dissolved in his stock tank?

    Solution:

    ounces/100 gallons = 275/20 $\times$ 1 $\times$ 0.75

    $$= 275/15$$

    $$= 18.33 \text{ pounds}$$

Proportioner
A device used in a fertigation system to control the rate of fertilizer applied through the system.

Fertigation
The application of fertilizers in soluble form through an irrigation system.

(a)   (b)

FIGURE 12–41 (a) Control and display units for a fertilizer and acid injection system, (b) Components of a fertilizer and acid injection system. Fresh make-up water and/or water returning from an irrigation cycle is checked and adjusted for the proper nutrient concentration (EC: electrical conductivity) and pH. (*Source:* Dr. AJ Both, Bioresource Engineering, Department of Plant Biology and Pathology, Rutgers University, New Brunswick, NJ 08901) ·

FIGURE 12–42 A Venturi-type proportioner.

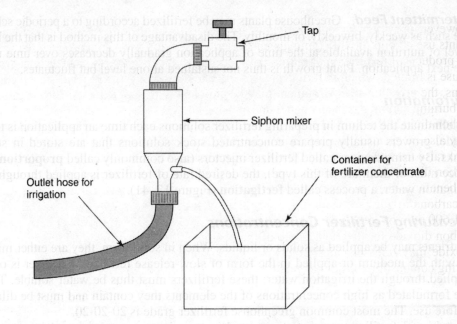

Tap

Siphon mixer

Container for fertilizer concentrate

Outlet hose for irrigation

2. Preparing the stock solution.

pounds to add to stock tank:

= ounces/100 gallons × second number of injector × stock tank volume (gallons)/100 × 16

= 18.3 × 200 × 50/100 × 16

= 183,000/1,600

= 114.4

Proportioners are calibrated in terms of the ratio of dilution of concentrated fertilizer with irrigation water. Some have fixed ratios (e.g., 1:100 or 1:200), and others are variable. They differ in mechanisms of operation, proportioning ratio, and cost. A relatively inexpensive type is the Hozon proportioner, which operates on the Venturi principle (Figure 12–42). Water enters the unit at very high velocity, generating a suction in a feeder line that is dipped into the soluble fertilizer concentrate. The suction draws the fertilizer into the watering hose, where it mixes with tap water according to a predetermined concentration. Proportioners may lose their accuracy over time and require periodic callibration.

Problem of Accumulation of Soluble Salts Pot media are prone to accumulation of soluble salts, which may result from factors such as poor drainage, excessive fertilization, or insufficient irrigation (resulting in inefficient leaching). Such accumulation may result in toxicity or deficiency of certain minerals. Monitoring the soluble-salt content of growing media, which can be done with an instrument called a *solubridge,* is important.

Fertilizers differ in solubility and *salt index* (a measure of the effect of a fertilizer on the soil solution. Potassium chloride has a salt index of 116, and urea, ammonia, and regular superphosphate have salt indices of 75, 47, and 8, respectively. Fertilizers of low salt indices are preferred to reduce salt accumulation. A greenhouse water supply may contribute to the amount of soluble salts in the soil or growing medium.

12.3.5 CARBON DIOXIDE FERTILIZATION

Plants utilize carbon dioxide and water in the presence of light to manufacture food by the process of photosynthesis. Carbon dioxide occurs in the atmosphere in a low concentration of about 350 ppm. As long as adequate ventilation and freely circulating air are present, greenhouses receive sufficient amounts of carbon dioxide for photosynthesis.

However, in winter, greenhouse vents are closed for more efficient heating. Because plants use carbon dioxide (animals and other combustion processes produce the gas as by-products of respiration or burning of fuel), the supply of this gas in an airtight greenhouse is limited, which in turn decreases the rate of photosynthesis. Under such conditions, the greenhouse environment may be enriched with supplemental carbon dioxide by burning natural gas in an open flame or using compressed gas or dry ice (solid, frozen carbon dioxide that is used in other laboratory procedures as well). Propane gas burners may also be used to generate carbon dioxide. The goal of **carbon dioxide fertilization** is to raise the concentration of the gas to about 1,000 to 1,500 ppm. This high level of carbon dioxide must be provided along with bright light (e.g., bright daylight) for it to be beneficial to plants. In addition to light, heat is a limiting factor to the effectiveness of carbon dioxide fertilization. Lettuce plant weight increased by more than 30 percent at 1,600 ppm of carbon dioxide. Certain crops have been known to flower earlier under carbon dioxide fertilization. Some of the equipment used to provide additional carbon dioxide may release undesirable toxic gases such as carbon monoxide and ethylene during combustion of the fuel; such gases are toxic to both plants and animals.

Carbon Dioxide Fertilization
Deliberately increasing the carbon dioxide concentration in the air of the greenhouse to increase the rate of photosynthesis.

12.4 GREENHOUSE PESTS

The use of pesticides (especially those that are volatile) in enclosed places is a potential health hazard to humans present in those areas. Every effort should be made to minimize the introduction of pathogens and weeds into a greenhouse. Weeds may grow in greenhouses with gravel or porous concrete floors. Apart from being unsightly, weeds may harbor insects and other pests. Weed seeds may be blown into the house or carried in potting media and impure crop seed. If required, only chemicals approved for greenhouse use (e.g., Roundup) may be used. Common greenhouse diseases include root rot, damping-off, botrytis blight, powdery mildew, and root-knot nematodes. Disease incidence can be reduced through strict observance of sanitation. Pots and all containers should be sterilized before reuse. After each crop cycle, the benches should be scrubbed and sterilized. Unsterilized media should not be allowed into the greenhouse. It is recommended that a greenhouse operator maintain a regular schedule of preventive programs. Since many greenhouse plants are grown largely for aesthetic uses, any blemish reduces the price that can be obtained for a product. A wide range of pests are found in the greenhouse, including aphids, fungus gnats, thrips, mealybugs, leaf miners, mites, and whiteflies.

Sometimes the grower has no choice but to use pesticides. On such occasions, the safest products and those recommended for greenhouse use must be selected. After a spray or fog application of a pesticide, the greenhouse must be aerated before people are allowed to work in the facility. Greenhouses may attract rodents (especially mice and rats), depending on the activities taking place in the facility and how it is kept. Baits and traps may be placed at strategic places to catch these rodents.

An effective approach to controlling pests in the greenhouse is the adoption of greenhouse-specific integrated pest management (IPM) programs. Such programs entail a combination of strategies, namely, sanitation, physical control, biological control, and use of pesticides. It should be pointed out that IPM will work properly in a greenhouse if the facility is used for a specific plant or crop or can be partitioned into sections for specific activities. IPM programs may include regular fumigation, washing and disinfecting floors, spraying, and other sanitary precautions. Plant debris should be removed and disposed of without delay, since debris may harbor pests.

One way of keeping plants healthy is to provide adequate growth factors (nutrients, light, temperature, water, and air). Healthy plants are more equipped to resist attacks from pests. To prevent entry of flying insects, ventilators may be covered with fine mesh screens. Other physical control measures include the use of yellow sticky traps. These traps have a dual purpose—monitoring the level of insect infestation and reducing their population (since once captured they die). For ground beds, plastic mulches may be used to suppress weeds.

Improved cultivars of horticultural plants with resistance to various diseases and pests have been developed by plant breeders. Some cultivars are better suited to greenhouse production than others. Tools should be cleaned and properly stored after use. Phytosanitary observance is also critical. All plant remains must be discarded.

SUMMARY

Plants may be grown in or out of season by growing them under controlled-environment conditions in greenhouses. Under indoor conditions, some or all natural growth requirements may either be supplemented or controlled in order to provide the appropriate amounts at the right times. Greenhouses differ in design, efficiency, and cost of construction and operation. Film-plastic models are cheaper to construct but less durable. More expensive and durable materials are glass and fiberglass-reinforced plastics.

An advantage of growing plants in an enclosed environment is that the optimal growth factors can be provided with minimal fluctuations. Heat during the cold season is provided by using heaters that burn fuel (e.g., unit heaters) or those that do not burn fuel (e.g., radiant heaters). Greenhouse heat may be lost through conduction, infiltration, or radiation, conduction being the major avenue. In summer, greenhouses are cooled by using cooling systems such as the evaporative cooling system. Light intensity, which increases during summer, is controlled by shading with fabric or whitewashing the glass outer covering of the greenhouse. During the winter months when light intensity decreases, the paint is washed away. Sunlight is supplemented with artificial lights from a variety of sources, including incandescent lights, fluorescent lamps, and high-intensity-discharge lamps.

Water used in greenhouses often comes from the domestic supply system. Care must be taken not to overwater greenhouse plants, which are generally planted in pots. The soil must be freely draining. The nutrient supply is important since the growing medium may be a soilless mixture, which will be low in nutrients or have none at all. Since the growing plant has a limited soil volume from which to forage for essential nutrients, the soil quickly becomes depleted of minerals and needs replenishing on a regular basis. Slow-release fertilizers are a good choice for greenhouse fertilizer applications.

REFERENCES AND SUGGESTED READING

McMahon, R. W. 1992. *An introduction to greenhouse production*. Columbus Ohio Agriculture Education Curricular Material Services.

Nelson, P. V. 1985. *Greenhouse operation and management*, 3d ed. Retson, Va.: Retson Publishing.

Ortho Book Staff. 1979. *How to build and use greenhouses*. San Francisco: Ortho Books.

Sunset Book Editors. 1976. *Greenhouse gardening*. Menlo Park, Calif.: Sunset-Lane.

Walls, I. G. 1991. *The complete book on the greenhouse*. London: Wardlock.

Greenhouse construction
http://www.umass.edu/umext/floriculture/fact_sheets/greenhouse_management/ jb_buildi_ng_gh.htm.

PRACTICAL EXPERIENCE

Conduct a field trip to commercial or research greenhouses. On the trip, find out about the greenhouse design type, materials used, purpose of the unit, how it is cooled and heated, various types of automation systems, layout of the benches, kinds of plants grown, and so forth.

OUTCOMES ASSESSMENT

1. Explain the underlying principles of a greenhouse design.
2. Discuss the advantages of gutter-connected greenhouses.
3. Compare contrast glass, polyethylene, and fiberglass as glazing material for greenhouse.
4. Discuss the management of heat in greenhouse production.
5. Describe how greenhouse producers manage light for optimal crop growth.
6. In what ways does fertilization of greenhouse plants differ from fertilization of field crops?
7. Describe how greenhouse design can optimize the use of greenhouse space.
8. The following exercises are designed to help the student better understand greenhouse energy issues. They were developed by Dr. AJ Both and Dr. David Mears of the Bioresource Engineering Department of Plant Biology and Pathology Rutgers University, New Brunswick, NJ:

Heat loss through any portion of a greenhouse structure can be calculated by multiplying a heat transfer coefficient times the area of the portion of the structure being considered times the temperature difference between inside and outside. The heat transfer coefficient depends on the material covering that portion of the structure and to some extent the external weather conditions. Approximate heat transfer coefficient for various glazing systems can be found in the reference and generally include a factor to account for some air infiltration for a reasonably well-sealed greenhouse. The total heat loss for any greenhouse can be calculated by adding up the heat loss the each portion. In the English systems of units the heat transfer coefficient is in British thermal units per hour per square foot per degree Fahrenheit, $Btu/(hr*ft^2*°F)$ so when coefficient is multiplied by the area and temperature difference it is the Btu/hr lost through that portion of the structure.

1. Consider a 96-foot long hoop house made by bending 12-foot water pipes into a semicircle with the roof and ends covered with double-layer polyethylene. If the heat transfer coefficient for plain double-layer polyethylene is $Btu/(hr*ft^2*°F)$ and it is 0°F outside when the crop requires 60°F inside what is the hourly heat requirement under these conditions?

2. Consider a larger, gutter-connected greenhouse with 7 bays, each 30 feet wide by 210 feet long with 12 feet height to the gutter and 19.5 feet to the ridge. The roof section, side walls, and gable end walls are all to be glazed with a single layer of glass with a heat transfer coefficient of $Btu/(hr*ft^2*°F)$. For the same inside and outside temperature conditions as in problem 1, what is the total hourly heat requirement for this structure?

3. To change this greenhouse to double-layer polyethylene on roof and all walls, the straight rafters are changed to curved bows each one 34.5 feet long. Assuming the average end wall heights is 14 feet and using the same heat transfer coefficient and the same temperature conditions as in problem 1, what is the total hourly heat requirement for this structure?

4. For each of the first three problems, divide the total heat requirement by the floor area of the greenhouse to compare the heat requirement per unit floor area. Discuss the differences of the results in problems 1 and 2 and the differences of the results of problem 2 and 3.

5. For an advanced exercise look up the heat transfer coefficient for double-layer polyethylene with an infrared heat-absorbing additive in the references or from an Internet source, and discuss the energy saving possible. Do the same for the gutter-connected greenhouse with the addition of a movable shade/heat retention curtain system.

13

Greenhouse Production

PURPOSE AND EXPECTED OUTCOMES

The purpose of this chapter is to discuss how greenhouses are used for producing horticultural plants on a commercial scale.

After studying this chapter, the student should be able to

1. Discuss the categories of greenhouse production.
2. Discuss the distribution of greenhouse production in the United States.
3. Discuss greenhouse ground culture.
4. Discuss hydroponic culture.
5. Discuss plug production in its importance to the horticultural industry.

[COLOR PLATES—*see color plates 19 and 20* for additional chapter photos]

OVERVIEW

Three primary factors should be considered when planning a horticultural production enterprise: *product quality, production cost,* and *transportation cost.* Whereas floricultural plants may be successfully produced in the field, their quality is often not consistent over time because of unpredictable and sometimes hard-to-control environmental factors. Certain plants are more environmentally labile than others. For example, chrysanthemums of acceptable quality may be produced in the field (as in Florida and California). However, roses produced in the field have inferior quality to those produced under greenhouse conditions. Because of bulk, potted plants are produced near major markets (i.e., localized competition). A successful production enterprise should produce high-quality plants at low production and transportation costs.

Floricultural plants adapted for greenhouse production may be grouped as follows:

Cut Flowers
Flowers grown specifically to be cut and displayed in vases or for other uses.

1. *Cut flowers.* Some plants are grown so that their fresh flowers may be harvested (cut) and sold.
2. *Potted plants.* There are two classes of potted plants:
   a. *Flowering plants.* Flowering plants are flower-bearing plants grown in pots.

b. *Foliage or green plants.* Foliage plants are nonflowering plants grown for the beauty of their foliage.

3. *Bedding plants.* Bedding plants are grown to the seedling stage and sold to be transplanted to beds and pots. There are two classes:

a. *Ornamental plants.* Ornamentals include certain vegetables that are grown for aesthetic purposes.

b. *Vegetables.* Vegetables are grown to maturity and harvested for sale.

Bedding Plants
Largely annual plants produced especially for planting in beds and in containers.

Another basis for grouping greenhouse plants is how they are grown. Plants may be grown in containers (pots), on benches or ground beds, in hanging baskets, or in soilless media (hydroponics).

13.1 IMPORTANCE OF GREENHOUSES IN PLANT PRODUCTION

Greenhouses may be used to produce crops on a small or large scale. In fact, for certain crops, commercial production is primarily done in a controlled environment for best quality. Greenhouse production has advantages and disadvantages.

Some of the major advantages and disadvantages of greenhouse production are as follows:

13.1.1 ADVANTAGES

1. Greenhouses may be used to provide a head start on field production. Seedlings of plants that are transplanted may be raised in the greenhouse in the off-season and timed to coincide with the beginning of the growing season so that early crops can be produced for premium prices.
2. Crops and ornamental plants may be produced in the off-season to prolong the availability of fresh produce or products.
3. Produce quality is usually high because growers can manipulate the growing environment for optimal production conditions.
4. Tropical crops can be grown in temperate zones and vice versa.

13.1.2 DISADVANTAGES

1. The initial costs of buildings and equipment are high.
2. Greenhouses operate at very high overhead (e.g., heating, cooling, and lighting), and thus their use is limited to the production of high-premium crops and plants.
3. Greenhouse production is not suitable for all crops and is economically applicable to small-sized plants (e.g., vegetables, ornamentals, and herbaceous plants) but not fruit trees.

13.2 PRODUCTION REGIONS OF THE UNITED STATES

The Netherlands, Japan, and the United States lead the world in floricultural production. The U.S. Department of Agriculture (USDA) data indicate the bedding plants are the most important greenhouse-produced floricultural plants, accounting for about 35 percent of total production. They are followed by potted flowering plants (24 percent), foliage plants (18 percent), cut flowers (18 percent), and cut cultivated greens (4 percent). The most important bedding plant production states are California, Florida, Texas, and Michigan, accounting for about 50 percent of total crop value. Plug technology has greatly facilitated the production of bedding plants and green potted plants. The most important production states for cut green plants are Florida, California, and

Texas whereas cut flowers are produced on the larges scale in California (69 percent), which, along with Florida, Washington, Hawaii, and Oregon, together account for over 80 percent of the total crop. On the world scene, the Netherlands and Colombia account for about 70 percent of the cut flower production.

U.S. vegetable production has traditionally been concentrated near population centers, especially in the northeastern region. However, as transportation improved and energy costs soared, the industry was forced to move to the southern states. Adequate light is a key factor to successful greenhouse production. Consequently, the Southwest is ideal for greenhouse vegetable production, especially in the winter months when tomato and cucumber prices are at a premium. Some production occurs in the Northeast, but the region is disadvantaged by relatively stabilized population and harsh climate, whereas the south and west have favorable climate for more cost-effective production, in addition to the proximity of expanding markets.

Unfortunately the southwestern greenhouses have challenges of their own. The summer heat makes cooling expensive for producing high-quality crops. Further, the expanding winter production in Mexico threatens to reduce greenhouse tomato prices and increase the competitive pressure on year-round production by U.S. producers.

13.3 THE ROLE OF IMPORTS

Modern delivery systems comprised of efficient transportation (jet) and storage facilities make it easy to transport fresh flowers across continents in a short period. Further, production costs are relatively lower in certain areas with appropriate climates. In terms of greenhouse production, the Netherlands has the largest number of these climate-controlling units. Cut flowers imported into the United States include carnation (80 percent), mum (57 percent), and rose (42 percent). Other plants involved in the import trade include astroemeria, tulip, daffodil, freesia, potea, and cut palm. Major exporters of floricultural products to the United States are the Netherlands, Spain, Italy, Israel, Kenya, Turkey, Brazil, Colombia, Costa Rica, Ecuador, Mexico, Peru, and Japan. Colombia is the main producer of cut flowers sold in the United States, especially roses, carnations, spray chrysanthemum, and *Astroemeria*. Second after Colombia in export to the United States is Ecuador, a major supplier of roses, *Delphinuims*, asters, and *Gysophila* (baby's breath). These two countries account for about 90 percent of roses, 98 percent of carnations, and 95 percent of chrysanthemums sold in the United States. To decrease the competition from imports, U.S. producers will have to reduce production costs (e.g., through improved and more efficient management of the enterprise, marketing, high-quality products, and increased productivity for a steady supply of flowers).

13.4 PRODUCTION COSTS

The cost of greenhouse production depends on many factors, the major ones including local climate, cost of labor, cost of materials, marketing costs, method of production, and scale of production. The costs associated with these factors may be grouped into direct, indirect, and marketing costs.

13.4.1 DIRECT COSTS

1. *Materials.* Cost for materials includes that for seeds and other planting materials, chemicals (including fertilizers, pesticides, and hormones), growing media, and containers (e.g., pots, trays, and flats).

2. *Labor.* The size of the labor force depends on the level of automation. Some activities are hard to automate and hence must be done by humans. These activities include spraying, preparation of the growing media, setting up containers on benches, harvesting, and cleaning.

13.4.2 INDIRECT COSTS

Indirect costs are generally described as *overhead costs* and include equipment depreciation, utility fees (e.g., water, fuel, and electricity), taxes, and administrative costs. Overhead costs may be about 25 to 40 percent of total production costs.

13.4.3 MARKETING

A major marketing cost is transportation. Others are packaging and advertising. Certain floricultural products require special packaging before marketing. Distribution and marketing costs may vary between 5 and 15 percent of total production costs.

13.5 PRODUCTION AND MARKETING STRATEGIES

Greenhouse producers operate one of three types of floricultural businesses. One group of producers *(growers)* limit their enterprise to producing plants, leaving the selling to others such as wholesalers. They usually concentrate on the production of one or a few types of plants. Some producers *(grower wholesalers)* produce some of their products but also purchase from other growers and sell on a wholesale basis. In addition to plants, they may also sell floricultural production accessories such as containers and wrappers. The third category of growers *(grower retailers)* market their products through a network of outlets. They may sell to other retailers or wholesalers. Brokers acting as sales agents arrange sales between growers and wholesalers. Flowers may also be auctioned. Full-service retailers add value to the fresh products through professional arranging (Chapter 24) or wrapping potted plants and tying with a bow, the function of the traditional florist. Florist prices are high because of their overhead costs. Floricultural products may be sold by the mass marketing strategy of selling in high-traffic locations (e.g., malls, airport terminals, street corners, and bus terminals). Prices at these locations are usually low.

13.6 THE CONCEPT AND APPLICATION OF DIF

Growing plants in a greenhouse offers opportunities for growers to manipulate the growing environment to control plant growth and development. Traditionally, greenhouse producers grow plants at a lower (cooler) nighttime temperature than daytime temperature, the rationale being that a cooler night temperature reduces respiration, thus conserving carbohydrates. For example, on a clear, sunny day, the nighttime temperature may be 15.5°C (60°F) while the daytime temperature would be about 24°C (75°F); a 15°F difference. On a cloudy day, indoor temperature is usually lower during the daytime (about 21°C or [70°F]), the night temperature remaining 15.5°C (60°F). This high-day–low-night temperature regime allows plants to photosynthesize and grow (stem elongation) more during the daytime and less at night.

Scientists have discovered that going against tradition and growing plants at a lower temperature during the day than at night is an effective strategy for controlling plant height (reduced growth or reduced stem elongation). This concept is called *DIF,* the difference between daytime and nighttime temperatures; that is, DIF-day temperature–night temperature. A positive DIF indicates a lower nighttime than daytime temperature (in the previous example, daytime temperature [21°C (70°F)] minus nighttime temperature [15.5°C (60°F)] equals a positive DIF [5.5°C (10°F)]). Similarly, when the nighttime temperature is higher than the daytime temperature, a negative DIF occurs.

Negative DIF treatments are now applied in the commercial production of certain crops to induce an effect similar to the application of growth retardants. This treatment makes plants short, compact, and fuller in form. Applying the negative DIF concept is problematic in warm climates and under conditions where daytime temperature control is erratic. However, the scientists who formulated this concept also discovered that giving plants a two-hour cool temperature treatment immediately after sunrise (the time when temperatures are usually the lowest in a twenty-four-hour period) has an effect equivalent to growing plants at that cool temperature all day long. This treatment can be applied in spring or summer by ventilating the greenhouse and cooling during that two-hour period. In winter, the thermostat may be set to delay the change from night temperature to day temperature to achieve the desired DIF effect.

Although many species exhibit no adverse side effects from the negative DIF treatment, others, including some Easter lily cultivars, may show curly or wilting leaves. Fortunately, these symptoms are usually temporary, especially if the negative DIF treatment is applied when the plant is young. The desirable DIF range is less than 4.4°C (8°F). Extreme temperature differences may permanently damage plants.

13.7 GREENHOUSE PRODUCTION SYSTEMS

Numerous production systems are used worldwide by commercial greenhouse producers. The discussion in this chapter focuses on the production of plant products (ornamentals and food) to be harvested and marketed to customers. All production systems require and use similar environmental controls and general greenhouse production practices as discussed in Chapter 12. The key distinguishing features:

1. Irrigation and nutrient delivery methods and controls
2. Medium characteristics and packaging

The two major categories of greenhouse production culture are **ground culture** and **soilless culture**, the latter occurring in receptacles or containers.

13.7.1 GROUND CULTURE

Also called **in ground culture** this production system entails growing crops in the ground in a greenhouse. Greenhouse construction involves significant soil compaction for the erection of the structure. For in-ground culture, the topsoil should be amended with large amounts of well-decomposed organic matter to allow good penetration of plant roots. The greenhouse structure limits the kinds of equipment that can be used in in-ground culture. The ground may be cultivated for planting on the flat, or raised beds may be constructed as needed (Figure 13–1).

Because of the enclosure, pathogen buildup is of concern with in-ground culture. To protect against soilborne pathogens, producers often sterilize or pasteurize the soil. Methods of soil disinfection used include solarization, steaming, use of electrical heat sources, and biological pest control.

Cover crops may also be used in in-ground systems. Species like legumes, buckwheat, annual ryegrass, oats, radish, the rapeseed have been used as cover crops in greenhouse production to enhance soil physical quality increase microbial activity, suppress soilborne diseases like nematodes, and add nitrogen to the soil.

FIGURE 13–1 Greenhouse production of cut chrysanthemum in soil. The heating pipes and attached wire support will be lifted in increments as the crop grows to provide heat and support close to the growing point. (*Source:* Dr. AJ Both, Bioresource Engineering, Department of Plant Biology and Pathology, Rutgers·University, New Brunswick, NJ 08901)

Weed control inside the greenhouse is best achieved without the use of herbicides for safety reasons. Mechanical cultivations, steam pasteurization, solarization, plastic mulching, and hand hoeing are all effective methods for weed control.

If needed, inorganic fertilizers may be applied to increase crop productivity. However, the crops should not be overfertilized, since fertilized soils do not readily leach out of the protected greenhouse environment. Fertilizers with a high salt index, such as potassium chloride, and those with a high ammonium content should be avoided.

13.7.2 CONTAINER CULTURE

Container culture entails the production of plants in containers to be sold as such to customers. The subject is discussed in more detail in Chapter 16 under nursery production.

13.8 SOILLESS CULTURE

Soil is a medium in which plants may grow. It provides the minerals needed for plant growth and development. When adequate moisture is present, these minerals are dissolved in water and can be absorbed by roots. When plants are grown in another kind of medium, all of the nutrients must be provided in the irrigation water. Over the years, a wide variety of attempts (with vary degrees of success) have been made at growing plants in soilless media (i.e., no mineral soil is used). The most successful attempt, which perhaps ushered in modern soilless culture, is credited to W. E. Gericke, who in 1936 grew a wide variety of crops in water supplemented with plant growth nutrients. He called this method of growing plants **hydroponics**, or *water culture*. Plants can be cultured in a variety of other inert substances besides water, including rockwool, sand (*sand culture*), or air (*aeroponics*) All of these methods (including hydroponics) are called *nutriculture*. The substances used as media are called inert because they do not add to or alter plant nutrient level in any way (unlike peat moss natural soil, which are both biologically and chemically active).

Hydroponics
The culture of plants in which the root medium is exclusively water fortified with dissolved nutrients.

13.8.1 TYPES OF SOILLESS PLANT CULTURE

There are two classes of **soilless plant culture:** *water culture* (hydroponic culture) and *substrate culture*. In terms of type of medium used, hydroponics may be broadly classified into two—**liquid** and **aggregate**. The liquid hydroponic systems include no physical substrate besides water. The aggregate systems utilize substrates that may be inert, organic, or a mixture of both as growing media.

Soilless Plant Culture
The collectivity of methods used to grow plants in media that do not consist of mineral soil.

13.8.2 HYDROPONIC SYSTEMS

The basic requirements for successful water culture or hydroponics are as follows:

1. *Root aeration.* The root environment must be aerated to prevent anaerobic respiration (due to waterlogging) from occurring. Preventing anaerobic respiration may include aerating the nutrient solution (as done in domestic aquarium tanks) or circulating the nutrients using a pump. Systems that use a continuous flow of nutrients provide the best cultural environment for plants.
2. *Root darkness.* Algae growth, which occurs around the roots when exposed to light, interferes with root function. Darkness around roots eliminates or reduces this problem.
3. *Physical support.* A system must have a means of holding plants erect in water.
4. *Nutrient supply.* Since water lacks the essential nutrient elements supplied by the soil, the hydroponic medium must be fortified with nutrients, both macronutrients and micronutrients.

In terms of design, there are two basic types of hydroponic systems:

1. *Nonrecycling (noncirculating) system.* In the nonrecycling system, excess nutrient solution is drained out of the container and lost.
2. *Recycling (circulating) system.* Excess solution is collected for reuse in the recycling system.

13.8.3 LIQUID HYDROPONIC SYSTEM

The major liquid hydroponic systems include:

The Gericke's System

The Gericke's system is designed so that plant roots grow through a wire mesh into the nutrient solution, in which they are either partially or fully submerged. This solution may be static or circulated on a continuous basis. Early designs were unsatisfactory because they lacked the air space that allows the solution to be aerated. Apart from poor aeration, another undesirable aspect of the system is the lack of self-support for seedlings. Users need to provide support for plants, which increases production costs. Commercial application of the Gericke's system is currently limited. For better support, some users include a solid substrate (e.g., soil, peat, or straw) in the seedbed.

The Floating Systems

The floating, raceway, or raft water culture system was first developed for lettuce production. Plants are raised in water beds about 6 to 8 inches (15 to 20 centimeters) deep. The nutrient solution in the bed is circulated through a tank. Before returning the nutrient solution to the bed, it is aerated, sterilized (by UV radiation), and chilled. The pH and electrical conductivity of the solution are also regularly monitored. Between crops, the system needs to be sterilized by using bleach, for example.

Lettuce is seeded into a peat plug mix and watered by using a capillary mat. When plants are about 12 to 14 days old, they are transplanted into beds. Planting is best done in the late evening when seedlings are bare rooted. The seedlings are planted in 1-inch-deep (2.5-centimeter) holes in a styrofoam board (raft) after placing them in paper supports (Figure 13–2). Lettuce is ready for harvesting about 32 days after transplanting.

Floating systems provide some support for plants by using lightweight material that floats (commonly a sheet of polystyrene). Some growers use thick (2.5-centimeter or 1-inch)

FIGURE 13–2 Lettuce plug is inserted into a Styrofoam board (raft) as physical support in a floating hydroponic systems. (*Source:* Dr. Louis Albright, Department of Biological and Environmental Engineering, Cornell University, Ithaca, NY.)

plastic material for support. Crops that have been grown successfully by this system include chard and strawberry.

Deep Recirculating Water System

Several variations of the Gericke's system are in use. These modern versions are designed to overcome the shortcomings of the previous system. The variations in design are also wide. For example, in the M system, the nutrient solution is circulated by a pump through an air mixer and then returned to the bed via holes in pipes located in the bottom of the container.

Ebb-and-Flow Systems

Ebb-and-flow systems are a type of subirrigation. They consist of a shallow bed, into which nutrient solution is pumped to a depth of about 1 inch (2.5 centimeters). The solution remains in the trough for about 20 minutes and then is drained back into the tank. Flats of plants are set in the shallow bed. Irrigation cycles can be automated; seedlings can be irrigated in plug trays or set in rockwool blocks.

Vegetables such as tomato, pepper, lettuce, broccoli, and cucumber may be propagated using the ebb-and-flow system. Similarly, rose cuttings and cuttings for hanging baskets may be propagated by this method.

Aeroponics

Aeroponics is used on a limited scale for commercial production. This system involves suspending bare plant roots in a mist of nutrient solution.

Aquaponics and Bioponics These systems are sometime used in organic hydroponic production (or hydro-organics) **Aquaponic** entails the use of irrigation effluent form aquaculture to fertilize crops growing in a medium (e.g., gravel, sand). **Bioponics** is a system of hydroponics in which microbes are incorporated into the liquid medium.

Nutrient-Film Technique

In the nutrient-film technique (NFT), there is no solid rooting medium. Plants' roots are placed in a shallow stream of recirculating water containing dissolved nutrients (confined to troughs or gullies). Plants produce a thin root mat, part of which is located above the solution. The technique derives its name from the film of nutrient solution on the parts of roots exposed to air. Because their roots are only partly submerged, plants are never in danger of the consequences of waterlogging. By using shallow water, the young seedlings can be set in the water in their propagation blocks or pots without any need for additional support. Furthermore, there is no need for the deep and heavy beds required by other systems.

The basic layout is shown in Figure 13–3. The catchment tank is located in the lowest point of the setup. It contains the dilute nutrient solution that is pumped up to the upper ends of the gullies. The gullies must be laid carefully and the flow rate of the pump set properly to prevent irregularities in the flow (i.e., there has to be a uniform gradient of about 1 percent slope). The NFT has other advantages that make it attractive. There is no need for pasteurization, the plastic film used for lining the trough is removed after each production cycle, and it is amenable to automation. Crops being grown in this system include tomato, lettuce, chrysanthemum, snapdragon, and cucumber.

A major problem with NTF systems is the high probability that a disease organism such as *Pythium* could be recirculated throughout the entire greenhouse to infect all plants.

The circulating pump used should be able to tolerate low levels of corrosion from the dilute nutrient solution and be sturdy enough to supply uninterrupted power. Pump failure can be disastrous, so commercial growers often use more than one pump (one serves as a backup). The NFT system may be assembled on the concrete floor or a raised platform. The channels require a covering, which helps to reduce evaporation of the nutrient solution, control root temperature, and prevent entry of light (which promotes algae growth). This covering should have reflective properties (not black) to reflect light and thereby reduce the danger of temperature buildup in the troughs, which could damage roots. The nutrient solution is circulated at a rate of about 2 liters (0.5 gallons) per minute. This rate of circulation is required for good aeration. The solution is collected in a sump by gravity.

Nutrient-film fertilizer may be purchased from chemical companies. The solution becomes spent with time and must be replaced periodically (e.g., biweekly). While in use, the pH and electrical conductivity must be monitored on a regular basis (daily). Desirable pH is between 6.0 and 6.5. To adjust pH toward acidity, sulfuric acid may be used; potassium hydroxide is used to increase pH. The electrical conductivity (soluble salts) of an NFT solution may be about 3 millimhos. With recycling and use, the soluble-salt concentration decreases. Replenishing is required when electrical conductivity decreases to about 2 **millimhos.**

The troughs may be prefabricated or can be formed by the grower from polyethylene sheets. The type of material used is critical. Some have phytotoxic effects that may kill plants or stunt their growth. Flexible polyvinyl chloride pipes and galvanized pipes have the potential to cause zinc poisoning, and copper pipes should be avoided. Plants to be grown are raised in media that are loose and will permit transplanting into the NFT channels without debris attached to roots, which can block the nutrient flow in the system. Materials that may be used include peat moss, Oasis foam, and blocks of rockwool. The seedlings are set in rooting blocks.

Millimho
A millimho is 1/100th of an mho (opposite of ohms, a unit of electrical resistance) or mho/cm × -3.

(a)   (b)

FIGURE 13–3 (a) Nutrient film hydroponic system (NTF), (b) Greenhouse production of lettuce in nutrient film technique. While the plant troughs are spaced close together in the forefront, this spacing is increased (mechanically) as the plants mature during their journey to the opposite side of the greenhouse where they will be harvested once they arrive. (*Source:* Dr. AJ Both, Bioresource Engineering, Department of Plant Biology and Pathology, Rutgers University, New Brunswick, NJ 08901)

13.8.4 AGGREGATE HYDROPONIC SYSTEMS

Under the substrate system, plant roots are surrounded by either inert or natural organic material. These substrates provide only limited physical support. They may be placed in bags, troughs, or trenches.

A variety of inert and organic materials are placed into containers to provide physical supports for plants in culture. The common aggregate systems are as follows:

Bag Culture

Bag culture is the preferred method of greenhouse vegetable production by many producers in the United States. It is relatively easy to establish and manage. It entails growing plants in a soilless medium placed 2–5 gallon polyethylene bags that may be laid flat or stood upright in the greenhouse. The former layout can handle 2–3 plants per bag, while the upright bag is usually limited to one plant per beg. The media may be peat, rockwool, peat/vermiculite, or mixtures of various soilless mix ingredients. Plants may be grown in pots with slits at the bottom and pot inserted into the bag (Figure 13–4) Bag-cultured plants are fertilized and watered through drip irrigation systems.

Vertical Towers

These are similar to bag culture. Because the bags are stood on their shorter end, support wires or beams are usually needed to stabilize them in the greenhouse. A company, Verti-Gro, markets square Styrofoam pots that are stackable and reusable. The media types are variable as in the case of bag culture.

Trough Culture

Materials that may be used as substrates include sand, vermiculite, horticultural rockwool, and perlite. The critical factor in the choice of material is that it be able to hold moisture and yet drain adequately for good aeration. Systems that use these materials are generally referred to as *sand cultures (or trough cultures)*. They are not widely used commercially since it is not easy to maintain a good balance for drainage, water retention, and aeration (Figure 13–5).

Commonly used containers include those made of concrete for permanent troughs or beds. Other materials such as timber coated with asphalt or fiberglass may be used. The nutrient solution is applied by using perforated pipes with suitable jets in fixed irrigation models or directly to the soil surface. Sand beds are often sterilized annually to control soilborne diseases and pests.

13.8.5 ORGANIC SUBSTRATES

Plants may be grown in organic substrates in various arrangements. As previously discussed, these substrates may also be used in bag or vertical tower culture.

FIGURE 13–4 Greenhouse production of tomato in rockwool bags. The hot-water heating pipes located on the floors of the isles also serve as tracks for carts used for plant maintenance and harvesting. ' (*Source:* Dr. AJ Both, Bioresource Engineering, Department of Plant Biology and Pathology, Rutgers University, New Brunswick, NJ 08901)

Straw Bale Culture

Bales of straw are laid out in rows on the greenhouse floor. Prior to planting, the bales are wetted with "manure tea" (liquefied manure) to initiate decomposition and to generate heat in the bale. The wetting process requires about 7 gallons of liquid per 50-lb bale. When the bale cools down to below 110°F, it is topped with about 6 inches of compost-based potting mix. This layer is needed for the transplant. Fertilization is by topdressing with liquid of dry fertilizers. Straw culture is useful in greenhouses with bare ground so the products do not get in touch with the soil.

Shallow Bed Culture

This is also called **thin layer culture.** It consists of 1–3 inches of potting mix or compost laid on plastic sheet or some other barrier. This system has been for crops including lettuce, greens, and herbs. If needed, the medium may be heated by bottom heat systems.

13.8.6   PLUG PRODUCTION (TRANSPLANT PRODUCTION)

Plug production is a method of large-scale nursery sexual and asexual propagation of plants. It lends itself to automation (Figure 13–6). Equipment types are becoming increasing more sophisticated. Plug production had advantages and disadvantages, including the following:

Advantages

*   Relatively easy to operate
*   Amenable to automation for quick and large-scale produciton
*   Operation is able to monitor the operation for uniform germination
*   Special seed treatments (e.g., vernalization) are easy to provide
*   Time from transplanting to sale is reduced
*   It is cost effective

Disadvantages

*   Initial equipment cost could be high, depending on the type
*   Employees require special training to use equipment

Media

A key to success to plug production is to find the best medium for the enterprise and consistently use it. It should be pasteurized. A common medium is 1:1 of sphagnum peat moss: vermiculite or perlite. Sand soil, or bark, are not recommended in the medium.

(a)

(b)

(c)

FIGURE 13–6 Plug production, (a) Drum seeder line used to precision-seed plug trays, (b) Robotic arm used to fill (or empty) a movable table with small potted plants. Each row of pots is placed on a conveyor belt, (c) High volume transplanter used to transplant plug (background) into liners (foreground). (*Source:* Dr. AJ Both, Bioresource Engineering, Department of Plant Biology and Pathology, Rutgers University, New Brunswick, NJ 08901)

Containers

Containers should be cleaned and disinfected prior fo filling with media. Working surfaces should also be cleaned and disinfected. There are plug trays for organic production.

Automation

Modern models of equipment are capable of full automation—filing plug flats or trays, sowing seed, transplanting, and labeling. It is easier to automate the production of annuals then perennial species.

Sowing

Week 1:   Seed is sown is plug trays and placed in a germination chamber maintained at 70–70°F and 80–90 percent relative humidity. Light intensity should be low during this period.

Week 2–4:   After a week in the germination chamber, the trays are placed in the propagation house at 70–75° F and 70–80 percent relative humidity. It may be necessary to provide bottom heating. The grower may use a precharged mix (contains basic nutrients). In week 2–4 the plants should be fertilized with 20-10-20 at 150 ppm, twice a week.

Week 5–6:   Prior to transplanting into larger containers to be prepared for sale, the seedling should be hardened at about 60–65°F and 35–40 percent relative humidity. Fertilization should be reduced to 15-10-15 at 125 ppm weekly.

Finishing

Finishing is the presale plant management. The time it takes for finishing depends on the plug size, the finish size, greenhouse temperature, and day length. The seedlings are transplanted into larger containers (e.g., 4-inch pots). Some species, like bulbs, can be forced to bloom earlier by modifying the day length (extending it for long-day plants).

Fertilization may be 20-10-20 or 15-5-15 applied once a week at 100–200 ppm depending on the natural growth rate of the plant. It might be necessary to control plant height. This can be done without the use of plant growth regulators by modifying the cultural environment (e.g., reducing watering rate).

Factors that affect the success of plug production

A producer must decide whether to raise his or her own seedling or purchase plugs. The economic decision varies from one enterprise to another. The provider should decide the appropriate equipment to purchase for the operation. Once selected, the employees should be trained to operate and equipment efficiently so that the plug trays are filled properly, seeded efficiently, and stacked such as to avoid compaction of the medium. It is critical to fertilize and water plants properly so they grow at the proper rate and attain the proper height.

SUMMARY

Soil has traditionally been the primary source of plant growth nutrients. It also provides physical support for plants. However, technological advances have enabled plants to be grown in media that contain no real or true soils. This soilless culture may take place in water (hydroponics or water culture) or in soilless substrates (bag culture). Water culture has two basic types—recycling and nonrecycling systems (i.e., excess nutrients drain away). Plants may be cultured in inert or organic substrates. Because these substrates provide only physical support, all nutrients must be artificially supplied through irrigation water.

REFERENCES AND SUGGESTED READING

Food and Agriculture Organization (FAO) of the United Nations. 1990. *Soilless culture for horticultural crop production: Plant production and protection paper 101.*
    Rome, Italy: Food and Agriculture Organization of the United Nations.

Nicholls, R. 1990. *Beginning hydroponics*. Philadelphia: Running Press.

Resh, H. M. 1995. *Hydroponic food production*. Santa Barbara, Calif.: Woodbridge Press.

Greenhouse fertilization
*http://www.umass.edu/umext/floriculture/fact_sheets/greenhouse_management/
    bedfert.html*

Greenhouse roofs
*http://www.umass.edu/umext/floriculture/fact_sheets/greenhouse_management/
    jb_retractable_roofs.htm*

Greenhouse production
http://pubs.caes.uga.edu/caespubs/pubced/B1182.htm

OUTCOMES ASSESSMENT

1. Give an overview of the geography of greenhouse production in the United States.
2. Discuss the impact of plug technology on modern greenhouse production.
3. Give the pros and cons of hydroponic production.
4. Discuss the challenge of imports to the U.S. horticultural industry.
5. Discuss the advantages of greenhouse production over field production of plants.

14

Growing Succulents

PURPOSE AND EXPECTED OUTCOMES

This chapter is designed to discuss how to grow and care for cacti and other succulent plants.

After studying this chapter, the student should be able to

1. Describe the basic characteristics of succulents.
2. Describe how succulents are propagated.
3. Distinguish between desert and jungle cacti.
4. Describe the methods of cacti propagation.
5. Discuss how to care for cacti for healthy growth.
6. Describe how to propagate and care for bromeliads.

[COLOR PLATES—*see color plate 21* for additional chapter photos]

14.1 WHAT ARE SUCCULENTS

The term *succulents* refers to a very large group of plants that spread across many plant families, and are characterized by a water-storing adaptation that makes them thrive in harsh, water-limited environments in which other plants perish (Figure 14–1). These plants live on dry land and have fleshy leaves and stems that are covered with a thick, waxy cuticle or surface. Their specialized cells tightly hold in water, while the waxy surface prevents water loss by evaporation. Succulents differ widely in shape and form and are widely used in the landscape as ground covers, bedding plants, and focal points. They are also used as container plants for the house.

Cacti are a specific group of succulents and perhaps the most well-known family of succulents. It is common for people to refer to succulents and cacti as separate categories, but technically, they are one group—succulents. Cacti differ from other succulents by having unique structure called *areoles*. An areole consists of two buds from which flowers, branches, fruits, and spines emerge. Another distinguishing feature

FIGURE 14–1 Succulents can grow under dry and marginal environments. *(Source: Tony Souter © Dorling Kindersley)*

FIGURE 14–2 Stem succulents: (a) Columnar cactus represented by *Pachycereus schottii*; (b) Barrel-shaped cactus represented by barrel cactus. *(Source: For (a) © Dorling Kindersley, (b) Jeremy Hopley © Dorling Kindersley)*

(a)   (b)

is the presence of thorns (spines), which when removed do not cause sap to be exuded. If sap, clear or milky, exudes upon removal of a spine, the plant is definitely not a cactus. Examples noncacti thorny succulents are hawthorns, black locust, roses, and raspberry brambles.

Succulents are geographically widely distributed, but occur mostly in frost-free regions with low rainfall. They are found in mostly arid regions and less frequently in the humid forests, but rarely in the driest desert. Succulents are tolerant of poor and shallow soils.

14.2 CATEGORIES OF SUCCULENTS

Any plant with fleshy leaves or stems is considered a succulent. Succulents may be divided into two broad categories based on form:

1. *Stem Succulent*—The most conspicuously adapted plant part is the stem. These species have fleshy stems that contain chlorophyll and hence have the capacity for photosynthesis. The stems may be columnar or barrel shaped (Figure 14–2).

FIGURE 14–3 Leaf succulent represented by *Agave Americana* 'Marginata' *(Source: © Dorling Kindersley)*

FIGURE 14–4 Flowering succulent Christmas cactus (*Schlumbergera* sp) *(Source: © Dorling Kindersley)*

When they occur, the leaves on these stems are drastically reduced. The Saguaro cactus is a stem succulent.

2. *Leaf succulents*—There is great variation in this group. Some leaf succulents have small fleshy leaves. Others have highly compressed stems from which a rosette of large, fleshy leaves radiate, as exemplified by the *Agave* group (Figure 14–3).

Succulents may or may not produce flowers (Figure 14–4). The blooming types often have spectacular shapes and colors. In the absence of blooms, succulents have attractive foliage colors and morphological features that provide excitement in the landscape. Succulents can be grouped in containers (mixed containers) to create stunning plant displays.

14.3 POPULAR SUCCULENTS (NONCACTI)

Some of the widely grown noncacti succulents include species from the genera *Aloe Agava, Sempervivum, Echeveria, Yucca, Euphorbia,* and *Sedum.*

Aloe

The *Aloe* genus of plants is native to Africa and the Arabian Peninsula. These plants have a compressed stem with radiating succulent leaves that are frequently spiny and patterned (Figure 14–5). Some species have well-developed stems and may grow into a bush or even a tree. Their flowers are erect spikes that come in color shades of orange, yellow, or pink. One of the widely popular species is the *Aloe vera*, the medicinal or Barbados aloe, which is widely known for its value as an ingredient in cosmetics. Other important species are the *Aloe maculata* (or *A. saponaria*), soap or zebra aloe, *A. arborescens* (touch or candelabra), and *A. variegata* (partridge breast aloe).

FIGURE 14–5 Aloe (*Aloe ferox*) *(Source: Craig Knowles © Dorling Kinsersley)*

FIGURE 14–6 Agave (*Agave parryi*) *(Source: © Dorling Kindersley)*

FIGURE 14–7 Common houseleek (*Sempervivum tectorum*) *(Source: Frank Greenaway © Dorling Kinsersley)*

Agave

The *Agave* genus (century plants) are widely adapted with cold-hardy species. They are also rosette-forming like the aloes (Figure 14–6). Most of the species are sharply spined and rigidly leaved, a popular species being the large, blue-gray foliages *A. americana*. However, *Agava attenuata* is soft leaved and very attractive.

Sempervivum

Sempervivum genus is native to southern and Central Europe. Known commonly as hen and chickens, they are also referred to as common houseleeks. They are generally frost-hardy and intolerant to extreme heat and dry conditions that promote rotting. The leaves are low growing with tightly rounded rosettes that occur in different shades and patterns of green, grey, and red. Being monocarpic, the rosette dies after flowering, leaving behind a cluster of offsets. Common blooms are purple or pink, and are borne on thick stems just above the foliage. The most common houseleek is the *S. tectorum* (Figure 14–7).

Echeveria

Also called hen and chickens, *Echeveria* species are native to Central America and are hence tolerant of higher temperatures than the *Sempervivum* species. They are not frost-hardy. Their rosettes are usually bigger than those of the *Sempervivum* genus. Also, they exhibit a wider variety of leaf shapes and colors, many of the leaves being edged in a contrasting color (Figure 14–8). Most of the species have a powdery of waxy surface. Their flowers are bell shaped. Some of the common species are *E. lilacina* and *E. shaviana*.

Yucca

Succulents in the *Yucca* genus are not as widely used in the landscape as the other families previously discussed in this section. Many species are sharply spined. There are variegated species that create interest in the landscape. A popular species, *Y. elephantipes*, is used as a houseplant. Another species of interest is the *Y. filamentosa*.

Euphorbia

This is the largest genus of succulents. Commonly referred to as spurges, species in the genus *Euphorbia* are characterized by plants with tiny flowers that lack petals. Instead, the showy parts of the plant are its brightly colored bracts. Another noteworthy distinction is milky sap or latex that exudes from the plant when cut or snapped. This milky sap is an irritant to the mucous membrane. When grown in the house, they should be kept out of reach of children and pets. The most popular species in this genus are the *E. pulcherima* (Poinsettia) (Figure 14–9) and *E. milli* (crown of thorns). This genus contains species with widely differing features. *E. horrida* and *E. echinus* are leafless with swollen spiny stems that resemble a cactus. The Mediterranean spurge, *E. characias*, has erect woody stems that can reach more than three feet tall.

Sedum

Commonly called the stonecrops, *Sedum* species are found mainly on rocky, mountainous regions (Figure 14–10). They belong to the family Crassulaceae. They may be divided into three general categories according to how they are used in the landscape. The group of upright and showy species, exemplified by *Sedum spectabile* (showy sedum), can grow to heights of about 2–3 feet and add color to gardens and borders. The group of trailing sedums is effective as edging plants for flower beds. The third group of sedums

FIGURE 14–8   Hens and chickens (*Echeveria* sp)   *(Source: Dorling Kindersley)*

FIGURE 14–9   Poinsettia (*Euphorbia pulcherima*) *(Source: Matthew Ward © Dorling Kindersley)*

FIGURE 14–10   Stone crop (*Sedum*)   *(Source: Jonathan Buckley © Dorling Kindersley)*

FIGURE 14–11   *Haworthia tessellate*   *(Source: Deni Brown © Dorling Kindersley)*

is used as grounds covers or container plants. They are easy to propagate from leaves, as well as from cuttings and seed, for example, *S. spathulifolium, S. spurium*, and *S. procumbens*.

Faucaria

Native to South Africa, these plants are very good as "practice plants" for the novice who wants to grow succulents at home. They are easy to propagate, rooting easily from vegetative parts. Should the plant begin to rot as a result of improper care, the grower may salvage the plant by retrieving a healthy part for planting in fresh soil. They are sunloving plants. Their beauty is in their compact form, which is a challenge to keep since the stem tends to elongate under improper care, especially low light and moisture in the rest period. Their flowers are relatively large for their size.

Haworthia

These plants are native to South African and Namibia. They occur either as a solitary plant or as short plants surrounded by a cluster of offshoots (Figure 14–11). They bloom once a year. However, because the flowers are unattractive, some growers prefer to cut the flower stalk when it emerges, to encourage more leaf growth. As houseplants, they may be located in the window where the sunlight is indirect. They grow mostly in the cool winter months and rarely outgrow their initial containers. They are not exacting in their demands for growth factors and can tolerate improper watering practices.

The plant families that contain succulents include Agavaceae, Aizoaceae, Asclepiadaceae, Compositae, Crassulaceae, Euphorbiaceae, Liliaceae, and Cactaceae. Because of their immense capacity to store water, succulents can survive as indoor plants with minimum care. A list of various succulents is provided in Table 14–1.

TABLE 14–1   Selected Popular Succulents (Excluding Cacti and Bromeliads)

Plant	Scientific Name
Houseleeks	*Sempervium* spp.
Century plant	*Agave americana*
Wart plant	*Haworthia* spp.
Milk bush	*Euphorbia tirucali*
Crown of thorns	*Euphorbia splendens*
Candle plant	*Senecio articulatus*
Mother-in-law's tongue or snake plant	*Sansevieria trifasciata*
Air plant or Panda plant	*Kalanchoe* spp.
Hen and chickens	*Echeveria* spp.
Agave	*Agave angustifolia; A. botterji*
Aloe	*Aloe variegata* and other species
Ox tongue	*Gasteria* spp.
Jade plant	*Crassula argentea*
Burro tail	*Sedum* spp.

14.4 PROPAGATION

Succulents may be propagated from seed, cuttings, or offsets. Aloes, haworthias, apicras, and gasterias may be propagated from suckers as well as seed and cuttings.

14.4.1 SEED

Seeds may be nursed in trays or pots containing a rooting medium that drains very well. Many succulent seeds are small and should not be buried during propagation. The soil surface should be of fine tilth. The seeds are sprinkled on the soil surface and then watered. The soil should be kept moist with either a glass plate or clear plastic covering. Germination occurs within two to three weeks.

14.4.2 CUTTINGS

Cutting are best taken in May and June for quick healing of wounds. A sharp blade should be used for cutting. Leaf cuttings of succulents can be propagated by first rooting them in water or soil. Succulents of the family Crassulaceae are particularly suited for propagation from leaf cuttings. After removing a leaf, the cut surface should be allowed to dry for a few days before planting in the medium.

14.4.3 OFFSETS

Nonbranching succulents often produce **offsets** that readily propagate the species. Offsets are identical plants that develop as side growths from the mother plant originating from either the main stem or the base of the mother plant, as occurs in bulbs. These young, full-fledged plants may be removed after they have grown to a size that will enable them to survive independently of the parent plant. The daughter plants are detached by cutting with a sharp razor blade or knife and inserted into a rooting mixture. They are nursed under warm, medium light conditions with sufficient moisture until they have formed adequate roots. Offsets are commonly produced by cacti, bromeliads, and bulbs.

Offsets
Side growth of the mother plant originating from either the stem or base of the plant.

Growth requirements include the following:

1. *Light.* An inadequate light supply is usually the cause of poor growth and development of succulents grown indoors. Since an indoor light supply is irregular, succulents grown indoors should be located on the windowsill or near a window where they can receive sunlight. Window-grown plants are prone to phototropic response and should be turned regularly to prevent the foliage from curving toward bright light. It is a good practice to place potted succulents outside for some time during the bright days of spring and summer.

2. *Temperature.* Succulents generally grow well under warm conditions. They are cold sensitive and as such should not be left outside during the cold season.

3. *Moisture.* By nature, succulents are able to store large amounts of water due to adaptive mechanisms that enable them to survive dry conditions. However, this should not be misconstrued to mean that they do not need watering. On the contrary, a good watering regime increases the success of succulents. Physiologically, they need watering during the period of active growth. The amount provided should be reduced during the rest period of the plant. Since the foliage of most succulents have great aesthetic value, it is best to water potted indoor succulents from below to prevent water from splashing on the plants, which often leaves unsightly markings from the salts in the water.

4. *Fertilizing.* Unless the succulents are fast growing, they are not likely to benefit a great deal from any fertilizer application regimen. However, some nutrition is needed to support basic growth and development. Nitrogenous fertilizers should be used with caution since they may cause weakness and flabbiness in top growth.

5. *Diseases and pests.* Indoor plant pests such as root mealybugs, spider mites, scales, and mealybugs affect succulents because the anatomical arrangement of the leaves is a conducive environment for such pests to hide and thrive. When root mealybugs become a problem, succulents should be repotted after removing the old medium. Observance of phytosanitation reduces the incidence of diseases and pests.

6. *Repotting.* Like other potted plants, succulents periodically need to be repotted into larger containers. In spite of their succulence, some of these plants are brittle and should be handled with care. The foliage may be cleaned with a mild detergent and water.

14.6 BROMELIADS

14.6.1 WHAT ARE BROMELIADS?

Bromeliads belong to the family Bromeliaceae. These tropical plants have certain distinguishing features. They have a rosette plant form and absorb food and moisture primarily through their leaves. The name *bromeliad* derives from this aerial feeding characteristic. As such, bromeliads are sometimes called *air plants*. Most bromeliads grown indoors are **epiphytes;** however, nonepiphytic terrestrial species exist. The most popular terrestrial species is the edible pineapple *(Ananas comosus)*. Bromeliads produce brilliantly colored flowers that may appear at any time of the year once the plant has attained maturity. Bromeliads also need to have water in the center of the rosette, which is the growing point. The two most common plant shapes are presented in Figure 14–12. Popular species are listed in Table 14–2.

Epiphyte
A plant that grows upon another plant but is not a parasite.

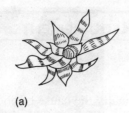
(a)

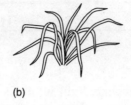
(b)

(c)

(d)

TABLE 14–2 Selected Popular Bromeliads

Plant	Scientific Name
Pineapple	*Ananas comosus*
Um plant	*Aechmea fasciata*
Patriotic plant	*Aechmea mertensis*
No common name	*Ananas bracteatus* or *A. comosus variegates*
Angel's tears or queen's tears	*Billbergig nutans*
Orange star	*Guzmania lingulata*
No common name	*Guzmania musaica*
Blushing bromeliad	*Neoregelia carolinae*; other species are *N. spectabilis* and *N. ampullaceal*
Earth stars	*Cryptanthus bromelioides, C. bivittatus, C. acaulis*, and others
Flaming sword	*Vriesia splendens*; other species are *V. hieroglyphica* and *V. fenestralis*
Blushing bride	*Tilandsia ionantha*
Pink quill	*Tilandsia cyanea*
Black Amazon bird nest	*Nidularium innocentii;* another species is *N. fulgens*

14.6.2 CREATING AN EPIPHYTE BRANCH

Epiphytic bromeliads are not planted in soil in pots but are attached to pieces of wood. To create a display, one needs sphagnum moss, a log, cork bark, wire, plastic wrap, and shears. The moss is moistened and wrapped around the base of a bromeliad rosette to cover all of the roots. The moss-covered plant is attached to the log and temporarily secured by tying with a piece of wire. The cork bark is wrapped around the moss and secured with wire permanently. Several rosettes may be prepared and attached to various parts of the log to produce a creative display (Figure 14–13). Different species may be used in one display.

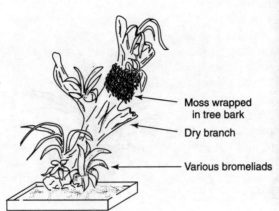

FIGURE 14–13 An epiphytic branch may be used to display a variety of bromeliads. *(Source: George Acquaah)*

Moss wrapped in tree bark
Dry branch
Various bromeliads

14.6.3 CARE

Care of succulents includes the following:

1. *Water.* The moss part of the display should be watered when it feels dry, and the middle part of the rosette that holds water should be kept full at all times. The receptacle should be emptied and refilled periodically (monthly).
2. *Light.* The display should be mounted in a part of the house that receives bright, filtered light.
3. *Temperature.* Warm temperatures (above 15.6°C or 60°F) and relatively high humidity are required for best growth. In a drier season, a periodic mist application may be needed to provide humid microclimates for bromeliads.
4. *Fertilizing.* Foliar application or addition of liquid fertilizer to the water in the rosette may be helpful during the period of active growth.

14.6.4 POTTED BROMELIADS

Terrestrial species may be potted in a medium that is porous but retains moisture adequately. Lime is not desirable in the medium. Bromeliads do not produce roots profusely and hence do not need to be grown in deep pots.

Propagation

Bromeliads may be raised from seed. The seeds are sowed and cared for as described for succulents. Commercial nurseries raise plants in this way for sale. However, it is easier to propagate bromeliads by using offsets.

Repotting

Plastic pots retain moisture longer than clay pots. Being air plants, repotting to renew the soil is not important in bromeliad culture. Repotting into larger pots is necessary on an infrequent basis.

14.7.1 WHAT ARE CACTI?

Cacti (plural for *cactus*) are mostly *succulent plants* that belong to the family Cactaceae. They differ from other succulents by having *areoles* that frequently carry spines and also are sites of flower production. There are two kinds of cacti—*desert cacti* and *jungle cacti*—each with its own growth requirements. Desert cacti are adapted to drought conditions *(xerophytic),* largely because they lack leaves or have greatly reduced leaf structures, thereby eliminating or minimizing stomatal transpiration. The stems of desert cacti are columnar or spherical in shape and also are ribbed. Most of them have spines that are often prickly (Figure 14–14). Jungle cacti, on the other hand, are generally *epiphytic* and adapted to humid and shady conditions. Their stems are often flattened and cylindrical structures. Jungle cacti lack ribs on their stems, which are jointed into long strings (Figure 14–15). Their stems and spines are not prickly.

Desert cacti have more aesthetic appeal than jungle species in their vegetative states. However, cacti, under proper conditions of light, produce attractive flowers, the finest and largest ones being produced by jungle species. Because the jungle species are adapted to shady conditions, they are better suited to indoor use. However, because of their stringy stems, they often require staking or physical support in cultivation. They also do well as hanging basket plants. Common cacti suited to indoor cultivation are listed in Table 14–3.

(a)

(b)

FIGURE 14–14 Desert cacti occur in a wide array of shapes, sizes, and forms. *(Source: George Acquaah)*

Cylindrical

Nonsegmented

Segmented

FIGURE 14–15 Basic stem types occurring in jungle cacti.

14.7 Cacti **461**

TABLE 14–3 Selected Cacti Suitable for Growing Indoors

Plant	Scientific Name
Bunny ears	*Opuntia microdsys;* others are *O. leucotricha,* *O. monacantha,* and *O. tuna*
Sea urchin cactus	*Astrophylum asterias*
Peanut cactus	*Cleistocactus strausii*
No common name	*Cereus peruvianus*
Queen of the night	*Selenicereus grandiflorus*
Rat's tail	*Aporocactus flagelliformis*
Crown cactus	*Rebutia* spp.
Golden barrel cactus or mother-in-law's arm chair	*Echinocactus grusonii*
Bishop's cap	*Astrophytum myriostigma*
Rose-paid cactus	*Gymnocalycium mihanovichii*
No common name	*Hematocactus stispinus*
Pincushion cactus	*Mammilaria* spp. such as *M. bocasana,* *M. bombycina,* and *M. parkinsonii*
Rainbow cactus	*Echinocereus pectinatus*
Easter cactus	*Rhipsalidopsis* hybrids
Christmas cactus	*Schlumbergera* hybrids

14.7.2 POPULAR CACTI

Cacti are grown as both houseplants and landscape plants. They are popular houseplants for several reasons. They are relatively easy to grow and care for, because, being adapted to harsh environment, they can tolerate some neglect. However, being slow growing, they are capable of hiding the consequence of flawed care for a long time, appearing healthy when in fact they are slowly deteriorating. Cacti display a wide range of stunning shapes, sizes, and blooms. They can also remain small in size for a long time. Some of the popular genera are discussed next:

Opuntia

Called the prickly pear, the genus *Opuntia* is characterized by pear-shaped pads that are often spiny or prickly (Figure 14–16). They grow well in the southwestern United States. A few species are nonglobular, growing into columnar structures. Some species are also spineless. Many species produce large branching mounds that may reach four to five feet high to sprawl in long chains along the ground. They are best grown in ample space. They also produce beautiful flowers, provided they receive adequate sunlight. They are best grown in a window location where they will receive some direct sunlight. Some varieties have food and medicinal value.

Echinocactus

This group of cacti is more challenging to grow and care for as houseplants, requiring a lot of sunlight to be induced to bloom (Figure 14–17). However, they can be sunburned if set outdoors in spring, unless they are properly hardened off. In the wild in the southwestern United States, some of the species in this genus can attain a height of over three feet. As houseplants cacti should not be watered in the cold season.

Echinocereus

This genus is very diverse in shape, size, and flower color (Figure 14–18). This species is adapted to a wide range of growing environments. They are generally faster growing than many genera of cacti. They are known to shrink during the winter season as a survival mechanism. They should not be watered in the cool season.

FIGURE 14–16 *Opuntia.* *(Source: Craig Knowles © Dorling Kindersley)*

FIGURE 14–17 *Echinocactus.* *(Source: © Deni Brown Dorling Kindersley)*

FIGURE 14–18 *Echinocereus.* *(Source: © Dorling Kindersley)*

FIGURE 14–19 *Echinopsis.* *(Source: Peter Anderson © Dorling Kindersley)*

Echinopsis

The genus *Echinopsis* is native to Argentina, Bolivia, Brazil, and Paraguay. They are characterized by globular stems and a wide array of spectacular flowers. They are also among the easiest of cacti to grow and care for as houseplants. They produce hairy buds that soon burst into flowers in a wide range of colors including pinks, deep reds, magentas, white, and oranges (Figure 14–19). Flowers often exude a sweet scent that comes out in the night. For optimum flowering, the plant should be kept dry during the cool season.

Escobaria

These are relatively small plants that bloom easily in a wide variety of colors including yellow, purple, pink, and red (Figure 14–20). They are found in the wild in the southwestern United States and Mexico. They usually require abundant sunlight and a protracted resting period in winter.

Ferocactus

These are also native to the southwestern United States and Mexico. They are noted for their pronounced and attractive spines (Figure 14–21). As houseplants, they are difficult to get to bloom. They can be kept outdoors during the growing season and returned indoors for the resting period.

Gymnocactus

Gymnocactus cacti are native to Mexico. These globular cacti bear small, brightly colored flowers, in white, pink, magenta, and others. As houseplants, they are best kept in the window so they receive some direct sunlight. It is also critical not to water them during the resting period in the cool season.

Gymnocalycium

Like the *Echinopsis* group, *Gymnocalycium* species are native to South America, occurring in Argentina, Bolivia, Brazil, Peru, and Uruguay. They are fast growing and flower easily in colors including white, orange, pink, green, and yellow (Figure 14–22). They exhibit a very wide diversity of color and texture on their globular stems. They can be propagated by the offsets they are noted for producing. They also shrink during their winter rest period when they must be kept cool and dry.

Mammillaria

Found in the wild in the southwestern United States and Mexico, these species of plant mostly occur in the mountain regions. They exhibit a wide variety of shapes, sizes, and spine colors (Figure 14–23). They produce small flowers that occur in a circular arrangement around the top of the stem; however, the stem is solitary in some species.

FIGURE 14–20   *Escobaria.*
(Source: © Dorling Kindersley)

FIGURE 14–21   *Ferocactus.*
(Source: © Dorling Kindersley)

FIGURE 14–22   *Gymnocalycium.*
(Source: © Dorling Kindersley)

FIGURE 14–23 *Mammillaria.* (Source: Andrew Lawson © Dorling Kindersley)

FIGURE 14–24 *Parodia.* (Source: © Dorling Kindersley)

FIGURE 14–25 *Rebutia.* (Source: © Dorling Kindersley)

Parodia

These globular plants are native to South America, occurring in the same places as the *Gymnocalycium* group. They are globular plants that bear flowers in a wide range of colors, including pink, deep red, magenta, white, green, and orange (Figure 14–24). Their natural growth pattern can be challenging to keep, but will generally do well as houseplants if provided abundant sunlight. Inadequate sunlight produces distorted growth. They are best watered sparingly during the winter period.

Rebutia

The genus *Rebutia* consists of small, globular plants that are native to Argentina and Bolivia. They are diminutive in size, reaching only a few inches height but with a tendency to produce copious numbers of offsets ("puppies") in a ring from around the mother plant (Figure 14–25). They bloom easily and often multiple times a year, in colors including white, pink, yellow, and red. During the rest period in winter, they should be kept dry and cool and out of intense sunlight.

Thelocactus

Found wild in the southwestern United States and Mexico, this group of cacti usually bloom as older plants in a wide range of colors and often in combinations of colors. The soil should be kept dry in the winter and cool season for about half the year, during which time occasional misting may be given if the air is very dry.

Astrophytum

The genus *Astrophytum* (star plants) has globular-shaped cacti, even though a few columnar species exist. They grow as native species of Mexico and southwestern United States. They are also commonly called "bishop's cap" because of their five-ribbed shape.

The genus contains five species. Some are spineless, with attractive felt where the spines would have occurred, and speckled patterns of their skin called *flocking*. The genus is characterized by large, bright yellow flowers sometimes with bright yellow orange or red center. These plants grow best in the windowsill where they receive some direct sunlight. Withholding water during the resting period in the cool season is critical for survival.

14.8 PROPAGATION

Cacti can be raised from seeds, offsets, or cuttings.

14.8.1 CONTAINERS

It is common to find cacti grown in decorative, glazed pots. However, as previously discussed, glazing transforms a clay pot into a plastic pot, without the natural pores for moisture loss. Unglazed clay pots are preferred containers for cacti.

14.8.2 SEED

To raise cacti from seed, fresh, viable seed should be obtained from a reputable nursery. A lot of moisture is needed for germination. First, a pot is filled with the soil mixture, leaving about 1 inch (2.54 centimeters) of space on top. The medium should be drenched with water. After the excess water has drained away, the seeds are scattered on the soil surface without burying them; large seeds (e.g., those from the opuntia group) may be partially buried. To maintain a moist soil, the pot should be covered (e.g., by tying a piece of plastic sheet over the top); the pot is then placed in a warm area (Figure 14–26). After about a year, the seedlings are ready to be transplanted into individual containers.

14.8.3 OFFSETS

As cacti grow, older plants develop plantlets, or offsets, around the base of the stem. The offsets can be harvested by either cutting or pulling them from the parent plant. The separation leaves a wound at the point of attachment that needs to be dried for a few days before planting to prevent rotting. Offsets are planted by pushing them slightly into the seed medium (Figure 14–27). After planting, they should be watered moderately and kept in medium light until they root, after several weeks. Since cacti have sharp needles, they cannot be handled with bare hands. Gloves, folded paper, tongs, and such items are used while cutting or planting cacti.

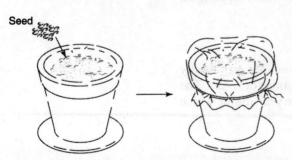

FIGURE 14–26 Desert cacti may be propagated from seed.

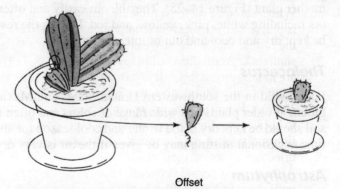

FIGURE 14–27 Desert cacti may be propagated by using offsets in certain species. This is simply accomplished by using a pair of tongs to carefully pull offsets and planting them in potting media.

(a)

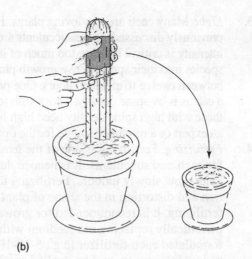
(b)

FIGURE 14–28 Both desert and jungle cacti may be propagated by cutting. (a) In segmented or branching species, a branch is simply cut off and planted (b) In nonbranching species, tip cutting is made. Care must be exercised to avoid injury from prickly spines.

14.8.4 CUTTING

Apart from whole plantlets, vegetative pieces can be obtained from the stem for propagation. For species such as opuntia that have segmented stems, individual segments can be removed for planting (Figure 14–28). If done carefully, the overall appearance of the plant is not ruined. Nonbranching species such as trichocereus are propagated by cutting off about 2 inches (5.1 centimeters) of the tip of a stem. The piece is planted after the cut end is dried.

14.9 CARING FOR CACTI

1. *Rest period.* Cacti and most succulents grow for only a few months of the year, resting the remainder of the time. Generally, the life cycle of these plants closely follow the seasons. They grow mostly in spring and fall, and rest in the hottest part of summer and through the winter. Whereas it is important to provide optimal growth factors during the active growing seasons, it is even more critical to observe their rest periods by withholding water. If grown in combinations with other houseplants, the grower should be careful not to treat all housplants alike by watering and feeding them year-round. As previously noted, cacti are slow growing and hence are less likely to react to improper care in a prompt manner.

2. *Water.* If unsure about sensitivity to domestic water, rain water should be used. When watering cacti, wetting the plant should be avoided Bottom watering (water is placed in the saucer) is recommended. It also eliminates the watermarks left on the foliage that is directly watered. Further, avoid placing a wet cactus in direct sunlight because this could cause sunburn. The soil should be kept dry while plants are in the resting stage. It is critical to respect the growth pattern of the plant in nutrient and water management. Some species grow in winter and rest during summer. When the active growth period is over and blooming has ceased, it is time to hold back water. Overwatering of cacti and other succulents may cause elongation and swelling of the stems. If plants are accidentally overwatered they may be dried by uprooting them and allowing them to dry out for about a week or more. After the rest period is over, it is important to withhold water from the plants until there is clear evidence of the beginning of growth. Premature and excessive water predisposes plants to rot, especially in sensitive species like those of the genus *Escobaria* and *Neoporteria*. To resume watering it is best to soak the roots of cacti by setting the pots in bowls of water for a brief period.

3. *Light.* Many cacti are sun-loving plants. However, some prefer partial shade. As previously discussed, some succulents are native to humid regions of the world. Light intensity is critical because too much of it during winter can hasten the entry of some species into their spring active growth phase. Photoperiod needs to cacti range between twelve to eighteen hours. One practical way of "guessing" the light needs of a cactus is by spine density. Those with fewer spines are more shade tolerant while those with high spine density need high light intensity. Better still, one should consult an expert or a reference source for the optimal light required for the species.

4. *Fertilizing.* Fertilizing is one of the least important inputs in growing and caring for cacti and succulents. It is needed during the active growing season. Succulents grow slowly indoors. Fertilizing them tends to promote undesirable elongation and distortion in the shape of plants, reducing their aesthetic value. In lieu of fertilizing, it is recommended for growers to refresh the growing medium by periodically replacing old medium with fresh medium. Some commercially formulated cacti fertilizer (e.g., 5-10-10, 7-10-6) are available. Fertilizers should be low in nitrogen, and be applied sparingly about every two months.

5. *Pests.* Cacti rarely experience pest problems while growing in the open. However, as indoor plants, some pests that may attack cacti include scales, mites, spider mites, white flies, and mealy bugs. Cleaning the plant after the rest period to remove dust particles, and also washing the roots under running water before resetting in the pot, help to stave off some of these potential pest problems. Insecticidal soaps or detergents should not be used.

6. *Shrinkage.* Shrinkage is part of the life cycle of many species of cacti. This occurs over about four to six months involving both aboveground and belowground structures. Plants that are still in their winter dormancy cannot make use of water. Whereas shrinking accompanies winter rest, summer shrinkage may be actually a call for water due to excessive due conditions.

7. *Temperature.* Desert cacti are adapted to warm conditions. However, extra indoor heat during the winter period coupled with reduced light may cause cacti to grow spindly and weak. A room temperature of between 7.22 and 18.3°C (45 and 65°F) is desirable for cacti. The low indoor humidity during winter is especially intolerable to jungle cacti, which need to be misted with water frequently during this season.

8. *Cleaning.* To keep plants attractive, cacti may be dusted, cleaned with a damp cloth, or washed. These cleaning activities should be done very carefully when handling species with thorns.

9. *Repotting.* Cacti require repotting every two to four years. To determine whether repotting is due, the plant should be removed from its pot and its roots checked for pot bounding.

14.10 MINIATURE ROCK GARDEN

Cacti are excellent plant species for creating rock gardens. They offer a wide variety of plant shapes and forms and can be used to develop desert gardens. The garden is created in a shallow container. The bottom of the container is lined with gravel or a suitable drainage material and then covered with a potting mixture (Figure 14–29). Stones of a variety of shapes and sizes are carefully chosen and placed to create a rocky terrain. A variety of cacti (both desert and jungle) are selected and planted around the stones.

14.11 GRAFTED CACTI

Cacti occur in a spectacular array of forms, as indicated in this chapter. The beauty of these slow-growing plants can be enhanced by grafting different species with contrasting forms and features onto one another (Figure 14–30). For example,

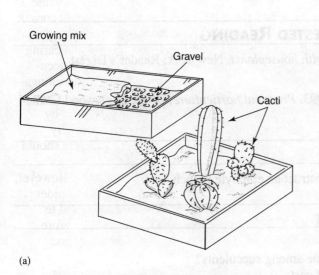

(a)

(b)

FIGURE 14-29 (a) A variety of desert cacti may be planted in a miniature garden. (b) Plant selection should include contrasting types for the best effect. *(Source: For (b) George Acquaah)*

FIGURE 14-30 Grafted cacti add interest to displays. A graft may be simple, involving just two species, or multiple, with several species growing on one stock. *(Source: © George Acquaah)*

a columnar species may be topped with a globelike species. Two species are commonly grafted, but some creative growers may graft more than two different species on one plant. In some cases, the scions develop into very colorful and attractive ornamental displays.

SUMMARY

Succulents are plants that are able to hold large amounts of water in their leaves or stems. Plant families that have succulents include Cactaceae, Liliaceae, Crassulaceae, and Agavaceae. Cacti are a special group of succulents that frequently carry spines. There are two kinds of cacti: desert (which are xerophytic) and jungle (which are epiphytic). Desert cacti have stems that are either columnar or spherical and may or may not be ribbed. Jungle cacti, on the other hand, have flattened and cylindrical stems that are jointed. Under proper light conditions, cacti may be induced to flower. They can be raised from seed, offsets, or cuttings; improper watering in cultivation is detrimental to cacti plants.

REFERENCES AND SUGGESTED READING

Reader's Digest. 1979. *Success with houseplants.* New York: Reader's Digest Association.

Rice, L. W., and R. P. Rice, Jr. 1993. *Practical horticulture*, 2d ed. Englewood Cliffs, N.J.: Prentice Hall.

PRACTICAL EXPERIENCE

Follow the steps in the text to construct an epiphyte branch.

OUTCOMES ASSESSMENT

1. What are succulents?
2. In what ways are cacti unique among succulents?
3. Discuss the seasonal care of cacti.
4. Describe how desert cacti adapt to drought conditions.
5. Distinguish between jungle cacti and desert cacti.

PART 5

GROWING PLANTS OUTDOORS: ORNAMENTALS

15
Principles of Landscaping

PURPOSE AND EXPECTED OUTCOMES

This chapter discusses the principles and steps involved in landscape design.

After studying this chapter, the student should be able to

1. Define the term *landscaping* and discuss its categories.
2. List and discuss the basic principles of landscaping.
3. Describe the steps involved in a landscape design.
4. Describe how plants are selected for a landscape.

OVERVIEW

Using plants outdoors to enhance the general view is not a modern-day invention. Although sometimes plants are used alone, at other times they are used in conjunction with nonplant elements such as sculptures, walkways, and fountains to create a view or environment that is aesthetically pleasing and nurturing to the human spirit (Figure 15–1). The key goals of landscaping design may be summed up into two—*function* and *aesthetics*. You may remember from an earlier chapter that horticulture is both a science and an art. Landscaping may be likened to using plants to paint a picture, with the open space as the canvas. One key difference is that unlike painting on canvas, the subjects in the picture are not static but change with time. The changes may be in form, size, and age. It takes time to stabilize plant characteristics, which can be controlled only with good maintenance. However, there is more to landscaping than appearance, even though aesthetics is what is most readily noticeable to most people and thus associated with the discipline. The landscape artist, properly called a *landscape designer*, can, with proper choice of plants and design or arrangement, elicit certain responses from people who use the landscaped area.

15.1 WHAT IS LANDSCAPING?

Landscaping
The use of plants and inanimate objects outdoors to fulfill aesthetic and functional purposes.

Landscaping may be defined as the use of plants outdoors to fulfill aesthetic and functional purposes. The term is identified with the outdoors, even though plants can be used to accomplish similar objectives indoors (sometimes called *interiorscaping* or *plantscaping*). Landscaping is an activity in which beauty, as well as function, may be determined by the customer. To one person, landscaping may mean a couple of fruit trees or just plants on the property. To another customer, plants in the landscape must not only be carefully selected but also strategically arranged.

15.1.1 GOALS OF LANDSCAPING

In fulfilling aesthetic and functional purposes, landscaping may be specifically used to accomplish the following:

1. *Enhance the aesthetic appeal of an area.* Home and business environments can be beautified to make them more attractive and nurturing to the human spirit. Homeowners can enjoy their surroundings and feel relaxed in the presence of an appealing display. People can walk in parks and horticultural gardens to enjoy the beauty of the exhibits.
2. *Enhance the neighborhood and increase property value.* Homes with curb appeal have higher property values on the real estate market. Landscaping can transform a simple structure into an attractive one.
3. *Blend concrete and architectural creations into the natural scenery.* Buildings tend to have sharp geometric edges that can be softened with plants. Brick and mortar in a city can be overwhelming and excessively artificial. Plants can be used to introduce life into the area.
4. *Provide privacy.* Landscaping can shield areas such as the backyards of homes, utility substations, and patios from the general public.
5. *Control vehicular and pedestrian traffic.* Just as pavements indicate where people should walk, trees, flower beds, and other features can be used to discourage people from making undesirable shortcuts across lawns. Trees and other plants on a median in the street prevent drivers from driving over the structure.
6. *Hide unsightly conditions in the area.* Plants can be used to create a wall around, for example, junkyards and storage areas.
7. *Modify environmental factors.* Trees can be planted to serve as windbreaks to reduce wind speeds, for example. Similarly, plants can be located to provide shade, block undesirable light, and modify local temperature.

8. *Create recreational grounds.* Such grounds provide places for relaxation and community interaction.
9. *Provide hobby activities for homeowners.* People can care for their gardens, water plants, and partake in other activities for exercise and enjoyment.
10. *Improve and conserve natural resources.* One such improvement is to reduce soil erosion, for example.
11. *Provide therapeutic relief.* Enjoying the landscape can be relaxing (horticultural therapy).
12. *Reduce noise and environmental pollution.* Plants in the landscape can be used to absorb noise.

These and other purposes of landscaping are discussed in this chapter.

15.2 CATEGORIES OF LANDSCAPING

The categories of landscaping do not have fixed boundaries but may overlap. They serve to show what is required in planning a landscape design. The general principles of landscape design are applied in each case to provide the best results by integrating function and aesthetics. In terms of customers or users and their needs or preferences, landscaping may be tailored to four categories of need, as described in the following sections.

15.2.1 RESIDENTIAL LANDSCAPING

Residential or *home landscaping* is geared toward individual homeowner and neighborhood needs. Developers may establish a theme for a residential project and landscape the area accordingly. For example, a residential community called Pine Acres may have a large number and variety of pine trees, whereas Cedarville may have a large number of cedar trees. Some developers landscape homes before sale. In such cases, they impose their theme on homeowners and the community. However, once the property has been purchased, a homeowner may add to the landscaping on the property. One problem results when neighbors become concerned by a nearby homeowner's exotic design, which may drastically offset the general neighborhood landscape. When homeowners are involved in the design of their homes, they are often also involved in the landscape design. Residential landscaping often has a strong personal touch to it, reflecting the taste and needs of the homeowner.

15.2.2 PUBLIC LANDSCAPING

Cities are more than brick and mortar. They are designed to look beautiful, and a large part of this goal is accomplished by blending architectural design with an effective and visually pleasing landscape design. Plants are used to enhance the frontage of edifices and to beautify the interior of offices and indoor open spaces.

Parks are designed and located for a variety of purposes. In the middle of sprawling skyscrapers, small parks may be located in strategic places to provide periodic and temporary rest and relaxation to weary pedestrians. Inner-city squares and plazas are designed for this purpose as well. Residential areas often have neighborhood playgrounds, parks, trails, pools, and ponds. On a much larger scale, a city may have community parks that include ball parks, tennis courts, and other recreational facilities.

At the state and national levels, large tracts of land may be developed for public use (e.g., fenced off as a nature reserve). Nature reserves usually include wildlife. Landscapes designed with the public in mind are found near schools, libraries, museums, and colleges.

A large city or community often has a grounds and gardens department responsible for designing, installing, and maintaining public grounds. Public landscaping may be in the form of trees planted along streets and flowers planted in the medians or on street corners. It may also take the form of a recreational park, where a piece of land is developed for residents to use during their free time. The personal or individual preference element associated with residential landscaping is not a debatable goal in the public arena since public areas are designed for a broad spectrum of people with broad backgrounds and preferences. This is not to say that individuals cannot enjoy public parks but rather that they must use what is offered.

15.2.3 COMMERCIAL LANDSCAPING

In a way, *commercial landscaping* has a public element, since businesses are open to the general public. Commercial places often have lots of space for parking. Both high- and low-traffic areas exist on company premises. Some businesses display merchandise in their windows and hence avoid obstructing the view in those areas. Commercial landscaping is found in places such as shopping malls, hotels, banks, and restaurants. When designing with the public in mind, one important though subtle factor to consider is safety. The landscaping installed should not pose a danger to the business's workers or patrons.

15.2.4 SPECIALTY LANDSCAPING

Specialty landscaping is found in places such as zoological gardens and botanical gardens, where formal designs are often used. A botanical garden is designed to exhibit a large variety of plant types. Their design usually has a strong educational component, plant species often being identified by their common and scientific names. However, the exhibits are organized and displayed in a manner that is very attractive to viewers. Golf courses are landscaped to provide the obstacles necessary for the game as well as for scenic beauty. Zoological gardens adopt landscape designs that are functional with respect to the animals on display. A jungle environment may be created in an inner-city zoo to simulate the natural habitat of jungle animals.

A commercial form of specialty landscaping is exemplified by *theme parks*. These amusement centers have landscape designs for the general compound in addition to unique landscaping designs as part of the key attraction.

15.3 LANDSCAPE DESIGNING

A landscape design should be prepared before installation of the landscape. Planning and design are both an art and a science. The environment must be thoroughly understood, including the area's topography, soil, and climate. The materials to be used should be selected properly and located to achieve the desired purpose. On a large scale, five professionals, the **landscape architect**, *landscape designer, landscape contractor, landscape maintenance supervisor*, and *nurseryperson* work together to execute a landscape project.

Landscape Architect
A professional who designs plans for the installation of plants and inanimate objects outdoors to fulfill aesthetic and functional purposes.

15.3.1 LANDSCAPE PROFESSIONALS

The Landscape Architect

The American Society of Landscape Architects defines *landscape architecture* as "the art of design, planning, or management of the land, arrangement of natural and man-made [human-made] elements thereon, through application of cultural and scientific knowledge, with concern for resource conservation, and stewardship, to the end that the resultant environment serves a useful and enjoyable purpose" (Section 2, Article II, Constitution of the American Society of Landscape Architects).

The landscape architect is thus a service provider who advises a client about plans that can enhance the client's environment. He or she is the consultant who provides the **site plan** and **planting plan** for the project. The landscape architect also provides detailed guidelines about how to install the landscape and then oversees the project to completion. Portions of the project are subcontracted to other professionals.

Landscape Designer

The Association of Professional Landscape Designers defines **landscape design** involving the analysis, planning, design, and creation of exterior spaces using plant material and appropriate hardscape elements. The landscape design process focuses on the client's overall goal of developing a specialized outdoor environment. The designer analyzes all factors of the natural environment, including views from inside the home, sun angles, privacy, architectural style of the house, slope, and drainage, and combines elements of science and art to create a functional, aesthetical pleasing extension of indoor living to the outdoors. Landscape designers have a sound knowledge in general horticulture and landscape architecture.

Landscape Contractor

The landscape contractor is a person who, using the architectural plans, installs the structures and plants in the landscape. It is important that the landscape contractor and architect thoroughly understand one another and agree on the practices and their implementation at a particular time. The landscape architect may recommend a specific contractor to a client.

Nurseryperson

After the plans have been clearly understood, the landscape architect contracts with suppliers for the materials to be used in a project. Plant materials are obtained from a nurseryperson. The landscape architect may participate at this level to ensure that the most suitable materials are selected for use. After installation of the landscape, the landscape architect inspects the work and approves it if it is done according to plan.

Landscape Maintenance Supervisor

The maintenance supervisor is responsible for managing the finished project to ensure that it becomes properly established according to plan and to the satisfaction of the client.

15.3.2 ELEMENTS OF DESIGN

Beauty is influenced by culture, traditions, and personal experiences; the elements that create beauty can be learned. The landscape designer or architect uses plants as the primary objects in creating a design. Plant species have certain characteristics or features that influence how they are used in a landscape. By themselves, each of these features is beautiful and desirable in its own way. However, when more than one feature is found in a place, their interrelatedness and interconnection become significant in how the viewer senses the visual scene. Choice of features can either enhance or diminish the overall appeal of the display. To make appropriate choices, one needs to understand the nature of the features.

Site Plan
A drawing of the locations of plants and inanimate objects in a landscape.

Planting Plan
A drawing specifying by means of symbols the types and names of plant species, the quantities, and their locations in a landscape.

Elements of Effect
Elements in a landscape design that elicit a response by creating moods or feelings in the viewer.

Consideration of plant features is important in the design of the landscape. They provide the aesthetic basis of landscape design. They are also called **elements of effect** because they create moods or feelings in the viewer.

Color

People respond differently to color. Certain colors—reds, oranges, and yellows—are described as warm colors and appear to advance toward the viewer. Cool colors—blues and greens—tend to recede in a landscape composition. The attributes of color are hue, value, and intensity or chroma. Some colors are enhanced when viewed against certain background colors, and others clash. Gray is a neutral color and, along with a cool color such as dark blue, can create an effective background. Some colors are overwhelming and loud, and others are soft and mild. Flowering plants have a wide array of colors in their petals. Some flowers have solid colors, while others are variegated.

Choice and arrangement of colors in the landscape are critical considerations to the overall visual appeal. Flower color is affected by light. Shade subdues and sunlight intensifies colors, which should be kept in mind when locating plants in the landscape.

Flowers are not the only sources of color in the landscape. Leaves, although predominantly green, may have variegation and seasonal color changes in autumn. Tree barks also produce variety in color.

Texture

Texture refers to an object's feel with respect to the sense of touch. Visual surface characteristics may project a soothing image or a harsh, coarse feeling to the viewer. A grass blade has a different texture from a herbaceous plant (Figure 15–2). Texture effect is pronounced when contrast exists in the display. For example, placing plants next to a wall enhances the textural differences between two contrasting types.

Texture may change with the season. While a deciduous tree has its leaves, it presents a smooth texture. However, when the leaves fall in autumn, the bare branches present a rough or coarse texture. Tree barks vary in texture, some being smooth and others, such as oak, thick and rough.

Texture in the landscape is not limited to plants. Other materials, such as those used as mulch, have varying textures. Gravel is fine in relation to rocks, and sawdust is fine when compared with tree bark. Texture is also modified by distance. A coarse-textured plant viewed at a distance may not appear as coarse. One of the goals in designing a landscape is for the elements to flow or blend together without abrupt changes. Gradual transition is always more aesthetically pleasing than sudden changes. To shift from a fine texture to a coarse one, the landscape architect should insert a transitional element between the two extremes. When materials in the landscape change on a seasonal basis, plants should be chosen such that changes are sequential. This practice is accomplished by thoughtful selection of plants so that mixtures are planted (e.g., deciduous and evergreen). Flowering plants can be selected to produce sequential flowering so that the landscape can be enjoyed across seasons.

Form

Form
The three-dimensional shape of the plant canopy.

Line
The one-dimensional effect produced by arranging three-dimensional objects in a certain fashion.

Form is a three-dimensional attribute. The outline of a plant against the sky, depends on the structure and shape of the plant. For example, trees may be conical, columnar, spherical, and so on (Figure 15–3). Plants of different forms may be grouped and arranged in a certain fashion to create a different overall form in the landscape. For example, a landscape architect may group a number of plants with narrow, columnar form to create a horizontal form. This strategy is used in creating a hedge around a house. Plants have form because they have visual mass and thus occupy visual space. Form is therefore directly related to one's ability to see it. The art of topiary (pruning plants with dense foliage into shapes) is a way of creating artificial form in plants.

FIGURE 15–2 The occurrence of texture among plants. (a) Contrast among succulents. (b) A broadleaf and (c) Grass display a sharp contrast in leaf form. *(Source: © George Acquaah)*

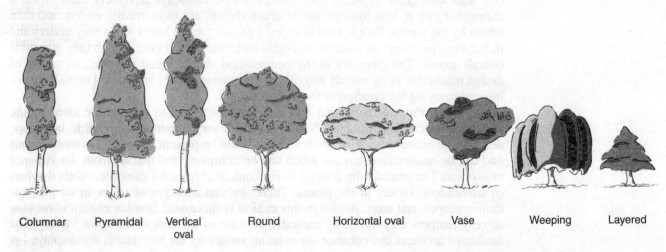

Columnar Pyramidal Vertical oval Round Horizontal oval Vase Weeping Layered

FIGURE 15–3 Tree forms.

Line

The effect of **line** is accomplished through the arrangement of objects. Line is a *boundary element* in design. Shape and structure are defined by lines. A design element line, when used effectively, has the capacity for eliciting emotional responses, making one display appear elegant and another disorganized. As indicated previously, form is a three-dimensional attribute, but it can be interpreted as one-dimensional by line. Line is the means by which form guides the eye.

Natural lines occur in nature but often are complex. Line is a design tool that a landscape architect uses to create and control patterns in the landscape. Formal, straight lines are found in pavement design. The monotony can be broken by arranging pavement elements (e.g., bricks) in a design or pattern that softens the effect of straight lines.

Arrangement of landscape objects in a line can be used to direct viewers to the focal point in the design. Lines do not have to be straight, and, when they are straight, they do not have to be continuous. A designer can deliberately introduce breaks to cause the viewer to pause and change views. Lines can be contoured or curvilinear to slow down viewing and encourage the viewer to spend more time to appreciate a particular display.

Landscape architects combine a knowledge of plant science, art, and creativity to design a functional and aesthetically pleasing product that meets the consumer's approval. It is not enough to know that a plant looks pretty; to serve a functional role, it may be necessary to know whether it is evergreen or deciduous, for example. A deciduous tree planted at the southwest corner of a house will provide shade in summer (when the sunlight is bright and intense), but when it sheds its leaves in winter (when it is overcast and not bright) it will allow light to reach the house, thus serving a dual role.

15.3.3 PRINCIPLES OF DESIGN

Regardless of the category of landscaping, the observance of five basic principles of design, *simplicity, balance, focalization, rhythm and line*, and *scale* or *proportion*, is necessary. These principles are applied in relation to the elements of design described previously. Landscape design pertains to the arrangement of objects to accomplish a purpose in the landscape. Since these objects may vary in color, form, and texture, the quality of results of the arrangement depends on creativity and successful application of the basic principles of design.

Simplicity (Unity)

A landscape designer is a three-dimensional artist working especially with plants (but also with other objects). Like canvas artists, landscape designers must create a theme, subject, or title for a project. Certain themes are more readily understood than others by the viewer. People tend to enjoy a painting much better when they understand it, but some paintings are abstract and difficult to understand even though they may have overall appeal. The elements in the composition should blend together, an aspect of design referred to as its overall *unity*. Also, the viewer should be assisted in understanding and enjoying the creation of the designer.

People who visit parks and botanical gardens expect to see and are awed by the variety of specimens displayed. Variety is thus a very important element in landscape design. The question is, how much variety should be present? Too little is monotonous and can be unattractive, but too much can be confusing and detract from the viewer's enjoyment. The annual tulip festival in Holland, Michigan, for example, offers displays of tremendous variety in the plants. There are vast acreages of tulips in all possible colors, shapes, and sizes. Although this exhibit is successful, another exhibit consisting of only junipers may not be as attractive because of the lack of adequate variety. The landscape architect can enhance the existing variety by the way plants are displayed in

GUIDELINES FOR LANDSCAPE DESIGN

DAVID BERLE, ASSOCIATE PROFESSOR
University of Georgia Horticulture Department

A beautiful man-made landscape does not happen by accident. Knowing commonly accepted principles of landscape design and following them are two different things. There are a few simple guidelines for landscape design that can improve the chances of creating a space that is truly beautiful and functional.

DESIGN IDEAS

A good sense of design comes from research. Start by looking at books and magazines that feature works of well-known designers. Visit botanical gardens for another source of inspiration. Garden clubs and Master Gardener groups often sponsor annual garden tours, which allow visitors to see the area's finest gardens. Ride or walk around different neighborhoods to get examples of good design using hardscape elements and plant materials suitable for the local area. You will also see examples of designs that don't work, which can be analyzed as well.

DESIGN AESTHETIC

Everyone prefers certain colors, plants and styles, so what looks beautiful to one person many not look beautiful to another. Expressing personal tastes, or those of the client's, is important to the design process. Whether it's an English cottage design, or sweeping drifts of native grasses, the look of a garden is influenced by personal tastes and opinions and should reflect the individual. Landscape design includes a wide spectrum of different styles, from formal to informal, symmetrical to asymmetrical, and naturalistic to highly-designed. The space between the street and the house is just another room of the house that just happens to be exposed for all to see. Some yards are cluttered, some perfectly clipped. Some yards are full of toys, some are poorly maintained, and still others have every shrub neatly arranged in straight lines. A professional designer gets to know the client before creating a landscape plan and combines knowledge of design with the preferences of the client.

PLANT/SITE SUITABILITY

It is impossible to successfully design using plants without thorough knowledge of plant hardiness and adaptability to a particular site. To make plant selection easier, use the USDA cold and heat hardiness maps, which indicate average cold or warm temperatures for each region of the country using a number system also used by nursery growers. Other factors to consider as you analyze a site for plants include sunlight availability, soil drainage and average rainfall. It is almost always cheaper to select a plant suitable to the site than adapt a site to make it suitable for the plant. The old adage "right plant, right place," is worth remembering.

LINES IN THE LANDSCAPE

Lines denote edges and outline objects. The human eye tends to follow lines created in the landscape, whether it's a row of trees, brick edging or a retaining wall. A line can be straight or curvilinear. To most people, straight lines denote formality and curved lines create a more relaxed feel to a landscape. Careful attention should be paid when using lines in landscape design and especially when installing a landscape. When a line, intended to be straight, turns out crooked, or a curved line comes off as "bumpy," the effect can be negative. A row of trees planted in a straight line with one tree out of place can ruin an otherwise careful design.

ACCESS AND MOVEMENT

People use residential landscapes on a regular basis. Homeowners move from the street to the house, often carrying things like groceries or children. Visitors seek out the front door. Meters must be checked, garbage picked up and mail delivered. From time to time, windows need washing and roofs need repairs. Many beautiful landscapes ultimately fail because the design limits or restricts access for these important functions. Fortunately, there are well-established design guidelines and standards for items such as walk and driveway widths, minimum step dimensions, planting spacing, and minimum/maximum slope requirements safe equipment operation and handicapped access. Some practical considerations are easy to forget, such as leaving access to the electric meter or providing access to every turf area for a riding lawnmower. A professional designer should spend sufficient time analyzing a site to insure that minor details are not ignored, thus preventing problems in the future.

PROPER CARE

An attractive landscape requires some level of maintenance. Even a well thought out design can be compromised by poor maintenance. For example, many lawn grasses can spread from the intended turf area into flower beds, at which time the grass becomes a weed. Large weeds growing amongst shrubs look unsightly and decrease the value of a good landscape design. Lack of water can slow growth or kill drought-intolerant plants. Before finalizing a landscape plan, realistic maintenance needs and a budget should be evaluated. Can the homeowner afford to properly maintain the proposed landscape? Often, changes in plant selection, plant density, mulching materials, edging treatments, and patio material can reduce maintenance needs without affecting the overall design.

BUDGET

Estimates vary on the amount that should be spent on landscaping a home. Generally, the cost for landscaping ranges from 5%–20% the cost of the home. With a good master plan, this cost can be spread out over several years if necessary, and completed in phases as time and money permit. In some situations, costs can be reduced by planting smaller plants. The cost to install a tree or shrub goes up exponentially as the size of plant increases, though the initial effect is not as dramatic with smaller plants. As an added benefit, research suggests that smaller plants adapt and establish quicker in the landscape than larger plants. Contractors, in an effort to save money, often narrow the width of concrete driveways and walks. This is not the place to save money. Irrigation systems can be expensive and must be installed prior to planting, however, a well-designed system provides reduces the risk of losing valuable plants.

THE WHOLE LANDSCAPE

Landscapes designed as one entire space look the best. However, this does not mean that everything must match across the entire yard, or that one style must be continued through

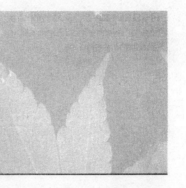

the landscape. Some very successful designs break the landscape into a series of individual rooms, much like the interior of a house. But like a house, movement from between rooms should flow smoothly and all the rooms should work combine to create a unified space. The professional uses repeated elements throughout the landscape, such as a type of stone or a certain color to unify the entire landscape, while maintaining a sense of excitement and diversity throughout. Each element added to the landscape, whether a small tree or a piece of sculpture, is selected with consideration for the entire landscape. Plants are not added because they were impulse purchases, but because they contribute in some way to the existing landscape. This holistic design approach often separates a professional landscape designer from a do-it-yourselfer.

the landscape. By using the design element of *repetition* or *massing* (Figure 15–4) he or she can give meaning and expression to variety in the landscape by controlling and limiting variety so as to introduce order in the design. Rather than displaying a single plant species in ten different colors, groups of ten or more plants of each color will produce a better visual impact on the viewer.

Distractions in the display should be eliminated, which may mean using edging to straighten out a lawn or flower bed. These strategies, when used appropriately, achieve the goal of **simplicity** in a design.

Balance

The concept of material **balance** implies stability resulting from equal distribution of weight around a central axis. Balance in horticulture refers to the visual weight a viewer is presented with by the materials in the general design. The distribution of the design materials should not be skewed. The viewer should have a sense that the amounts of things to see on both sides in the viewing frame are fairly equal. The two halves of the design need not be identical, just balanced. When the design is such that the materials on one side of the viewing frame are identical (mirror image) to what are on the opposite side, it is said to be *symmetrical* and formal (Figure 15–5); if the balance is achieved by different materials, it is called *asymmetrical* and informal (Figure 15–6). Most designs are asymmetrical.

Focalization

The design principle of **focalization** or *emphasis* is employed to satisfy an expectation of the viewers while fulfilling the "vanity" of the designer. It may be described as the center-of-attraction principle. Instead of the viewer's eyes wandering aimlessly to and fro, designs are composed around central pieces on which viewers focus first before looking around. Some natural focal points exist in the landscape. For example, a residential landscape design, at least from a distance, should draw attention to the point of entry into the house, which is usually the front door. If there are fountains, sculptures, or exotic or uniquely attractive plants (**specimen plants**) that one wants to emphasize,

Simplicity
A landscape design principle that employs a number of strategies to reduce excessive variation and distractions in the landscape.

Balance
A landscape design principle that presents an equal visual weight of elements to a viewer.

Focalization
A landscape design principle that creates interest and accent for a particular arrangement.

Specimen Plant
A plant with attractive features that is used to fulfill the principle of focalization or emphasis in an arrangement.

FIGURE 15–4 The concept of repetition or massing enhances the simplicity in landscape design. *(Source: © George Acquaah)*

FIGURE 15–5 A demonstration of symmetrical balance in landscape design.

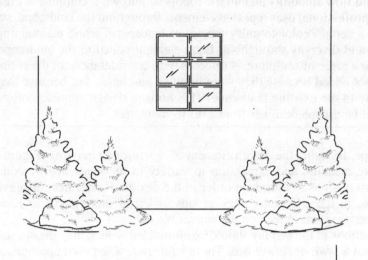

FIGURE 15–5 A demonstration of symmetrical balance in landscape design.

FIGURE 15–6 A demonstration of asymmetrical balance in landscape design.

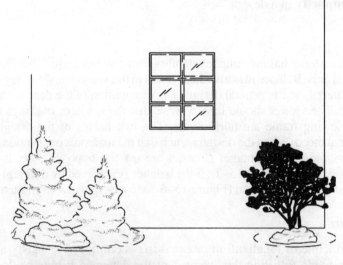

FIGURE 15–7 Using a fountain as focal point in a landscape design. *(Source: © George Acquaah)*

the designer may make these objects the focal points (Figure 15–7). Focalization is in effect a strategy for guiding the viewer to the must-see exhibits in the landscape. A landscape can be planned such that the focal point changes with the seasons, perhaps by strategically locating a flowering plant and a deciduous plant in the landscape. When the interest in the deciduous plant fades away after a spectacular display of fall colors, the flowering plant will create interest in spring with its attractive blooms.

Rhythm and Line

Panoramic view of a landscape design is often possible from one or several strategic viewpoints such as above or overhead (which very few people have the privilege to experience), especially if the design is not a straight-line display of plants. An elaborate and extensive design may incorporate several concepts into one overall picture. To avoid a disjointed display and create a sense of flow or continuity, the different concepts or sections of the landscape should be linked, such as by use of beds of appropriate plants. This linkage creates movement in the design. The principle is visible on avenues and in parks where the same kinds of trees are arranged in long rows (Figure 15–8). It is applicable to the home landscape where the display in the front of the house can be linked to the rear display by avoiding an abrupt ending in front. Instead, plant types are repeated or extended from the front bed or display around the corner. This layout suggests to the viewer that the design continues around the house.

Scale or Proportion

Scale, or proportion, is not only desired with respect to the plants in the landscape but also in terms of their relationship with other structures and the general functionality of the design. In choosing plants for the landscape, it is important to take into account their size at maturity. Since inanimate objects such as sculptures and houses maintain their

Scale
The landscape design principle that creates proportionality among design elements.

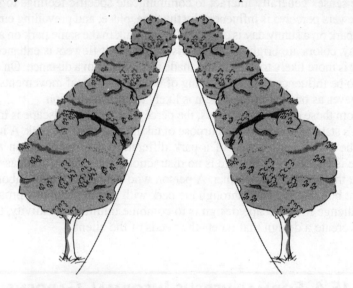

FIGURE 15–8 A demonstration of rhythm and line in landscape design.

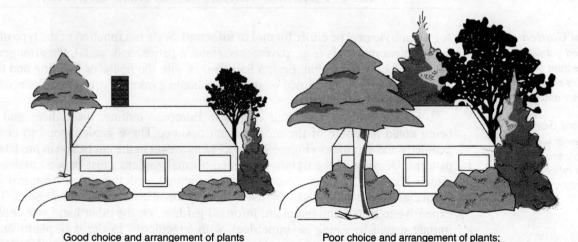

Good choice and arrangement of plants

Poor choice and arrangement of plants; house overwhelmed by plants

FIGURE 15–9 Scale or proportion.

sizes, it is important that trees located in their vicinity do not overshadow and make them inconspicuous when they are fully grown (Figure 15–9).

Transition

By definition, transition is gradual change in a factor. In terms of color, transition occurs in the radial sequence on the color wheel. In horticulture, it applies to the three-dimensional perspective of composition of the landscape design, not just a flat or facial view. The designer can combine elements of differing sizes, forms, texture, shape, and color to create the effect of transition in the landscape. For example, one may arrange objects to exhibit transition from coarse to fine textures, round to linear structural forms, or cylindrical to globular to prostrate stem characteristics. Effective use of transition can gradually guide the viewer to the focal point in the design and further enhance the display.

15.3.4 LANDSCAPE APPRECIATION

When people walk through a landscape, they perceive their environment through the engagement of their senses—smell, touch, sight, and sound (not tasting, since it could be dangerous to their health). Landscape architects design the landscape to evoke a certain response. The senses generally interact to communicate specific feelings to viewers.

What viewers perceive is influenced by the time, place, and prevailing circumstances. A walk in the park on a sunny day is different from a walk in the same park on a cloudy day. On a sunny day, colors are brighter and the visual appeal of flowers is enhanced. On a hot afternoon, one is more likely to walk in the shade and view from a distance. On a windy day, one is likely to be influenced by the swaying of branches and leaf movements. In autumn, the ruffle of leaves as one walks over them is likely to attract attention.

Apart from these extraneous factors, the perception of the landscape is influenced by the individual's state of mind and the purpose of taking a walk in the park. A happy person responds to the sights and sounds of a park differently than someone in a sad mood. Further, if one is walking alone, there is no distraction from conversation as would occur if one were in the company of another. A person who is knowledgeable about landscape design or plant botany may walk through the park with an intellectual approach.

The challenge in landscape design is to combine intuition, creativity, training, and experience to create a design that meets the needs of the client.

15.4 FORMAL VERSUS INFORMAL GARDENS

Formal Garden
A stylized garden in which arrangement of the materials emphasizes symmetry and geometry.

Informal Garden
A garden in which the materials are located without emphasis on regularity and symmetry.

A garden style may be either **formal** or **informal**. Style is a function of the type of plants, the nonplant materials (e.g., pavements, statues, patios, and walls), the arrangement of plants, and how the overall design harmonizes with the house or building and the general surroundings. The choice of style for a home garden is strongly influenced by the homeowner's personality.

Formal gardens have their origins in European culture, the Italians and French being noted for some of the most elegant designs. These gardens tend to emphasize geometry and symmetry (Figure 15–10). Plants are set in the landscape in predetermined patterns. Because of the rigidity in design, formal gardens must be well maintained to remain beautiful. Hedges should be well manicured, with their edges trimmed straight. Frequently, the arrangements are made to be symmetrical around a focal point. They are expensive to install and maintain. Informal gardens, on the other hand, are designed to imitate nature by being asymmetrical, with irregularity in the way plants and other objects are located. Straight, rigid lines are not an objective of the design (Figure 15–11). This style originated in the Eastern cultures of Japan and China. The lack of symmetry does not imply lack of balance in the design.

FIGURE 15–10 A formal garden. The emphasis is on symmetry in the location of plants and other landscape design elements. *(Source: © George Acquaah)*

FIGURE 15–11 An informal garden. It lacks symmetry in arrangement of landscape elements. *(Source: © George Acquaah)*

The most popular ornamental bedding plants include geranium, zinnia, petunia, marigold, impatiens, and begonia. When planning a garden design, the color intensity of flowers is a critical consideration. The impact of this factor on the general appeal of the design is influenced by the prevailing climate. Some colors develop best when formed under intense sunlight (e.g., marigolds). Certain colors overshadow others when they occur side by side. Another strategy used to improve display is to draw attention to plant size. A large plant located next to a small one may produce a situation in which the latter may be diminished by the former. One strategy to reduce this effect is to mass plants (group like plants together). If one desires to include garden ornaments (e.g., sculptures), care should be taken to avoid using an oversized piece that overwhelms the surrounding plants.

For best results, a garden design should be approached methodically. Drawing a field plan before going out to plant helps one to visualize the garden on paper before installing it. A plan can be designed and drawn on a computer using commercial software. The purpose of the garden should be in the forefront of the planning activity. For example, annual bedding plants are widely used to fill spaces in the landscape. While waiting for perennials to grow to blooming stage or, as in the case of bulbs, waiting for the next season to arrive, annuals may be planted so that the space is not left vacant. It is important that plants in the landscape complement each other. As such, one should know what already exists before adding new plants. There may already be a hedge or shrub border against which annuals may be planted.

Residential designs are usually small-scale designs. Viewers are much closer to plants and hence perceive certain details. Further, plant masses are smaller, though still effective. Larger plants could easily overwhelm the arrangement because of the scale of the landscape.

15.5.1 DESIGN CONSIDERATIONS

Landscaping is an expensive undertaking. Unless one purchases a prelandscaped home, some landscaping will be required, even if it involves installing only a lawn or a few trees. A homeowner may design his or her own landscape and may or may not need help in installing it, depending on the background and experience of the homeowner. Alternately, a homeowner may develop the design and contract its installation to a professional or commit the entire project (design and installation) to a professional service. The expense obviously increases as the involvement of the owner decreases, but the quality of work likewise increases with more professional involvement.

Notwithstanding which route the homeowner takes to landscape the property, three considerations are central to all landscape undertakings:

1. *The design should satisfy the homeowner's preference.* The homeowner is paying for the job and must live with it indefinitely, so the design must consider his or her preferences. In a way, the customer is always right. However, this is not to say that a professional should stand by and allow the homeowner to make mistakes without offering professional advice.
2. *The design should be aesthetically pleasing.* The view of the landscape must be aesthetically pleasing to the homeowner. Some if not all homeowners are pleased to be complimented on the beauty of their landscape designs, much the way they enjoy receiving complements on the interior decor of their homes. A landscape in effect is an extension of the indoor environment, a kind of outdoor room. If one's home is located on a large plot by itself, there is more room to be creative and fancy in the design. However, when it is located on a block in an urban area where the residential area was developed under a specific theme, the plot shapes and sizes may be very similar. Whatever the landscape design installed, it must take into consideration the general neighborhood and especially the immediate neighbors.
3. *The design should be functional or practical.* Landscaping is devoted to developing the outdoor environment of a residence. It must serve the practical purposes that the homeowner desires such as creating barriers, offering shade, and providing privacy. The finished work should be easy to maintain; otherwise, the homeowner must make a prior commitment to paying for the required care.

15.5.2 DESIGNING FOR RESIDENTIAL PURPOSES

Planning the Design

Assessment of the Homeowner's Needs   To satisfy the customer, the first step in planning a landscape project is to consult with the homeowner to learn firsthand about his or her preferences and what is expected from the completed project. At this fact-finding session with the client, the landscape designer should obtain information pertaining to the following:

1. What is the family size, and what ages are its members? If there are children, does the homeowner desire to have a playground?
2. What is the lifestyle of the family members? Do they prefer the outdoors or indoors for recreation? Do they love a closed (private) or open (outdoor) environment?

How frequently do they entertain? Are they avid gardeners? Do they prefer traditional or contemporary designs?

3. Are there any special preferences for certain plants?
4. How much work are they willing to put into (or willing to pay for) the maintenance of the landscape?
5. Do they desire to have an all-season or seasonal landscape?
6. How much are they willing to spend on the project?
7. Do they prefer walking through the landscape or enjoying it from a distance?
8. What time of day might they use the grounds?
9. Are there any service or utility needs?
10. Are there any nonplant installations (e.g., walkways and statues)?
11. Must a permanent irrigation system be installed?
12. Do they want to conform to neighborhood patterns or be unique?

One critical factor that a client must understand during the landscape planning period is that the landscape has a maturity period. Depending on the nature of the project, the landscape may mature and be ready for enjoyment a short time after installation, or it may take a while. Because some clients want to see results almost instantly, a designer may have to compromise and create a design with instant appeal.

Site Analysis **Site analysis** may be described as a survey of a landscape project site to ascertain the presence, distribution, and characteristics of its natural and human-made features and the environmental conditions prevailing at the site. It is important to know all of the existing characteristics of the site since they control the success or failure of the project. The designer must recognize and work with these characteristics to achieve a product that is desirable and sustainable.

A site analysis helps the landscape architect to formulate an appropriate strategy for enhancing the site. Designing for a rural setting requires considerations different from those for an urban setting. Most landscape designs are conceptually artificial in the sense that the finished product shows a great deal of order and tidiness. Further, the product is maintained by a regular cosmetic regimen to keep the curves and lines well defined and the site clean. Another approach to design—the naturalistic approach—depends primarily on nature to make the major choices in plant selection and placement. The species used are not only adapted to the area but also compatible with each other. The result is a product that is self-sustaining.

After a needs analysis has been conducted, the designer should visit the site for a thorough study of what is available. The information to be gathered on this visit includes the following:

1. *General setting of the property in relation to others in the neighborhood (i.e., the landscape of the neighborhood).* Some real estate developers install certain landscape features as a standard part of the design in a neighborhood. Certain neighborhoods have regulations regarding fencing and activities on the public side of the property.
2. *Size of property (i.e., lot size, dimensions, or space to be utilized for project).* The size of the property determines to some extent the variety, size, and number of plants that can be installed. Playgrounds, pools, fountains, and other similar structures may be practical only on large properties.
3. *Architectural design.* It is important that the design complement the architecture of the home. The size of the home is an important consideration for the purposes of the proportionality of the design.
4. *A record of the land characteristics.* It is important to know characteristics regarding the terrain (slopes and flat parts), drainage (any wet spots or areas in the flood plain), soil characteristics (texture, structure, pH, and organic matter content), rocks, and any natural features (e.g., creek or stream).

Site Analysis
An inventory of existing natural and human-made features at a proposed landscape site.

5. *Existing landscape.* It is important to know how many of the existing materials on the property will be retained in the design. For example, a rocky area may be developed into a rock garden. A mature tree or wooded area may be retained.

6. *Existing functionality of the design.* It is important to decide which sides offer the best views and what elements can be enhanced, removed, or hidden. If a client has recreational facilities (e.g., swimming pool), installing large trees on the south and west sides of the property is undesirable because of the shade they cast and the litter they produce.

7. *Climatic conditions of the area.* One should know the general climate and microclimate of the area. Plant species to be installed depend on their adaptation to cold weather. Local rainfall distribution and winds should also be considered.

8. *Site plan.* A site plan showing walkways, fences, sewer lines, and other utility lines should be made. Buried and overhead cables should be included as well.

Preliminary Design When the customer's needs are known and the site characteristics have been ascertained, the designer may proceed to the drawing board to create a drawing, starting with sketches and moving on to a scale drawing. The designer should pay attention to the three basic functional areas of the house (Figure 15–12):

1. Public area (the entryway area [front door] that often faces the street)
2. Private living area (patio or deck)
3. Service and utility area (e.g., vegetable garden, pet house, and storage)

Public Area
The part of the house that faces the street.

1. *Public area.* Most homeowners are most concerned about the public area—the part of the house most visible to passersby and that first approached by visitors to the property (curb appeal). This side of the house creates the first impression. It often indicates what the visitor will see indoors. An entryway made of concrete or brick usually leads to the door. This area could be straight from the street or designed to curve on approach to the door. Some interest may be introduced into the design by mounding or terracing a flat lot. Flower beds may aid in creating this effect. The design should complement the architecture of the home. This area is truly public and thus some communities restrict what can be done next to the street, especially regarding the erection of walls or the installation of fences and hedges.

2. *Private living area.* The private living area is where decks and patios are located. If shading is important to the homeowner, the patio should be located on the east side of the house, so that it will receive the warmth of the early morning sun and be shaded by the house at noon. If sunlight is desired most of the time,

FIGURE 15–12 The three basic functional areas of a home to consider in a home landscape design: private area, public area, and service area.

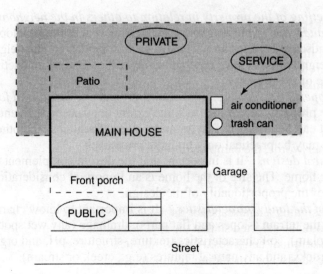

the patio should be located on the south side of the house. The private living area should be screened from the view of neighbors to be fully functional.

3. *Service and utility area.* The service and utility area may be described as the odds-and-ends section of the landscape. Although important activities occur or structures appear in this area, the homeowner does not want them to be in view of the public. In fact, the service area is a second private area. This section is always in the backyard of the house and may be fenced off. It is not meant to be aesthetically enjoyed but, as its name implies, is a real service area for things such as a doghouse, garbage cans, clotheslines, storage shed, and vegetable garden.

Landscaping of Planned Residential Developments

Some modern developers purchase a large tract of land and designate it for residential development. Streets and sewage and other utility lines are laid down. However, in addition to the infrastructure, developers deliberately set aside portions of the land to be developed into recreational facilities (e.g., golf course, park, tennis court, or swimming pool). They also leave a stretch of land called a **greenbelt** to be an open space where no construction occurs. This part of the land is usually unsuited for residential construction. The development may also include walkways and bicycle paths to be utilized by the residents. Greenbelts are used to control construction (and thus prevent sprawling) and to enhance the neighborhood.

15.6 PLANNING A NONRESIDENTIAL LANDSCAPE

The principles described for residential landscape designing apply to nonresidential landscaping as well. A variety of scenarios with unique design needs occur in nonresidential landscaping.

15.6.1 LANDSCAPING SCHOOL GROUNDS

School grounds require space in which children can roam freely. Trees often dominate the landscape, with some functional plants (such as shrubs planted as foundational plants) and a limited area for annuals or bedding plants. The goal of landscaping school grounds is to achieve low-maintenance and childproof areas. Many schools operate on a small budget and thus cannot afford expensive grounds-maintenance services. Because children are bound to play around trees, species selected for school grounds should be resistant to rough, mechanical treatment.

15.6.2 LANDSCAPING COLLEGE CAMPUSES

Unlike primary, middle, and high schools, college campuses can often afford grounds-maintenance services. The goal in landscaping a college campus is to provide visual continuity by linking the diverse structures on-site by using trees, ground covers, and shrubbery. Since funds are available, campuses often can afford high-maintenance landscapes. On a campus with a horticulture academic program, the campus provides an opportunity for installing plant materials in the general landscape for instructional purposes. In other words, the campus may be turned into a kind of giant arboretum.

15.6.3 LANDSCAPING PARKS AND RECREATIONAL AREAS

A key goal in designing a landscape for public use such as a park is public safety. Appropriate plants should be selected so that the park remains open, without hiding places that may encourage criminal activities. A park may have a significant number of nonplant materials in the landscape, including fountains, benches, playground equipment, and statues. Plants are used to complement these objects. Trees and shrubs grouped and spaced randomly are effective ways of landscaping parks.

15.6.4 LANDSCAPING URBAN CENTERS

Modern urban centers are characterized by steel and concrete structures. Soil for planting is very limited since the areas that are not streets have concrete pavement for use by pedestrians. Container planting *(raised planters)* enables soil to be imported into downtown areas for planting trees. The plant species selected should be adapted to growing in a confined area and tolerant of urban air pollution. Trees may be planted along streets or in the median. Urban species should be slow growing and tolerant of moisture stress. Some irrigating is usually needed to keep plants growing in a healthy way. In the business district, trees should not block window displays. Further, the trees selected should not interfere with power lines or light poles. With planning to provide appropriate structural support, irrigation, and drainage, plants may be planted on roofs *(roof planting)*.

15.6.5 LANDSCAPING SHOPPING CENTERS

Shopping centers offer a variety of services and merchandise to the general public and thus attract many shoppers to the complex. The rationale of their design is to sustain the interest of the shopper. A great deal of money is invested in plants, many of which are specimen plants, which provide focal points. Because of the shelter provided by shopping centers from the elements, a wide variety of plants can be used in interiorscaping these complexes. Annuals and perennials are used in the design. Skylight and artificial lighting are provided for the proper growth and development of plants. These features contribute to the overhead costs of operating these complexes, but such costs are offset by increased patronage because of the attractiveness of the surroundings.

15.6.6 LANDSCAPING CEMETERIES

Modern cemeteries do not use the ornate, elaborate, and massive headstones that were popular in the past. The cost of maintaining a cemetery is high, and thus live flowers such as annuals are not commonly used. Normally, a well-kept lawn is the primary landscape element, with a few trees planted in an informal design. Trees should preferably have horizontal form.

15.7 PLANTS IN THE LANDSCAPE

Up to this point in the designing of a landscape, no plant materials have been specifically included in the design. Space has been allocated for walkways, driveways, private areas, and utility areas. It is now time to allocate plants strategically to complete the design objectives. Plants in the landscape serve more than aesthetic purposes. If selected and located judiciously, they can provide functionality, as described in a later section. On paper, the architect represents plants by graphic symbols. There are symbols for trees, shrubs, flowers, buildings, and all of the elements in the design. A completed landscape design includes the land dimensions and all of the symbols drawn proportionally, or to *scale*. This scale drawing shows what materials are involved in the design, where they are to be located, and how they are to be installed on the property. The landscape architect is now ready to translate the paper drawing into real results on the grounds after obtaining the homeowner's approval of the proposed design.

15.7.1 SELECTING PLANTS

A homeowner may prefer a certain plant species, but a number of factors determine what can be planted. To make a wise choice, one must know the plants and how they behave at various stages in their life cycles. The following are important factors to consider in deciding which plant species to include.

Climate

The two critical climatic elements to consider are temperature and moisture. The species selected must be adapted to the local area with respect to critical elements. In terms of temperature, **cold-hardiness** is the most important factor. If a plant type cannot tolerate cold, it will not only cease to grow in winter but suffer severe damage, leading to deadwood that must be pruned. Plants need water for good growth. Some areas are climatically drier than others, requiring supplemental irrigation to maintain a decent landscape. To reduce the need for irrigation, drought-resistant varieties or species should be used.

Cold-hardiness
The ability of a plant to survive the minimum temperature of the growing area.

Soil Reaction (pH)

If the property is located on acidic soils, species such as azalea and rhododendron are appropriate, but others such as carnation, dahlia, and buttercup will not grow properly.

Sunlight

The general amount of sunlight the house receives is important in choosing plant species for the landscape. If the general area is open, sun-loving plants should be selected. Some homes are located in heavily wooded environments, in which case shade-loving plants should be considered. Even if the house is located in an open area, the architecture may cause certain parts of the land to receive less light. The areas under large trees are shaded and thus require shade-loving plants.

Features at Maturity

The location of a plant depends on its size, shape, maturity, form, and habit. The plant may be small in initial stages of growth but after about two to four years of growing could be a huge bush or a tall tree. Some plants grow slowly, while others grow rapidly. Some plants have narrow profiles, and others spread their canopies.

Maintenance Level

Plants differ in the level of care they need to grow and produce the best results. The homeowner should declare a certain level of commitment to maintenance of the landscape after installation. Some owners handle the maintenance themselves; others may not want such responsibility but may or may not be prepared to pay for someone to care for the plants. A poorly maintained landscape is unsightly and wastes the funds required for its installation. The plants used must meet the level of care the homeowner is willing to provide.

Customer Preferences

The homeowner pays for his or her needs to be met by the landscape developer. Therefore, every effort should be made to satisfy the customer. If the customer likes yellow flowers, blue flowering species should not be selected without permission.

FIGURE 15–13 A sample planting plan for a home landscape project.

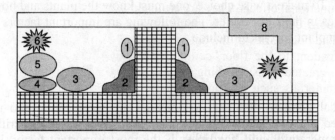

1. Pink cosmos
2. Daisies
3. Blue campanulas
4. Geraniums
5. Blue canterbury bells
6. Pine or other evergreen
7. Short flowering tree
8. Hedge

TABLE 15–1 A Sample Plant List Showing the Variety of Specifications According to the Type of Plant and How It Is Produced in the Greenhouse or Nursery for Sale

Key	Plant	Quantity	Size
AE	*Aspidistra elatior* (cast-iron plant)	10	10-inch pot
EI	*Hedera helix* (English ivy)	60	2-1/4-inch pot
FE	*Ficus elastica* (rubber plant)	4	15 gallons
MY	*Myoporum parvifolium* (Myoporum)	100	1 gallon
WR	*Washingtonia robusta* (Mexican fan palm)	2	12 feet
AS	*Aster spp.* (aster 'Chorister')	10	15 inches
AB	*Abies concolor* (white fir)	2	8 feet
FU	*Fraximus undei* (Shamel ash)	4	36-inch box

15.7.2 PREPARING PLANTING PLANS

Preparing planting plans is an activity that requires drafting and graphics skills. It is a job for professionals. A plan uses symbols to represent different kinds of plants (e.g., shrubs, deciduous plants, and evergreen trees) (Figure 15–13). The plan is a medium of practical communication between the landscape architect and the landscape contractor describing the designer's intentions. Such a plan includes specifications as to spacing between plants and where other structures in the landscape are to be installed. Planting plans should, whenever possible, include the name of each plant. The scientific name of the plant is used in all descriptions. A plant list should then be added to indicate the common names, qualities, sizes, and other specifications of all plants listed on the plan (Table 15–1).

All clients may not be able to interpret a planting plan. In such a case, a *perspective sketch*, which shows three dimensionally how the finished project will look, may be produced. The planting plans also contain additional sheets that describe in more graphic detail how plants are to be planted, staked, guyed, and so forth. Plans are made on a vellum, linen, or Mylar surface for durability. The client should receive a copy of the original plan on Mylar or sepia paper.

Plant Arrangement in the Landscape

Plants are carefully selected and strategically arranged in the landscape for maximum aesthetic and functional effects. They are arranged according to a design concept called the **outdoor room** concept; the landscape is designed as an extension of the indoor environment. The boundaries of the outdoor room are provided through the creation of structures equivalent to the floor, ceiling, and walls of an indoor environment. An outdoor floor is created by establishing a turf or some other appropriate ground covering (e.g., natural materials such as gravel, sand, or wood or synthetic materials such as concrete). The outdoor ceiling establishes the height of the landscape display and is provided through the planting of trees or the installation of structures such as a covered patio. The walls of an outdoor room may be provided by constructing a fence, creating a hedge or flower beds, or using shrubs.

Outdoor Room
A landscape design concept that extends the indoor room outside by using plants to create walls and a ceiling.

The landscape architect selects and allocates plants to the site according to the outdoor room concept by adopting four basic plant arrangements:

1. *Corner planting.* Corner planting starts with creating a bed in the corner of the building or the area to be landscaped. By so doing, the corners of the outdoor room are demarcated. This bed contains a few species of plants, with the tallest in the back. The designer may create interest in the design by including specimen plants located in the corner created by the intersection of the two walls or corner lines.
2. *Foundation planting.* As the name implies, certain plants are located close to the foundation or walls of the building. One should be careful to locate the tallest plants in the corners and the shortest below the window so the view is not obstructed. Generally, low-growing plants are used as foundation plants.
3. *Line planting.* Line planting is also done in beds along the property line. The function of line planting is to create a screen to provide privacy. A variety of shrubs are usually used for this purpose. These plants provide the walls to the outdoor room.
4. *Accent planting.* Accent planting has primarily an aesthetic purpose in the landscape. As the name indicates, it enhances the area by its attractiveness in the color of blooms or leaves, form, or some other unique characteristic. Single specimen plants are often strategically located in the landscape. Sometimes plants and nonplant materials (e.g., statues) may be used in combination. Accent planting may also be created by massing flowering herbs in a bed.

Projected Cost

Cost estimation, made after a landscape plan has been prepared, is done by both landscape architects and contractors. The contractor should attempt to obtain the most accurate prices possible to avoid underbidding or overbidding and losing the project or losing money on the project. For large projects, specific components can be bid on separately. Otherwise, the contractor who wins the bid can subcontract various portions in which his or her expertise is required. For example, the irrigation system may be subcontracted to a company that specializes in that area. Similarly, driveway construction and other concrete structures may be subcontracted to a masonry company.

The plants required should be readily obtained at a reasonable price. A cost analysis made before submitting a bid should address the following:

1. Variable costs (or direct costs), including materials, labor, equipment rentals, and so forth
2. Overhead costs (fixed costs), including costs that will be incurred whether or not the bid is accepted (e.g., fringe benefits, management expenses, and salaries of employees)
3. Profit, which varies according to the specific business owner

15.8 OTHER FUNCTIONAL USES OF PLANTS
IN THE LANDSCAPE

15.8.1 PRIVACY FROM ADJOINING PROPERTY

No matter how good one's neighbors, homeowners usually demand some privacy from adjoining property. A fence may be installed as a divider. High-growing shrubs can be planted to create a dividing wall. Plants behind bathroom and bedroom windows may be selected to be aesthetically pleasing as well as adding privacy from neighbors.

15.8.2 CLIMATE MODERATION

Trees with large canopies provide shade and protection from the sun's radiation on hot days. At night, however, radiation from the soil is reduced, creating a microenvironment under the canopy in which temperatures are more even. By planting evergreen trees or shrubs close to west- or south-facing walls, a dead-air space can be created between the "plant wall" and the wall of the house (Figure 15–14). This space has insulation capability similar to the dead space deliberately created by some architects in home design. The effect of this condition is that summer temperatures are moderated and kept even. Ivy-covered concrete walls (or those covered by any other climber) reduce the temperature of the wall relative to the bare wall when exposed to full sunlight.

15.8.3 GLARE REDUCTION

A streetlight in front of a house may provide light in undesirable parts of the house. Blinds may have to be pulled down at night. A tree can be located in the path of the light rays to block or reduce the amount of light reaching the house (Figure 15–15). Another light moderation strategy is to plant deciduous trees near the sunniest area of the house to reduce light and provide shade. In winter, these plants shed their leaves, allowing more light to reach the house through the bare canopy. To reduce glare throughout the day as the sun's position changes with the earth's rotation, plants of different heights may be planted in the path of the sun, the shortest plants nearest to the sun.

FIGURE 15–14 Planting trees close to the wall can create a dead-air space for temperature modification.

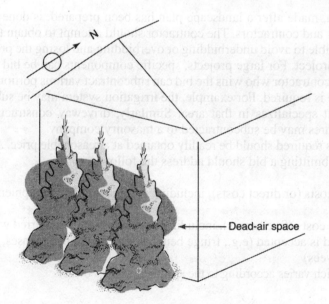

Dead-air space

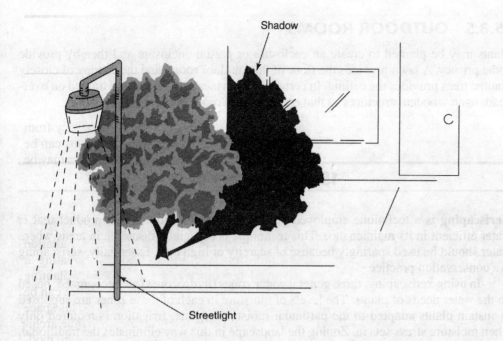

FIGURE 15–15 Planting a tree between the streetlight and home can reduce the glare of streetlights.

Shadow

Streetlight

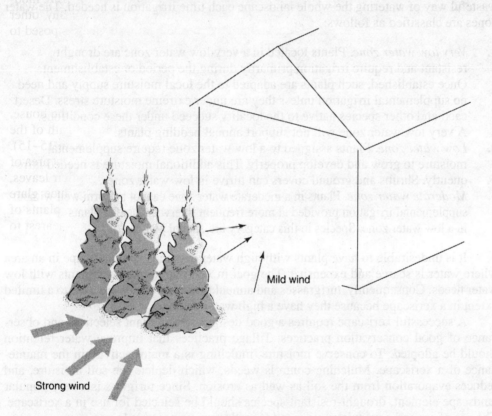

FIGURE 15–16 Using plants as windbreaks to reduce wind speed.

Mild wind

Strong wind

15.8.4 WINDBREAKS

Plants such as coniferous evergreens are effective windbreaks. They reduce the speed of strong winds considerably, so that a cool breeze reaches the house rather than a storm (Figure 15–16). The amount of wind reduction depends particularly on the height and shape of plants and the density and width of planting. Multiple rows of plants may be used for more effective reduction. Multiple rows of plant types (e.g., a shrub followed by a tall pine followed by a tall tree) provide a dense wall with minimum penetrability by wind.

15.8.5 OUTDOOR ROOMS

Plants may be planted to create an enclosure or partial enclosure and thereby provide some privacy. A lawn provides the floor of this outdoor room, and the canopy of closely planted trees provides the ceiling. In certain parks, vines are planted and trained on overhead, open wooden structures so that eventually a "roof" is formed.

15.9 XERISCAPING

Xeriscaping
A landscape installation strategy that groups plants according to water needs in order to improve irrigation efficiency.

Xeriscaping is a technique employed in landscape design to create a product that is water efficient in its maintenance. This technique is especially desirable in areas where water should be used sparingly because of scarcity or high cost. Essentially, xeriscaping is a conservation practice.

In using xeriscaping, three general water zones (hydrozones) are recognized, based on the water needs of plants. The levels of moisture in each of these zones are supposed to sustain plants adapted to the particular moisture regime. Irrigation is required only when moisture stress sets in. Zoning the landscape in this way eliminates the traditional, wasteful way of watering the whole landscape each time irrigation is needed. The water zones are classified as follows:

1. *Very low water zone.* Plants located in a very low water zone are drought resistant and require irrigation primarily during the period of establishment. Once established, such plants are adapted to the local moisture supply and need no supplemental irrigation unless they are under extreme moisture stress. Desert cacti and other species native to the locality succeed under these conditions. A very low water zone will not support annual bedding plants.
2. *Low water zone.* Plants assigned to a low water zone require supplemental moisture to grow and develop properly. This additional moisture is needed infrequently. Shrubs and ground covers can thrive in low water zones.
3. *Moderate water zone.* Plants in a moderate water zone cannot perform well without supplemental irrigation provided at more frequent intervals than for plants in a low water zone. Species in this category are annual plants.

It is undesirable to have plants with high water demands in a landscape in an area where water is scarce and expensive. The goal in xeriscaping is to use plants with low water needs. Consequently, turfgrasses and annual flowering plants are used to a limited extent in a xeriscape because they have a high water demand.

A successful xeriscape requires a good design, careful plant selection, and observance of good conservation practices. Tillage practices that improve water retention should be adopted. To conserve moisture, mulching is a major activity in the maintenance of a xeriscape. Mulching controls weeds, which deplete the soil moisture, and reduces evaporation from the soil as well as erosion. Since turfgrass is a very popular landscape element, drought-resistant species should be selected for use in a xeriscape. The use of ground covers is encouraged for reducing evaporative losses.

When moisture is needed, high-efficiency irrigation systems should be used. The drip method of irrigation is the most water efficient, but it is not adapted to watering all plant types in the xeriscape. Highly efficient sprinkler systems (low volume) can be installed to reduce water use. Plants should be watered when most of the water will be retained in the soil (early morning). Using a watering hose or watering can is wasteful under these circumstances.

After installation, a good maintenance schedule is necessary for success of a xeriscape. Weeds and excessive plant growth must be controlled (pruning).

SUMMARY

Landscaping enhances the surroundings, be they residential, commercial, or public areas. Landscaping means different things to different people. However, a good landscape is the result of careful planning and implementation of a sound design that includes the proper choice and location of plants, the functionality of the design, and the general aesthetic appeal. Whether done by professionals or by the homeowner, five basic principles should be followed for success: simplicity, balance, focalization, rhythm and line, and scale or proportion. If contracted to a professional landscape designer, the design process includes an assessment of the owner's needs, site analysis, and preliminary design. Plants are selected according to climatic adaptation, local soil characteristics, features and size at maturity, and customer preference and level of maintenance desired.

REFERENCES AND SUGGESTED READING

Carpenter, P. L., and T. D. Walker. 1990. *Plants in the landscape*, 2d ed. New York: W. H. Freeman.

Crockett, J. V. 1971. *Landscape gardening*. New York: Time-Life.

Hartmann, H. I., A. M. Kofranek, V. E. Rubatzky, and W. J. Flocker. 1988. *Plant science: Growth, development and utilization of cultivated plants*, 2d ed. Englewood Cliffs, N.J.: Prentice Hall.

Rice, L. W., and R. P. Rice, Jr. 1993. *Practical horticulture*, 2d ed. Englewood Cliffs, N.J.: Prentice Hall.

Robinette, G. O. 1972. *Plants, people, and environmental quality*. Washington, D.C.: U.S. Government Printing Office.

Schroeder, C. B., E. D. Seagle, L. M. Felton, J. M. Ruter, W. T. Kelly, and G. Krewer. 1997. *Introduction to horticulture: Science and technology*, 2d ed. Danville, Il: Interstate Publishers, Inc.

OUTCOMES ASSESSMENT

1. Discuss the purpose of landscaping.
2. Distinguish between residential landscaping and commercial landscaping.
3. Explain the landscape design principles of balance and focalization.
4. Describe the role of the homeowner in planning the design of a landscape.
5. Discuss the use of landscaping to accomplish functional purposes outdoors.
6. Give and discuss three major factors to consider in selecting plants for the landscape.
7. Discuss the concept of landscape appreciation.
8. Describe what a landscape architect does.

16

Nursery Production

PURPOSE AND EXPECTED OUTCOMES

This chapter is designed to discuss the nursery and its role in landscaping.

After studying this chapter, the student should be able to

1. Describe how a site for locating a nursery is selected.
2. List the categories of plants produced by a nursery business.
3. Discuss container and field nursery production systems.
4. List at least five plants in each of the categories of bedding plants, ground covers, ornamental grasses, trees, shrubs, and plants with underground modified structures.

Nurseries produce the plant materials used in the landscape. They also produce seedlings for gardens, fruit seedlings for orchards, and tree seedlings for forests and other uses. A good landscape design is only as good as the quality of materials used to implement it.

16.1 THE ROLE OF THE NURSERYWORKER

The success of the landscape industry depends on the *nurseryworker*. The landscape designer depends on the nurseryworker to do the following:

1. *Supply the correct plants in terms of species, size, and other specified characteristics.* The nurseryperson should be knowledgeable about the species and be exact in labeling plants. It would be unfortunate to purchase seedlings that are supposed to produce red flowers only to find out midseason that they produce white flowers.
2. *Supply healthy plants.* The plant material provided should be high quality and free from diseases and insect pests. Plants grown in the field and potted plants should be free from weeds.

3. *Supply materials on a timely basis.*   The materials should be ready when they are needed to avoid delays in completing the project.
4. *Deliver well-packaged plant materials.*   Plants harvested with a ball of soil around the root should be properly packed. Cracked soil balls can seriously jeopardize the survival of plants in the landscape. Plants should be protected from bruising and damage to the bark.
5. Provide at least basic instructions for minimal care of the plants.

16.2 LOCATION OF THE NURSERY

Just as in locating a greenhouse, a nursery site should be selected after careful analysis, considering both economic and ecological factors. The ecological or environmental considerations include soil and climate. Since production is largely under open-air environments (i.e., not controlled like a greenhouse), the factors are more critical now than when considering the location of a greenhouse. These factors are discussed in detail in Chapter 12. Thus, discussions in this module are limited to certain aspects of these factors and how they specifically affect outdoor open nursery production. These factors are described in the following sections.

16.2.1 CLIMATIC CONSIDERATIONS

Important climatic factors to consider in locating a nursery include temperature, rainfall, wind, light, and air pollution.

Temperature

Nurseries produce young plants or seedlings, which are more sensitive than older plants to changes in climatic conditions. Seedlings are generally intolerant of rapid changes in temperature. If a nursery is being considered for the West Coast of the United States (e.g., California) where winters are mild and the growing season longer, the need for winter protection of plants (overwintering) is not critical for container culture. On the other hand, an East Coast production enterprise should consider erecting structures for winter protection of plants in containers.

Rainfall

The rainfall pattern for an area should be well understood. Certain operations cannot be delayed in a nursery enterprise. Rainfall can be supplemented with irrigation if needed, but rains that come during field preparations (e.g., tillage and making beds) or planting time could be very problematic for an operation. Production schedules are delayed because, for example, the field may be too wet to prepare it for planting. Areas that are prone to unpredictable severe weather should be avoided. If seedlings are damaged by hail or storms, for example, the nursery is likely to take a loss in revenue because the plants may be too old to sell by the time the damage is corrected.

Wind

Nursery plants need to be sheltered from strong winds, which can topple plants in containers and damage young plants. Because plants in the nursery are meant to be around for only a short period of time before being marketed, spacing is closer than it should be in the landscape. Consequently, a delay in selling could make plants compete for space and become top heavy and prone to being blown down by even slight winds. Further, the containers used are generally relatively light to facilitate transportation, which contributes to their susceptibility to wind effects. To overcome this problem, a nursery should be located in an area where natural windbreaks occur; otherwise, artificial windbreaks must be installed.

Light

Unlike a greenhouse, in which supplemental lighting can be provided, field production relies solely on sunlight. Shade houses can be erected for plants that need such conditions. Unwanted shading sometimes is experienced where trees are used to provide shelter from the winds.

Air Pollution

A nursery should be located where it will not suffer from air pollution. If it has to be established in a heavily industrialized area, it should be located upwind to escape the pollutants emitted from the various industrial facilities.

16.2.2 SOIL FACTORS

Soil factors that affect the location of a nursery include drainage, topography, soil texture and structure, and soil fertility.

Drainage

The proposed site for a nursery should be naturally well drained. If it is not, artificial drainage is required, adding to production costs. Drainage is required for good aeration of the soil and to reduce the incidence of soilborne diseases. Well-drained soils allow rapid soil warming for early production in spring.

Topography

The terrain of the site has implications in drainage, soil erosion, ease of land preparation, and general ease of production operations. If the site is rolling, use of machinery is hampered and irrigation systems are more difficult to install and operate. It may become necessary to spend additional money to level or terrace the site to facilitate production operations. On a rolling site, low parts of the land are likely to experience drainage problems and be susceptible to frost damage.

Soil Texture and Structure

Field production of seedlings for sale requires that plants be dug up at some point. If bare-root production is intended, a soil with loose structure (sand or loam) is preferred. For balled and burlapped production, the soil should be cohesive enough to form a ball around the roots. A properly textured soil also drains well, holds moisture at a desirable level, and is easy to work and well aerated.

Soil Fertility

The soil must be fertilized sooner or later for optimal production. However, the site should have some native fertility and be responsive to fertilization. The higher the soil quality (in terms of organic matter content, pH, and nutrition), the fewer the initial amendments.

16.2.3 NURSERY STRUCTURES

The type of structures needed depends on the region in which the nursery is located. As previously indicated, an area's climate may require the provision of overwintering facilities. Some plants may need shelter from intense sunlight, necessitating the construction of shade houses. Because some greenhouse-type production may be necessary to successfully produce certain types of plants, nurseries may construct greenhouses. For propagation, a cold frame or hotbed may be required at a nursery site.

A variety of storage facilities are needed on-site. Storage is needed for supplies, including seed, chemicals (e.g., fertilizers and pesticides), equipment, and temporarily for planting materials awaiting shipment. These facilities are in addition to basic ones such as preparation rooms (for mixing and potting), propagation houses, and other administrative rooms.

16.2.4 ECONOMIC CONSIDERATIONS

For profitability, several economic considerations should be taken into account in deciding on the best place to locate a nursery. These include:

1. *Markets.* Nursery products may be transported to near or far markets. These products are generally bulky, whether container or field grown. Nurseries should be located near highways, if possible, to make them readily accessible to customers. Whereas some nurseries serve local markets, others serve clients out of state and long distances from the production sites. If the operation is large, the company may consider operating its own transportation system. Sometimes nurseries deliver large plants in mechanical augers after digging. This undertaking is economical only if the nursery is located close to the market or clients.

2. *Land.* Virgin land costs more to develop into a usable site than an area that has previously been in cultivation. It is advantageous to acquire a large piece of land and expand the operation as time goes by. Land near metropolitan areas may be expensive. Land in rural areas may be cheaper, but transporting materials and products to and from the nursery and markets would be costly.

3. *Labor.* Nursery production is seasonal in terms of labor needs. Container production is more labor intensive than field production. A limited number of permanent staff should be employed, with a seasonal labor pool readily available.

16.3 CONTAINER NURSERY PRODUCTION

Container nursery production is done on a large scale in many states, especially Florida, Michigan, Pennsylvania, Virginia, and Ohio. In container nursery operations, plants are grown and marketed in containers that differ in sizes and types according to the species and marketable size desired (Figure 16–1). Containers were discussed in Chapter 12. Similarly, the media ingredients and mixes discussed for greenhouse production apply here. The conditions described for successful container culture are also the same for the nursery operation.

Seeds and cuttings (Chapter 10) may be used for propagation. Nurseries may maintain blocks of parent stock in the field, which are plants used as a source of materials for propagation. Parent stock may be maintained less expensively in containers than in fields. These stock plants must be well maintained to produce healthy planting materials.

FIGURE 16–1 Container-grown tree seedling. *(Source: © George Acquaah)*

16.3.1 ADVANTAGES AND DISADVANTAGES

Container nursery production has certain advantages and disadvantages over field nursery production. Some of these are as follows:

Advantages

1. The seedlings are easier to market, being already "packaged" in independent containers.
2. The growing season can be extended by starting the material indoors ahead of the growing season.
3. Containerized plants are easier to transport.
4. Containerized seedlings are easier to transplant with minimal transplanting shock because the plant roots are intact.

Disadvantages

1. Container production requires more intense management.
2. Plant roots are more exposed to rapid fluctuations and greater extremes in temperature than plants in the ground in the field nursery. There is little environmental buffering against the environmental conditions because of the large surface-area-to-volume ratio.

16.3.2 CONTAINERS

Containers differ in shapes and sizes, according to root morphology and the marketable size of the plant species being produced. In greenhouses, pots are usually arranged on benches (and sometimes on the floor) during production. In container nurseries, container beds are created such that plants of similar size that require the same cultural conditions are grouped together during production. These beds vary in design and size depending on the sizes of pots, spacing, shade house and overwintering facility installed, and irrigation system used.

16.3.3 MEDIA FOR CONTAINERS

Container media composition was discussed in detail in Chapter 4. Factors to consider in developing media for container nurseries include the plant marketing size and form, and the need to stably support the plant in an erect position in an open environment without toppling. The container medium should be suited to the irrigation method to be used. Also, the cost of transportation to markets should be factored into media composition. The medium composition should be developed for specific production systems, rather than developing a universal mix.

Tree seedlings remain longer in the containers. The medium should be stable enough to support proper growth and development throughout the production period. Container medium volume generally decreases with time as the soil medium's physical conditions are altered by the force exerted by root penetration, soil compaction, shrinkage, and erosion from the impact of irrigation and natural precipitation.

Over time, the particle size distribution, soil porosity and air space, and water-holding capacity change. Particle size alteration is due in part to microbial action through decomposition of the organic component, resulting in the decrease in soil volume. Media that incorporate sand are prone to the migration of smaller particles to the bottom of the pot, and may clog the drainage hole and thereby reduce aeration and increase the potential for waterlogging. The particle size distribution also influences the root distribution in the container. Plant roots would tend to concentrate in the top of the container if aeration is reduced. Water saturation in the container predisposes the plants to root infections like *Pythium* and *Phytophthora*.

The root zone of containerized plants is subject to rapid environmental fluctuations. First, the container surface-area-to-soil volume is high and thereby provides little buffering of environmental fluctuations. Further, the container sidewalls are exposed to direct solar radiation, making the container soil temperature about 15°C higher than the air temperature. However, in winter, night temperature of the container soil could be lower than the air temperature as a result of rapid heat loss from the container surfaces; this could lead to root injury.

16.3.4 SITE PREPARATION

The site is leveled in one of two basic ways (Figure 16–2). In one design, the center of the bed is raised so that excess irrigation water flows away to the edges of the bed. This design may be undesirable because it compels workers to walk through mud to get to the bed. In the other design, the slope is toward the center of the bed. The bed is covered with natural materials, such as gravel or crushed sea shells, or artificial materials, such as black ground cloth or black polyethylene. Black cloth is made of durable natural materials. The problem with gravel and shells is that they allow weeds to grow through, and plant roots may also grow through drainage holes in the pots and through the gravel layer into the ground, making moving plants around problematic.

16.3.5 PROTECTION FROM COLD INJURY

Tropical and subtropical plants are more susceptible to cold injury. Two basic cold injuries are recognized (see also Chapter 4). Chilling injury results from cold temperatures above freezing, while freezing injury causes freezing injury.

1. *Chilling injury*   Characteristic symptoms of chilling injury are not very different from drought injury, root rot diseases, chemical injury, heat stress, and light stress. They include the following:
   - Surface lesions, pitting, large sunken areas and discoloration
   - Water-soaked tissues (as cells rupture to release content solutes into intercellular spaces); Wilting and browning.
   - Internal discoloration of pulp, pith, and seed
   - Accelerated rate of senescence
   - Slowed growth
2. *Freezing injury*
   - Desiccation or burning of foliage
   - Water-soaked areas, resulting in necrotic spots on the plant

Container plant roots are less resistant to cold than field roots because they are less protected than roots in the ground. The ground is warmer in winter than the soil in pots. Thus, in container culture, plants need protection from the cold. One way to provide winter protection is to crowd plants together and wrap the pots in black plastic. In place of plastic, an outer border of containers filled with growing media can be used. White polyethylene-glazed overwintering houses are widely used for winter protection of plants in nurseries.

One strategy of growing container plants with winter protection is called the *double pot* (pot-in-pot) *production system*, whereby larger pots (*holder pots*) are placed

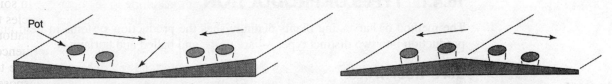

(a) Water drains into center of center-depressed plot   (b) Water drains away from center-elevated bed

FIGURE 16–2   Ways of leveling a field nursery for pot culture: (a) water is drained from the sides of the field into a central channel, (b) water is drained into channels on both sides of the field.

in holes in the ground and buried up to their lips. Tree seedlings may also be grown in pots placed in raised beds containing soil and wood chipping (Figure 16–3). These pots then become holes in which containerized plants are grown through the season. The use of holder pots eliminates the need for additional winter protection. However, this year-round insulation may expose plant roots to high temperatures during the summer season.

16.4 FIELD NURSERY

Methods of cold protection include sprinkling with water. A disadvantage of sprinkling is that the ice formed may weigh down plant limbs, breaking some of them, eventually. To reduce this incidence, container plants may be positioned on their sides prior to sprinkling. Fog application retards the loss of heat from soil and plant surfaces. This treatment is more effective in an enclosed structure such as a greenhouse. Some producers use erected structures like wind tunnels or cold frames. Cold injury to container plant roots may not be detected until it manifests later in the warmer season as high-temperature stress.

A fundamental difference between container and field nurseries is that in field nurseries plants are grown to the desired size in ground beds (e.g., Christmas tree farms). This system is often used for producing shade trees (e.g., red maple, pin oak, green ash, honey locust, white ash, and red oak), flowering trees (e.g., crab apple, redbud, flowering plum, and flowering dogwood), and evergreen and deciduous shrubs.

The soil is broken up and prepared for planting by plowing and harrowing. The land is divided into sections, with turfgrass-covered access ways between sections. Planting materials may be cuttings or grafted plants or from tissue culture. Trees are planted in rows under two basic systems, which differ according to how they are harvested for the market.

16.4.1 TYPES OF PRODUCTION

The method of harvesting plants distinguishes the production systems in field nursery production into two distinct types—bare roots, and balled and burlapped.

Bare-Root Trees

Bare Root
A tree or shrub seedling that is offered for sale without soil around its roots.

Bare-root trees are dug up without soil around the roots (Figure 16–4); they do not store well and are prone to transplanting shock. This system is suited to small trees and shrubs. Bare-root plants are lighter and easier to transport than balled and burlapped trees.

FIGURE 16–4   A bare-root tree seedling.   *(Source: © George Acquaah)*

Balled and Burlapped Trees

Balled and burlapped systems require plants to be planted in the ground and dug with a ball of soil around the roots (Figure 16–5). Mechanical harvesters (hydraulic augers or tree spades) are used for this purpose. The ball of soil is wrapped with burlap material and tied. If they are not needed immediately, balled and burlapped plants can be stored for a period of time. Harvesting by tree spade can severely prune roots, jeopardizing their establishment in the field. Balled and burlapped plants are best harvested when the soil is moist.

Balled and Burlapped
A tree or shrub seedling that is offered for sale with a ball of soil around its roots and wrapped in burlap.

16.4.2 IRRIGATION AND FERTILIZATION

Overhead sprinklers are commonly used in container nurseries. If there is the need, sprinklers are convenient to use for protection during a cold spell. The major drawback of this method of irrigation in container nurseries is that water application is very inefficient, involving significant water runoff loss. It is estimated that the average efficiency of overhead sprinkler systems in the container nursery is only about 25 percent. Plants may be grouped according to water needs and more closely together to reduce water waste. Also, the nursery ground may be lined with plastic or some impervious material to collect and pond the surface runoff for recycling. This strategy is implemented at additional production cost. Some producers use microirrigation in some instances.

16.5 RETAIL NURSERY

A retail nursery or garden nursery represents the retail outlet of the nursery industry. Garden centers sell nursery products (planting materials) and production materials (pesticides, simple tools, fertilizers, garden or landscape furniture, and various horticultural literature). The personnel at these facilities include a manager for administrative and general oversight purposes and a plant technician who is knowledgeable in a variety of plant problems and capable of advising customers. A garden center may employ a landscape designer who can design small-scale projects for homeowners.

SUMMARY

Nurseries are depended on to provide planting materials for the landscape. The plants they specialize in are perennials—shrubs, trees, and fruit trees. The site for the nursery should be carefully selected, following the guidelines utilized in selecting a greenhouse site. The site may require some preplanting preparation, including leveling and installation of drainage systems to ensure good drainage. Greenhouse-type structures are often erected for certain production operations and for protecting plants in adverse weather.

The two basic nursery production types are container and field. In container production, the prepared ground is covered with gravel or another suitable natural material or artificial materials such as black ground cloths. Plants produced in the field are marketed as either bare-root or balled and burlapped plants.

REFERENCES AND SUGGESTED READING

Schroeder, C. B., E. D. Seagle, L. R. Felton, L. M. Ruter, W. M. Kelly, and G. Krewer. 1997. *Introduction to horticulture: Science and technology*, 2d ed. Danville, Il: Interstate Publishers, Inc.

OUTCOMES ASSESSMENT

1. Describe the role of the nursery in modern horticultural industry.
2. Compare and contrast bare-root and balled and burlapped tree seedlings as landscape planting materials.
3. Discuss the incidence of cold injury in container nursery production.
4. What are the advantages and disadvantages of container production?

17

Installation of the Landscape

PURPOSE AND EXPECTED OUTCOMES

The purpose of this chapter is to discuss the activities involved in installing a landscape, following the plans produced by landscape designers. The materials used in a landscape may be plant materials or nonplant materials.

After studying this chapter, the student should be able to

1. Define hardscaping.
2. Distinguish between formal garden and informal garden.
3. List five common plants in each of the categories of bedding plants, ground covers, ornamental grasses, trees, and shrubs.
4. Discuss how the plants in each of the categories in (3) above are planted.

OVERVIEW

Plants used in the landscape may be grouped into certain operational categories—trees, shrubs, vines, bedding plants, ground covers, bulbs, corms, tubers, and rhizomes. Plants in each group have common methods of propagation and require similar care. They differ in various characteristics including adult size, shape, color, texture, and growth environment. These categories of plants have certain specific roles in the landscape. When different categories are used simultaneously in the landscape, they have to be properly located to be effective and functional. This chapter is devoted to discussing how these categories of plants are installed and used in creating effective designs in the landscape. The role of the nursery and its operations are also discussed.

509

Once a planting plan has been prepared, the installation of the landscape can begin. Frequently, however, the site cannot be planted without some modification. A landscape usually consists of more than just plants. Most of the static features are best installed before planting.

17.1.1 HARDSCAPING

Hardscaping
The installation of nonplant elements in the landscape.

Hardscaping is a term used for the installation of hard or static features in the landscape. These features range from simple ones such as fences, walls, patios, and walks to major constructions such as fountains and pools (Figure 17–1). These hard features can significantly enhance the landscape and increase functionality and property value. Walks may be constructed out of concrete, stone, brick, or some other similar material. Concrete is easy to install and inexpensive; however, it has low aesthetic value and creates little interest in the landscape. Bricks themselves are expensive, as is their installation; they are used

(a)

(b)

(c)

FIGURE 17–1 Examples of hardscaping materials include (a) brick, (b) wrought iron, and (c) stones. *(Source: George Acquaah)*

for walks, driveways, and patios (Figure 17–2). A layer of sand is spread on the ground before bricks are laid. With creativity, a work of art can be created with bricks to add tremendous interest to the general landscape design. Stones add a natural touch to the landscape, but they are very expensive to install. In the category of permanent material are decorative patio stones. These stones are made by molding crushed stones and other materials into attractive patterns that can be laid like bricks.

To add beauty to the landscape at night, some homeowners install low-voltage lamps along sidewalks and among plants for ornamental purposes (Figure 17–3). This use of light is called **night-lighting.** Other hardscaping activities include the construction of a patio or swimming pool on the private side of a house.

Erecting a fence around a property is a common activity undertaken by homeowners. The style of fencing chosen depends on the kind of privacy and security desired. The fence may be solid or with breaks. Chain-link fences are inexpensive but provide the least amount of privacy. While some people are interested only in demarcating the property boundaries, others use decorative fences to enhance the landscape. A common type of fence is the stockade type, which can be purchased in easy-to-install 6 × 8-foot (height × width) panels from a local lumber store. For durability, the wood in the panel may be treated with pesticides and thus cost a little more than the untreated type. To create a sturdier fence, steel pipe fence posts may be used.

Constructing the hard features before planting prevents workers from trampling on and damaging established plants. Sometimes large implements (earth-moving equipment) may be involved in the construction, in which case it is best to have no plants obstructing the operation. It is important that the topsoil removed during the construction of the home be replaced.

Night-lighting
The installation of special lights to illuminate and beautify the landscape.

17.1.2 PREPLANTING SITE MODIFICATION

Terrain

Modifications of the site before planting are necessary to ensure that plants are grown in an environment in which they will perform well. Modifications may be made to introduce additional interest in the landscape by creating variations. Instead of planting on flat areas, mounds may be constructed at certain parts and the area contoured where a slope occurs. On a steep slope, railroad ties may be used to create embankments. As previously mentioned, whenever an earth-moving operation is undertaken in the landscape, it is important to stockpile the topsoil for later use. Mounding may not be necessary in a landscape. Instead, holes or depressions may have to be filled.

Drainage

An important site modification that may be necessary is drainage. Information about *internal soil drainage* at the site can be obtained from the National Resources Conservation

(a)

(b)

FIGURE 17–2 Bricks are used for (a) patios and (b) walkways. *(Source: For (a) USDA, (b) George Acquaah)*

Service (NRCS). This property of the soil depends on its type. To avoid the issue of poor internal drainage and other soil-related problems, it is best to check the suitability of the building site before construction. *Surface drainage* is easier to handle than internal soil drainage. Drainage channels can be created to remove from the property excess water resulting from rains. It is critical that the drainage always be away from the foundation of the building, flower beds, and other such structures. Drainage channels can be incorporated during the final grading stage. Where adequate surface drainage occurs, the need for internal drainage is minimal.

Subsurface Irrigation

The landscape can be watered in a variety of ways. However, if a *subsurface irrigation system* (pipes buried in the ground with nozzles that pop up when in use) is to be used, it is best to establish it before installing the turf. An irrigation engineer often provides the best advice as to the most suitable system to install and the site modification necessary to accommodate the system. If the site slopes, pressure will be gained or lost, depending on the part of the slope in question. The type of irrigation system installed depends on the plant type to be irrigated, soil type, wind factors, source of water, terrain, and cost. Irrigation is discussed in detail elsewhere in this text.

Soil Fertility

Even though fertilizers can be applied to plants later on, it is important to start with good soil conditions at the time of planting. A soil test should be performed to determine the native nutrition status. The topsoil should first be replaced where it was removed; otherwise, the turf will be installed on subsoil, which offers less nutrition. If soil amendments are needed, they should be undertaken before the final grading for planting the turf. Whereas liming increases soil pH, sulfur application lowers it.

17.1.3 THE CONCEPT OF CURB APPEAL IN LANDSCAPING

The concept to curb appeal is often stressed by real estate agents when assisting homeowners in preparation to place their property on the market. Simply, it means how the house elements and landscape elements tie in to provide the viewer a favorable first impression from the curbside. Specific elements include the landscape design, porches, fences, lighting, mailbox, outdoor furnishing, driveway, walkways, and windows. The driveway may be made of solid material, such as concrete or asphalt, and hence smooth and seamless. It could also be made of aggregate material, such as gravel, crushed stone, and hence not seamless. It may be heated or unheated. The entryway and driveway are key elements in curb appeal. A combination of hardscaping and softscaping (use of plant materials) may be used to accent the entrance to a home.

Planting may be limited to accenting the entrance or implemented along the entire length of the driveway. A homeowner may build a path through the yard using concrete slabs or flat rocks, rather than having a contiguous pavement. Apart from being aesthetically pleasing, stepping stones are used to reduce compaction in the lawn and unmulched areas in the yard.

17.2 ROLE OF ANNUAL BEDDING PLANTS

The term *bedding plants* is used to refer to a broad range of largely annual plants (i.e., herbs, vegetables, and flowering ornamentals) that are grown especially in flower beds (but also in containers such as hanging baskets and window boxes). The bedding plant industry has grown tremendously in recent years due in part to convenient packaging of the seedlings by nursery growers. This packaging increases homeowners' success in growing bedding plants. One factor limiting success with bedding plants is transplanting shock. Previously, seedlings were raised in seedling trays or flats. The high density of sowing did not allow seedlings to be dug out individually with adequate soil attached to the roots, which predisposed the seedlings to wilting from moisture stress. Today, nursery and greenhouse producers raise seedlings in plastic cell packs, each seedling occupying a cell with adequate soil around its roots. Home growers can purchase packs of seedlings and transplant them conveniently. The continued efforts of breeders make it possible to have a wide variety (in terms of shape, size, color, and maturity) of bedding plants to meet different customer tastes and climatic conditions. Hybrid cultivars of these plants produce superior flowers or edible produce. Ground covers are generally low-growing plants with the ability to spread. They include shrubs, vines, grasses, and perennials.

Vegetable bedding plants, are usually restricted to gardens, where they are grown for their edible parts. Some ornamental types of certain vegetables exist. The use of bedding plants discussed in this section is limited to ornamental plants.

The use of *ornamental annual bedding plants* is based on their size or height, form (spreading or trailing versus erect), foliage, light requirements (shade, partial shade, or high light), and color of flowers, among others.

Because of their relatively small size, bedding plants can be readily and effectively raised to form a patch of uniform display of color, texture, or other desired characteristics. They can be used to fill open spaces between or around objects. For example, bedding plants may be grown around a sculpture or fountain in the landscape. These plants may be grown in the foreground of permanent shrubbery or along fences and walls. When grown in containers, bedding plants may be displayed in windows or hanging baskets on patios. They may be used to accentuate the border of the walkway. It is easy to be creative with bedding plants. Even the gardener prefers a particular species; plant breeders have developed numerous cultivars of many species to provide for variety in the landscape, such as by using cultivars with different colors in the design. Some bedding plants may serve the dual purpose of providing interest in the landscape and being used for *cut flowers* for indoor use. In short, bedding plants can be used in a variety of ways to beautify the landscape.

17.3 DESIGNING A FLOWER GARDEN

To maximize the aesthetic value of flowers, it is important to choose the right plants for the area and also locate or display them attractively in the landscape. In fact, simple or rather unattractive flowers can be greatly enhanced by the way they are displayed. Instead of locating plants haphazardly in the landscape, specific designs can be created and adopted in planting the flower garden. The following is a discussion on the principles involved in designing a successful flower garden.

17.3.1 SELECTING A SITE

A garden site should be freely draining since waterlogged conditions are intolerable to most plants and a nuisance to gardeners as they care for their plants. High soil moisture levels may cause bulbs and roots to rot before they sprout. Where soils drain slowly or poorly, raised beds may be used to improve drainage and provide a warm seedbed. The site of a garden should be strategic. The purpose of planting a garden is to make it readily visible in order to be enjoyed. It is easier to enjoy a garden for a prolonged period if it is located within view of where the gardener usually sits to relax (e.g., a deck or patio). Because it is also gratifying if others can enjoy the garden, it may be located on the public side of a house.

Apart from water and air, light is another factor that is critical to the success of plants. Most flowering plants grow best under conditions of full sunlight. Shading causes some plants to produce more foliage than flowers or to grow spindly, weak, and unattractive.

17.3.2 CHOOSING PLANTS

Some gardeners will grow any plant they find pretty. Others are very particular about their choice of plants and plant only certain species and colors. Gardeners often like to grow a variety of types (e.g., bulbs, herbaceous plants, and annuals). In the case of mixtures, care must be taken in designing the garden so that the different species blend well together. Different species may have different physical features and environmental needs, requiring that the layout be designed such that no component is obscured or diminished. General guidelines for choosing plants are as follows:

1. *Height.* It is important to know the plant height at adult stage so that taller species are planted in the background and shorter ones in front. This way, all plants can be seen very clearly in the display. If the contrast is too great, one species may overwhelm the others.
2. *Habit or form.* Some species stand erect, and others are procumbent (spreading). Many hanging basket species produce long vines that hang down from the container.
3. *Color.* Flowers come in a large variety and intensity of colors. A successful flower garden displays species whose colors blend well. A good display of colors does not necessarily mean contrasting colors. Some stunning and effective displays involve shades of one or a few colors.
4. *Sunlight required.* When plants are located close to the house or trees, shading (partial light) becomes an important consideration. Inadequate sunlight reduces flowering capacity.
5. *Blooming.* Species bloom at different times and for different periods. If the gardener desires continual blooming in the landscape, the species should be selected such that they bloom in succession throughout the season.
6. *Water needs.* The domestic water supply is the source of water for home gardens. In summer when demand for water is at its peak, some areas experience water shortage. Plant breeders develop drought-resistant cultivars of various bedding plants that may be used in such drought-prone regions. Certain species require more water for growth than others. When growing mixtures, water can be used more efficiently by grouping plants with similar needs, the principle of *xeriscaping*.
7. *General care.* Some plant species require constant vigilance for best results, while others need minimal attention. Generally, annual bedding plants need more hands-on involvement of the grower than do trees and shrubs. The gardener should choose plants he or she is ready to care for adequately.

17.3.3 PREPARING THE BED

The soil should be dug up and turned over to a depth of about 12 to 18 inches (30.5 to 45.7 centimeters) with a spade or rototiller. During the tillage operations, compost or peat should be incorporated to improve drainage and moisture retention. It may be necessary to purchase topsoil to mix into the native soil to improve its physical structure. A complete fertilizer (e.g., 10:10:10) should be spread and mixed in at the rate of about 2 pounds per 100 square feet (1 kilogram per 9 square meters) of land. Other soil amendments such as liming may be necessary where the soil is acidic. A pH of 6.5 is preferred by most annual species.

Where drainage is a problem, raised beds may be constructed for bedding plants. Beds should not be designed to have straight edges. Straight lines are not only hard to maintain but also less attractive than those with sweeping curves. A variety of materials (e.g., bricks, plastic, or boards) may be used to edge beds to define their perimeter and to avoid encroachment of lawn grass.

Flower beds may be attached to hedges or fences and thereby serve as borders. Beds may be constructed to be unattached (freestanding or island) in the landscape, thus providing viewing opportunities from all angles, as opposed to from the front only in the case of border beds.

17.3.4 SEEDING

Bedding plants may be *direct seeded* or *transplanted*.

Direct Seeding

Direct seeding is done in early spring when there is no danger of frost. The bed should be prepared to a fine tilth. The proper spacing and planting depth should be observed for good germination. Annual plants such as cleome, poppy, baby's breath, and stock may be direct seeded (Table 17–1). It is important that the seeds used be viable in order to obtain a good stand. If possible, fresh seeds should be purchased each season. The bed should be watered after seeding and kept moist but not wet (which promotes rotting).

Transplanting

Raising seedlings for transplanting is an activity that requires good strategy. Seedlings are raised indoors while the weather outside is cold and timed to coincide with early spring. Seeds are sown in flats containing a lightweight soil medium; the medium should be pasteurized to avoid damping-off of seedlings. Such a medium is freely draining but also has good moisture-holding capacity, which makes transplanting easier. Small seeds

TABLE 17–1 Selected Direct-Seeded Bedding Plants

Plant	Scientific Name
Spider flower	*Cleome* spp.
Coreopsis	*Coreopsis* spp.
Baby's breath	*Gypsophila* spp.
Sunflower	*Helianthus annuus*
Poppy	*Papaver* spp.
Forget-me-not	*Myosotis* spp.
Zinnia	*Zinnia elegans*
Marigold	*Tagetes* spp.
Nasturtium	*Tropaeolum majus*

are sown in rows in flats (Figure 17–4). When they attain a good size to be conveniently handled, they are transplanted individually into peat pots or cell packs. When sowing larger seeds, the cells or peat pots are arranged in the flat before filling with soil. Seeds should be sown such that each pot eventually holds one or two successful seedlings. Examples of transplanted bedding plants are presented in Table 17–2.

Freshly sown seeds should be thoroughly watered and kept moist. A spray nozzle should be used to avoid burying small seeds too deeply in the soil. Also, the flat may be covered with a sheet of glass to reduce the light and transpiration, and also maintain a high relative humidity. Poor lighting, however, induces etiolation. Overcrowding caused by a high seeding rate also results in plant etiolation. Alternatively, the seeding flat should be periodically misted. Seedlings should be hardened off for better transplanting success. Transplanting should not be delayed.

The advantage of using peat pots is that the pots can be inserted directly into the soil. Before transplanting, the plants should be thoroughly watered. The rim of the pot should then be torn off and the bottom opened up before inserting it into the soil. Plants should be set according to recommended spacing. A starter solution may be applied at planting to promote good and quick establishment. The solution is usually high in phosphorus, but soon after the seedling becomes established, nitrogen should be applied.

Commercial greenhouses grow and sell bedding plants. Using greenhouse plants is a convenient way to establish bedding plants if one does not want to go through the process of raising seedlings. For best results, one may invest in a **propagation case,** which may be heated and enclosed to keep the humidity at a desirable level for germination (Figure 17–5).

Propagation Case
A transparent and enclosed container used for raising seedlings.

17.3.5 CARE

The flower bed should be kept clean of weeds, which not only compete with bedding plants for nutrients but also are unsightly and reduce the aesthetic value of the display. It is important to maintain a good watering schedule to avoid drying of plants, which can induce premature flower drop. Application of a mulch helps to control weeds and also reduces moisture loss. Fertilizers should be applied judiciously so that the vegetative cycle is not overextended to the detriment of flowering. Water-soluble fertilizers may be applied in the irrigation water. If insects or diseases occur, they should be controlled by using appropriate and safe pesticides. In commercial nurseries, some growers apply a hormone (e.g., B-nine or diaminozone) to control growth in bedding plants so that they become stocky, compact, and appealing. These features may be obtained by *pinching* (removing the terminal bud) to induce lateral branching. Since many annual flowering plants die after their fruits mature (i.e., monocarpic), they can be maintained in bloom for a long time by regularly removing faded flowers and thereby preventing fruiting.

TABLE 17–2 Selected Bedding Plants That Are Transplanted

Plant	Scientific Name
Petunia	*Petunia* spp.
Pansy	*Viola tricolor*
Dahlia	*Dahlia* spp.
Lavender	*Lavandula officinalis*
Larkspur	*Delphinium* spp.
Ageratum	*Ageratum* spp.
Snapdragon	*Antirrhinum majus*
Coleus	*Coleus blumei*
Cosmos	*Cosmos* spp.
Impatiens	*Impatiens* spp.

FIGURE 17–4 Bedding plants raised in cell packs. *(Source: George Acquaah)*

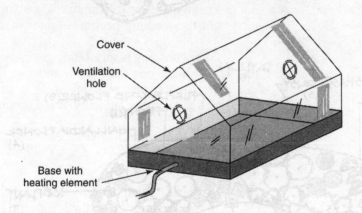

Cover

Ventilation hole

Base with heating element

FIGURE 17–5 A propagation case for home use.

Flower gardens may also be designed with specific themes in mind. One may capitalize on floral characteristics to create a theme. Certain flowers bloom in the evening, such as evening primrose (*Oenothera* spp.), angel's trumpet (*Datura* spp.), pastel evening stock (*Mathiola longipetala*), and four-o'clocks (*Mirabilis jalopa*). A garden that comes alive in the evening could be a viable theme. A grass garden using species such as bromegrass (*Bromus madritenis*), broom corn millet (*Panicum miliaceum*), Job's tears (*Croix lacryma Jobi*), and foxtail millet (*Betana italica*) is also a viable garden theme. Fragrance is another design possibility, whereby flowers such as pastel evening stock (*Mathiola longipetala*), petunia (*Petunia x hybrida*), and flowering tobacco (*Nicotiana sylvestris* and *N. alata*) that produce sweet fragrances are incorporated into a garden design. Some simple garden designs are presented in Figure 17–6.

17.4 COMMON PERENNIAL BEDDING PLANTS

Bedding plants are mostly annuals. However, certain garden designs include perennial species. In fact, growing mixtures of species is a strategy for creating a **continual bloom garden** in which plants bloom in succession. This way, the garden can be enjoyed for a long period. Bulbs are included in mixtures for their early bloom in fall; perennials bloom in late spring and throughout the summer. Popular flowering perennials are described in Table 17–3.

Continual Bloom Garden
A garden planted with a mixture of plant species that bloom in different seasons so that flowers occur year-round.

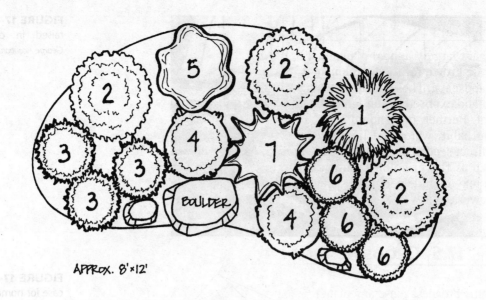

APPROX. 8'×12'

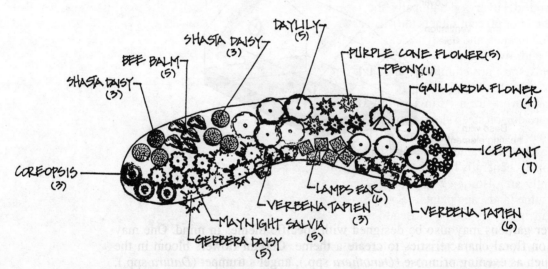

FIGURE 17–6 Samples of simple garden designs. *(Source: Courtesy of TLC, Oklahoma City)*

TABLE 17–3 Selected Perennial Bedding Plants

Plant	Scientific Name
Canterbury bells	*Campanula medium*
Carnation	*Dianthus caryophyllus*
Columbine	*Aquilegia* spp.
Daisy, Shasta	*Chrysanthemum maximum*
Delphinium	*Delphinium elatum*
Foxglove	*Digitalis purpurea*
Daylily	*Hemerocallis* spp.
Iris	*Iris* spp.
Peony	*Paeonia* spp.
Sweet pea	*Lathyrus latifolius*
Sweet william	*Dianthus barbatus*
Lupine	*Lupinus polyphyllus*
Daisy, golden	*Anthemis tinctoria*

SUMMARY

Bedding plants are largely annual plants that are grown in beds. Whereas vegetable bedding plants are grown for food, ornamental bedding plants are grown for aesthetic reasons in the landscape. These plants are generally small in size. Flower beds should be well drained and exposed to sunlight. Plants selected for use should be adapted to the environment. Further, one should also consider the adult height, habit or form, color, blooming habit, water and light needs, and general care required. Bedding plants may be direct seeded or transplanted. Garden plants can be designed along certain themes such as flower color, fragrance, or species (e.g., grass garden). Annual gardens, which may include perennial species, generally require a degree of involvement by the grower.

17.5 CHOOSING A GROUND COVER

Even though in the broadest sense any plant that spreads its foliage over the soil can be called a **ground cover**, operationally the term is reserved for low, spreading plants (less than 2 feet or 60 centimeters tall). This group of plants includes shrubs (e.g., dwarf yew, creeping juniper, and dwarf azalea), vines (e.g., English ivy), perennials (e.g., lily of the valley and twining strawberry), and grasses. Some species such as daylilies (*Hemerocallis* spp.) are clump forming, and others such as ajuga (*Ajuga reptaris*) are rhizomatous or stoloniferous.

> **Ground Cover**
> *A low-growing plant that spreads and forms a matlike growth over an area.*

Ground covers are used in a variety of ways. For example, they may be used to reduce soil erosion on steep slopes; cover rocky and rough areas that are difficult to mow; cover up areas under trees that are poorly lit; hide unattractive parts of the landscape; or enhance the aesthetic value of the landscape by their attractive form, foliage, and flowers. These plants generally have the capacity to grow in a manner as to blanket the ground and frequently are also quick spreading. They do not require the regular maintenance needed by some landscape plants.

Ground covers should be chosen to meet certain conditions:

1. *The hardiness zone.* Unless the selections are adapted to the local climate, they will not perform to their full capacity. Like other plants, some species are adapted to cool climates and others prefer hot and dry climates. Some plants such as hostas are adapted to a wide variety of climates.
2. *The site characteristics.* A good site analysis is needed to find out the specific problems and how to select a ground cover to solve them. This analysis often includes a soil test to determine the nutritional status of the soil in the area. If an area in the landscape is bare, it might be due to a number of factors, such as shade, shallow soil, low nutrients, improper pH, and others. The soil may be sandy and drain too quickly or clay and hold too much water. The soil may have an adequate amount of nutrients to support growth but a pH that does not make the nutrients available to plants.

   Table 17–4 provides some suggestions of plants to grow in shady conditions such as under trees. Junipers and cinquefoil (*Potentilla fruticola*) perform well if the area is a dry hillside of poor fertility. Table 17–5 lists some species adapted to steep and rocky slopes. One hard-to-manage area in the landscape is the wet patch that will not support a lawn. For such spots, possible choices include the creeping Jenny (*Lysimachia* spp.), certain ferns, blue flag (*Iris versicolor*), and Japanese primrose (*Primula japonica*).
3. *Special effects.* Ground covers are used for more than protection of bare ground in the landscape. Some species have qualities to make them appropriate for use as a focal point in the landscape. Apart from green foliage, ground covers can be used for specific roles in the landscape. Ground covers with attractive colors

TABLE 17–4 Selected Ground Covers Adapted to Shade

Plant	Scientific Name	Zone	Comments
Bishop's weed	*Aegopodium podagraria*	3–9	Fast spreading; 12 inches (30 centimeters) high
Ajuga	*Ajuga reptans*	3–8	Short (3 inches or 7.7 centimeters); forms solid carpet
European ginger	*Asarum europaeum*	4–8	5 to 7 inches (12.5 to 17.5 centimeters) high; leathery leaves
Chinese astilbe	*Astilbe chinensis*	5–8	Flowers in summer; 8 to 12 inches (20 to 30 centimeters) high
Winter creeper	*Euonymus fortunei*	5–9	Evergreen; long climbing vines; 1 to 2 feet (30 to 60 centimeters) high
Sweet woodruff	*Galium odoratum*	3–8	Fast spreading; 6 to 12 inches (15 to 30 centimeters) high; sweet fragrance when dried
English ivy	*Hedera helix*	5–9	Excellent spreader; 6 inches (15 centimeters) high
Hosta	*Hosta* hybrids	3–8	Easy to grow; versatile; 6 to 24 inches (15 to 60 centimeters) high
Strawberry geranium	*Saxifraga stolonifera*	6–9	Good houseplant; 6 inches (15 centimeters) high
Common periwinkle	*Vinca minor*	3–9	Quick spreading; 6 to 10 inches (15 to 25 centimeters) high
Japanese pachysandra	*Pachysandra terminalis*	4–8	Popular; good spreader; 8 to 10 inches (20 to 25 centimeters) high

TABLE 17–5 Selected Ground Covers Adapted to Steep Slopes and Rocky Areas

Plant	Scientific Name	Zone	Comments
Wooly yarrow	*Achillea tomentosa*	3–7	Short (2 inches or 5 centimeters); full sun
Saint-John's-wort	*Hypericum calycinum*	6–8	Easy to grow; vigorous; 12 to 18 inches (30 to 45 centimeters) high
Japanese pachysandra	*Pachysandra terminalis*	4–8	Popular; good spreader; 8 to 10 inches (20 to 25 centimeters) high
Creeping juniper	*Juniperus horizontalis*	3–9	Erosion control; good for foundation planting; 6 to 18 inches (15 to 45 centimeters) high
English ivy	*Hedera helix*	5–9	Excellent spreader; 6 inches (15 centimeters) high
Common periwinkle	*Vinca minor*	3–9	Quick spreading; 6 to 10 inches (15 to 25 centimeters) high
Ajuga	*Ajuga reptans*	3–8	Short (3 inches or 7.7 centimeters); forms solid carpet

include shrubby cinquefoil, lenten rose (*Helleborus orientalis*), Bethlehem sage (*Pulmonia saccharata*), Japanese primrose (*Primula japonica*), and moss phlox (*Phlox subulata*). Other ground covers have fragrant flowers, such as lily of the valley (*Convallaria majalis*) and sweet violet (*Viola ordorata*). Thyme, a popular herb, can also be used as an effective ground cover. Ground covers can serve to tie together contrasting areas (e.g., turf and shrubs) in the landscape.

4. *Installation and maintenance.* Ground covers are utilized in areas of the landscape that are difficult to reach or manage. The plants installed should require relatively little maintenance and be easy to install. They should be chosen for their high probability of success in an area.

5. *Size of space available.* Since ground covers are by nature quick spreading, it is important that the species selected not overwhelm the area where they are installed. Additional maintenance is required to keep the ground cover in control. Plant selection is especially important when ground covers are planted in combination. A list of some aggressive spreaders is presented in Table 17–6.

17.5.1 SOIL PREPARATION AND PLANTING

Even though ground covers are perceived as plants used in marginal parts of the landscape, they nonetheless require adequate soil preparation for good establishment. Further, if the purpose of using the ground cover is for something other than

TABLE 17-6 Selected Ground Covers That Are Aggressive Spreaders

Plant	Scientific Name	Zone	Comments
Mazus	*Mazus reptans*	5–8	Forms quick ground mat; 1 to 2 inches (2.5 to 5 centimeters) high
Creeping jenny	*Lysimachia nummularia*	3–8	Stems root rapidly as they spread; 4 to 8 inches (10 to 20 centimeters) high
Creeping lilyturf	*Liriope spicata*	5–10	Rapid rooting; 4 to 8 inches (10 to 20 centimeters) high
Crown vetch	*Coronilla varia*	3–9	Tough ground cover; 18 inches (45 centimeters) high
Ajuga	*Ajuga reptans*	3–8	Short (3 inches or 7.7 centimeters); forms solid carpet
Bishop's weed	*Aegopodium podagraria*	3–9	Fast spreading; 12 inches (30 centimeters) high
English ivy	*Hedera helix*	5–9	Excellent spreader; 6 inches (15 centimeters) high
Sweet violet	*Viola odorata*	6–8	Fragrant; runners; 5 to 8 inches (12.5 to 20 centimeters) high

environmental protection, the site should be appropriately prepared. The ground should be cleared, dug up, and prepared like a bed. For example, sandy soil should receive an application of organic matter; drainage in clay areas can be improved by using raised beds for planting. A popular ground cover such as periwinkle (*Vinca minor*) cannot be grown in poorly draining soils or soils with a low pH (less than 6.5).

Species such as crown vetch (*Coronilla varia*), fringe cups (*Tellima grandiflora*), and mother-of-thyme (*Thymus serpyllum*) are relatively easy to start from seed. Potted plants, though expensive, are easier to handle than seed. For low-budget planting, bare-root stock may be used to establish the ground cover. However, such plants need more care to be successful. Small shrubs such as creeping juniper (*Juniperus horizontalis*) may be planted as bare roots. They must be watered thoroughly after planting and mulched to retain moisture and suppress weeds.

Ground covers are seeded on slopes where manual planting is a challenge or a large area must be planted. Steep slopes (more than 1:1) along roads may be conveniently seeded by using a *hydroseeder* or *hydromulcher*. Seed is mixed in a water slurry, which may include some fertilizer and pumped under high pressure onto the slope. Hydromulching includes wood cellulose fiber mulch in the slurry.

Potted ground cover plants are planted like other potted plants. The seedling should be set in the hole no deeper than it was in the pot. Potted cuttings of species such as English ivy (*Hedera helix*) and periwinkle may be used to establish ground covers. Cuttings are spaced closer than potted plants.

17.5.2 CARE

Water is critical during early establishment. Seeds, divisions, and transplants should not be allowed to dry. Mulching helps to prevent drying. Plants should not be overwatered. Fertilizer application of about 10 pounds of 20:10:10 analysis may be applied to promote growth and development. Ground covers spread over the soil surface, and thus irrigation must follow immediately after an application of fertilizer to wash away residue on leaves and prevent fertilizer burn.

Mulching at planting is necessary to control weeds and thereby give the ground cover time to establish. The mulch may have to be renewed annually to keep weeds under control. If weeds appear, they should be removed. Watering is necessary when a prolonged dry spell occurs. Fertilizing is not critical unless the soil is particularly poor in nutrients. Sandy soils generally need fertilizer supplementation more frequently than clay soils.

The pruning of ground covers may be necessary after years of growing under favorable conditions. Under such conditions, growth must be controlled by pruning shrubby species such as junipers and vines such as English ivy (*Hedera helix*) in early spring. Pruning reduces overcrowding, which causes undesirable competition among plants and subsequent loss of vigor. Renewal pruning, which helps to rejuvenate the ground cover, may be accomplished by mowing vines with a trimmer.

Ground covers may be attacked by spider mites, Japanese and other beetles, caterpillars, powdery mildew, aphids, and other pests. However, diseases and insects are usually not a problem for ground covers in the landscape. When conifers are grown by the roadside in cold climates, the salts used on icy roads in winter may damage the needles.

If the ground cover is not uniform (empty spots occur), the spaces can be filled by vegetatively propagating the species using applicable methods. For example, creeping junipers (*Juniperus horizontalis*) can be layered, and moss phlox (*Phlox subulata*) can be propagated by cuttings.

17.6 ORNAMENTAL GRASSES

Grass is one of the basic elements in a landscape design. The establishment of a lawn is discussed in detail in Chapter 18. The discussion in this module is limited to grasses planted in spots in the landscape for decorative purposes.

Grasses used as ornamentals in the landscape may be grouped into four categories: *true grasses, sedges, rushes*, and *bamboos*, the last three sometimes being described as grass relatives. They are used in the landscape for the color of their foliage and the variety in their sizes, shapes, and forms. These plants are easy to grow and care for in the landscape. They can be grown in beds or in containers. Like ground covers, certain grasses are clump forming, others form stolons or rhizomes, and some form low mounds (e.g., fountain grass [*Pennisetum alopecuroides*]).

17.6.1 CHOOSING GRASSES

As discussed in Chapter 18, turfgrasses may be placed into two general categories: *cool* and *warm season*. Warm-season grasses become dormant in winter and turn brown. Cool-season grasses tend to be evergreen or semievergreen. The space to be allocated to the grass must always be considered. Clump-forming species tend to be contained and less aggressive or invasive. A limited number of species, including blue lyme grass (*Elymus arenarius* 'Glaucus'), are notorious for being very aggressive. When such species are grown, they may be held in check by planting them next to pavements or installing edging strips. Apart from climate, soil pH, salinity, and drainage should be considered in making choices. Table 17–7 presents a list of popular ornamental grasses. A number of annual grasses can be grown in the garden; they can be cut and dried or used fresh for cut flowers.

17.6.2 SOIL PREPARATION AND PLANTING

If many grass clumps are to be planted, a bed may be prepared for the purpose. For a few clumps, the spots for planting should be prepared in the same way as a flower bed. It is critical that the area be free of weeds. Regular lawn grasses should not be allowed to invade the space of ornamental grasses since they are difficult to control after the invasion. Aggressive species such as quack grass (*Agropyron repens*) and popular lawn grasses such as Bermuda grass (*Cynodon dactylon*) should be kept away from ornamental species.

Ornamental grasses should be allocated ample space for growth. Clump-forming grasses can be assigned space since their adult size is predictable. When planting grasses for ground cover, spacing should be closer than when planting a few clumps. Grass for planting may be purchased as container-grown or bare-root plants. Thorough watering and mulching are needed after planting. Some grasses may be started from seed. Species

TABLE 17–7 Selected Ornamental Grasses

Plant	Scientific Name	Zone	Remarks
Shade loving			
Variegated Hakone grass	*Hakonechloa macra* (Aureola)	6–9	Slow spreading; 18 to 24 inches (45 to 60 centimeters) high
Snowy woodrush	*Luzula nivea*	4–9	One of the best woodrushes; 9 to 12 inches (22 to 30 centimeters) high
Bottlebrush grass	*Hystrix patula*	5–9	Cool season; 1 to 2 feet (30 to 60 centimeters) high
Tufted hairgrass	*Deschampsia caespitosa*	4–9	Blooms early in spring; 2 feet (60 centimeters) high
Dry, sunny sites			
Ravenna grass	*Erianthus ravennae*	5–10	Warm season; perennial; 5 feet (1.5 meter) high
Indian grass	*Sorghastrum nutans*	4–9	Showy fall colors; 3 feet (90 centimeters) high
Little bluestem	*Schizachyrium scoparium*	3–10	Good ground cover, erosion control; 1 foot (30 centimeters) high
Side oats gramma	*Bouteloua curtipendula*	4–9	Good meadow plant; 2 feet (60 centimeters) high
Prairie dropseed	*Sporobulus heterolepis*	3–9	Drought resistant; 1 foot (30 centimeters) high
Moisture loving			
Bulbous oat grass	*Arrhenatherum elatius*	4–9	Clump forming; 1 foot (30 centimeters) high
Prairie cord grass	*Spartina pectinata*	4–9	Deciduous; 2 to 5 feet (60 to 150 centimeters) high
Giant reed	*Arundo donax*	7–10	Warm season; 6 to 20 feet (1.8 to 6 meters) high
Quacking grass	*Briza media*	4–10	1 to 2 feet (30 to 60 centimeters) high; easy to grow
Showy grasses			
White-striped ribbon grass	*Phalaris arundinacea*	4–9	Invasive; 2 to 3 feet (60 to 90 centimeters) high
Fountain grass	*Pennisetum alopecuroides*	5–9	Adaptable; 3 feet (90 centimeters) high
Pampas grass	*Cortaderia sello ana*	8–10	One of the showiest; sharp leaves; 5 to 12 feet (1.5 to 3.6 meters) high

that are easy to start from seed include velvet grass (*Holcus lanatus*), northern seas oats (*Chasmanthium latifolium*), Indian grass (*Sorghasrum nutans*), blue fescue (*Festuca cinera*), and fountain grass (*Pennisetum alopecuroides*). Some species may have to be started in a nursery indoors and transplanted into the landscape later.

Grasses may be planted alone or in combination with other bedding plants or ground covers. For shady areas, sedges adapted to shade may be combined with shade-loving ground covers such as hosta and lily of the valley. In sunny areas, poppy, peony, and chrysanthemum may be mingled with ornamental grasses. Grasses can be grown in combination with bulbs (e.g., tulip, crocus, or daffodil). Grasses may also be planted in containers. Small- and medium-sized grasses may be planted in decorative pots and other containers. Like all potted plants, moisture management is the key to success.

17.6.3 CARE

When grasses are planted in the garden, watering is critical, especially in the first year of establishment, when it should be done fairly frequently. After establishment, watering is required less frequently. Similarly, only minimal fertilization is required. Organic fertilizer may be used as needed, and regular mulching is recommended. To keep the form and shape, grasses may be trimmed, clipped, or pruned periodically. Such measures may be taken at any time during the year to remove unwanted growth, but in late winter or early spring, grasses may be cut more severely. Cool-season grasses may be pruned to about two-thirds of their height; warm-season grasses may be cut even closer to the ground to leave about 4 inches (10.2 centimeters) of growth.

Grasses usually can remain at the same spot and in good health for a long time. Stoloniferous and rhizomatous species are able to spread, but clump-forming species often exhibit signs of aging, losing quality. When this occurs, the clumps should be dug up and divided into smaller clumps. Overfertilization predisposes plants to disease. Generally, grasses have few pests, provided care is taken to select the proper species and they are planted after adequate site preparation. Beetles, aphids, scale and sucking insects; moles, mice, and other rodents; and other pests and diseases may attack grasses to varying extents. However, grasses stay relatively trouble free in the landscape with minimal care.

17.7 BAMBOOS

Bamboos originate in the tropics and semitropics. They are woody, producing hardwood canes or culms that vary in color and size. They may be as short as 12 inches (30 centimeters) or more than 100 feet (30 meters) tall. Once established, they cannot be eradicated. They spread by rhizomes and can rapidly invade an area. Some species form clumps. Short-growing bamboos may be grown in containers. Hardy bamboos that are adapted to climate zone 6 include fountain bamboo *(Fargesia nitida), Shibatae kumasaca,* and *Sasa palmata.*

17.8 SEDGES

Sedges may be distinguished from true grasses by their angular stems filled with pith. They are generally shade-loving plants and used where grasses may not grow well. They are adapted to climate zones 4 to 9. Sedges may grow vertically or have a weeping plant form. They also vary in foliage color. Sedges may be used in a variety of ways to accent the landscape, and some are good ground covers.

17.9 RUSHES

Rushes differ from grasses and sedges by having cylindrical stems that are stiff and solid. They prefer shade and moist soil but can be grown in drier parts of the landscape. Popular ornamental rushes include big rushes *(Junus* spp.) and wood rushes *(Carex glauca).*

SUMMARY

Ground covers are low-growing, spreading plants that stand less than 2 feet (60 centimeters) tall. They may be shrubs, vines, grasses, or other perennials. They are able to grow in shade and other hard-to-manage areas in the landscape and have attractive foliage of varying color. Ornamental grasses are used for their shapes, sizes, and forms. Some are cool-season and others warm-season plants. They may form clumps or spread aggressively. Bamboos, the largest in the grass group, are woody and can grow to heights in excess of 100 feet (30 meters). Other ornamental grasses are sedges and rushes.

17.10 CHOOSING TREES

Trees in the landscape may be classified as *narrowleaf* or *broadleaf,* and *evergreen* or *deciduous.* Long-lived, trees are large plants in their adult stages. Narrowleaf evergreen plants are particularly popular in landscapes.

Trees in the landscape have both functional and aesthetic roles. Because trees are large and long-lived, they must be selected and located with care. In selecting trees for the landscape, numerous factors should be considered. Some factors are critical because they determine the success and survival of the plant at the site; other factors deal with economics and aesthetics.

1. *Site and space.* The space available for landscaping determines the size of plants one can install. At maturity, trees are the largest plants in the landscape and as such need a relatively large space per plant to grow properly. In certain areas, homeowners are not allowed to plant any trees at all or only certain ones in front of their houses if the property is situated next to a street. Further, species such as birch, elm, and sycamore are adversely affected by street lighting. Other species such as little leaf linden *(Tilia cordata)* and pin oak *(Quercus palustris)* are excellent street plants.

2. *Adaptation.* Regardless of the attractiveness of a particular tree, if it does not grow well in the intended environment, one should not purchase it. Some trees prefer temperate conditions and others tropical. The species should be selected with the hardiness zone in mind. In terms of adaptation, the most important environmental factor is temperature. Every so often, unseasonable weather conditions occur in an area. The winters may be unusually cold or warm, which may cause damage from winter chilling or prevent blooming. Unless one is willing to invest in irrigation, the trees selected should be tolerant of moisture stress, which is prevalent in summer. For example, the weeping European birch *(Betula pendula)* is adapted to zone 2, red sunset *(Acer rubrum)* to zone 3, redbud *(Cercis canadensis)* to zone 4, Japanese maple *(Acer palmatum)* to zone 5, pecan *(Carya illinoinensis)* to zone 6, and live oak *(Quercus virginiana)* to zone 7.

3. *Plant size and characteristics at maturity.* Even though tree growth may be controlled by pruning, it is best to select a tree whose mature characteristics will not pose maintenance problems. For example, certain trees branch extensively. If located near the property boundary, its branches may grow over the fence and into the neighbor's yard. This overextension could initiate turf wars between neighbors, especially in the fall season when leaves drop. The flowering dogwood *(Cornus florida)* has a horizontal branching pattern, and shademaster honeylocust *(Gleditisa triacanthos)* has open branching. Even if one is able to control the top of the tree by pruning, the roots may spread and damage pipelines, house foundations, pavements, or drainage systems. Large trees may grow and touch overhead electrical cables or shade the lawn and thereby suppress grass growth.

4. *Maintenance.* Some species are low maintenance, requiring no pruning or other landscape maintenance practices. Others must be nurtured with care. Deciduous trees shed their leaves annually, necessitating fall cleanup.

5. *Aesthetics.* The shape of the canopy, the foliage (e.g., texture, color, and size), and the general appearance of a tree may be used to create dramatic scenery in the landscape. The inflorescence of flowering trees can be stunning in beauty and design. A weeping tree form is always attractive in the landscape; cut leaf weeping birch *(Betula pendula* 'Laciniata') and weeping European birch *(Betula pendula)* both have weeping forms, the former being oval and the latter pyramidal.

6. *Seasonal enjoyment.* Avid plant lovers look forward to seasonal changes in the plant cycle and their enjoyment from viewing the changes. The fall colors produced by trees such as dogwood, oak, ash, aspen, and maple are very impressive. Flowering plants such as flowering crab apple, magnolia, redbud, and flowering dogwood produce bursts of very attractive flowers that many look forward to each year.

7. *Fragrance.* The inflorescence of some plants produce very pleasant fragrances. A good example is the amur maple *(Acer ginnala)*, with purplish flowers, which is often used as a specimen plant.

8. *Fruiting.* Certain trees have the capacity to produce edible fruits (e.g., apple, cherry, plum, and peach). Other fruiting trees such as mulberry and olive, when used in the landscape, should be discouraged from flowering because they litter the ground with many dropped fruits.

9. *Cost.* Tree species vary in cost. Specimen trees are usually relatively more expensive than regular plants. Cost also depends on whether the tree is sold as balled and burlapped or bare root.

10. *Use.* Trees may be chosen for use as specimen trees (highly ornamental) or for other practical roles such as providing shade or serving as a windbreak. Pecan (*Carya illinoinensis*) is an excellent nut tree, and copper beech (*Fagus sylvatica* 'Atropurpurea') has attractive foliage. The shademaster honeylocust *(Gleditisa triacanthos)* is an excellent shade tree, and sweet bay *(Magnolia virginiana)* has very attractive flowers and is used as a specimen tree.

11. *Rooting characteristics.* Some trees produce roots close to the soil surface, which can crack pavements or driveways (Figure 17–7). Other trees have aggressively growing roots that can clog drainage pipes.

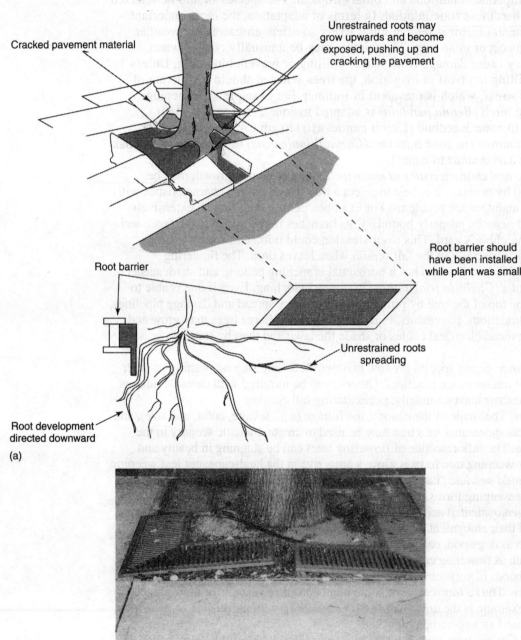

Cracked pavement material

Unrestrained roots may grow upwards and become exposed, pushing up and cracking the pavement

Root barrier should have been installed while plant was small

Root barrier

Unrestrained roots spreading

Root development directed downward

(a)

(b)

FIGURE 17–7 (a) Roots of an adult tree cracking a pavement due to lack of root deflector. (b) Signs of a tree outgrowing its boundaries. *(Source: For (b) George Acquaah)*

12. *Wildlife attraction.* Trees in the landscape and other ornamentals attract birds into the area. Fruiting plants attract birds more than nonfruiting types. Examples of good wildlife-attracting trees are *Crataegus phaenopyrum*, which produces bright-red fruits in fall, and American beech *(Fagus grandifolia)*.

13. *Diseases.* Certain species have devastating disease problems, making their use problematic. For example, the American elm *(Ulmus americana)* is susceptible to Dutch elm disease. A tree that matures only to be attacked by diseases must be removed from the landscape at high cost.

14. *Allergies.* Flowering trees that produce copious amounts of pollen may pose allergy problems in affected homeowners.

17.11 Purchasing Trees for Planting

Care must be taken to select very healthy plants for installing in the landscape. The following are factors to consider in purchasing trees for use in the landscape.

17.11.1 TYPE OF SEEDLING

Nurseries raise tree seedlings for sale to homeowners and landscape contractors. In terms of how they are grown and packaged for sale, there are three classes of tree seedlings—bare-root trees, balled and burlapped trees, and container-grown trees.

Bare-Root Trees

As the name indicates, a bare-root tree seedling is dug up without a ball of soil around the roots. Deciduous species with stem diameters of less than 1 inch may be transplanted as bare-root seedlings. Seedlings are prepared in this way when the plants are dormant (i.e., winter). Deciduous plants are usually sold as bare-root seedlings. Conifer seedlings that are not more than three years old are also frequently sold this way. Bare-root plants are inexpensive to raise and purchase. Seedlings tend to lose some of their roots when uprooted, which places them in jeopardy of dying during transplantation. If it cannot be planted immediately, the bare-root seedling should be *heeled in* (roots covered up in a shallow trench).

Balled and Burlapped Trees

A tree seedling may be harvested for transplanting by digging a certain distance around the trunk and lifting it with a ball of soil around the roots. The soil ball around the roots is usually at least 12 inches for each 1 inch of trunk diameter. The soil is then tightly wrapped in a burlap sack, thus the name balled and burlapped (B&B) seedling. Balling and burlapping is an expensive operation, which increases the price of such seedlings. Evergreen trees (narrowleaf and broadleaf) are marketed in this way. Balling and burlapping can be done any time of year. Deciduous trees may sometimes be handled by this method. Transporting balled and burlapped trees is difficult because of their bulk, but the seedlings establish quickly. The operation is mechanized, especially when seedlings are large. Large trees, as previously indicated, are not burlapped but carried in mechanical spades to the site at which they are to be transplanted.

Container-Grown Trees

Tree seedlings may be raised in containers (e.g., plastic, concrete, or wooden) for sale. Seedlings may be raised in this restricted soil environment for twelve months or more depending on the species. An overgrown plant may experience pot-bounding (i.e., roots grow over each other in circles). Another problem with container-grown plants is rapid soil drying. Potted plants should be irrigated on a frequent schedule. An advantage of container plants is that they can be readily relocated in the nursery in adverse weather, such as winter, into a place where they can be protected from the cold. This transportability allows a wide variety of species to be raised and also makes seedlings available year-round. Container plants are easy to transport over long distances.

17.11.2 CHARACTERISTICS OF A GOOD TREE SEEDLING

The method of raising notwithstanding, the buyer should always purchase seedlings from a reputable nursery and select healthy plants. For container plants, one should not select those with exposed roots on the soil surface, which indicates pot-bounding and overgrown seedlings. Such plants establish very poorly in the field. Plants with large tops may not be advantageous, since they may be prone to being blown down by the wind. Such seedlings also may be too old and may not establish properly. Like all seedlings, they should be disease free and without physical injury, have a well-developed stem and good branching, and be generally healthy and vigorous.

17.12 PREPLANTING STORAGE

It is best to prepare the site before bringing in purchased seedlings from the nursery. This preparation eliminates additional care of plants and handling in the preplanting stage. Sometimes a short period of storage may be required while waiting for the proper soil and weather conditions for planting. Preplanting care basically involves prevention of drying. In bare-root seedlings, the seedlings are uprooted while the plant is dormant. Nonetheless, many roots are lost in the process, and freshly bruised surfaces may provide avenues for moisture loss. Burlapped seedlings have some soil around the root to hold moisture for a short period but eventually will begin to dry out. Bare-root and burlapped seedlings may be heeled in while in storage. Heeling in may be accomplished in several ways in the soil or by using a variety of materials. The roots may be placed in a shallow ditch or covered in mulching material (e.g., straw, wood bark, peat moss, and well-rotted sawdust) that can hold moisture. The roots are kept moist by frequent watering. To reduce evaporation, the storage environment should be kept very humid. The seedlings should be protected from direct sunlight to reduce the rate of transpiration.

17.13 FACTORS FOR TRANSPLANTING SUCCESS

When we talk about planting trees, we actually mean transplanting trees. There are several factors to consider for increasing the success of transplanting of trees. A critical factor in all transplanting operations is the condition of plant roots. In greenhouse seedling production, techniques such as the use of individual peat pots or cells, ensures that seedling roots remain intact and in the best state of health, thereby reducing transplanting shock. Digging up tree seedlings raised in field nurseries is more challenging and could result in the loss of 25 percent of the roots, and sometimes as much as 75 percent of the roots in the case of transplanting established landscape plants.

It is important to evaluate woody transplant materials to see their condition and assess their transplanting success before transplanting them. The plant material should be in good health. Transplants of younger trees and shrubs experience less stress and survive better than older plants. Also, shrubs tolerate transplanting better than trees, while deciduous species survive transplanting better than evergreens. Similarly, shallow-rooted species generally survive transplanting better than deep-rooted species because the latter tend to lose a significant amount of roots during the digging process. Container plants are more tolerant of transplanting than field-grown or landscape-established plants.

Other factors that influence the success of transplanting trees are season or time of transplanting, the site soil conditions, natural tolerance to transplanting, and the after-transplanting care. Species that are tolerant of transplanting include green ash (*Fraxinus pennsylvanica*), hackberry (*Celtis* spp.), American elm (*Ulmus Americana*), poplar (*Populus* spp.), willow (*Salix* spp.), sumac (*Rhus* spp.), and silver maple (*Acer saccharinum*). Species that are not tolerant of transplanting include walnut (*Juglans* spp.), oak (*Quercus macrocarpa*), and buckeye (*Aesculus* spp.).

17.14 PLANTING TREES

The success of a transplanted tree seedling depends on the timing of planting, seedling preplanting preparation, soil preparation, and planting technique, among other factors.

17.14.1 TIMING

Spring offers the best conditions for planting many tree species. The conditions at this time provide adequate moisture and warm soils for plant root establishment and growth. The relatively cool temperatures of spring minimize moisture loss through transpiration and thus reduce the incidence of transplanting shock. The cool temperatures of fall (in areas where winters are mild) also provide good conditions for planting trees. The limitation to planting under this condition is frozen soil. Many deciduous and evergreen broadleaf trees as well as conifers may be planted during this period. Planting in summer is most challenging because of the high temperatures and intense sunlight that induce rapid drying of plant tissue. Some container plants may be planted during this period but will require great care for success.

17.14.2 LOCATING PLANTS

Trees live for a long time in the landscape. Mistakes in locating them can be costly. Locating plants in the landscape should be done very judiciously, taking into account structures like sidewalks, pavements, light posts, buildings, and the adult plant size and form. Trees should be located where they will have ample room for both root and crown to develop fully. The light conditions, soil pH, and soil moisture are critical factors to consider as well.

17.14.3 DIGGING THE HOLE

Some general guidelines should be observed in digging a hole for planting trees. First, the hole should be large enough to contain the plant roots without the need to squeeze or pack them tightly. There should be ample room around the roots for soil to be added. The hole should be at least 12 inches wider than the ball of roots. The depth of the hole should be such that when the plant is set, the original soil level on the plant is maintained after filling the hole with soil. It should be about 6 inches deeper than the soil ball around the roots. The topsoil should be carefully piled up near the hole in a separate heap from the subsoil, which is called the **backfill soil.** This practice may not be possible when a tractor-mounted power take-off is used to dig the hole.

Backfill Soil
Topsoil dug out of a hole and used to fill it during seedling transplanting.

17.14.4 PLANT PREPARATION

Bare-root plants should be sent to the field in a container of water to avoid drying roots. The roots are then carefully pruned before setting in the hole. In container plants, the pot-bound roots should be straightened and spread out before placing them in the hole.

17.14.5 PLANTING

Bare-root plants need to be held while setting them in the hole. First, some backfill soil is placed in the hole. The plant is then held such that the crown is slightly above the soil level, and the hole is refilled with topsoil or, as some growers prefer, amended soil (soil mixed with organic matter and sometimes fertilizer). After filling, the soil should be packed firmly by tamping with a foot or stick, making sure the trunk remains erect (Figure 17–8). In the

FIGURE 17–8 Planting a bare-root tree seedling.

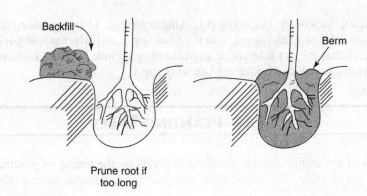

Backfill

Berm

Prune root if too long

FIGURE 17–9 Planting a balled and burlapped tree seedling.

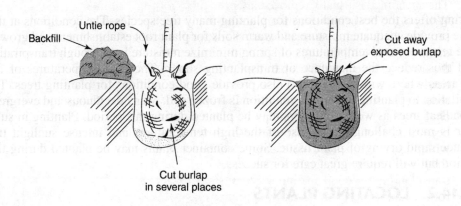

Backfill

Untie rope

Cut away exposed burlap

Cut burlap in several places

case of burlapped seedlings, the ball is set in the hole before untying the ropes. A broken soil ball may result in the seedling's death. The crown should also be set above the soil line. The burlap material is usually biodegradable and need not be removed before planting. Instead, only the overhanging top is trimmed off (Figure 17–9). The remainder of the space is filled with topsoil and patted firm. If the burlap material is not biodegradable, it must be removed by making a slit in the bottom of the wrapping and pulling it up after properly setting the seedling in the hole. Under no circumstances should a plant be planted at a depth lower than it was before transplanting. Plants are easily killed when seedlings are planted too deeply.

It may be helpful to mark the original soil level on the seedling prior to transplanting.

17.15 POSTPLANTING IMMEDIATE CARE

Newly planted tree seedlings require immediate care to increase the chance of successful establishment. This care package includes the following:

Berm
A circular ridge of soil constructed around the base of a newly transplanted tree to hold water.

1. *Installing a berm.* After firming the soil, a water-retaining wall or ridged structure called a **berm** may be installed by using the excess soil to form a ring around the trunk (Figure 17–10). This structure forms a basin to hold water around the base of the tree.
2. *Mulching.* A mulch should be placed around the base of the stem to control weeds and retain moisture in the bare soil. Mulching also prevents the soil from cracking and aids in soil infiltration by water and rapid root development.
3. *Staking and anchoring (or guying).* Balled and burlapped seedlings are often self-supporting. Newly planted tree seedlings, especially bare-root seedlings, are prone to toppling by the wind. Without additional support, the tree may be tilted

by winds. A stake, which is often a metallic rod, is positioned close to where the stem will be and driven into the soil before planting the tree. The stake should be positioned on the west or northwest side of the trunk. The stem height of the stake should be such that after tying the stem it remains upright. Any bare-root seedling taller than 8 feet (2.4 meters) should be staked. Tying should not completely immobilize the tree but permit some degree of movement with the wind, which helps in the development of a strong trunk. To prevent injury to the tree, the bare wire used for tying should be covered in a piece of rubber hose. Sometimes, double stakes may be used (Figure 17–11). In this case, the stakes are fixed outside of the planting hole on opposite sides of the stem. In place of staking, a newly planted tree may be anchored in place by using three well-positioned *guy wires* (Figure 17–12). These anchors may be removed after about a year or two (sooner for small trees). The anchorage is usually removed after the first growing season.

4. *Wrapping.* This is less commonly done these days. Trees (especially those with sensitive bark such as *Acer rubrum*) often need to be protected against trunk damage from sunlight and cold in cold climates. They are protected by wrapping the trunk with strips of burlap or tree wrapping paper after treating with an insecticide. This material is left in place for about twelve months. The wrapping also reduces moisture loss. Without the stabilizing effect of the wrapper, rapid changes in temperature in winter will cause the bark of the tree to crack or become sun scalded. The paper used must not be black or dark colored. In lieu of wrapping, tree tubes are increasingly being used by tree growers.

5. *Pruning.* In bare-root seedlings, about 30 percent of the top should be removed at transplanting for good and quick establishment. Because of root mass loss, bare-root seedlings need severe pruning to minimize water loss. Thinning of the top also reduces the dangers of toppling from wind.

6. *Antitranspirants.* To reduce transpiration and subsequently transplanting shock, antitranspirants may be sprayed with a foliar application of antitranspirants before transplanting. This treatment is used when large plants are being transplanted. It has only a temporary effect.

7. *Watering.* New transplants should be watered deeply for quick establishment. However, care should be exercised to avoid waterlogging of the soil. Although watering next to the trunk is proper during tree establishment, after the tree has grown older it should be watered only in the area outside of the *drip line* where the roots occur.

8. *Fertilization.* Nitrate fertilizers (3 to 6 pounds per 100 square feet or 1.53 to 2.7 kilograms per 9 square meters) may be applied in moderate amounts after planting. Adding fertilizer directly to the backfill soil may scourge the roots.

9. *Installing a wire mesh.* To protect against pests such as rodents, transplants may be encircled with a wire mesh, plastic, or metal guard installed around the tree trunk. These tree guards also protect against accidental damage from mowers.

10. *Installing a root deflector.* Trees that produce roots close to the soil surface should not be planted near pavement. If they have to be planted near such materials, damage to the pavement may be prevented by installing a root deflector (a sheet of impervious material inserted between the pavement and the roots to force the roots near the surface to grow downward and away from the pavement material).

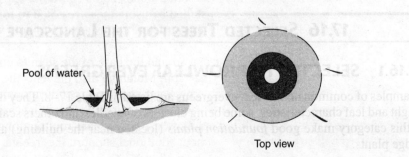

FIGURE 17–10 A berm.

Pool of water

Top view

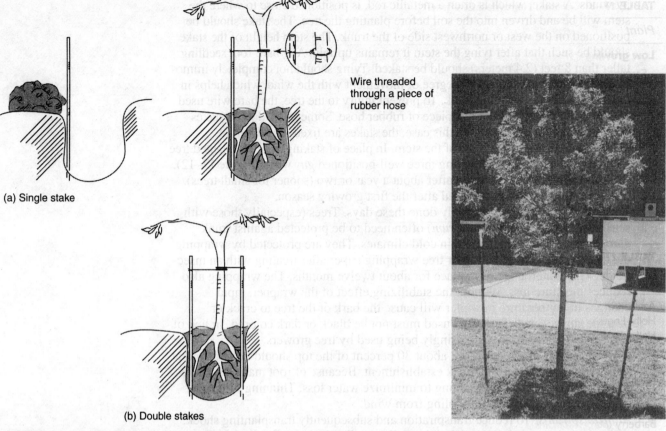

(a) Single stake

(b) Double stakes

FIGURE 17–11 Staking newly planted trees in the landscape. (a) Single stake and (b), (c) double stakes. *(Source: For (c) George Acquaah)*

Wire threaded
through a piece of
rubber hose

FIGURE 17–12 Guying newly
planted trees in the landscape.

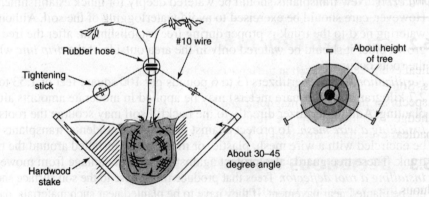

Rubber hose

#10 wire

Tightening
stick

About height
of tree

About 30–45
degree angle

Hardwood
stake

17.16 SELECTED TREES FOR THE LANDSCAPE

17.16.1 SELECTED NARROWLEAF EVERGREENS

Examples of common narrowleaf evergreens are listed in Table 17–8. They differ in plant height and leaf characteristics, some being clusters of needles and others scalelike. Plants in this category make good *foundation plants* (located near the building) and screen or hedge plants.

TABLE 17–8   Selected Narrowleaf Evergreens

Plant	Hardiness Zone
Low growing	
Sargent juniper (*Juniperus chinensis Sargentii*)	4–8
Spring heath (*Erica carnea*)	5–7
Spreading English yew (*Taxus baccata repandens*)	4–7
Blue rug juniper (*Juniperus horizontalis wiltoni*)	2–8
High growing	
Mugho pine (*Pinus mugo Mughus*)	2–6
Hicks yew (*Taxus media hicksii*)	4–8
Leyland cypress (*Cypressocyparis leylandi*)	4–8
English yew (*Taxus baccata*)	6–9

TABLE 17–9   Selected Broadleaf Evergreens

Plant	Hardiness Zone
Azalea (*Rhododendron* spp.)	4–8
Holly, English (*Ilex aquifolium*)	6–9
Holly, American (*Ilex opaca*)	6–9
Holly, Japanese (*Ilex crenata*)	6–9
Holly, Chinese (*Ilex cornuta*)	6–9
Magnolia, Southern (*Magnolia grandiflora*)	7–10
Nandina (*Nandina domestica*)	7–8
Privet (*Ligustrum japonicum*)	6–7
Barberry (*Barberry darvinii*)	4–9
Boxwood, English (*Buxus sempevirens*)	6–8
Oak, Southern live (*Quercus virginiana*)	9–10
Orange (*Citrus sinensis*)	9–10
Weeping fig (*Ficus benjamina*)	10

17.16.2   SELECTED BROADLEAF EVERGREENS

Broadleaf evergreens are used in the landscape in much the same way as narrowleaf evergreens. Some are good foundation plants (e.g., azalea and Japanese holly) and others good specimen plants (e.g., magnolia and English holly). Japanese holly also makes a good hedge. Rhododendrons are frequently located in the corner of the area. Examples of broadleaf evergreens are given in Table 17–9.

17.16.3   DECIDUOUS TREES

Deciduous trees vary widely in adult height, some being less than 30 feet (9.1 meters) and others more than 70 feet (21.2 meters) tall. They are used to provide shade in the landscape and for ornamental purposes through flowering or fall color changes. The characteristics of a selected deciduous tree used in the landscape are described in Table 17–10.

17.17   USING TREES IN THE LANDSCAPE

Apart from adaptation, other factors affecting use of deciduous species in the landscape include plant height, fall color, tree form (e.g., conical or rounded), leaf texture, and growth rate (slow or fast). Some species, such as Japanese maple (*Acer palmatum*) and flowering dogwood (*Cornus florida*), make good specimen plants; copper beech (*Fagus sylvatica*) is a good accent plant.

TABLE 17–10 Selected Deciduous Trees for the Landscape

Plant	Hardiness Zone
Alder, gray (*Alnus incana*)	3–8
Ash, Arizona (*Fraxinus velutina*)	8–10
Aspen, quaking (*Populus tremuloides*)	3–8
Beech, European (*Fragus sylvatica*)	5–10
Birch, European white (*Betula pendula*)	3–9
Chestnut, Chinese (*Castanea mollisima*)	5–9
Crab apple, Siberian (*Malus baccata*)	3–8
Dogwood, flowering (*Cornus florida*)	7–9
Elm, Chinese (*Ulmus parvifolia*)	7–10
Fig, common (*Ficus carica*)	7–10
Honey locust (*Gladitsia triacanthos*)	5–9
Larch, European (*Larix decidua*)	3–8
Sycamore (*Platanus x acerifolia*)	5–10
Poplar, Lombardy (*Populus nigra* 'Italica')	2–10
Redbud, western (*Cercis occidentalis*)	6–9
Walnut, English (*Juglans regia*)	7–9
Willow, weeping (*Salix alba*)	3–10

17.18 INSTALLATION OF SHRUBS

17.18.1 SHRUBS VERSUS TREES

Shrubs play a major role in the landscape. In terms of nomenclature, it is common for the scientific name of the shrub to be part of the common name of the plant; for example, common camellia is *Camellia japonica* L., glossy abelia is *Abelia x grandiflora*, and forsythia is *Forsythia x intermedia*.

Shrubs are distinguishable from trees in several ways:

1. *Height.* Shrubs are usually low growing (less than 10 feet or 3 meters).
2. *Central axis.* Trees usually have one stem or trunk, and shrubs produce multiple stems from a low crown.
3. *Size.* Overall, shrubs are smaller and (as individuals) require less space than trees.
4. *Branches.* Shrubs branch more profusely than trees, starting low on the stem. Shrubs may be deciduous or evergreen plants. Broadleaf or narrowleaf species, such as oleander and Russian olive, may be grown to be shrubs or trees depending on how they are trained when they are young. Shrubs may also be flowering or nonflowering.

17.18.2 CHOOSING SHRUBS

The factors for consideration described for choosing trees (i.e., climatic adaptation, plant size, characteristics at maturity, maintenance, aesthetics, seasonal appeal, use, and cost) also apply to shrubs.

17.18.3 PURCHASING SHRUBS FOR PLANTING

Just like trees, shrubs may be purchased as bare-root, balled and burlapped, or container-grown seedlings.

17.18.4 PLANTING AND IMMEDIATE CARE

The methods of planting trees are applicable to shrubs. Since shrubs are small in size, staking or anchoring is not necessary; besides, the multiple stems do not have to grow vertically.

TABLE 17–11 Selected Deciduous Shrubs

Plant	Hardiness Zone
Low to medium growing	
Cotoneaster (*Cotoneaster horizontalis*)	5–9
Daphne (*Daphne genkwa*)	5–8
Cinquefoil (*Potentilla fruiticosa*)	2–8
Abelia (*Abelia grandiflora*)	6–8
Flowering almond (*Prunus glandulosa*)	4–8
Butterfly bush (*Buddleia davidii*)	6–9
Barberry (*Barberis thunbergi*)	6–9
High growing	
Arrowwood (*Viburnum dentatum*)	3–7
Cranberry bush (*Viburnum opulus*)	3–8
Lilac, Chinese (*Syringa chinensis*)	5–7
Bottlebrush buckeye (*Aesculus parviflora*)	5–8
Mock orange (*Philadelphus* spp.)	6–9
Winterberry (*Ilex verticillata*)	4–8

17.19 USING SHRUBS IN THE LANDSCAPE

Unlike trees, shrubs are not grown for shade. Structurally, they provide bulk and mass in the landscape. Shrubs may be grouped into three size classes (Table 17–11):

1. Small: less than 3 feet (1 meter)
2. Medium: 3 to 6 feet (1 to 2 meters)
3. Large: 6 to 12 feet (3 to 6 meters)

As with trees, when including shrubs in the landscape, the appropriate size should be selected so that at maturity the plant will not overwhelm the building. Small- and medium-sized shrubs are suited to traditional uses; large species fit best in commercial landscapes.

Shrubs and trees have some common uses. Shrubs and trees are major flowering species that add color to the landscape. Their leaves vary in shape, size, and color, and they also influence the texture of the landscape design. Many shrubs produce attractive fall colors, and fruiting types attract wildlife.

In addition, many shrubs produce fragrant flowers. Other functional uses include hedges, screens, erosion control on slopes, foundation plantings, and background material in the landscape. They are readily massed and pruned to form a contiguous plant wall or hedge. The lower branches and some of the multiple stems may be removed so that one trunk is trained to give the shrub the appearance of a tree.

17.20 SHRUBS, BUSHES, AND VINES WITH ATTRACTIVE FALL COLORS

Selecting plants for the landscape should be made according to the USDA plant hardiness zone classification. There is a wide variety of plants with dazzling fall colors for all the regions. However, there are several with spectacular colors that stand out among the rest. These include:

1. *Burning bush (Euonymus alatus)*—There are several varieties of this species, the 'Rudy Haag' variety being one of the most attractive. This dwarf bush stands

3–5 feet tall and spreads the same length. In spite of its beauty, the plant is actually classified as an invasive species and must be kept in check in the landscape. To optimal color development, the plant must be properly watered and grown in sunny locations.

2. *Sumac (Rhus spp.)*—The name *sumac* conjures up negative images because it has both toxic and nontoxic species. The staghorn sumac (*Rhus typhina*) is a very tall bush, while smooth sumac (*R. glabra*) is shorter, reaching about 10 feet. The fall colors of the varieties include reds, maroon, and gold.

3. *Forthergilla (Fothergilla major)*—This is a white-flowered, sun-loving shrub with a pleasant fragrance, reaching a height of 6–10 feet. Its fall colors include yellow, orange, and scarlet.

4. *Spirea (Spiraea betulifolia)*—The 'Tor' variety of this shrub stands as tall as it is wide, reaching 2–3 feet. It produces white flowers in spring, but in fall its dark green foliage changes color to red.

5. *Black viburnum (Viburnum prunifolium)*—This shrub can attain a height of 12–15 feet, and produces white flowers in spring. In fall, it changes color from purple to reddish-bronze to crimson.

6. *Oakleaf hydrangea (Hydrangea quercifolia)*—These species attains a height of 4–6 feet and about the same spread. It is partially shade-tolerant, bearing white flowers in summer that fade to pinkish-brown in fall, along with foliage that changes color to purple, orange, and red.

7. *Oriental or American bittersweet vines (Celastrus orbiculatus)*—The former is an invasive species. A striking feature of the bittersweet plants is the spectacular morphing over the seasons. In summer, they bear green berries that turn yellow in early fall, as the foliage starts to change color as well. As the fall season advances the yellow husk of the fruit peels back to reveal an orange berry as the foliage turns bright yellow.

8. *Red chokeberry (Aronia arbutifolia)*—This shrub attains a height of 6–10 feet and spreads 3–5 feet. It bears white flowers in early spring that change to red berries in summer. In fall, the berries change to deep purple.

9. *Virginia creeper (Parthenocissus quinquefolia)* —This vine is relatively easy to grow. The caution with this vine is that, once it attaches to the wall, it is difficult to get rid of it. Consequently, unless one wants to have this permanently on the wall, it should not be grown near a building. In fall, its leaves change color from green to red and then burgundy.

10. *Viking black chokeberry (Aronia melanocarpa)*—The 'Viking' variety of this shrub produces white flowers in spring. It reaches a height of about 3–5 feet and about the same spread. In fall, its foliage changes color from red to purple. It produces dark, purplish berries that persist through fall, attracting birds into the landscape.

Other shrubs and vines with great fall foliage and flowers include:

Attractive foliage

1. *Barberry (*Berberis *spp.)*—This shrub is adapted to zones 4–8. They produce red and yellow foliage with berries in fall.

2. *Clethra (Clethra spp.)*—Adapted to zones 3–8, these plants change foliage color to yellow or orange.

3. *Virginia sweetspire (*Itea virginica*)*—It produces red foliage and is adapted to zones 6–9.

4. *Winged euonymus (Euonymus spp.)*—This plant is adapted to zones 3–8 and produces red foliage in fall.

5. *Ornamental grape (*Vitis *spp.)*—This vine is adapted to zones 5–9 and produces burgundy foliage in fall.

Blooming bushes

1. *Blue mist shrub* (Caryopteris *spp.)*—This bush is adapted to zones 6–9 and has beautiful flowers in fall.
2. *Scotch heather* (Calluna vulgaris)—The species thrive best in zones 4–7 and bloom in fall.
3. *Witch hazel* (Hamamelis virginiana)—This fall-blooming shrub is adapted to zones 5–8.

Shrubs with colorful fruits

1. *American cranberry bush (*Viburnum trilobum)—This species is grown in zones 3–7.
2. *David viburnum* (Viburnum davidii)—Adapted to zones 7–9.
3. *Firethorn* (Pyracantha *spp.)*—The shrub is adapted to zones 5–10.
4. *Heavenly bamboo* (Nandina domestica)—The shrub is adapted to zones 7–9.
5. *Linden viburnum* (Viburnum dilatatum)—Adapted to zones 5–8.
6. *Red chokeberry* (Aronia arbutifolia *'Brilliant')*—This shrub is adapted to zones 4–8.

SUMMARY

Trees and shrubs are perennial plants. The largest plants in the landscape, trees may be deciduous or evergreen and broadleaf or narrowleaf. Principles for selecting annual bedding plants apply to selecting trees and shrubs. The critical caution is that once planted, trees remain for a long time in their spots (i.e., until they are cut down or die) and as such should be selected and located with care. Some trees and shrubs flower; they are purchased from the nursery as either bare-root, balled and burlapped, or container-raised plants. After planting, trees may be staked or guyed to hold them upright. Certain trees change color during the fall season and can be strategically located to enhance the landscape during the season. Trees provide shade, and shrubs are common hedge plants.

17.21 BULBS, CORMS, TUBERS, AND RHIZOMES

Plants with underground structures (e.g., bulbs, corms, tubers, and rhizomes) have a wide variety of uses in landscape design. These plants are modified roots, stems, and leaves that have the capacity to store large amounts of water and plant food. Sometimes the term *bulb* is used loosely to include all of the categories of plants described.

Bulbs are used to add color to the landscape. They are very effective when placed in a bed with perennial plants. They are most effective when massed. Bulbs such as tulips have a spectacular array of colors. Flowers of bulbs, as well as plant form and height, vary widely. For example, lilies are tall and should be planted behind short bulbs such as grape hyacinth. Fall-planted bulbs provide landscape color in early spring. Some bulbs are planted in spring (Table 17–12). After the fall crops have withered, summer annuals

TABLE 17–12 Spring-Planted Bulbs

Plant	Scientific Name
Giant allium	*Allium giganteum*
Amaryllis	*Hippeastrum x hybridum*
Peruvian daffodil	*Hymenocallis narcissiflora*
Dutch iris	*Iris hollandica*
Tiger flower	*Tigridia pavonia*

may be planted in the same area as the bulb. Certain species of bulbs such as *Crocus* and *Galanthus* may be planted to **naturalize** in the lawn. In naturalizing, these bulbs are dormant in fall and summer so that the lawn can be enjoyed during that period. In winter and early spring, when the lawn is dormant, these naturalized bulbs flower to keep the space attractive year-round. Species that lend themselves to this treatment include crocus, daffodil, scilla, early narcissus, spring start flowers, and glory-of-the-snow. When a lawn is planted in this way, it should not be mowed until the bulb begins to wither, which may take eight to twelve weeks after peak flowering.

17.21.1 ESTABLISHMENT

Site Selection and Preparation

Bulbs prefer neutral soils that are well drained and loamy. Acidic soils (less than pH 5.9) should be limed. If necessary, the organic matter content of the soil may be increased by adding compost or sphagnum moss. The bed should be well prepared and loose since some bulbs are planted as deep as 10 inches (25.4 centimeters) in the soil. Some form of complete fertilizer (10:10:10) or slow-release bulb fertilizer should be incorporated into the soil during preparation for planting. Because bulbs generally prefer sunny and warm locations, the planting site should experience full sun for at least four hours daily and be protected from strong winds. Beds that face south or west receive adequate exposure to light.

Planting Bulbs

As indicated previously, some bulbs are planted in spring and others in fall. Bulbs differ widely in depth of planting (Figure 17–13). Begonias are planted shallowly (about 1 inch or 2.54 centimeters deep) and daffodils deeply (about 10 inches or 25.4 centimeters deep). It is important that planting depth be uniform in the bed to promote even flowering. Spacing is also variable. Since bulbs have more aesthetic appeal when massed, close planting is desirable. For large bulbs such as daffodils, five bulbs per square foot (0.18 square meter) is adequate; ten to fifteen bulbs per square foot (0.18 square meter) is recommended for small bulbs such as crocus. However, the deeper they are planted, the wider they are spaced. Spacing is also influenced by the garden plan. Bulbs such as daffodils are easy to orient in the soil since they show roots at the bottom. Others, such as dahlia and anemone, do not have clear upward-facing parts. If roots are hard to find, the bulb can be planted sideways. Bulbs can be planted with the aid of a trowel or spade. A *bulb planter* (hand and foot models are available) facilitates the planting activity. It is used to remove plugs of soil from the ground, into which the bulbs are placed and covered up. The recommended depth of planting and spacing are indicated on the packaging. The plot should be watered well after planting.

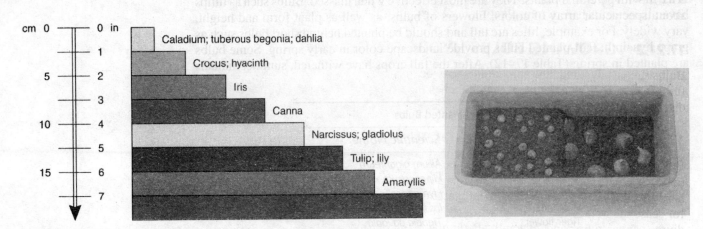

FIGURE 17–13   Planting depth for various plants with underground swollen structures.   *(Source: For (b) © Dorling Kindersley)*

Planting Bulblets and Bulbils

Species such as fritillary, lily, and onion produce underground offspring called *bulblets*. In lily, bulblet formation may be encouraged by removing the flowers and flower buds. Also, certain structures called *bulbils* may form in the leaf axils and be harvested for use in planting. Since these structures are small, they are planted at a depth of about 2 to 3 inches (5.1 to 7.6 centimeters).

Planting Cormels

Cormels are produced by species including freesia and gladiolus. After digging up the corms and cormels at the end of the fall growing season, the cormels are picked off and the top growth of the corm cut off. These parts are treated with a fungicide and stored in a fresh paper bag containing dry vermiculite in a cool place (10°C or 50°F) through the winter. In spring, the corms are planted in the same way as bulbs. The cormels are planted in a nursery (similar to bulblets) and transplanted after about two years.

Planting Scaly Bulbs

Scaly bulbs, such as lilies, have plump leaves or scales that can be picked apart. The outermost ring of overlapping leaves is used for propagation. It is important that each scale have at least some basal tissue for rooting to occur. These loose scales are rinsed in tap water and air dried. After shaking in a plastic bag filled with fungicide, the scales are planted in a flat containing moist sand or vermiculite. The flat is placed in a plastic bag with holes for ventilation, and the setup located in a bright and warm place (21.1°C or 70°F). Rooting occurs in about six weeks. These rooted scales are planted in the same way as bulblets.

Planting Sliced Tunicate Bulbs

Tunicate bulbs are dug up when their top foliage withers in late summer or early fall (for the spring bloomers). The bulbs are split in half and planted in a flat in the same manner as the scales of the scaly bulbs. Rooting occurs within six to eight weeks.

Scoring and Scooping

Scoring and *scooping* are applicable to tunicate bulbs. The object of these techniques is to induce the formation of bulblets. Scoring entails making three half-inch cuts across the basal plate with a sharp knife; in scooping, the basal plate is sliced away. The cut surface is treated with a fungicide, placed on dry vermiculite or sand, and subject to warm conditions (18.3 to 21.1°C or 65 to 70°F) to promote callus formation. Callus is formed in about two weeks, after which the bulbs are incubated in a dark, warm (29.4°C or 85°F), humid place for six to eight weeks. The bulblets formed need to be nursed for about three years before transplanting.

17.21.2 GROWING BULBS HYDROPONICALLY

Bulbs such as hyacinth and some tulips may be propagated by placing the bulb in a vase full of water such that the basal plate touches the water. *Hydroponics* on a large scale is discussed in Chapter 13.

17.21.3 TREATMENT AFTER DORMANCY BEGINS

Bulbs wither and die after flowering. Some species are annual in the sense that they have to be replanted each season. These species are dug up after they wither since they are not hardy and are damaged by cold soil temperature (Table 17–13). Digging and preparation for seasonal storage are initiated when the rest period starts. Tender bulbs include caladium, canna, tulip, and hyacinth. Perennial bulbs include crocus, daffodil, and lily. Perennials are planted for naturalizing and remain in the same area year after year.

TABLE 17–13   Selected Cold-Sensitive Bulbs That Must Be Dug Up after the Season

Plant	Scientific Name
Lily of the Nile	*Agapanthus africanus*
Garden canna, common	*Canna x generalis*
Elephant ear	*Caladium bicolor*
Dahlia, garden	*Dahlia* spp.
Freesia	*Freesia x hybrida*
Gladiolus, garden	*Gladiolus* spp.

Bulbs are dug up using a spading fork or nursery spade. The bulbs should not be injured in the process. Loose soil should be removed immediately after digging; the bulbs are then allowed to dry for a few days so that the remaining soil may be removed easily. It is a good practice to dust the bulbs with appropriate fungicides to reduce spoilage from mold attack.

Bulbs should be separated (offsets broken off from the parent bulb) and the broken surface dried before storage. Bulbs such as *Dahlia, Canna*, and *Caladium* require about two to three days of curing at about 15.6 to 21.1°C (60 to 70°F); others, including *Gladiolus, Freesia*, and *Watsonia*, require two to three weeks of curing to heal the bruised surfaces. If bulbs require long storage, they may be stored, after burying in dry sphagnum moss, at a temperature of about 1.67°C (35°F). Not all bulb species tolerate this treatment.

17.21.4   DISEASES AND INSECT PESTS

Bulbs are attacked by a variety of insect pests and diseases. Observance of good phytosanitation and the use of healthy bulbs for planting reduces the incidence of diseases and pests. Bulb diseases include soft rot, basal rot, blight, nematode, and mosaic. Thrips, mites, and aphids are among the common insect pests of bulbs.

17.21.5   GROWING BULBS INDOORS

Bulbs can be planted in pots. It is possible to treat certain species such that they flower early or outside of their natural conditions. The cold treatment for this purpose is called **forcing.** Spring-blossoming bulbs, that respond well to forcing include daffodil, tulip, hyacinth, and crocus. Bulbs to be forced are planted in a pot with an appropriate potting medium (e.g., 3:1:1 of peat to vermiculite to perlite plus a teaspoonful of 10:10:10 fertilizer or slow-release bulb fertilizer). The bulbs are not completely covered with the medium, but the top parts are slightly exposed. They are watered from below and placed in a cold environment (e.g., cold frame or refrigerator) at about 10°C (50°F) for about nine to twelve weeks, after which the pots are transferred to a cool environment maintained at 15.6°C (60°F). This treatment induces flowering in the bulbs. Different species are treated differently during the forcing process. Various cultivars should not be forced in the same container, since they may bloom at different times.

Forcing can be done in a trench in the ground. The container should have drainage holes. The forcing mix is placed in the container at an appropriate depth after which about 1 inch (2.54 centimeters) of mix is spread on top. A trench is dug about 6 to 12 inches (15.2 to 30.5 centimeters) deep and should be freely draining. After placing the container in the trench, soil is used to fill in the space. The site is then mulched and watered periodically. The bulbs are ready to be dug up when shoots begin to appear. The pots or containers are then placed in a warm place to await flowering.

17.21.6   TUBERS

Tuberous ornamental species include begonia, cyclamen, caladium, and dioescorea. Most tubers do not produce offsets and have to be propagated by other means. A tuber

Forcing
A cultural manipulation used to hasten flowering or plant growth outside their natural season.

may be divided such that each section contains an eye, or bud. The cut surface is dusted with a fungicide such as captan before planting. Some tubers produce tiny tubers that are used for propagating without dividing the tuber. Cyclamen is propagated from seed.

SUMMARY

Certain horticultural plants produce underground structures (e.g., bulbs, tubers, rhizomes, and corms) by which they may be propagated. Bulbs add color to the landscape and are most effective when massed in the pot. Bulbs may be planted indoors in containers. They may be planted as naturalizing plants in lawns to make use of the plot when the grass becomes dormant in winter. Tubers generally do not produce offsets and are propagated by division.

REFERENCES AND SUGGESTED READING

Hartman, H. T., and D. E. Kester. 1983. *Plant propagation: Principles and practices*, 4th ed. Englewood Cliffs, N.J.: Prentice Hall.

Hartman, H. T., A. M. Kofranek, V. E. Rubatzky, and W. L. Flocker. 1988. *Plant science: Growth, development, and utilization of cultivated plants*, 2d ed. Englewood Cliffs, N.J.: Prentice Hall.

Landscape plants
http://classes.hortla.wsu.edu/hort231/

Sunset Magazine and Book Editors. 1985. *Bulbs for all seasons*, 4th ed. Menlo Park, Calif.: Sunset-Lane.

OUTCOMES ASSESSMENT

1. What are bedding plants?
2. Discuss the role of ground covers in the landscape.
3. Distinguish between formal and informal garden designs.
4. Discuss three specific factors to consider in planting tree seedlings in the landscape to enhance their success.
5. List five key factors that affect the selection of landscape trees.
6. Give three shrubs with attractive fall colors in the landscape.
7. What is the purpose of forcing in bulb propagation?
8. Discuss the planting of bulbs in the landscape.

18

Turf Production and Use

PURPOSE AND EXPECTED OUTCOMES

This chapter discusses the principles of establishing and maintaining a lawn. The basic equipment used for planting and caring for a lawn is also presented.

After studying this chapter, the student should be able to

1. Distinguish between the terms *lawn* and *turf*.
2. List three examples each of popular cool- and warm-season turfgrasses.
3. Discuss the guidelines for selecting turfgrass species.
4. Describe how a lawn may be established by seeding, sodding, sprigging, or plugging.
5. List advantages and disadvantages of each method of lawn establishment.
6. Discuss how a lawn mowing schedule is developed and implemented.
7. Describe how pests and diseases are controlled in a lawn.

OVERVIEW

Before starting a discussion on lawns and turfgrasses, it is important to distinguish between the terms *lawn* and *turf*. Ordinarily, grass used in the landscape is referred to by most people as a lawn; grass used on a football field or golf course, however, is referred to as turf. Technically, the definition of *lawn* is a piece of land on which grass grows, including residential, commercial, and recreational areas. The term *turf* is used by horticulturists to refer to grass that is mowed and maintained, which again includes the uses in residential, commercial, and recreational areas (Figure 18–1). A lawn installed as part of a landscape is seeded to *turfgrass* so that it can be mowed and cared for.

Lawns are very important in the landscape for several reasons. For many, the aesthetic value is most readily appreciated, but there are also secondary benefits. A lawn provides a relatively inexpensive ground cover that protects the soil against erosion. While conserving soil, this "natural carpet" also reduces dust on a dry day, mud on a wet day, and heat and glare from the ground on a sunny day. Lawns have recreational use in both residential settings and public places where people gather to relax or play.

FIGURE 18–1 A lawn.
(Source: George Acquaah)

A healthy and beautiful lawn is obtained through good installation and effective management practices. It starts with the proper turfgrass species and is followed by good management practices including mowing, irrigating, fertilizing, and pest control. The culture and management of turfgrasses often impose stress on the growth of individual shoots. However, it is the totality (population) rather than the individuality that counts in turf culture. To begin, turfgrass is cultivated to provide a dense ground cover (a carpet), and thus seeding rate is excessive, resulting in crowding. Turfgrasses are mowed regularly, reducing the photosynthetic surface of the plants. Under limited moisture conditions, there are more shoots per unit area to compete for the available moisture. Careful stress management is, thus, critical to good turfgrass culture.

18.1 PURPOSE OF LAWNS

Turf has three main functions in the landscape—ornamental, sports and recreation, and utility.

18.1.1 ORNAMENTAL

A lawn is often the least one can provide by way of landscaping a home environment. In this capacity, turf has a decorative value and enhances the home or site where it is installed. Turf is found not only in the home landscape but also in public parks and commercial building sites.

18.1.2 SPORTS AND RECREATION

Many sports surfaces, including tennis courts; golf courses; and soccer, football, athletic, and baseball fields, are covered with turf. Horse racing tracks and polo grounds may also be turf covered. Community and home playgrounds use turf to some extent as ground cover.

18.1.3 UTILITY

Bare areas on slopes along roads, ponds, and other construction work sites are prone to soil erosion. To prevent this potential soil loss, turf is used in an ecological role to stabilize the soil.

The ornamental role of turf depends on the visual quality it projects. Visual quality is a function of several factors including texture (fine or coarse), color (pale or rich green), uniformity or evenness in appearance, growth habit, and other characteristics. To be used in sports fields, a turf's functionality depends on its resistance to wear (capacity to rebound after traffic, or its elasticity and resilience). To be used to cover bare grounds, the utility quality of a turf depends on its aggressivity, or colonizing habit. These factors are further discussed in this chapter.

18.2 ESTABLISHING A LAWN

Once established, a lawn can remain indefinitely, provided a sufficient management schedule is adopted. It is therefore important that a good deal of planning go into its establishment.

18.2.1 REGIONAL ADAPTATION OF SPECIES

Grass species should be selected based on regional adaptation, use of the lawn, maintenance level required, and of course aesthetic value. Like other plants, turfgrass species differ in their climatic growth requirements. Some species prefer cooler temperatures and others warmer conditions. Turfgrass species may be divided into two general groups on the basis of climatic adaptations (Figure 18 -2).

FIGURE 18–2 Areas of turf-grass adaptation: 1 and 2 = cool-season grasses, 3 = transitional zone, 4 = warm-season grasses.

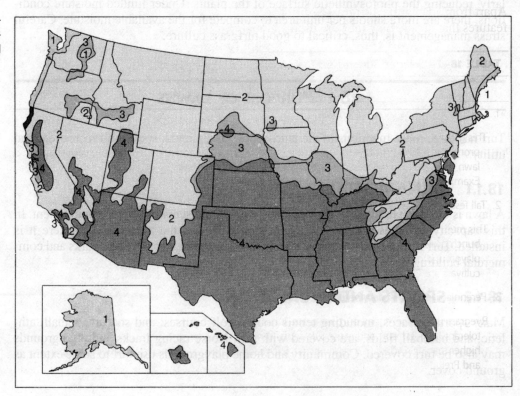

Cool-Season (Temperate) Grasses

In the United States, cool-season grasses are grown in the northern states where the temperature ranges between 15 and 24°C (60 and 75°F) during the growing season. These grasses perform well during the mild temperatures of spring and fall. They may become dormant during the hot temperatures of summer and be killed altogether if extreme heat persists. Active growth of these grasses ceases when the temperature rises above 27 to 29°C (80 to 84°F) in summer. Examples of cool-season grasses are bentgrass, annual ryegrass, bluegrass, red fescue, tall fescue, and perennial ryegrass. Cool-season grasses are intolerant of heavy shade.

Warm-Season (Subtropical) Grasses

Warm-season grasses are grown in the warmer southern areas where the temperature ranges between 27 and 30°C (80 and 86°F). Soil temperature should average about 15.5°C (60°F) for best growth. Warm-season grasses become dormant when cold temperatures arrive and are susceptible to permanent cold injury during seedling establishment. Examples are Bermuda grass, bahiagrass, zoysia, carpetgrass, buffalograss, Saint Augustine grass, grama, and kikuyugrass. To keep a warm-season lawn looking green throughout the winter season, some homeowners overseed their lawns with a cool-season species such as fescue or ryegrass.

Transitional Zone

States located in the region in which these two zones of adaptation meet straddle the two climates and are described as belonging to the *transitional zone*. In this region, cool-season species perform well during the cooler months of the year but cease to grow or are even damaged during the high-temperature periods of summer. Likewise, warm-season species perform poorly under the cold conditions of winter, often turning brown.

18.2.2 CHOOSING TURFGRASS SPECIES

Apart from adaptation, turfgrasses differ according to growth habit and other anatomical features that dictate how they are used and maintained (Table 18–1).

TABLE 18–1 Selected Turfgrasses: Their Adaptation, Characteristics, and Uses

Cool-Season Grasses

1. Colonial bentgrass (*Agrostis tenuis*) — Zone of adaptation: 3–8

   This grass is shallow rooted, aggressive, and pale colored. It is tolerant of light shade. It is drought prone and intolerant of heavy traffic. If mowed more than 1 inch (2.5 centimeters) high, the lawn looks puffy and coarse textured. It is suitable for use as utility turf and decorative lawns. Examples of cultivars are Astoria and Exeter.

2. Tall fescue (*Festuca arundinaceae*) — Zone of adaptation: 2–7

   This multipurpose grass is drought resistant, deep rooted, and robust. It is coarse textured, with a bunch growth habit. It is best grown in pure stands and provides erosion control. It is usable as playground or sports turf and best mowed higher than 1.5 inches (3.8 centimeters). Examples of cultivars are Colchise, Arid, Bonanza, Mustang, and Olympic.

3. Perennial ryegrass (*Lolium perenne*) — Zone of adaptation: 3–7

   Ryegrass is an excellent all-purpose grass. It has good texture and color similar to bluegrass. It is tolerant of high traffic and is used as sports turf or in utility or decorative lawns. It is best mowed higher than 1.5 inches (3.8 centimeters). Examples of cultivars are Derby, Sunrise, Tara, Citation II, and Prelude.

TABLE 18–1   Selected Turfgrasses: Their Adaptation, Characteristics, and Uses *(continued)*

4. Kentucky bluegrass *(Poa pratensis)*   Zone of adaptation: 4–7

This grass makes one of the most beautiful lawns. It is fine textured and has perhaps the best lawn color but is susceptible to diseases. The grass is used for sports turf and decorative lawns. It is best to mow above 1.5 inches (3.8 centimeters) (e.g., 2.5 inches [6.4 centimeters]). Examples of cultivars are Touchdown, Adelphi, Baron, and Pennstar.

5. Annual ryegrass *(Lolium multiflorum)*   Zone of adaptation: 3–7

This grass is short-lived (dies after one season) and is used commonly to overseed a lawn during the winter in the South. It is winter hardy and quite disease tolerant. Mowing height may be about 2 inches (5.1 centimeters). Examples of cultivars are Gulf and Tifton 1.

Warm-Season Grasses

1. Bermuda grass *(Cynodon dactylon)*   Zone of adaptation: 7–9

Bermuda grass is a dense-growing, vigorous grass. It propagates by rhizomes and stolons. It is drought and salt tolerant but turns brown in winter. If desired, it may be overseeded in winter for color in the landscape. Bermuda grass builds up thatch rapidly and requires frequent dethatching. It is best when mowed low (1/4 to 1 inch [0.6 to 2.5 centimeters]). It is a multipurpose grass that is used as a decorative lawn or on sports fields. It makes good turf grass for putting on the golf course. Examples of cultivars are Texturf 10, Cheyenne, Tifway, and Common.

2. Centipedegrass *(Eremochloa ophiouroides)*   Zone of adaptation: 7–9

Like Bermuda grass, centipedegrass is dense growing and vigorous. It is a relatively low-maintenance grass that can perform well on marginal soils. It is also a heavy thatch builder. It can be used for a decorative or utility lawn and responds to low mowing (1 inch [2.5 centimeters]). Examples of cultivars are Centennial, Centiseed, and Oaklawn.

3. Bahia grass *(Pasalum notatum)*   Zone of adaptation: 3–9

This grass is very difficult to mow and produces a coarse, low-quality turf. Because of its coarse, open growth pattern, it is readily invaded by weeds. Bahiagrass may be used for decorative and utility lawns, and is good for erosion control. It is best mowed high (2 to 2.5 inches [5.1 to 6.4 centimeters]). Examples of cultivars are Paraguay, Saurae, Argentine, and Pensacola.

4. Saint Augustine grass *(Stenotaphrum secondatum)*   Zone of adaptation: 6–9

This grass has a dense, vigorous, and coarse growth habit and propagates by stolons. It is adapted to shade but is disease prone. When used as a decorative or utility lawn, it should be mowed high (2 to 2.5 inches [5.1 to 6.4 centimeters]). Examples of cultivars are Servile, Sunclipse, Bitter blue, and Floratam.

5. Buffalo grass *(Buchloe dactyloides)*   Zone of adaptation: 3–9

This a slow-growing and fine-textured grass adapted to dry and hot areas. It is clump-forming and needs little fertilization and moisture. It can be used for decorative lawns and for erosion control. Mowing height is between 1.5 and 2 inches (3.8 and 5.1 centimeters). Examples of cultivars are Bison and Prairier.

6. Zoysia *(Zoysia japonica)*   Zone of adaptation: 6–9

This tough, very dense-growing grass has good color and fine texture. It is vegetatively propagated by stolons or rhizomes. It is good for erosion control but can be used for a decorative or utility lawn. Examples of cultivars are Emerald, Meyer, and Midwest.

Growth Habit

Turfgrasses are the most durable ground covers. The base of the grass is critical to its survival and should be well protected from damage. Each grass blade grows upward from the base (not the tip). In terms of growth habits, grass may be described as *bunching* or *creeping* (Figure 18–3). Bunching grasses grow upright in clumps. They spread by means of new growth called tillers, which arise from the crown. Grasses adapted to cool climates such as fescue and ryegrass have bunching habits. Creeping grasses spread far by means of modified stems, which could be stolons or rhizomes. Examples of creeping grasses are those adapted to warm climates such as Bermuda grass and kikuyugrass.

Texture

Grasses differ in texture, some being fine, with narrow blades, as in bluegrass, Bermuda grass, or zoysia, or coarse, as in Saint Augustine grass, Bahia grass, and tall fescue. Fine-textured grasses such as bentgrass are used on golf courses in the cool-season zones of the northern United States. Likewise, fine-textured bluegrass is used on golf course fairways in these areas. These grasses also make excellent lawns. Bluegrasses are the most commonly used cool-season grasses. In the South, fine-textured Bermuda grass is the most commonly used grass. It is found on golf fairways and greens as well as lawns. Coarse-textured Bahia grass is used on playgrounds and along roads.

Competitiveness

Turfgrass species differ in aggressiveness. Some species are described as colonizing species because they are aggressive and quickly take over the area where they are introduced. For example, in the cool-season zone, bentgrass in a bluegrass lawn poses a major problem because the former is very competitive. The conditions under which grasses are grown affect their competitive abilities. When bluegrass occurs in a mixture that is planted in full sun, the bluegrass will soon become the dominant species. Similarly, when fine fescues are mixed with bluegrasses under full sun conditions, the fescues tend to be disadvantaged. However, under less favorable growing conditions (like shade), the fescues are superior to bluegrasses. Bermuda grass is a good competitor provided it is grown in full sun. The stolons of zoysia have been known to be so aggressive that they grow under edging material (border-control materials) to invade adjacent plots.

Resistance to Wear

Grasses differ in degree of resistance to wear. Saint Augustine grass is intolerant of heavy use. On the other hand, tall fescue is rugged and very tolerant of traffic, making it a popular choice for playgrounds, athletic fields, and areas where pedestrian use is heavy. In the warm-season zone, Bahia grass is used on playgrounds and along roads. Similarly, Bermuda grass is a high-wear grass.

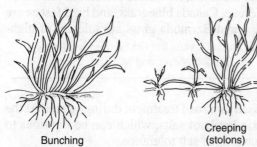 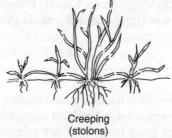 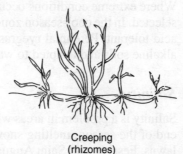

Bunching   Creeping (stolons)   Creeping (rhizomes)

FIGURE 18–3 Types of growth habit of grasses: bunching or creeping.

Maintenance

Once established, turfgrasses differ in their requirements for care to remain attractive. In this regard, certain species are low maintenance and others high maintenance. Bentgrasses (colonial and creeping) produce a thick, matlike growth and must be dethatched (removal of thatch or dead grass accumulation) on a regular basis. When warm temperatures occur, bentgrasses are prone to disease attack. A lawn of bentgrasses should be mowed low (3/4 to 1 inch [1.9 to 2.5 centimeters]) and frequently to maintain a good appearance. Because of their high maintenance requirements, bentgrasses are best planted as a pure stand rather than in mixtures. Bluegrasses are also high-maintenance species that require frequent mowing. They vary in susceptibility to diseases and adaptation and thus are best established as mixtures (of different cultivars) or blends (of different species). Tall fescue is resistant to drought and most turfgrass diseases and insect pests. It is low maintenance and prefers to be mowed high (2 to 3 inches).

High-maintenance, warm-season grasses include Bahia grass and Bermuda grass. They are susceptible to diseases and insect pests and require frequent mowing to maintain a good appearance. Bermuda grass should be fertilized frequently for good growth. It responds well to low mowing (3/4 to 1 inch high). Zoysia is also high maintenance and susceptible to diseases and insect pests. Centipedegrass is a relatively low-maintenance turfgrass that responds well to good fertilization.

18.2.3 CHOOSING GRASS FOR CHALLENGING SITES

Most turfgrasses prefer bright and sunny sites and are generally intolerant of shade. Lawn sites should be well drained and of good fertility. When lawns are established in less-than-ideal locations, they grow poorly and less uniformly. However, with planning, correct choices, and good care, it is possible to establish a fairly good lawn in these challenging areas. Some of these challenging locations are discussed in the following sections.

Drought Prone

Water is a critical factor in lawn maintenance. In dry areas, homeowners may have to water their lawns twice daily on some days to create a healthy and lush lawn. Bermuda grass or buffalo grass may be selected for drought-prone, hot-summer areas. For similar conditions in temperate zones, wheatgrass or tall fescue may be chosen.

Shade

Maintaining a lawn under trees is a challenge. Lighting under such a condition is filtered and diffuse. Grasses (and, for that matter, other plants) grow spindly and weak under reduced light. Shade-tolerant grasses include Pennlawn red fescue and chewing fescue in the cool-season zone. For warm-season zones in the South, Saint Augustine grass is a good choice.

Extreme Soil Reaction

Proper soil acidity or alkalinity is required to make soil nutrients available at safe levels. Where extreme conditions occur, species that are tolerant of those conditions should be selected. In the cool-season zone, chewing fescue, Canada bluegrass, and hard fescue are acid tolerant. Perennial ryegrass, wheatgrass, and Bermuda grass are tolerant of high-alkaline soils and adapted to warm regions.

Salinity

Salinity is a problem in areas where salt is used as a road treatment during winter. At the end of the season, melting snow carries toxic levels of salts, which can be injurious to lawns. Fescues and Saint Augustine grass have some salt tolerance.

Heavy Use

Lawns on playgrounds and sports fields come under intense traffic and rough use and should be able to withstand considerable wear and tear. In cool-season areas, tall fescue and perennial ryegrass may be used; zoysia, Bermuda grass, and Bahia grass may be used in warm regions of the South.

18.3 PLANTING TURFGRASS

Several methods are used for establishing new lawns, each with advantages and disadvantages. The most common methods are the use of *seed* and *sod;* others are *plugging* and *sprigging* (or *stolonizing*). These methods differ in cost and how quickly a lawn can be started.

18.3.1 SOIL PREPARATION

Preparing the soil at the site where the lawn will be installed is the first major undertaking; it involves several activities including clearing of debris, grading, providing good drainage, amending soil fertility, providing a good seedbed, and controlling weeds. As previously indicated, the primary objective of a builder is first to ensure the structural integrity of the building. Therefore, loose topsoil is moved for the foundation of the building to be established. Incidentally, the topsoil is the medium in which plants grow. If efforts are not made to return it, successful plant cultivation will be difficult without soil amendments. The topsoil moved is usually replaced such that water will drain away from the foundation. The area left for landscaping should be cleared of all rocks and large plant debris. Topsoil should be redistributed and graded to no more than a 15 percent slope. This degree of slope provides good drainage without severe consequences of erosion. It also ensures the safety of operators during mechanical mowing. Some soils may require additional provision for effective drainage, such as the installation of drainage tiles. It may be necessary in some cases to haul in additional topsoil so that the depth of topsoil is at least 6 inches (15.2 centimeters).

A soil test is always recommended before using a piece of land for cultivation. It is easier to establish a lawn on good soil than to amend the soil when the lawn is well established. Soil pH, which should be about 6.5, can be corrected for acidity by applying lime to raise it or sulfur to lower it. Sulfur should be added to a lawn with caution. Approximately 10 pounds (4.5 kilograms) of garden lime per 100 square feet (9 square meters) is required to raise soil pH by one unit. Soil fertility may be boosted by applying a starter amount of fertilizer. To improve its organic matter content, organic amendments such as peat or other wastes may be incorporated into the topsoil. *Starter fertilizers* for lawns with high phosphorus content may be used. Fertilizers should be spread as evenly as possible.

For seeding, it is important that the bed has very fine tilth for the tiny grass seeds to germinate properly. A rake is useful not only for removing clods and large debris for a fine tilth but also for incorporating starter fertilizer. If subsurface drainage tiles and underground irrigation systems are to be installed, they should be in place before the final seedbed preparation.

18.3.2 SEED SELECTION

As previously discussed, choosing turfgrass species depends on several factors—adaptation, aesthetics, maintenance level, cost, competitiveness, and resistance to wear. In addition, the planting material can be obtained in several forms, based on genetic and physical constitution. These qualities depend on the source (supplier) of the seed.

Seed Constitution

Blend
Seed consisting of a mixture of two or more cultivars of the same grass species.

When seeding a bare soil, it is important that the cultivar be aggressive (a colonizing species) so that it will be quickly established before weed species emerge. Another consideration in choosing a seed for planting is the genetic purity of the seed. Seeds are sold as *straight* (or *pure*), consisting of only one species or cultivar, or as a **blend** (consisting of a mixture of two or more cultivars of the same grass species).

Seeds may also be sold as a *mixture* of two or more species. When a mixture is chosen as planting material, it should contain at least 60 percent of the *permanent species* desired and other species of similar characteristics. That is, if Bermuda grass is the permanent species, 60 percent of the mixture does not have to be only Bermuda grass but could also include species such as fescue that have similar characteristics. Sometimes, to obtain a quick cover of the ground, a seed mixture containing a species such as ryegrass that establishes rapidly may be used. The ryegrass is the *temporary species* and thus the area must be *overseeded* with the desired permanent mixture at a later date. Some cultivars are clones and hence genetically pure. Clonal cultivars are common for species such as Kentucky bluegrass because of the phenomenon of *apomixis* (the production of seed without fertilization). Such genetically uniform cultivars have a disadvantage in that the entire lawn responds similarly to any adverse environmental factors (e.g., disease) and can be completely destroyed by a single attack. This uniform susceptibility is why bluegrass seed is commonly sold as a blend of several cultivars (e.g., 'America,' 'Manhattan,' and 'Princeton'). Blends are formulated for a variety of growing conditions (e.g., shade or marginal soil) and available for species besides bluegrass. The rationale for constituting a good permanent mixture is to include a species for beauty (e.g., 50 percent consisting of bluegrass); a species for toughness, and disease and pest resistance (e.g., 25 percent consisting of fescue), and a species for quick establishment and durability (e.g., 25 percent consisting of perennial ryegrass). Examples of good mixtures are as follows:

1. Kentucky bluegrass and red fescue (for dry, shady, and marginal soils)
2. Kentucky bluegrass and ryegrass
3. Kentucky bluegrass, fescue, and ryegrass

Pure seed may be used for establishing Bermuda grass or carpetgrass. If a mixture contains bentgrass, it must be cared for properly to prevent this grass from becoming a weed in the lawn.

Since several species are adapted to a single region, the choice of one species or cultivar over another is influenced by other properties of the species, such as tolerance to drought, shade, cold, and diseases prevalent in the region; tolerable mowing height; and appearance. Some species are low maintenance, and others require more than the regular care needed for a good lawn.

Source

Seed should always be purchased from a reputable source, and certified seed is preferred. It is worth the investment to pay a little more for quality seed than to use bargain seed. The seed industry has an obligation to declare certain facts to the customer. This information may differ from place to place but generally includes the following:

1. Company name and address
2. Cultivar name
3. Percent germination
4. Date of testing
5. Purity (proportion of usable grass seed)
6. Nongrass seed
7. Inert material (rocks and other debris)
8. The seed lot number may be included

The seed should be free from weeds (especially noxious ones) as much as possible and have a high germination percentage (at least 80 percent). If the germination percentage is low, the seeding rate should be increased. Whenever possible, freshly harvested seed should be purchased.

Time to Sow

The best time to sow grass seed differs from one region to another and is chosen strategically to benefit from the weed cycle and adverse weather. Timely sowing ensures grass establishment before weed seeds germinate or cold weather sets in. In the cool-season zone, the best time to sow temperate grasses is late summer or early fall, which allows the lawn to be established before freezing temperatures set in. Furthermore, when grasses are sown in fall, the need to irrigate is reduced because of cooler temperatures and less evaporation. In the warm-season zone of the South, a good strategy is to sow in early summer after clearing away the weeds. Sometimes delays in construction projects may not allow the timely sowing of seeds. The result is poor seed germination and thus poor lawn establishment.

Seeding Rate

Grass seeds are very tiny. Species such as bentgrass may have more than 10 million seeds per kilogram (4.8 million seeds per pound). The objective of seeding is to obtain a quick establishment and produce a dense lawn resembling a carpet. However, overseeding leads to overcrowding and additional stress to plants, which consequently grow poorly and delay the attainment of a quality lawn. Similarly, low plant populations delay the covering of the ground, allowing weeds to infect the lawn. Sowing at the rate of 1 pound per 1,000 square feet (0.45 kilograms per 90 square meters) will suffice for most grasses that are sown in due season. Tall fescue and perennial ryegrass require much higher rates of between 3 and 6 pounds per 1,000 square feet (1.35 and 2.7 kilograms per 90 square meters). Seed companies indicate the recommended seeding rates on package labels.

Seeding

Small plots may be effectively seeded by hand, even though this method has the disadvantage of uneven spreading. Mechanical seeders, which should be used for large areas, distribute seed by one of three ways—drill, gravity feed, or broadcast. If a narrow strip is to be seeded, using a drill may be most appropriate. However, drilling places seeds in narrow strips, leaving wide bare spaces between them. Because ground covering is slow, weed control is required during the establishment of a lawn. Gravity feeders may be manually pushed or tractor operated. Similarly, broadcast spreaders may be portable or tractor mounted. For very large areas, helicopters may be used to broadcast the seed. To reach steep slopes, hydroseeding or hydromulching may be used. When one of these methods is used, frequent watering is needed during lawn establishment. To increase the seeding efficiency for uniform coverage, the recommended seeding rate may be divided into two so that one-half is distributed in one direction on the first pass and the other spread crosswise on the next pass (Figure 18–4). Mixing grass seed with sand in a mechanical spreader has been found to aid in the even spreading of seed. Since grass seeds are so fine and lightweight, sowing on windy days should be avoided. Furthermore, because they are so tiny, grass seeds should not be seeded too deeply in the soil (less than 1 centimeter or 0.4 inch). Proper depth of planting is accomplished by lightly raking the area after sowing.

Mulching and Firming

Mulching a freshly sown lawn has several purposes:

1. To protect grass seeds from predators (birds)
2. To prevent seeds from washing away during irrigation
3. To conserve moisture for germination
4. To control erosion of soil

FIGURE 18–4 Seeding of a lawn by the crosswise method.

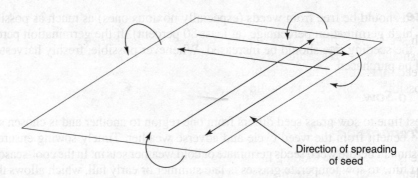

Direction of spreading of seed

The mulch used should be spread thinly so that emerging seedlings are not impeded. Straw mulches are commonly used, although other coarse plant materials are also appropriate. To aid in germination, the mulched area is firmed by rolling over it with a lightweight roller. Rolling firms the soil for seeds to effectively imbibe moisture while also anchoring them in the soil.

Watering and Fertilizing

Keeping the newly seeded lawn moist during seed establishment is vital. After the first watering, frequent irrigation (about two times daily) should be provided until germination and seedling establishment is attained. A brief drought spell during the germination period can wipe out an entire lawn. Excessive moisture predisposes the plants to disease, especially damping-off caused by a number of fungi. For most species, germination starts within about a week of planting and continues for another week. Slow-germinating species such as bluegrass may have an extended germination period of several weeks; the frequent watering schedule thus lasts a little longer in such species. The frequency of watering is reduced gradually after germination is completed, but supplemental nitrogen may be required soon after that. An application of nitrogen at the rate of about 0.5 pounds per 1,000 square feet (0.23 kilograms per 90 square meters) will maintain seedling vigor.

Advantages and Disadvantages of Seeding

Seeds are less expensive and less bulky than sod. Plots can be seeded easily by the owner. However, seeds establish rather slowly.

18.4 PLANTING GRASS BY VEGETATIVE METHODS

Grass may be established in the landscape by vegetative methods, the most common including sodding, plugging, sprigging, and stolonizing.

18.4.1 SODDING

Sod
A shallow (1–3 inches) strip of topsoil that is bound by grass roots and usually harvested and sold in narrow strips.

Sodding is the establishment of a lawn by using **sod**. Sod is grass that is specially cultivated, mowed, and cut into strips (1 to 2 × 4 to 6 feet) like pieces of carpet, including about 1 to 2 inches (2.5 to 5.1 centimeters) of roots. Long strips are rolled, and short ones are sold flat. These strips are stacked on pallets and transported to the site where the lawn is to be established. Establishing a lawn in this way provides an instant ground cover. Sodding may be likened to *transplanting* of seedlings, except that it involves a large mass of seedlings. Sodding involves activities similar to those of seeding. Although it is the most expensive means of establishing grass, sodding produces the most rapid results and is the least problematic.

Source of Sod

As with seed, sod suppliers differ in the quality of product they sell. Certified sod producers should be used as suppliers of the planting material, since poor-quality sod has a high weed infestation. The best cultivar adapted to the region should be selected. Whenever possible, freshly cut sod should be used in lawn establishment.

Soil Preparation

The site is prepared for sodding in the same fashion as for direct seeding. Erosion is not a problem, which allows steep slopes to be planted, as long as the lawn is not intended to be mowed, especially by a tractor. The soil surface should provide a loose medium in which roots from the sod may be established. The soil bordering walkways should be piled up to a lower depth so as to accommodate the thickness of the sod. The seedbed should be moistened before laying rolls of sod. To achieve a good level of moisture, the plot may be irrigated several days before the planting date.

Installation

Soil fertility may be boosted by a starter application of nitrogen and phosphorus. Sod laid in fall or spring establishes more quickly than that laid in summer or winter. However, sod of subtropical grasses establish well in summer. It is important to lay sod as soon as possible after harvesting, which means that the sod should be delivered after the ground has been prepared. If sod is left to sit in a stack, it will rapidly deteriorate because heat builds up in the pile. In case of an unexpected delay, the edges of the stack should be sprinkled lightly with water to prevent drying. High-quality sod should be free of weeds. Similarly, the ground should be well prepared and weed free. To suppress weeds, sod should be tightly laid, edge to edge, without gaps between adjacent strips or between rolls and structures such as concrete walkways against which they are laid (Figure 18–5). It is best to lay the rolls in a staggered, checkerboard pattern. A sharp knife should be kept handy to cut smaller strips to fit challenging areas. Staggering of sod strips prevents the formation of noticeable lines in the lawn, especially in the early stages after establishment. If narrow strips of bare soil remain after laying a full piece, it is better to cut a small strip to complete the job than to stretch a larger piece. If sod is stretched, the edges will shrink later to expose gaps between the pieces for weeds to grow through. As in direct seeding, newly laid sod should be rolled over with a roller to ensure good contact between roots and soil (Figure 18–6).

FIGURE 18–5   Laying sod.   *(Source: For (b) Peter Anderson © Dorling Kindersley)*

FIGURE 18–6 Rolling newly laid sod.

Immediate Care

The first thing to do after laying sod is to water it thoroughly to wet the topsoil for root establishment. Thinly cut sod tends to dry more quickly than thick sod but also establishes more quickly. Even though freshly laid sod gives the appearance of an established lawn, all heavy traffic should be kept off of the lawn until it has rooted. Because of the thick soil cover sod produces, the soil does not dry up quickly. However, the area should be watered frequently during the first several weeks to ensure proper establishment.

Fertilizing

Applying small amounts of lawn fertilizer after the sod has rooted is helpful for good establishment.

Advantages and Disadvantages

The major advantages to using sod are that it provides instant cover (instant lawn), promotes a high-quality lawn, is good for a quick fix of high-traffic areas of already-established lawns, and is easy to lay.

The disadvantages of using sod include that it is bulky to handle, expensive, and once purchased must be laid without delay.

18.4.2 PLUGGING

Plugging
A method of lawn establishment involving the use of small pieces of sod.

Plugging is a method of lawn establishment that involves the transplanting of small pieces of sod plugs into holes in the seedbed (Figure 18–7). The holes are spaced about 6 to 12 inches (15.2 to 30.5 centimeters) apart, depending on how the species spreads. Zoysia spreads more slowly than Bermuda grass and Saint Augustine grass and should be spaced much closer (6 inches). Plugging is a labor-intensive operation and takes time to cover the plot with grass; fortunately, it can be done mechanically. After the operation, the plot may be rolled or firmed to provide good soil contact with plant roots. This method of planting sod is sometimes called *spot sodding*. Timing is critical to the success of plugging. Warm-season turfgrasses must be planted about two or more months before the first frost of fall for good establishment.

18.4.3 SPRIGGING

Pieces of short stems or runners (called *sprigs*) may also be used to establish a lawn. This method of lawn establishment, called *sprigging*, is accomplished by placing the sprigs in shallow (1 to 2 inches or 2.5 to 5.1 centimeters) furrows at about 4- to 6-inch (10.2- to 15.2-centimeter) spacing. The sprigs are covered such that at least one-fourth of the material is above ground. Again, it is important to allow about two months before the onset of adverse weather (e.g., frost) for establishment.

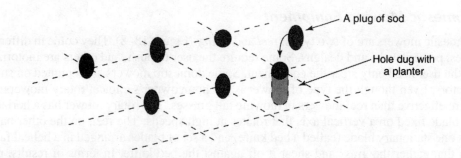

FIGURE 18–7 Plugging method of lawn establishment.

A plug of sod

Hole dug with a planter

18.4.4 STOLONIZING

Stolonizing is a form of sprigging in which the recommended number of sprigs are spread uniformly over the seedbed. Stolonizing is sometimes called *broadcast sprigging*. After spreading, the sprigs are partially covered with soil by disking or rolling. This method is usually adopted for planting large areas.

18.5 TURF MANAGEMENT

The grass should be allowed to be well established and grow to a height of about 1 or 2 inches (2.5 or 5.1 centimeters) above the mowing height for the period or season and species before the first mowing. It is important that watering be suspended for the topsoil to dry slightly before mowing.

Once established, a lawn should be maintained according to a schedule that promotes healthy growth of the grass while serving the purpose or purposes for which it was established. In putting together a management program, factors to be considered include the type of grass, climatic zone, use of turf, equipment, and owner's level of commitment to maintenance. For example, more frequent watering may be required in areas that are prone to drought; the cultivar or composition of the lawn material affects the height of mowing and response to fertilizer and watering. High-traffic areas such as playgrounds are maintained differently from lawns established primarily for aesthetic purposes. Some homeowners are willing to put in time and effort (or pay for such) to have the "best lawn on the block"; others just want to have grass growing around the house.

Whatever the management practice, it should include certain basic maintenance activities: mowing, watering, fertilizing, weed control, and disease and pest control. If diligently pursued, these practices will result in a healthy and attractive lawn. It should be stressed that a good lawn does not come naturally. The homeowner has to invest in some kind of regular maintenance schedule. Such maintenance should start after installation and be sustained thereafter. A variety of aggressive grasses and plant species can invade even the very best lawn if the maintenance schedule is irregular. Just as neglect can lead to disastrous consequences, overmanagement is equally undesirable and largely wasteful. As stated earlier in this chapter, with good management, a lawn can remain indefinitely once installed.

Turf culture essentially entails the management of stress in grasses for healthy growth and development. First, an unusually high number of plants are maintained per unit area, creating a situation in which competition occurs for plant growth requirements. Second, the photosynthetic area required for food manufacture is drastically reduced periodically. Good growth and development are therefore critical in turf management and are attained through three primary practices: *mowing, watering*, and *fertilizing*.

18.5.1 MOWING

A homeowner may not remember or care to provide supplemental irrigation and fertility to the lawn, but an unkept lawn may invite problems with neighbors. Mowing a lawn is the least that can be done, and even this is often a chore for many. To be effective, mowing should be done with the proper equipment, at the right frequency, and to the proper height.

Domestic Mowing Equipment

Domestic mowers are of two types: *reel* and *rotary* (Figure 18–8). They come in different sizes, power levels, and designs. Some require the user to push, and others are motorized so the user need only steer the equipment. Some domestic mowers are mounted on small tractors. Even though the type of mower is the homeowner's choice, rotary mowers are more effective than reel mowers in mowing tall grasses. The rotary mower has a horizontal blade fixed on a vertical axis that rotates at high speeds. The reel, on the other hand, has one stationary blade (called a bed knife) and a set of blades arranged in a helical fashion that gather the grass and shear it off against the bed knife. In terms of results, reel mowers produce the best mowing finish. They are excellent for use around homes, resorts, and other areas where noise is a problem. They are also used to mow golf course fairways.

Some mowers are designed to not only cut the grass but also to reduce it to mulch. These implements are called *mulching mowers*. Dual-type mowers allow owners to change the mowing type from regular to mulching. A good mower should have sharp blades because dull blades produce a rough cut and bruise the leaves, which may discolor at the tips and not recover quickly from mowing. Sharp blades are more critical in the case of rotary mowers, which cut by impact and even under the best conditions are likely to produce ragged cuts. A maintenance schedule for mowers should include changing or sharpening the blades as needed. Operator care is also critical in the use of rotary mowers because of the high energy required by the rotating axle to move the blades.

Commercial Mowers

When the lawn to be mowed is expansive and a fine finish is not the goal (such as mowing roadsides), a *flail mower* is used (Figure 18–9). It has the capacity to mulch and mow tall grasses and weeds. Such commercial mowers are designed to have broad coverage with each pass of the equipment. The *sickle bar mower* is used where the clippings are going to be collected, because it does not mulch but arranges the cut leaves such that they can be readily collected.

Mowing Frequency

Since mowing has physiological implications, it must be done judiciously. The rule of thumb, if one exists, is that at any mowing time, no more than 30 percent of the leaf should be removed. If the lawn is left to grow too tall, it will be necessary to cut more than 50 percent of the leaf in some cases, thus drastically offsetting the photosynthetic machinery and limiting translocation of food to the roots for proper growth. Based on the grass variety and season, it is desirable to establish a height and adopt a mowing schedule to maintain it. In this

FIGURE 18–8 A rotary mower. The bag may be removed to convert it into a mulching mower. *(Source: George Acquaah)*

FIGURE 18–9 A flail mower. *(Source: George Acquaah)*

way, plants are able to adapt to the routine and not experience shock. When plants do not have an adequate leaf surface to support the photosynthetic requirements, they grow pale or yellowish until new growth occurs. To maintain an attractive lawn, the kind that is the envy of the neighborhood, a mowing frequency of once a week should be maintained. When the lawn overgrows, it encourages the growth of tall weed species.

Mowing Height

Mowing height depends largely on the species and the culture and varies from 1/2 to 4 inches (1.3 to 10.2 centimeters). Bentgrass should be mowed low. A low cut gives a lawn a carpetlike appearance, but, unfortunately, not all turf species are amenable to cuts of less than 1 inch (2.5 centimeters) in height. The opposite of a carpet appearance is puffiness, which occurs when grasses such as fescue and bluegrass are mowed higher than 3 inches (7.6 centimeters). Under such conditions, the grass becomes more open and exposes more of its stems. It is not uncommon to see two adjacent and well-kept lawns mowed at different heights, which happens when two neighbors have different preferences, one for a low cut and the other for a high cut. Low mowing should be accompanied by other maintenance activities such as effective weed control to suppress weeds since the lawn is unable to suppress weeds through shading.

Clippings and Thatch

In a mowing activity, the operator, depending on the type and design of the equipment, may choose between allowing the fresh clippings to fall on the ground or collecting (bagging) and discarding them. Mulching mowers are designed to cut the clippings into small pieces so they do not lie on the lawn but fall to the ground. Clippings on the ground eventually decompose to improve soil fertility. The undecomposed plant organic material (**thatch**) can build up over a period. This buildup of thatch is attributed more to other lawn maintenance activities such as watering and fertilizing than to clippings per se. If a good mowing schedule is adopted, the clippings from each mowing will be small and fall to the ground without problem. However, in overgrown lawns, mowing leaves behind visible clumps of clippings that are not only unsightly but also detrimental to the growth of the grass by reducing the photosynthetic surface and producing disease-causing conditions. On such occasions, bagging of clippings is not only desirable but necessary. Some mowers are fitted with containers for bagging the clippings. Bagging clippings is additional work that many homeowners would rather not add to the chore of mowing. When thatch buildup becomes excessive, it must be reduced, in part because insects and other pests thrive in thatch.

Thatch
Accumulated undecomposed organic material between the turf and soil surface.

Edging

Edging is a cosmetic activity in which the edge of a lawn, especially next to a walkway or driveway, is trimmed in a straight line or smooth fashion. Edging machines may be purchased separately for this purpose (Figure 18–10). However, a combination trimmer-edger may also be purchased for tidying up a lawn near walls and in places that are too hard to reach with a mower. Gas-powered and electric trimmers and mechanical edgers are available.

Mowing Tips

For best mowing results, an operator should observe certain guidelines including the following.

1. Grass should not be mowed when it is wet. The mower performs more efficiently on dry grass. Wet lawn mowing leads to soil compaction, and the mower may clog up frequently and require interruptions in the mowing operation to clean the system. These problems extend the time required for mowing. Further, wet grass does not fall to the ground but forms clumps.

FIGURE **18–10** An edger.
(*Source: George Acquaah*)

2. A mowing pattern should be developed. Mowing the area in one direction one time and at right angles the next time reduces compaction of the soil.
3. A mower with sharp blades should be used at each mowing.
4. An overgrown lawn should be mowed at least two times over. The first time, the mower should be set to mow to a higher height to avoid clogging the machine. It may be wise to bag at least the first round of clippings.
5. Each pass should slightly overlap the previous one to ensure 100 percent coverage of the lawn.
6. When mowing a rough lawn with debris and rocks, it is best to remove these objects before beginning and also to wear goggles.
7. A large lawn may be mowed in a spiral pattern. This method eliminates backtracking and stops, as well as direction changes. The recommended practice is to mow clockwise in the first instance and counterclockwise the second time.

18.5.2 WATERING

Watering is another seasonal chore that many homeowners in areas experiencing seasonal drought feel obligated to perform. Where the drought spell is protracted and occurs regularly, some homeowners invest in permanent automatic irrigation systems, which are discussed in detail in Chapter 4. Pipes are buried during the ground preparation for the installation of the lawn. Pop-up sprinklers, which are located at strategic spots on the lawn below the mowing height, pop up when irrigation is needed. Lawns can also be watered with lawn sprinklers that oscillate. Such units are fed by water hoses connected to the outside taps of homes.

Irrigation, unlike mowing, is not done according to a set schedule but is provided only when needed. The rule of thumb is to water heavily and infrequently. The lawn needs watering just before wilting sets in. Watering should be thorough so as to wet at least the top 4 inches (10.2 centimeters) of soil where most grass roots are found. It is important that watering be thorough since light sprinkling or partial wetting encourages roots to grow up (not down) the soil surface in search of water, thereby making plants more susceptible to drought.

At each watering time, at least 1 inch (2.5 centimeters) of water should be supplied. It takes about thirty minutes to soak to 1-inch depth in sandy soil, two hours for loam, and about three and one-half hours for clay loam soil. A homemade rain gauge in the form of a can placed on the lawn within the area of coverage of the sprinkler may be used. When the water in the can rises to the level of 1 inch (2.5 centimeters), it is time to move the sprinkler to another location or shut it off. The amount and rate of application are affected by soil characteristics. Sandy soils drain fast and clays drain slowly. The infiltration rate in sandy soils is faster than in clay soils.

The best periods to apply water are early in the morning and late in the afternoon. Evaporation of water, which is a major source of water waste in irrigation, is minimal during these times. Overwatering a lawn is wasteful, but inadequate moisture may encourage the growth of aggressive and hardy weeds. Healthy grass growth shades out weeds in the lawn and impedes their growth. A combination of the alertness of the homeowner and the nature (genetics and botany) of the species, as well as familiarity with the regional climate and weather patterns, is helpful in the judicious application of water. Information on turf culture is available from local extension agents and horticulturalists. The homeowner should know the characteristics of the turf cultivar in the lawn. Some cultivars are shallow rooted and benefit from shallow soaking, while others are deep rooted and benefit from deep soaking. By listening to weather forecasts, one can take advantage of the rain or know when to increase or decrease the frequency of watering.

Turfgrasses differ in their response to and recovery from adverse weather. Extreme conditions of temperature or drought cause browning or yellowing of the grass. Lawns under stress become dormant but recover with varying degrees of success when the stressor is removed. A soaking rain after a drought rejuvenates lawns quite successfully, provided the proper species is used.

18.5.3 FERTILIZING

A good green color is often associated with a healthy lawn. In trying to maintain this color, some homeowners may go overboard and be in danger of overfertilizing their lawns. Fertilization should be preceded by a soil test for best results. Fertilizers should be applied when the lawn is actively growing. Since the main purpose of fertilizing is to promote vegetative growth, the principal component of a fertilizer analysis is nitrogen; however, excessive nitrogen may predispose plants to diseases. Fertilizers specially formulated for lawns may be purchased from nursery shops. Some of these preparations contain pesticides (e.g., herbicides, fungicides, and insecticides) and must be used cautiously.

18.5.4 WEED CONTROL

The secret to a weed-free lawn is keeping the turfgrass healthy so that it develops into a thick carpet. If the sod is not laid properly, the gaps between strips provide room for weeds to grow. If the lawn is not mowed at the appropriate frequency and to the appropriate height, weed growth is encouraged. Poor nutrition predisposes grasses to disease and weakens them, making them less competitive against weeds.

When weeds appear, they should be removed before they set seed. Weed species such as crabgrass are seasonal in occurrence, and thus when they infest a lawn they die after the season is over, leaving bare spots in the lawn. Preemergence or postemergence chemicals may be used. A popular chemical, 2,4-D, is used to selectively control broadleaf weeds in lawns. Common lawn weeds include dandelion, plantain, burclover, and puncture vine. Table 18–2 presents a sample of effective lawn herbicides against common weeds. The final choice of a herbicide and for that matter any pesticide is according to regional or state recommendations.

A few days before spraying a herbicide, the lawn should be mowed and watered well. Lawns should not be watered after application of a herbicide, since the chemical will be washed away. For a small lawn, a backpack tank sprayer or compression tank sprayer may be used. This type of sprayer may hold up to 5 gallons (19 liters) of fluid.

TABLE 18–2 Some Common Weed Situations in the Lawn and Turf and Suggestions for Their Control

	Preemergence	
Common weeds	Crabgrass	
	Foxtail	
	Annual bluegrass	
	Barnyard grass	
Control	Use Bensulide, Dacthal, Siduron, or Benefin	

	Young Seedlings of Turfgrass	
Common weeds	A wide variety of broadleafs are common at this stage	
Control	Bromoxynill	

	Postemergence (Established Lawn or Turf)	
Common weeds	Grasses:	Nutsedge
		Crabgrass
		Quackgrass
Control		Use Bentazone, Fenoxaprop-ethyl, or Glyphosate (spot treatment)
Common weeds	Broadleafs:	Black medic
		Chickweed
		Dandelion
		Plantain
		Clover
Control		Use 2,4-D amine

	Nonselective Control of Grass Weeds (Many Species)	
To remove existing grass to establish new turf		
Control	Use Glyphosate	

Note: Some of these chemicals are more effective against certain weeds than others; some may damage desired grasses. Labels must be read and directions followed very carefully.

18.5.5 DISEASES AND PESTS

Lawn diseases are frequently fungal in origin. They are readily spread by people and pests as they walk on the lawn and shake off the fungal spores on their bodies. Overfertilization and excessive moisture predispose turfgrasses to diseases. Table 18–3 summarizes the characteristics of lawn insect pests and diseases. The Japanese beetle is the most devastating lawn insect pest. Its destructive stage in the life cycle is the larva (or grub), the same stage biological control of this pest is most effective. The dormant form of a bacterium called *Bacillus popilliae*, in the form of an insecticidal powder (sometimes called milky spore powder), is applied to spots under the grass. Patches of the lawn are lifted up using a spade. After application, the lawn should be watered thoroughly.

18.5.6 AERATION

Aeration
A method of improving soil infiltration and air penetration of compacted soil by, for example, removing small cores of soil.

After a lawn has been walked over for a long period, the soil underneath becomes compacted, depriving the lawn grass of air and impeding water infiltration. To increase aeration and drainage, cores of soil may be removed using an aerifying machine called a *plunger* or *core* **aerator**. The holes poked in the soil may be left to fill up naturally or may be plugged by adding a topdressing material such as peat moss. It is best to aerate a lawn when it is actively growing.

TABLE 18–3 Some Common Lawn and Turf Diseases and Suggestions for Their Control

1. General problems (all grasses affected)	
Nematodes	No chemical control
Fairy rings	No effective chemical control; remove infested patch and reseed
Algae	Use Mancozeb as needed
Toadstools and mushrooms	Drench spots with Dinocarp or Thiram
Slime mold	Use Mancozeb as needed
2. Fusarium blight	Avoid excessive thatch buildup; use Benomyl
3. Brown patch (*Rhizoctonia*)	Use Benomyl, Mancozeb, or Anilazine; avoid excessive nitrogen application
4. Pythium blight (*Pythium*)	Use Zineb or Thiram; treat promptly
5. Dollar spot (*Sclerotinia*)	Use Anilazine or Chlorothalonil
6. Crown rot (*Helminthosporium*)	Use Anilazine or Chlorothalonil

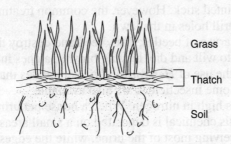

Grass

Thatch

Soil

FIGURE 18–11 Thatch in a lawn.

18.5.7 DETHATCHING

Thatch is an accumulation of old, dead grass; bits of unraked leaf; and other plant material above the soil (Figure 18–11). Beyond just being unsightly, excessive thatch reduces oxygen and moisture entry into the soil and harbors pests and diseases. Warm-season grass species produce more thatch than cool-season species. When thatch accumulates to more than 1/2 inch (1.3 centimeters), it should be removed. Lawns are dethatched when the grass is actively growing, which allows for quick recovery. A variety of dethatching tools exists, ranging from a simple *thatch rake* to *motorized* **dethatchers**. A dethatching rake is first run in one direction and then repeated in a perpendicular direction.

Dethatching
The removal of thatch.

18.6 COMMON PROBLEMS IN THE LAWN

In the May 2007 issue of *Consumer Reports*, the top ten lawn problems were identified as follows:

1. *Crabgrass.* Being adaptable, vigorous, fast-growing, and competitive, crabgrass thrives best when the lawn is underfertilized and mowed too low. Corn gluten applied early in spring is an effective preventive measure. Other herbicides may be used. It is important to fertilize and water the lawn properly for the desired species to grow to keep the crabgrass in check.
2. *Dandelions.* Dandelions spread quickly and are persistent in the soil, possessing underground structures for propagation. To kill the plant, the large taproots must be destroyed or pulled out. It is critical to control the plant before it flowers and sets seed. Broadleaf herbicides such as dicamba and 2, 4-D are effective for chemical control.

3. *Other weeds.* Apart from being unsightly in the lawn, several grass weeds including dallisgrass, quackgrass, and tall fescue have the habit of forming patches and clumps in areas of the lawn where there is shade or excess moisture. No suitable elective herbicide control measures have been developed for these grass weeds.

4. *Fungus.* To treat fungal problems effectively, early identification is critical. If found out too late, it is a waste of time and money to invest in fungicides.

5. *Moss.* The presence of moss to a significant degree indicates the lawn is shaded, or the soil is wet, compacted, or acidic. Planting shade-tolerant species, aerating the soil, liming, and improving drainage are methods to control moss growth.

6. *Excessive shade.* Lawns are generally shade intolerant. Where trees occur in the landscape, excessive shading causes sparse growth under the trees. One measure to curb this incidence is to sow shade-tolerant grasses in those areas, or replace the grass with shade-tolerant ground covers.

7. *Compacted soil.* Soil compaction occurs as the people traverse the lawn during maintenance operations like mowing. Compacted soil impeded water infiltration and promotes poor rooting. For a small lawn, the homeowner may poke holes in the lawn with a pointed stick. However, the common treatment is to use machines (core aerators) to drill holes in the lawn.

8. *Grubs.* Grubs are larvae of beetles. They feed and destroy the roots of grasses, causing the plants to wilt and die, leaving brown patches in the lawn. A biological control method is the use of *Heterorhabditis* nematodes that can be purchased in a pastelike form. Some insecticides are also available.

9. *Dog urine.* Urine is high in nitrogen. When a house pet urinates on a spot, a high concentration of this chemical is deposited on a small areas, causing the grass to die in the areas receiving most of the urine, while the edges become dark green from nitrogen enrichment.

10. *Moles.* Moles are rodents that tunnel through the soil in search of grubs and worms. In the process, they leave unsightly trail of raised soil. These critters may be trapped or baited to kill them.

18.7 TURF FOR ATHLETIC PURPOSES

Athletic fields are subjected to intense and rough traffic, especially in the cases of sports such as soccer and football. Sports such as golf are more gentle on the playing surface. Designers and managers of athletic fields take the wear and tear factors into account in planning the design and maintenance of a field. To reduce wear and tear, the game field should be reserved for playing only scheduled games, and not used for team practice, physical education classes, or marching band rehearsals.

18.7.1 SELECTION OF TURFGRASS AND INSTALLATION

Selection of turfgrass for an athletic field should take into account the desired characteristics of the finished surface in terms of playability, safety, tolerances to traffic, durability, and ease of maintenance, among other factors. Turfgrass for athletic fields include warm-season grasses such as Bermuda grass and zoysiagrasses, as well as cold-tolerant ones like Kentucky bluegrass, perennial ryegrass, and tall fescue.

18.7.2 INSTALLATION

To ensure timely delivery, sod should be ordered from a reputable producer well in advance of the time of use. The site should be well prepared, free from all preexisting sod and weeds. A nonselective herbicide may be applied to remove all weeds effectively. A soil test should be conducted to determine the soil amendments needed for establishing a healthy turf. A light roller may be used to roll over the prepared field to provide an even surface soil surface for laying the sod. Sod for athletic fields is often delivered in special large rolls that are laid with the help of special equipment. Light rollers are then used to roll over the sod to ensure that it makes good contact with the soil. The sod should be watered immediately and frequently during the next two weeks following installation.

18.7.3 MAINTENANCE

Many athletic fields are in poor condition not because of lack of maintenance inputs, but because of poor maintenance scheduling. Athletic turf managers should develop and implement desirable maintenance practices to provide year-round care for the turf, especially during critical times. Athletic field surfaces are not subjected to uniform traffic. Certain areas, such as the goal line of a soccer field, are subjected to more intense trampling and hence more wear and tear than the corner of the sidelines. The management calendar should take into account the different management needs of these distinct parts of the playing field. There are two general goals of management of athletic fields—to promote growth and to prevent pest problems. Cultural practices that promote growth include watering, fertilizing, mowing, and aerification, while pest protection, weed control, and insect and disease control are all measures for preventing disease.

Maintenance scheduling may be designed to suit the budget available. It varies from true professional quality maintenance to a low-budget schedule in which nature is depended upon for moisture and most maintenance work is done by volunteers. Whatever the level of maintenance, certain critical maintenance practices are included in a maintenance schedule. These are mowing, fertilizing, watering, dethatching, aerification, overseeding, and weed control.

Mowing frequency varies from month to month. Depending on the region, it may be weekly in February to March and biweekly in April to October. Mowing in December to January may be done as needed. The turf should be mowed at the appropriate height recommended for the species. Scalping should be avoided. Mowing directions may be periodically altered to minimize repeated scalping of the same spot. Rotary mowers cannot adequately handle mowing heights of less than one inch that many sports fields require.

Fertilizing should be preceded by a soil test. Turfgrass species such as bluegrass that grow even through winter need to be fertilized all year-round. The rates of application of fertilizer range from 5 to 7 pounds per 1,000 square feet in Kentucky bluegrass, to 6 to 9 pounds per 1,000 square feet for Bermuda grass. Zoysiagrass may be fertilized at the rate of 5 to 6 pounds per 1,000 square feet. The recommended fertilizer ratio is 5-1-4. The sources of fertilizer preferred are the slow-release formulations, such as Nutralene, IBDU, and poly-S.

Turfgrasses used for southern athletic fields (e.g., Bermuda grass and zoysiagrass) that produce rhizomes are prone to forming thatch that may build up to between 0.25 to 0.50 inch thick in a short period. When thatch accumulation reaches more than 0.50-inch mulch, the field should be dethatched. Proper fertilization and mowing, as well as periodic aerification help to control thatch buildup. Aerification improves aeration of the soil for rapid decomposition of thatch. High-traffic areas of the field are prone to compaction. Core aerification helps alleviate soil compaction and also promotes soil drainage and decomposition of organic matter.

As previously stated, the rule of thumb in watering is to water deeply and infrequently. During each round of watering, water should be applied to soak the soil to a depth of about 6 inches. The water should be distributed evenly over the field. To reduce soil compaction, the field should not be watered at least two days before use.

In areas where grasses go dormant in winter months, athletic fields may be overseeded with species such as annual ryegrass or perennial ryegrass, to keep the turf looking green year-round. This activity should be performed after the first frost and at a rate of about 5 to 10 pounds per 1,000 square feet.

Weed control may be accomplished by using preemergent or postemergent herbicides. Pest control involves treating the field against weeds and managing insect pests like white grub, cutworms, and webworms.

18.7.4 PUTTING GREENS

Unlike football and soccer fields in which the entire field is uniformly structured and planted to the same cultivar of turfgrass, golf courses have two distinct parts—*fairways* and *putting greens*. Fairways are the long stretches of turf between the tee (starting point) and the end region. The end region, the putting green, consists of a specially designed area around a pin or hole. Putting greens are designed to resist compaction, drain well, and provide a smooth surface for unobstructed roll of the golf ball. To attain this condition, the U.S. Golf Association recommends that putting greens be underlain by a 12-inch root zone mixture of sand and organic matter placed over a gravel layer for good drainage. This layer should be as uniform as possible to avoid any perched water table from forming. Poor drainage will also cause anaerobic conditions to develop. Anaerobic conditions may lead to problems such as shallow rooting of the turfgrass, black layer, and various diseases.

As the turfgrass grows, the nature of the top layer is modified by the presence of a network of roots. Further, if the mower does not bag the clippings properly, clippings may drop on the green, contributing to thatch buildup. Thatch buildup may be prevented by promoting rapid degradation of clippings and other organic matter through the practice of topdressing with sand. Periodic light sprinkling of the green with sand of texture that is similar to that of the top layer promotes aeration and water movement for good growth of microorganisms. With time, topdressing may lead to an accumulation of several inches of topdressing sand. Further, if a finer-textured soil is used for topdressing, this may lead to the development of layered greens. This layering is caused by the lack of mixing of the topdressing soil with the existing soil in the root zone. Flooding of the golf course may also lead to layering of the field. When layering occurs, core aerification and sand topdressing may be used to correct the condition. As a last resort, the turf should be removed and the root zone rototilled before replanting.

SUMMARY

A lawn, basic to most landscape designs, is established by using turfgrasses (grasses grown to be mowed and maintained). Certain turfgrass species, such as bluegrass and ryegrass, are adapted to cool climates. Other grasses (e.g., Bermuda grass and buffalo grass) prefer warm climates. Between these two climatic zones is a transitional one in which either class of grass grows well. A new lawn may be established by seed, sod, or sprigs. The selection of species should take into account the use for which the lawn is intended and the maintenance level the homeowner is willing to provide. Seeds are less expensive and less bulky than sod.

Once established, a lawn needs regular maintenance to keep it healthy and attractive. The three primary elements of turf management are mowing, watering, and fertilizing. Lawn mowers vary in design and efficiency. Mowing should be done in a timely fashion, under the proper conditions, to the correct height, and at the right frequency.

REFERENCES AND SUGGESTED READING

Beard J. B. 1973. *Turfgrass science and culture*. Englewood Cliffs, N.J.: Prentice Hall.

Carpenter, P. L., and T. D. Walker. 1990. *Plants in the landscape*. New York: W. H. Freeman.

Crockert, J. V. 1971. *Landscaping and ground covers*. New York: Time-Life.

Hartmann, H. T., A. M. Kofranek, V. E. Rubatzky, and W. J. Flocker. 1988. *Plantscience: Growth, development, and utilization of cultivated plants*, 2d ed. Englewood Cliffs, N.J.: Prentice Hall.

MacCaskey, M. 1987. *All about lawns*. San Francisco: Ortho Books.

Turgeon, A. J. 1985. *Turfgrass management*. Reston, Va.: Reston Publishing.

Excellent turf ID tool
http://www.agry.purdue.edu/turf/tool/index.html

PRACTICAL EXPERIENCE

1. Visit a local golf course to see the types of grass used and how the course is maintained (watering, fertilizing, mowing, and disease and pest control).
2. Tour local residential and commercial areas. Observe how the lawn is featured in the landscape. Look for differences in style of mowing, quality of maintenance, species, color, mowing height, watering methods, and other characteristics.
3. Visit a department store to see the various kinds of lawn maintenance tools and machinery available.

19

Pruning

PURPOSE AND EXPECTED OUTCOMES

This chapter discusses the importance and methods of pruning horticultural plants. After studying this chapter, the student should be able to

1. List and discuss the general purposes of pruning.
2. List the basic pruning tools and their uses.
3. List and discuss the basic strategies of pruning.
4. Describe how roots, fruit trees, ornamental trees, and shrubs are pruned.
5. Describe specialty pruning strategies such as espalier, topiary, and pollarding.

OVERVIEW

Plants have different growth habits and produce different adult forms. Uncontrolled, plants produce vegetative growth in response to the environmental provisions for growth. Branches form profusely and grow upward in search of light. Strong winds may twist limbs of plants and sometimes even break them off of the stem. The general appearance of plants under such conditions is not always appealing to humans. Under cultivation, humans employ a variety of procedures to manage plant growth and development for a number of reasons including the improvement of aesthetics and productivity.

Pruning
The technique of cutting selected plant parts to accomplish a desired purpose.

Management of plant growth entails removing excessive and undesirable growth and structures by cutting, a procedure called **pruning**. Pruning is an art and a science. Manipulating the growth of plants in this way requires an understanding of plant botany and physiology. It is important to know plant structure and growth habits, as well as how plants respond to their environment and to removal of vegetative growth. The attractiveness of plants after pruning depends on the gardener's creativity and understanding of plant form and texture. Pruning is a standard cultural practice in orchards and vineyards, as well as in landscape management. The principles of pruning are generally the same in all situations. However, the specific methods or techniques are varied, depending on the species and the goal of pruning; that is, apples, citrus, grapes, and roses are pruned in different ways.

Pruning is sometimes done in conjunction with another horticultural procedure called *training*. Training involves cutting, repositioning, and guiding the course of development of branches and limbs of plants according to a specific objective. During training, limbs may be bent and tied to support structures or even removed altogether, resulting in creative and attractive shapes. In the landscape, aesthetics appears to be more important than productivity, whereas the reverse is true in orchard management.

19.1 GENERAL PRINCIPLES OF PRUNING AND TRAINING

The success of pruning and training plants depends on the understanding and observance of certain principles:

1. *Evaluate the whole plant.* Pruning affects the entire plant, whether physiologically or physically. Removing a limb may change plant form or shape and may also affect the plant's capacity for performing certain physiological functions such as photosynthesis and transpiration. By assessing the whole plant, one can make a decision as to which part of the plant to cut to give the overall best results.

2. *Think before you cut.* Cutting is an irreversible operation. Thus, a limb should be cut only when there is a good reason to do so. It is best to cut in stages, especially when one is relatively inexperienced in pruning. More of the branch or plant part can be removed if the first cut is not adequate.

3. *Apical dominance is broken when a stem is cut.* Apical dominance resides in the terminal bud and gives direction to plant growth. While the apical bud is present and in control, lateral buds are suppressed. Breaking apical dominance stimulates new growth. New growth tends to arise below a wound on the stem because of interference in apical dominance. Apical dominance is strongly associated with vertical growth. Thus, any attempt to alter vertical growth induces a response in plants to correct the change. For example, when a branch that is growing vertically is bent and forced to remain horizontal, the buds in the leaf axis are stimulated to grow vertically. This happens because apical dominance is reduced by changing the vertical growth to horizontal growth. The new side shoots are likely to develop into reproductive shoots, flowers, and fruits.

4. *Pruning invigorates regrowth.* When pruning is used to reduce the size of a plant, it encourages vigorous new growth. The more severe the pruning, the more vigorous the regrowth. Thus, if a plant is growing in an unbalanced fashion, for example, the weaker side should be pruned severely to encourage vigorous new growth. For this reason, it may be best to select plants that will fit the available space when they are mature, thereby eliminating pruning that would produce vigorous new growth.

5. *Pruning can be used to direct growth.* By removing apical dominance, the direction of growth is transported to the topmost lateral bud. Thus, by selecting which bud will become the topmost bud, the regrowth is given direction because buds are positioned to face certain directions.

6. *Timing is critical.* Plants have different flowering habits that must be considered in pruning. Shrubs that flower in late summer and autumn produce flowers on the current season's growth. These plants are pruned in spring so that they will produce vigorous shoots that will flower later the same year. On the other hand, shrubs that flower in spring or early summer produce flowers on the previous season's growth and thus are pruned after flowering. This way, the new growth has time to develop and be ready for flowering in the following year. Certain plants lose much sap when cut. Such plants should not be pruned in spring when sap production is at its peak.

7. *Pruning can be used to create special effects.* With pruning and training, plants can be manipulated to produce unique shapes and forms in the landscape. Such techniques include pollarding and coppicing.

19.2 OBJECTIVES OF PRUNING

Although the manner of pruning varies, the general objectives remain similar. All of the objectives may not be required or accomplished in any one particular instance, since pruning may be used for a specific purpose at a particular stage in the growth of a plant.

The four general purposes of pruning are plant sanitation, aesthetics, reproduction, and physiology.

19.2.1 PLANT SANITATION

Pruning may be undertaken to remove plant parts that create an unsanitary condition. Specific actions geared toward improved plant sanitation include the following:

1. Broken branches and dead tissue on plants provide surfaces on which disease-causing organisms grow and thus jeopardize the health of plants. Broken branches pose grave danger to people.
2. Diseased plant parts may be removed to prevent the spread of infection.
3. The plant may be cleaned by removing unsightly dried or dead parts.
4. The canopy can be opened up so that air can circulate freely and thereby reduce humid conditions that predispose plants to disease.
5. An open canopy enables effective spraying by allowing pesticides to penetrate the canopy.
6. Removal of excessive undergrowth not only keeps the landscape clean but also reduces hazards from brush fires.

19.2.2 AESTHETIC OBJECTIVES

In ornamental horticulture, the visual appeal of plants is of paramount importance to gardeners, especially if plants are in the landscape. Pruning is employed for shaping the form of the plant. After determining the desired shape, branches are strategically removed or their growth controlled to maintain the shape.

In *formal gardens* or on certain public grounds such as those found in zoological or botanical gardens, certain plant species are grown, trained, and trimmed into geometric figures or readily recognizable or abstract shapes. This art form is called *topiary*.

Pruned plants can by themselves be attractive elements in the general landscape. However, more pleasing components can be produced if the style of pruning takes into account other elements in the landscape such as the architecture of the house, the terrain, and artificial structures such as statues and fountains.

19.2.3 REPRODUCTIVE OBJECTIVES

Pruning may be undertaken to enhance the reproductive capacity of the plant in several ways:

1. The canopy may be opened up by cutting out the branches in the center. This allows light to penetrate the canopy for fruiting to occur on inner branches.
2. Fruiting may be regulated by encouraging the growth and development of fruiting shoots while reducing nonreproductive shoots.
3. Pruning may be done to balance reproductive and vegetative growth for optimal yield.

4. Pruning may be done to reduce the number of fruiting branches per plant (*thinning out*) in order to increase fruit size and quality.
5. Generally, proper pruning enables a fruit-bearing tree to produce higher-quality fruits over a longer period. Flowering plants also produce bigger flowers over a longer period of the plant's life when pruned.
6. Properly pruned trees have good fruit distribution throughout the plant canopy (not only at the edges) and bear fruit of good size, color, texture, and sugar content.
7. Pruning allows the gardener easier access to fruits during harvesting.

19.2.4 PHYSIOLOGICAL OBJECTIVES

Pruning, if not done judiciously, may have adverse physiological consequences on plant growth and development. However, pruning may be employed to manipulate plant physiology in a variety of ways to enhance the performance of the plant:

1. Pruning roots before transplanting reduces the chance of transplanting shock.
2. Pruning shoot tips in species with apical dominance (e.g., apple, pear, and cherry) induces lateral branching and thereby prevents the tree from growing straight without sufficient branching.
3. Pruning deciduous species during the dormant period in winter conserves the plant's stored food for use in spring for vigorous new growth.
4. Severe pruning may have a dwarfing effect on a plant by reducing total vegetative growth.
5. Older plants may be rejuvenated by pruning to stimulate new growth.

Apart from these four general purposes of pruning, the procedure may be employed on specific occasions for practical reasons. For example, when plants grow bigger and exhibit destructive tendencies such as roots cracking pavements or foundations of buildings, roots clogging sewage pipes, and branches destroying the roof or touching utility cables, the affected plant parts need to be pruned to contain the plant in the available space.

19.3 PLANT RESPONSE TO PRUNING

Removing vegetative parts of plants affects certain plant physiological processes and subsequently growth and development. The two basic plant responses to pruning are described in the following sections.

19.3.1 INTERFERENCE WITH APICAL DOMINANCE

As previously stated, apical dominance of terminal buds suppresses the growth of lateral buds. The removal of terminal buds removes this inhibitory effect, allowing lateral buds to grow. In certain plants, gardeners deliberately remove terminal buds (pinching or **pinch pruning**) to encourage lateral bud growth so that plants look fuller and more appealing. The vertical shoots that arise on the upper side of branches, called *water sprouts* are an example of a plant response to interference with the process of apical dominance.

Pinch Pruning
Breaking by hand of the terminal bud.

19.3.2 GROWTH STIMULATION

A physiological balance exists between the top and bottom growths of plants. Removing parts of the top growth upsets this balance. Plants respond with a burst of new growth, especially just below the cut. In spite of the new growth, pruned plants do not exceed the size of the plant before pruning. This dwarfing effect on plant size occurs because the amount of new growth does not match what was removed in addition to what would have been produced by the plant in its prepruned form. Similar to the practical application of interference with apical dominance, gardeners employ this dwarfing effect of pruning in creating art forms. The epitome of such an art form is the Japanese art of dwarfing plants called *bonsai*.

19.4 PRUNING TOOLS

Most pruning tools are handheld and operated manually. A motorized chain saw may be used for cutting large branches. Cuts are made by either sawing or scissor action of cutting tools. Pruning tools are hence a variety of saws and shears designed to cut different sizes of limbs at different heights and different locations on the plant. When the plant is tall and the limbs are hard to reach, pruning aids may be used to lift the operator to the desired height. Some of the common pruning tools are described in the following sections.

19.4.1 SHEARS

Figure 19–1 shows a variety of shears.

Hand Shears (Hand Pruners)

Hand shears are the most commonly used pruning implements. They can be held in one hand and are available in two basic designs. One design has a true scissor-cutting action produced by two cutting edges or blades (*bypass action* type). The other design uses one sharp blade that cuts against a metal piece (*anvil* type). The limitation of this tool is that it can only cut limbs that are less than 1/2 inch (1.3 centimeters) thick.

Lopping Shears (Loppers)

Loppers
Long-handled shears operated with two hands and used for cutting larger branches.

Lopping shears (**loppers**) are designed to cut larger branches (up to 2 inches or 5.2 centimeters in diameter) by a two-handed action. Their long handles provide the needed leverage for cutting thicker limbs. The long handles also extend the reach of the operator so that limbs located high on the stem may be pruned without using a pruning aid such as a ladder or lift. Short-handled loppers are available. The common loppers have hinge action, but more expensive designs with different types of action are available.

Hedge Shears

Two-handed tools, hedge shears are designed for trimming and shaping hedges and ground covers. Manual models are common, inexpensive, and easy to use. Electric models are also easy to use and have a fast-cutting action. However, they may be frequently jammed by twigs during operation and also be limited in operation by the length of the extension cord.

FIGURE 19–1 A variety of shears used in pruning. The type used depends on the size of the branch.

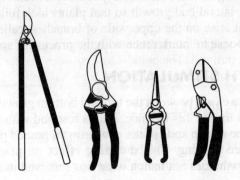

19.4.2 SAWS

A saw may be designed to cut only on the forward stroke and thus make it easier to maneuver when cutting limbs located high on a tree. A saw may also be fine toothed for smooth, close cuts and is especially appropriate for cutting deadwood. Coarse-toothed saws are easier to use on greenwood. Common horticultural saws can be placed into four general categories: manual saws, power saws, pole saws, and pole pruners.

Manual Saws

Folding Saw The folding saw can be folded to make it even smaller and more convenient to carry around. It is fine toothed and used for small branches.

Rigid-Handle Curved Saw The rigid-handle curved saw may be designed to have all lance teeth for cutting deadwood or raker teeth (a deep slot after every five even-sized teeth to carry away sawdust) for greenwood.

Bow Saw The blade on the bow saw is thin and replaceable. It can be used to make quick cuts of even large branches but is restricted to use in unobstructed areas because of the pronounced arching of the bow.

Tree Surgery Saw The tree surgery saw comes closest to the common carpenter's saw but differs in that it is designed to cut only on the forward stroke. It is more difficult to use than the other types and requires more effort because of its fine teeth.

Two-Edge Saw Because of its design, the two-edge saw can cut on both edges and therefore must be used with great care.

Power Saws

Motorized saws, or *chain saws*, are easy to use and very efficient. They can be used to cut all sizes of plant limbs. However, they pose a great danger and can inflict serious injuries to operators if not handled properly. According to the source of power, there are two basic models:

1. *Electric-powered chain saws.* Electric power makes this model of chain saw quiet during operation. It is also easy to use. Models with cords are limited by the length of the extension cord.
2. *Gasoline-powered chain saws.* Gasoline models are completely portable, larger in size, and generally more expensive than electric-powered chain saws. They also require more maintenance and are noisy during operation.

Pole Saws

A pole saw has a small, curved saw blade mounted on the end of an extendable pole. This type allows branches on tall trees to be easily pruned while the operator is standing on the ground.

Pole Pruners

The pole pruner has a J-shaped hook mounted on a pole along with a saw blade, which is operated by a rope or pull rod. The hook is used to grab and hold the branch while the saw cuts it. A combination pole saw and pruner may be purchased.

19.4.3 PRUNING KNIFE AND RASP

The pruning knife is very sharp and is used when minor pruning involving a few small branches is needed. The knife may also be used to clean and smooth large cut surfaces. A rasp is like a file and is used for shaping or smoothing tree wounds.

19.4.4 LADDERS

Ladders, tools for extending the reach of an operator during pruning, should be used with care. They must be set up properly to ensure good stability. Leaning while standing on a ladder should be avoided. Of the different types of ladders available, those most recommended include the following:

1. *Orchard ladder.* This three-legged tool has added stability from its wide stance.
2. *Extension ladder.* This ladder can be adjusted in length and is useful for reaching high places on a tree.

19.5 PRUNING TECHNIQUES

19.5.1 GENERAL GUIDELINES

The exact way a particular pruning method is implemented is determined by a number of factors including species, goal to be accomplished, whether the plant is grown strictly for ornamental purposes or for producing fruits, and the environment in which the plant is growing. Fruit trees are pruned differently from ornamental landscape trees and bushes; flowering plants are pruned differently from foliage plants.

In selecting and implementing a method of pruning, one should consider not only the desired outcome but also how the species responds to pruning, especially in terms of the extent of pruning. Further, one method may be suited to one species but not to another.

Notwithstanding the method, certain general guidelines may be followed for successful pruning:

1. Have clearly defined goals.
2. Prune at the appropriate time. Some plants may be pruned any time of the year, while others are best pruned when dormant (late fall to early winter).
3. Proceed cautiously. Take time to look at the plant to determine which limb needs to be pruned. It is better to cut less and revisit the plant later for further pruning than to cut too much in one instance.
4. Use sharp tools and make clean cuts. Avoid tearing off the bark of the plant. Clean cuts heal much faster and reduce the chance of disease infection.
5. Prune the parts that must be pruned first. Phytosanitation is important in any pruning operation. All dead or dying parts and broken limbs should be removed.
6. Branches that grow inward toward the center of the canopy are prime candidates for pruning. Outward-growing branches should be encouraged. Branches that are acutely angled with respect to the central axis are also candidates for pruning. Similarly, stems and branches that are squeezed cause cracks to form.
7. Look for abnormal growths. Species have certain natural forms, and as such pruning is more successful when the natural tendencies of plants are taken into account. For example, it is easier to prune a species with a cone-shaped canopy to remain cone shaped than to force it to assume a spherical shape.
8. For fruiting plants, it is critical to know the fruiting habits (i.e., lateral or terminal) and identify and distinguish between vegetative and fruit buds or branches.
9. Seek the help of a professional arborist if a large limb or high branches require the use of a ladder.

19.5.2 CUTTING

Cutting is the primary activity in pruning. After determining which branch or limb to cut, the next critical step is deciding how to cut it. A wrong cut may ruin a bud or defeat the purpose of pruning. The way a plant part is cut depends on the size of the part and the location of the cut to be made. The following are some general guidelines for cutting:

1. A cut should be clean, which is made possible by using a sharp tool. If a saw is used, any rough edge should be smoothed with a pruning knife. A clean cut accelerates callus formation for quick healing.

2. When cutting a branch, first identify the branch collar. This structure forms at the base of the branch from stem tissue. A folding or ridge, called a *branch bark ridge*, is often found in the branch axil. It is important that these two structures are not damaged during pruning. The cut should be close to the main branch or stem so as to leave very little stub without being flush with the stem (Figure 19–2). Without an active bud, a stub will gradually wilt and die back. Deadwood can become infected with disease.

3. Avoid splitting and tearing, which are caused by the weight of the branch. When cutting a large branch that cannot be cut with shears, it is best to cut in stages (Figure 19–3). First, make a shallow cut on the underside of the branch, about 6 inches (15.2 centimeters) away from the trunk or main branch. This cut should go only about halfway deep. Next, make a cut on the top side at about 1 to 2 inches (2.54 to 5.1 centimeters) away from the first cut and away from the main stem or trunk. This cut goes through the entire branch. The remaining stub is then removed closer to the trunk or main branch (outside the branch collar and branch bark ridge).

4. The cutting angle is important for two main reasons. Too sharp of a cutting angle produces a larger surface area, thus increasing the time for healing and predisposing the wound to infection (Figure 19–4). All cuts die back from the surface, but the dieback is more extensive for a sharp-angled cut. A 45-degree or less slanted cut is recommended.

(a)   (b)

FIGURE 19–2 (a) Pruning cuts should not be made flush to the trunk or branch. (b) A well-healed wound. *(Source: George Acquaah)*

FIGURE 19–3 Large branches should be cut in stages. Cut 1 is made to prevent tearing of the bark; cut 2 is made to remove the weight of the branch; cut 3 is made just above the branch collar (never flush to the stem) to finish the pruning.

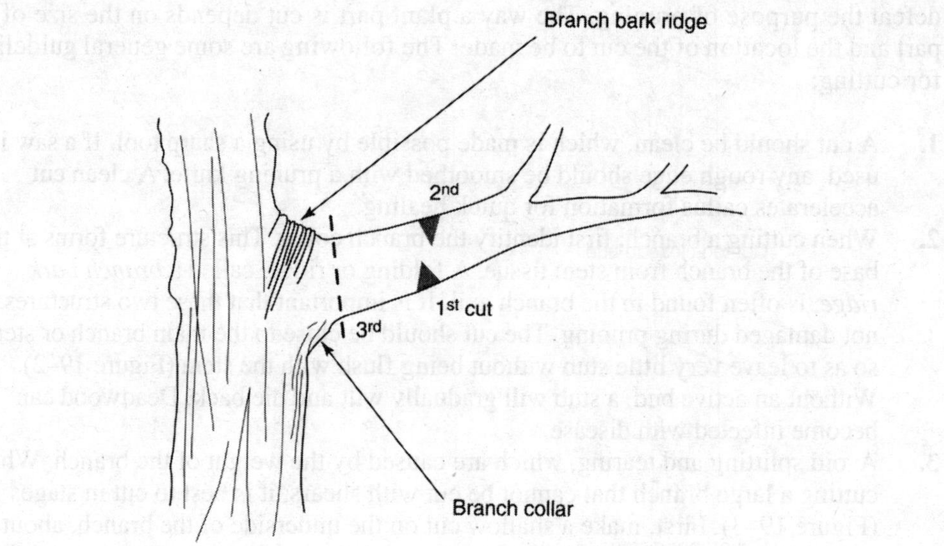

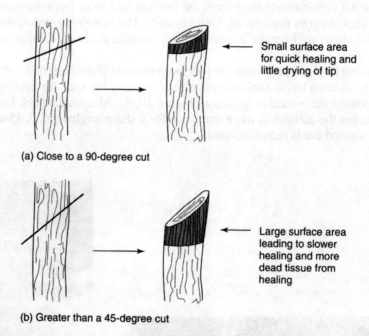

Branch bark ridge

2nd

1st cut

3rd

Branch collar

FIGURE 19–4 (a) Pruning cuts should be made as close to a 90-degree angle as possible. (b) Cut angles greater than 45 degrees create large surface areas, slow healing, and a larger amount of dead tissue during the healing process.

Small surface area for quick healing and little drying of tip

(a) Close to a 90-degree cut

Large surface area leading to slower healing and more dead tissue from healing

(b) Greater than a 45-degree cut

5. The distance of the cut from a bud is important. Since all cuts die back a little, cutting too close to a bud (or cutting at a sharp angle) might cause the dieback to kill the nearest bud in the process (Figure 19–5).

6. The direction of cut determines the direction of the new growth from the immediate bud. Slanted cuts are approximately parallel to the direction of the tip of the immediate bud below. An outward slant (upper tip pointing out of the canopy) indicates that the bud immediately below will produce an outward growth (Figure 19–6). This direction of growth is desirable and is one of the objectives of pruning—opening up the canopy for ventilation and light penetration. An inward growth achieves the opposite effect. Therefore, when pruning, the operator should select the appropriate bud above which a cut is to be made.
   It should be mentioned that there may be situations in which pruning to obtain a tight center may be preferable. If the plant has opposite buds, one of them should be removed to leave the outward-pointing bud.

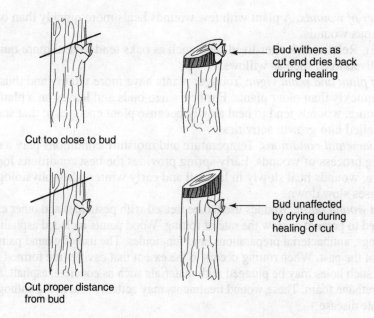

Cut too close to bud

Bud withers as cut end dries back during healing

Cut proper distance from bud

Bud unaffected by drying during healing of cut

FIGURE 19–5 Distance of cut from the nearest bud is critical to the survival of the bud. If a cut is too close to the bud, it might wither with the advance of drying tissue as part of the healing process.

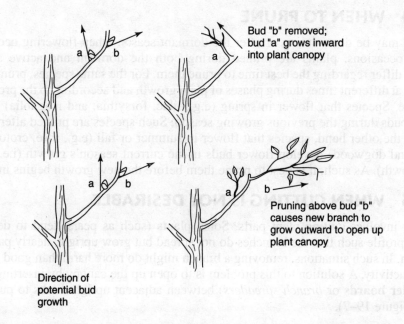

Bud "b" removed; bud "a" grows inward into plant canopy

Pruning above bud "b" causes new branch to grow outward to open up plant canopy

Direction of potential bud growth

FIGURE 19–6 The direction of new growth after pruning depends on the potential direction of growth of the bud closest to the cut. If an outward-pointing bud is the last bud, the shoot will grow outward. An inward-pointing bud should be targeted with care since it defeats the purpose of pruning in certain cases by encouraging new growth to crowd the inner part of the tree canopy.

7. The ideal cutting position is close to a bud at a fork or branch or just above the collar of a branch.

8. When cutting with shears or pruners, the thin blade should be nearest the bud or the trunk, which permits the desired cut.

19.5.3   CARING FOR WOUNDS

Plants have natural defense mechanisms that are triggered upon injury. First, a layer of waterproof material called **suberin** is produced to protect the exposed tissues of the wound from drying. Next, *callus* growth occurs to produce new tissue to close up or heal the wound. It is important that wound closure occur without delay to avoid invasion by decay organisms. The rate of healing depends on a number of factors:

1. *Size of wound.* A large wound heals slowly.
2. *Location of wound.* Generally, wounds occurring at lower levels on the plant heal more quickly than those at higher levels.

Suberin
A hydrophobic material that occurs on the inner surface of a cell wall.

3. *Number of wounds.* A plant with few wounds heals more quickly than one with numerous wounds.
4. *Species.* Relatively longer-lived trees such as oaks tend to heal more quickly than short-lived trees such as willows.
5. *Age of plant and plant vigor.* Younger plants have more vitality and thus heal more quickly than older plants. Further, when buds and leaves on a plant are expanding, wounds tend to heal slowly because plant energies at that stage are channelled into growth activities.
6. *Environmental conditions.* Temperature and moisture conditions play a role in the healing process of wounds. Early spring provides the best conditions for wound closure; wounds heal slowly in late fall and early winter when physiological processes slow down.
7. *Use of wound paint.* Wounds used to be treated with pesticides and other chemicals believed to prevent or slow the rate of rotting. Wood paints included asphalt-based dressings, antibacterial preparations, and fungicides. The use of wound paint is a thing of the past. When rotting occurs to the extent that cavities are formed in the tree trunk, such holes may be plugged with materials such as concrete, asphalt, and polyurethane foam. These wound treatments may actually seal in the pathogens and promote disease.

19.5.4 WHEN TO PRUNE

Pruning may be done during or after the dormant season when flowering occurs. On certain occasions, plants are pruned during both the dormant and active seasons. Species differ regarding the best time to prune them. For the same species, pruning may be done at different times during phases of plant growth and according to the production schedule. Species that flower in spring (e.g., lilac, forsythia, and magnolia) develop flower buds during the previous growing season. Such species are pruned after flowering. On the other hand, species that flower in summer or fall (e.g., rose, croton, blueberry, and dogwood) develop flower buds in the current season's growth (i.e., on the new growth). As such, it is best to prune them before the new growth begins in spring.

19.5.5 WHEN CUTTING IS NOT DESIRABLE

Pruning involves cutting plant parts. Some plants (such as pears) tend to develop a narrow profile such that the branches do not spread but grow upright, nearly parallel to the stem. In such situations, removing a branch might do more harm than good in terms of productivity. A solution to this problem is to open up the canopy by inserting boards (**spreader boards** or *branch spreaders*) between adjacent upright limbs to push them apart (Figure 19–7).

Spreader Board
A flat piece of board with V-cuts at both ends that is forced between the stem and a branch with a narrow crutch to widen it.

FIGURE 19–7 A spreader board may be used to open up the canopy of a tree for the development of strong and wide crotches.

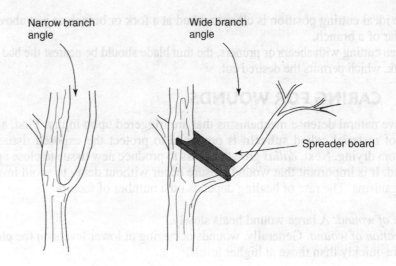

Narrow branch angle

Wide branch angle

Spreader board

19.6 STRATEGIES FOR PRUNING ABOVEGROUND PLANT PARTS

19.6.1 BASIC PRUNING PRACTICES AND TERMINOLOGIES

As previously indicated, cutting is the primary activity in pruning. Cutting permanently removes plant parts to accomplish a desired objective. Vegetative material can be removed in one of two basic ways, each with distinct effects on the plant. Entire shoots or limbs can be removed by *thinning cuts*. Alternatively, parts (terminal parts) of a shoot or limb can be removed by *heading cuts*. Thinning cuts open up the canopy for ventilation, light penetration, and other benefits. Removing the terminal parts of shoots by heading affects auxin movement through the plant. Groups of lateral buds are stimulated. Horizontal limbs tend to produce vertical shoots called *water sprouts*.

The major tree branches extending from the trunk are called *scaffold branches*. They define the tree's outline and hence its canopy shape. Removing a scaffold branch hence has the potential to alter the shape of the canopy. The central stem is the trunk, while the junction between the trunk and scaffold branch is the *crotch*. The main growing point of the tree (the tip end of the trunk) is called the *leader* or terminal. Removing the leader alters the shape of the tree.

19.6.2 PRUNING DECIDUOUS TREES

There are several approaches to pruning trees, the most common being crown thinning, crown raising, and crown reduction (Figure 19–8).

1. *Crown thinning.* The principal objective of **thinning** is to open up the plant canopy for light to penetrate to lower branches for better fruit set and increased productivity. Without adequate light, shaded branches become unproductive but nonetheless use up nutritional resources available to the plant. In thinning, the operator strategically removes certain branches, such as those that are inward growing. The operation involves limited or no trimming at all so that the general shape of the plant is preserved. To avoid stress to the plant, no more than 25 percent of the crown should be removed at any time. The limbs are evenly spaced on the stem, and the low and unproductive ones are removed. Thinning is a common orchard management practice for keeping fruit trees in the best shape for high productivity.

2. *Crown raising.* In crown raising, the lower one-third of the branches of a tree are removed. This pruning approach is used to develop stems for timber production. In residential areas, crown raising provides clearance for pedestrians, vehicles, and building.

3. *Crown reduction.* Also called drop crotch pruning, crown reduction is used to reduce the height of a tree. Trees growing under utility lines are cut back to avoid contact with lines, some of which carry electricity. It has the potential to alter the natural appearance of the tree and hence is considered a pruning method of last resort by some experts. Furthermore, it is used on trees with pyramidal growth forms. Growth reduction is accomplished by pruning back the leaders and branch terminals.

19.6.3 PRUNING FLOWERING SHRUBS

1. *Rejuvenation.* Rejuvenation pruning is a severe method of pruning in which all the canes of a shrub are cut back to about 6 inches above the ground (Figure 19–9). This method is applied when a shrub has outgrown its allocated space or stopped flowering. It is done in late winter before plants start their spring growth. Such a severe cutback may cause a plant to miss a cycle of blooming while it regrows.

2. *Renewal Pruning.* Renewal pruning is employed to rejuvenate old plants by removing old, unproductive branches, which allows for fresh and vigorous replacement growth. Flowering shrubs may be rejuvenated in this way. Fruit trees in the landscape

Thinning
Removal of excess vegetative growth to open the plant canopy and reduce the number of fruiting branches for larger fruits.

FIGURE 19–8 Crown thinning, crown raising, and crown reduction.

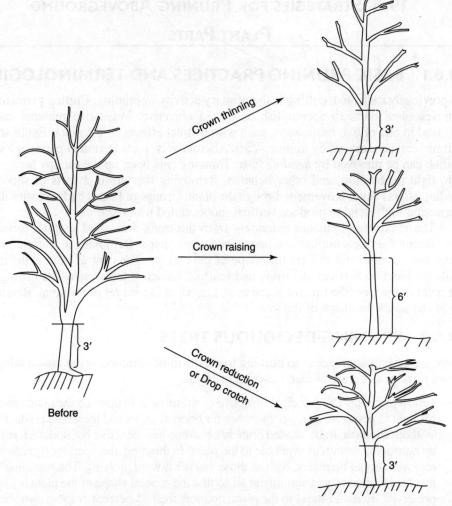

neglected by previous homeowners may require renewal pruning by new owners. This method is used in early spring, prior to the start of spring growth, to selectively remove about 30 percent of the canes of the shrub at the ground level. The practice is to remove three- to four-year-old canes so that the more vigorous canes that produce the best flowers are left to grow. Long canes can be headed back. This method of pruning is similar to thinning out in its effect, allowing better air movement through the plant. Renewal pruning may be practiced in trees and shrubs (Figure 19–10).

19.6.4 PRUNING EVERGREEN SHRUBS

Evergreen shrubs (yew, juniper, boxwood, arborvitae) are commonly used in foundation planting in the landscape. They vary in size, color, and shape. They need pruning to keep them from outgrowing their space. However, rather than shearing them, the current trend is to preserve their natural look by clipping judiciously with a hand pruner. Care should be taken not to prune into the dead zone (6 to 12 inches of space below the green needles at the bottom of the plant). Most species are unable to develop new leaf buds following such pruning.

19.7 TREE TOPPING

Though practiced by some homeowners, professionals do not consider tree topping an acceptable pruning technique. It entails indiscriminate cutting back to reduce tree height by about 50 percent, by reducing the upper scaffold branches to stubs, disfiguring the tree

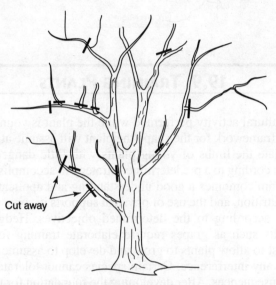

FIGURE 19–9 Renewal pruning and rejuvenation.

Cut canes to about 6 inches above ground

Rejuvenation Pruning

Renewal pruning

Remove 1/3 of shrub canes

Before

FIGURE 19–10 Renewal pruning of an old tree removes old and unproductive or damaged branches and heads back limbs to encourage new growth.

Cut away

in the process. Homeowners who request or undertake this procedure themselves feel their trees are overgrown and pose a hazard. Because of the severe reduction in the canopy, the tree is deprived of most of its photosynthetic surface, leading to stress from inadequate food supply. The tree trunk is weakened and predisposed to disease and insect attack, as well as bark splitting from sunburn. The stubs are prone to decay and also produce many rapidly growing weak new shoots. Topping reduces the life of the tree and is expensive, since a weakened tree is prone to weather-related damage and often needs pruning after a few years.

19.8 PRUNING ROOTS

Unlike the pruning of aboveground plant parts done as part of the plant management operation, roots are pruned once during the plant establishment process. Roots of large plants are pruned immediately or shortly before transplanting (Figure 19–11). If pruned long before transplanting, the roots have the opportunity to develop a new mass of secondary roots for better establishment when transplanted. Sometimes pruning is necessary to reduce the root size in order to fit the hole for transplanting. Tractor-mounted mechanical root pruners are used by large commercial nurseries that produce and sell large plants.

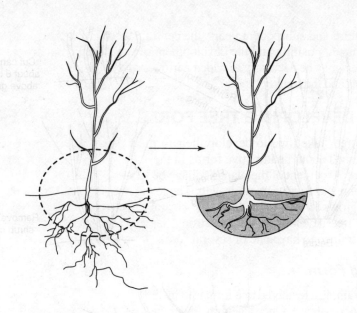

FIGURE 19–11 Root pruning is accomplished by using a spade for a small plant or using commercial tree augers for large plants. Bare-root plants may be pruned before planting to remove damaged roots.

Training
A system of plant management that involves pruning and tying to create and maintain desirable plant size and shape.

19.9 TRAINING PLANTS

Training, a horticultural activity performed while the plant is young, entails laying the basic architectural framework for the shape the plant will assume at maturity. Further, it is easy to manipulate the limbs of young plants with little danger of breaking them. Plants are trained according to a predetermined strategy to accomplish specific purposes. A successful program combines a good understanding and application of the practices of pruning, plant nutrition, and the use of physical supports in some cases. Plant training requirements vary according to the determined objectives. Hedge plants are rarely trained. Small fruits such as grapes require elaborate training for good production. Sometimes it is best to allow plants to grow and develop to assume their natural shapes and forms without any interference. Certain species cannot tolerate limb manipulation without adverse consequences. After developing the foundation for the adult plant shape and form, the gardener must prune or reposition limbs periodically to maintain these characteristics.

19.10 TRAINING AND PRUNING ORNAMENTAL TREES

The primary goals of training ornamental trees are to develop a strong tree trunk, develop an attractive plant form, and establish a heading height.

19.10.1 DEVELOPING A STRONG TRUNK

Central Leader
The main upright shoot of a tree.

The training strategy for developing a strong trunk is called the **central leader**. One strong, upward-growing branch is identified and encouraged to grow to become the central axis of the tree. One way of developing a strong trunk is as follows:

1. Cutting back (heading back) the plant in the first year will allow new growth to occur just below the cut. Unless a young tree is weak, it should not be staked. If required, staking should be loose to allow the trunk free movement in the wind in order to develop strength.
2. A strong, upward-growing branch is identified in the second year, and other branches (competing leaders) below the selected leader are removed or pruned back. Water sprouts will develop as a result.

3. In the third and subsequent years, the central leader is encouraged to maintain its dominant position and the development of secondary branches is controlled.
4. Spreaders may be necessary to widen narrow crotch angles between secondary branches and the trunk.

19.10.2 DEVELOPING TREE FORM

Ornamental trees take time to develop their form, and therefore growers should not be overly concerned about unattractive forms in the early years of their growth. It is important that about 30 percent of the plant's foliage be located in the lower half of the tree during the first three to four years of growth. The lower branches are progressively removed as the plant grows to establish a desirable clearance beneath the limbs. By adopting this strategy, the tree develops a straight, strong, tapered, and attractive trunk. Ornamental trees can be trained to have one of several forms, described in the following sections.

Feathered Form

The goal of training a feathered tree form is to maintain a simple main stem with well-spaced laterals for good balance. Once a central leader has been identified, crossing laterals should be pruned by cutting them to the main stem (Figure 19–12). A desirable clearance is established beneath the limbs by removing the lowest branches. If staking is needed, a low stake allows the main stem to flex for strength development. In the second and subsequent years, regrowth at the stem base is pruned along with any vertical shoots that compete with the central leader. Crossing branches are removed as they occur. Once adequate strength has been developed in the trunk, the stake should be removed. This system of training is the easiest to perform. Evergreen trees are commonly trained to have a feathered form.

Standard Form

A standard tree form can develop naturally. There are two variations of this form. The central leader standard is a modification of the feathered form but with more clearance beneath the limbs (Figure 19–13). Laterals on the lowest one-third of the tree are pruned in stages. In the first year, laterals in the top one-third are left untouched, with the exception of dead branches. Those in the midsection are shortened by half, and those in the lower one-third are removed completely. In the next two years, the pattern in year one is repeated, except that the laterals that were shortened in the previous year are removed. In addition, any existing cross branches are removed in the top section of the tree. This process continues until a desired length of clear stem is attained.

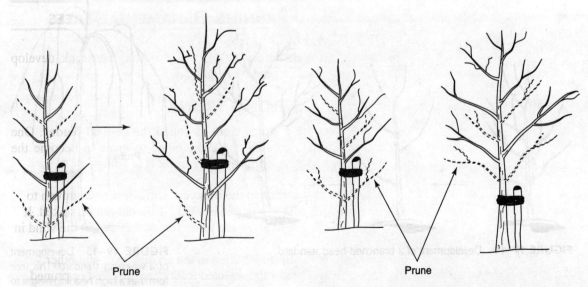

Prune

FIGURE 19–12 Feathered tree form development.

Prune

FIGURE 19–13 Development of a standard tree form.

Branched-Head Standard

In the branched-head standard, the tree is trained as a central leader in the first two to three years before the leader is cut back such that three to four strong laterals remain (Figure 19–14). The growth of these branches is controlled by pruning to outward-facing buds to open the crown of the tree.

Weeping Standard

Weeping tree forms may be natural or grafted. The tree in natural weeping standard form is trained as a single stem to a suitable height and then the branches are allowed to arch down (Figure 19–15). Commonly, a high stake is needed to support the downward-arching branches until a strong trunk has developed. In the top-grafted weeping standard, a short stem is grafted onto the stock.

Multistemmed Tree Form

Certain trees naturally develop multiple stems and branches that are very low on the base of the tree. They also tend to produce suckers. To create this form, the stem of a young tree (about two years old) is cut as close to the ground as desired (Figure 19–16). This practice induces new shoot growth. Two to three healthy shoots, well spaced around the base, are selected and retained while all others are pruned. Any regrowths are removed in subsequent years.

19.10.3 DEVELOPING HEAD HEIGHT

Scaffold Branch
The main branch growing from the trunk of a tree.

The head height determines the height of **scaffold branches** above the ground in the adult stage. Whether a low or high head is chosen depends on the natural form of the tree and the desired amount of clearance beneath the tree. Generally, trees with narrow forms, such as conifers, have a low head height, whereas spreading trees have a higher head height (Figure 19–17). Trees with weeping forms (such as weeping willow) need very high head height for proper display of their low-hanging branches and good clearance. For a low adult-stage head height, the initial heading height should be about 2 to 3 feet (0.61 to 0.91 meter) above the ground. If a high head height is desired, the initial heading may be 3 to 5 feet (0.91 to 1.5 meters) or even higher.

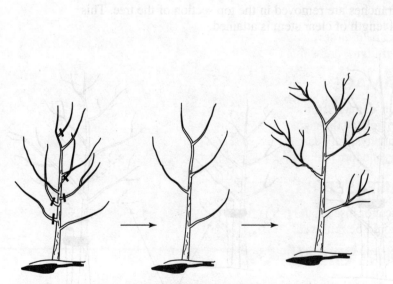

FIGURE 19–14 Development of a branched-head standard.

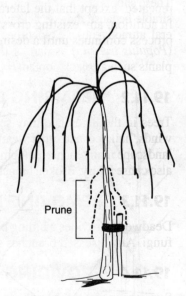

FIGURE 19–15 Development of a weeping standard. This tree form has a high heading height to allow the branches room to hang.

Prune

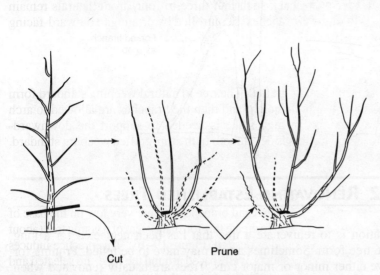

FIGURE 19–16 Steps in the development of artificial multistem tree form.

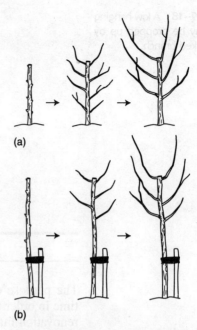

FIGURE 19–17 Developing heading height of trees. (a) Low heading height and (b) high heading height.

19.11 MAINTENANCE OF ESTABLISHED TREES

Once established, ornamental trees need occasional pruning to remove unwanted growth, correct growth, or repair damage. Specific pruning activities include those described in the following sections.

19.11.1 REMOVING SHOOTS

A tree has dormant buds under its bark that may be stimulated to produce shoots on the stem. These shoots are called **epicormic shoots** (or water sprouts or water shoots). They are undesirable because they deplete plants of food and also distract from the tree's form and general attractiveness. Sometimes shoots arise from the roots of adult trees such as aspen (*Populus tremula*) as part of their natural development. Suckers may arise when certain plants such as black poplar (*Poplar nigra*) are wounded. These shoots should be removed.

19.11.2 REPAIRING DAMAGE

Trees in the landscape may suffer damage from a variety of sources. Lightning, strong winds, hail, ice, and other weather-related damage may occur. Humans may vandalize and landscape maintenance equipment physically damage trees. Animals in the landscape may also cause injury. Broken branches and torn barks need to be repaired by cutting them away.

19.11.3 REMOVING DISEASED BRANCHES

Deadwood provides a hiding place for insects and tissue for disease organisms including fungi. Any diseased branches should be removed.

19.11.4 PROVIDING PHYSICAL SUPPORT

Sometimes tree branches become excessively inclined and need to be physically propped up to avoid snapping (Figure 19–18). Propping with a forked branch may help to enhance the appearance of a tree by improving its form.

Epicormic Shoots
Shoots that develop from previously dormant buds under tree bark after being stimulated by external factors such as wounding.

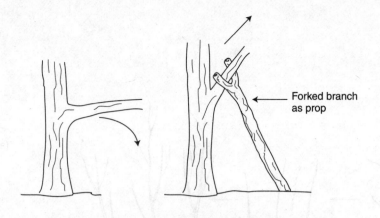

Forked branch
as prop

19.12 RENOVATING ESTABLISHED TREES

The purpose of renovation is to rejuvenate a tree that has been neglected for a long time in order to restore tree form. Sometimes a tree may have to be felled. Pruning for renovation may involve either minor or major cuts. Trees are usually renovated when they are dormant. To avoid disease infection, wounds should be properly treated for quick healing.

A tree may grow unevenly in terms of form or shape because it encounters an obstruction that suppresses normal growth and development on one side of the tree. When the obstruction is removed, the tree may be renovated to stimulate growth on the suppressed part. As previously indicated, vigorous growth is restored to the suppressed side by pruning that area.

19.13 SPECIAL TRAINING AND PRUNING TECHNIQUES

Sometimes trees may be cut back drastically to allow for new growth. The severe pruning may be used to create unique and fascinating structures in the landscape. Examples of such artistic creations are described in the following sections. It should be noted that few species will tolerate this degree of pruning.

19.13.1 POLLARDING

Pollarding entails a severe pruning of the plant after it has attained its maximum desirable height. Trees may be headed when they attain a height of 8 to 12 feet (2.4 to 3.6 meters). The tree top is cut back drastically during its dormant period (winter). Scaffold branches are headed when they are about 2 to 5 feet (0.61 to 1.5 meters) long. When spring starts, new buds sprout below each cut. These water sprouts are removed each year as they recur. Repeated pruning leaves the tops of branches in clumps of growth resembling stubs. Infection by decay organisms is minimal because the branches that are pruned are small in diameter and hence incur only small wounds. This look is desirable in spring, but in the fall and winter seasons, the plants look unattractive without the foliage, though the stumps create some interest in the landscape. Ornamental trees that may be pollarded successfully include elm, sycamore, poplar, and willow. The colorful stems of dogwood (*Cornus* spp.) and willow (*Salix* spp.) add attraction to the stumps in winter.

19.13.2 COPPICING

In coppicing, pruning is even more extreme than in pollarding. The tree is cut back to leave a short stump (forming the stool) from which new growth emerges. Trees such as

Greenhouse structures: (a) Double poly hoop house covered with a woven plastic shade screen. (b) Venlo style greenhouse used for vegetable production. (c) Open-roof greenhouse. (d) Retractable roof greenhouse used for overwintering of nursery crops. (e) Aspirated box containing temperature and humidity sensors connected to the computereized environmental contral system. (f) A high pressure sodium (HPS) lamp. (g) Dual-fuel boiler system. (h) Greenhouse floor heating. (i) A layer of insulation along the knee wall (curtain wall) helps reduce unwanted heat loss. (j) Evaporative cooling pads. (k) Moving tables allowing for maximized space efficiency of the greenhouse growing area. *(Source:* Courtesy of Dr. A.J. Both, Ph.D. Bioresource Engineering, Department of Plant Biology and Pathology, Rutgers University, New Brunswick, NJ.)

(a)

(b)

(d)

(c)

(f)

(e)

(g)

Greenhouse irrigation: (a) Automated irrigation boom can be programmed to deliver different amounts of water to different crops as it travels the length of the greenhouse. (b) Overhead sprinkler irrigation system. (c) Irrigation carrousel for hanging baskets; an irrigation point can service an entire string of hanging baskets as they are automatically moved one-by-one past the irrigation point. (d) Components of a fertilizer and acid injection system. **Bag Culture:** (e) Tomato plants growing in rockwool bags; these plants are drip-irrigated. (f) Fruiting tomato plants; the spindly stems are supported by strings dropped from the roof. The two hot water pipes located on the floor between plant rows are also used as tracks fro carts for general maintenance and harvesting of fruits. (g) Ripe tomato fruits packaged for the market. *(Sources:* Photos a–d are courtesy of Dr. A.J. Both, Ph.D. Bioresource Engineering, Department of Plant Biology and Pathology, Rutgers University, New Brunswick, NJ: photos e–g, are courtesy of Dr. Louis D. Albright, Professor of Biological and Environmental Engineering and Stephen H. Weiss Presidential Fellow, Cornell University, Ithaca, NY.)

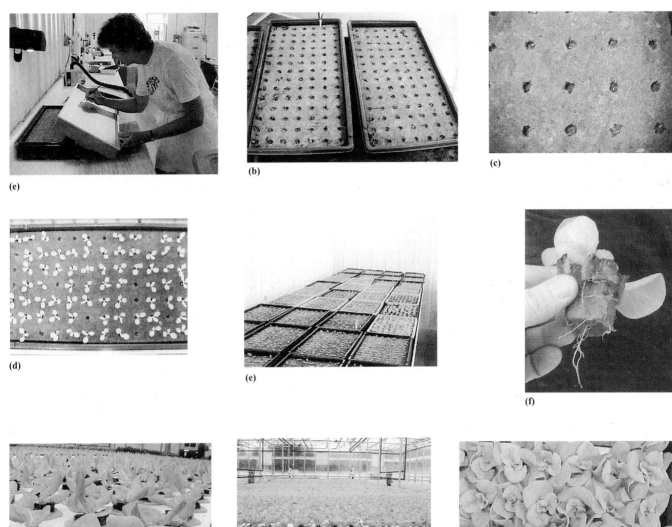

(e)

(b)

(c)

(d)

(e)

(f)

(g)

(h)

(i)

(j)

Hydroponic culture of lettuce by the NTF (nutrient film) system: (a) A worker uses a vacuum seeder to sow lettuce seeds into rockwool slabs. (b) Little suction holes in the seeder tray line up with small indentations on the rockwool slab. (c) Seeds starting to germinate. (d) Young seedlings. (e) Seedlings in growth room. (f) Seedling plug ready (after 12 days) to be transplanted onto Styrofoam™ floaters. (g) Blue plastic rings are used to hold each seedling cube in an upright position. (h) Styrofoam™ floaters with seedlings are place on top of nutrient solution in a pond. (i) Seedlings crowd each other after about 10 days and must be respaced. (j) Plants are ready for harvesting after 36 days. *(Source:* Courtesy of Dr. Louis D. Albright, Professor of Biological and Environmental Engineering, and Stephen H. Weiss, Presidential Fellow, Cornell University, Ithaca, NY.)

(a)

(b)

(c)

(d)

(e)

(f)

Greenhouse production: (a) Greenhouse production of cut lettuce in soil. (b) Greenhouse production of strawberry in troughs suspended from the greenhouse frame. (c) Drum seeder line used to precision-seed plugs trays. (d)Robotic arm used to fill (or empty) a movable table with small potted plants, each row of pots is placed on a conveyer belt. (e) High volume transplanter used to transplant plug (background) into liners (foreground). (f) Roll-out benches used by spring bedding plant growers. *(Source:* Courtesy of Dr. A.J. Both, Ph. D. Bioresource Engineering, Department of Plant Biology and Pathology, Rutgers University, New Brunswick, NJ.)

Succulents: (a) *Agave Americana* 'Marginata, (b) *Aloe ferox*, (c) *Beschorneria yuccoides*, (d) Zebra plant (*Haworthia altenuata*), (e) Common house-leek (*Sempervivum tectorum*), (f) Milkweed or spurge (*Euphorbia candelabrum*), (g) *Kalanchoe blossfeldiana*, (h) Donkey's tail (*Sedum morganianum*). (*Sources:* (a–d,g) © Dorling Kindersley; (e) Frank Greenaway © Dorling Kindersley; (f,h) Deni Bown © Dorling Kindersley.)

Sempervivums: (a) *Sempervivum montanum*, (b) *Sempervivum tectorum*. **Sedums:** (c) *Sedum kamtschaticum*, (d) *Sedum telephinum*, (e) *Sedum lydium*, (f) *Sedum spectabile*, and (g) *Sedum spurium*. *(Sources:* (a,b,e,f) © Dorling Kindersley; (c) Beth Chatto © Dorling Kindersley; (d) Andrew Lawson © Dorling Kindersley; (g) Jonathan Buckley © Dorling Kindersley.)

Cacti genus: (a) *Parodia leninghausii* (gold ginger), (b) *Echnocactus grusonii*, (c) *Echnocactus pulchellus*, (d) *Echnopsis* 'Forty niner', (e) *Rebutia krainziana*, (f) *Escobaria vivipara* (pincushion), (g) *Mammillaria sempervivi*, (h) *Gymnocalycium saglionis*, and (i) *Ferocactus hamatacanthus* (Turk's head cactus). (*Sources:* (a,b,e,f,h,i) © Dorling Kindersley; (c) Deni Bown © Dorling Kindersley; (d) Peter Anderson © Dorling Kindersley; (g) Andrew Lawson © Dorling Kindersley.)

Evergreens also exhibit tremendous variation in form, size, and other characteristics (a, b). Popular examples include the Blue spruce (c), Black Hills spruce (d), Dwarf Alberta spruce (e), and the Colorado Blue spruce (f). Low-growing evergreens are used in a variety of ways in the landscape. Examples are the Mugho pine (g) and the Blue Chip Juniper (h).

(a)

(b)

(c)

(d)

(f)

(e)

(g)

Planting Trees: Newly planted young trees may be given physical support during the first year by using (a) Single tall stake, (b) Double low stakes, (c) Guying. Guy wires are passed through pieces of rubber tubes to prevent damage to the tree (d). **Training Trees:** In the first year tooth picks and clothespins may be used to spread young limbs to develop desired crotch angle (e–f). In succeeding years, limb spreaders are used to spread tree limbs for proper growth and fruiting (g). (*Source*: (a,b,d) Peter Anderson © Dorling Kindersley; (c) © Dorling Kindersley; (e–g) Courtesy of Dr. Michael L. Parker, Associate Professor and Tree Fruit Extension Specialist, Department of Horticultural Science, North Carolina Cooperative Extension Service, North Carolina State University.)

Pruning cuts: (a) Proper way and position to cut a limb. (b) Improper procedure (cutting from the top first) used in cutting a large limb can result in a snap and tear of the bark (c) Variety of cuts (from left to right): cut is too close to the bud; angle of cut is too steep and too close to the bud; cut is a good distance from bud, but better to be slanted than flush; a snapped branch. **Steps in cutting a large limb:** (d1) The first cut is always from the bottom (undercut). (d2) The second cut is from the top and to the side of the first cut away from the trunk to remove the limb. (d3) The third cut is used to remove the stump. (d4) A clean cut close to the collar of the limb is desired. (*Sources*: (a,d) © Dorling Kindersley; (b,c) Peter Anderson © Dorling Kindersley.)

Pruning: (a1) Quince tree before pruning, (a2) Quince tree after pruning, (b1) Gnarled spurs of unpruned pear in winter, (b2) Pruned spurs, (c) a well-trimed yew (*Taxus* sp.) hedge with tapering top, (d) Topiary. (*Sources*: (a–c) Peter Anderson © Dorling Kindersley; (d) Steven Wooster © Dorling Kindersley.)

Pollarding of *Catalpa bigniodes,* before (a1) and after (a2). **Coppicing** of Hazel, before (b1) and after (b2). **Pruning** gooseberry bush, before (c1) and after (c2), pruning black currant bush, before (d1) and after (d2). (*Sources*: (a2) Jeffrey Harpur © Dorling Kindersley; all other photos Peter Anderson © Dorling Kindersley.)

Fall leaf color changes: (a) Maple leaf color changing; (b) Color changes in a variety of leaves. (*Sources*: (a) Peter Chadwick © Dorling Kindersley; (b) Dave King © Dorling Kindersley.) **Plasticulture:** (c) Use of floating row covers placed over a potato crop to increase ambient air temperature around plant and keep Colorado potato beetles from feeding on potato foliage. (*Source*: Couresy of Dr. William Lamont, Pennsylvania State University.) (d) Different mulch colors are currently being used in commercial vegetable production including red, blue, white, reflective silver, and IRT green. (*Source*: Courtesy of Dr. Mike Orzolek, Pennsylvania State University.) (e) Low November in central Pennsylvania. (*Source*: Courtesy of Catie Rasmussen, Pennsylvania State Center for Pasticulture.) (f) Snapdragon production in high tunnel at Penn State High Tunnel Research and Education Facility, Rock Springs, PA. (*Source*: Courtesy of Dr. Mike Orzolek, Pennsylvania State University.)

(a)

(b)

(c)

(d)

Floral design: (a) *Abstract Designs* use non-realistic use of natural and/or man-made materials solely as pure elements to create a statement suggesting a specific emotion. (b) *Formalinear Designs* have relatively few, but well organized materials that emphasize bold forms and clean lines. Notice in this design that each material has its own space to emphasize its unique form. (c) *Geometric Designs* have radial stem placement and are based on the fundamental forms of geometry, i.e. triangles (shown), asymmetrical triangles, round centerpiece, fan-shaped, etc. (Synonyms include Western Line and Line-Mass designs). (d) *Ikebana Design* – Ikebana is the Japanese art of floral design, when literally translated means "to arrange flowers." It is characterized by simplicity of materials, with well thought-out placements that represent different aspects of nature and/or man's relationship with nature. Typically there are three primary lines placements called Shin (heaven), Soe (man), and Tai (earth). (*Source:* Photographs by Laura Cicarella, Michael Klein and James Lyle - used by permission of San Jacinto Publishing Co.)

(a)

(b)

(c)

Floral design: (a) *Interpretive designs* are organized to evoke a desired theme, idea, occasion, style or period. This design has a theme of both color (green) and materials used (fruits/vegetables). (b) *Parallel designs* use parallel stem placement of groupings of flowers. This design would be considered a "decorative" parallel, because much of the negative space (which is typical in parallel designs) between the groupings is massed with additional materials. (c) *Vegetative designs* use plant materials in a naturalistic manner to resemble plants growing together in specific environment. Most commercial vegetative designs, such as the one shown, are not "pure" vegetative designs, but rather adaptations for easier marketability that appeal to customer aesthetics. (*Source*: Photographs by Laura Cicarella, Michael Klein and James Lyle. Used by permission of San Jacinto Publishing Co.)

(a)

(b)

(c)

(d)

(e)

The variety of bonsai designs include: (a,b) multiple plants or forest bonsai; (c,d,e) single plants; (b,d) species that change color in fall; and (c,e) creative forms. (*Sources*: (a–d) Paul Goff © Dorling Kindersley; (e) Linda Whitman © Dorling Kindersley.)

Eucalyptus and *Paulownia* are amenable to such treatment. Coppicing and pollarding both have dwarfing effects on plants.

19.13.3 PLEACHING

Pleaching is a technique used to weave together the branches of a row of trees that, with appropriate pruning, can develop into a hedge. Species adapted to this kind of treatment include linden, hornbeam, and holly.

19.13.4 TOPIARY

Topiary may be described as the art of plant sculpture in which plants are trained and pruned into formal shapes. These shapes may be abstract or geometric and sometimes may be readily recognizable objects such as animals. Topiary may be created in container plants, in the garden, or in the general landscape. Sometimes the top of a hedge is capped with a topiary.

Topiary
Training and pruning of plants into formal shapes, sometimes geometric or abstract but highly stylized.

    The simplest designs are those closest to the natural shape of the plant. To create complex forms, a metal framework is first designed and placed over the plant so that it grows into and over it. The plant is then carefully clipped to shape, following the outline of the framework. Horticultural techniques such as pinching, training, and tying are used to encourage dense growth to cover and hide the framework. When pruning, a straightedge and other guides often are required for accuracy. Without such guides one may cut too much on one side, which may require that the whole piece be reworked to obtain the geometric symmetry desired.

    Geometric shapes are difficult to create and maintain. To keep them attractive, the sides and surfaces must be properly cut to the symmetrical, sharp, and well-angled shapes. Round shapes are relatively easier to create and maintain. It is very important to use sharp tools in pruning and for the operator to exercise patience, proceeding cautiously. Common and more or less standard shapes are the poodle or cake stand and the spiral (Figure 19–19). To create complex and irregular shapes, one must be very creative and patient. The species most frequently used for topiary include those that are easy to train such as yew (*Taxus*), boxwood (*Boxus*), and bay (*Laurus nobilis*). These plants are evergreen and long-lived.

    Topiaries need to be maintained to keep them in form and attractive. Like all plants, they require fertilizing and watering to enable regrowth after cutting. They also need frequent routines of maintenance clipping during the growing season. The frequency of clipping depends on the species, plant vigor, form, design, and demands of the owner. If owned by a perfectionist who must have the plant in great shape all of the time, very frequent pruning will be required. Species such as the yew can be presentable with about two clippings per year. However, if the design is geometric, a monthly schedule may be required to remove any new growth. Over time, certain portions of the plant may become damaged and require repair. The damaged part should be removed and a nearby shoot trained to fill the gap. Depending on the damage, it may take up to several years to restore the topiary to its original form.

19.14 TRAINING AND PRUNING FRUIT TREES

Fruit-bearing tree training goals are similar to those of ornamental trees. These goals include the following:

1. To develop strong branches to bear the weight of fruits.
2. To properly space and retain an appropriate number of branches for enhanced productivity.
3. To control the time of first fruiting. While fruiting should not be delayed, the quality of fruits and the duration of fruiting period are increased when trees

a)

b)

c)

d)

FIGURE 19–19 Common topiary designs: a) pompon, b) spiral, and c), d) topiary shaped into recognizable forms ("plant sculpturing") such as animals. *(Source: George Acquaah)*

are not allowed to fruit in the early years (three to five years). The heavy weight of fruits may injure young plant limbs and jeopardize productivity in later years.

4. To facilitate production operations such as harvesting, pruning, and spraying.
5. To produce attractive tree shapes, which is particularly important if fruit trees occur in the landscape.
6. To provide physical support for weak stems. In dwarf and semidwarf fruit trees, some kind of support system is needed to aid the tree in bearing the weight of heavy fruits. The limbs may be propped with a notched-end piece of wood.
7. To confine the tree to the space available.

Training of fruit trees may involve developing wider crotches, perhaps by using spreaders. A crotch alteration should be done when the trees are young. The degree of

Training & Pruning Deciduous Fruit Trees

Michael L. Parker, Ph.D.

Associate Professor and Tree Fruit Extension Specialist

Department of Horticultural Science
North Carolina Cooperative Extension Service
North Carolina State University

Growers of fruit trees often neglect the annual training and pruning of fruit trees. Without training and pruning, however, fruit trees will not develop proper shape and form. Properly trained and pruned trees will yield high quality fruit earlier, produce more high quality fruit and live significantly longer than poorly or unmanaged trees.

A primary objective of training and pruning is to develop a strong tree framework that will support fruit production. Improperly trained fruit trees generally have very upright branch and crotch angles, which result in limb breakage under a heavy fruit load. This significantly reduces the productivity of the tree and may greatly reduce tree life. Another goal of annual training and pruning is to remove dead, diseased, or broken limbs. Proper tree training also opens up the tree canopy to maximize light penetration. For most deciduous tree fruit, flower buds for the current season's crop are formed the previous summer. Light penetration is essential for flower bud development and optimal fruit set, flavor, and quality. Although a mature tree may be growing in full sun, a very dense canopy may not allow enough light to reach 12 to 18 inches inside the canopy to allow for fruit production. Opening the tree canopy also permits adequate air movement through the tree, which promotes rapid drying to minimize disease infection and allows thorough pesticide penetration. Additionally, a well shaped fruit tree is aesthetically pleasing, whether in a landscaped yard, garden, or commercial orchard.

Pruning vs. Training

Historically, fruit tree form and structure have been maintained by pruning. Tree training, however, is a much more efficient and desirable way to develop form and structure.

Pruning is the removal of a portion of a tree that is used to correct or maintain tree structure. Training is a relatively new practice in which tree growth is directed into a desired shape and form. Training young fruit trees is ideal for proper tree development. It is better to direct tree growth with training than to correct it with pruning.

Pruning is most often done during the winter, commonly referred to as dormant pruning. Training includes summer training and summer pruning as well as dormant pruning. The goal of tree training is to direct tree growth and minimize pruning.

Types of Pruning Cuts

Thinning Cut

Removal of an entire shoot. Thinning cuts do not invigorate the tree in comparison to other pruning cuts.

Heading Cut

Removal of only the terminal portion of a shoot. This type of cut promotes the growth of lower buds, which is most vigorous in the 3–4 buds directly beneath the cut. When lateral branches are headed into one-year-old wood, the area near the cut is invigorated. The headed branch is much stronger and rigid, resulting in lateral secondary branching. Older trees can be held in their allotted space by "mold and hold cuts", which are devigorating heading cuts made into at least two-year-old wood. Young trees and branches where heading cuts are made will be referred to as headed.

Bench Cut

Removal of vigorous, upright shoots back to outward growing side branches. Bench cuts are frequently used in open center systems to open the center of the tree and spread the branches outward. *This is a major cut and should only be used only when necessary.*

One criterion that will determine the type of cut being made in fruit trees is where the fruit is borne on the tree. For pome fruit and pecans, the fruit are borne primarily on the terminal buds of shoots and spurs (short branches). If many heading cuts are used on these trees the fruit is being removed. However, in most stone fruit the fruit are borne on lateral buds on one-year-old wood and heading cuts are used to stiffen the branches to bear the fruit load as well as to thin the crop to a management level for the coming season.

When making pruning cuts, it is important to use techniques that will allow the cut surface to heal quickly. Rapid healing minimizes the incidence of disease and insect infection. Pruning cuts should be flush with the adjacent branch outside of the branch collar without leaving stubs. Also, when large horizontal cuts are made, they should be slightly angled so that water does not set on the cut surface, allowing the growth of rot and disease organisms.

Many compounds are available as wound dressing or pruning paints. But the best treatment is to make proper pruning cuts and allow the tree to heal naturally. If preferred, tree paints and wound dressing may be used for aesthetic reasons, but they will not promote healing.

DORMANT PRUNING VS. SUMMER PRUNING

Trees respond very differently to dormant and summer pruning. Dormant pruning is an invigorating process. During the fall, energy is stored primarily in the trunk and root system to support the top portion of the tree. If a large portion of the tree is removed during the winter, while the tree is dormant, the tree's energy reserve is unchanged. In the spring, the tree responds by producing many new vigorous, upright shoots, called water sprouts, which can shade the interior of the tree and inhibit proper development. Heavy dormant pruning also promotes excessive vegetative vigor, which uses much of the tree's energy, leaving little for fruit set, growth and development.

Historically, much of the vigorous, upright vegetative growth has been removed during the dormant season; heavy dormant pruning results in a yearly cycle with excessive vegetative growth with little to no fruit production.

Dormant pruning should begin as late in the winter as possible to avoid winter injury. Apple and pecan trees should be pruned first, followed by cherry, peach, and plum trees. A good rule to follow is to prune the latest blooming trees first and the earliest blooming last. Another factor to consider is tree age. Within a particular fruit type, the oldest trees should be pruned first. Younger trees are more prone to winter injury from early pruning, especially in climates where large fluctuations in winter temperatures occur.

Summer pruning eliminates an energy or food producing portion of the tree and can result in reduced tree growth in the year of pruning and increase light penetration. Summer pruning is not as severe as dormant pruning and usually only results in the removal of current seasons' growth done by hand or with hand pruners. Pruning can begin as soon as the buds start to grow, but it is generally started after vegetative growth is several inches long. For most purposes, summer pruning should be limited to removing the upright and vigorous current season's growth; only thinning cuts should be used. To minimize the potential for winter injury, summer pruning should not be done after the end of July in the Southeastern United States.

TRAINING SYSTEMS

One of the most frequently asked questions is, "To what shape should I train my fruit tree?"

It is difficult to give one answer. You can choose from many different training shapes and forms with multiple variations on each form. This chapter will focus primarily on the central leader and open center training systems for medium density orchards. A list of fruit trees conventionally trained to each system is also included. A fruit tree may be trained to any system. Depending on the form and function of the desired shape, you may want to train a tree to a nontraditional system.

Whatever system you chose, keep in mind that the objectives of training and pruning are to achieve maximum tree life and productivity.

CENTRAL LEADER TRAINING – APPLE, CHERRY, PEAR, PECAN, PLUM

A central leader tree is characterized by one main, upright trunk, referred to as the leader. Branching generally begins on the leader 24 to 36 inches above the soil surface to allow equipment and labor movement under the tree. The first year, 3 to 4 branches, collectively called a *scaffold whorl,* are selected. The selected scaffolds should be uniformly spaced around the trunk, not directly across from or above one another. Above the first scaffold whorl, leave an area of approximately 18 to 24 inches without any branches to allow light into the center of the tree. This light slot is followed with another whorl of scaffolds. Alternating scaffold whorls and light slots are maintained up the leader to the desired maximum tree height. See Figure 1.

The shape of a properly trained central leader tree is like that of a Christmas tree. The lowest scaffold whorl branches will be the longest and the higher scaffold whorl branches will be progressively shorter to allow maximum light penetration into the entire tree.

DEVELOPING A CENTRAL LEADER TRAINED TREE AT PLANTING

Fruit trees are frequently purchased as whips, which are unbranched trees ranging from 1/2 to 3/4 inch diameter. The tree should be planted in early winter with the graft union 2 inches above the soil surface. Just before the buds start to grow in the spring, the tree should be headed, or cut off, at 30 to 34 inches above the soil surface. The height at which the tree is headed depends upon where you want the first whorl of branches. Once the tree is headed, permanent branches will be selected from buds growing within 4 to 12 inches below the heading cut. See Figures 1 and 2.

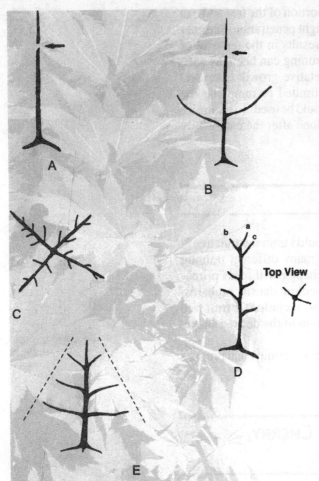

A At Planting
As the buds begin to swell, head the tree at 30 to 34 inches above the soil surface.

B Dormant Pruning
Head the tree at 24 to 30 inches above the highest branch of the first scaffold whorl.

C Top View

D First-Year Summer Pruning
Summer prune when new growth is 3 to 4 inches long. Leave a as the new leader, and remove b and c. Select four uniformly spaced laterals for the first scaffold whorl, and remove the remaining lateral branches.

Steps in Pruning:
• Leave only one trunk for the central leader.
• Remove branches with crotch angles less than 60 degrees.
• Remove all branches directly across from one another on the leader.
• Space lateral branches uniformly around the leader to prevent crowding as the limbs grow in diameter.

E After pruning the third year
Three scaffold whorls have been developed with three to four branches uniformly spaced around the tree in each whorl. A light slot of 18 to 24 inches is left between each scaffold whorl. Note the pyramidal tree shape that allows light penetration to the lower branches and interior of the tree.

FIGURE 1 Pruning a central leader tree

Summer Pruning

After the new vegetative growth has reached 3 to 4 inches in length, summer pruning should begin. The first step is to select one upright shoot near the top of the tree to be the leader. After selecting the leader shoot, remove all other competing shoots for approximately 4 inches below it; rehead the tree above this leader. See Figures 3 and 4.

At this time, side shoots (laterals) should be spread out to form a crotch angle of at least 60 to 70 degrees between the leader and the side shoot. This angle is referred to as the branch or crotch angle. Branches that do not have a wide crotch angle are overly vigorous and have a weak point of attachment to the leader. These branches frequently break under a heavy fruit load. Spreading the lateral branches will also reduce the growth of the branches to a manageable level and promote the development of secondary or side shoots on the scaffolds. When growth is only 3 to 4 inches, toothpicks or spring clothespins can be used to spread branches. See Figure 5. However, with a flat crotch angle the branch will grow upward so that the orientation of the branch will be more upright than the angle of the crotch. After a proper branch angle is attained, clothespins can be moved to the ends of longer limbs to weigh down the branches as they start to grow upward.

FIGURE 2 Newly planted apple tree headed back
(Source: Michael L. Parker)

a)   b)

FIGURE 3 a) Heading an apple tree at planting results in several competing shoots below the cut.
b) For central leader tree, a single leader needs to be selected by removing the undesired shoots. *(Source: Michael L. Parker)*

a)   b)

FIGURE 4 Central leader plum trees must also have competing shoots removed. *(Source: Michael L. Parker)*

During the first year, minimize further summer pruning. Limit it to the removal of shoots growing upright. Summer is the optimal time to select the leader and scaffold branches and remove undesirable growth. Branches lower than the desired height should also be removed. A young orchard or tree should be summer trained and pruned once a month through July to remove unwanted growth and to properly orient young branches. Summer pruning will greatly reduce the amount of dormant pruning needed.

a)　　　　　　　b)

c)　　　　　　　d)

FIGURE 5 Central leader apple trees. Toothpicks and clothespins can be used to spread the lateral branches outward during the first growing season. *(Source: Michael L. Parker)*

Failure to summer prune the first year will result in an improperly trained tree, and drastic dormant pruning will be required to correct tree structure.

Succeeding Years

Managing the central leader is one of the most important aspects of dormant pruning. The leader should be headed at approximately 24 to 30 inches above the highest whorl of scaffolds to promote continued branching and scaffold whorl development. Dormant pruning should also eliminate dead, diseased, and damaged wood. Unwanted growth, such as upright growing shoots and laterals with sharp branch angles not removed during summer pruning, should also be removed at this time. Unbranched lateral branches should be headed back by approximately 1/4 of their length to encourage side branches and to stiffen lateral branches.

Summer pruning in succeeding years should eliminate competing shoots where dormant heading cuts were made (on the central leader and laterals) as in the first year. Summer is also the optimal time to remove unwanted side shoots and excessive growth.

FIGURE 6 Wooden limb spreaders can be made from wood and finishing nails in various lengths.

(Source: Michael L. Parker)

FIGURE 7 Well-trained semi-dwarf apple tree. Note the wide branch crotch angles and the development of scaffold whorls.

(Source: Michael L. Parker)

All laterals should have a wide crotch angle, and spreading of lateral branches is essential for many varieties. Lateral branches will need to be spread for about the first five years, using a larger spreader each year. The ideal is to encourage fruit development on the laterals close to the trunk to aid in spreading the lateral branches.

In addition to commercially purchased spreaders, spreaders can also be made with one inch square wood pieces with a finishing nail driven in the end and cut off at an angle. Spreaders are frequently made in lengths of 6, 12, and 18 inches. See Figure 6. The wood used for the spreaders should be commercial grade lumber and not branches from the orchard which could harbor disease pathogens.

Spreading branches in later years reduces vigor and promotes fruit development on the lateral branches. The reduced growth rate and the weight of the crop load will also help pull the branches down to a proper angle. However, it is important that the young tree is not allowed to crop too early where the weight of the fruit pulls the branches below horizontal. Once the branches are below horizontal, they are weak and nonproductive and need to be removed and replaced. See Figure 7.

Another objective of dormant pruning is to control the length of the lateral branches. In order to maintain the pyramidal tree shape (Figure 1), lateral branches need to be cut back. Once the tree has reached its desired height and lateral spread, it will be necessary to "mold and hold" the lateral branches and the central leader with heading cuts. This can be done by cutting the laterals and leader back into two-year-old wood to a side growing shoot. It is a good rule to cut back to a side shoot that is close to the same diameter as the lateral or leader being cut.

Mature Trees

Mature trees that have been properly trained and summer pruned will require minimal pruning. The first step would be to remove dead, diseased, and damaged wood and then upright shoots and shoots below horizontal. To prevent shading, it is important to maintain the pyramidal tree shape by heading lateral branches with mold and hold cuts. See Figure 8. For quality fruit production, it is also essential that the light slots between the scaffold whorls be maintained.

FIGURE 8 Mature, well-trained apple tree. Note that the distance between branches needs to be increased for larger trees.
(Source: Michael L. Parker)

Mature fruit trees that have not been properly trained frequently do not have a true central leader shape. For those trees, the objectives of training and pruning, as discussed earlier, must be considered. In many cases, too many lateral branches and upright limbs (some may be 6 or more inches in diameter) have been left and need to be removed to allow proper light penetration. This pruning needs to be done during the dormant season.

Neglected trees often have overgrown tops that act as an umbrella, shading the rest of the tree. The tops of these trees need to be cut back or removed. Remember, if the principles of pruning are followed, there are no perfect cuts and no incorrect cuts. However, do not remove more than 30 percent of the tree at a time to avoid shifting the tree into an excessively vegetative state with little fruit development.

Pecan Tree Consideration

Pecan trees should be trained to a central leader. The lateral branches, however, should be spiraled up the leader. Approximately 12 to 15 inches should be left between branches for adequate light penetration initially. As the tree matures it will be necessary to remove branches to prevent crowding and allow light penetration.

MODIFICATIONS OF THE CENTRAL LEADER

Multi-leader Tree

A multi-leader tree is the goal of another training system and an ideal option for pear varieties in regions that are very susceptible to fire blight. With a multi-leader tree, if one leader is infected with fire blight, it may be removed without loss of the major portion of the tree. See Figure 9.

The multi-leader tree uses the same concept as the central leader tree except there are several leaders in the center of the tree. Each leader is maintained the same as an individual central leader tree. The only difference in training a multi-leader from the central leader is that in the first and second year instead of removing the competing leaders, several should be left and maintained. On the tree in Figure 1, it would be necessary to leave shoots a, b, and c for a multi-leader tree. However, it would be necessary to put spreaders between the selected leaders to get the shape of the tree in Figure 9.

FIGURE 9. An apple tree trained to a multi-leader system. This would be an ideal training system for pear trees in the southeastern United States where fire blight is a serious threat, even on fire blight resistant cultivars.
(Source: Michael L. Parker)

Higher Density Central Leader Training Systems

In the commercial apple industry, there is a need and trend to establish higher density orchards with 1,000 or more trees per acre. There are many types of higher density training systems, some with elaborate trellis systems. Two of the better known higher density training systems are the slender spindle and vertical axis. Both are central leader trees with branches continually along the central leader to the top of the tree. The first requirement for higher density systems is smaller trees, which is accomplished with size controlling, dwarfing, rootstocks. High density systems must also use a trunk support for each tree, either a stake or trellis, or combination of the two. Light penetration is not a problem as the maximum height of the tree is limited to approximately 6 to 12 feet, with a canopy spread of 3 to 4 feet outward from the leader.

OPEN CENTER OR VASE TRAINING - PEACH, NECTARINE, PLUM

With the open center system, the leader is removed, leaving an open center. Instead of having a central leader, the open center tree has three to five major limbs, called scaffolds, coming out from the trunk. This training system allows for adequate light penetration into the tree, which minimizes the shading problem prevalent in higher vigor trees such as peach.

At Planting

At planting, peach trees should be set so that the graft union will be two inches above the soil surface. As the buds begin to swell, the unbranched trees (whips) are generally headed approximately 30 to 34 inches above the soil surface. As discussed with the central leader system, new branches with wider crotch angles will come from the buds that are 6 to 9 inches below the heading cut.

Trees that are branched at planting are handled differently than the whips. The work that needs to be done under the tree determines the appropriate height for branching, which is usually 24 to 32 inches. Remove branches that are too low. If there are three to four uniformly spaced branches around the tree that can be selected as scaffolds, the tree is headed just above the highest selected scaffold. Any remaining branches not selected as scaffolds should be removed. However, if there are less than three scaffolds the tree should be cut back to a whip and the side branches removed. See Figures 10a and 10b.

Summer Pruning

After the new vegetative growth is approximately three to four inches long, it is time to select the shoots that will become the major scaffolds. The lowest scaffold should be 24 to 32 inches above the soil surface to avoid interfering with cultural work under the tree, such as harvesting and weed control. It is best to select three to four scaffolds that are uniformly spaced around the tree, with wide crotch angles, and not directly across from another scaffold. See Figure 10a. During the summer it is best to come back through every month during the summer to remove upright growth that is shading the primary scaffolds.

Succeeding Years

After the first year of growth, the primary scaffolds should be selected and properly trained outward. Scaffolds should be headed during the dormant season of the first three

a)

b)

FIGURE 10 (a) Training and pruning young peach trees.
Left: Well-branched peach tree to be trained to an open-center system
Right: 3 to 5 well-spaced scaffolds re selected and the tree is headed above the highest scaffold.
(b) Training and pruning young peach trees.
Left: Tree after heading, branches lower than 24 inches are also removed.
Right: Top view of uniformly spaced scaffolds. *(Source: Michael L. Parker)*

years to promote continued lateral branching on the scaffolds and to stiffen and strengthen the scaffold. At two to three foot from the trunk the primary scaffolds will also be allowed to fork to allow two secondary scaffolds in order to fill the allotted space of the tree. Scaffolds should be headed to outward growing shoots similar in angle to those being removed. Bench cuts should be avoided. See Figure 11a.

If summer pruning is being practiced, undesirable shoot growth can be removed as soon as growth is four to six inches long. Summer pruning can also be used to direct scaffold growth outward to the desired growing points instead of waiting until the dormant season.

For bearing trees, the goal of dormant pruning is to remove vigorous upright growth on the scaffolds and trunk that was not removed during the summer. See Figure 11b.

The upright growth left in the tree during the growing season may shade out lateral growth near the trunk. This shading results in lateral fruiting wood only on the ends of the scaffolds, which results in broken scaffolds under a heavy fruit load. It is best to keep the fruiting wood on the scaffolds as close to the tree trunk as possible to reduce tree breakage and to produce the highest quality fruit.

Also, during the dormant season, damaged, dead, and diseased wood, such as cankers, should be removed from the tree. Shoots with shriveled and dried fruit from the previous season, called mummies, should also be removed from the orchard to reduce disease pressure for the coming season.

a)

b)

FIGURE 11 (a) Dormant pruning a mature open-center peach tree.
Left: One-half of tree pruned.
Right: Heading a scaffold to an outward growing shoot.
(b) Dormant pruning a mature open-center peach tree.
Left: Removal of vigorous upright shoots in the center of the tree.
Right: Tree after pruning.   (Source: Michael L. Parker)

spreading or bending affects shoot growth and development. If too wide (e.g., 90 degrees), water sprout growth is stimulated. These shoots should be pruned. Narrower crotches (about 30 degrees) slightly suppress terminal growth while increasing the number and length of side branches. Moderate angles (45 to 60 degrees) have an intermediate effect between the narrow and wide crotches. Whenever physical support is needed, tying is often involved. Tree trunks should not be too tightly restrained to a support but allowed some room to move in the wind. Wind movement allows the trunk to develop strength in its wood for additional support. Wide-angled crotches encourage the development of strength in the wood of the limb and thereby improve its resistance to damage from the weight of fruits or snow accumulation. Narrow-angled crotches are prone to damage because of weakness resulting from the formation of *bark inclusions* (Figure 19–20).

19.14.1 TRAINING SYSTEMS FOR FRUIT TREES

Pruning and training of fruit-bearing trees are done together to increase productivity and ease harvesting and other operations. These practices start early in the growth of plants, a strategy that prevents young trees from overbearing too early, an event that adversely affects plant structure and productivity later in life (see chapter boxed reading.)

19.14.2 TRELLIS TRAINING SYSTEM

Trellis training involves tying limbs of plants to wires strung between posts or constructed against a wall or fence. Materials for tying range from wires to masking tape and should be of a material that will not damage the limbs. Common trellis training systems are described in the following sections.

Espalier

Espalier
A training system in which the tree or shrub is made to grow flat against a wall or on a trellis, often in formal branch patterns.

The goal of **espalier** training is to create a work of art confined to a specific space; as such, it requires heavy pruning to control shoots on top of horizontal limbs. The tree forms produced are usually two dimensional since frequently a wall or fence provides the background of the trellis. All designs require some support system, at least in the formative training. When forming espaliers, one should take into account the species and the vigor of the plant. The space between horizontal limbs, for example, is wider for peach trees (20 to 24 inches or 50.8 to 61 centimeters) than for apple trees (12 inches or 30.5 centimeters). About three tiers of limbs are adequate for small plants, but vigorous plants can have more. All bending should be done when the limbs are still flexible. A balance should be maintained between limbs on either side of the central axis by keeping opposite limbs at each tier equal in length. The limbs should be tied snugly to the support or trellis, as already mentioned. Espaliers may be formal or informal in design.

FIGURE 19–20 Development of bark inclusion occurs when a branch angle is too narrow. It results in the development of weak crotches.

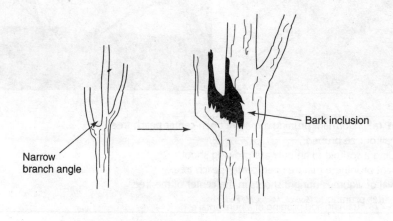

Narrow branch angle

Bark inclusion

Horizontal Espalier The horizontal espalier training system consists of a set of horizontal wire trellises attached to walls, fences, or posts. When starting from a *whip* (seedling with a single slender stem), it is cut just below the first wire. This practice causes new shoots to develop from lateral buds. Two lateral shoots of equal vigor are selected and trained on stakes tied diagonally to the wires (Figure 19–21). These stakes are later (in summer) lowered to the horizontal wires and tied. Stakes may not be necessary. Horizontal limbs are developed by first heading the plant just below each wire. Growth toward the wall should be pruned. Horizontal espaliers produce uneven vigor in the plant. The whole process is repeated to form the next tier of lateral branches. The ends of the lower scaffold branches usually lose vigor.

Once established, side shoots will be produced, first on the lower limbs. These shoots are pruned in summer to form fruiting spurs in the next season. As fruiting spurs increase in number over the years, they should be thinned out to avoid overcrowding and reduced plant vigor.

Palmette The palmette training system consists of several designs—*baldessari, v-form, verrier, oblique*, and *candelabra*. This system is a variation of the espalier system whereby plants are trained at about a 40-degree angle instead of having horizontal branches. The candelabra palmette training system uses a lattice framework consisting of horizontal and vertical arms to create balanced and attractive trees (Figure 19–22).

Cordon

The cordon training system requires the use of wire, similar to a horizontal espalier system. A single main stem is tied at an oblique angle to the wires. Cordons perform best if the angle is oblique. Laterals, which grow from the main system, are pruned to form fruit-bearing spurs (Figure 19–23). Double cordons (U) and four-armed Kniffen are also used in training plants (Figure 19–24).

19.14.3 PRUNING EVERGREEN BROADLEAF FRUIT TREES

Broadleaf evergreen fruit trees are pruned only lightly, especially once established. Species such as citrus and avocado are rarely pruned. Light pruning may be done to control plant height, remove deadwood, and induce fresh growth, as in species such as lemon, coffee, olive, and mango. Citrus and lemon fruits are heavy, and hence fruiting should be encouraged on strong branches to prevent breakage. The productivity of citrus trees declines with age, requiring that trees be rejuvenated by topping and hedging to remove old and weak limbs.

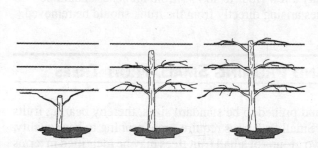

FIGURE 19–21 Training and pruning of a horizontal espalier.

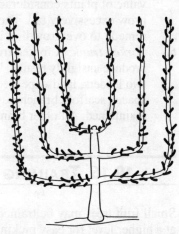

FIGURE 19–22 Training and pruning of a candelabra palmette.

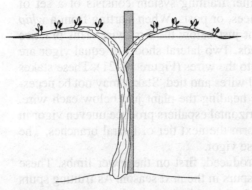

FIGURE 19–23 Training and pruning of a cordon.

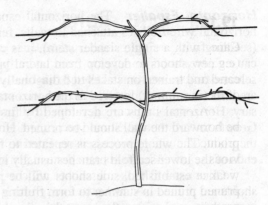

FIGURE 19–24 A four-armed Kniffen training system.

19.15 COMMON TREE PROBLEMS

As trees and shrubs grow and age, they develop characteristics that reduce their visual appeal or pose problems in the general environment. Many of these problems can be corrected by pruning. The major ones include the following:

1. *Excessive height.* Ornamental trees in open space are normally allowed to grow freely to attain maximum height. Excessive tree height becomes a problem if it interferes with utility lines or overwhelms structures such as buildings. When this happens, the height of the tree may be reduced by *drop crotching* (cutting a main branch on the leader back to a lower crotch).
2. *Excessive spread.* When large branches located high on the tree spread excessively, they become prone to damage by wind. The condition may also cause the tree to be deformed and lose its visual appeal. When branches spread excessively, limbs from the highest and outermost parts should be pruned.
3. *Low-hanging limbs.* Low-hanging limbs pose clearance problems for humans and vehicles. It is desirable to establish clearance early in the growth of the plant.
4. *Deadwood.* When deadwood occurs, it should be removed to prevent disease infestation and spread. Deadwood also detracts from the beauty of a tree.
5. *Overcrowding of trees.* As trees grow and mature, they take up more space in the landscape. That is why it is critical to know the mature characteristics of trees before installing them in the landscape. Overcrowding can reduce the aesthetic value of plants considerably. It also causes trees to compete for light and thereby grow excessively tall. Their natural shapes and forms are often ruined. The remedy to overcrowding is complete removal of trees or pruning of limbs.
6. *Forked trunk.* A forked trunk stands the danger of splitting in strong winds to produce unsightly results. Unless there is an overwhelming advantage to maintaining two leaders, landscape trees should be trained early to have one trunk and well-spaced scaffold branches. Only a few (four to six) scaffold branches should be maintained. All other branches arising directly from the trunk should be removed.

19.16 TRAINING AND PRUNING SMALL FRUIT TREES

Small fruit trees may be trained and pruned to be standard sizes, thereby bearing fruits at a higher level for easy picking. Small fruit trees require some pruning to bear quality, large fruits and have high yield. Two groups of small fruit trees may be identified in terms of pruning and training needs—cane and bush fruits.

19.16.1 CANE FRUITS

Cane fruits are temperate fruits and include raspberry, blackberry, and hybrid berries (e.g., boysenberry, sunberry, and tayberry). They bear their fruits on long canes. These cane fruits, sometimes called **brambles**, are pruned in summer or winter to remove all of the canes that fruited in the previous season and any unwanted canes and suckers.

An important consideration, in all pruning operations, is knowing where fruits will be borne on a plant. Some species, including many brambles, bear their fruits on canes produced in the previous season. Pruning removes all of the canes that fruited in the previous season. Pruning is also done in summer or winter when the plant is dormant. Also, weak canes and broken branches are cut off. Under such circumstances, plants must be pruned judiciously such that enough buds are left from the current season's growth for production in the next season.

Cane fruits can be trained on trellises or on a fence or wired wall. Fruiting and new canes occur simultaneously. Once harvested, the fruited canes are removed so that the new canes can be positioned for fruiting in the next season. The goal of pruning is to ensure that year-old canes are in position each season. Pruning of individual species differs slightly.

19.16.2 BUSH FRUITS

Popular bush fruits include currant (black, red, and white), gooseberry, and blueberry. The goal of pruning these crops is to remove older and less productive wood to allow new and more vigorous shoots to grow. Horizontally growing wood is removed and the bush thinned to avoid overcrowding and improve circulation of air. This aeration decreases disease incidence. Black currant (*Ribes nigrum*) is produced as a "stooled" bush whereby the old wood is cut back close to the ground to allow a set of new shoots to develop. The highbush blueberry (*Vaccinium corymbossum*) can remain productive for a long time, and thus removing fruited wood is not necessary for several years.

19.17 PRUNING ORNAMENTAL PLANTS

19.17.1 PRUNING CONIFERS

Conifers are cone-bearing plants. They may be low growing, as in prostrate junipers, and useful as ground covers. Some conifers are used as hedge plants.

Ground Covers and Hedges

Conifer hedges require pruning to maintain the desired shape, whereas ground covers seldom need it. Conifers have different branching habits. Some plants branch only once a year (as in pine, spruce, and fir), starting with the beginning of the season's growth. This growth pattern results in circular (whorl) growth of branches at the growing tip. These plants lack latent buds on old wood and as such will not regrow when cut back severely. The *candles* (new growth) on the whorls may be shortened or pinched back while the needles are small to control growth (Figure 19–25). Junipers, on the other hand, branch as growth proceeds and produce fresh growth at the point of pruning. Junipers may be thinned or sheared.

Pruning Coniferous Trees

Coniferous trees commonly develop a single dominant central axis with an overall narrow pyramidal shape. This shape makes it impossible to shorten a mature plant without destroying its natural look. Some conifers such as junipers and digger pines have multiple central leaders and are more tolerant of height reduction. Conifers are amenable to pruning to fit symmetrical shapes. When pruning conifers, one should always cut back to visible buds and leave no stocks. Conifers tend to grow low branches. Pruning of some

FIGURE 19–25 Pruning conifers.

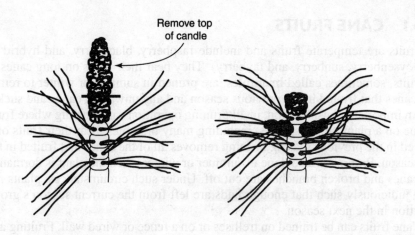

Remove top of candle

of these branches may be necessary to provide for clearance under the tree. Conifers are best pruned in spring or early summer, when most (e.g., pine, cypress, cedar, and spruce) experience rapid growth. Some new growths (candles) may be removed or cut in half.

Pruning Christmas Trees

Christmas trees are characterized by a conical shape. To attain this desirable shape, growers maintain a schedule of shearing to produce plants that are symmetrical and of uniform canopy and density and with uniform spacing between branches. Shearing of Christmas trees may begin in the third or fourth growing season, depending on the species. It is important to shear pines in their active growing periods or no new buds will form near cuts and dieback may occur. In the case of species such as fir and spruce, shearing causes shoot growth to cease while buds form. These species may be sheared after new growth begins. Pines tend to lose their shape readily (they grow less tight) and hence require more frequent shearing than fir and spruce.

The density of the canopy depends on how the central leader is headed. The first heading is done when the pine is about 12 inches (30.5 centimeters) tall. This lead shoot is headed again in the next and subsequent seasons (up to four years) in the same manner. If the lead shoot is cut short, the tree will be denser and more attractive but attain harvest height after additional growing seasons. Whorls of branches develop in tiers as the tree grows. Side shoots should be headed to about half the length of the lead shoot. The sides are sheared to approximately 50 percent taper. To facilitate harvesting, handling, and installation of the tree for display, up to about 12 inches (30.5 centimeters) of the trunk from the ground is pruned to leave a clean base.

Pines characteristically have a conical or pyramidal shape. A significant difference between pines and broadleaf trees is that pines mostly have one axis that does not branch if cut back. Once a limb is removed, no replacement limb will be produced. When pruning, no stubs should be left. The limb should be cut back to a visible live bud. Christmas trees are *sheared* to obtain an attractive symmetrical and conical shape with uniformly dense foliage (Figure 19–26). Pine, spruce, and fir produce circular growth of branches (whorls) and branch once a year. To obtain a compact plant, the tips of the branches may be pinched. Once formed, the internode between whorls is fixed and cannot be shortened.

19.17.2 PRUNING NONCONIFEROUS SHRUBS

Shrub problems in the landscape include the following:

1. *Plant overgrowth*. Shrubs may grow such that the canopy is too large. When this occurs, the size of the plant may be reduced by carefully removing the long side branches (thinning) or removing all large branches in the top of the shrub (*dehorning*). Thinning should be done such that the shape of the plant is not

FIGURE 19–26 Shearing of Christmas trees. Shearing is designed to create a symmetrical shape with uniform distribution of branches and foliage throughout the plant. Plants are sheared to about 50 percent taper. The maximum width should be about 40 to 60 percent of the height of the plant.

destroyed. Plants that sprout very easily from old wood are amenable to dehorning, which is a severe pruning technique.

2. *Canopy too dense.* Dense shrubs cannot receive light in the center of the canopy. This situation may be corrected by thinning spindly growths and the top of the shrub.

3. *Canopy too loose.* A loose canopy results from spindly, weak branches, which tend to sprawl. These branches should be removed or shortened.

Shrubs, unlike trees, are low growing in terms of height and have small stems. Several stems often arise from the ground and are bunched together. This close arrangement encourages upward growth as the response to competition for light. The foliage at the bottom part of the plant is shaded, leading to poor growth in those parts and bare stems. Shrubs are pruned by removing old stems from the ground level to open up the clump by thinning out.

Some smaller branches and twigs are also removed. Shrubs may be headed back slightly to encourage new growth in the right direction by making appropriate cuts. Overgrown shrubs may be pruned back drastically to rejuvenate them through production of fresh growth.

19.18 PRUNING HEDGES

Hedges are planted for several purposes, including to demarcate property boundaries, to hide utility areas, or to provide decorative borders. Hedge plants are shrubs that are planted very close together. The plants may be allowed to grow tall or dwarfed through frequent trimming. For rapid results, a fast-growing species may be selected, but slow-growing hedge plants live longer and produce dense hedges that require less frequent clipping.

There are two basic styles of hedges:

1. *Formal hedges.* Formal hedges are created by planting and shearing plants according to geometric shapes (Figure 19–27). For best effect, formal hedge species should have a dense growth habit and tolerate close clipping. It is important that hedges be uniformly dense from top to bottom. Formal styles of hedges are more difficult to maintain. Hedges should be sheared on a regular basis. Because the shapes and sizes are monitored regularly, formal hedges require less space in the landscape.

2. *Informal hedges.* Plants may be allowed to grow freely according to their natural shapes, and pruned only to restrict size and maintain an attractive visual appearance (Figure 19–28).

FIGURE 19–27 A formal hedge. The emphasis is on symmetry and details in shearing to keep the symmetry and cosmetic appearance. *(Source: George Acquaah)*

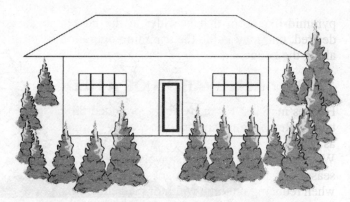

FIGURE 19–28 An informal hedge. The emphasis is more on privacy and less on symmetry.

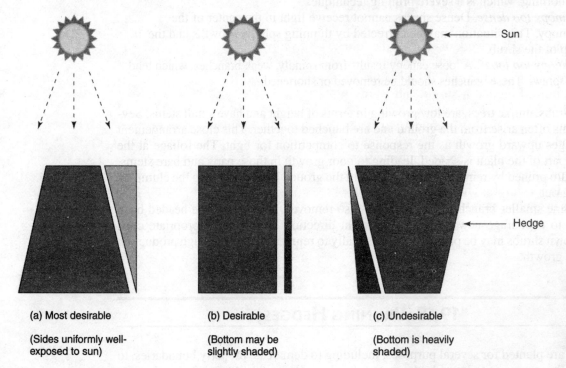

(a) Most desirable	(b) Desirable	(c) Undesirable
(Sides uniformly well-exposed to sun)	(Bottom may be slightly shaded)	(Bottom is heavily shaded)

FIGURE 19–29 Shapes of hedges.

19.18.1 CLIPPING OR SHEARING OF HEDGES

Plants vary in their tolerance of shearing, density of growth, leaf size, growth rate, and adaptation. The best hedge plants should be upright, small leaved, and slow growing. For formal hedges, the species should be tolerant of frequent shearing (e.g., boxwood, holly, and privet). Flowering shrubs (e.g., camellia, oleander, and azalea) may be used as informal hedge plants. Conifers that sprout from old wood are good hedge plants. To have a good hedge, the plants should be shaped early. Frequent trimming of hedge plants in early seasons promotes the development of a dense hedge.

The shapes of columns of trimmed hedges are varied. Individual plants are not trimmed but rather the whole bunch is trimmed to blend together as a solid column. A very common yet improper hedge form is one that is wide and flat at the top, resulting eventually in thinning in the foliage at the bottom (Figure 19–29). A columnar form that is as wide at the top as it is at the bottom is more desirable. The best shape is a pyramid-like form that is wider at the base than at the top. If straight hedges are desired, one may guide the trimming operation by stretching a string between stakes along the hedge.

19.18.2 RENOVATION OF A HEDGE

Hedges may last for many years, provided the plants are fertilized and properly maintained. Renovation may involve severely cutting back an overgrown hedge. Species such as yew (*Taxus*), holly (*Ilex*), and hornbeam (*Carpinus*) tolerate such *hard pruning*. Whenever severe pruning is involved, it is best to spread out the operation over several seasons; that is, one should not reduce plant height and width at the same time. Even when reducing only the width of the hedge, it is best to start with one side of the hedge in one season and the other in the next season. Some kinds of damage may be repaired by removing the older material and replacing it with younger plants.

19.19 ORNAMENTAL STEMS

Apart from creating a work of art with the foliage of plants, the stems of certain shrubs may be twisted or woven together (Figure 19–30). This training must be done while the plants are young and flexible. To create the single stem shape, the young leader of the shrub is trained around a strong and sturdy pole. All growths on the stem are then removed. When the plant develops adequate strength, the pole is removed. Similarly, the barley sugar stem involves training two stems simultaneously around a pole. A more fancy and eye-catching stem effect is produced by plaiting three young and flexible stems to form a braid. To obtain multiple stems, the central axis is cut back like a coppice to produce new shoots. As the plants grow, the braided stems become bound together in a natural graft by fusing at all of the sites where contact is made between stems, as in approach grafting. A pole may be needed to provide temporary support until

(a)

(b)

FIGURE 19–30 Woven and twisted stem designs. (a) Creative designs using a golf ball. (b) Shrubs may be trained to stand up as single stemmed trees by reinforcing the stem with a stake or combining several weak stems to grow as one strong stem through braiding. *(Source: For (a) George Acquaah)*

the stem is strong enough to be self-supporting. The foliage may then be trained and pruned into attractive shapes. Shrubs that can be manipulated in this way include boxwood (*Buxus*), bay (*Laurus nobilis*), and weeping fig (*Ficus benjamina*).

19.20 TRAINING AND PRUNING CLIMBING PLANTS

Climbing plants are a versatile group of landscape plants that can be utilized in a variety of creative ways. They require physical support and training to control and manage their fast-growing shoots (Figure 19–31). Climbers can be trained along walls and fences or to climb poles and other nearby plants. They are utilized in decorative topiary and as free-standing specimen plants growing over a frame.

Climbing plants differ in how they attach themselves to physical supports, which affects the way in which they are pruned. Ivy has aerial roots by which it clings to supports. *Parthenocissus tricuspidata* uses adhesive pads that are touch activated to hold onto objects. Unfortunately, these climbing aids remain part of the physical support even after the climbing plant is dead, leaving unsightly marks. Plants such as climbing roses and bougainvillea utilize thorns to hook onto the support, and *Wisteria* simply twines around the support upon contact. Some plants, such as *Passiflora racemosa*, climb by coiling their tendrils around objects. Some species neither twine nor cling but simply scramble over objects by producing long shoots; once over the object, they cascade down.

Plants that climb by twining or tendrils can be grown near posts, pillars, fences, or walls provided these supports have objects or materials (such as netting or wires) to which these plants can anchor themselves. On the other hand, plants that cling to their support need flat surfaces such as fences, tree trunks, and walls or masonry. When trellises or other wires and fixings are provided for twiners, it is important that they not be attached directly to the wall or surface. Some room is needed for the plant to move to twine around the surface. Further, the space provides a means of aeration to reduce disease incidence.

(a)

(b)

FIGURE 19–31 Climbers can be trained on physical structures such as (a) the frame of a patio or over a walkway or (b) a wall.   *(Source: George Acquaah)*

After selecting the appropriate species and the area to plant it, the plant should be set at least 6 to 9 inches (15.2 to 22.9 centimeters) away from the base of the support. The growing shoot is led to the support by providing it with an angled stake on which to climb. Once on the support, it is allowed to grow without much interference in the first year. Thereafter, the shoot should be trained in the desired direction. Where a shoot is growing at a rapid pace without producing side shoots, it should be pruned to stimulate branching.

During the dormant season, deadwood should be removed. Any shoot that has overgrown the space allotted should be cut back. Excessive growth should be removed to avoid congestion.

Training is important to guide the growth of the plant and to contain it within desirable boundaries. Vines that bloom on the previous season's wood should be pruned after they bloom in spring so that new growth will occur during the summer period to produce flower buds for the next spring. Those that bloom on the current season's growth should be pruned before growth starts in spring to stimulate growth later in spring for more flowers. It is important to contain vines, especially aggressive ones such as trumpet vines, so that they do not damage a home's roof and gutters. When vines are old and show deadwood, renewal pruning may be necessary.

19.20.1 USING CLIMBERS IN THE LANDSCAPE

Vines may be used in a variety of ways to enhance the landscape and for other functional purposes:

1. *Ground cover.* Vines may be used as a ground cover by allowing the plants to trail on the ground. Species that can be used in this way include ivy (*Hedera*), *Vitis*, *Akebia*, and *Ampelopsis*.
2. *Hedge plants.* Climbers with thick, woody stems, including climbing roses, bougainvillea, and *Hedera*, can be trained over appropriate structures such as tightly stretched wire to form a fence.
3. *Container grown.* Climbers can be grown in containers and trained over wire supports to form a variety of decorative shapes. Climbers such as philodendrons and epipremnums that produce aerial roots can be used in creating moss poles.
4. *Cover vertical structures.* Climbers can be trained to grow over arches or other vertically erected structures. These species are vigorous and include *Humulus lupulus* 'Aureus,' *Adlumia*, *Mina lobata*, and *Codonopsis*.
5. *Climbing a pergola.* A *pergola* is a structure consisting of pillars or posts linked by cross beams or arches. Climbing plants can be grown, one at each post, to climb over the structure and around the posts.

19.20.2 CLIMBERS AS STANDARDS

Climbers generally do not have enough wood to be self-supporting even when mature. However, some plants such as *Wisteria sinensis* and *Jasminum polyanthrum* can be trained to stand up as single-trunk, self-supporting plants. Most species trained as standards never achieve self-support and have to rely indefinitely on a support of some sort, usually metallic. Standard climbers are also used as border plants around patios.

SUMMARY

Perennial plants, especially, require periodic management in which parts of the plant are selectively clipped to control growth and remove unproductive and diseased parts. This activity, called pruning, is designed to improve and sustain quality plant products and aesthetic value. The four general purposes of pruning are phytosanitary, aesthetic, reproductive, and physiological. Trees and shrubs are pruned differently. Fruit trees are pruned to improve light penetration into the canopy and to remove unproductive and diseased limbs. Pruning strategies include central leader, modified central leader, and open center types. Plants may be thinned out, headed back, or renewed by pruning methods. Hedges and vines are pruned differently from trees. Sometimes the technique of training is combined with pruning to force plants to assume certain forms, called the espalier method of pruning. This plant art form reaches a high level in topiary, the art of training and pruning trees to assume geometric or other recognizable shapes.

REFERENCES AND SUGGESTED READING

American Horticultural Society. 1980. *Pruning*. Alexandria, Va.: American Horticultural Society.

Brickell, C., and D. Joyce. 1996. *Pruning and training*. Alexandria, Va.: American Horticultural Society.

Harris, R. W. 1992. *Arboriculture: Integrated management of landscape trees, shrubs, and vines*, 2d ed. Englwood Cliffs, N.J.: Prentice Hall.

OUTCOMES ASSESSMENT

1. Discuss the general purposes of pruning.
2. Discuss how deciduous fruits are pruned.
3. How is pruning different from training of plants?
4. Describe how a hedge should be pruned for best growth and development.
5. What is a topiary?
6. What is coppicing, and what is its purpose in the landscape?

PART 6

GROWING PLANTS OUTDOORS: VEGETABLES, FRUITS, AND NUTS

20

Growing Vegetables Outdoors

PURPOSE AND EXPECTED OUTCOMES

This chapter discusses the general principles of designing, planting, and caring for a vegetable garden, as well as the cultivation of selected vegetables.

After studying this chapter, the student should be able to

1. Describe the characteristics of a home garden.
2. Discuss the benefits of a home garden.
3. Design a vegetable garden.
4. List and describe the basic tools required by a gardener.
5. Discuss the choice of garden site and vegetable varieties to grow.
6. Describe how selected vegetables are cultivated.

OVERVIEW

Vegetables are grown on a small scale as well as a large commercial scale. Some vegetables are grown on commercial scale in greenhouses, as previously discussed in Chapter 13. However, most vegetable production occurs outdoors in the field.

Small-scale vegetable production is an activity that may be undertaken year-round (except in extreme weather) by people in a wide variety of situations. It is applicable to rural as well as urban dwellers. The size of the project depends on what is available in terms of land and how much time and effort one is willing to devote to the activity. Urban dwellers may be limited to only a fraction of an acre, whereas rural dwellers may have more than an acre with which to work. The space available may have to be devoted to both ornamentals and vegetables, since people who enjoy gardening usually like to grow some flowers as well.

Gardeners have a wide variety of crops from which to choose, including roots, cole crops, cucurbits, and solanaceous crops. There are crops for the cool season and others for the warm season. Small-scale vegetable farming can be undertaken as a hobby, where the primary purpose of the project is recreational while also providing fresh produce for the table. Larger-scale vegetable farming may be used to produce more than one needs so that the surplus can be marketed for supplemental income. This kind of small-scale production, whether as a hobby or for commercial purposes, is commonly called *home gardening* or **backyard gardening**.

When growing to sell, postharvest handling and marketing become very important considerations in planning a garden. In herb gardening, one has to decide whether to grow mainly for culinary use or also for ornamental purposes. Some herbs may be grown indoors in pots for ready access for culinary use.

20.1 NUTRITIONAL AND ECONOMIC VALUE OF VEGETABLES

Vegetables vary widely in their nutritional value. Some are high in carbohydrates (e.g., dry bean, white and sweet potatoes), while others are high in protein and amino acids (e.g., legumes and brassicas). Others are rich in minerals (e.g., greens, brassicas, and root crops), and pro-vitamin A (e.g., carrots, peppers, and greens), vitamin C (e.g., brassicas, peppers, tomatoes, and greens), and dietary fiber (e.g., carrot). Because they are generally high in bulk but low in dry matter as a result of the high water content (often more than 90 percent), a person needs to consume large quantities of vegetables in order to obtain the FDA recommended daily requirement of the nutritional factors they supply. Vegetables are often called "high value crops" because they account for only about 1 percent of the crop land in the United States but almost 15 percent of the cash receipts from crop production.

20.2 ADAPTATION OF VEGETABLES

As previously discussed in Chapter 4, plants may be classified according to temperature requirements as either cool season or warm season. This is an operational classification and hence the categories are only approximate.

Cool-Season Vegetables

Some cool-season vegetables are slightly freezing tolerant (e.g., spinach, cabbage, broccoli, radish, beet, turnip, rutabaga, and cauliflower), while others are damaged by temperatures near freezing (e.g., lettuce, celery, artichoke, endive, mustard, carrot, and chard). A few vegetables are frost tolerant (e.g., asparagus, garlic, kale, Brussels sprouts).

Warm-Season Vegetables

Warm-season vegetables are frost intolerant and include sweet corn, pepper, snap bean, squash, pumpkin, lima bean, cucumber, tomato, and muskmelon. Some warm-season species are long-season (e.g., watermelon, sweet potato, eggplant, and okra).

20.3 REGIONALIZED PRODUCTION OF VEGETABLES

Whereas backyard gardening can be undertaken by all homeowners who have suitable space for the activity, commercial vegetable production is largely a regionalized activity. Based on plant adaptation, production of vegetables is localized in the United States in the various USDA plant adaptation zones. In fact, because of seasonal variation within regions, various states in a production region can alternate in leading the production of one specific crop. That is, one state may lead in spring production of a crop, while another leads in fall production of the same crop. Further, vegetable production on the commercial scale is produced for two markets—fresh market and processing market. Different states or parts of the production state may lead in the production of one market type but not the other.

The National Agricultural Statistics Services of the USDA indicates that vegetable production in the United States occurs on the eastern and western coastal areas, as well as the South and the Midwest regions (Figure 20–1). The ten top producers of both market types in 2005 were California, Wisconsin, Minnesota, Washington State, Florida, New York, Oregon, Georgia, Michigan, and Arizona.

20.3.1 FACTORS FOR REGIONALIZATION OF PRODUCTION

There are several reasons why vegetable production is localized in these regions.

1. Fertile soils and terrain that is conducive to mechanization occurs in these regions.
2. Field crops are relatively more tolerant of wide variations in meteorological factors than vegetables. An unstable environment is unable to support the production of high-quality produce. Vegetables are intolerant of large fluctuations in temperature.
3. Vegetables comprise large amounts of water, as previously indicated. Successful production of quality produce depends on the availability of water throughout the growing season. Consequently, large-scale vegetable production is economically feasible in regions where water is plentifully for irrigation at a reasonable cost.
4. Vegetable production is labor intensive. In spite of the increasing rate of infusion of mechanization into field production, human labor is indispensable for some operations that are still challenging to automate or mechanize in some crops. Vegetable production is hence economical in regions where cheap labor is plentiful.
5. Vegetables are in high demand year-round. Regions where crop production is possible year-round are suitable for vegetable production.

20.3.2 WHY CALIFORNIA IS IDEAL FOR VEGETABLE PRODUCTION

These ideal factors previously discussed in 20.3.1, can be obtained in the California production region. California has fertile soils for vegetable production. More importantly, California has cool coastal valleys like the Salinas Valley with rich, fertile soil that are used to

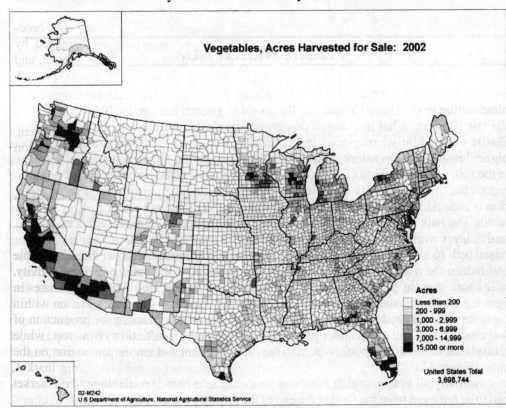

FIGURE 20–1 Regional distribution of vegetable production in the United States. *(Source: USDA)*

PLASTICULTURE IN NORTH AMERICA

DR. MICHAEL D. ORZOLEK, PROF. VEGETABLE CROPS
Department of Horticulture, The Pennsylvania State University
University Park, PA 16802

INTRODUCTION

Plasticulture very simply is the use of plastics in agriculture. There are more uses of plastics in horticultural crop production than any other form of agriculture. Use of plastics in horticulture can be traced back to the 1960's when Dr. Emery Emmert at the University of Kentucky constructed the first double layer inflated polyethylene greenhouse with 6 mil thick clear greenhouse grade plastic for producing vegetable transplants and commercial crops. Emmert also realized the tremendous advantage of using plastic film for growing vegetables outside and also placed thin plastic film (1.25 to 1.50 mil thick) in the field for the production of field grown vegetables. Dr. Emmert observed that placing black plastic film over soil resulted in higher soil temperatures, higher soil moisture levels, reduced leaching of nutrients, and control of most annual and perennial weeds compared to no plastic mulch. Chemical composition of plastics used in horticultural crop production are general either polyethylene or polypropylene in nature with additives to reduce the affect of ultra violet (UV) light on plastic degradation. From these resins, many plastic products have been manufactured for modifying the environment when growing horticultural crops in the field. The list of plastic materials used in horticultural crop production include; transplant trays, plastic pots, plastic mulch film, drip irrigation tape, low tunnels, row covers, floating row covers, high tunnels, and greenhouses. All of these materials will modify the environment and optimize conditions for optimum plant production.

PLASTIC MULCH FILM

Because of the many advantages of using plastic film to grow horticultural crops, use of plasticulture in the United States and the world in general has grown 10% each year for the last 10 years. What has caused this growth of plasticulture use in the last 10 years? Plastic mulch film when placed in the field will increase soil temperature, maintain higher levels of soil moisture, maintain optimum soil tilth, reduce leaching of nutrients in the soil, reduce leaching of chemicals, reduce/eliminate weed problems, and generally reduce the time to maturity of the crops being grown on the plastic film. Plastic mulch film is manufactured in rolls 2,400 to 4,000 linear feet long and either 3, 4, or 5 feet in width. The bulk of plastic mulch used in the US is applied in the field with a raised bed, mulch layer with drip irrigation tape applicator. The reason the plastic film is placed on raised beds (6 to 12 inches in height) is to increase soil temperature faster than flat culture and reduce the risks of root diseases since excess water in the root zone of most plants will cause disease problems and/or deplete oxygen in the soil. Prior to placing the non-degradable plastic mulch in the field, the soil must be tilled to leave small soil particles that will produce a very firm bed for seeding or transplanting without any large soil clods. Large soil clods under plastic mulch will make it difficult to firm soil around transplants, eliminate air pockets next to the roots and firm soil around and above the soil cube (Figure 1).

Initially all plastic mulch film was produced as a non-degradable material which had to be retrieved from the field at the end of the growing season or when the horticultural

FIGURE 1 Black plastic mulch applied in the field on raised beds for the production of muskmelons. *(Photo courtesy of Dr Mike Orzolek – PSU)*

crop was finished being harvested (multiple crops in southern states such as Florida and Texas). As more acreage of plastic mulch film increased within the last 20 years, it was apparent that new types of plastic mulch film would have to be developed to help the growing problem of sending non-degradable plastic mulch to landfills. The plastic film manufacturers answer to the problem was to produce a photodegradable plastic mulch in the mid eighties which would degrade when the film was exposed to light (specifically ultra violet light). After several years of trial in the field, two problems became obvious; 1) the plastic film under the soil of the shoulders on the bed did not degrade during the growing season since it was not exposed to the UV light and 2) it was very difficult if not impossible to accurately determine/predict when the photodegradable plastic film would degrade and become ineffective. Photodegradable plastic film that should have lasted for 90 days in some cases lasted only 30 days and film that should have started to breakdown in 40 to 50 days didn't degrade until 120 days. The unpredictability of the photodegradable plastic mulch resulted in most plastic manufacturers dropping the product by the 1990's. Within the last 5 years in both Europe and North America, vegetable crop growers were looking for a truly degradable plastic film that did not have to be retrieved from the field at the end of the growing season. Plastic mulch manufacturers, especially in Europe, developed a biodegradable plastic mulch that would be effective for 30 to 45 days after being placed in the field before the mulch became brittle and started to breakdown in the field. At the end of the growing season, the biodegradable plastic mulch can be rototilled into the soil and a cover crop planted into that field 7 to 10 days later. The biodegradable plastic mulch degrades in response to both moisture and microbial activity in the soil.

The color of plastic mulch was initially either black or clear when introduced in the sixties. Black was the preferred color because of the increase in soil temperature compared to no plastic mulch and black eliminated photosynthetic active radiation (PAR) from reaching the soil, thus eliminating weed growth. Clear plastic mulch increased soil temperature at least 5°F to 8°F warmer than black mulch, but clear mulch allowed for weed growth under the film. Within the last 10 years, other colors have been introduced into the industry including red, Infrared Thermal green (IRT), IRT brown, blue, metalized or reflective silver, white, and co-extruded films with two colors, black on one side and white on the other side for example. The change in vegetable crop yield in response to the different mulch colors is due in part to an increase in soil temperature and the range of reflected wavelengths produced by individual mulch colors. Different colors will absorb and reflect different wavelengths of light and plants are very sensitive to the color of light their leaves intercept from the sun and reflected surfaces. Red and far-red light (between 600 and 800 nanometers) produces the largest growth responses in plants. Light that has a lower far-red to red (FR/R) ratio will cause a plant to develop shorter stems and larger roots (Table 1). A higher FR/R ratio will cause a plant to direct more new growth into shoots, resulting in a taller plant with more leaves. Different mulch colors reflect different wavelengths of light and thus different FR/R ratios (Figure 2).

Research over the last 10 years has concluded that certain crops grow best with certain colors. Tomatoes appear to produce maximum production and quality when grown on red mulch, cucurbits (melons, cucumbers, squash) when grown on blue plastic mulch, peppers when grown on IRT green, eggplant grown on red and potatoes grown on co-extruded reflective silver over black.

DRIP IRRIGATION

Drip or trickle irrigation is a very efficient method of applying water and nutrients to crops. For many crops, the conversion from sprinkler to drip irrigation can reduce water use by 50% and increase yields. This is a result of both improved water and fertility management as well as reduced disease and weed pressure. When drip irrigation is used with polyethylene mulch, yield increases can even be increased further.

These benefits are only possible when a drip irrigation system is properly designed, managed, and maintained during the growing season. Irrigation system design is complex and is beyond the scope of this publication. You should consult with a qualified agricultural engineer or irrigation equipment dealer to design your drip irrigation system. However, there are many design factors you should understand in order to assure that your drip irrigation system is properly designed and operating efficiently.

Drip irrigation was introduced into agriculture in the U.S. in the early 1970's to reduce water applied to crops compared to overhead irrigation, maintain plant health, optimize nutrient management, protect ground water from contamination, and increase both crop marketable yield and quality. Currently, there are several manufacturers of drip tape as well as the other critical components of a drip irrigation system. Components required for a effective and efficient drip irrigation system include: water source, pump, sand filter (depending on water source), backflow valve, flow meter, chemical/fertilizer injector and delivery system including, mainline distribution to field, sub-mainline (header line), feeder tubes or connectors and drip lines.

A clean, non-contaminated, consistent water source is required with a drip irrigation system. Since a drip irrigation system does not require large water volumes and high pressure, well water, ponds, streams or lakes are ideal water sources for drip irrigation.

Water quality can impact horticultural crop production both directly and indirectly. Direct effects may result from irrigation water with a high or low pH, a high dissolved mineral content, or high soluble salts. All of these water characteristics can affect plants by altering the chemistry of the soil plants are growing in, especially over time. Indirect water quality issues primarily affect plant growth by affecting the irrigation system that will be used. Water with a high amount of dissolved organic materials, for example, can clog irrigation fittings or drip tape orifices. This, in turn, will change the rate of flow and wetting patterns in the drip tape, resulting in the potential for wilting in the crop or a reduction in nutrient uptake. There are three simple, and relatively inexpensive, steps that growers should take to determine and mitigate irrigation water quality. The first is to select a good source of water. The second is to have the water tested for contaminants and relative concentrations of nutrients. And the third step is to use filtering technology in all the necessary irrigation supply lines (i.e. lines that will be used for drip/trickle irrigation or overhead sprinkler/emitter delivery).

Compared to other forms of irrigation such as furrow or overhead irrigation, drip irrigation is 90% efficient in delivering the amount of water applied to the soil compared to approximately 50% with the other forms of irrigation.

Drip tape is manufactured with specific characteristics based on thickness of the plastic tape, distance between orifices (holes where water exits through the drip tape), amount of water volume the drip tape will deliver (standard delivery rate is 0.45 gallons/minute/100 linear feet of tape), pressure compensation and self cleaning orifices. Drip tape operates very efficiently at low pressures of 6 to 10 pounds per square inch (psi) and water volume of 30 to 40 gallons/minute/acre. Pressure compensation refers to a drip line's ability to maintain a specified emission rate over a range of pressures. A pressure compensating line will emit water at the same flow rate over a range of pressures. A non-pressure compensating line emits water at a rate that increases linearly with pressure. Commonly used drip lines fall somewhere in the middle and are called "partially pressure compensating". For example, many drip lines will experience a 10% increase in emission rate when pressure is increased 20%. Drip tubes with internally attached emitters are fully pressure compensating. These emitters are more complicated to manufacture and are more expensive (Figure 3).

Filters are essential to the operation of a drip system. Many devices and management techniques are available for cleaning irrigation water. Depending on the water source, settling ponds, self-cleaning suction devices, sand separators, media filters, screen filters, and disk filters are used to filter any organic debris in the water before delivered to the drip irrigation system. Keeping a drip system free of debris is critical because most types of clogging of the orifice will irreparably disable a system.

In the last 10 years in North America, there has been mild to severe droughts in many locations of North America. Concurrent with drought has been an increased demand for residential water as a result of a significant increase in the population of the United States. Demand for water has not only caused water prices to dramatically increase, especially in the western U.S., but also has impacted the type of crops many growers are producing. For those vegetable and small fruit growers that have been using raised beds with plastic mulch, addition of drip irrigation was a necessity. However, there has been an ever increasing use of drip irrigation with crops grown on bare ground such as grapes, sweet corn and small fruit. The use of drip irrigation even on bare soil compared to overhead irrigation can reduce water consumption for crop production by 50 per cent. In addition, use of drip irrigation with crop production on bare soil can also reduce incidence of foliar diseases and the total amount of fertilizer applied to produce crops (Figure 4).

FIGURE 3 Use of drip irrigation tape to water broccoli and romaine lettuce crop in high tunnel. Note wetting pattern on soil from water being emitted from drip tape. *(Photo courtesy of Catie Rasmussen, Penn State Center for Plasticulture)*

ADVANTAGES OF DRIP IRRIGATION

1. Smaller water sources can be used, because trickle irrigation may require less than half of the water needed for sprinkler irrigation.
2. Lower operating pressures mean reduced energy costs for pumping.
3. High levels of water use efficiency are achieved because plants can be supplied with more precise amounts of water.
4. Disease pressure may be less because plant foliage remains dry.
5. Labor and operating costs are generally less, and extensive automation is possible.
6. Water applications are made directly to the plant root zone. No applications are made between rows or other non-productive areas, resulting in better weed control and significant water savings.
7. Field operations, such as harvesting, can continue during irrigation because the areas between rows remain dry.
8. Fertilizers can be applied efficiently through the drip system.
9. Irrigation can be done under a wide range of field conditions.
10. Compared to sprinkler irrigation, soil erosion and nutrient leaching can be reduced.

DISADVANTAGES AND LIMITATIONS OF DRIP IRRIGATION

1. Initial investment costs per acre may be more than other irrigation options.
2. Management requirements are somewhat higher. Delaying critical operation decisions may cause irreversible damage to crops.
3. Frost protection is not possible with drip systems; if this is needed, sprinkler systems are necessary.
4. Rodent, insect, and human damage to drip lines are potential sources of leaks.
5. Water filtration is necessary to prevent clogging of the small openings in the emitters.
6. Compared to sprinkler irrigation, water distribution in the soil is restricted.

LOW TUNNELS

Low tunnels have been used in field production in North America for the last 50 years. Use of low tunnels (24″ to 36″ wide by 18″ to 30″ tall) for vegetable crops helps to warm the soil, maintain higher air temperatures under the tunnel, maintain higher levels of soil moisture, reduce plant stress from wind, reduce/eliminate insect pests and reduce/ eliminate hail damage to the crops growing under the low tunnels. Generally, number 9 wire that is six feet long is bent into a semi-circle and placed in the soil every eight feet over the crop row. Polyethylene film with either 300 or 600 holes per square yard or polypropylene row cover is than placed over the wire hoops to form the low tunnel. Clear polyethylene provides increased temperatures in the low tunnels because of the greenhouse effect. In most northern locations, the polyethylene as a low tunnel cover works best when applied after transplanting crops in mid-April to early June. Because of the unpredictability and fluctuation of temperatures, low tunnels with polyethylene over the top must be monitored daily to prevent plant growth inhibition or crop loss because of elevated temperatures inside the tunnel that could be in excess of 100°F. Low tunnels made with clear plastic mulch usually increase air temperatures too high for most days during the spring in southern locations, so the tunnels need to be ventilated by perforating the plastic or rolling back one side of the low tunnel between noon and 4:00 PM. White polyethylene can provide some growth enhancement while avoiding the extremely high temperatures in the tunnel. Polypropylene and non-woven covers are fabric-like and can be placed over rows in tunnel fashion or can be laid on the crop in a floating fashion. Since the fabrics are porous, temperatures in the low tunnel are generally 5° to 10°F lower compared to the plastic film covers (Figure 5).

ROW COVERS AND FLOATING ROW COVERS

Floating row covers were developed to provide season extension for vegetable producers in areas that are susceptible to early and late frost events (temperatures between 28°F to 36°F) during the growing season. Row covers will increase both soil and ambient air temperatures in the crop canopy, maintain higher levels of available soil moisture, act as an insect barrier, and reduce wind stress on especially young and immature plants.

Insect control is effective with spunbonded row covers when all of the edges are completely sealed. For example, maggots in radish (and in other crops in the cabbage family) are controlled when a cover is applied at seeding with a complete seal around the edges. When the adult maggot flies search out the young seedlings for laying eggs, the flies will be unable to get under or through the cover. Placing the outside edge of the floating row cover in a continuous shallow furrow and than covering the row cover

FIGURE 5 Low tunnels used in conjunction with high tunnel for the production of table beets in November in central Pennsylvania. *(Photo courtesy of Catie Rasmussen, Penn State Center for Plasticulture)*

edge with soil is probably the best method of securing floating row covers in the open field. It is feasible, however, that row covers could actually increase insect damage on some crops. The environment under the cover is pretty "cozy" for insects, so it is important that all transplants that are to be covered be free of insects at transplanting. To prevent a heavy population of Colorado potato beetles under a cover, do not plant potatoes in the same place in successive years and use a cover the second year. Overwintering adult Colorado potato beetles could emerge from the soil under the cover and lay an abundance of eggs that would soon hatch into a dense population of larvae.

There are a couple of disadvantages of floating covers. One is the weed populations that develop under the row covers. Between strips of plastic mulch or with crops such as sweet corn where plastic mulch is not used, weeds grow rapidly and competitively with the crop. A pre-emergence herbicide application is recommended for the effective control of weeds germinating and growing under the row cover. There is also some inefficiency in covering the space between strips of plastic, but here again the trade-off is reduced installation labor of wide covers versus narrow covers (Figure 6).

Most all vegetable crops as well as strawberries, raspberries, and cut flowers have been grown with row covers. Although the primary crops for row cover use are high value crops such as melons, tomatoes, pepper, summer squash, sweet corn, and strawberries, many growers find row covers to be valuable for a number of crops for varying reasons: 1) earliness, 2) higher yields, 3) overwintering protection, and 4) insect and rodent control. Crop selection and cover selection are important to the economical success of the extra inputs. Crop production requirements such as temperature sensitivity, pollination methods, and growth habit dictate the type of row cover that is best to use.

For most crops, floating row covers require no support because they are lightweight. They literally "float" or lie directly over the crop, whether direct seeded or transplanted. Materials include perforated plastic film, spunbonded polyester, and spunbonded polypropylene. These materials do not impede seedling emergence or subsequent growth of the crop (for an exception, see below). To secure the cover against wind, all the edges are buried or weighted down with sandbags, rocks, or other materials. There are two types of these covers: perforated polyethylene which is about 1 mil thick and spunbonded polyester or polypropylene which is available in several weights (rather than in thickness). Perforated polyethylene has a uniform pattern of 3/8-inch holes (74 holes/sq ft) for ventilation. However, the holes allow for heat loss at night and are an entry point for insects. Overall, many growers have found these covers to be very beneficial for growth enhancement.

Spunbonded covers are comprised of a thin mesh of white synthetic fibers that entrap heat and serve as a barrier to wind, insects, and various animals trying to feed on the crop. Water from rain or overhead irrigation and air freely passes through the fabric row cover materials. The weight of these covers range from 0.3 to about 2.0 ounces per

FIGURE 6 Use of floating row covers placed over a potato crop to increase ambient air temperature around plant and keep Colorado potato beetles from feeding on potato foliage. *(Photo courtesy of Dr William Lamont – PSU)*

square yard (10 to 68 grams per square meter). The lightest covers are used primarily for insect exclusion while the heaviest of the covers are used for frost protection. The most common weights of row cover used by growers are 0.5 to 1.25 ounces per square yard (17 to 42 grams per square meter). With row covers under 0.5 ounces per square yard there is minimal heat retention at night and with row covers over 1.75 ounces per square yard, there is a significant reduction in light transmission. The heavy covers are basically used for nighttime frost protection since they do not transmit sufficient light for optimum crop growth.

Floating covers require much less installation labor than hoop supported covers. The wider and longer the covers, the less labor required per unit area since only the edges are secured. These covers vary in width from 6 to 50 feet and up to about 800 feet long. Regardless of width, the cover is secured by weighting down the edges (sides and ends) with soil, sand bags, stones, or long pins. In extremely windy areas, additional weighting in the middle of the cover is advisable. Even though most crops can be grown without damage under floating covers, tomatoes and pepper are an exception. If the spunbonded material is not supported with wire hoops for these crops, flapping of the cover in the wind will damage the growing points of young plants. Also, with summer squash under windy conditions, many of the leaves might be broken by the cover. For these three crops, a series of strategically placed wire hoops will prevent crop damage.

At the Penn State Center for Plasticulture, evaluation of floating row cover materials is being conducted on crops in the field as well as crops being grown in high tunnels (Table 1).

HIGH TUNNELS

What is a High Tunnel? High tunnels, although resembling a traditional plastic covered greenhouse, are a completely different technology. With no electrical service or automated ventilation or heating systems, high tunnels are classified as non-permanent (removable) structures, an important distinction for taxation purposes. Unlike greenhouses traditionally covered with a double layer of polyethylene plastic, high tunnels are covered with only a single layer of 6-mil thick greenhouse grade plastic. Traditional high tunnels do not require a permanent heating system, although it is advised to have a standby portable propane heater to protect against unexpected frosts in the spring and fall. High tunnel ventilation is accomplished by manually rolling up and down the length of each side of the high tunnel by using the roll bar with T-handle. Many high tunnels do however make use of a drip irrigation system for water management. The purchase and construction cost of a high tunnel is approximately $1.50 per square foot compared to a permanent automated greenhouse at a minimum cost of $30.00 per square foot (Figure 7).

FIGURE 7 Production of a mixed vegetable crop in a 17' x 36' high tunnel located at the Penn State High Tunnel Research and Education Facility, Rock Springs, PA. (Photo courtesy of Dr Mike Orzolek – PSU)

Table 1 A description of available floating row covers currently available from manufacturers.

Brand Name	Material	Weight in oz/sq yard	Light transmitted
Reemay 2006	Spun-bonded Polyester	0.6	85%
Melon, cucumbers, other vine crops, lettuce, carrots.			
Typar T-518	Spun-bonded polypropylene	1.25	70%
Up to 6°F or more frost protection and will last 3-4 seasons.			
Agrofabric Pro 10	Spun-bonded polypropylene	0.3	90%
Super lightweight, designed to protect crops against insect pests.			
Agrofabric Pro 17	Spun-bonded Polypropylene	0.5	85%
Up to 4°F frost protection and UV Stabilizers increase expected field life to 2-3 years if used seasonally.			
Agrofabric Pro 30	Spun-bonded Polypropylene	0.9	70%
Up to 6° F frost protection for citrus, strawberries, vegetables, nursery stock.			
Agrofabric Pro 50	Spun-bonded Polypropylene	1.5	50%
Up to 8°F frost protection. Protects crops and nursery stock in freezes down to 24°F.			
Agrofabric Pro 70	Spun-bonded Polypropylene	2.0	30%
8°F + frost protection. Highly effective for over-wintering ornamentals, superior durability for re-use through multiple seasons.			
Agribon AG-15	Spun-bonded Polypropylene	0.45	90%
Super-lightweight, designed to protect vegetable crops from insects.			
Agribon AG-19	Spun-bonded Polypropylene	0.55	85%
Up to 4°F frost protection. UV stabilized, usable 2-3 seasons.			
Covertan	nonwoven fabric	0.5 & 0.9	90%
Lightweight, provides growth enhancement and insect control.			
Tufbell 3800 N	Polyvinyl alcohol (PVA)		92-95%
Up to 10°F freeze protection. A net-type material with absorption properties that allow moisture to freeze within the row cover and form protective cover over a crop. Double-thick material is reinforced every 1" to prevent tears, with additional reinforcement every 39". Washable, antistatic, chemical and light stable material. Most durable row cover on the market.			

High tunnels better enable growers to produce crops in an economical, ecological and more efficient manner, thus increasing the likelihood of capturing a longer market window and producing an overall higher quality product due to the protective nature of the structure itself. Most importantly, high tunnels allow growers the opportunity to enter the regional marketplace first by having a saleable product earlier in the season than their competitors growing in the field and for less capital expenditure than greenhouse growers. High tunnels offer the opportunity for family farms to diversify their farming operations and keep the family farm a viable opportunity for the next generation of farmers.

High tunnels help increase the profitability of family farms in five ways:

1) by extending the production season
2) by increasing the quality and shelf life of the horticultural crop being produced
3) by minimizing the use of pesticides
4) by ensuring a continuous flow of product when the outside environment is not favorable for field production
5) by increasing the opportunity to grow more value-added and specialty products.

Vegetables

Extended field production of horticultural crops and in particular vegetables is difficult because of the extreme fluctuations in temperature and moisture – the two most significant environmental factors controlling plant growth. Growers producing vegetables have been using some type of environmental modification in the form of plastic mulch, drip irrigation, row covers or low tunnels to mitigate the effects of cool temperatures or fluctuations in moisture. In the United States and other countries where short growing seasons occur, substantial periods of temperature and moisture extremes represents a major limitation on crop productivity and an invitation for a host of insect and disease organisms to infest a stressed crop. This has led growers in these countries to look at other technologies such as modified environmental structures for intensive production of horticultural crops. The use of high tunnels for production of horticultural crops in the United States offers growers several advantages: 1) reduce temperature and moisture fluctuations during the growing season, 2) lessen disease and insect pressure and enable the use of biological pest control for both insect and disease control, 3) extend the Spring and Fall growing seasons 4) enable the production of crops that have a time to maturity beyond normal field production practices, 5) provide more precise control over water and nutrient application to optimize crop yield and quality as well as reduce non-point source pollution, 6) reduce/eliminate wind stress to plants, and 7) deter animals .

Small Fruits

Season extension technologies have been used with small fruit, but most of the utilization has been for strawberries . Strawberries have been shown to produce extremely high yields in winter when grown in a vertical system in greenhouses. Winter greenhouse raspberry production has been investigated in New York. However, the costs associated with greenhouse small fruit production are higher than those for high tunnel production. Ideal small fruit crop candidates for production in high tunnels are primocane-bearing raspberries and thornless blackberries. In many northern states, early fall frost dates results in only a small portion of the crop of most primocane-bearing raspberry cultivars being harvested. High tunnel production would extend the period during which raspberries could be harvested for a much longer period of time, increasing profitability greatly for the grower. Under field conditions, thornless blackberries often suffer damage to the flower blossoms during periods of low winter temperatures. Low-temperature mitigation would improve the percentage of the crop that would be harvested, or in some cases, make production possible. A preliminary trial of primocane-bearing raspberries and blackberries in a containerized system, while only recently established, has shown improved plant growth over that of in-ground plants (unpublished data). Through the use of greenhouses and/or high tunnels for primocane- and floricane-bearing raspberries and blackberries, it would be possible to have year-round bramble production in the Mid-Atlantic States. Constant supply is helpful in increasing willingness of buyers to purchase produce from a particular source.

Cut flowers

Production of cut flowers in the field had been increasing with many of these flowers destined for local farmer's markets and roadside markets. During the regular growing season market growers have an ample supply of cut flowers although the quality can be negatively impacted by rainfall. As the fall approaches, the numbers of cut flowers produced begins to decrease rapidly after the first frost. Generally farmer's markets are operating long past the first frost so a method of extending the production of cut flowers would be very important for the producer of field grown cut flowers; however, information on methods of extending the growing season has been limited. Many researchers have now demonstrated in the last 3 years that cut flower species can be successfully grown in high tunnels for approximately 10 months of the year (Figure 8).

GREENHOUSES

Because the cost of glass was prohibitive, greenhouse crop production was not fully established in the United States until the introduction of polyethylene. The first plastics were not produced on a commercial scale until 1939. Of these, polyethylene was easy to manufacture, resistant to chemicals, durable, flexible and relatively free of odor and toxicity.

In the U.S., the first use of polyethylene as a greenhouse cover occurred in 1948, when the late Professor Emery Myers Emmert at the University of Kentucky, used the material in place of glass. Prior to his use of polyethylene, he designed crude wooden structures over which he placed wooden frames covered with stretched cellophane supported by wires. In these structures, he grew commercial crops of lettuce, tomato, cucumber and bedding plants for several years. The first plastic greenhouse was constructed at the Kentucky Agricultural Experiment Station in 1953 and remained in use until 1959. Its primary appeal was its comparatively low cost of construction and maintenance.

Currently, many growers have constructed small to medium size greenhouses (1,500 to 10,000 square feet) using two layers of greenhouse grade polyethylene film (6 mil thick) covering the metal frames and inflated with a small blower to provide stability to the structure under high winds and to increase the insulation value of the plastic films (Figure 9). These smaller greenhouses are generally heated with propane, natural gas, #2 fuel oil, wood or in some cases coal. Greenhouses are generally constructed on a cement or stone base and are considered to be non-movable structures and taxable. In the last 25 years, construction of multiple-bay greenhouses with plastic film for their top or roof has been the standard structure for producing horticultural crops in a large area, 10 to 40 acres. In these large growing structures, the common growing system is some form of hydroponics (using water as a carrier for nutrients). Crops

FIGURE 8 Snapdragon production in high tunnel at Penn State High Tunnel Research and Education Facility, Rock Springs, PA. *(Photo courtesy of Dr Mike Orzolek – PSU)*

FIGURE 9 Commercial greenhouse covered with two layers of greenhouse grade polyethylene plastic film and inflated with small fan blower for stability of plastic and insulation value. *(Photo courtesy of Atlas Greenhouse, Alapaha, GA)*

FIGURE 10 Multi-bay gutter connected greenhouse range covered with two layers of greenhouse grade polyethylene plastic film and inflated with small fan blower for stability of plastic and insulation value. *(Photo courtesy of Atlas Greenhouse, Alapaha, GA)*

generally grown in the multi-bay greenhouses are vegetables (tomato, lettuce, cucumber and pepper), small fruits (strawberry and red raspberries), bedding plants and flowering plants and ornamental tropical plants (Figure 10).

References

Abbes, A., D. D. Hemphill, Jr. and N. S. Mansour. 1987. Response of an autumn romaine lettuce crop to nonwoven polyester and perforated polyethylene floating row covers. Proc. Nat. Agr. Plastics Conf. 20:9–13.

Bayer, G., R. Hargan, and J. Cialone. 1962. The influence of petroleum mulch on the performance of several herbicides. Proc. Northeast Weed Contr. Conf. 16:69–74.

Begin, S., J. Calandriello, and P. A. Dube. 1995. Influence of the color of mulch on development and productivity of peppers. HortScience 30(4):883.

Decoteau, D. R., S. B. Wilson, C. L. Ray, and H. H. Graham. 1996. A plant physiologist's view of the perception of light and color by plants. Proc. Natl. Agr. Plastics Congr. 26:158–163.

Granberry, D.M., K.A. Harrison, and W.T. Kelley. "Drip Chemigation-Injecting Fertilizer, Acid and Chlorine." Cooperative Extension Service, University of Georgia, Bulletin 1130, 1996.

Hall, B. J. 1986. New developments in row crop drip/trickle irrigation. Proc. Nat. Agr. Plastics Conf. 19: 65–71.

Hatt, H. A., M. J. Mcmahon, D. E. Linvil, and D. R. Decoteau. 1993. Influence of spectral qualities of mulch film on bell pepper growth and production. Proc. Natl. Agr. Plastics Congr. 24:233–239.

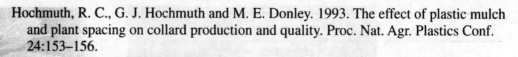

Hochmuth, R. C., G. J. Hochmuth and M. E. Donley. 1993. The effect of plastic mulch and plant spacing on collard production and quality. Proc. Nat. Agr. Plastics Conf. 24:153–156.

Khan, V. A., C. Stevens, M. A. Wilson, J. E. Brown, D. J. Collins, J. Y. Lu and E. G. Rhoden. 1994. Walk-in-tunnels as an alternative method of extending the growing season for small scale vegetable producers in Alabama. Proc. Nat. Agr. Plastics Conf. 25: 117–121.

Locascio, S. J. and G. C. Smart, Jr. 1968. Influence of polyethylene mulch color and soil fumigants on strawberry production. Proc. Fla. State Hort. Soc. 81:147–153.

Lamont, W.J., Jr., J.K. Harper, A.R. Jarrett, M.D. Orzolek, R.M. Crassweller, K. Demchak, and G.L. Greaser. "Irrigation for Fruit and Vegetable Production." *Agricultural Alternatives* series. University Park, PA: Penn State Cooperative Extension, 2001.

Lamont, J. L. Jr. 1996. What are the components of a plasticulture vegetable system? HortTechnology. 6(3):150–154.

Mawardi, M. and K. Stewart. 1993. Effects of mini-tunnels and thermal tubes on soil and air temperatures. Proc. Nat. Agr. Plastics Conf. 24:31–42.

Orzolek, M. D. 1993. The effect of colored polyethylene mulch on the yield of squash and pepper. Proc. Natl. Agr. Plastics Congr. 24:157–161.

Orzolek, M. D. and L. Otjen. 1996. Is there a difference in red mulch? Proc. Natl. Agr. Plastics Congr. 26:164–171.

Orzolek, M. D., S. J. Fleischer and L. Otjen. 1996. Interactions of mulch color and 'Adios' on cucumber beetle populations and cantaloupe production. Proc. Natl. Agr. Plastics Congr. 26:164–171.

Schales, F. D. 1973. Principles, practices and problems involved in using plastic mulches for vegetable production. Proc. Nat. Agr. Plastics Conf. 11:145–148.

Storlie, C. "Treating Drip Irrigation Systems with Chlorine". Rutgers Cooperative Extension Service Factsheet FS795, 1995.

Storlie, C. "Irrigation Scheduling with Tensiometers". Rutgers Cooperative Extension Service Factsheet FS657, 1995.

Wells, O. S. and J. B. Loy. 1986. The current status of row cover use in the United States. Proc. Nat. Agr. Plastics Conf. 19: 4–9.

Wells, O. S. and J. B. Loy. 1993. Row covers and high tunnels enhance crop production in the northeastern United States. HortTechnology. 3(1):92–95.

produce cool-season vegetables like lettuce, broccoli, spinach, and cauliflower through most of the year for the rest of the country. The Central Valley is well suited for warm-season summer vegetables that require a long growing season and fertile soil like tomatoes and melons. Production areas like the Imperial Valley on the Mexican border in extreme Southern California can be used for vegetable production during the winter months. California has a dry climate with seasonal rainfall that inhibits fungal diseases of plants. Vegetable production uses large amounts of water. Federal water projects in the 1930s helped develop a sophisticated irrigation network of dams and reservoirs system that captures mountain runoff and redistributes water through a series of canals to fields during the dry summer months. In terms of markets, vegetable production targets one of two markets—fresh market or processed market.

20.4 VEGETABLE MARKET TYPES

Fresh Vegetable Market Production

Major fresh market vegetable producing states are California, Florida, Arizona, Texas, and Oregon. It is common for production of a crop to be conducted in progression as the season changes. Florida produces "new" (not stored) potatoes in March, followed by Georgia in April, and North and South Carolinas in May. Virginia supplies the fresh market potatoes on the eastern United States in June and July, while Maine produces most of the "new" potatoes in summer to early fall. However, with competition from other production areas, this traditional production pattern has been significantly disrupted.

Processing Vegetable Production

Vegetables for processing are commonly produced in regions where summer temperatures are moderate. The cool temperature allows vegetables to mature more slowly, thereby giving producers some flexibility in the development of harvesting times. Warm-season vegetables are produced in the Great Lakes regions, focusing on crops like sweet corn, peas, cabbage, beets, and carrots. The lake effect moderates the climate in the region for high-quality produce. Major producing states are Minnesota, Wisconsin, Ohio, and New York. Irrigated vegetable production also occurs in the western states of California, Oregon, and Washington.

20.5 SOILS OF MAJOR PRODUCTION REGIONS

As previously stated, vegetables are produced commercially in the field or the greenhouse. Field production generally occurs on soils that are well drained, loamy, and high in organic matter. Vegetables have high water content, some containing about 90 percent by weight of water. Regular supply of water is critical to the production of high-quality vegetables. It is important that the soil drain well while maintaining the capacity to retain adequate amounts of water all the time, hence the preference for loam and high organic matter for optimal soil textural properties. However, light sandy soils may be used, if adequate irrigation and fertilization are provided. High organic matter provides high CEC for nutrient retention for high soil fertility. Some soils in production areas in places like New York, Michigan, and Florida have high organic content. Few crops require special production media that has excessive moisture. In fact, crops like Chinese water spinach and watercress are aquatic vegetables.

20.6 GREENHOUSE VEGETABLE PRODUCTION

Greenhouse vegetable production is by the method of in-ground culture or hydroponics. Hydroponics is the technology of growing plants by delivering the plant growth nutrients through a liquid medium (see Chapter 13). Sometimes, the plant roots are suspended directly and only in water fortified with fertilizers. However, most producers commonly grow plants in artificial media for physical support, and deliver nutrients by the drip fertigation (i.e., the fertilizer is delivered through the irrigation) system. Because vegetables are eaten fresh, it is critical that they not be contaminated with soil in production. Greenhouse production of vegetables using the hydroponics culture is a very attractive and most desirable method of production of fresh produce.

20.7 THE IMPORTANCE OF MULCHES IN VEGETABLE PRODUCTION

Mulching is an old practice in crop production used to accomplish several goals, chief among which are to control weeds, to retain soil moisture, reduce soil compaction, add organic matter to the soil (in the case of organic mulches), and keep produce clean from soil contamination. Materials used for mulching may be natural (organic) or artificial, each with its advantages and disadvantages.

Organic Mulches

Originally, mulches were of plant origin, the most common being straw. Organic mulches are an inexpensive way of achieving the benefits of mulching in addition to the potential to enrich the soil upon decomposition. However, to be effective, organic mulches should decompose slowly. Further, they were also prone to contamination by weed seeds.

Plastic Mulches

Plastic mulches are widely used in modern commercial vegetable production. Their use in horticultural production began in the 1960s. Plastic mulches modify the microclimate of plants, by modifying the absorbidity and reflectivity of solar radiation. They also reduce the soil water loss via evaporation from the soil. The plastic material is available in several colors, of which three are most widely used. These are black, clear, and white-on-black.

In modern production, plastic mulch is often used in a production system called *plasticulture*. In this system, growers use drip irrigation as the means of watering and fertigation. The system is also used for weed control and some pest control in the soil by way of fumigation. Advantages of plastic mulches include the following: they provide weed control, reduce soil moisture loss and increase water use efficiency, reduce soil compaction, provide a means of soil pest control by solarization or fumigation, and modify soil temperature keeping soil warm in cool weather. Some crops mature early because of modified soil conditions. Further, the produce is clean because of lack of contact with soil.

Disadvantages of plastic mulching include the following: producers require special equipment for laying the mulch. The used mulch has to be disposed off because it is not biodegradable. Also, the microirrigation system needed is initially expensive to install.

Installation of the Plastic Mulch

The first step is to prepare the soil to incorporate organic matter properly and with the proper tilth. Clods, coarse organic matter, and other hard objects like rock interfere with the laying of the plastic. All soil amendments and soil nutrient evaluation should be performed prior to laying down the plastic. Plastic is laid on firm, flat, raised beds for easier installation and improved drainage. Raised beds allow the edges of the plastic to be more securely tucked under the soil and resist dislodging during strong winds. Also, it is important for water not to collect on top of the bed. Plastic laying machines are available. Many of these are multipurpose and are capable of forming the bed, laying the mulch, as well as laying the microirrigation system.

It is advantageous to install plastic mulch in the fall season when the nematode population is high, the weather is conducive (not wet), and creates and opportunity for early spring planting.

Establishing the Crop

Planting into plastic mulch can be done as a manual or mechanized operation. Planters burn or punch holes in the plastic at predetermined spacing. It is critical that the hole be clean-cut without any flaps that can be agitated in the wind to cause tears in the plastic. Also, the holes should be large enough such that the seedling does not come into direct contact with the plastic, which can be hot on hot days to the extent of scorching the soft plant tissue. If seeds are sown, they should be placed such that the seedlings would emerge through the holes and not be trapped under the plastic. Planting is a more precise and delicate operation for these and other reasons like potential to damage the microirrigation system. Growers using microirrigation systems usually apply 25–50 percent of their fertilizers at planting and balance through fertigation at a latter date. Where fertigation is not an option, up to 75 percent of the fertilizer is applied as preplant.

Disposal of Used Plastic Mulch

Being mostly biologically nondegradable, disposal of used plastic mulch is one of the major problems with this technology. Most plastic mulching are single use, even though some may be adapted for multiple cropping or used for several seasons before replacement. Some photodegradable plastic is available, although not widely in use because the edges tucked under the soil during installation do not decompose, among other problems. Most producers depend on cheap migrant labor to remove these mulches at the end of the growing season.

20.8 IRRIGATING VEGETABLES

Being largely water by weight (more than 90 percent), vegetable production is highly dependent on the availability of water. Further, many vegetables are shallow rooted. Some production areas (e.g., some producers in the eastern United States) produce vegetables as rain-fed with some success. However, for optimal yield and highest quality for premium prices, vegetables need to be watered at critical times.

It is worthwhile investing in a reliable irrigation system for vegetable production since the industry is generally profitable. In the western United States reliable water supply through canal systems help support a vibrant vegetable production industry.

Selecting an Irrigation System

Irrigation was discussed in detail in Chapter 4. All the methods are used to varying extents in various production regions according to soil conditions, crops being grown, and rainfall patterns. For example, furrow irrigation is popular in the western United States, while seepage irrigation is widely used in parts of Florida where an impermeable hardpan occurs beneath a permeable layer. Drip irrigation is widely used in places where water is scarce. The design that is widely used in vegetable production is the thin-walled (called *tape*) plastic tube design. The tubes may be buried in the soil or laid on top of the soil to trickle water. This system is effective but very delicate, prone to clogging and breakage and hence needs to be replaced annually. Vegetables need large amounts of water in production, as previously indicated. The general recommendation is to supply at least 1 inch of water each week to vegetables. Tensiometers may be used to determine when to irrigate (when it reads 20–30 centibars).

20.9 HOME GARDEN

No two home gardens are exactly alike. Home gardens reflect the creativity and idiosyncrasies of the gardener. Generally, they tend to be more cosmetic than commercial or large-scale farming enterprises. One reason may be that they are often located on the premises of the dwelling place and in a residential area so that they have to be kept clean. Also, since it is near the house, the gardener is able to visit it more frequently than if it were located in a distant place. The general characteristics of a home garden include the following:

1. It is usually located in close vicinity of a home (often in the backyard).
2. The garden is usually less than 1 acre (0.4 hectares) in size.
3. More than one crop is usually grown.
4. Most of the crops grown are annuals.
5. Labor for the garden is supplied solely by the gardener and his or her family.
6. It involves the use of hand implements. When the plot is large, simple powered machines such as a garden cultivator may be used.
7. It depends on the home water supply for additional moisture.

20.9.1 BENEFITS OF A HOME GARDEN

Avid gardeners usually make it a point to show their projects to visitors or to brag about their accomplishments in conversations (sometimes with a bit of exaggeration, for example, about the size of the tomato fruits or the yield of some crops). As a hobby or an income earner, a garden has a number of benefits to the gardener, including the following:

1. It brings pleasure, satisfaction, and a sense of achievement.
2. It reduces the grocery budget.
3. It is a source of fresh produce for the table.
4. It provides a means of exercising the body.
5. When engaged in by the family, it provides valuable time of family interaction.
6. Gardeners may participate in clubs in the community for social interaction.

20.9.2 CHOOSING A SITE

People in urban areas who live in apartments may not have access to land in the immediate vicinity of their residences. Some property owners are gracious enough to provide tenants with a vacant lot that may be devoted to gardening projects by those who wish to do so. Some avid gardeners go to varying extents to grow plants, even in high-rise apartments, by using pots and wooden boxes in their balconies, for example.

In choosing a site for a garden, certain general guidelines may be followed. Even vegetables that require partial shade should not be denied sunlight, especially at the midday period. It should be kept in mind that longer shadows tend to be cast in northern than in southern areas. Further, spring and autumn shadows are longer everywhere than the shadows of June and July. To make maximum use of light, the orientation of the beds in which crops are planted is critical. Following are some general guidelines for site selection:

1. *Adequate sunlight.* The garden should be located in a place where it will receive full, direct sunlight or at least partial sunlight. Gardens should not be planted in the close vicinity of trees, not only because they cast shade but also because they compete with the garden crops for sunlight and with their extensive root systems deplete the soil of nutrients and moisture.
2. *Well-drained soil.* Plant roots need to breathe. Because gardeners tend to visit their gardens on a frequent basis (daily in most cases), gardens receive heavy traffic from humans and are prone to soil compaction. The soil structure, especially in the paths, can be ruined and thereby cause poor drainage and the formation of puddles after rainfall. Loamy soils are best for gardening because they drain well and are also easy to work.
3. *Source of water supply.* Many garden crops require a good supply of moisture for growth and quality produce. The primary water source for garden crops is the

home water supply from the tap. This supply may be accessed by means of a long water hose. If the garden is located too far away, a watering can may have to be used for watering, making the project more tedious.

4. *Flat or gentle slopes.* Whenever possible, steep slopes should be avoided for a garden project. Steep slopes are prone to soil erosion once the natural vegetative cover has been removed for farming.

5. *Windbreaks.* Garden crops are tender and should be sheltered from strong winds. The garden receives some protection from winds if it is located on the sheltered side of a hedge or a row of trees acting as a windbreak.

Because a garden is only a miniature farming operation, the preceding restrictions may be altered. Characteristics that normally would be a major problem for large-scale farming are much easier to correct or manage in home gardens. For example, if the land is not well drained, garden crops may be planted on raised beds, an activity that is not difficult on a small scale. Where the land slopes, beds should be oriented across the slope. Shade-loving plants should be allocated to sections of the land where there is partial lighting. If the land is far from the house and not within reach of a watering hose of reasonable length, water may be carried to the garden.

20.9.3   DESIGNING A VEGETABLE GARDEN

After choosing a site, a decision must be made about which crops and how much to grow. The following are some factors that influence decision making in this respect.

Gardener's Preference

Gardeners grow what they want to grow. Since gardening has a strong hobby element, people devote time to what they enjoy doing. They do not grow crops just to be growing something.

Crop Adaptation

Even though a grower's preference comes first, this factor may be overruled by the reality of what *can* be grown. If one likes strawberries but the environment cannot support this crop, it ceases to be an option (unless artificial growing conditions, such as greenhouse facilities, will be provided). Even when a crop can be grown in a general region, specific varieties or cultivars are adapted to particular areas (Chapter 2). An additional operational classification is important in choosing the season and planting dates for crops. Based on the temperature plants can endure during the growing season, vegetables may be classified into four groups:

1. *Hardy.* **Hardy plants** are frost resistant and may be planted before the last killing frost in the region.
2. *Semihardy.* Plants that are tolerant of light frost but will succumb to severe frost are said to be semihardy.
3. *Tender.* **Tender plants** will grow in cool weather just like semihardy plants but will be severely damaged or killed by even a light frost.
4. *Very tender.* Plants in this category range from very sensitive to intolerant of cold temperatures; even cool weather could kill them.

Market

If an objective of the garden project is to provide supplemental income, it is important that the crops chosen be readily marketable. At the very least, friends and neighbors should be interested in purchasing small quantities of the produce.

Culture

Some crops are easier to grow than others in terms of land preparation, plant care, harvesting, and postharvest handling. Once planted, some crops require only minimal care and attention. Others may require special attention such as staking, pruning, and other activities and expenses that some growers may not be willing to provide. Before deciding on a crop, it is important for the gardener to find out as much as possible about it.

Growth Cycle

Some plants are annuals, while others are biennials or perennials. Certain cultivars of crops are early and others late maturing.

Plant Form and Size

Some plants grow erect, while others climb or are runners. Each type has ideal space requirements. Some plants are small, and others grow to be large bushes. Knowing the crops in this way helps in locating plants in the garden. You do not want plants shading or climbing onto others. Further, tall plants may cast shadows over short ones (unless strategically located in the garden).

Hardy Plants
Plants adapted to cold temperatures (or other adverse climatic conditions).

Tender Plants
Plants that are sensitive to cold temperatures (or other adverse climatic conditions).

20.9.4 GARDEN PLAN

Crop rotation is key to a good garden design. It entails shifting crops from one location in the garden to another according to a strategic and predetermined sequence (Figure 20–2). This strategy has several advantages:

1. *It helps to control insect pests and diseases.* Diseases and pests tend to be associated with a group or family of plants. Their population soars when the host plants are planted year after year in the same location. This is especially true of pests that inhabit the soil and over winter. For example, whiteflies, Colorado potato beetle, and hornworms are associated with the family Solanaceae, which includes potato, eggplant, tomato, and pepper. If such crops are shifted to another location in the garden and replaced with an unrelated species such as corn, the pests will be starved to death and their numbers drastically reduced.
2. *Plants feed at different levels and at different intensities.* Some crops are generally heavy feeders (e.g., corn). Others consume large amounts of specific nutrients (e.g., leaf crops such as lettuce consume large amounts of nitrogen). By rotating crops, the soil fertility will be properly utilized.
3. *Variety of crops may be produced.* Since gardeners frequently grow a fairly large variety of crops, grouping crops according to some sound and strategic basis is an important consideration in the design of a garden plan. For example, cucumber and summer squash belong together; eggplant, tomato, and pepper are related; and carrot and beet, which attract the same pests, can be grouped together. Because a gardener may want to grow perennial vegetables, such species (e.g., rhubarb and asparagus) should be separated from the annuals and not included in the crop rotation cycle.

20.9.5 COMMON GARDEN PROBLEMS

A garden may suffer from neglect and general improper management. Table 20–1 presents some of the common problems and how they can be corrected or avoided.

Garden plants are also plagued by a host of insect pests and diseases. A variety of strategies may be adopted to minimize pest infestation. The control of pests is discussed in detail in Chapter 8. In addition to these general strategies, the gardener may make use of the repellent action of scents exuded by certain plants to reduce pest attacks. For example, aphids are known to be repelled by garlic, and radishes repel beetles that attack

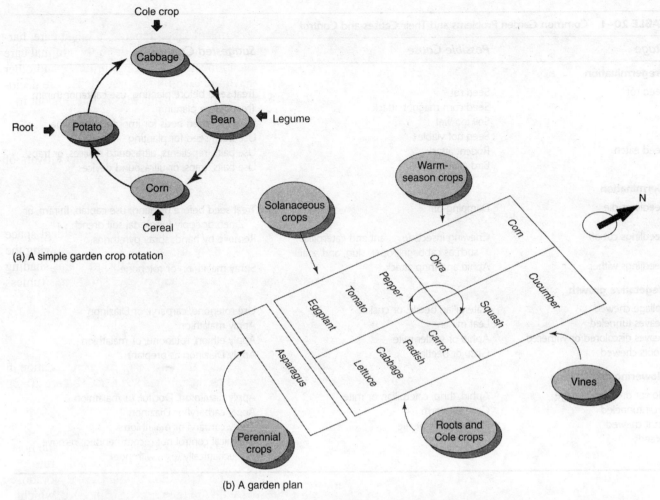

(a) A simple garden crop rotation

(b) A garden plan

FIGURE 20-2 A crop rotation and garden plan. In locating plants, attention must be paid to the heights to avoid shading problems. Gardens frequently have more than the four crops that are often used to illustrate the concept of crop rotation.

plants such as tomato, squash, and eggplant as well as mites. Other repellant actions of plants are presented in Table 20-2.

20.9.6 INCREASING EARLINESS OF VEGETABLE CROPS

The early bird catches the worm, according to the adage. Vegetable growers may want to take advantage of the preseason or early season limited supply of fresh produce to obtain premium prices by taking certain calculated risks to produce an early crop. Particular strategies may increase the production cost of the crop. Some activities and provisions help in this regard, the key ones including the following:

1. *Site selection.* Where the growing season is preceded by cold weather, the site chosen for vegetable production should be such that it encourages rapid warming of the soil. A piece of land that slopes (about 20 degrees) to the south absorbs more of the early sunlight and warms up to a greater depth. Soils that are sandy (light) and drain freely also warm up much faster than cold (clay) soils.
2. *Cultivar selection.* Early maturing cultivars should be chosen.
3. *Use transplants.* Instead of direct seeding, plants can be started indoors in a nursery during the adverse weather conditions preceding the growing season. This practice gives plants a head start on growth and reduces the field growing

TABLE 20–1   Common Garden Problems and Their Causes and Control

Stage	Possible Cause	Suggested Control
Pregermination		
Seed rot	Seed rot	Treat seed before planting; use captanor thiram
	Seed corn maggot attack	Treat before planting
	Soil too wet	Plant on raised beds for improved drainage
	Seed not viable	Use fresh seed for planting
Seed eaten	Rodent attack	Use baits, repellents, ultrasound devices, or traps
	Bird attack	Use baits, traps, or ultrasound devices
Germination		
Seedlings die	Damping-off	Treat seed before planting; use captan, thiram, or Zineb or apply fungicidal soil drench
Seedlings cut off	Chewing insects (e.g., ant and caterpillar such as cabbagelooper, slug, and snail)	Remove by hand; spray pyrethrins
Seedlings wither	Aphid and thrip attack	Spray malathion or rotenone
Vegetative growth		
Foliage chewed	Caterpillar, beetle, or cricket	Use rotenone, carbaryl, or Diazinon
Leaves tunneled	Leaf miner	Apply malathion
Leaves discolored or withered	Aphid or spider mite	Apply ethion, rotenone, or malathion
Roots chewed	Grub or beetle	Apply Diazinon as preplant
Flowering and fruiting		
Flower drop or damage	Aphid, thrip, caterpillar, or mite	Apply disulfoton, Docifol, or malathion
Fruit tunneled	Corn earworm	Apply carbaryl or Diazinon
Fruit chewed	Fruitworm or beetle	Apply carbaryl or malathion
Weeds		Chemical control not recommended; remove mechanically (e.g., with hoe)

TABLE 20–2   Selected Plants Known to Repel Insects and Other Pests

Plant	Insect Repelled
Basil (*Ocimum basilicum*)	Flies and mosquitoes
Marigold (*Tagetes* spp.)	Many insects
Garlic (*Allium sativum*)	Many pests
Mint (*Mentha piperita*)	Cabbage moths
Onion (*Allium cepa*)	Ants
Radish (*Raphanus sativus*)	Many insects
Rosemary (*Rosemarinus officinalis*)	Cabbage moths, bean beetles, and carrot flies
Tansy (*Tanacetum vulgare*)	Beetles and flying insects

time. Although crops such as pepper and tomato are routinely transplanted, vines such as cucumber and muskmelon are not.

4. *Protection from weather elements.* Planting on slopes helps to protect against frost damage. The soil may be irrigated the day before a predicted frost to increase the soil's capacity to retain heat. Windbreaks reduce wind speeds and soil loss while increasing soil temperature. Some growers use plant covers to shield plants from inclement weather.

5. *Mulching.* Mulching controls weeds, keeps soil warm, and increases soil water retention. Crops such as tomato, watermelon, and pepper tend to mature earlier when mulched.

6. *Adequate nutrition.* While overfertilization is detrimental to crops and often delays maturity, providing adequate nutrition encourages rapid plant development. The quality of produce is high with sufficient nutrition. Plants need to be watered adequately to ensure a proper rate of growth.

20.9.7 EXTENDING THE HARVEST

A garden's harvest may be extended such that the grower is able to harvest fresh produce over a prolonged period. This strategy maximizes the use of garden space and increases productivity per unit area. It entails overlapping the planting of vegetable crops by planting crops in combination. It makes use of the fact that certain crops are early maturing while others are late maturing. Early season and early maturing crops are planted first, but before they mature, they are interplanted with midseason crops. There is minimal competition between the two sets of plants. The same effect can be realized with one or several crops by staggering the planting dates. The grower may be able to purchase different cultivars of a crop with varying maturity dates (early, medium, and late). Some crops that can be interplanted are cucumber and pepper, corn and squash, broccoli and pepper, lettuce and onion, and carrot and beet.

REFERENCES AND SUGGESTED READING

Abraham, G. 1977. *The green thumb garden handbook.* Englewood Cliffs, N.J.: Prentice Hall.

Knoot, J. E. 1988. *Handbook for vegetable growers*, 3d ed. New York: John Wiley & Sons.

Newcomb, D., and K. Newcomb. 1989. *The complete vegetable gardener's source book.* Englewood Cliffs, N.J.: Prentice Hall.

Ortho Books. 1981. *All about vegetables.* San Francisco: Ortho Books.

Yamaguchi, M. 1983. *World vegetables.* Westport, Conn.: AVI Publishing.

20.10 GROWING CUCURBITS

Cucurbitaceae is commonly called the gourd family. Commercially produced cucurbits are warm-season annual. Reproductively, they are cross-pollinated even though some cultivars are parthenocarpic (fruit without pollination), the latter commonly grown in greenhouse production systems. Sex is a critical issue in cucurbit cultivation. Most of the commonly cultivated cultivars are monoecious. Some growers manipulate flowering by using auxin and ethephon to stimulate female flower production and gibberellin application to stimulate the production of male flowers. The fruit of cucurbits contain compounds called *cucurbitacins* that are widespread through the entire plant and responsible for bitter taste of the fruit.

20.10.1 CUCUMBER (*CUCUMIS SATIVUS*)

Two basic types of cucumbers are grown—slicing or pickling. Slicing types have dark-green skin and are longer, while pickling types are light green and shorter in length. Cucumber fruits may have white or black spines according to the cultivar, the white-spined cultivars being more preferred for commercial production. Cucumbers are harvested prematurely (or physiologically immature) so the seed are only partially developed.

Most modern cultivars are hybrids. The leading fresh market production areas are Georgia, Florida, North Carolina, and Virginia, in that decreasing order of importance.

Cucumber for pickling is grown widely in Michigan, North Carolina, Texas, Florida, and California, in that decreasing order of importance.

The soil should be deep, well-drained, and slightly acidic for optimal production. Spacing for fresh market production is commonly 9×12 inches (23–31 cm) within rows and 36–72 inches (0.9–1.8 m) between rows. Excessive nitrogen fertilization in the early growth may delay flowering. Irrigation is critical during fruiting period; drought causes small fruit with one shriveled end ("nubbing"). Similarly, pollination is critical for maximum production. For this, bees should be rented for field production. Common diseases of cucumber include bacterial wilt and powdery mildew, others are cucumber mosaic, scab, and angular leaf spot. Common insect pest is the cucumber beetle that is a vector for bacterial wilt, and others like aphids and mites. After harvesting, cucumber should never be stored below 55°F (warm season; susceptible to chilling injury).

20.10.2 MELONS (*CUCUMIS MELO*)

Muskmelon or cantaloupe? Botanically, these two fruits belong to the same species and are one and the same crop, even though the melon industry favors the term *cantaloupe*, because "musk" smacks of foul odor. However, traditionally, in terms of appearance, cantaloupes are those cultivars with less distinct ribs and sutures on the skin, while muskmelons have more pronounced ribbing. Internally, cantaloupes have thicker flesh and smaller, drier seed cavity, while muskmelons have a juicier flesh with larger seed cavities and a strong, fruity aroma. The third melon category is winter melon (e.g., honeydew) that is adapted to high temperatures and semiarid environment.

The key production states of fresh market muskmelons are California, Arizona, Texas, Georgia, and Indiana. Production on the West Coast is largely cantaloupes for shipping, while production on the East Coast is for muskmelons.

Muskmelon produces both male and complete flowers. Producers need about one to two colonies of bees per acre for effective pollination. Fruit quality factors are netting quality, soluble solids (sugar), flesh color, flesh thickness, flesh texture, and cavity size. Of these, fruit thickness is largely genetically determined and most stable. Other traits depend on the cultural environment. A minimum of 9 percent soluble solids (indicator of sweetness) as measured by a refractometer is the industry standard for production in California. Tastier cantaloupes register about 14 percent. Warm, sunny days and cool, clear nights promote higher sugar content. Poor netting is an indication of poor fruit quality.

Muskmelon is generally grown on 6–8 inches raised bed, spaced 80 inches apart, center to center. The crop is sensitive to acidity and salinity, preferring a pH of 6.8–8.0. Growers on the East Coast use drip irrigation with or without plastic mulch. Growers on the West Coast use furrow irrigation more frequently. Excessive irrigation leads to poor fruit netting and low sugar content of mature fruit.

Netted melons are ready for harvesting when the fruit naturally separates (called "slip") from the vine. For local markets, fruits may be harvested earlier as 1/2 or 1/2 slip (partially attached). For distant markets, it is better to harvest sooner. Fruits on the market with attached stalks are generally poor quality. It should be pointed out that winter melons do not slip even when fully mature. After harvesting, melons should be kept cool to retain quality. If shipping, temperature should be 50–55°F to avoid cold injury.

Diseases of melons include powdery mildew (*Erysiphe cichoracearum*), and bacterial wilt that is the most serious pest on the East Coast. Other pests are the cucumber mosaic virus and melon aphids.

20.10.3 WATERMELONS (*CITRULIS LUNATUS*)

Fruit shapes and sizes are variable. Some cultivars are globular while others are oblong, with others in between. Fruit skin color ranges from green to blackish green. Some cultivars are yellow. The color may be solid, stripped, or marbled. The flesh color is also variable, ranging from creamy yellow pink to orange reds. The fruit wall (rind) thickness is between 1–4 cm of white inner flesh between hard outer skin and softer pulpy interior.

Watermelon varieties vary in maturity days between 75–120 days. The average size is about 40 lb., however, the so-called "ice box" cultivars weigh only about 20–25 lb. Seedless melons are triploids produced by the crossing of $4n \times 2n$.

Major producing states for fresh market watermelons are Texas, Georgia, Florida, California, and North Carolina, in this order of descending importance.

The crop is frost intolerant. Production areas must have between 85–150 frost-free days and a high daytime temperature of 25–33C° (77–95F°), and nighttime temperature of 17–25C° (62–77F°). Soil pH of 6.0–6.8 is desirable for watermelons. Watermelon is monoecious. Proper fruiting is aided by bees as pollination agents.

The crop is grown on raised beds in the western United States and in the East. The beds are spaced 80 inches from center to center. Closer spacing results in smaller fruits. For premium yield, watermelon is grown with irrigation and mulching. The crop is established primarily by direct seeding. However, because of poor germination, seedless melons are transplanted.

The crop is moderately fertilized with nitrogen mainly, but with some phosphorus and potassium as the soil test may reveal. Excessive nitrogen produces vegetative growth and delayed reproductive growth that can lead to reduced fruit setting.

The fruits are mature when the ground spot changes color from white to pale yellow. The general color of the rind also changes from glossy to dull green. Another sign of maturity is when the tendril at the same node as the fruit dies. Unlike muskmelon, watermelons do not slip or detach from the stalk when mature and ripe. They have to be cut by hand. The sugar content of the fruit at maturity ranges between 9–13 percent. Shelf life is 10–14 days, if not refrigerated.

Diseases and insects common to watermelon production include anthracnose, fusarium, downy mildew, pickleworm, rindworm, and corn seed maggot.

20.10.4 PUMPKIN (*CUCURBITA PEPO*)

Pumpkin or squash? Just like muskmelon or cantaloupe, the distinction between pumpkin and squash is debatable. Some consider *C. pepo* as true pumpkins, while all *C. maxima* are considered as squash. Pumpkin is one of the most visible festive fruits in the United States, being associated with Halloween as a fresh fruit, and other occasions in which pies are served. It has a distinct appearance and bright orange color when ripe. The flesh of pumpkin is coarse and has a strong flavor. It is used as livestock feed and of course as pumpkin pie.

Squash, winter and summer species, have fine-grained flesh that has a mild flavor and is baked or cooked for food for humans. Summer squash is used as an immature fruit and can be also be fried. Summer squash is early maturing, usually attaining maturity in 45–60 days. Winter squash and pumpkin mature in 80–120 days.

Pumpkin cultivars are classified according to use as follows:

1. *Mini pumpkins.* very small size and used for desktop decoration; it has a flattened shape and light orange color.
2. *Baby pumpkin.* these are also used for desktop decoration; it is small sized and dark orange in color.
3. *Pie pumpkin.* this weighs 5–10 lbs and has a near global shape; it is used for decoration and cooking.
4. *Multipurpose.* it has naked seeds that are edible; the flesh is used for cooking while the rind is carved.
5. *Carving pumpkin.* this is also called a Jack-o-lantern pumpkin and weighs between 15–25 lbs and has variable shapes.
6. *Exhibition pumpkin.* this is enormous in size, weighing more than 100 lbs; this *C. maxima* species has a smooth surface and pale orange color.

Winter squash and pumpkins are grown mainly in the northern United States, the key states being Illinois, New Jersey, California, Indiana, New York, Ohio, Michigan, and Pennsylvania.

Winter and summer squash and pumpkins are monoecious species and mostly day neutral. Summer squash production is more widely distributed than winter squash. There are bush and vining cultivars.

Pumpkins and squash are mostly direct seeded. Spacing is 6–8 feet by 6–8 feet, wider spacing promoting larger fruits. Fruits grow best in the northern United States where day length is longer for extended photosynthesis. To reduce the mishapening of the fruit, specifically flattening of one side, some growers periodically turn the fruits.

Summer squash is harvested prematurely when seeds are just beginning to develop and fruit shows a glossy outer appearance. Where smaller fruits are preferred, they are harvested just after the blossom has abscised. These premature fruits tend to shrivel or are easily bruised and hence are sometimes wrapped in plastic upon harvesting. Fresh fruits should be sold within 7–10 days before fruit quality starts to deteriorate.

If winter squash and pumpkins are to be stored for longer times, they should be harvested when the rind has hardened. Also, curing at 75°F and 80 percent relative humidity for 3–5 days allows wounds to heal to prevent rot in storage.

Key diseases of pumpkins are viruses and powdery mildew. Others are bacterial leaf spot, angular leaf spot, and phytophthora blight.

20.11 TOMATO (*LYCOPERSICON ESCULENTUM*)

Tomato is a warm-season perennial that is cultivated as an annual in temperate regions. This yellow-flowered plant bears berries of various sizes and shape, according to cultivars. Its wild relative is the *L. pimpinellifolium* (wild or currant tomato) from which *Fusarium* resistance is obtained for breeding modern cultivars. Mature fruits may ripen to red or remain green. Cherry tomato (*L. esculentum var cerasiforme*) is roundish in shape, while pear tomato (*L. esculentum var pyriforme*) is pear shaped. Green-fruited species include *L. peruvianam* and *L. chilense*. They have been sources of genes for important disease such as root-knot nematodes, tobacco mosaic virus, and potato virus Y. Green tomato is also high in calcium. Other less common colors are white, orange, and yellow.

Tomato cultivars vary widely in plant growth habit, some being determinate, semi-determinate, or indeterminate. The first two cultivar types are cultivated as freestanding without staking. Leaf type variation in tomato is also vast, including potato and fernlike leaves. Some cultivars are early-maturing, reaching harvest stage in 50–60 days. Some cultivars are later-maturing, requiring 80–90 days to attain maturity. Fruit set is optimal when temperatures range between 55–85°F. Most commercial cultivars have been bred to develop full and uniform color, without the "green shoulder" pattern (top of fruit remains green) trait. Apart from color variation, tomato cultivars come in varying sizes, some being large (over 150 g per fruit), while others are small (55–110 g per fruit) or cherry shaped (20–25 g). Fruits are more flavorful when harvested vine-ripened.

Traits of key importance that have received significant attention from plant breeders include blossom end closure (a source of disease infection), high solids (for good canning quality), crack resistance, firmness of flesh (to reduce bruising during mechanical harvesting and transportation), reduced fibrous core, and lack of pedicel attachment to the fruit (to reduce bruising during harvesting).

Tomato is susceptible to several nonpathogenic fruit disorders, some of which are attributed to nutritional problems. Calcium deficiency resulting from drought stress causes a condition called *blossom end rot* of the fruit, while potassium deficiency causes blotchy or uneven ripening. Potassium deficiency can also cause a condition called *gray wall*, whereby the pericarp turns gray and does not develop the red color in red tomato cultivars.

There are two general production practices—tomatoes for processing and tomatoes for the fresh market. Fresh market tomatoes are transplanted and often staked. In some eastern states like Pennsylvania, they are produced under plasticulture. Black and clear plastics have a warming effect on the soil. In places like Florida, white plastic helps to cool the soil. Tomato for processing may be direct seeded or transplanted onto raised beds without plastic mulching, and mechanically harvested.

Tomato is very intolerant of waterlogging so the soil should be well drained. Soil pH should be between 5.5 to 6.8. Direct-seeded tomato is seeded in clumps of three seeds per hole at a spacing of 12–18 inches in double rows on both sides of a 40-inch bed. At this density, no thinning is necessary. Beds may be spaced 4–6 feet apart, depending on the cultivar. Tomato responds to a moderate to high rate of fertilization. Transplant spacing is similar to that of direct seeding. Spacing may be used to modify fruit size. At transplanting, a starter application that is high in phosphorus (e.g., 8-24-8) is helpful. Fertigation is practiced under plasticulture. Side-dressing with nitrogen after fruit set is desirable. However, high nitrogen levels reduce reproductive growth. Plasticulture uses drip irrigation. California growers primarily use furrow irrigation; sprinklers are common in the Midwest for processing tomatoes.

Staking is a highly specialized and labor-intensive production operation that includes stinging, vine pruning to control plant growth, and fruiting. Unpruned plants produce smaller fruits. Staked plants are easier to harvest.

Being a climacteric fruit, they can be harvested at the physiologically mature green stage and forced-ripened at the point of sale in an ethylene-rich environment. Forced-ripened tomato is less flavorful. The first attempt at using genetic engineering to modify food crops was accomplished with the release of the '*Flavr Savr*' tomato, a product with a reduced capacity for producing the fruit-softening enzyme polygalacturonase. However, this product was not commercially successful.

Diseases of tomato include root knot nematodes, fusarium and bacterial wilts, septoria, and potato virus Y. Insect pests include the European corn borer, aphids, cutworms, and tomato horn worm.

20.12 PEPPER (*CAPSICUM* SPP.)

The cultivated specis of *Capsicum* are *C. annuum, C. frutescens, C. chinende, C. baccatum,* and *C. pubescens*.

Peppers are noted for their pungency, a trait that is not related to size, shape, or stage of maturity of the fruit. The pungency is caused by a chemical called *capsaicin* that is concentrated in the placenta of the fruit. Scientists measure pungency in Scoville units, the most pungent cultivars including *C. chinense*, Thia hot, and Scotch bonnet or 'habernero' pepper. Based on pungency, peppers are classified into two groups, as follows:

1. *Nonpungent peppers*. This groups includes pimento cultivars that are used in processed or canning production, the bell peppers used in salads, and the paprika types used in dried and processed products.
2. *Pungent peppers*. This group of peppers includes the Tabasco (used for processed hot sauce), Cayenne (processed as dried powder), jalapeno (bullet-shaped fruits are often pickled), cherry (has both pungent and sweet types for pickling of used in salads), and scotch bonnet or habernero (cultivated for fresh market sales).

Another group of peppers, "wax peppers," are yellow-fruited and comprise pungent and nonpungent cultivars. Apart from use in flavoring food, and as food items in salads or main dishes, peppers have medicinal value. Also, there are ornamental peppers that are used as potted plants or bedding plants.

Peppers vary in height, some being determinates while others are indeterminate. Some cultivars are early-maturing (75 days) while others are late-maturing (110 days).

Mature fruit color is usually red, but also green and yellow cultivars and other colors exist. Red cultivars are more expensive than green cultivars because color development takes a long time and the yields are lower. Fruit size can be very small in some cultivars and very large in bell peppers, the latter used in food preparations such as stuffed peppers.

The leading production states for fresh market peppers include California, Florida, North Carolina, New Jersey, and Texas, in that order of decreasing production. Bell peppers make up over 2/3 of the total pepper production.

Pepper is frost sensitive. The soil should be well drained and have a pH of about 6.5–7.0. Commercial production is usually done on raised beds. Establishment of the field is by transplanting. Double rows spaced 18–24 inches within rows are commonly used. Plasticulture is practiced in the eastern United States. Just like tomato, pepper responds to nitrogen fertilization.

Pepper is not a climacteric fruit and must be harvested vine-ripened. Bell peppers are hand harvested to avoid damaging the fragile branches. Fruits should be stored at temperatures above 50°F to avoid damage. For powdered pepper production, growers usually cut entire plants and dry them in the field.

20.13 POTATO (SOLANUM TUBEROSUM)

White or Irish potato is *Solanum tuberosum*. It is a tetraploid that grows in the wild as perennial but is commercially cultivated as an annual. Most cultivars have a white flesh, but yellow potato (e.g., Yukon Gold) is increasing in acreage. Over 50 percent white potato crop is produced using a few cultivars—Russet Burbank, Kennebec, Katadin, and Sebago.

Potato cultivars are distinguished by traits that determine their food use. High starch content cultivars are used for baking in salads, while low starch tuber content is preferred for cooking by boiling. Low sugar content is required for processing (fries), while low sugar is preferred for boiling or cooking. Cultivars for boiling also have large cells. Tubers differ in size, shape, length, width, and end shape (blunt or round). Skin or periderm characteristics are also widely variable. Skin color may be red, tan, or brown, and be netted (russet) or smooth. White tuber flesh is most popular in the United States while yellow is most popular in Europe.

Potato is best cultivated in cool climates. Top-producing states are Idaho, North Dakota, Washington, Minnesota, and Wisconsin. Early summer potatoes are produced in Virginia, Maine, and North Carolina, while production for late summer and fall harvests occur in Idaho, North Dakota, Washington, Oregon, Wisconsin, New York, and Colorado. Winter and late spring potatoes are harvested in Florida, California, and Texas, while late spring harvests occur in California, Alabama, Arkansas, and North Carolina.

The potato crop is established by seed potatoes (whole tomatoes) or seed pieces (large tubers cut into pieces so that each piece has at least one "eye"). Potatoes grow best under daily temperatures of 60–65°F. To control soilborne diseases like fungal scab, the crop performs best on acidic soils with a pH of 4.5–5.5. The soil should be free from stones and loose for proper tuber formation. Seed potato is spaced at 6–12 inches within rows and 34–36 inches between rows, the wider spacing being used when whole seed is used for crop establishment. Cut pieces should be treated against rot by applying a fungicide (e.g., Captan).

Tubers form best under short days, low temperatures, and high sunlight intensity. Excessive nitrogen fertilization delays tuberization, tuber maturity, and tuber solids. Irrigation is critical during the tuber formation. If moisture is not uniformly applied during that period, the tuber becomes knobby. On the other hand, if moisture is excessive, the lenticels (pores in the periderm) increase in size. Irrigation is by sprinkler or drip and never flood irrigation, since it is a tuber crop.

It is important for the tubers to be completely burring in the soil during production. Exposure to sunlight causes greening, a condition that causes the chlorophyll and solanine to form in the skin. Mechanical injury to the tuber can also cause solanine to form.

This toxin is heat resistant and not destroyed by cooking. Peeling away the skin removes this toxin. Green potato should not be eaten.

Tubers are ready for harvesting when the vines begin to dry. However, some producers harvest potatoes prematurely for a specific market at premium price by using chemicals to defoliate the plants. Also, producers may delay harvesting without damage to the tubers left longer in the ground. Low temperature storage is used to store potatoes. Prior to storing, the tubers undergo a process called *curing*, whereby they are placed under high humidity (95–99 percent) and low temperature (60°F) for any wounds to heal. Storing at a lower temperature (34–36°F) and 95 percent relative humidity causes starch to be converted to sugar. Tubers stored this way can keep their harvest condition for several months but are rendered unsuitable for processing as fries (sugar caramelized when heated). To have the sugar reconverted to starch, potatoes removed from low temperature storage may be stored at 64–68°F and 85–90 percent relative humidity. This process is called *reconditioning*, and used by grocery stores to reduce the sugar developed in low temperature stored potatoes. Storing potatoes at high temperatures can cause tuber dormancy to be broken, resulting in sprouting. An application of sprout inhibitors such as maleic hydrozide can delay sprouting that reduces the market quality of the tubers.

The most economic disease of white potato is blight (both early and late types). Incidentally, this was the disease that devastated potato farms in Ireland, prompting the mass migration of Irish people to other countries such as the United States. Potato is also plagued by scab, a disease that can be prevented by growing potatoes in acid soils (pH of 4.5–5.5). Root-knot nematode, various viruses, and bacterial rot are also important diseases. The major insect pests of potato include the Colorado potato beetle, potato tuberworm, and aphids.

Potato is also susceptible to physiological disorders, the chief being hollow heart, a condition whereby the tuber develops a hollow inside. This occurs when the plant and therefore the tuber grows rapidly. This may be caused by excessive nitrogen fertilization. Also, excessive heat causes necrotic spots to develop in the flesh of the tuber.

20.14 SWEET POTATO (*IPOMEA BATATAS*)

Unlike Irish potato that is a modified stem, sweet potato is a modified root. The root shape is variable but tapers at both ends. Skin color is also variable, being white, buff, brown, pinkish, purple, magenta, or copper, according to variety. The flesh of cultivars in the United States is yellow or orange because of the high carotene content. The flesh has high sugar content, limiting its use in processed foods, especially fried products. White flesh dominates cultivation in other parts of the world. The stem color is either purple or green.

Apart from being used for food, a wide variety of ornamental cultivars are available for use in the landscape, foliage colors ranging from green to deep purple.

China leads the world with about 80 percent of total world production. In the United States the leading producing states are North Carolina, Louisiana, California, Texas, Georgia, and Alabama, in that order of decreasing production.

The crop is produced as annual in temperate areas and as a perennial in the tropics. The desirable soil is one that is well drained, loamy, and slightly acidic (pH of 5.0–6.8). Producers in the United States establish their crop by using transplants called **slips** produced by inducing adventitious roots and shoots from parent seed roots. To do this, seed roots are buried in specially prepared beds and covered with plastic sheets, keeping temperatures below 85°F.

Slips are set into well-tilled soil that is free of clods for proper formation of swollen roots. Starter fertilization application may be applied. Transplants are spaced about 8–18 inches within rows and about 32–42 inches between rows. Fertilization should be kept to low rates. A high amount of nitrogen promotes vegetative growth at the expense of economic product. Similarly, excessive moisture late in the season results in oversized roots that are prone to developing cracks. Mature roots should be harvested before the soil temperature falls below 50°F. Some producers dig the mature roots and leave them in the field to dry before collecting them. Delaying harvesting after the vines die risks having root decay.

Prior to storage, the harvested root products should be cured at 85°F and 90 percent RH for about 7–10 days for bruises to the skin to be healed. Thereafter, the roots retain peak quality for about six months if stored at 55–59°F and 85–90 percent relative humidity. Sweet potato is intolerant of colder temperatures.

Disease in production include *Fusarium* wilt (stem rot), *Rhizopus* (soft rot), and internal cork.

20.15 CORN (ZEA MAYS)

Sweet corn is *Zea mays* var. *saccharata*. The sweetness is caused by mutant genes that cause the accumulation of sugar instead of starch in the endosperm of the corn kernel. The standard sweet corn has the *su* gene. To keep its sweetness, the harvested corn must be stored at a cool temperature without delay. A new breed of sweet corn cultivars with a new gene, the **sugary enhancer** (*se*) gene, causes a higher accumulation of sugar than the standard cultivars. Also, the gene slows down the rate of deterioration or conversion of sugar back to starch, and increases shelf life in terms of sweetness. These cultivars are described as extra sweet. A third category of sweet corn, the supersweets, carries the **shrunken-2 gene** (*sh2*) that further promotes sugar accumulation. These cultivars retain sweetness longer in the field and in storage. However, the *sh2* is linked with poor seed germination and low vigor leading to poor crop establishment, and hence reduced acceptability by producers.

Sweet corn is interfertile with regular or field corn. The starchy condition of field corn is dominant to the mutant sugar allele. Consequently, when sweet corn is cross-pollinated by field corn, the sweetness is suppressed. It is imperative that sweet corn farms be isolated from field starchy corn farms. Only about 1 percent of corn acreage in the United States is devoted to sweet corn production.

Like sweet potato, some corn cultivars are grown for ornamental purposes. Most cultivated corn in the United States is from hybrid seed. Corn cultivars differ in maturity, some being early (65–74 days), midseason (81–90 days), and late (over 90 days).

Sweet corn may be produced for the fresh market or for processing. Fresh market production is led by Florida, followed by California, New York, Georgia, and Pennsylvania, while processing corn is concentrated in Minnesota, Wisconsin, Washington State, Oregon, and New York, in this order of decreasing production.

Corn is frost sensitive and intolerant of high soil acidity (below pH 5.5). The soil should be well drained. Unless furrow irrigated, corn is not planted on raised beds. Corn is direct seeded at 6–18 inches within rows and 2–4 feet between rows, wider spacing resulting in larger ears. Corn responds to high fertilization, especially, nitrogen. The crop is ready for harvesting when the kernel attains the "milk" endosperm stage. To keep its sweetness, corn must be refrigerated immediately after harvesting.

Diseases of corn include, corn smut, bacterial wilt, leaf rust, and maize dwarf mosaic virus. Major insect pests include the European corn borer, corn root worm, and cutworms.

20.16 ONION (ALLIUM CEPA)

Other members of the onion family of interest are garlic (*A. sativum*), leek (*A. ampeloprasum*), and chive (*A. schoenoprasum*).

The onion is a biennial crop, the economic part being the bulb. The onion bulb varies in size, shape, inner leaf thickness, skin color, pungency, and other traits. Skin color can be tan, yellow, white, brown, purple, or red, while bulb size may be small, large, or jumbo. The bulb may be sweetness and pungency. Pungency is caused by the presence of methyl and propyl disulfides (e.g., thiopropanyl sulfoxide). The pungent smell that causes tearing in humans is the result of bruising or cutting of the tissue that causes enzymes to be released. There is no relationship between skin color and bulb pungency. However, pungent cultivars store better than the sweet cultivars.

Garlic cultivars differ in clove size, being larger in elephant garlic. The bulb color may be red, tan, or white. Some cultivars are pungent while others are mild. The bulb may be compact or large.

The United States, Japan, Spain, Turkey, Italy, and Egypt are among the top producers in the world. In the United States, the leading onion-producing states are Georgia, Texas, California, and Arizona. California is the primary garlic-producing state.

Onions may be cultivated for fresh immature bulbs (green onions) or as dry mature bulbs, the latter being most challenging to produce. Being a biennial, flowering or bolting occurs after vernalization (cool temperature treatment). Photoperiod is critical to optimal bulb formation, cultivars varying in the critical day length desired. Similarly, temperature conditions are critical to bulb formation, optimal range being 20–25°C.

Onions are cultivated on soils that are rich in organic matter and are well drained. The seedbed should be finely tilled and free from physical obstructions like stone that can interfere with bulb formation. Soil pH preferred is 5.3–6.5. The planting material can be seed, sets (small bulbs), or seedlings, direct seeding being the choice in commercial production. Sets and transplants are popular with home gardeners and small commercial growers.

Weed control is essential for a good crop, since the onion plant does not compete well with weeds. If grown in organic soil, nitrogen and phosphorus fertilizers are less important. Instead, potassium becomes more important. Both sprinkler and furrow irrigation methods are used.

Bulb onions are mature for harvesting when the tops fall over. The bulbs are dug and wind-rowed in the field in desert areas. In humid areas, the crop is dried in forced-air dryers. Prior to storing, the bulbs are cured at 25–35°C for two days. Cured bulbs are stored at low temperature (0–7°C) and low humidity for up to about 12 months. Generally, the pungent cultivars store better than sweet cultivars.

Onion diseases include downy mildew, pink rot, neck rot, purple blotch, and white rot. Insect pests include beet armyworm and thrips.

20.17 LETTUCE (*LETUCA SATIVA*)

Lettuce cultivars vary in leaf shape and head firmness. The **crisphead** types have overlapping and brittle leaves that form a firm, roundish head. They have a strong and sometimes bitter flavor and taste. They are easy to handle and transport. The **butterhead** types are similar to the crisphead, except that the leaves are smooth and oily. The flavor is less overwhelming. The **cos** or **romaine** lettuce have narrow, erect leaves that form a loose head. Their flavor is most desirable. Being delicate plants, they are not suited for long-distance transportation. The **loose leaf** or **bunching** cultivars have leaves that form a rosette or cluster. The leaves are smooth and not crisp. A type of lettuce, **stem lettuce**, forms enlarged seed stalks that can be eaten raw or cooked. It is not popular in the United States, though very popular in Japan and some parts of Asia.

Lettuce is the principal salad crop in the United States. Major production states are California, Arizona, and Florida. The Salinas Valley of California has the ideal condition for head lettuce production. The climate is consistently cool (65–70°F) and dry. Warm temperatures cause some cultivars to bolt and produce small heads.

Lettuce is best grown on well-drained organic soils that are slightly acidic (6.0–6.8). It may be established by transplants or direct seeding, the latter method involving precision seeders and pelleted seeds. Seed germination may be inhibited by high temperature and dormancy, the latter requiring after-ripening to overcome. Seedbeds should be of fine tilth and well drained. Double rows spaced 12–20 inches apart are used in some areas, and within-row spacing ranging from 2 inches (leaf types) to 12–18 inches for head types. Lettuce responds well to nitrogen, 50 percent applied at planting and 50 percent as side dressing. Phosphorus and potassium are commonly applied at planting. Furrow irrigation is common in the commercial production areas. Excessive irrigation causes puffy heads and reduced storage life.

Commercial lettuce is harvested by hand. A major problem with lettuce production is uniformity of maturity. Harvested produce should be cooled immediately to avoid deterioration. Crisp lettuce head may be chopped and bagged for marketing.

Common diseases in production include downy mildew, big vein virus, lettuce mosaic, and sclerotinia. Common insect pests include cutworms, aphids, thrips, leaf hopper, and cabbage looper.

20.18 BRASSICA

The genus *Brassica* is characterized by species with strong pungency in the plant parts. However, there some of the widely eaten species that lack pungency, including mustard, horseradish roots, cress, and watercress foliage. The bitter taste of *Brassica* species is caused by the presence of high levels of glucosinolates that are broken down to give compounds like isothiocyanates, thiocyanates, nitriles, and goitrin, which result in the bitter principle.

The cultivated *Brassicas* include *B. nigra* (black mustard) and the *B. oleracea* that is classified into major groups: *Capitata* (cabbage), *Botrytis* (cauliflower), *Italica* (sprouting broccoli), *Gongylodes* (kohlrabi), *Gemmifera* (Brussels sprout), and *Acephala* (kale, collards). There is also *B. rapa* that comprise a number of varieties such as *rapifera* (turnips) and *B. napus* var *napobrassica* (rutabaga or Swede turnip). *Brassica* species may be used as fresh leaves (e.g., watercress, garden cress, sea kale) or as roots (e.g., radish, turnip, and rutabaga).

20.18.1 RADISH (*RAPHANUS SATIVUS*)

Radish is a popular early spring vegetable. This cool-season crop does not tolerate temperatures above 25°C (77°F). High temperatures cause plants to bolt (bloom) or the tissue to be pithy and poor in quality. Cultivars differ in skin color (usually red, but mixed colors occur), pungency, and size. Winter cultivars are larger in size and more pungent.

Radish may be planted on raised beds or flat beds. Sandy loams are preferred for good tuber formation. Plants are spaced about 10–12 inches between rows. Good fertility produces a good crop. Delayed harvesting causes the root to be pithy and bitter.

Common diseases include *Phytophthora, Rhizoctonia, Pythium*, anthracnose, and powdery mildew. Insect pests include aphids, flea beetles, and cabbage root maggots.

20.18.2 CABBAGE (*BRASSICA OLERACEAE* OR *CAPITATA*)

Cabbage is characterized by a terminal bud whose leaves are arranged into a ball of tightly wrapped and overlapping leaves called a *head*. Cabbage can be direct seeded or transplanted. For direct seeding, the bed should be of fine tilth. Varieties differ in head size, shape, or color (pale, dark, blue-green, or red). Leaves may be smooth or coarse. Recommended spacing is 3 × 1 feet (0.91 × 0.3 meter). Delayed harvesting causes the head to split.

Common diseases during production include downy mildew, black rot, alternaria leaf spots, and club root. Root knot nematodes and cysts are a problem.

REFERENCES

Growing selected vegetables
http://www.thompson-morgan.com/growing-vegetables/index

How to grow selected vegetables
http://www.farm-garden.com/growing-vegetables

OUTCOMES ASSESSMENT

1. Discuss the nutritional value of vegetables. Compare vegetables with field crops in terms of nutritional value.
2. Discuss the regional distribution of vegetable production in the United States.
3. Discuss giving specific reasons why places like California are suited for vegetable production.
4. Discuss vegetable production in terms of market types.
5. Discuss the importance of irrigation in the production of vegetables.
6. What is plasticulture? Discuss its application in field vegetable production.

21
Herb Gardening

PURPOSE AND EXPECTED OUTCOMES

This chapter discusses the use of herbs and their cultivation.

After studying this chapter, the student should be able to

1. List ten herbs.
2. Discuss the use of herbs in the landscape.
3. Discuss the medicinal and culinary uses of herbs.
4. Describe the general cultivation and care of herbs.

OVERVIEW

Herbs are plants that include a variety of types—annuals, biennials, perennials, woody, herbaceous, roots, leaves, bulbs, flowering, and nonflowering. They may be grown in the landscape as ornamentals, in gardens (flower and vegetable), or in containers for medicinal and other uses. They are also adapted to a wide variety of growing conditions.

21.1 USES

Characteristics of common herbs are described in Table 21–1.

21.1.1 MEDICINAL

Herbal medicine was the primary form of therapy for treatment of diseases in ancient times and still plays a significant role in the treatment of diseases in many cultures today. Medicinal herbs are used in a myriad of ways. They may be brewed to extract the essential chemicals and drunk like a tea. Some are burned as incense or vaporized and inhaled, and others have essential oils that can be extracted and used as ointments or balms.

TABLE 21–1 Popular Herbs and Their Parts Used

Plant	Scientific Name	Parts Used
Bay	*Laurus nobilis*	Leaves
Basil (sweet)	*Ocimum basilicum*	Leaves
Chives	*Allium schoenaprasum*	Leaves
Cumin	*Cuminum cyminum*	Seeds
Coriander	*Coriandrum sativum*	Leaves or seeds
Dill	*Anethum graveolens*	Leaves
Ginger	*Zingiber officinale*	Root
Mint	*Mentha* spp.	Leaves (seasoning or tea)
Marjoram (sweet)	*Origanum marjorana*	Leaves
Oregano	*Origanum vulgare*	Leaves
Parsley	*Petroselinum crispum*	Leaves (seasoning or garnish)
Rosemary	*Rosemarinus officinalis*	Leaves
Sage	*Salvia officinalis*	Leaves
Thyme	*Thymus vulgaris*	Leaves

Sometimes herbs are ground into a thick slurry and applied to parts of the body for a variety of purposes. Using herbs for medicinal purposes should only be on the advice of qualified practitioners and is discouraged for pregnant women.

21.1.2 ORNAMENTAL

Herbs have great decorative value in the landscape. They may be used in edging, for either their attractive foliage (e.g., sage, rosemary, lavender, and thyme) or color (e.g., parsley, chives, and pot marigold). Plants such as sage, hyssop, bushy thyme, and lavender can be trimmed to amenable sizes and attractive shapes.

21.1.3 FRAGRANCE

Part of the use of herbs in the landscape is to provide pleasing scents in the environment. Herbs are known for their scents, which emanate from flowers and foliage. Some of the most notable herbs with sweet scents include thyme, lavender, rosemary, and rosebuds. Certain herbs are cut and dried (leaves and flowers) and included in the mixture used to make potpourri, which is widely used in perfuming indoor environments.

21.1.4 CULINARY

A number of herbs are used in cooking to add their characteristic flavors to foods. Fresh leaves, where available, may be picked and added to foods for this purpose; dried forms may be purchased in stores for culinary use. Flowers of chives and borage, among others, may be used in salads, and seeds of dill, coriander, and cumin are good flavoring aids. Certain herbs are dried and used in brewing teas (herb teas), which have refreshing and medicinal values. Apart from these common uses, certain herbs such as hyssop, clover, thyme, and sage have flowers that attract insects such as bees and butterflies. Others, such as tansy, pyrethrum, and santolina, on the other hand, repel insects with their scent.

21.2 CULTIVATION

21.2.1 SITE SELECTION

Herbs grow vigorously and attain the most flavor when exposed to full sun. The soil must be well drained with a neutral to alkaline soil reaction. Clay and sandy soils should be avoided since they present water-related problems in cultivation, clays being prone to water-logging and sandy soils being prone to drying out. Many herbs are adapted to marginal soils.

21.2.2 SOIL PREPARATION

Raised beds should be used where drainage is poor. If required, soils should be limed to reduce acidity. Herbs may be grown in containers in the kitchen using regular potting mixes; such herbs are readily accessible for culinary use (Figure 21–1).

21.2.3 DESIGN OF AN HERB GARDEN

Herbs, as mentioned previously, have both ornamental and culinary uses. For ornamental purposes, and like other ornamental species, herbs may be set in a formal design in the landscape by judiciously selecting species according to the principles of landscaping. Herbs may be arranged in a fashion similar to bedding plants. In herb gardening, themes are important in creating attractive designs. These themes should take into account the adaptive characteristics, along with growth habits and other botanical features such as flower color. A popular design is the checkerboard, in which the site is divided into squares with walkways between squares and each square planted with one species.

21.2.4 PROPAGATION

The most common method of propagation of herbs is by seed. Herbs have not received the attention that vegetables and many important field crops have from the standpoint of breeding and improvement. As such, wild characteristics may be present in some species, making their germination unpredictable and sometimes very poor. Species with some degree of germination problems include rosemary, lavender, catnip, mint, and winter savoy. Instructions on seed packs should be followed with care. Vegetative propagation (by cuttings or division) may be used in propagating certain seed-bearing plants; it is the only method for seedless species such as French tarragon. Mints are widely used in the confectionery industry and have received some attention in terms of improvement. They are often propagated from division of rootstocks and runners to make them come true to type. Tansy and bergamot are also propagated from root division.

21.2.5 CARE

Herbs, being relatively wild, are quite hardy and can be produced on marginal soils, eliminating or reducing the need for additional fertility in cultivation in many cases. Herbs, such as basil, chives, and parsley, whose foliage is frequently cut benefit from moderate fertilization. Mulching improves moisture retention and suppresses weeds.

Herbs grown in restricted areas in containers generally need more attention than those grown in beds. They are more likely to experience moisture stress and also more prone to danger from excessive moisture. Herbs that do best indoors are those with preference for low light, unless artificial light supplementation is provided. They may be grown in window boxes or hanging baskets. Few diseases and pests are a problem in herb cultivation. Chives and mints are known to be susceptible to rust attacks. Under damp conditions, fungal diseases such as molds, mildews, and rots may occur on some herbs, as is generally the case in many plants in cultivation.

21.2.6 HARVESTING AND DRYING

Herbs may be used fresh or cut and dried. For culinary uses as seasonings, young leaves should be picked. Plants attain peak flavor when flowers open, which is the best time for harvesting for drying of stems and leaves. The plants to be dried are cut when leaves exhibit no moisture. Slow drying at low temperatures produces the best results. Drying is done not in the sun but in a well-ventilated dry room or in an oven at low temperature. This drying condition helps to retain the green color, essential oils, and aroma of the leaves and stems. Seeds are harvested when brown or black by cutting the stems. The stems are then hung upside-down over a receptacle so that

FIGURE 21–1 Selected herbs: (a) rosemary, (b) garden sage, (c) catnip, (d) common thyme, (e) English lavender, and (f) basil. *(Source: George Acquaah)*

FIGURE 21–2 Methods of drying herbs.

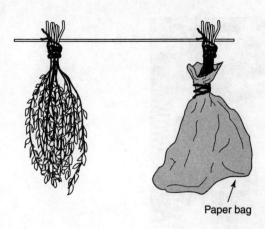

Paper bag

when completely dry the seeds will drop into a container (Figure 21–2). After drying, the products (seeds and leaves) should be stored in an opaque container or in the dark to retain color and flavor.

SUMMARY

Herbs are relatively hardy plants that are cultivated for their medicinal value and used as flavorings in food. Some have pleasant scents and attractive blooms and can be grown as landscape plants. They generally have wild tendencies and can tolerate marginal soils. Herbs may be grown in pots or beds. Commonly propagated from seed, they may be used fresh or dried.

REFERENCES AND SUGGESTED READING

Rice, W. R., and R. P. Rice. 1993. *Practical horticulture*, 2d. ed. Englewoods Cliffs, N.J.: Prentice Hall.

Stern, K. R. 1997. *Introductory plant biology*. Dubuque, Iowa: Wm. C. Brown Publishers.

Sunset Magazine and Book Editors. 1972. *Herbs: How to grow*. Menlo Park, Calif.: Sunset Lane.

Herb gardening
http://herbgardening.com/

How to grow selected herbs
http://www.urbanext.uiuc.edu/herbs/

Key tips on herb gardening
http://www.herbgardeningtips.com/

Miscellaneous information of herb cultivation
http://www.gardenguides.com/plants/factsheets/herbs/

Notes on growing herbs
http://www.wvu.edu/~agexten/hortcult/herbs/ne208hrb.htm

OUTCOMES ASSESSMENT

1. Discuss the common uses of herbs in society.
2. Discuss the container production of herbs.
3. Discuss the garden cultivation of vegetables.

22

Organic Farming

PURPOSE AND EXPECTED OUTCOMES

This chapter is designed to show the importance of organic matter in plant nutrition and how it is utilized as the principal source of additional fertility, apart from rock minerals. Methods of composting are also described.

After studying this chapter, the student should be able to

1. List the major sources of organic matter for gardening.
2. Describe the importance of organic matter in soil fertility.
3. Discuss the sources and importance of mulches.
4. Discuss the methods of disease and pest control in organic farming.
5. Describe how composting can be done on a small scale.

OVERVIEW

Is *organic farming* a new method of growing crops or an ancient practice? Like many bandwagon terms, such as *biotechnology*, there is always the question of novelty. The term has gained prominence in society in the face of a strong move toward healthy eating and environmental protection. Organic farming is certainly not a new method of growing crops. In fact, it is as old as agriculture itself. To appreciate the resurgence into the limelight of organic farming, it is important to understand how it differs from modern methods of cultivation. Modern methods of plant cultivation are greatly influenced by technological advancements that enable scientists to duplicate or mimic natural conditions. To qualify as an organic producer, one must be duly certified by the state after complying with certain standards.

The fundamental differences between the two systems of plant production lie in the ways in which plants receive nutrition and protection from diseases and pests in cultivation. However, what launched organic farming into the limelight were the side effects of modern crop production practices on the general environment. Natural resources in the soil environment for plant growth are exhaustible. Unless there is a way to replenish the nutrients extracted from the soil by plants, the land soon becomes depleted of plant food and consequently incapable of supporting plant growth. Natural nutrient recycling systems exist to replenish the soil nutrients. These cycles are largely dependent on the activities of soil microbes and occur at a slow pace. Nutrient recycling is the organic way of fertilizing crops. Scientists have identified these plant growth nutrients and produced synthetic versions (chemical fertilizers) that are easier to regulate and apply.

Regarding disease and pest control, organic farming depends on nature for control, while modern farming depends on chemicals. Nature has a way of regulating itself, maintaining balance so that one organism does not dominate the community. Further, prey–predator relationships occur in nature; some potentially harmful organisms fortunately have natural enemies. Pesticides often indiscriminately kill organisms, the good and the bad.

Organic production is not without its problems or critics. It is generally a more expensive cultural practice. Crop yields and quality are significantly lower than under traditional production. People are willing to pay more for organically produced crops because of the fear of chemical residues from the application of pesticides under traditional systems of vegetable production. However, the absence of chemicals in the production system may encourage the presence of natural toxins, which could also be harmful. Disease and insect pest buildup is increased under this system of production. In fact, the benefit to humans of organic production is largely experienced through a safer environment because of the reduced amounts of chemicals entering the soil and polluting the water supply.

22.1 What Is Organic Farming?

The National Organic Standards Board (NOSB), which serves in advisory capacity to the USDA, defines *organic farming* as "an ecological production management system that promotes and enhances biodiversity, biological cycles and soil biological activity. It is based on minimal use of off-farm inputs and on management practices that restore, maintain and enhance ecological harmony." This formal definition notwithstanding, organic farming tends to be defined in society by one of its characteristics as an approach to farming that does not utilize synthetic pesticides or conventional fertilizers.

22.2 Importance of Organic Farming in Modern Crop Production

Organic farming is widespread, practiced in its modern form in over 120 countries and on over 31 million hectares of farmland in 2005. The leading producing nations include Australia, Argentina, United States, and Italy; the United States and the European Union account for 95 percent of the world market of organic foods. Organic farming is rapidly expanding in the United States at the rate of about 20 percent annually. According to the USDA, organic foods are found in about 75 percent of conventional food markets, bringing nearly 15 billion dollars in revenue in 2005. Currently, about 5 percent of the total domestic market for fresh market fruits and vegetables is supplied by organic farmers. Australia, New Zealand, and Latin America account for many of the organic fruits and meat imported into the country.

22.3 PRINCIPLES OF ORGANIC FARMING

Organic farming is governed by certain general principles and concepts, chiefly biodiversity, diversification and integration of enterprises, sustainability, natural plant nutrition, natural pest management, and integrity. Producers use these principles as guidelines in designing farm-specific organic production plans. These principles are implemented through the use of sustainable farming practices such as crop rotation; intercropping; composting; mulching; biocontrol; and use of cover crops, green manures, and natural pesticides.

Biodiversity

It is known that the stability of an ecosystem increases with diversity in species composition. Organic producers enhance the biodiversity of the agroecosystem by adopting practices such as intercropping, crop rotation, and companion planting. These practices have the capacity to naturally enhance nutrient recycling, soil physical quality, disease suppression, and nutrient augmentation.

Integration

Enterprise diversification is a strategy used by some organic producers to implement the principle of diversity. For example, some organic producers may raise livestock along with crops, recycling the manure as fertilizer for crop production. Similarly, the practice of crop rotation replenishes soil fertility when nitrogen-fixing legumes are included in the rotation cycle.

Sustainability

Organic farming exhibits the key characteristics of sustainable agriculture—reduced soil erosion, reduced energy (fossil-fuel) consumption, reduced leaching of nitrates into groundwater, greater carbon sequestration, and restricted or excluded pesticide use. In terms of economic sustainability, many organic producers realize high market premiums for their products.

Natural Plant Nutrition

Nutrient recycling is at the core of providing nutrition for crops in an organic production enterprise. Harsh, soluble, synthetic chemicals, and tillage practices that reduce the population of beneficial soil microbes, are abandoned in favor of nutrients derived from natural rock minerals or the decomposition or mineralization of organic matter.

Natural Pest Management

Conventional pest management in modern agriculture is heavily dependent on pesticides. Organic producers, on the contrary, adopt practices such as crop rotation, sanitation, genetic resistance, and natural pesticides, if necessary, to manage diseases and insect pest incidence in production.

Integrity

Integrity is the principle that speaks to the observance of guidelines for operating an agricultural enterprise certified as organic, so that consumers get what they expect. In other words, certified organic producers literally pledge to manage all aspects of agricultural production and handling in accordance with prescribed organic regulations.

22.4 Organic Farm Certification

Organic farmers, as previously stated, are required to produce their crops in accordance with stipulated guidelines. The guidelines are developed by the National Organic Programs (NOP) and the National Organic Standards Board (NOSB), entities created under the authority of the Organic Foods Production Act of 1990. The purpose of organic certification is to protect the consumer through third-party confirmation that the production and handling operations for all products labeled organic in the U.S. marketplace are in compliance with uniform standards. Successful certification entitles the producer to market his or her products under the USDA Certified Organic seal. This seal assures the consumer of organic integrity. Located in the USDA Agricultural Marketing Service, the NOSB provides recommendations to the Secretary of Agriculture as pertains to the implementation of the NOP.

22.5 The Certification Process

The organic certification process follows certain basic steps.

22.5.1 THE CERTIFIER

Organic certification is conducted by a USDA-accredited certifying agency, which can be private for-profit, private non-profit, public, or state-run agency. The producer or handler seeking certification chooses a certifier. A list of accredited certifiers is found at *http://www.ams.usda.gov/nop/indexIE.htm*. Third-party, independent certifiers usually charge a fee for their service, based on factors like the size or the enterprise and travel cost of the certifier. The farmer is not obligated to use one agent but can change if a certifier performs unsatisfactorily. A farmer with gross annual sales of $5,000 is obligated to submit to certification. Certification is voluntary for producers with sales of less than $5,000 per annum. Some farmers submit to additional certification standards through entities such as the International Foundation for Organic Agriculture (IFOAM), the European Union, and the Japanese Agricultural Standards (JAS).

To convert a farming operation from conventional to organic requires a thirty-six-month waiting or a transitional period during which the land is kept free from all prohibited substances in the organic program. Once certified, the status is permanent, unless it is suspended or revoked by the NOP. Also, the producer may voluntarily surrender the certificate. However, the operation is subject to annual visual inspection and the organic system plan recertified.

22.5.2 THE ORGANIC SYSTEM PLAN

The certification process centers around the Organic System Plan (OSP), or simply a Farm Plan, which the producer or handler submits along with an application to the certifier. This written statement describes the soil and pest-management approaches that are specific to the applicant's operation.

In a crop production enterprise, specific information required includes land use history, field maps, crop rotation plans, soil improvement and pest-management plans, seed sources, planting, production, harvest, sales records, specific production inputs (soil amendments, fertilizers, compost, manure, pest control materials, etc.), nutrient monitoring systems, and product labeling of products. It is important to show how organic integrity will be maintained (e.g., the use of buffers and borders, planting and harvesting equipment, post-harvest handling and storage).

For a livestock operation, the specific information supplied includes source of animals, feed and feed supplements, housing and living conditions, health care practices and the specific materials to be used, management practices, manure management, record-keeping system, and product labeling.

If the applicant is engaged in a handling operation, specific information to provide will include sources of ingredients, processing aids, materials and standard operating procedures for equipment cleaning, sanitation, and pest control. It is also important to show how the organic integrity will be maintained (i.e., prevention of contamination), packaging, product formulation, record-keeping system, and product labeling. It is permissible for applicants to request and receive help in the development of the OSP.

22.5.3 REVIEW OF OSP

The certifier reviews the information to determine if the applicant is capable of operating the proposed enterprise in accordance with NOP guidelines, and whether the operation, as described in the OSP, meets the requirements for certification. Once the OSP is approved, the certifying agency will subsequently assign an organic inspector to conduct an on-site inspection of the operation.

22.5.4 ORGANIC INSPECTION

The inspector's job is to ascertain whether the daily practices of the operation are as described in the OSP, and whether the inputs and management practices are in compliance with the USDA National Organic Standard. Also, the inspector verifies the record-keeping practices for adequacy and compliance with standards. Records inspected include input materials, production, harvest and sales records, and product packaging. The risk of contamination from prohibited materials is verified. The inspector may decide to take samples of soil and products for off-site critical evaluation. The information gathered is sent back to the certifier who is the decision maker, but not before the farmer or handler has been furnished a copy for his or her approval at an exit interview.

22.5.5 REVIEW OF THE INSPECTION REPORT

The certifier reviews the inspector's report to determine the eligibility of the applicant's operation for organic certification. The decision types are (a) unqualified approval, (b) request for additional information for a conclusive decision, or (c) denied, if significant noncompliance is evident. Where noncompliance is only minimal, the certifier will instruct the applicant the specific corrective actions to take and the time frame within which documentation of compliance is required.

22.5.6 ORGANIC CERTIFICATION

When a certifier is satisfied that an applicant's operation meets the NOP compliance, an organic certificate is summarily issued, granting the permission for the operator to market the product as organic. The USDA organic label (Figure 22–1) may be displayed on the packaging along with the seal of the certifying agency. When the product comprises a single ingredient (e.g., unprocessed, raw or fresh vegetables and fruits), the certification and labeling is straightforward. The "100% organic" label is applicable. However, sometimes an enterprise may contain multiple ingredients, in which case one of four categories of labels may be used:

- "100% organic" means 100 percent of the ingredients (excluding salt and water) are certified organic.
- "Certified organic" means 95 percent of the ingredients (excluding salt and water) are certified organic.
- "Made with organic ingredients" means at least 75 percent of the ingredients (excluding salt and water) are certified organic.
- "No label claims" means less than 70 percent of the ingredients are certified organic.

FIGURE 22–1   USDA organic
certification label.   *(Source: USDA)*

22.6 AMENDMENTS APPROVED FOR ORGANIC PRODUCTION

Organic producers may use a variety of nonsynthetic biological, botanical, or mineral inputs to manage pests only if preventative approaches are inadequate to provide effective control. The NOP defines the term *synthetic* as any substance that is formulated or manufactured by a chemical process, while *natural* is defined as any substance created as the result of naturally occurring biological process. It publishes the National List of Allowed and Prohibited Substances annually, following rigorous review by the NOSB. The "National List" as it is called, may be obtained from a certifying agency or the NOP website. Being natural per se is not sufficient for a substance to be eligible for use in organic production. For example, arsenic is a natural substance but is prohibited in organic production. On the other hand plastic is allowed (as mulch), provided it was not made of polyvinyl chloride.

Organic producers may also consult a list of materials published by the Organic Materials Review Institute (OMRI), a private non-for-profit organization, for approved substances. Further, substances approved for use in pest management in organic production are subject to state and federal labeling laws, as well as EPA tolerance criteria.

22.7 PLANTING MATERIAL

Organic crop farms may be established by direct seeding or transplanting. Planting material includes crop seed, cover crop seed, vegetable transplants, perennial plants, seed inoculants, and other seed treatments. These materials must meet NOP criteria and be organic. New and improved varieties must be developed using only allowed methods. Allowed methods of crop variety development include traditional breeding, hybridization, in vitro fertilization, and tissue culture. Prohibited methods include recombinant DNA technology, cell fusion, and micro- or macroencapsulation. In other words, genetically engineered varieties and even GMO (genetically modified organisms)-derived pesticides are prohibited from organic crop culture.

Should a producer decide to produce his or her own seedlings, it must be done using the proper media and containers and other inputs. Because many commercially formulated soil mixes contain prohibited materials, media used in organic culture must be specially constituted. Those who grow perennial crops like tree fruits and berries may obtain their planting stock from conventional sources. However, production from such plantings cannot be marketed as organic for at least twelve months following transplanting.

22.8 Managing Soil Physical Quality

A good farming soil should be maintained in a condition such that soil compaction and erosion are reduced, while soil water-holding capacity, aeration, and tilth are enhanced. Tillage and mechanical cultivation can be used judiciously to incorporate organic matter and other soil organic amendments into the soil to improve its physical quality. Incorporation of organic matter into the soil stabilizes soil aggregates and reduces soil erosion. Practices such as crop rotation also maintain good soil physical condition since crops vary in root depth and characteristics.

22.9 Soil Fertility Management

Soil fertility management is one of the key activities in organic production. As previously stated, one of the key foundational principles in organic production is the use of natural plant nutrition.

22.9.1 NUTRIENT MANAGEMENT PLANNING AND MONITORING

Just like conventional production, nutritional balance is important in organic production. However, because of the more stringent production guidelines, nutrient management in organic culture should be carefully planned and monitored to remain compliant with NOP guidelines. The plan should include the approaches for using natural plant nutrition through practices like crop rotations as well as incorporating nutrient amendment and environmental protection from contamination. These should be detailed in the OSP. Another key aspect of nutrient management is soil testing to monitor nutrient concentration in the soil.

22.9.2 REPLENISHING SOIL NUTRIENTS BY NATURAL PLANT NUTRITION

This approach to fertility management in organic production relies on natural cycles and carefully planned human practices to replenish the soil with nutrients extracted during a production cycle. Organic matter is incorporated into the soil to be decomposed by soil microbes to release nutrients by the process of mineralization. The major practices for natural plant nutrition are:

1. *Green manures*. Specific plants are cultivated with the sole purpose of incorporating into the soil while green.
2. *Cover crops*. Cover crops are grown for the primary purpose of soil and nutrient conservation. If leguminous, they can enrich the soil through nitrogen fixation. Cover crops may be used as green manures. Examples of cover crops are sunhemp (*Crotalaria juncea*), velvet bean (*Mucuna deringiana*), hairy vetch (*Vicia villosia*), and crimson clover (*Trifolium incarnatum*). If an inoculum is to be used for a legume species, it must be of the approved kind.
3. *Animal manures*. See book
4. *Compost*. General composting is discussed in Chapter 22. To be allowed for use in organic production, composts must be prepared according to NOP guidelines. Raw animal manure may be applied to crops grown for livestock feed but not for human consumption. If applied to a crop whose edible portion does not touch the soil, it cannot be harvested earlier than ninety days postapplication. If the edible portion touches the soil, harvesting must be delayed until 120 days postapplication. Municipal waste is prohibited from organic production. The carbon-to-nitrogen ratio (C:N ratio) of the raw materials should be between 25:1 and 40:1. Further, the

compost heap temperature must be maintained at between 131°F to 170°F for at least three days if the compost system is static-aerated, and for at least fifteen days if composting occurs in a wind-row system whereby the heap is periodically turned.

22.9.3 REPLENISHING SOIL NUTRIENTS BY SUPPLEMENTAL PLANT NUTRITION

Deep, fertile, organic soils and other prime farmlands can support high crop productivity if properly managed with little or no supplemental nutritional inputs. On marginal farmlands and those that previously were under conventional production practices, conversion to organic production requires significant management not only to be compliant but to sustain high productivity.

Organic producers may apply natural products like powdered rock minerals in their operations. These include dolomitic limestone, rock phosphates, gypsum, and mined potassium sulfate to supply phosphorus, potassium, calcium, magnesium, and sulfur, applied as needed. Materials like hydrated lime (slaked lime) and burnt lime (calcium oxide) are prohibited because of the synthetic method of production. Providing supplemental nitrogen, often the most limiting nutrient in vegetable production, is challenging because the organic sources are highly variable in their nitrogen concentrations. In addition to organic sources of nitrogen, producers may use sodium nitrate from mined rock to supply up to 20 percent of the crop's total nitrogen requirement. Further, if the producer can document a specific nutrient deficiency, the certifying agency may approve the use of a synthetic material with relatively high solubility for corrective action. All supplements that have been pelleted are prohibited. Some companies now market low-analysis organic fertilizers (e.g., 8-5-5 and 4-2-2) composed of dehydrated granular by-products of animal production (e.g., feathers, bone meal, etc.). Fish emulsion is also used in organic production.

22.10 WEED MANAGEMENT

Some consider weeds to be the most economic pests in organic culture. Herbicides are a major component of modern conventional crop production. However, since synthetic pest control is prohibited in organic culture, the most widely used weed management approach to weed control is prevention. The key approaches to weed control in organic production include the following:

1. *Avoidance.* Whenever possible, the producer should avoid locating plants in fields that are known to have high weed infestation. As previously discussed, the predominance of certain weeds in an area is indicative of the soil physical and nutritional condition. The producer may allocate crops to the field on the basis of plant growth requirements and competitive abilities, to make the best of the environment.
2. *Solarization.* This is the method of killing weeds by heating the soil using the sun as the source of heat. Solarization can control some weeds as well as soil pathogens.
3. *Flame weeding.* Flame weeding may be conducted as a preplant, preemergent, or postemergent treatment to control weeds. As preplant, the goal is to control the first flush of weeds that follows tillage. This method of weed control is noted to be more effective on hot, dry days. Further, just searing the plant is more effective and economical than charring, which is known to stimulate root development and plant regrowth.
4. *Tillage.* Tillage and cultivation are the most commonly used nonchemical weed management methods in traditional crop production. Tillage may be conducted as preplant operation to prepare the soil for seeding. *Blind tillage* is conducted as a

preemergent or early postemergent operation. Tillage tools are variable and used to accomplish various purposes. The shallower the depth to which the soil is disturbed, the fewer the weed seeds that will be brought to the soil surface to grow. *Row crop* and *interrow cultivation* are other tillage operations for weed control. They improve the soil physical condition by breaking surface crusts while removing young weeds.

Tillage is found to be more effective in controlling biennial and perennial weed species than annual weeds, except in perennial weeds that propagate by rhizomes (e.g., johnsongrass, quackgrass). In the latter cases, tillage exposes these underground materials and reduces propagation of the plant.

5. *Allelopathy.* Allelopathy is the ability of some plant species to inhibit the growth of other plants in their vicinity by exuding toxic chemicals into the soil. Rye mulch has been successfully used to suppress weeds in no-till cultures of crops like pea, corn, and cucumber.

6. *Crop rotations.* Crop rotation is the strategy of growing several judiciously selected crops in a cyclical fashion on the same piece of land. By varying the crops on the land, the growth of weeds is disrupted by the lack of consistent favorable environment that favors them, since each crop has unique requirements. The buildup of weed populations is limited by this cycling of crops.

7. *Intercropping.* Intercropping is the strategy of growing two or more crops together on the same piece of land in one growing season. Because the crops have different spacing requirements and morphological features, the ground is more effectively shaded to restrict weed growth.

8. *Mulching.* Plasticulture is discussed in Chapter 20.

9. *Herbicides.* Synthetic herbicides are prohibited in organic production. However, a number of preparations with low herbicide toxicity are permitted, including corn gluten meal and herbicidal soaps. Commercial products such as WeedBan™ and Corn Weed Blocker™ are available. Herbicidal soaps such as Scythe™ may also be purchased by growers. Vinegar is a component of several newly released herbicides, such as Burnout™ and Biorganic™

22.11 DISEASE AND INSECT PEST CONTROL

An effective pest management plan is rooted in an understanding of the biology of the pest, including factors such as the life cycle, stage in the cycle it is most vulnerable, stage in which it causes economic damage to crops, and method of dispersion. Pest control strategies are discussed in detail in Chapters 7 and 8. Like nutrient supplementation, synthetic pesticides are forbidden in organic culture. Consequently, preventive measures are relied upon in pest management in organic production. Avoidance strategies include the use of pest-resistant cultivars, sanitation, crop rotation, and timing of planting, among others.

22.11.1 TIER APPROACH TO PEST MANAGEMENT

Just like nutrient management, some synthetic products are allowable under some circumstances. However, producers are required to first exhaust all avenues for using physical, biological, legislative, and cultural methods of pest control, before considering the use of approved materials. To this end, the NOP recommends that a pest management plan be three-tiered, the distinction between the first two levels often being minimal:

Level One—This includes proactive management practices that reduce the potential for the development of disease and pest (e.g., the avoidance measures).

Level Two—The management at this level includes the use of cultural and mechanical measures (e.g., planting dates, cultivations, etc.).

Level Three—This level of protection against diseases and insect pest entails the use of biorational pesticides (see next section). To resort to the use of pesticides, the producer must clearly document his or her efforts at implementing the methods in the first two levels, to justify using curative instead of preventive measures in pest management.

22.11.2 BIORATIONAL PESTICIDES

Permitted biorational pesticides may be classified as follows:

1. *Minerals*—These include sulfur, copper, and clay-based material such as the commercial preparation called Surround®.
2. *Botanicals*—Botanicals derive from plants, the common ones including rotenone, neem, and pyrethrum. Highly toxic botanicals like strychnine are prohibited from organic production.
3. *Soaps*—A variety of commercial insecticidal, herbicidal, fungicidal, and algicidal soaps are available to producers. However, detergent-based products are prohibited.
4. *Pheromones*—These are products that impact the mating behavior of insects and lure them into traps to be captured and disposed of.
5. *Biologicals*—Biopesticides are becoming more important in crop culture, a widely used one being the formulation *Bacillus thuringiensis (Bt)*, which is used to combat lepidopterous pests like the Colorado potato beetle. Another is Contan® consisting of the fungus *Coniothyrium minitans*, and effective against sclerotia (*Sclorotina sclerotium*).

22.12 BUFFERS AND BARRIERS

Buffers and barriers are constructed from plants like sod and surround the field being organically farmed. Their purpose is to prevent or reduce the contamination of the organic crop from biological or chemical intrusions. For example, if the organic farm borders a conventional farm, it is critical to protect the former from contamination with synthetic chemicals. The buffers may also harbor beneficial insects that may aid pollination. Also, strips of sod help reduce erosion and contamination of surface water.

22.13 RECORD KEEPING

Effective record keeping is not only required for annual recertification of an organic enterprise, but it can be used by the producer to improve the profitability of the enterprise. It can be used to aid in planning pest and nutrient management as well as establishing and protecting product integrity in compliance with NOP guidelines.

22.14 COMPOSTING

Plants obtain inorganic nutrients from the soil and air and convert (fix) them in organic form (e.g., protein and carbohydrates) as plant material through complex biochemical processes. When they die, the organic matter decomposes, or breaks down, and thus inorganic nutrients that were locked up become available to plants once again. There are well-known natural recycling processes, including the nitrogen, phosphorus, and carbon cycles, in which specific elements undergo alteration of form between inorganic and organic.

Composting is a deliberate activity by gardeners aimed at accelerating what occurs naturally—*rotting*, or the decomposition of organic matter. As previously mentioned, a typical mineral soil consists of about 5 percent organic matter. Organic matter affects both the physical and chemical properties of soil. It improves the aeration and moisture retention of the soil and, through gradual decomposition, releases both major and minor nutrient elements into the soil for plant use. Composting in effect is organic matter recycling. In the soil, compost acts like a source of slow-release fertilizer, in addition to its desirable influence on the physical characteristics of soil.

Compost
An organic soil amendment consisting of highly decomposed plant organic matter.

22.14.1 PRINCIPLES OF COMPOSTING

To be successful at composting, one needs to understand the underlying science of the biological processes involved. Composting involves both biotic and abiotic factors, the essential ones being decomposers (microorganisms), organic material (plant or animal), environmental factors for growth (of the decomposers), and time (over which decomposition occurs).

22.14.2 DECOMPOSERS

Decomposers are the agents that convert organic matter into compost through the process of decomposition.

Decomposers
Microorganisms that break down organic matter.

Types

There are two groups of decomposers that inhabit the soil—microorganisms and macroorganisms.

Microorganisms The major microorganisms (or microbes) involved in decomposition are bacteria, fungi, and actinomycetes.

Macroorganisms The major macroorganisms include earthworms, grubs, and insects. These groups of organisms should be provided the appropriate environmental factors for their growth and development in order to have large enough populations to work effectively in the compost pile. Microbes have four basic requirements for growth:

1. *Source of energy.* Microbes obtain energy from the carbon inorganic materials. Plant materials differ in their carbon content, and thus proper materials must be selected for the compost pile.
2. *Source of protein.* The protein source for microbes is the nitrogen from materials such as blood meal, manure, and green vegetation. Protein is required in only small amounts.
3. *Oxygen.* Aerobic microbes, which use oxygen for respiration, are more effective and efficient decomposers than anaerobic microbes, which do not use oxygen for respiration. As such, a compost pile should be well aerated. When a pile is poorly aerated and thus dominated by anaerobic bacteria, the decomposition process produces foul odors.
4. *Moisture.* Moisture is required by organisms for metabolism, but excess moisture in the compost pile fills up the air spaces and creates anaerobic conditions.

An active compost heap is, in effect, an environment teeming with a wide variety of microorganisms that operate in succession, depending on the temperature in the heap. The temperature in the heap changes because the by-product of a metabolic reaction is heat. It is important to note that bacteria operate over a broad spectrum of temperature conditions. Some prefer cool conditions while others prefer warm conditions. A group of microbes called *psychrophiles* can operate at temperatures below freezing ($-2.22°C$ or $28°F$) but work best around $12.8°C$ ($55°F$). They dominate a compost heap when the temperature is cool (at the initiation of the pile), but soon the by-products of their metabolic activities cause the temperature to increase. A temperature range of between 21.1 and 32.2°C (70 and 90°F) ushers in another group of microbes called *mesophiles*. Mesophiles are the workhorses of composting. However, at 37.8°C (100°F), they are replaced by *thermophiles*, heat-loving bacteria that work to raise the temperature of the compost heap to a much higher level, reaching a peak of about 71.1°C (160°F).

After bacteria have operated on the organic matter, cellulose, lignin, and other hard-to-metabolize substances are left behind in the pile. Fungi and actinomycetes are able to decompose these substances. Their presence in the heap is indicated by the occurrence of whitish strands or cobweblike structures.

Larger microorganisms such as earthworms are important in the compost heap. They feed on organic matter and excrete materials rich in nutrients for plant growth. Earthworms abound in soils that have high microbial activity.

22.14.3 COMPOSTABLE MATERIAL

The quality of compost depends in part on the materials included in the compost heap. The secret to quality is variety. Avoid including too much of one type of material. Good compostable materials include the following:

1. *Grass clippings from mowing a lawn.* A mulching mower may be used to spread fine clippings on the soil. When clippings are bagged, they may be used as a good source of plant material for composting, provided a few cautions are observed. Do not use clippings from a lawn that has been recently sprayed with pesticides. A fresh pile of grass clippings has a tendency to form a slimy and soggy product with a foul odor. It is best to spread grass clippings in thin layers or to mix them in with dry leaves.
2. *Household garbage that is void of fats and oil.* Greasy materials are hard for microbes to metabolize.
3. *Leaves.* During the fall season, leaves drop from trees. Dry leaves may be gathered for use in composting. Leaves decompose slowly and need some help to accelerate their breakdown. Instead of using full-size leaves, they should be chopped before adding them to the compost pile. Leaves should be added in thin layers.
4. *Sawdust.* Sawdust from softwoods, pine, and cedar decompose more quickly than those from hardwood (e.g., birch and oak). When including sawdust, it should be sprinkled lightly and in layers like the other materials.
5. *Straw or hay.* Old (highly weathered), not fresh, hay makes a good compost material. Straw or hay should be chopped before adding it to the pile.
6. *Ash.* Wood ash from the fireplace contains potash and is a good material to include in a compost heap.

22.14.4 MATERIALS TO AVOID

Some materials are undesirable in a compost heap because they cither are not biodegradable or produce toxic factors that are harmful to microbes. These materials include:

1. *Diseased plants.* All pathogens may not be killed by the heat generated, even at the peak temperature of about 71.1°C (160°F).
2. *All nonbiodegradable material* (e.g., plastics, synthetic cloths, and styrofoam).
3. *Pesticides.* Pesticides should not be used under any circumstance because they destroy the organisms that are the agents of decomposition.
4. *Pet litter.*

Other materials should be used with caution. For example, the plant remains from corn harvest, including cobs and husks, are hard to decompose. If they must be added, they should first be chopped into small pieces.

22.14.5 THE CARBON-TO-NITROGEN RATIO FACTOR

Grass clippings have a high nitrogen composition and hence a lower C:N ratio than dried leaves. If the nitrogen in the compost heap is too low, it will heat up. However, if the nitrogen proportion is too high, the heap may become too hot, killing the decomposers, or become anaerobic, resulting in a foul-smelling compost heap. Usually, a good starting C:N ratio is 30:1. This ratio reduces to 10:1 at the end of a good composting process.

The carbon-to-nitrogen (C:N) factor is a measure of the material's relative proportion of carbon to nitrogen. The higher the value, the lower the nitrogen content and the longer it takes to decompose. A C:N ratio of 30 is best for composting. Straw has a C:N ratio of 80, while sawdust has a ratio of 400. Materials of leguminous origin have a low C:N ratio (e.g., 15). While a high C:N ratio material decomposes slowly, using materials of low C:N ratio produces excess nitrogen that is expelled from the heap in the form of ammonia gas.

22.14.6 TIME FACTOR

Plant breeders in a way cause artificial evolution to occur in their breeding programs. The difference between their activities and natural evolution is the fact that natural evolution requires an estimated millions of years while a plant breeding program may be completed within ten years. Natural evolution depends on *natural selection* to guide it, while plant breeding relies on *artificial selection* imposed by the breeder. Similarly, a biodegradable material eventually decomposes, if left in the soil long enough. However, a gardener may not be able to wait for nature to take its course. To accelerate the process of decomposition, a compost pile is inoculated with materials called *activators*. They contain good populations of decomposers and a nitrogen-protein source to sustain the decomposers in the initial stages of composting.

22.14.7 COMPOST ACTIVATORS

There are natural and artificial compost activators.

Natural Activators

Natural activators include the following:

1. *Loamy soil.* The decaying organic component of a loamy soil contains soil microbes.
2. *Compost.* For the person who composts frequently, finished compost from a previous pile may be used to inoculate a fresh compost heap.
3. *Protein meal.* Protein meal may be derived from high-protein plant material, such as alfalfa and cotton seed. Animal sources include fish meal, bone meal, and blood meal.
4. *Manure.* Manure from a variety of farm animals including poultry, cattle, and sheep is a good activator. However, it should not be used fresh, since it is safest when well decomposed. Manure may be decomposed by allowing the fresh substance to sit exposed to the weather for several weeks. Unfortunately, manures contain weed seeds, which could be a problem if the composting process does not reach the peak temperature required to kill weed seeds.

Artificial Activators

Artificial activators include the following:

1. *Fertilizers.* Fertilizers are less efficient than natural activators because they lack protein. Compound fertilizers consisting of nitrogen, phosphorus, and potassium (10:10:10) may be used.
2. *Inoculant.* Commercially prepared dormant bacteria and fungi that are packaged as tablets or granules may be used.

Methods of composting are varied and adaptable to one's needs and situation, once certain general guidelines are observed. There are designs for small-scale and indoor use, and others for large-scale and outdoor production of compost. They also vary in terms of ease of aeration, cost of setup and maintenance, time to completion, quality of product, and odor. The two types of compost systems are categorized on the basis of the receptacle.

No-Container Method (Sheet Composting)

The ultimate goal of composting is to decompose plant material for incorporation into the soil to improve its nutrient level and physical characteristics. The most direct way of accomplishing this is to use in situ composting, in which the plant material is composted in the soil where it will be used. The material used may include leaves, plant residue after harvesting, grass clippings, and manure hauled onto the field. These materials are incorporated by an appropriate implement such as a spade or a mechanical tiller. Another version of this method, called *green manuring*, involves the growing of leguminous species, such as clover, alfalfa, peas, and soybean, and plowing them under while still fresh.

Sheet composting allows organic materials to be applied to large fields. A negative side of this method is that it takes several months for the incorporated material to decompose. Also, when materials of high C:N ratio are used, the soil experiences a short period of nitrogen deficiency (*nitrogen starvation*) because the existing nitrogen is used in decomposition. Crops therefore should not be planted until several months after composting, when the nitrogen deficiency has been corrected. Another negative factor is that heat does not build up to a level at which weed seeds are killed.

Container Methods

Gardeners also compost in specially constructed containers or pits. These methods of composting follow certain recipes, depending on the design. The compost is prepared in one place and transported to another for use.

22.16 General Principles of Constructing and Monitoring a Compost Heap

The success of composting depends on the observance of certain principles including layering, moisture supply, size of pile, and aeration. When monitoring the compost heap, be sure to take multiple measurements of temperature, pH, and moisture content, since these factors vary within the heap.

Right Mix and Layering

Layering or arrangement of the organic material in the compost pile is important. However, the key to a successful composting is to start with the right mix of ingredients. In this regard, the key factors of concern are the moisture content and the C:N ratio of the ingredients.

Since one is encouraged to use a wide variety of materials in a compost pile, the way they are arranged in the pile is important. Materials are not haphazardly mixed up in the pile but rather are placed strategically in layers. For example, layers of dry materials such as straw should be alternated with fresh materials such as clippings and vegetative matter. Materials high in nitrogen (low C:N) should be alternated with high-carbon (high C:N ratio) material. After a number of layers, the activator should be spread evenly before another set of material is added. This pattern is repeated until the container is filled. Particle size also affects the rate of decomposition of the organic materials. Particles in the heap should preferably not exceed 2 inches in size.

Moisture Supply

Water is required by microorganisms for decomposition. It is best to keep the moisture content of the compost heap at 40–60 percent. If too wet, pieces of newspaper or wood chips may be added to the heap to remove excess moisture. Too much of it may cause anaerobic conditions to develop in the pile leading to foul odor, while too little slows decomposition. Efforts should be made to provide moisture uniformly throughout the pile, accomplished by moistening the material layer by layer as it is being piled and as needed. A well-moistened compost heap material feels as moist as a wet sponge that has been wrung. Overwatering a compost pile is a waste of water and also causes leaching of nutrients. Rain water is ideal for watering since it contains useful microorganisms, minerals, and oxygen.

Size of Pile

An effective pile size is one that is manageable and self-insulating without causing compaction in the layers. A large pile may cause overheating and anaerobic conditions to prevail in the inner part, a situation that is detrimental to bacteria. A small pile, on the other hand, may be overventilated and thus not be able to reach peak temperatures; it may also require artificial insulation. Since a pile should be turned over regularly, a huge pile may be unmanageable.

Aeration

A compost heap should be well ventilated for good growth of aerobic bacteria. A pile may be built around ventilating pipes or a tube of wire mesh. Such a practice may be necessary in methods where the pile is left unturned or turned infrequently.

Temperature Monitoring   Heat is generated as a by-product of decomposition of organic material by the microbes. The temperature at each point in time depends on how much heat is being generated by the microbes and how much is lost to aeration. If well constructed, a compost heap would attain a temperature of 40–45°C within two to three days and drop as the decomposable material becomes depleted. Be sure to insert the thermometer deep into the compost pile for a reliable measurement.

pH   Compost decomposers operate best at a pH of neutral to slightly acid conditions (pH = 5.5–8.0). Organic acids form at the start of the process of decomposition, favoring the growth of fungi and breaking down lignin and cellulose. Once the organic acids are neutralized, the mature compost heap would have a pH of 6–8. Aeration and mixing of the heap are two practical ways of achieving a good pH in the compost heap. Soil test kits may be used for pH monitoring. However, if the heap is moist, a pH paper may suffice.

Odor   A composting process will not be odor free. However, the presence of a foul odor is an indication of improper composting environment. Ammonia gas indicates a low C:N ratio, while a musty odor indicates a wet pile. These conditions may be corrected, as previously suggested.

22.17 CONSTRUCTING OUTDOOR COMPOSTING SYSTEMS

Two critical factors to consider in constructing an outdoor composting unit are location and container type and design.

Location

The compost site should be near the garden or a place where it is easy to manage. The pile should not be allowed to dry out, so locating it in the shade in tropical areas is desirable. In the temperate zone, however, sunlight is required to keep the heap warm. It is wise to locate the heap so that the house is not downwind from it; in the case of poor decomposition, the foul odors will not blow into the house with the wind. The site should be well draining.

Container Design

Containers or retaining walls may be constructed out of a wide variety of materials including blocks, plastic, wood, and even baled straw (Figure 22–2). On a well-drained location, the ground may be used as the bottom wall of the container (Figure 22–3). The advantage of using bare earth for the bottom of the container is that natural decomposers in the soil have the opportunity to act on the material in the pile. Wooden and wire bins are also used (Figure 22–4). Since wood is biodegradable, a wood preserver or latex paint coating reduces the danger of its decomposition. Wire bins are well ventilated and as such lose heat rapidly. Barrels, drums, tumblers, and plastic bins may be used as containers for composting (Figure 22–5).

Pit composting is simply burying the composting materials in a pit dug in the soil until they decompose (Figure 22–6). When ready, which may be up to a year, the

FIGURE 22-2 Composting in a concrete pit.

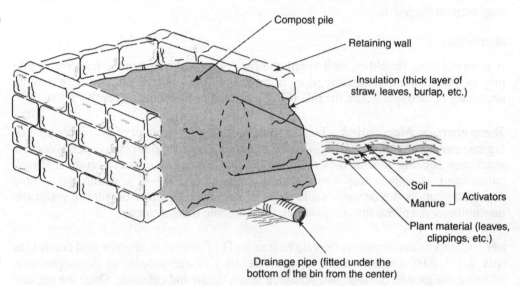

Compost pile

Retaining wall

Insulation (thick layer of straw, leaves, burlap, etc.)

Soil
Manure } Activators

Plant material (leaves, clippings, etc.)

Drainage pipe (fitted under the bottom of the bin from the center)

FIGURE 22-3 Composting directly on the ground.

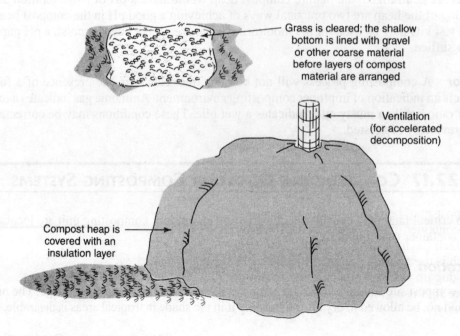

Grass is cleared; the shallow bottom is lined with gravel or other coarse material before layers of compost material are arranged

Ventilation (for accelerated decomposition)

Compost heap is covered with an insulation layer

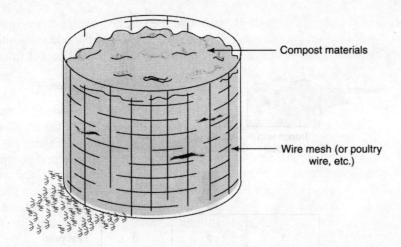

FIGURE 22-4 Composting in a wire basket.

Compost materials

Wire mesh (or poultry wire, etc.)

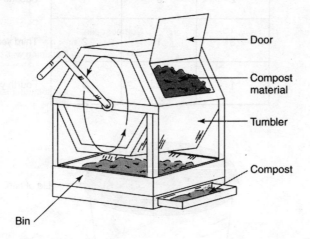

FIGURE 22-5 A compost tumbler.

Door

Compost material

Tumbler

Compost

Bin

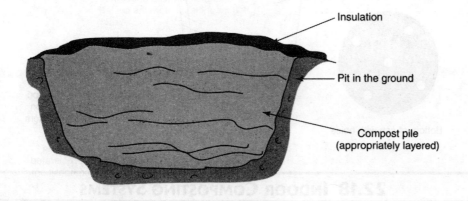

FIGURE 22-6 Pit composting.

Insulation

Pit in the ground

Compost pile (appropriately layered)

compost may be dug up and used elsewhere or left in place and crops planted in it. The container in this case is the earth. A variation of this method is *trench composting*, in which the material is buried in long trenches (Figure 22–7). Once decomposed, the trench is used as a bed for growing crops, while the adjacent row separated by a path is then dug up as a new trench for composting. The compost trench becomes a walkway before it is used for growing crops, thus giving the material two years to decompose properly.

FIGURE **22-7** Trench composting.

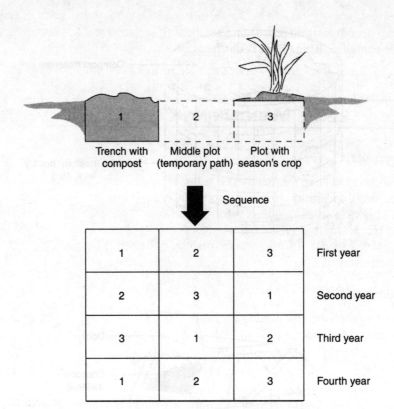

Trench with   Middle plot   Plot with
compost   (temporary path)   season's crop

Sequence

1	2	3	First year
2	3	1	Second year
3	1	2	Third year
1	2	3	Fourth year

FIGURE 22-8 An indoor composting setup.

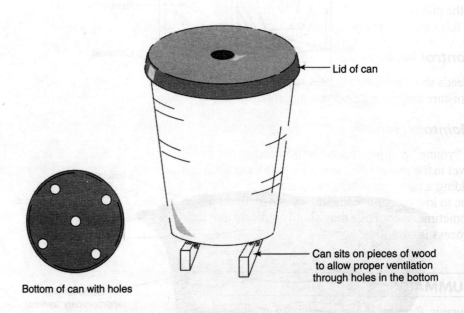

Lid of can

Can sits on pieces of wood
to allow proper ventilation
through holes in the bottom

Bottom of can with holes

22.18 INDOOR COMPOSTING SYSTEMS

Indoor composting systems are portable and can be readily located and relocated in
small areas such as a garage (Figure 22–8). Small-scale composters with worms as the
principal decomposers are used to decompose domestic waste (kitchen garbage). Their
success depends to a large extent on protecting the worms from exposure to extreme
temperatures.

In one design, a 20-gallon can with perforated wall (about twenty 1-inch holes) is
inserted into a 32-gallon plastic container. The inner can is the bioreactor. In this design,
the wood blocks are placed inside the outer container to separate the two containers.

As microbial decomposition proceeds, a leacheate ("compost tea") collects at the bottom of the outer container. This liquid is nutrient rich and a useful plant fertilizer.

22.19 MAINTAINING COMPOST PILES

Turn Regularly

Turning the compost heap frequently is a tedious but worthwhile chore since it quickens the rate of decomposition. Home composters may turn their heaps less frequently (every six to twelve weeks), unless a foul odor develops earlier. In turning frequently, one should be careful to do it each time after peak temperature has been attained in the pile (to kill weed seeds). Turning too frequently, however, is detrimental to the activity of the decomposers.

Keep Aerated

Aeration is accomplished by turning the heap or poking it. Poor aeration encourages the development of a foul odor.

Keep Moist

It is best to moisten the pile after each layer is added. If watering becomes necessary later on, it should be done very carefully to avoid creating anaerobic conditions in the pile. If the pile is generally damp and warm only on the inside, the pile size may be too small. In this case, it must be rebuilt on a larger scale.

Control Weeds

Weeds should not be allowed to grow on a compost heap since they deprive the pile of moisture and the nutrients being produced through mineralization of the organic matter.

Maintain Heat

A "young" compost heap should heat up quite rapidly. If it remains cool, the nitrogen level in the pile may be low. This factor may be remedied by poking holes in the pile and adding a nitrogen source (e.g., fresh manure or blood meal). Lack of heat may also be due to low moisture content; water may thus be added through holes poked in a dry pile. Sometimes a cool pile may simply indicate that it is time to turn it or that the composting process is complete.

SUMMARY

Organic farming is the practice of growing plants by depending primarily on natural sources of fertility for plant nutrition and nonchemical strategies for controlling diseases and pests. The management of organic matter is a critical activity in organic farming. Organic matter may be obtained from plant or animal sources. To obviate the need to use chemicals in controlling weeds, mulching, crop rotation, use of cover crops, and mechanical weeding are alternative methods employed. The use of disease- and pest-resistant cultivars, observation of strict phytosanitation, and good crop production practices reduce disease incidence in cultivated crops. Composting, an activity in which raw organic matter is processed for use, is a primary activity for organic gardeners.

A successful composting operation depends on the use of compostable material, good activators, proper layering of materials in the pile, and good management of the compost pile in terms of aeration, moisture supply, and temperature. Composting systems are designed for either indoor or outdoor use.

REFERENCES AND SUGGESTED READING

Campbell, S. 1990. *Let it rot: The gardener's guide to composting*. Pownal, Vt.: Storey Communications.

Minnich, J. 1979. *The Rodale guide to composting*. Emmaus, Penn.: Rodale Press.

PRACTICAL EXPERIENCE

Construct a small-scale compost pit following the steps described in the text.

23

Establishment and Management of an Orchard

PURPOSE AND EXPECTED OUTCOMES

The purpose of this section is to discuss the general principles and cultural practices employed in the establishment of a small-scale fruit orchard.

After studying this chapter, the student should be able to

1. Discuss the establishment of an orchard.
2. Discuss the management of an orchard.

OVERVIEW

The science and art of producing and marketing fruits and nuts is called *pomology*. The classification of fruits was presented in Chapter 2. Vegetable fruits are discussed in Chapter 20. These fruits are usually annual plants or cultivated as such (e.g., tomato and pepper). Further, the term *fruits* technically includes nuts, which are dry fruits. However, the terminology *fruits and nuts* is conventionally used to make the distinction between the two kinds of fruits. The discussion in this section is limited to fruits borne on trees (**fruit trees** or tree fruits).

Fruit Trees
Trees that bear fleshy fruits.

23.1 IMPORTANCE OF FRUIT AND NUT TREES

Fruit and **nut trees** are utilized for food and are also found in the landscape. They are used as shade trees and as ornamental plants. As sources of food, fruits are rich in vitamins (A, C, B_6, and folacin) and minerals (potassium, magnesium, copper, and iron). Fruits are important sources of fiber in the diet, and the pectins they contain are known to be effective in controlling blood cholesterol levels. Important temperate fruits include apple, pear, peach, plum, cherry, and apricot. Nuts are dry fruits. Generally, they are also rich in vitamins (riboflavin, thiamin, and niacin) and minerals (calcium, phosphorus, iron, and potassium).

Nut Trees
Trees that bear dry, indehiscent, single-seeded fruits with a hard pericarp or shell.

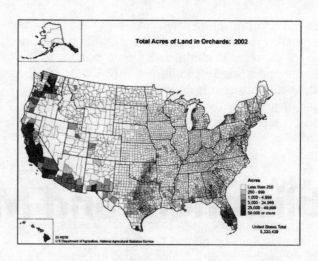

23.2 PRODUCTION REGIONS

Deciduous tree fruit (e.g., apple, pear, sweet cherry, plum, nectarines) production is currently concentrated in the Pacific Northwest states of Washington, Oregon, and Northern California (Figure 23–1). These regions benefit from the temperate, dry conditions and the water from snowmelt from the mountain ranges that feed the streams and rivers for irrigation use. The region is influenced by the Pacific Ocean that tempers the climate during the winter. The mild winter temperatures (0–10°C) are ideal for developing dormancy as well as for the chilling treatment needed by trees. Citrus production is concentrated in Florida.

23.3 LOCATING A FRUIT ORCHARD

Orchard
A parcel of land devoted to the cultivation of fruit trees.

The success of an **orchard** depends on the soil, site, and management of the enterprise. Areas in the United States where commercial orchards occur in large numbers include the Great Lakes region, the Central Valley of California, the Washington Valley, and the Fort Valley Plateau of Georgia.

These areas are characterized by climatic and soil conditions that are ideal for fruit tree production. However, the home grower living outside of these ideal regions can successfully grow adapted fruit trees by observing certain basic factors described in the following sections.

23.3.1 TEMPERATURE

Temperature-related injury to fruit trees can occur in any of the four seasons—winter, spring, summer, or fall. The U.S. Department of Agriculture (USDA) hardiness zone map should first be consulted in deciding the kind of fruit plants to grow. The effect of temperature is moderated by the presence of features such as hills and large bodies of water. Low winter temperatures can damage not only flower buds but also the whole plant. To prevent frost injuries, low-lying areas should be avoided. The upper parts of hills are preferred for fruit culture.

All fruit crops are prone to damage as a result of a late spring freeze, when blooming occurs. Because the blooms are sensitive to low temperature, they are easily damaged permanently when temperatures drop to about −22.2°C (28°F) or lower. The freeze may occur by one of two mechanisms, which are wind dependent. On a windless, calm night, freezing can occur in spring when cold, heavy air settles in low-lying areas. This type of freeze is called *radiation freeze*. By locating the orchard on higher grounds, damage from this type of freeze is minimized. On the other hand, crops can be exposed to cold temperatures under windy conditions, called *advective freeze*. This wind-aided freeze is problematic because it is difficult to protect crops from it.

When late-maturing cultivars are planted, they are prone to freezing in early fall. Certain fruit trees such as apple are intolerant of the high heat prevalent in summer. The orchard should thus be located on the northern or eastern slopes in regions in the Northern Hemisphere.

23.3.2 LIGHT

Light is critical to fruit tree productivity, which is highest in full sunlight. It is important for light to penetrate the plant canopy to reach the inner fruiting branches for fruiting to occur; fruit trees must thus be pruned to open up the canopy to increase reproductive growth. Certain fruit trees exhibit a photoperiodic response by slowing growth in one season or producing flowers only under certain light conditions.

23.3.3 WATER

Fruit trees need adequate soil moisture for proper growth and good yield of high-quality fruits. Fresh fruits may consist of about 90 percent or more water. However, they are intolerant of waterlogged conditions. In fact, a significant amount of fruit production occurs in areas where rainfall is inadequate to sustain production. These dry areas depend on irrigation for successful production. Fruit trees, especially in dry regions, are irrigated by *microirrigation methods* (drip). It is critical that the trees have adequate moisture during the last 30 days of fruit development. An erratic or insufficient moisture supply leads to reduced productivity, and the fruits grown under such conditions are prone to physiological disorders.

23.3.4 SOIL

The soil should have a good texture that poses minimal resistance to root penetration and is easy to till. Sandy loams are ideal for fruit tree production. Fruits such as peach, nectarine, and apricot prefer well-drained, coarse-textured soils in the region of sand or silt loams. Cherry prefers silt loams, while apple grows well on silt loams to clay loams. Pear and quince, on the other hand, prefer finer-textured soils in the region of silt loam to clay. In considering soil, one should pay most attention to the texture of the subsoil. It might be necessary to use a subsoiler (a plow capable of being operated to depths in excess of 15 inches [38.1 centimeters] to break any pans that may occur at the site) as part of the land preparation activity.

The soil used for fruit tree production should be deep (4 to 6 feet deep or 1.21 to 1.82 meters). Peach and nectarine are deeply rooted and require deep soils, while pear and quince are not as deeply rooted. Tree roots prefer freely draining soil. Excessive moisture in the soil in spring (during bud and shoot development) is undesirable; the water table should not be high. Further, accumulated irrigation water or rain water should drain within a few days. Certain fruits such as peach and nectarine perform best under very well-drained soil conditions.

23.3.5 SLOPE

The slope of the land should encourage both air and water drainage. Land that is very flat is not desirable unless it occurs at a higher elevation than the surrounding land. Thus, valley floors and river bottoms are not good fruit tree lands, because they are prone to flooding and frost damage. Land with excessive slope is difficult to cultivate and manage and soil erosion is likely. Generally, a 1 to 10 percent slope is acceptable. Further, west slopes should not be selected in cold regions or areas of high elevations since they may not have sufficient heat units to properly mature the crop. North slopes minimize the potential for plants to be damaged by frost or sunburn. However, these sites provide conditions that delay the blooming of plants and thus also harvesting.

Most fruit trees perform well on slightly acidic soils (pH 5.5 to 6.5). Some plants, including plum, prefer a soil pH of 6 to 7. In terms of choosing a site for fruit tree production, one should pay more attention to the soil's physical characteristics, since soil fertility can be readily amended.

23.3.6 LABOR

For a small garden, labor is usually not a problem. However, for a large operation, labor is needed for fruit harvest and also for various pruning operations. A commercial orchard should be located where seasonal labor is readily available and affordable.

23.3.7 MARKET

Home gardens are designed primarily for home consumption. However, contingency plans should be made to handle surplus produce. The surplus can be preserved by processing it in a variety of ways. If a large operation wishes to serve the general public, markets and marketing strategies should be carefully considered. Dry fruits can be stored for long periods. However, fresh produce is highly perishable and thus markets must be known before production. Strategies for marketing were further discussed in Chapter 27.

23.4 PROPAGATION

Fruit tree production depends on the selection of the right cultivar. The right cultivar is adapted to the production area, resistant to major diseases in the area, high yielding, of desirable quality, and ripens to coincide with market demands. Planting materials are of two basic types—asexual and seed.

23.4.1 ASEXUAL PROPAGATION OF FRUIT TREES

Asexually propagated planting materials are widely used in establishing orchards. These seedlings are produced by either grafting or budding. In selecting cultivars, one should pay attention not only to the fruit cultivars (the scion or bud cultivar) but also to the rootstock. Rootstocks are used for several purposes, as already described in Chapter 10. They are resistant to soilborne diseases and insect pests and tolerant of the local soil conditions (to which the fruiting cultivar is not). Such conditions include pH, salinity, and soil moisture. Sometimes dwarfing rootstocks or mauling rootstocks are used to dwarf the plant and control its size. Suitable dwarfing rootstocks are available only for certain fruits. Asexual propagation ensures that the fruits produced are true to variety (true to type). Certain fruit species are asexually propagated but without grafting or budding. The planting materials are raised from cuttings, suckers, layers, and other methods. Species amenable to such procedures include olive, fig, quince, and pomegranate.

23.4.2 PROPAGATION OF FRUIT TREES BY SEED

Propagation of fruit trees by seed results in fruits that are not true to type, due to the consequence of meiosis. The degree of deviation from type depends on the species in question. Seeds are needed sometimes to produce the rootstock (or understock) used in asexual propagation. Most fruit seeds need special treatment to germinate. The causes of delay in germination for fruit seed are several, the most common being dormancy of the embryo. When embryo dormancy occurs, the seed must undergo a period of postharvest physiological modification (after ripening) at the appropriate temperature and in the presence of air and moisture. In practice, after ripening of seed is accomplished by stratification. It entails mixing seed with a moisture-holding material such as peat, sawdust, or even sand. These materials are also porous enough for aeration. The mixture is then held at a cool temperature in storage for the appropriate duration according to the plant species. Plum and apple seeds require stratification at 1 to 5°C (34 to 40°F) for about 60 to 90 days, while peach is stratified for 75 to 100 days at 0 to 7°C (32 to 45°F). Black walnut and hickory may be stratified at 1 to 10°C (33 to 50°F) for about 60 to 90 days.

Certain seeds experience a delay in germination caused by a hard seed coat. In this instance, the seed may be soaked in hot water (or dropped in boiling water momentarily), mechanically scratched (scarification), or soaked in sulfuric acid.

23.5 THE ANNUAL CYCLE OF A FRUIT TREE

A temperate fruit tree undergoes a certain developmental cycle during which a number of physiological and developmental changes occur. These changes are influenced by the environment. In winter, fruit trees enter a dormant period that affects seeds and buds. This type of dormancy, *endodormancy*, is caused by certain internal, physiological mechanisms. Upon exposure to cold temperature, the dormancy is effectively broken. This *winter chilling requirement* is essential for the plant to be prepared for proper development when spring arrives. For most fruit trees, the winter chilling requirement temperature is 7°C (45°F) or lower. The duration of chilling varies both within and among species.

Springtime brings the warm temperatures and heat units needed for the dormant buds that have been successfully winter chilled to develop into either flowers or shoots. At some point during the growth cycle of the tree, the flowers become pollinated, fertilized, and then produce fruits. Many trees have an inherent capacity to self-regulate the load of fruits borne during the season by the process of self-thinning. Excessive blossoms as well as fruit drop occur at certain times. However, species such as apple and peach are ineffective in self-thinning. Generally, fruits require seed development for fruits to set properly. As previously indicated, fruits differ in growth pattern. Apple development follows the classic sigmoid curve, while peach development follows the double sigmoid curve.

Flower buds for the next year's crop are formed in mid- and late summer. Deciduous fruits generally follow this pattern. The environmental conditions must be appropriate for the desired number of fruiting branches to be formed. An unfavorable condition may cause most buds to develop into vegetative buds. Fruit tree flowers are generally perfect. However, fruits such as walnut and pecan are monoecious. Endodormancy starts in the late fall, and plants remain in this state until winter chilling occurs to break the dormancy.

23.6 SPACING FRUIT TREES

The proper spacing among trees in an orchard is determined by the following:

1. *The adult size of the plant.* Trees grow slowly but eventually occupy a significant amount of space. It is important to know what size the plant will ultimately attain before deciding on plant spacing for the orchard.
2. *Rootstock.* Certain rootstocks, as previously discussed, have the capacity to affect the size of the fruiting cultivar. While some rootstocks have a dwarfing effect (e.g., M9 in apple), others, such as MM1110, enhance the growth of the flowering cultivar.

3. *Growing environment.* The growing environment determines how much of the plant's potential will be achieved in cultivation. Under conditions of proper temperature, high soil fertility, and adequate moisture, plants generally grow large.

4. *Predetermined planting density.* In terms of tree density, three strategies of planting are adopted in orchards. Stone fruits and nuts are highly productive under a *low-density* planting strategy (with a plant population of about 250 trees per hectare [100 trees per acre]). Using dwarfing rootstocks enables the grower to increase plant density because of the size-reducing effect of the rootstock. This practice allows a *high-density* strategy to be adopted whereby a plant population of 500 to 1,235 plants per hectare (200 to 500 plants per acre) can be achieved. This close spacing is employed under intensive plant culture; effective management and high fertility are required for success. Operations using close spacing make use of various plant training systems, coupled with regular pruning to control growth and plant size. Fruit trees may also be spaced moderately in the orchard. This *medium-density* spacing is possible if plants are small in adult size. It allows a density of about 250 to 500 plants per hectare (100 to 200 plants per acre).

23.7 FRUIT TREE PLANTING STYLES

Trees in an orchard may be arranged in one of several ways, the most common being the *square system.* In this system, all plants are equally spaced between adjacent plants. The *quincunx* arrangement is a variation of the square system whereby the permanent crop is interplanted with a temporary crop that is grown, harvested, and completely removed from the field after several years. Consequently, the open space between trees is utilized until the trees have attained adult size. Other plant arrangements are also in use.

23.8 GROWTH REGULATORS

Growers of certain tree fruits like apples and pears use growth regulators to modify tree growth and structure, remove excess fruit (fruit thinning), modify fruit maturity, and for preharvest drop control. Training plants successfully requires that seedlings have a certain minimum number of branches (3–5) arranged in a certain way. Growers may use growth regulators to stimulate additional branching for the specific training system to be used. Those consisting of cytokinins and gibberellic acid (e.g., Promalin, Typy) help stimulate additional branch growth. Excessive shoot growth may be suppressed by applying growth regulators like Apogee®. Another important application of chemicals in tree fruit production is the use of growth thinners (containing, e.g., NAA, 6-BA) to control actual fruit size and to sustained high productivity of the tree. Growth regulators are also used to manage fruit harvest. Application of a chemical like ReTain on apples can help expand the harvest window while fruit retain their firmness without dropping. Delayed ripening can promote proper and more complete fruit red color development provided warm days and cool nights persist. Other fruit disorders associated with ripening (e.g., water core, stem end cracking) can also be reduced with such treatment.

23.9 PEST CONTROL

Nematodes are an economic pest in fruit crop production. They parasitize on tree roots, reducing vigor and crop yields. Also, they predispose tree fruits to diseases and reduce winter hardiness of the plants. The tomato ringspot virus (ToRSV) is transmitted by the dagger nematode (*Xiphinema* spp.) and causes peach stem pitting and apple union necrosis. Perhaps the most widely known nematode pest of fruit trees is the root-lesion nematode (*Pratylenchus penetrans*) that destroys the tissue of the cortex, promoting infection by root-rotting microbes. Nematode control in orchards is challenging. Growers may use nematicides or cultural practices in their orchards. Treating the soil prior to planting trees will not only help control parasitic nematodes, but also reduce the incidence of soilborne viral infections (e.g., stem pitting in stone fruits and union necrosis in apple). Fumigation with broad-spectrum fumigants is also effective.

Tree fruits are also attacked by numerous insect pests and other pathogens. Common diseases include scabs, mildews, blotches, cankers, and rots. Insect pests include aphids, leaf miners, borers, scales, moths, and various hoppers and flies. Mites also plague fruit trees.

Pest control in orchards is accomplished by two basic kinds of spraying—tree spraying for disease and insect pests and ground spraying for weed control. Aerial spraying of trees is commonly achieved by using air-blast sprayers, while hydraulic sprayers are used for herbicide application. The use of herbicides in orchards has the advantage of eliminating tree bark damage from mechanical weeders and leaving the soil undisturbed, thereby reducing soil erosion.

23.10 GROUND COVERS

It is important to prepare the soil prior to fruit crop establishment such that perennial weeds are excluded from the field. It is best to establish a ground cover of grass at least a year prior to planting the crop. An application of 2,4-D helps to eliminate perennial weeds. Immediately before planting, the rows where the trees will be planted should be treated with glyphosate or paraquat to kill the grass to facilitate planting.

23.11 HARVESTING

Producers should establish the proper harvest maturity for the crop for optimal produce quality. A schedule of harvesting should be planned ahead to enable labor to be scheduled for the operation. The optimal harvest maturing depends on the cultivar, the intended use, and postharvest storage and shelf life desired. Proper timing is of the essence since prematurely harvested fruits are less flavorful, have poor color and taste, small fruit size, and poor storage. On the other hand, delaying the harvest operation can predispose the fruit to developing watercore, excessive softness, and reduced storage and shelf life.

Maturity indices have been developed for various fruits. Elements in these indices include starch, sugar, acid content, fruit firmness, flesh color, and seed color, as well as presence of watercore and internal ethylene concentration (requires the use of a gas chromatograph). These elements are not equally important. Background color, starch content, and firmness (e.g., by using the Effigi fruit tester) are key indicators since they correlated well with sugar content, flavor, aroma, texture, acidity, and shelf life. Fruits with poorly developed background color will fetch low prices on the fresh market. Other key factors to consider include the immediate use of the crop. Will the fruit be sold on the fresh market or for processing? Is the fruit climacteric or nonclimacteric? If the fruit color will not change in storage, it is critical to harvest it at peak color in the field.

23.12 Pruning and Training

Training and pruning are critical operations in orchard management for high and sustained productivity of tree fruits. Pruning of tree fruits is discussed in detail in Chapter 19.

Outcomes Assessment

1. Discuss the geographic distribution of orchards in the United States.
2. Discuss the key factors to consider in locating an orchard.
3. Discuss the importance of pruning and training in orchard management.
4. Discuss the propagation of tree fruits by vegetative methods.
5. Discuss the use of growth regulators in orchard management.

PART **7**

SPECIAL TECHNIQUES AND HANDLING OF HORTICULTURAL PRODUCTS

24

Cut Flowers and Floral Design

PURPOSE AND EXPECTED OUTCOMES

This chapter is designed to discuss the field culture and handling of cut flowers and how they are used in creating floral displays.

After studying this chapter, the student should be able to

1. List five plant species that make good cut flowers.
2. List five plant species that make good dried flowers.
3. Describe how cut flowers are managed for longevity.
4. Describe how flowers are dried for preservation.
5. Describe the principles of flower arranging.
6. List five tools or materials used by the florist.
7. Describe how plants are chosen in creating a floral design.
8. List four different floral designs.
9. Describe the steps in creating a floral design.

[COLOR PLATES—*see color plates 30 and 31* for additional chapter photos]

OVERVIEW

Flowering plants are frequently grown outside (in beds) or inside (in containers) to be enjoyed and admired as whole living plants in the landscape or interior plantscape. Flowers are used in a variety of ways to convey sentiments. For most of these uses, flowers are detached from the parent plant and used individually or in groups. As such, **cut flowers** (i.e., detached flowers) are an important part of the horticultural industry. *Florists* are the specialists who use cut flowers in their trade. To add value to cut flowers, florists often use them to create *floral designs* for a variety of occasions. Using cut flowers in this art form is called *flower arranging*. Whereas fresh cut flowers last for only a short period, flowers may be dried and preserved for a long time. Dried flowers may also be arranged into durable arrangements.

Cut Flowers
Flowers grown for the purpose of cutting for display in a container or for other uses.

Cut flower displays are found in restaurants and homes, as accessories to dressing (corsages and boutonnieres), at weddings (e.g., as a bridal bouquet), at funerals (e.g., as casket spreads and wreaths), on special occasions to express love and appreciation (e.g., Valentine's Day and Mother's Day), and to offer congratulations (e.g., on graduation days). The use of flowers in this fashion is enormous. Some flowers are more suited than others for use as cut flowers. In fact, scientists have developed special qualities in some plants that are used this way to extend their postharvest lives and qualities.

24.1 CUT FLOWER SPECIES

Many species used as cut flowers are herbaceous (Table 24–1). However, a number of woody species can be cultivated for cutting (Table 24–2). The most popular cut flower species are rose, carnation, and chrysanthemum. On the whole, the quantity of major cut flowers sold steadily declined between 1989 and 1998. The decline ranged from two-fold

TABLE 24–1 Selected Species Commonly Grown for Use as Cut Flowers

Plant	Scientific Name
African daisy	Dimorphotheca sinuata
Astroemeria	Astroemeria spp.
Baby's breath	Gypsophila elegans
Celosia	Celosia plumosa
Cleome	Cleome hasslerana
Carnation	Dianthus caryophyllus
Cornflower	Centaurea cyanus
Cosmos	Cosmos bipinnatus
Chrysanthemum	Chrysanthemum spp.
Cyclamen	Cyclamen persicum
Freesia	Freesia refracta
Kalanchoe	Kalanchoe spp.
Fountain grass	Pennisetum setaceum
Gerbera daisy	Gerbera jamesonii
Snapdragon	Antirrhinum majus
Zinnia	Zinnia elegans
Nasturtium	Tropaeolum majus
Globe amaranth	Gomphrena globosa

TABLE 24–2 Selected Woody Species Used for Cut Flowers

Plant	Scientific Name
Rose	Rosa spp.
Buttersweet	Celastrus orbiculatus
Redbud, eastern	Cercis canadensis
Red osier dogwood	Cornus stolonifera
Hydrangea	Hydrangea arborescens
Nadina	Nadina domestica
Pussy willow	Salix matsudana
Forsythia	Forsythia x intermedia
Hollies	Ilex spp.
Virburnum	Virburnum spp.
Beauty berry	Callicarpa americana
Weigela	Weigela florida

to more than four-fold in standard carnations. The popular species (and many others) are predominantly grown in greenhouses for best quality. Greenhouse production of cut flowers has been discussed previously. Herbaceous plants used for cut flowers are mostly annuals and require planting each season and proper maintenance to ensure high-quality products. Once established, woody plants have the advantage of being perennial and require relatively less maintenance in production as sources of cut flowers. A significant disadvantage in using woody plant species for cut flowers is that they require several years to grow to the stage where they are usable. Species and even cultivars within species differ in **vase life** (the duration of time within which a cut flower retains its desirable qualities before deteriorating), the equivalent of shelf life for perishable garden products.

Vase Life
The duration of time in which a cut flower retains its desirable qualities while on display in a vase.

24.2 CULTURE

24.2.1 GROWING SCHEDULE

Cultural procedures for cut flowers are the same as described for the production of garden plants in the landscape. The profitability of the enterprise depends on increasing production efficiency to reduce production costs. In field production, effective scheduling of production activities coupled with sound irrigation and fertilizer management are needed for efficient production.

Plants grown for cut flowers require good management in cultivation to produce healthy, disease-free, vigorous plants and durable cut flowers. Since flowers are expected to live for a period after being detached from the parent plants and deprived of new nutrients, it is critical that plants for cut flowers be cultivated with care so that at the time of harvesting the detached portion has appreciable nutritional reserves to depend on for some time. Malnourished plants produce poor quality cut flowers with short vase lives. For high carbohydrate levels, cut flowers need a good fertilizer program in cultivation, proper temperature and light (quality and intensity), and adequate moisture. Diseases and pests should be effectively controlled since they not only reduce the value of products but also accelerate deterioration and reduce the longevity of cut flowers.

Because species bloom at different times and have different degrees of temperature adaptation, the gardener can maintain a nearly year-round active cutting garden through judicious selection of plants. One such growing schedule is described in Figure 24–1. The strategy is to select plants that will provide continuous blooms in the garden.

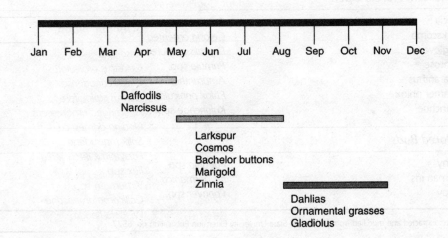

FIGURE 24-1 A growing schedule for cut flowers.

24.2.2 HARVESTING

Flowers should be harvested at the optimal stage of development and under the best environmental conditions. Whereas some species, such as *Helianthus annus* and *Chrysan themum* spp., are harvested when fully open, others, including *Hemerocallis* spp. and *Trollus* spp., are best harvested when half open (Table 24–3). Because warm temperatures tend to accelerate plant development, summer flowers may have to be harvested at a less mature stage. In terms of time of day, advantage should be taken of morning's low temperatures to conserve tissue moisture content; fresh flowers should be cut in the early morning hours. Cut flower longevity can be extended by placing the flower stems in water immediately after cutting. The water should be tepid, not cold. Water uptake is impeded if the stem is cut with a dull blade, so it is important that all cutting tools be very sharp and all cuts be as clean as possible. Cuts should be angled to create a wider surface area and increased water absorption. Cut flowers may be handled dry (stems not placed in water) during transportation under low temperatures. At the destination, flowers are then rehydrated, but the vase life of such flowers is generally reduced. Flowers should be harvested with care to avoid mechanical damage that not only reduces aesthetic value but also accelerates aging and reduces vase life. Bruised plants also become prone to diseases.

24.2.3 POSTHARVEST MANAGEMENT

To increase cut flower longevity before sale and after purchase, growers and consumers have to manage the environment of the products with respect to temperature, humidity, moisture, and noxious gases.

TABLE 24–3   Best Stage of Harvesting Selected Cut Flowers for Immediate Sale

Fully Open Flowers

Chrysanthemum	*Chrysanthemum* spp.
Stonecrop	*Sedum* spp.
Sunflower	*Helianthus annuus*
Camellia	*Camellia japonica*
Cyclamen	*Cyclamen persicum*
Marigold	*Tagetes erecta*

Partially Open Flowers

Rose	*Rosa* spp. (first two petals starting to unfold)
Daylily	*Hemerocallis* spp.
Fritillaria	*Fritillaria* spp.

50 Percent Florets Open

Acacia	*Acacia* spp.
Cockscomb	*Celosia argentea*
Foxglove	*Digitalis purpurea*
Primrose	*Primula* spp.
Amaranthus	*Amaranthus*
Summer phlox	*Phlox paniculata*
Kalanchoe	*Kalanchoe* spp.

Colored Buds

Peony	*Paeonia* spp.
German iris	*Iris germanica*
Poppy	*Papaver* spp.

Source: Extracted and modified from Oklahoma State University Extension Publication no. 6527

Temperature and Humidity

Wilting reduces the vase life of cut flowers. To reduce respiration and water loss, flowers should be held at temperatures between 0 and 7°C (32 and 45°F) immediately after harvesting until they are ready to be used. A relative humidity of about 90 percent should be maintained. Beading and droplets of water on flowers indicate excessive humidity, a condition that predisposes flowers to fungal attacks such as the gray mold caused by *Botrytis*.

Water

After harvesting, flower life depends on the availability of good-quality water and the capacity to absorb it. Hard water is harmful to cut flowers, as are fluoride, sodium, and sulfate salts when present in high concentrations. Whenever possible, cut flowers should be placed in warm (43°C [110°F]) deionized and distilled water of acidic reaction (pH 3 to 4). The pH of water can be lowered by adding citric acid to it. Acidic water not only improves water uptake but also has antiseptic properties, reducing infection of the cut surface, which is known to clog the xylem vessels and prevent water absorption. Passages are also blocked by trapped air bubbles. To correct these problems, flower stems should be recut under warm water using a sharp cutting instrument before being set in a vase or arranged for display. Some species, such as poppy and dahlia, require a flame treatment in which the cut surface is passed over a flame for a very brief period. This treatment hardens the sap. The milky sap that oozes from plants such as poppy clogs the stems of other species held in the same container unless flame treated. The leaves on the part of the stem that will be submerged in water in the vase should be removed. Depending on the moisture status, rehydration may take between thirty and sixty minutes to restore plants to full turgidity. Flowers that are purchased from a store or transported over a long distance often need rehydration. Flowers obtained from the home garden for use indoors can be maintained fresh by placing them in water immediately after cutting.

Nutrition

The nutrition of plants during growth is critical to the success of flowers after cutting. Flowers must be harvested at the right time, which is when they have accumulated enough sugars and starches to open and sustain them after cutting. During rehydration, sucrose may be added to the holding water to extend vase life and improve flower qualities. Commercially formulated floral preservatives that contain pH adjuster, biocide, wetting agent, food source, and water can be purchased from a local nursery store. Homemade concoctions such as 1 tablespoon of corn syrup plus 10 drops of household bleach in a quart of warm water may be used. Also, one part of soda (lemon-soda) plus two parts of water was developed at the University of California to extend vase life. These preservatives work because the sugar is nutritious and the lime reduces the pH of the water to suppress bacterial growth.

Ethylene Reduction

Ethylene is a by-product of gasoline or propane combustion and is emitted through vehicles' exhaust systems. More importantly, this chemical is a natural plant growth hormone involved in several physiological processes such as fruit ripening, seed maturation, aging, and wound healing. Certain flowers are ethylene sensitive (Table 24–4). In the presence of excessive amounts of the gas, flowers of these plants deteriorate rapidly. Ripening fruits and vegetables produce large amounts of ethylene and as such should not be stored or transported with cut flowers. Treatment with a commercial preparation of *silver thiosulfate* reduces the effects of ethylene on cut flowers.

TABLE 24–4 Selected Ethylene-Sensitive Species Used for Cut Flowers

Plant	Scientific Name
Astroemeria	*Astroemeria* spp.
Carnation	*Dianthus caryophylus*
Celosia	*Celosia* spp.
Delphinium	*Delphinium elatum*
Larkspur	*Delphinium* spp.
Freesia	*Freesia* spp.
Gladiolus	*Gladiolus* spp.
Baby's breath	*Gypsophila paniculata*
Lily	*Lilium longiflorum*
Phlox	*Phlox* spp.
Snapdragon	*Antirrhinum majus*
Stock	*Matthiola* spp.
Speedwell	*Veronica spicata*
Moneywort	*Lysimachia nummularia*

Diseases

In an attempt to reduce moisture loss, cut flowers should be kept under humid conditions. However, high humidity provides an environment that is conducive to the growth of gray mold (*Botrytis*).

24.3 FLOWER ARRANGING

Flower design and arranging is an art whose success depends on the observation of certain basic principles, similar to those for landscape designing. Throwing a couple of flowers together in a bunch produces a bouquet, but it takes creativity to use flowers to make a statement, influence mood, or enhance the ambience and general decor of a place. Floral designers can create flower arrangements for specific occasions. Arrangements are designed for happy occasions such as weddings and sad ones such as funerals. Flowers such as roses may be displayed individually in tiny vases and thus do not require arranging.

24.3.1 PRINCIPLES OF DESIGN

Even though flower arranging is an art, the following principles underlie basic floral designs. These basic principles are described in detail in Chapter 15, as pertaining to landscape design.

Balance

Balance in a design is sought both in physical and visual terms. To achieve balance, the plant materials need to be physically equally distributed about an imaginary central axis or perceived as such.

Balance in design relates to the display's visual weight projected to the viewer. In a *symmetrical design*, viewers on opposite sides of a display see similar things; *asymmetrical designs* do not offer the same view from two different angles. The centerpiece for a formal dinner may be arranged in a symmetrical design. Balance is critical in a design because it is a major element that makes a design beautiful.

FLORAL DESIGN: AN OVERVIEW

BY WM. J. McKINLEY, AIFD
Associate Dean, Career Technologies
Kishwaukee College

The floral design industry is dynamic and exciting. Few industries encompass the artistry (principles of design), scientific details (post-harvest physiology), and intrinsic beauty of raw material (flowers) to create such an aesthetically pleasing finished product. Florists are unique in that they not only deal with the present sale, but they are also part of a long term relationship with customers and their special life events - from birth, to celebrations of marriage, anniversaries, parties, and finally death. These events involve a wide range of emotions that are directly affected by the use of flowers and plants. Studies done by Rutgers University and the Society for American Florists (SAF 2007) indicated that receiving flowers is a natural and healthy way to modify moods, increasing a feeling of happiness and well being.

The floral industry encompasses a wide range of diverse specialties. **Weddings/Parties, Personal Flowers, Sympathy, Permanent Botanical,** and **Plants** are a few of these specialty areas. A florist may focus on one or two of these areas, or they may choose to offer expertise in many areas, concentrating on providing something for everyone.

Many schools, both public and private, provide educational opportunities specifically designed to train students in the art and techniques of floral design. There is much to learn, and even the most experienced, veteran florists will assert that there is always something new to learn. For the beginning student, it is important to get a combination of formal education through a school (public or private) and on-the-job training from a professional florist. This combination will ensure that the student has the theoretical knowledge, as well as the practical skills to be successful.

The material presented here is a short review of some of the basics of floral design taken from the book *Flower: Creative Design* by Johnson, McKinley, and Benz. Images are also used with permission from the publisher from original photographers Laura Cicarella, Michael Klein, and James Lyle.

PRINCIPLES AND ELEMENTS OF DESIGN (ARTISTRY)

Elements and principles of design might well be called "Tools of Design." These concepts are not arbitrary; they are constant. They are the tools of all the arts, and no artist should modify them until they are mastered. A careful study and understanding of these elements and principles of design enable a designer to express his or her personality in floral art. It is through this mastery that distinction and individuality are created in design.

Elements of Design—basic visual and/or tangible qualities of a design that are inherent to the design's components themselves. They are the most basic tools for the designer to use.

Principles of Design—fundamental guidelines that are created by using combinations of elements of designs. Principles are organized into two categories; primary and secondary. Primary principles can stand alone as tools to enhance and interpret elements of design, while secondary principles supplement the primary principles and are commonly used as techniques for enhancing the primary principles.

Element	Definition	Design Application	Types
Line	The visual path the eye follows to produce motion	1. The use of linear material, such as curly willow, snapdragons, or scotch broom will clearly delineate a line form. (see curly willow and ginger in Formalinear image) 2. The use of materials in a sequential placement (dot-to-dot) format to create an implied line path. (see lily placement in Geometric image)	a. Vertical b. Horizontal c. Straight d. Curved e. Multiple variations of a-e
Form	The shape or contour of the individual components in a composition and the overall three-dimensional configuration or shape of a design.	1. Intrinsic to the materials used, form should be contrasted to create interest and prevent monotony. (see ginger, gerbera, and anthurium in Formalinear image) 2. The placement of materials to create a desired design shape, such as triangle, round centerpiece, etc. (see triangle shape in Geometric image)	1a. Mass flowers/foliage 1b. line flowers/foliage 1c. filler flowers/foliage 1d. form flowers/foliage 2. see "Design Styles"
Space	The open areas around or between the individual components and/or the entire area occupied by the composition	The placement of materials relative to each other, giving the opportunity to; 1. emphasize through solitude, 2. diminish through crowding, or 3. create movement through gradation. (see cattail mat in Interpretive image)	a. positive space b. negative space
Texture	The physical surface qualities of the materials used	Selection of textures should be based on the natural quality of the materials used. Contrast is desired to create interest and prevent monotony, but too many textures can create a "busy-fussy" design. (see texture contrasts in Interpretive image)	Unlimited texture variations are possible, i.e rough, smooth, coarse, delicate
Pattern	A repeated combination of lines, space, color, or texture. Texture enlarged is also referred to as pattern	By repeatedly placing a combination of materials relative to each other, such as groups/clusters of color or repeating similar lines with the same material/spacing, pattern will be established. (see artichoke in Interpretive image)	Unlimited combinations are possible
Color	The visual response of the eye to various reflected wavelengths of light	Color is basic to the materials used, though interpreted on a personal level. Color creates emotions, gives personality to a design, and may provide the foundation for establishing a design.	See page ?? for more information about color
Size	The measurement of the amount of space something occupies	Size is obviously intrinsic to the materials used and should be contrasted to create interest and prevent monotony. However, large size contrasts, without transitions, may cause disruption of rhythm or harmony.	Unlimited size variations are possible

Principle	Definition	Types (or Uses)
Balance (primary)	A state of equilibrium achieved when the components of a design are composed so that they give a feeling of stability and security. (see overall symmetrical balance with asymmetrical placement of lilies in Geometric image)	1. mechanical/structural 2. visual 3. symmetrical 4. asymmetrical
Proportion (primary)	The relationship of the units of a composition to each other in size, quantity and degree of emphasis. (note the phi relationships of flowers:container ratio in Geometric image)	Phi relationships (2:3:5 or 3:5:8 –container:flowers: complete design) are aesthetically pleasing to most people
Scale (secondary)	The relative ratio of the size of a composition to its surroundings or environment.	Should be approximately 1/9 of intended environment
Dominance (primary)	The visual organization of a design that emphasizes one or more aspects. Dominance is synonymous with "authority" in a design. (see begonias in Ikebana image)	
Focal (secondary)	Area(s) of greatest visual impact or weight; center(s) of interest which naturally attract the eye. (see lilies in Geometric image)	For geometric design, focal should be at the junction of vertical and horizontal axis
Accent (secondary)	Detail added to a design to enhance interest and emphasize other stronger elements; "punctuation" to other components. (see arching fern fronds above anthuriums in Formalinear image)	
Emphasis (secondary)	An area in a composition that is given importance to make it stand out; to give special attention. (see tall cattail leaves in Parallel image)	Typically done with larger material (size) or contrasts of color, texture, or form
Rhythm (primary)	The visual movement throughout a design; the flow of a design. (see free and variable rhythm in Vegetative image)	1. regular and repeated 2. free and variable
Depth (secondary)	Placement of materials at different levels in and around an arrangement. (see base materials in Vegetative image)	Created by placing materials deep within a design, or lightly covering other materials, as well as using light colored materials deep in the design.
Repetition (secondary)	The repeating of similar elements within a composition such as line, space, form, size, etc. (see spray orchids in Formalinear image)	Gives importance to materials that are limited in number or weak visually
Transition (secondary)	The easy visual movement that comes from gradual degrees of change between the design components. (see gladiolus in Geometric image)	Accomplished by gradating size (small to large), flower facing (vertical to horizontal), and color (light to dark).
Contrast (primary)	The differences between objects when they are placed next to each other; emphasis by means of differences.	
Variation (secondary)	Basic similarities but with minor differences. (see artichokes, limes, and grapes {variations of the round form} in Interpretive image)	Example – using pink roses and pink carnations, both are round forms, but shaped differently.
Opposition (secondary)	Total contrast that bring about contradiction. (see grapes {round form} and cattail mat {flat form} in Interpretive image)	Example – using pink roses and yellow gladiolus, forms are opposites (linear vs round) and colors also have strong contrast
Tension (secondary)	Aesthetic quality developed through careful use of opposition to create an expression of action, or implication of energy use. (see curly willow and ginger interaction in Formalinear design)	
Harmony (primary)	The aesthetic quality (personally pleasing relationship) created through the pleasing interaction of the components of a design. (see Interpretive image)	
Unity (primary)	Oneness of purpose, thought, style and spirit; a cohesive relationship of all components. (see Vegetative image)	

Good and consistent care and handling procedures when using cut flowers/foliage will pay big dividends in terms of longer vase life. A quality, long lasting flower or foliage is certainly a major objective of professional florists. Whether flowers are purchased locally or transported great distances, the basic rules of flower care must be observed. Cut flowers and foliage, even when separated from the parent plant, are living, actively metabolizing plant parts. These parts undergo the same aging processes as the parent plant, however the rate of metabolizing can be manipulated. This is done by supplying the cut material with its basic needs and by supplementing those needs through environmental controls and the addition of post-harvest chemicals. The following table summarizes the major factors that affect the keeping quality of cut flowers and foliage.

Factor	How controlled	Who controls
1. Production	Plant genetics, growing environment and management practices	Grower
2. Transpiration	Lower environmental temperature and higher environmental humidity reduce transpiration rate	Wholesaler, retailer, consumer
3. Floral Food	Provides energy for plant metabolism, increases water uptake, helps control bacteria growth in water	Grower, wholesaler, retailer, consumer
4. Temperature	Lower environmental temperatures slow transpiration as well as respiration	Grower, wholesaler, retailer
5. Humidity	Higher humidity reduces transpiration and the need for the flower to absorb large quantities of water	Grower, wholesaler, retailer
6. Ethylene	Ethylene scrubbers on the refrigeration system, chemical treatments such as Ethybloc®, do not mix fresh fruit with cut flowers in refrigerated storage	Grower, wholesaler, retailer
7. Microbial Activity	Use of floral food greatly decreases microbial activity, use of clean buckets and storage in a clean refrigerator also reduce microbial activity	Grower, wholesaler, retailer, consumer

Basic Care and Handling Terms

Acidifier–additive to floral foods to reduce the pH of water for better water uptake

Anti-Transpirant–a spray or dip that reduces water loss from the flower/foliage by reducing the transpiration rate

Bio-inhibitor–additive to floral foods to reduce the microbial activity in bucket or vase solution

Citric Acid Hydration Solution–a pre-treatment used prior to floral food to stimulate rapid water uptake

Conditioning–allowing flowers/foliage to absorb a water floral food solution at room temperature

Dehydration–excessive loss of moisture (wilting)

EthylBloc^R–chemical used to prevent ethylene damage (1-MPC)

Ethylene–naturally occurring plant hormone that causes rapid aging of flowers

Floral food–contains three primary ingredients to prolong the vase life of cut flowers/foliage; 1. sugar (dextrose) for energy, 2. bio-inhibitor to reduce microbial activity, and 3. acidifier to lower water pH for better water uptake.

Hardening–allowing flowers/foliage to cool in a refrigerated environment

pH value–a measure of the acidity or alkalinity of a solution. The range is from 0-14, with 7 being neutral, below 7 considered acidic, and above 7 considered alkaline

Pre-Treatment - special procedure use prior to and in conjunction with a floral food solution, i.e. hydration solution

Respiration–the use of energy (carbohydrates/sugars) by the flower to sustain itself

FIGURE 1 Abstract Design–Abstract designs use non-realistic use of natural and/or man-made materials solely as pure elements to create a statement suggesting a specific emotion.

(Source: Wm. J. McKinley)

FIGURE 2 Formalinear Design–Formalinear designs have relatively few, but well organized materials that emphasize bold forms and clean lines. Notice in this design that each material has its own space to emphasize its unique form.

(Source: Wm. J. McKinley)

FIGURE 3 Geometric Design–Geometric designs have radial stem placement and are based on the fundamental forms of geometry, i.e. triangles (shown), asymmetrical triangles, round centerpiece, fan-shaped, etc. (synonyms include Western Line and Line-Mass designs). *(Source: Wm. J. McKinley)*

FIGURE 4 Ikebana Design–Ikebana is the Japanese art of floral design, when literally translated means "to arrange flowers." It is characterized by simplicity of materials, with well thought out placements that represent different aspects of nature and/or man's relationship with nature. Typically there are three primary line placements called Shin (heaven), Soe (man) and Tai (earth). *(Source: Wm. J. McKinley)*

FIGURE 5 Interpretive Design–Interpretive designs are organized to evoke a desired theme, idea, occasion, style or period. This design has a theme of both color (green) and materials used (fruits/vegetables). *(Source: Wm. J. McKinley)*

FIGURE 6   Parallel Design–Parallel designs use parallel stem placement of groupings of flowers. This design would be considered a "decorative" parallel, because much of the negative space (which is typical in parallel designs) between the groupings is massed with additional materials.   *(Source: Wm. J. McKinley)*

FIGURE 7   Vegetative Design–Vegetative designs use plant materials in a naturalistic manner to resemble plants growing together in specific environments. Most commercial vegetative designs, such as the one shown, are not "pure" vegetative designs, but rather adaptations for easier marketability that appeal to customer aesthetics.   *(Source: Wm. J. McKinley)*

Vase life–the length of time a cut flower or foliage will be aesthetically pleasing after being harvested.

Transpiration–the loss of water through small openings (stomata) on the leaves and flowers

Underwater Cutting–cutting the stem ends of flowers/foliage under water to prevent air from entering the stems

References

Johnson, James L., McKinley, William J., Benz, M (Buddy), *Flowers: Creative Design* (2001). College Station, TX: San Jacinto Publishing Co.

Society of American Florists, Flower Therapy, retrieved May 15, 2007 from, www.aboutflowers.com/flowertherapy/information.htm

Society of American Florists, Flowers=Happiness, retrieved May 15, 2007 from, www.aboutflowers.com/happier.html

Society of American Florists, Mother Nature's Social Security, retrieved May 15, 2007 from, www.aboutflowers.com/seniorstudy.htm

The AIFD Guide to Floral Design - Terms, Techniques, and Traditions (2005). The American Institute of Floral Designers, Baltimore, MD.

Proportion and Scale

Proportion describes the desired relationship between size and shape among objects (or parts of objects) displayed together. Scale, a component of proportion, deals with relative size of objects displayed together.

Several elements go into producing a proportional design—the characteristics of the flowers, container, table (where applicable), and room. Although tall containers can be used for tall displays, low containers should not hold tall flowers. The general recommendation is that the arrangement be about one and a half to two times the container height or width. The display should not overwhelm the table or the room. An oversized display is out of place in a small room, and a tiny display is ineffective in a large room or on a large table.

Focal Point and Accent

Rather than creating a design with all-around appeal, it is best to have emphasis or dominance in which one or several parts generate most interest.

A focal point can be created by including an exotic or very attractive flower (**accent plant**) in the design. This flower could be described as a conversation piece that draws the immediate attention of viewers. In lieu of such a specimen, a designer can use other techniques such as *repetition* and *massing* to draw attention to a design. A focal point should be located at the top of the container.

Contrast

Without contrast, a design can be monotonous and boring. Flowers differ in color, size, texture, and shape; these characteristics should be used to enhance the arrangement.

Unity

If a designer observes the principles of good balance, proportion, scale, and contrast and includes an effective focal point, the resulting creation blends together to produce an effective display that is aesthetically pleasing and functional. Unity is achieved in a design when the viewer gets the sense that all elements are working together. The design elements are not seen individually when there is unity.

The Role of Containers

Containers serve important roles in flower arranging other than just holding flowers. In some displays, they can hardly be seen. In many others, however, they provide a background for the arrangement. The size of the container determines the size of the finished product (remember that the arrangement should be one and a half to two times the size of the container). Containers can be ceramic, plastic, crystal, or some other material (Figure 24–2). Bright colors should be avoided and preference given to shades of white, green, gray, or beige. Solid colors should be chosen, although simple patterns may add to the display; elaborate patterns distract from the floral display and should be avoided.

Accent Plant
A plant strategically located in a landscape to draw attention to a particular feature in the area.

FIGURE 24-2 Containers for cut flowers. There is variety and room for creativity in selecting containers.

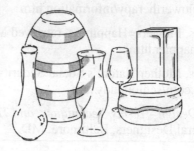

24.3.2 TOOLS AND MATERIALS

The tools used in the cut flower industry are simple (Figure 24–3):

1. *Cutting tools.* The basic cutting tools are the florist models of hand pruners, wire cutters, knives, and scissors. These instruments should be sharp and capable of providing clean cuts.
2. *Straight wire.* Wires of 16 to 20 gauge are used to provide additional support to the stems of cut flowers and also for creating certain shapes.
3. *Chicken wire.* Chicken wire may be placed in a tall vase to hold stems so that they do not slump and bunch together.
4. *Floral foam.* Instead of using water alone, flowers in certain displays may be arranged in a block of absorbent material called **floral foam**. The foam is soaked to saturation in water before being placed at the bottom of the container. The block then acts as the soil medium in which the cut flowers are "transplanted."
5. *Floral tape.* Floral tape can be used in a variety of ways, such as for creating cells (similar to chicken wire) on top of a vase to separate the flowers and prevent them from bunching together.
6. *Floral clay.* Floral clay is a putty used to hold materials such as chicken wire in place.

Floral Foam
A block of material with a high capacity for water absorption and retention that provides mechanical support for cut flowers in an arrangement.

24.3.3 BASIC FLORAL DESIGN

A floral designer should decide on the shape of the overall display to be created before beginning to arrange the flowers. Basic shapes are shown in Figure 24–4. The shape of the design is determined by where the arrangement will be placed and the occasion. A round shape is ideal on a table that can be viewed from all directions. For a dinner

(a)
(b)

(c)

(d)

FIGURE 24-3 Materials and tools used by the florist. (a) The florist's desk showing some basic tools and materials, (b) cut flowers, (c) refrigerated display case for completed arrangements and cut flowers, and (d) ribbons for decorating the arrangements. *(Source: George Acquaah)*

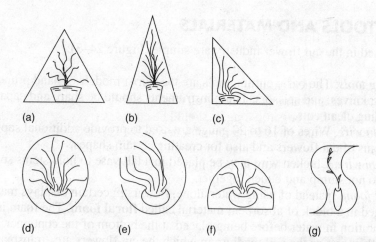

FIGURE 24-4 Selected basic floral shapes. (a) symmetrical triangle, (b) vertical triangle, (c) asymmetrical triangle, (d) round, (e) crescent, (f) half-circle, and (g) Hogarth or S-curve. Arrangements that are sometimes described as horizontal are flatter in the center and more drawn out than the half-circle design.

(a) (b) (c)

(d) (e) (f) (g)

occasion, the design should be low (e.g., half-circle or horizontal) so that it does not obstruct the view across the table. If the arrangement is intended to be displayed where it can be viewed from only the front, a half-triangle design is suitable.

Choosing Flowers

Flowers should be chosen with the occasion and the shape of the design in mind. In certain cultures, specific flowers are associated with funerals; consequently, it would be an unfortunate mistake to present these flowers at a wedding. Based on anatomy, individual flowers are suited for certain roles in a display. Some are used to create the skeletal structure or framework of the basic design and are called **line flowers** (e.g., gladiolus, delphinium, and snapdragon). They establish the height and width of the arrangement. The proper placement of the first flower creates the height of the arrangement. Flowers are arranged by working down from the top of the arrangement to the container. As previously described, the focal point in a display is provided by an exotic, unique, or very attractive flower (e.g., orchid and potea); these flowers are called **form flowers**. The bulk of the remainder of an arrangement is occupied by the base flower, which is most abundant in the overall arrangement. Flowers used in this fashion are called **mass flowers** (e.g., carnation, aster, and rose). After these three categories of flowers have been incorporated, spaces may occur in the design, causing the overall appearance at this stage to be coarse and somewhat fragmented. Sometimes nonplant materials (e.g., wires and foam) used in the design remain exposed in a manner that reduces the aesthetic value. These gaps and rough edges can be covered by using **filler flowers** such as palms, heather, fern, and baby's breath.

Other design elements to consider are color, texture, and pattern of both plant materials and container. Plant parts (vegetative and flowers) differ in texture related to physical structure (shape and form) and surface characteristics. The way flowers are arranged can also impact the texture of the design. Color, an element that has strong visual effect, can be warm (red, yellow) or cool (blue, green). Plant foliage varies in pattern due to color variation or arrangement of leaf parts. Dark colors should be placed near the container and lighter colors on top.

Creating a Design

The following steps provide a guide for creating a *low design*:

1. Place a block of floral foam saturated with water at the bottom of the container. It may be cut (if necessary) to fit the container. The foam should rise about 2 inches (5.1 centimeters) above the rim of the container.
2. Establish the height and spread of the arrangement.

Line Flower
A flower with a splice appearance.

Form Flower
A flower with a unique shape that is used to provide a focal point in an arrangement.

Mass Flower
A flower that is usually round-shaped and is used most abundantly in an arrangement.

Filler Flowers
A flower used to complete an arrangement by filling in gaps to tie in the various aspects of the design.

3. Establish the focal point.
4. Add massing flowers.
5. Add filler flowers.

In creating the design, it may be necessary to work by trial and error, cutting and recutting, twisting and turning, and doing all that is necessary to produce the most desirable arrangement. If a flower is too long, it should be cut back. Some leaves may have to be removed. Flowers may have to be repositioned in the floral block. It is critical that all cuts be made under water. It is also important to the display that all of the flowers and foliage appear to begin from a common spot. Examples of designs are shown in Figure 24–5.

(a) (b) (c)

(d) (e) (f)

FIGURE 24-5 Examples of simple arrangements. *(Source: George Acquaah)*

(g)　　　　　　　　　　(h)　　　　　　　　　　(i)

(j)　　　　　　　　　　(k)

FIGURE 24-5　Examples of simple arrangements. (*continued*)　(*Source: George Acquaah*)

24.4 DRIED FLOWERS

Garden plants brighten the landscape with their wide variety of colors and textures, and many may be cut and used fresh indoors in containers. Some species may be cut and dried and used just like fresh flowers in a variety of arrangements. In this way, flowers can be enjoyed year-round. Cut and dried flowers usually lose their scent but frequently maintain their color. Preparing flowers in this way is a means of preserving them.

24.4.1 DRYING

Flowers may be dried by natural or artificial means. One method may suit particular species more than others. Flowers should be cut in dry weather and when they are not covered with dew.

Natural Drying

To dry naturally, flowers are cut and hung upside-down in bunches or singly in a room that is dry and well ventilated until they feel dry and crisp. Species that may be dried naturally include lupins (dry singly), *Gypsophila, Delphinium* (dry singly), holly *(Eryngium)*, strawflowers, and statice *(Limonium)*. Some species require special treatment during drying. For example, *Hydrangea* flowers dry to the best quality when dried with the stems in water.

Grasses can be dried naturally, a good species being pampas grass *(Cortaderia selloana)*. Cereal plants such as wheat and barley may be dried and used successfully in arrangements. If the flower stock is too short to be hung, the flowers may be dried in an upright position using long pins (Figure 24–6). Plants with fruits or pods may be dried and used in very attractive displays. Such plants should be harvested for drying after the fruits or pods have ripened and begun to turn brown. Plants with pods such as poppy, foxglove, and hollyhock make excellent dry specimens. The Chinese lantern is a perennial favorite for dried flower displays.

Artificial (Chemical) Drying

Instead of air drying, special drying agents may be used to quickly dry cut flowers. Examples of drying agents are silica gel crystals (or powder) and a mixture of silver, sand, and borax. Chemical drying is done in a box. First, about an inch-deep (2.54-centimeters-deep) layer of drying agent is placed in the bottom of the box before placing the plant or flower inside. Additional drying agent is then spread carefully over the top (Figure 24–7). The box is set in a warm place for about three days to complete the drying process. Flowers that can be dried chemically include *Delphinium, Pelargonium*, rose, *Fuchsia*, and gentian.

Dry flower arrangements often include preserved leaves from trees. Preservation of leaves is accomplished by standing the ends of the petioles in glycerine mixed with water in a ratio of 1:2. To increase the uptake of glycerine, the ends of the petioles are hammered before standing in a container of the mixture (Figure 24–8). Leaves of horse

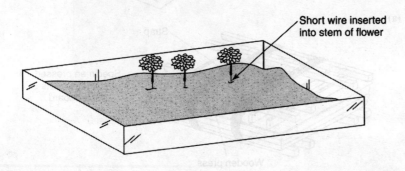

Short wire inserted into stem of flower

FIGURE 24–6 Drying cut flowers naturally.

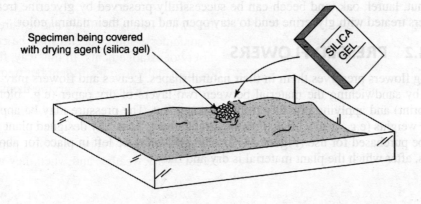

Specimen being covered with drying agent (silica gel)

SILICA GEL

FIGURE 24-7 Drying cut flowers by using chemicals.

24.4 Dried Flowers **699**

FIGURE 24-8 Cut flower preservation.

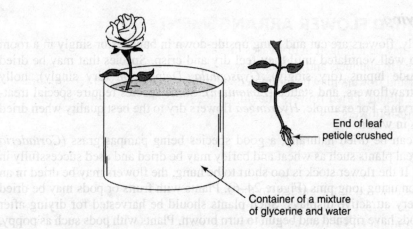

End of leaf petiole crushed

Container of a mixture of glycerine and water

FIGURE 24-9 Pressing cut flowers and plant specimens. (a) Homemade method and (b) commercial press.

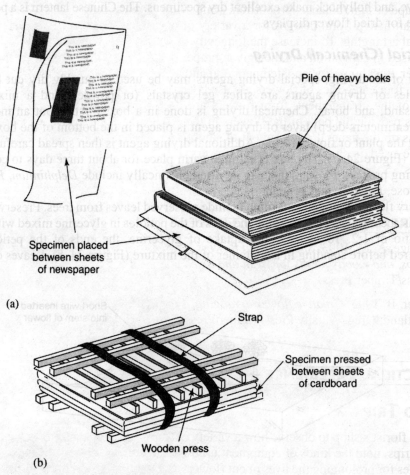

Pile of heavy books

Specimen placed between sheets of newspaper

(a)

Strap

Specimen pressed between sheets of cardboard

Wooden press

(b)

chestnut, laurel, oak, and beech can be successfully preserved by glycerine treatment. Flowers treated with glycerine tend to stay open and retain their natural color.

24.4.2 PRESSED FLOWERS

Drying flowers preserves them in their natural shapes. Leaves and flowers may also be dried by sandwiching the material between two layers of dry paper (e.g., blotting or newsprint) and applying pressure to the arrangement. The pressure may be applied by piling weights (e.g., heavy books) on the arrangement. Specially designed plant presses may be purchased for use (Figure 24–9). The press may be left in place for about four weeks, after which the plant material is dry and flat.

24.4.3 DRIED FLOWER ARRANGEMENTS

Dried flowers may be arranged in dry vases just as fresh cut flowers are arranged. They may be arranged in bouquets and wall displays after fastening them to decorative bands. Pressed leaves and flowers may be laminated, which extends the life of the product, and arranged in an album. Dried flowers should be handled with care since they are more delicate than fresh flowers.

SUMMARY

Flowers can be enjoyed in the garden, in the landscape, and as potted plants. They can also be enjoyed as cut flowers when they are detached from the parent plant and displayed in containers. Florists employ basic principles similar to those that govern landscape design (balance, proportion, scale, focal point, accent, contrast, and unity) to create attractive floral designs for a variety of occasions. There are five basic designs in floral arranging. To increase the longevity of cut flowers, they first need to be properly raised in cultivation and then given proper postharvest care that includes provision of water, high humidity, cool temperature, and absence of ethylene gas. In a basic floral design, four categories of flowers are used: Line flowers are used to set the height and width of the arrangement, form flowers are used for creating the focal point, mass flowers provide the bulk of the flowers in the arrangement, and filler flowers are used to dress up the general arrangement to smooth roughness and fill in gaps. Cut flowers may be used fresh or dried. Dried flowers are arranged in the same way as fresh flowers.

REFERENCES AND SUGGESTED READING

Armitage, A. M. 1993. *Specialty cut flowers: The production of annuals, perennials, bulbs, and woody plants for fresh and dried cut flowers*. Portland, Oreg.: Varsity Press/Timber Press.

Belcher, B. 1993. *Creative flower arranging: Floral design for home and flower show*. Portland, Oreg.: Varsity Press/Timber Press.

PRACTICAL EXPERIENCE

FIELD TRIP

Visit a florist's shop to observe how a variety of floral arrangements are created. During these trips, note the kinds of equipment used for creating the arrangements, the storage facilities for prolonging the lives of cut flowers, the training required to do the work, and the like.

LABORATORY WORK

1. Select any five cut flower species. Obtain cut flowers for these species and conduct an experiment to study the differences in the vase lives of the various species.
2. Collect, press, and dry cut flowers from the landscape. Create an album of dried flowers.
3. Collect and dry flowers from the landscape.

Outcomes Assessment

1. Discuss the methods used to extend the vase life of cut flowers.
2. Explain why cut flowers are recut under water prior to placing in a vase.
3. Discuss the principles of floral design.
4. Give five examples of species used as cut flowers.
5. Describe how cut flowers may be preserved by drying.

25

Terrarium Culture

PURPOSE AND EXPECTED OUTCOMES

This chapter is designed to discuss the principles and methods of growing plants in restricted environments.

After studying this chapter, the student should be able to

1. Describe how a terrarium works.
2. Discuss the selection of containers and plant species for a terrarium.
3. Discuss the maintenance and care of a terrarium.

OVERVIEW

In Chapter 12, greenhouses are described as controlled-environment structures for growing horticultural plants. Miniature versions of greenhouses are exemplified by indoor plant growth chambers that may be purchased for domestic use. Like greenhouses, growth chambers are equipped with devices for automatic control of certain growth factors such as light, water, and temperature. Very simple homemade controlled-environment plant growth chambers can be constructed, primarily for aesthetic purposes. Nathaniel B. Ward is credited with inventing the method of growing plants in closed containers. His original invention was based on the principle that when plants grow in an enclosed and restricted environment, moisture from transpiration and evaporation from the soil is not lost but retained through condensation and returned to the soil. This *water cycle*, coupled with adequate provision of other growth factors, enables plants to be grown in a variety of closed containers. This system for plant culture is called a *terrarium* (or *plantarium*) or *plant case*.

25.1 TYPES OF TERRARIUMS

In terms of design, there are two basic types, with some variation. In one design, the container for retaining moisture and maintaining high humidity does not come into direct contact with the growing medium. Instead, a potted plant is placed inside of a larger container with a lid (Figure 25–1). A very large container can hold several pots. In the second design, the potting medium is placed directly in the container (Figure 25–2). *Bottle gardens* are a very attractive variation of the traditional **terrarium** and *Wardian case* (named after Dr. Ward). They work on the same principle and are designed like the traditional terrarium. A terrarium may be sealed or openable.

Terrarium
A unit with a high capacity to retain moisture that is used for displaying plants.

25.2 DESIGNING A TERRARIUM OR BOTTLE GARDEN

25.2.1 CONTAINER

The container should be of clear transparent (preferred) or translucent material (glass or plastic). It should be noted that water runs off glass better than plastic. The plant in the container should be clearly visible. Scratches, cloudiness, and water marks distract from the beauty of the display. Glass reduces the amount of light that enters the container, more so if the material is tinted. However, lightly colored material can enhance the display. Shape is limited only by the grower's creativity, since a terrarium is purely for decorative use. Wine glasses, bell jars, glass bowls, glass bottles, and aquarium tanks are a sample of the containers that can be used (Figure 25–3). The shape and size of the

FIGURE 25–1 A terrarium display may involve a container-in-container design in which the potted plants are enclosed in an outer container such as a bell jar.

FIGURE 25–2 Commonly a terrarium is created in one container such as an aquarium tank.

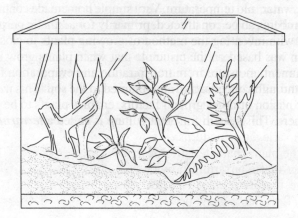

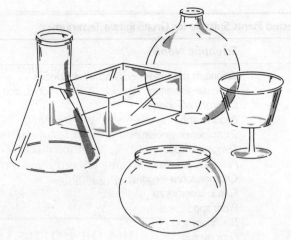

FIGURE 25–3 Terrarium containers are varied in shape and size. A key requirement in container type is clarity of material to allow adequate light to reach plants and also for plants to be visible. *(Source: For (c) Peter Gardner © Dorling Kindersley)*

(a) Horizontal bottle

(b) Vertical bottle

FIGURE 25–4 Bottle terrarium designs: (a) horizontal bottle and (b) vertical bottle display.

container and the size of the neck opening determine the sizes and types of plants that can be grown. Further, if the container is tinted, only plants that are adapted to subdued light (e.g., peperomia and pteris fern) can be grown. It is critical that the container be watertight and without cracks. A bottle may be used in either a vertical or horizontal position for a terrarium (Figure 25–4).

25.2.2 SELECTING PLANTS

In selecting plants for a terrarium, it should be kept in mind that the primary advantage of a terrarium is maintenance of humidity for plant growth. Cacti and succulents are therefore not recommended, unless the container will be left open, which in a way defeats the primary principle of holding moisture inside. Since the walls of the container reduce the amount of light entering the system, plants that are adapted to low or medium light intensities are desirable. It is desirable to select plants that are slow growing, such as bonsai (Chapter 26). If several plants are to be planted together, it is best to choose plants that vary in leaf shape, size, and color. Small leaves prevent overshadowing of one plant by another and allow all plants in the display to be visible. Terrarium plants are commonly foliage plants, but good plant selection can introduce some color and variety to break the monotony of green by including plants with different leaf arrangements, forms, shapes, and variegation patterns.

Apart from the plant characteristics described, another factor to consider in plant selection is the fact that a terrarium provides a highly restricted growth environment. Therefore, if more than one plant is to be grown, they must all be adapted to the same conditions. Terrariums may be designed according to environmental themes

TABLE 25–1 Selected Plants Suitable for Growing in a Terrarium

Plant	Scientific Name
Maidenhair fern	*Adiantum capillus-veneris* and other species
Spleenwort	*Aspleniun fontanum, A. viride, A. trichomanes,* and *A. ruta-muraria*
Scaly spleenwort	*Ceterach officinarum*
Begonia	*Begonia* spp.
Killarney fern	*Trichomanes speciosum*
Irish moss	*Selaginella* spp.
Button fern	*Pellaea rotundifolia*
Parlor palm	*Chamaedorea elegans*
Lace flower vine	*Episcia dianthiflora*
Table fern	*Pteris* spp.
Hard fern	*Blechnum* spp.
Creeping fig	*Ficus pumila*
Christmas cactus	*Schlumbergera* spp.
Prayer plant	*Maranta leuconeura*
Siper plant	*Sinningia pusilla*

(e.g., tropical plants or ferns). Good terrarium plants include those that originate in the forest region and thus are adapted to humid and shaded conditions. Examples are lichens, ferns, mosses, violets, and ground ivy, which are suited to closed-container terrariums. Cacti and other succulents make good open-container terrarium plants. Table 25–1 provides a list of plants suitable for terrarium culture.

25.3 TOOLS

When planting a large terrarium, such as one using a fish tank, ordinary hand tools used in the garden are adequate. However, in bottle gardens, creativity may be necessary in choosing instruments to plant and maintain the unit. The operation becomes more challenging as the neck of the bottle becomes longer and narrower. A number of tools may be improvised for placing growing medium into the container, scooping soil, inserting and planting, firming soil after planting, cutting, cleaning the inside of the container, and retrieving material (Figure 25–5). To deliver the planting medium into a bottle, for example, a funnel may be used to direct the soil placement in order to avoid dirtying the inner walls and having to clean them later, sometimes with great difficulty. A disposable funnel can be made out of paper. A spoon with a long handle, or tied to a long stick or wire for increased reach, may be used as a minispade to make planting holes and fill them after transplanting. For firming the soil, the spool from sewing machine thread mounted on a stick or dowel may be used. Long forceps, a forked stick, or a pair of long sticks may be used to deliver plants into planting holes. Dirt on the inner wall of the container may be wiped with a damp piece of cloth or foam attached to the end of a flexible wire. When a leaf or branch must be cut off after planting, a scalpel blade mounted on the end of a stick may be used.

25.4 THE PLANTING MEDIUM

Some general principles should be observed in selecting and preparing a growing medium for a terrarium. Good drainage is critical since most plants do not tolerate waterlogging. Good drainage also ensures that plant roots have adequate air for proper growth

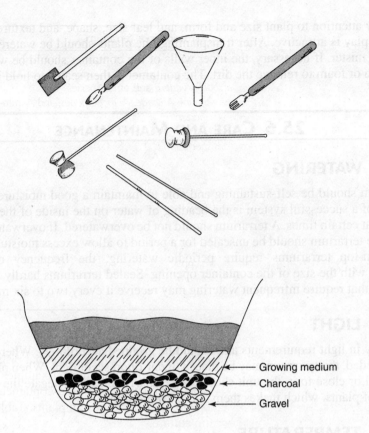

FIGURE 25–5 Assortment of tools used in creating a terrarium. These tools are largely home-made and include cutting, cleaning, scooping, picking, grabbing, and compacting tools.

FIGURE 25–6 Typical layering of a terrarium. Drainage material lines the bottom, followed by a sprinkle of charcoal for deodorizing, and topped with the growing medium.

Growing medium
Charcoal
Gravel

and development. To provide good drainage, the bottom of the container should first be lined with a layer of coarse material such as washed gravel, sand, or pieces of broken pottery (Figure 25–6). To prevent this reservoir for excess water from being destroyed, a layer of sphagnum moss may be spread over the drainage layer as a retaining layer before adding the growing medium. In a closed system, odors tend to build up over time because of the decomposition of organic matter by bacteria. To deodorize the closed environment, a small amount of activated charcoal may be sprinkled over the sphagnum moss. Alternately, lumps of charcoal may be used in place of gravel to line the bottom of the container to about 1 to 2 inches (2.54 to 5.1 centimeters) deep. The planting medium may be purchased from a nursery store or made at home. Fertility management is important in a terrarium, since in a closed environment certain nitrogenous fertilizers tend to release ammonia gases over time; these gases can be toxic to plants and kill them. Using chemical fertilizers in a terrarium, especially a sealed one, is therefore not recommended.

25.5 PLANTING

The tools described earlier may be used for planting: the spoon to dig a hole, the forked stick or pair of sticks for lowering the plant into the planting hole, and the dowel for firming the soil around the plant. The hole should be large enough to hold the root mass. After removing the plant from the original container, some of the potting medium should be removed before transplanting. Plants to be located near the side of the bottle should be planted first. For a bottle garden intended for all-around viewing, the tallest specimens should be located in the center and the shortest near the container walls. If the unit is intended to be displayed against a wall, a slope design may be a better choice. In this design, the soil is banked up against the wall rather than leveled off. Plants with a lot of foliage may have to be gently bent to maneuver them through the narrow neck of a bottle. Plants should be arranged such that no plant is obscured by another. The arrangement should pay attention to plant size and form, and leaf size, shape, and texture so that the overall display is attractive. After transplanting, the plants should be watered by spraying with a mister. If necessary, the inner walls of the container should be wiped with a moist cloth or foam to remove the dirt. The container is then sealed to hold in moisture.

25.6 CARE AND MAINTENANCE

25.6.1 WATERING

A terrarium should be self-sustaining and able to maintain a good moisture cycle. The evidence of a successful system is the beading of water on the inside of the wall of the container at certain times. A terrarium should not be overwatered. If overwatering is suspected, the terrarium should be unsealed for a period to allow excess moisture to evaporate. Open-top terrariums require periodic watering, the frequency of watering increasing with the size of the container opening. Sealed terrariums hardly need watering; those that require infrequent watering may receive it every two to six months.

25.6.2 LIGHT

Plants vary in light requirements and should be grouped accordingly. Where additional light is needed, the terrarium may be placed under fluorescent light. When placed on the windowsill or close to it, the unit should be regularly rotated to negate the phototropic response of plants, which makes them curve toward light.

25.6.3 TEMPERATURE

A terrarium with a tropical theme requires a warmer temperature than one with a subtropical theme. Ideal temperatures are similar to those required by other indoor plants (about 18.3 to 23.9°C or 65 to 75°F). As previously indicated, potted plants placed on windowsills are subject to greater temperature fluctuations than those placed away from windows.

25.6.4 FERTILIZING

When needed, organic fertilizers should be used. However, if the initial growing medium is well composed, additional fertilizing may not be necessary. Since slow growth is desired, fertilizer application should be minimal. Chemical fertilizers may be used in open terrariums but not in closed types.

25.6.5 PRUNING

When vigorously growing species are used or when growing conditions are very favorable, plants may grow too big too soon and crowd the restricted space in the container. In this situation, excess foliage should be removed. Pruning plants in narrow-necked containers is a challenge but may be accomplished by using a razor blade or scalpel mounted on the end of a long stick. All clippings should be retrieved from the container, lest they decay and cause a foul odor.

25.6.6 DISEASE AND INSECT PEST CONTROL

To reduce the incidence of diseases and insect pests, the growing medium should be sterilized to kill pathogens. The plants used should be disease free, and the foliage should be examined for insects and other pathogens before transplanting into the container. Insect pests found in terrariums include mites, whiteflies, aphids, and mealybugs, which may be controlled by spraying appropriate chemicals.

25.6.7 ENHANCING THE DISPLAY

Certain terrarium designers enhance the display by topping the soil with pebbles or pieces of driftwood. As already mentioned, the containers used should be clear, but light tinting adds beauty to the display, even though it further reduces light penetration.

25.7 TROUBLESHOOTING

The following are some common problems associated with terrarium culture, and how they may be remedied.

Symptom	Possible cause	Action
1. Yellowing of foliage	Poor drainage or inadequate fertility	Renew soil and ventilate for evaporation of excess water
2. Poor growth or stunting	Inadequate fertility or poor drainage	Replace soil and add organic fertilizer
3. Browning of foliage	Lack of moisture or burning from direct sunlight	Water plants and move away from direct sunlight
4. Odors	Decomposition of material or presence of nitrogenous fertilizer	Ventilate and add activated charcoal

SUMMARY

Terrarium culture entails growing plants in an enclosed container such that a water cycle is established in the chamber to make further watering unnecessary for an indefinite period of time. A variety of container types and shapes may be used, but clear glass is most preferred for sufficient light provision for the plants. Plants that are adapted to low or medium light intensities are most desirable. The planting medium should drain freely. Chemical fertilizers should be avoided since certain nitrogenous fertilizers release toxic ammonia gases that are injurious to plants. In terms of moisture, a terrarium should be self-sustaining and able to maintain a good moisture cycle. The growing medium and the plants included should be free of diseases.

REFERENCES AND SUGGESTED READING

Reader's Digest. 1979. *Success with houseplants*. New York: Reader's Digest Association.

Wright, M., ed. 1979. *The complete indoor gardener*. New York: Random House.

OUTCOMES ASSESSMENT

1. Discuss the principle of terrarium culture.
2. Discuss the criteria for selecting plants for growing in a terrarium.
3. Discuss the care and maintenance of a terrarium.

26

Bonsai: The Art of Miniature Plant Culture

PURPOSE AND EXPECTED OUTCOMES

This chapter is designed to describe the principles and show the techniques of creating and maintaining miniature plants.

After studying this chapter, the student should be able to

1. Describe the art of bonsai.
2. Discuss the principles of bonsai design.
3. Describe the steps involved in creating a bonsai.
4. List plant species that are amenable to this art form.
5. Discuss how to use and care for a bonsai.

[COLOR PLATES—*see color plate 32* for additional chapter photos]

OVERVIEW

In Chapter 6, we learned that the expression of genes in an environment produces a phenotype. For the genetic potential to be fully expressed, optimal environmental conditions must be provided for the development of the genotype. In other words, it is possible to manipulate phenotype to some extent by altering the environment in which an organism is developing. Plants in the landscape are usually nurtured to quickly establish a vigorous vegetative growth and to develop to full size. However, when growing plants indoors, it is desirable to nurture plants such that they grow and develop at a much slower pace. An extreme case in the application of this concept of slowing plant growth and development is found in the Japanese art form called **bonsai** (*bon* meaning tray and *sai* meaning tree). Bonsai is the art of growing and training plants (trees, shrubs, and vines) to be miniatures of their natural forms (Figure 26–1). In effect, bonsai is a cultural technique for dwarfing plants. Dwarfing is accomplished through creative design, pruning, and culturing plants in shallow containers.

Bonsai
The art of growing and training plants to be miniatures of their natural forms.

(a)

(b)

FIGURE 26–1 Bonsai can be created using a variety of species for specific effects. (a) A juniper bonsai shows the traditional bonsai shape. (b) A fruiting bonsai created from an orange plant. *(Source: George Acquaah)*

26.1 PRINCIPLES

To successfully produce a bonsai plant, four general principles—plant selection, design, pruning and training, and management—should be understood and observed.

26.1.1 PLANT SELECTION

All plants are not suitable for bonsai. Those with small leaves (deciduous or evergreen) are most desirable. It is also desirable that the species be able to grow in restricted space. Bonsai are essentially outdoor plants, although recently they have been adapted for indoor display. In China and Japan, where the art originated, bonsai plants are obtained from temperate and humid forests. The three groups of plants used in creating bonsai are discussed in the following sections.

Conifers

Conifers are hardy plants and tolerant of the pruning and other manipulations customary with bonsai culture. The beginner may fare best with conifers as a starter material. Conifers require a short period (usually a few years) to be ready for displaying, and therefore keep the enthusiasm of the novice alive. Another desirable characteristic of conifers is that they are mostly evergreen and as such can be enjoyed year-round. A selection of conifers suited to miniaturization is presented in Table 26–1.

Deciduous Trees

Deciduous plants shed their leaves in the fall season, after displaying dazzling fall foliage colors. During the dormant period, when all leaves drop, the tree offers a good opportunity for pruning and reshaping. Vigorous growth resumes in spring. As such, deciduous

TABLE 26–1 Selected Conifers Used for Bonsai

Plant	Scientific Name
Cedar	Cedrus spp.
Silver fir	Albies alba
Japanese cedar	Cryptomeria japonica
Chinese juniper	Juniperus chinensis
Japanese white pine	Pinus parviflora
Japanese black pine	Pinus thubergii
Spruce	Picea spp.
Yew	Taxus baccata
Larch	Larix spp.
False cypress	Chamaecyparis spp.

These are evergreen species (except for the larch, which has deciduous needles). Silver fir has upright cones, and spruce has pendant cones. Cedar has dark green needles, and Japanese white pine has a bluish-green color.

TABLE 26–2 Selected Deciduous Trees Used for Bonsai

Plant	Scientific Name
Trident maple	Acer trifidum
Japanese maple	Acer palmatum
Chinese elm	Ulmus parvifolia
Hornbeam	Carpinus laxiflora
Crab apple	Mallus floribunda
Black birch	Betula nigra
Beech	Fagus crenata
Gray-bark elm	Zelkova serrata

bonsai require regular pruning to keep their leaves small. Species from Asia are desirable because their leaves are naturally small in size. Table 26–2 presents a selected number of deciduous trees adapted to bonsai culture.

Ornamental Shrubs

Conifers are most commonly used in creating bonsai. However, ornamental shrubs that bear small fruits and flowers also make good bonsai. Their spectacular display of flowers and fruits is a sight to behold. Ornamental shrubs that are suitable for use in creating bonsai are listed in Table 26–3.

26.1.2 DESIGN

Because bonsai is an art form, creativity is critical to the overall appeal of a finished product. Longevity is an important aspect of bonsai; designs are meant to produce plants that appear old, rugged, and weathered. It should be acknowledged that, to a large extent, the art of bonsai imitates nature. Therefore, some designs portray plants responding to the impact of natural forces such as the wind, as is the case in the *Fukinagashi* design and the *Nejikan* twisted trunk design (Figure 26–2). Designs may involve a single tree with a single trunk, a single tree with multiple trunks, or a group of trees. Group designs offer an opportunity to create a miniature landscape. Some designs are very creative, with cascading branches that hang over the edge of the container.

TABLE 26–3 A Selection of Popular Ornamental Shrubs and Trees Used for Bonsai

Plant	Scientific Name
Azalea	*Azalea* spp.
Rhododendron	*Rhododendron* spp.
Rock cotoneaster	*Cotoneaster horizontalis*
Crab apple	*Malus* spp.
Japanese apricot	*Prunus mume*
Almond	*Prunus amygdalus*
Japanese cherry	*Prunus serrulata*
Wisteria	*Wisteria* spp.
Winter jasmine	*Jasminum nudiflorum*
Japanese camellia	*Camellia japonica*

Plants such as cotoneaster and crab apple produce small flowers and fruits.

FIGURE 26–2 Bonsai designs: (a) single plant and (b) multiple plants (forest bonsai).　*(Source: Paul Goff © Dorling Kindersley)*

26.1.3 PRUNING AND TRAINING

Pruning to control plant size is critical to bonsai culture. Roots and shoots are judiciously pruned to obtain the planned shape and size and to control the rate of development. It is often necessary to use wires during the training process to force the plant to assume a desired shape.

26.1.4 MANAGEMENT

After establishment, pruning is periodically required to contain the roots and maintain the shape of the bonsai. The plant needs to be watered, fertilized, and placed under appropriate environmental conditions at all times.

26.2 CREATING THE BONSAI

26.2.1 TOOLS

A variety of pruning and cutting tools are used in bonsai culture. The cutting ends of these tools should be small enough to cut parts of the miniature plants (Figure 26–3). A pair of pinchers is used for cutting the taproot, and pliers are used for stripping away the bark of limbs. The clippers are used for shaping the top of the tree. Apart from cutting tools, copper wires of various gauges (10 to 20) are used in creating bonsai plants. The wires are required for forcing plant limbs to assume shapes and to grow in the direction desired by the designer.

FIGURE 26–3 Tools for creating a bonsai. These include: (a, b, e) a variety of cutting implements (c) a pair of forceps, (d) a pair of pliers, (f) a brush, (g) a hand trowel, (h) a scalpel, and (i) a wire.

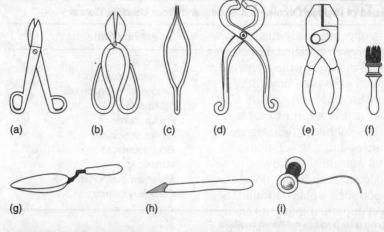

(a)   (b)   (c)   (d)   (e)   (f)

(g)   (h)   (i)

FIGURE 26–4 Typical bonsai containers have an Asian design. They are usually shallow. *(Source: George Acquaah)*

26.2.2 CONTAINER

The plant selected can be left in its original container for the initial stages of the culture (the training and primary or initial pruning). After the topwork is completed, it should be transplanted to a bonsai container, which is characteristically very shallow (Figure 26–4). The bonsai container is usually round but may also be oblong or rectangular in shape for certain planting designs involving more than one plant. The color of the container should not be bright (browns and greens are preferred). Earthen pots that are unglazed on the inside are best. Drainage holes should be provided in the bottom of the container.

26.2.3 PLANT SELECTION

As previously mentioned, both deciduous and evergreen plants, purchased at a local nursery, can be used for bonsai. Species such as pine, juniper, and pyrachantha are excellent bonsai material. In selecting a plant, it is best to look for one that already has a rugged and irregular appearance in order to have a head start on the design. As indicated, deciduous species shed their leaves at some point. If green leaves are desired year-round, conifers should be selected. Further, conifers require relatively little maintenance.

26.3 TRAINING BONSAI

Plants for bonsai may be collected from nature, raised from seed, or vegetatively propagated.

26.3.1 COLLECTING BONSAI PLANTS FROM NATURE

The Japanese name for collecting ready-made bonsai from natural surroundings is called *Yamadori*. The natural bonsai is called *Yamadori shitate*. These specimens have the advantage of having been molded by the elements (weather-beaten) and usually exhibit some of the features, such as twisted branches, stunting, and aging, that are artificially induced when bonsai are created from scratch. However, should the plant not be perfect, it is difficult to remold it to conform to an acceptable style. Old specimens are not flexible and do not readily submit to twisting and bending without damage.

The best environment under which bonsai material can be collected is one that is harsh (poor to marginal nutrition, shallow soil, unseasonable temperature, and windy conditions). Plants under such conditions do not grow normally and may be stunted and possibly deformed. When such a plant is found, it should be dug up and transplanted in the dormant period. It is important to dig up (rather than pull) all of the roots including a ball of soil. Some root or shoot pruning may be required before transplanting.

26.3.2 GROWING PLANTS FOR BONSAI

Starting from Seed

Starting from seed is a slow process, requiring several years to obtain a plant of decent size that can be trained. Seeds may be collected from the wild or purchased from a nursery. Seeds differ in preplanting preparation, some requiring soaking and others stratification.

Using the Vegetative Propagation Method

Any of the methods for vegetative propagation described in Chapter 10 may be used to raise plants for training as bonsai.

26.3.3 PLANT SHAPE AND PRIMARY PRUNING

The selected plant should be examined for desirable natural features such as natural curvature and twists in the stem. The designer should determine the best viewing angle (or front) of the finished product and work to enhance it. The primary branches are also identified, starting with the lowest ones, which determine how low the display will be. All unwanted branches below the lowest ones should be removed flush from the trunk. Sometimes dead branches below the selected lowest one may be retained and incorporated into the overall design. The maximum height of the bonsai must be determined next. The plant should then be pruned to that height. The branches between the top and bottom ones are judiciously pruned such that they alternate along the stem and are shorter at the top than at the bottom. Some downward-pointing branches may be removed. During the initial pruning stage, one or two of the lowest branches may be cut back to leave 2 to 4 inches (5.1 to 10.2 centimeters) of limb that is stripped of its bark to kill it. This action creates deadwood (aging), which enhances the design. The taproot should be removed to encourage the growth of lateral or secondary roots. When starting from seed, pruning is initiated when the seedling is young. The taproot and main stem are pruned to induce lateral branching (Figure 26–5).

26.3.4 SECONDARY (MAINTENANCE) PRUNING

Secondary pruning is done very frequently to preserve the plant shape, remove unwanted growth, and control growth (Figure 26–6). Leaves are clipped and sometimes completely removed in deciduous species. Further, deciduous species are pinched on a regular basis to remove buds, which has the effect of producing smaller leaves.

26.3.5 WIRING

The central stem may or may not be vertical. Vertical stems are desirable when a mini-forest design is being created, whereby several to many bonsai plants are grown in one container. The stem or branches may be forced to assume unnatural shapes by twisting a copper wire around a limb and bending it in the new direction or into a new shape (Figure 26–7). Wiring starts from the lower part of the stem or branch and progresses to the tips. Thinner wires are used for thinner limbs. Branches that are close together can be pushed apart by first wiring and then bending. These operations should be done very carefully to avoid bruising the bark or breaking off the limb caused by excessive tension from bending or wrapping the wire too tightly around the limb. The ends of the wires should be tucked away from view. Conifers are wired at the end of the dormant period in late winter, while deciduous plants are wired in spring. Wires should be removed after the shape is set (about six to twelve months). If left for a long time, the wire may become embedded in the bark of the plant. The base of the trunk may be deliberately wired to induce thickening (Figure 26–8). After wiring, bending, and determining the final shape, additional secondary pruning may be required to finish the product. Typical bonsai top shapes are flattened and layered foliage.

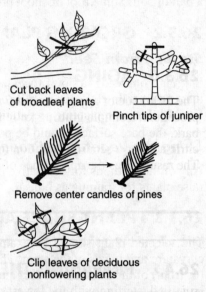

Cut back leaves of broadleaf plants

Pinch tips of juniper

Remove center candles of pines

Clip leaves of deciduous nonflowering plants

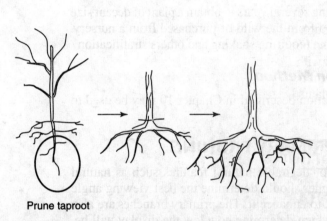

Prune taproot

FIGURE 26–5 Root pruning. One training goal in creating bonsai is to discourage the growth of the taproot. Bonsai plants have a taproot system. Root pruning also slows plant growth.

FIGURE 26–6 Shoot pruning. Leaves on bonsai need to be pruned at certain times to control growth.

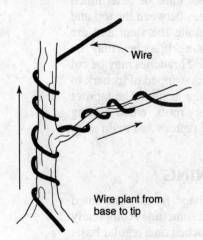

Wire

Wire plant from base to tip

FIGURE 26–7 Wiring is a primary activity in creating bonsai. Wiring is done to force branches to grow in a desired manner to create the desired bonsai shape. Wiring must always start from the base of the stem or branch.

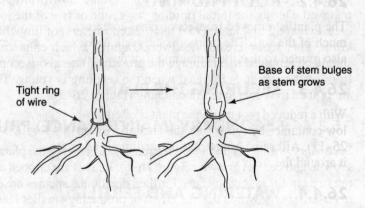

Tight ring of wire

Base of stem bulges as stem grows

FIGURE 26–8 A technique of creating a bulging stem base is used to create additional interest in bonsai.

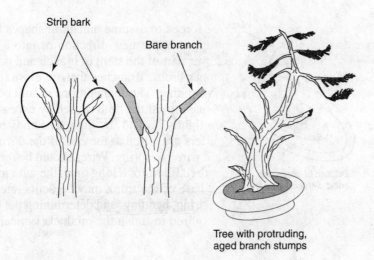

Strip bark

Bare branch

Tree with protruding, aged branch stumps

26.3.6 AGING

The technique of aging is called *jin*. Although a special knife may be purchased for this procedure, a simple grafting knife may also be used successfully. After stripping off the bark, the bare surface should be polished with fine-grade sandpaper, after which dilute citric acid or a scouring solution may be rubbed on the bare surface to bleach the area. The result gives the appearance of aged plants (Figure 26–9).

26.4 REPOTTING BONSAI

26.4.1 PREPARING THE CONTAINER

When repotting bonsai, a piece of wire is passed through the holes in the bottom of the container to anchor the plant (Figure 26–10). A fine wire mesh is stretched over the drainage hole, and a layer of gravel or potting medium (sterilized mix of equal amounts of coarse sand, soil, and sphagnum moss) is placed to a depth of about 1 inch (2.5 centimeters) in the container.

26.4.2 ROOT PRUNING

The plant is removed from its original container and the roots examined after removing much of the soil. The taproot is cut back to leave a short stump. Other lateral roots are also pruned so that the remaining root mass fits the bonsai container.

26.4.3 SECURING THE PLANT

With a reduced root mass, the plant is often top-heavy and needs to be secured in the shallow container by tying with the anchor wire passed through the drainage holes (Figure 26–11). After that, more potting medium is added to cover the roots, slightly mounding it around the stem.

26.4.4 WATERING AND FERTILIZING

Watering and fertilizing are two operations that are very critical to the success of a bonsai. As previously indicated, the miniature plant depends on one's ability to control and slow the growth and development of the plant. Growth control relies to a great extent on the management of watering and fertilizing. Since the bonsai container is shallow, the

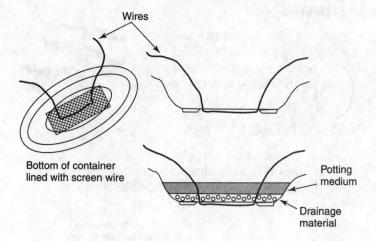

FIGURE 26–10 Bonsai are repotted periodically as a maintenance activity. The container should be lined with a drainage material and then topped with the potting medium.

Wires

Bottom of container lined with screen wire

Potting medium

Drainage material

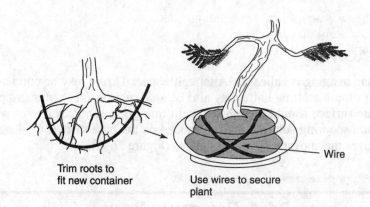

FIGURE 26–11 Wires are used to stabilize the plant in a shallow container.

Trim roots to fit new container

Use wires to secure plant

Wire

plant should be watered thoroughly, especially in summer. Hard and polluted water should be avoided; rain water is the most recommended but may not always be available. Chlorine in an urban water supply is injurious to plants. If tap water must be used, the container of water should sit open outside to evaporate the chlorine. The spout of the watering can should be capped with a head that delivers a fine spray.

For fertilizing, slow-acting fertilizers are most desirable. Specially constituted bonsai fertilizer may be purchased from a nursery. Organic fertilizer pellets contain nitrogen, phosphorus, and potassium in proportions of 50:30:20 compounded from materials such as bone meal and fish meal. Bonsai are fertilized during the active growing period. Fertilizing of flowering and fruiting bonsai plants should be delayed until after flowering.

26.5 POSTESTABLISHMENT CARE

26.5.1 PRUNING AND REPOTTING

A bonsai plant needs periodic pruning to maintain its shape and control growth. Depending on the species, roots require pruning every three to five years, since they quickly become pot-bound in the restricted area of the bonsai container. The plant to be pruned is removed from the container and the roots trimmed below the soil level. Pruning should also be geared toward providing room for new growth over the next three to five years. The plant should then be resecured, if necessary, by tying with a wire before fresh potting medium is added and the plant watered.

26.5.2 SANITATION

It is critical to maintain clean surroundings and thereby reduce the chances of disease and pest attacks. Because of its small size, any disease or pest attack can be devastating to a bonsai plant. Routine cleaning includes scraping and brushing off moss growth on the trunk and removing liverworts and other weeds from the soil.

26.5.3 PEST CONTROL

Pests of bonsai include aphids (or greenflies), caterpillars, scale insects, red spider mites, and ants. Aphids and mites may be controlled by spraying with insecticides. Ants may attack and destroy roots and should be removed. Caterpillars are readily removed by hand and destroyed.

26.5.4 DISEASE CONTROL

Powdery mildew is a problem where humid conditions prevail. Rust and black spot may also occur. Black rot may be controlled by applying sulfur. Root rot may occur if water-logged conditions prevail, or if poorly decomposed organic fertilizer is applied. The bonsai plant should be lifted and all contaminated soil brushed away. Canker is effectively controlled by cutting away affected plant parts.

26.5.5 SEASONAL MAINTENANCE

Winter

When winter temperatures become severe (below freezing), protection may be required for outdoor bonsai. Plants may be brought indoors and kept at temperatures below 5°C (41°F). Fertilization should cease during the dormant period. Water should be provided as needed but sparingly. Deciduous plants are best pruned in winter, when they shed all of their leaves. The plants can also be cleaned during winter.

Spring

Outdoor bonsai should be returned to the outside environment only after it is safe to do so (frost free). Plants begin to bud as active growth resumes. Watering should be increased, but very carefully. As spring advances, the growth rate increases, and some pruning may be necessary to prevent excessive growth. When blooms wither, plants should be pruned before new buds appear. Blooms occur on the previous year's wood, and any delay in pruning will prevent blooming in the next year. Coniferous bonsai may be repotted in midspring.

Summer

Foliage growth is intense in early summer. Pinching and pruning are required to control growth. Water is critical in late summer when it is hot; however, hot and humid conditions predispose plants to fungal diseases.

Fall

A key activity in fall is to prepare the plant for winter by boosting its nutrition with fertilizers. Deciduous species display their most intense colors in midfall. Late fall ushers in the time of leaf drop and the approach of winter. As leaves drop, the plants may be pruned. Preparations should be made to protect plants in case of an unexpected frost when bonsai are displayed outdoors.

SUMMARY

Young trees, shrubs, and vines can be manipulated and managed such that they grow to become miniature versions of the adult plants. The technique of miniaturizing plants is called bonsai and originated in China and Japan. Bonsai can live for more than 100 years. One of the key elements in design is to create the appearance of old age and the effects of weathering. Materials can be selected or manipulated to appear old and weather-beaten. Pruning and nutrition are two major management activities in the successful culture of a bonsai. Both the roots and shoots of a plant are regularly pruned to create the desired shape and to control growth. Bonsai are generally designed for the outdoors, and thus when used indoors, the appropriate adjustments should be made to provide the necessary environmental conditions for proper growth and development.

REFERENCES AND SUGGESTED READING

Koreshoff, D. 1984. Bonsai: *Its art, science, history, and philosophy*. Beaverton, Oreg.: ISBS/Timber Press.

Pessey, C., and R. Samson. 1989. *Bonsai basics: A step-by-step guide to growing, training, and general care*. New York: Sterling Publications.

Wright, R., ed. 1975. *The complete indoor gardener, revised edition*. New York: Random House.

Young, D. 1990. Bonsai: *The art and technique*. Englewood Cliffs, N.J.: Prentice Hall.

OUTCOMES ASSESSMENT

1. Discuss how a plant can be miniaturized.
2. Discuss the proper care of bonsai plants.

Postharvest Handling and Marketing of Horticultural Products

PURPOSE AND EXPECTED OUTCOMES

This chapter discusses the methods used to preserve the quality of horticultural products after harvesting and strategies for marketing products.

After studying this chapter, the student should be able to

1. Describe the various methods of cold storage of horticultural products.
2. Describe how products are handled while being transported.
3. Describe methods of processing products.
4. Discuss the advantages and disadvantages of direct and nondirect product marketing alternatives.
5. List and describe the basic elements in a product marketing operation.
6. Discuss the role of intermediaries in the marketing process.

OVERVIEW

Horticultural crops and ornamental plants are grown with certain markets (consumers) in mind. Whereas some operations are small and limited to home consumption, others are large scale and designed to sell produce. Some horticultural products are harvested as mature and dry items, while others are harvested fresh. Some products are designated for processing and others for table use. Whether planted for the table or processing, the producer may target a multitier of consumers—those with discriminating taste and willing to pay premium prices and those looking for bargains. All of these and other factors affect how crops are managed in production and handled after harvesting. If ornamental plants and crops are grown for sale, a paramount consideration in postharvest activities is preservation of product quality so that it reaches the consumer in the best desirable state. The discussion in this chapter focuses on edible products. Handling of nonedible products such as cut flowers is discussed in Chapter 24.

27.1 ECONOMIC IMPORTANCE OF POSTHARVEST LOSSES

Horticultural production is a business. Consequently, the goal of the producer is to maximize the yield of the economic product and to deliver it to the market or consumer at the highest quality for maximum profitability. Because many harvested horticultural products (fruits, vegetables, flowers, etc.) are perishable, they are prone to rapid deterioration soon after harvesting. Product spoilage is responsible for reduction in farm income by about 25 percent and sometimes much higher in tropical developing countries. Such places often experience extreme abiotic conditions that favor diseases and plant physiological abnormalities that lead to spoilage of products. Socioeconomic constraints in these regions also prevent the acquisition of appropriate technologies for harvesting, processing, and handling horticultural products.

27.1.1 CAUSES OF POSTHARVEST LOSSES

Fresh produce consists of about 65–95 percent water, depending on the plant species and the economic part harvested. Physiological activities (respiration and transpiration) continue for some time after harvesting, because the tissues are living. Consequently, as the produce loses its water reserves, the cells die and start to decay. High temperature and low atmospheric humidity tend to accelerate the rate of natural deterioration, causing abnormal ripening, development of off-flavor, and changes in texture of the produce. Improper handling during harvesting may cause mechanical or physical damage to the produce. Bruising provides access to microbes that cause tissue decay or exposure of internal tissue for accelerated dessication. Another major cause of postharvest losses is disease and pests that may originate in the field or the storehouse. It is important to stress that these factors usually interact to cause deterioration of fresh horticultural produce.

27.1.2 POSTHARVEST PHYSIOLOGY

Respiration and transpiration are the two key physiological processes that occur in harvested fresh produce. Because no new dry matter is added to the produce after harvesting, respiration depends on stored photosynthates while transpiration depends on stored water in the tissues. As both processes occur, the stored resources are gradually depleted. Poor ventilation of the storage environment depletes the oxygen concentration and brings about fermentation, which causes off-flavors and rapid ageing of the produce. Similarly, fresh produce is prone to moisture loss, an event that occurs rapidly under low atmospheric humidity and fast air circulation. Produce such as leafy green vegetables (e.g., spinach) are more susceptible to dessication than others with a thicker epiderminal layer (potato). The greater the surface area of the plant part to its volume, the more rapid will be the loss of water. As previously discussed, fruit ripening may be a postharvest event in some crop produce (e.g., banana, tomato). Furthermore, ethylene gas is important in initiating ripening of fruits.

27.2 HARVESTING

Since postharvest activities have a significant bearing on how products are handled, it is useful to precede discussions on postharvest activities with how horticultural products are harvested. It is fair to say that, regarding storage performance, if poor-quality products go into storage, poor-quality products come out. Harvesting is a very timely and expensive operation. The difficulty (or ease) of the harvesting operation and how it is done depends on factors such as the crop, the part of economic importance, the growth habit (annual or perennial), the market needs or uses, the maturity pattern, and others. Peppers are harvested differently from apples. Potatoes are dug up (they have underground tubers of economic importance), whereas oranges are picked (they have fruits borne above ground on branches). In harvesting annuals, the whole plant may be cut or destroyed in the process without any consequence to the enterprise as a whole. On the other hand, when harvesting perennial crops such as apples and oranges, one must be careful to leave the trees healthy for production in subsequent years. The same crop may be harvested in two different ways for two different target markets. High-premium produce for the table is harvested with great care (e.g., handpicked), whereas produce for canning can have bruises and cracks without any adverse consequences. Some cultivars are determinate in growth habit and therefore exhibit even maturity and ripening. In other cultivars and certain species, the product matures at different times and hence requires multiple rounds of harvesting. Growers devise harvesting strategies to suit various production operations in order to cut costs.

27.2.1 PREPARING TO HARVEST

It would be a shame to invest resources into growing a good crop to maturity only to lose the crop at harvest time. A poor harvesting operation would result in poor-quality produce and a low selling price. The grower should plan the harvesting operation with great care, especially when the enterprise is on a commercial scale. Labor equipment and transportation should be prearranged. Labor should be trained to pick the produce at the right stage (market-harvest) and the proper manner (e.g., plucking, cutting, digging) without bruising the produce. Mechanical injury is reduced by training workers to use the appropriate containers in the best shape (not rough edges of lining), to avoid rough handling (throwing, dropping), and to pack properly. Some produce many be harvested and packed in the field and transported directly to the market. Workers should be trained to sort as they pick and avoid contact with soil. Some products are placed in special market packages. Harvesting equipment should be cleared and readied for the operation.

27.2.2 WHEN TO HARVEST

From a physiological standpoint, a crop is ready for harvesting when it has attained *physiological maturity*. At this stage, no additional dry matter accumulates, even if production inputs are increased. This stage may have readily recognizable signs in some crops. In practice, fresh produce is harvested at *harvest maturity* when it has developed to its optimum stage for marketing or consumption. *Ripening* follows physiological maturity and consists of processes that result in changes such as the fruit's texture, sugar content, flavor, and color. These qualities differ depending on whether the fruits are ripened on the vine or in storage. Generally, while **vine-ripened fruits** are tastier, they are also more prone to rotting. Growers often have ways of determining readiness for harvesting their crops from experience. On certain occasions (e.g., commercial production), special instruments may have to be used for precision to obtain the highest quality of product. For example, the percentage of soluble solids (primarily sugars) is important in fruits such as pear, whereas sugar-acid balance is important in blueberry. In certain crops, color development is critical for premium price; growers may thus delay harvesting until the desired color has developed. In certain fruits, the degree of softness (upon applying a gentle squeeze or thumb pressure) is used to indicate readiness for harvest. In pod crops, the way the pod snaps may indicate maturity.

Sometimes crops are harvested prematurely for certain markets and uses. For example, green beans or peas may be harvested when the pods are only partially filled so that they can be eaten fresh. When the pod matures it becomes too stringy (fibrous) to be desirable for use in this fashion. Fiber development is also not desired in celery. In crops such as banana and others that have to be transported over long distances, harvesting is usually done at physiological maturity but before ripening. The fruits are forced to ripen artificially under a controlled environment (enriched with ethylene gas) to obtain the characteristic bright-yellow color for the market. Most horticultural products are highly perishable and should be harvested and used promptly.

Vine-ripened Fruits
Fruits picked after they are ripe and ready for immediate use.

Apart from developmental readiness for harvesting, the time of harvesting depends on weather conditions and the market demand. Whenever possible, fresh produce should be harvested in the cool of the day (early morning or late afternoon) to reduce desiccation. Harvesting wet produce predisposes it to disease in storage and hence should be avoided. The producer will obtain a high price for the produce if it is sold at a time when demand for it is high. Whereas some crops can be harvested over a protracted period, others (e.g., berries) have a short window during which they must be harvested or risk severe losses. The vagaries of the weather may prohibit timely harvesting of crops. A wet field is not suitable for mechanized farming, and, of course, the produce will be wet.

27.2.3 METHODS OF HARVESTING

Hand harvesting of vegetables varies with the economic parts being harvested and may or may not be aided by a tool. For crops with aboveground economic parts, the stem may be snapped off by hand only (e.g., spinach, broccoli, rape, Brussel sprout) or cut with a knife (cabbage, lettuce). For those with underground parts, they are harvested by pulling (e.g., onion, leek) or digging with a fork (mature bulb of onion, garlic).

Ripe fruits with a natural break-point attachment to the stem of a branch (e.g., apple, tomato) are harvested by first lifting, twisting, and then pulling. Highly located fruits may be picked by using aids such as picking pole. Immature fruits are more delicate and best cut with a sharp knife (e.g., okra, papaya, peppers, zucchini).

Hand harvesters may carry sacks or bags with shoulder or waist sling (e.g., for citrus). Containers should be free from rough lining that can bruise the fresh produce.

Harvesting may be done by hand or as a mechanized operation (Figure 27–1). Several factors are considered in deciding on the appropriate method of harvesting a crop. Some crops offer no choice since machines have not yet been developed for harvesting them. In other cases, the product is so delicate that mechanical harvesting becomes a great challenge and is not cost effective. Where human labor is plentiful and inexpensive, handpicking may be economical. Sometimes the acreage of the crop is too large for hand harvesting to be carried out in a timely fashion. Crops that are commonly machine harvested include corn, tomato, carrot, beet, and potato. In vegetable production, machine-aided hand harvesting is commonly used. Crops such as cauliflower, cabbage, pepper, and broccoli are directly packaged in the field and loaded onto trucks. They are hand harvested and sometimes wrapped and packed in boxes that are then placed on conveyor belts and transported into trucks. Certain crops, such as onion, require some drying or curing in the field after being dug and cut. The harvesting operation is therefore multistage; in the first pass, the vegetables are cut or dug, and in the second, they are picked up and transported. In the production of nuts such as almonds, fruit shakers are used for shaking down the mature fruits, which are then swept into windrows. The rows are picked up by vacuuming into bins.

Hand harvesting is labor intensive, expensive, and slow, but this produce will usually not have cracks or other injuries associated with harvesting by machines. Hand harvesting also allows fruits and other produce to be picked selectively. This approach saves the extra time and cost of cleaning and sorting after harvesting, which is required for certain crops. It is suitable for crops that mature over a protracted period (not all at once), requiring the plant to be visited multiple times during the growing season. Mechanized harvesting, on the other hand, is generally indiscriminate, picking up good and bad fruits along with plant debris. Mechanization is also capital intensive. However, a large acreage can be harvested in a shorter time with mechanization. Further, it reduces the tedium of harvesting crops such as roots and tubers that require digging. Products are more prone to bruising and other physical injuries when mechanically harvested. Plant breeders often breed special cultivars of crops for mechanized harvesting. Mechanized harvesting is also adapted to crops that mature uniformly so that they can be harvested all at once.

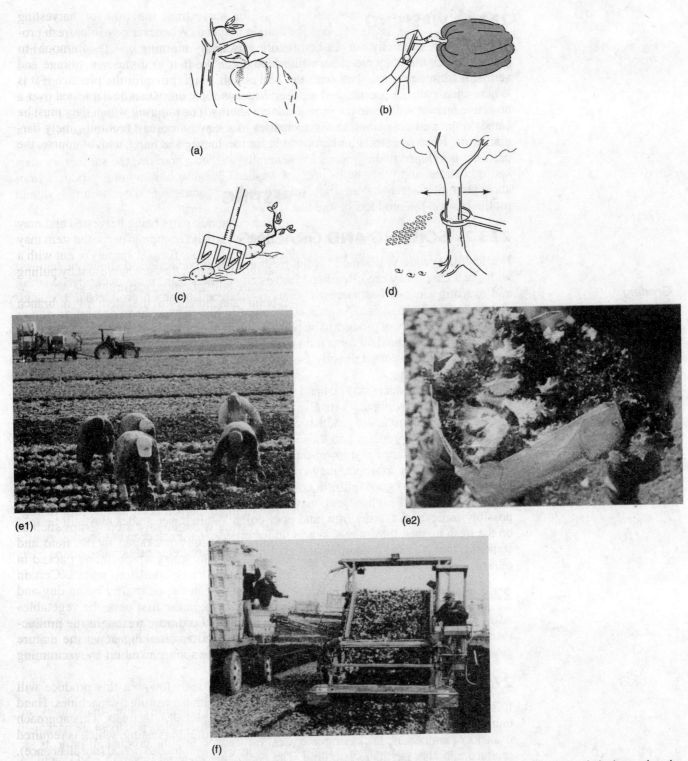

FIGURE 27–1 Some methods of harvesting horticultural produce: (a) handpicking of fruits, (b) harvesting vining fruits by cutting the vine, (c) lifting underground modified structures such as tubers of potato by the potato rake, (d) harvesting nuts by mechanical tree shaker, (e) harvesting lettuce by hand, and (f) harvesting lettuce by machine. (*Source:* For (e) and (f), USDA)

27.3 HANDLING

Before a horticultural product reaches the table or the consumer, it undergoes a number of postharvest handling processes, as described in the following sections.

27.3.1 WASHING

Vegetables are generally not washed before packaging or marketing. They are usually managed such that they are clean while growing in the field (e.g., by mulching to prevent soil from being splashed onto the harvestable parts during rainfall or irrigation). Where chemicals (i.e., pesticides) are used in production, they should be timed such that no active residue will be on the produce at harvesting. The proper waiting period is indicated on the pesticide label. Fruits such as apples may be washed before packaging or marketing. Root vegetables and crops (e.g., carrot, turnip, and beet), whose commercial parts are developed underground, are generally washed to remove the soil before marketing. Onions and other bulbs are not washed. Because horticultural products from aboveground plant parts are not washed before packaging, the consumer should routinely wash the products before use.

27.3.2 SORTING AND GRADING

Grading
The process of assigning products to categories according to predetermined standards.

Warehousing
Holding of products in storage prior to sale.

Horticultural products destined for the fresh market are delicate and should be handled with great care. They are often hand harvested and hence are more expensive. *Sorting* and **grading** are two postharvest operations designed to group products into quality classes for pricing and use. As indicated earlier in this section, hand harvesting allows only a certain quality of product to be picked, and hence sorting and grading may be done in one operation in the field for certain crops. In fact, some products are packaged as they are picked and transported directly from the field to the intended market or consumers, without **warehousing.**

Harvested products may be hand sorted, especially those destined for the fresh market. Mechanized grading units are also used for certain crops. During the process of sorting, defective and immature products are eliminated, as are diseased products. However, cracked or broken products and those with blemishes are removed but not always discarded. They are placed in a lower-quality category or grade and sold at a lower price. Premium grade, for example, may comprise products with no blemishes, uniform in maturity and size, of good uniform color and firm flesh, and with unbruised, clean skin. A lower grade, on the other hand, may have a mixture of sizes, different maturity days, possibly some cracks in the fruit, and poor color. While lower grades may still be sold on the fresh market, they may also be sold for processing. Each crop has its own quality standards that are used for sorting and grading. Fruits are frequently graded on the basis of size.

27.3.3 TREATMENT

After washing, some produce may be given additional cosmetic treatments to enhance their appearance (e.g., waxing) or treatments to protect from diseases and pests (e.g., fungicidal sprays, fumigation). Sprout suppressants may be applied to tubers and root crops.

27.3.4 PACKAGING

It is most convenient to market most fresh produce in quantities rather than individual units. Consequently, many products (e.g., tomato, onions, apples, potatoes) are packaged in sacks or containers. Packaging is critical for transporting the produce. It protects the produce and also facilitates handling. The packaging material is variable and includes wood, plastic, foam, or cardboard. It is desirable that the container is reusable and light weight. Natural materials are less rigid, difficult to clean, and susceptible to collapsing when not staked properly. Molded plastics and wooden crates are easy to clean and stack. Although packaging has obvious advantages, it can be a source of substantial postharvest losses. Rigid containers may have rough sides that may bruise the produce. Improper packing or an unsuitable container type may cause squashing of soft produce. Injury to produce may be caused by dropping and throwing of crates by workers, and shaking during transportation. Improper packing and poor ventilation may cause heat buildup in the container, leading to produce deterioration.

To reduce packaging injury, containers may be lined or individual fruits may be prevented from touching by wrapping each fruit or including loose-filling materials. Only boxes that are rigid should be stacked to avoid collapsing into lower boxes. The boxes or containers should be adequately ventilated to avoid heat and carbon dioxide buildup. The size of containers should be selected for easy handling and for adequate ventilation on inner parts. Separator trays may be used when packing multilayers of produce.

27.3.5 TRANSPORTING TO MARKET

As previously discussed, proper packaging is essential for safe transportation of produce. Fresh produce is best transported in a refrigerated truck or vehicle for long-distance transportation. The container should be stacked safely and prevented from shifting (poor stowage) in transit. Ventilation should be adequate to avoid overheating. Loading of packages onto pallets enhances air circulation.

27.4 POSTHARVEST CHANGES IN PRODUCTS

As mentioned previously, many horticultural products are highly perishable and hence should be handled appropriately to maintain good quality (appearance and condition) for the market. The shelf life of produce is reduced drastically if harvesting occurs under unfavorable conditions. While some crops do not continue ripening after harvest, others do. Products tend to lose moisture from bruises or the point of attachment to the plant, which results in weight loss, wrinkling, and, in extreme cases, shriveling. Fruits that continue to ripen after harvesting (e.g., pear and banana) experience changes in flavor and sugar content (carbohydrates change to sugars), skin color, and softness. Dormancy may be broken in certain crops to initiate sprouting, as is the case in potatoes. If not properly protected, eventually the perishable product begins to rot.

27.5 STORING UNPROCESSED PRODUCTS

Dry products such as nuts and grains store for long periods in dry environments. Fruits and vegetables have a much shorter shelf life, unless preservation measures are taken to prolong it. The storage conditions (especially temperature, humidity, and light) and the kind of crop (regarding quality characteristics and condition at time of storage) affect the duration of storage the crop can withstand before deteriorating (Table 27–1). Even under the best conditions, poor-quality produce deteriorates rapidly. The general goals of storage are to slow the rate of respiration occurring in living tissues, which also slows the rate of microbial activity, and to conserve moisture in the tissues (prevent excessive dehydration). These goals are accomplished by providing the appropriate temperature (usually cool to cold), maintaining good levels of oxygen and carbon dioxide, and controlling humidity. Bruised products respire at a higher rate than intact ones, and the areas around the wounds become discolored. Certain crops have an inherent genetic capacity for prolonged storage. Those with dormancy mechanisms have a reduced respiration rate in storage.

As a general rule, cool-season crops are stored at low temperatures (0 to 10°C or 32 to 50°F) while warm-season crops are stored at warmer temperatures (10 to 12°C or 50 to 54°F). However, sweet corn, a warm-season crop, should not be stored at warm temperatures, which causes sugar to convert to starch, an event that reduces the sweetness of the corn. Instead, sweet corn that is not going to be used soon after harvesting should be placed in cool storage. Fresh fruits and vegetables should be stored at high relative humidity to retain their succulence and general quality. Crops such as lettuce and spinach require higher relative humidity (90 to 95 percent) than crops such as garlic and dry onion (70 to 75 percent).

TABLE 27–1 Selected Vegetables and Fruits and Their Susceptibility to Injury from Cold Temperature When Stored below Freezing

Crop	Susceptibility
Fruits	
Apricot (*Prunus armeniaca*)	VS
Apple (*Pyrus malus*)	MS
Blueberry (*Vaccinium* spp.)	VS
Blackberry (*Rubus argustus*)	VS
Grape (*Vitis* spp.)	MS
Peach (*Prunus persica*)	VS
Plum (*Prunus domestica*)	VS
Squash (*Cucurbita mixta*)	VS
Pear (*Pyrus communis*)	MS
Vegetables	
Asparagus (*Asparagus officinalis*)	VS
Brussels sprouts (*Brassica oleraceae* var. *gemmifera*)	RR
Carrot (with top) (*Daucus carota*)	MS
Cucumber (*Cucumis sativus*)	VS
Celery (*Apium graveolens*)	MS
Cauliflower (*Brassica oleraceae* var. *botrytis*)	MS
Onion (dry) (*Allium cepa*)	MS
Turnip (*Brassica rapa*)	RR
Rutabaga (*Brassica campestris* var. *napobrassica*)	RR
Beet (with top) (*Beta vulgaris*)	RR
Spinach (*Spinacia oleracea*)	MS

VS, very susceptible; MS, moderately susceptible; RR, relatively resistant

Darkness or subdued light should be provided in storage areas. Light may cause products such as potato tubers to green (from the development of chlorophyll). The two general methods of storage for unprocessed products are described in the following sections.

27.5.1 LOW-TEMPERATURE METHODS

Fresh products retain the capacity for certain physiological activities such as respiration. Because respiration produces heat, ventilation in storage is critical for fresh produce to prevent excessive heat buildup, which causes rotting. The respiration rate of crops such as spinach is very high. At a given temperature, strawberries can respire about six times as much as lemons. Temperature is known to affect the rate of respiration; lower temperatures slow biochemical and enzymatic reactions. Temperate or cool-season crops generally tolerate lower temperatures than tropical crops, which are readily injured by cold.

Whether at home or in a commercial setting, the *mechanical refrigerator* is the mechanism for cooling. Refrigerated trucks and containers are used to transport fresh horticultural products over long distances. For products such as cut flowers, strawberry, and lettuce that should be stored dry (no contact with moisture), a *forced-air cooler* system is used to pass cooled air through a stack of the product in a cold room. Some commercial growers use *vacuum cooling* for the direct field packaging of leafy crops. *Package icing* involves the use of slush ice for certain crops. In fall, vegetable produce may be stored outside in earthen mounds or trenches.

The rate of respiration is affected by the concentration of carbon dioxide and oxygen in the environment. Where carbon dioxide levels are very high (low oxygen), respiration slows down. The normal levels of oxygen and carbon dioxide in the air are 21 and 0.03 percent, respectively, nitrogen being 78 percent. Incidentally, in an airtight room full of fresh fruits such as apples, the oxygen soon gets used up in respiration and is replaced by the by-product of respiration (carbon dioxide). As such, after a period in storage, the carbon dioxide level reaches about 21 percent (the previous level of oxygen). At this stage, the fruits respire anaerobically (fermentation), a process that produces alcohol. Fermentation is undesirable, and hence growers should ventilate such a storage room before anaerobic respiration sets in. It has been determined that when the carbon dioxide level is raised, fruits can be stored at high temperatures of 3 to 7°C (37 to 45°F) instead of low temperatures of −1 to 0°C (30 to 32°F).

The gaseous environment during storage can also be enriched with a variety of volatile organic compounds to influence ripening. One of the most common is ethylene, which is used to commercially ripen banana. Bananas are harvested when mature but still green in skin color. When left to ripen on the tree, they split and lose quality in terms of taste and texture. The bunch is cut into "hands" consisting of about 4 to 15 fruits. These are then shipped in polyethylene wraps. At the destination, bananas are kept at temperatures of between 13.5 and 16.5°C (56 and 62°F) and humidity of about 85 to 95 percent. While in this airtight room, 1 percent (1,000 ppm) ethylene gas is introduced for about 24 hours. To initiate ripening, additional ethylene is introduced at the rate of 0.09 cubic meters (3 cubic feet) per 90 cubic meters (3,000 cubic feet) of space. Fruits are ready for sale when they begin to yellow.

Certain fruits produce ethylene naturally as they ripen. Since the gas is harmful to cut flowers, fruits (e.g., apples) should not be stored in the same room with cut flowers. The storage environment should be maintained at an appropriate humidity level to prevent excessive moisture loss from fresh products. High humidity predisposes stored products to decay. A relative humidity of 90 to 95 percent is appropriate for most fruits including apple, banana, pear, and pineapple. In the case of leafy vegetables that are prone to wilting, a high relative humidity of 95 to 100 percent is recommended. Examples of such crops are lettuce, broccoli, celery, and root crops such as carrot and turnip. On the other hand, vegetables such as garlic, dry onion, and pumpkin store better at 75 to 85 percent relative humidity. It is important to maintain good ventilation when manipulating relative humidity to prevent condensation and the accumulation of undesirable gases.

27.5.2 LOW-MOISTURE METHODS

Many crops including grape, plum, date, fig, and apple may be preserved for long periods by drying. **Solar dehydration** is a relatively inexpensive method for drying in areas where a long, dry, and reliable sunny period occurs (Figure 27–2). The product is spread in appropriate containers and exposed to dry and warm air. For more rapid dehydration of large quantities of product, the *forced hot air* method, which involves air heated to 60 to 70°C (140 to 158°F), is used. This method removes water by

Solar Dehydration
Drying of produce by direct energy from the sun.

FIGURE 27–2 Dried grapes between fresh grapes.
(Source: USDA)

dehydration. However, water may also be removed by *sublimation* to ice at temperatures below the freezing point by using the *freeze-drying* method. This method is expensive, but the product quality is restored by rehydration to the level of quality of products stored by freezing. As occurs in cold storage, the oxygen concentration of the storehouse may be reduced by increasing the carbon dioxide concentration. Fresh products stored in conditions of reduced oxygen, as indicated previously, respire slowly and thus deteriorate slowly.

The succulence of fresh products depends on how well they retain their moisture content. A high relative humidity reduces the rate of water loss from plant tissue, but in the presence of high temperature, the combination might encourage the growth and spread of disease-causing organisms. Storage room ventilation ensures that condensation of moisture does not occur, and that harmful gases do not build up.

27.6 TEMPERATURE-INDUCED INJURY

Fresh horticultural products, both ornamentals (e.g., cut flowers) and food (e.g., fruits and vegetables), are stored at a low temperature to slow down deterioration after harvesting. However, extreme temperature is injurious to fresh products, the susceptibility varying widely among products. Freezing is usually not tolerated by fresh produce; it often becomes soft and soggy after thawing. Some products are tolerant of chilling, but not freezing, temperatures, especially temperate species. Symptoms of chilling injury vary among species. They include external discoloration (e.g., browning of skin in banana), pitting (lime, beans, cucumber), internal discoloration (potatoes), abnormal ripening of fruits (tomato, mango), and decay (pumpkins). To avoid low temperature-induced injury, store bananas at 12–14°C (54–57°F), ripe tomatoes at 7–10°C (45–50°F), sweet peppers at 7°C (45°F), potatoes at 4°C (39°F), and oranges at 7°C (45°F). Fresh produce may also be injured by exposure to high temperatures. It is important that freshly harvested field produce be placed in a cool and well-ventilated environment to avoid scorching by the sun.

27.7 FUMIGATION

Storage of dry grain and fruits, such as grapes and citrus, benefits from fumigation to rid the environment of rodents, insect pests, and decay-causing organisms. One of the widely used fumigants is methyl bromide, which is effective against insects in storage houses. Sulfur dioxide is used to protect grapes from decay.

27.8 PROCESSING OF HORTICULTURAL PRODUCTS

27.8.1 FREEZING

One of the quickest and most commonly used methods of crop product preservation is *quick freezing,* whereby a fresh product is kept in a freezer. The main disadvantage of this method is the damage it causes to the physical or structural integrity of some products. For example, frozen tomato does not remain firm after thawing but assumes a soft texture; consequently, use of the product may be limited by freezing. For best results, freezing should be done rapidly. Slow freezing causes larger ice crystals to form in the cells of the tissue and ruptures them. These large reservoirs of water in fractured cells give frozen products a soft texture upon thawing. Rapid freezing results in tiny crystals that do not rupture cells. Quick freezing temperatures are around −22.3°C (−10°F).

Stored produce may lose some color, flavor, and nutrients. To protect against dehydration, products to be frozen must be packaged (e.g., in plastic wrap). Failure to do so will lead to *freezer burn*, resulting from sublimation of water to ice, with adverse consequences such as deterioration of flavor, color, and texture.

27.8.2 CANNING

A common household processing method is the preservation of products in sterilized water. *Canning* is another method used in processing (Figure 27–3). After placing the products in airtight or hermetically sealed containers, they are sterilized in a pressure cooker. Instead of using water, *brine* (a salt solution) may be used to process vegetables such as onion, beet, and pepper. The intense heat used in sterilization changes some quality traits such as color, texture, and flavor, as well as nutritional value. Low-acid products (pH 4.5 to 7.0) such as vegetables require very high temperatures for sterilization to kill the bacteria that cause food poisoning *(Clostridium botulinum)*. Canned products can stay in good condition for several years. However, because heat treatment does not kill all bacteria, spoilage sets in after some time in storage. The salt in canning corrodes the can and reduces the shelf life. Likewise, humidity and high temperatures accelerate spoilage.

27.8.3 FERMENTATION

Fermentation involves bacteria that decompose carbohydrates anaerobically. Some of the products of fermentation prevent the growth of bacteria. The products differ according to the organism, conditions, and duration of the process. Fermentation may produce alcohol and lactic acid, products that affect the flavor of fermented foods. Alcohol may further ferment to produce vinegar. Certain fruit juices are deliberately fermented to produce alcoholic beverages (e.g., grape juice becomes wine). A special fermentation process involving the use of salt is called **pickling.** Vegetables that are pickled include cucumber, onion, cauliflower, and tomato; pickled cabbage is called *sauerkraut.* Instead of using bacteria in pickling, pickles may be produced by placing products directly in citric acid or vinegar.

Pickling
Fermentation of produce in high concentration salt.

27.8.4 PROCESSING WITH SUGAR

High concentrations of sugar may be used to process certain fruit products. The sugar increases the osmotic pressure to a degree that prohibits microbial activity and thereby reduces spoilage opportunities. Different fruit products may be preserved in this way. When fruit juice is used, the product is called *jelly.* *Jam* involves concentrated fruit, while *marmalade* is sugar-processed citrus fruit and rind. When whole fruits are used, the product is called a *preserve.*

FIGURE 27–3 Preservation of fruits. Fruits are processed to varying degrees in canning. They may be ground into sauce, diced, sliced, or canned whole. *(Source: George Acquaah)*

Intermediaries
*Persons who provide
services that link the
producer to the consumer.*

Add Value
*The processing of raw
products into secondary
products, the latter being
more expensive than the
former.*

Marketing in its simplest form entails the supply of satisfactory products by a producer to a consumer at a price acceptable to both. In more advanced market economies (and even in less advanced ones), where division of labor occurs, a host of service providers (called **intermediaries**) operate between the producer and the consumer. The services provided include packaging, storage, transportation, financing, and distribution. Sometimes the fresh product changes in nature between the farm gate and the consumer's door, as is the case when intermediaries **add value** to the product by processing it into other secondary products. In spite of the activities of intermediaries, some growers deal directly with consumers. Notwithstanding the mechanics of marketing, certain general principles and characteristics of a horticultural enterprise should be well understood:

1. Horticultural products are highly perishable; they lose quality rapidly.
2. Many horticultural products are bulky to transport.
3. Prices for horticultural products are not stable.
4. Some storage may be required in a production enterprise.
5. It is important to identify a market before producing horticultural products.

Ultimately, the market is the most critical consideration in a crop production enterprise. Growers should not grow what they cannot sell, since horticultural products are highly perishable. Marketing alternatives should be discussed *before* production starts. The various marketing methods are described in the following sections.

Two basic marketing alternatives are available to the producer—direct marketing and nondirect marketing. Either one has advantages and disadvantages.

27.9.1 DIRECT MARKETING

The producer may market produce directly to consumers via one of several alternative mechanisms, the common ones being pick-your-own, roadside sales, and farmers' markets. The producer interacts with customers on a one-on-one basis and should be ready to provide honest and convincing information about the operation.

Pick-Your-Own

In pick-your-own (U-pick) operations, consumers go to the farm where they harvest their own produce (usually fruits and vegetables) and present the produce to the farmer for pricing. Pricing may be on a weight, volume, or count basis, depending on the produce. To be successful, the crop should mature uniformly and be of very high quality, and the farm should be located near potential customers. It is advantageous if the farmer produces different varieties of the crop or different crops so that customers have choices. Consumers patronize this system of marketing for the high quality of fresher produce they expect.

The layout of the farm should facilitate easy and safe movement of customers. Some fruits may require some supervision for proper and safe harvesting by customers. The sale should be advertised to the public through local newspapers, fliers, radio, and so on. The most effective advertisement is probably by word-of-mouth from satisfied customers. Signs should be placed near roadsides and sometimes throughout the farm to direct customers. Furthermore, adequate parking should be available for customers.

Proper pricing is critical to the success of such an operation. Customers expect to pay less than they would pay in grocery stores because they are aware that overhead cost is low (no transportation cost, no labor for harvesting, no packaging, no intermediaries, no storage costs, etc.). However, if the quality of produce is excellent, the farmer can obtain a high price for it. Some farmers allow some haggling, whereas others are firm with pricing. When selling by volume, it is advantageous to provide containers to customers, even though some will find a way to overfill a container.

The checkout station should be readily visible to customers and provide some storage space since some customers may make several trips to the field. It may help to have chairs and tables for weary customers to rest. For a large operation, farm assistants should be available to assist customers. The disadvantages of pick-your-own include liability for accidents assumed by the producer, and the need to work long hours during harvesting season. Inclement weather would prevent an open field sale from taking place.

Roadside Sale

Heavy traffic may create congestion and discourage some potential customers from stopping to buy items. Weekends (when people are not hurrying to or from the workplace) may attract more customers. Furthermore, locating the operation along roads with low or moderate speed limits (35–50 mph) will be safer for drivers to pull over and will attract more customers. The produce should be attractively displaced to draw customers. Sales increase when a diversity of products are offered for sale. Prepackaging of produce diminishes from the fresh-farm image of roadside marketing.

Farmers' Market

Farmers' markets are owned by a grower organization, community development groups, or a state or local government. The partners in the operation share operating costs (insurance, advertising, facilities, etc.). Consumers associate farmers' markets with lower prices, fresh produce, and high-quality produce. Unlike pick-your-own, the business hours of farmers' markets are set by the coordinator or organizer. The produce should be competitively priced since there may be other producers selling the same produce.

27.9.2 NONDIRECT MARKETING

In nondirect marketing, the producer reaches the consumer through a third party that may include terminal market firms, wholesalers, brokers, processors, cooperatives, private packing companies, and buyers for retail outlets.

Terminal Market Firms

Terminal market firms purchase produce for chain stores or large wholesalers. They are usually interested in doing business with producers who can supply large volumes of consistently high-quality produce. However, they have specific stipulations concerning product quality, quantity, and packing. Furthermore, because prices are based on current retail prices, the prices they pay for produce are variable. Producers are also responsible for delivering produce to the designated terminal market.

Brokers

Brokers are agents, individuals, or firms that negotiate sales contracts between producers (sellers) and buyers, without taking physical custody of the produce. The producer retains responsibility for most of the marketing functions (grading, handling, packing). The broker (selling or buying) locates the produce of desired quality and quantity at a price acceptable to both seller and buyer and arranges the appropriate contract. Though brokers may be involved in invoicing and collecting payments, they are not responsible for payment if the buyer defaults on the contract.

Processors

Processors add value to fresh produce. They often purchase large amounts of produce. They contract some of their needs to growers. The producer has the advantage of an assured sale of large quantities of produce. Often, the processor provides some technical expertise to the producer to ensure that the desired produce quality is attained. On the other hand, the producer is expected to supply a produce at a specified time and quality, demands that may be hard to satisfy all the time.

Cooperatives

Producers of specific produce may join together to form cooperatives for collective bargaining for high prices and guarantee of markets. Members are able to benefit from the use of communal equipment and facilities (e.g., for harvesting, grading, storage, and transportation), some of which they could not afford on their own. By coming together, small producers are able to pool their outputs to satisfy the needs of processors and other purchasers of large quantities.

Whereas cooperatives provide bargaining power for producers, the producers lose their independence to sell for better prices when consumers demand changes. Furthermore, the more efficient producers subsidize the less experienced producers, not being able to receive the optimum returns for their produce.

27.9.3 RETAIL OUTLETS

Retailers usually service relatively smaller markets such as schools, hotels, and prisons. The produce may not require special packaging prior to delivery. Some of these customers may be niche markets that are counted and developed over time (Figure 27–4).

27.10 THE ROLE OF INTERMEDIARIES IN MARKETING

Pick-your-own and roadside sales provide customers direct access to the grower. The product is usually fresh, and the cost is generally lower to the buyer because the grower has less overhead to pass on to consumers. A grower's operation may not be equipped to service individual customers, a role filled by intermediaries. Intermediaries, acting as intermediaries, help in distributing products to customers over a large area. They provide warehousing and storage facilities and transportation that the grower may not have the resources to own or manage. Some intermediaries are processors who are able to preserve the fresh product, thereby extending its shelf life. Because of the added value to fresh farm products, the resulting products usually sell for much higher prices.

FIGURE 27–4 Fresh and dried fruits are sold in small quantities or individually by retailers. *(Source: George Acquaah)*

(a)   (b)

FIGURE 27–5 Horticultural produce is packaged in a variety of ways: (a) fresh or (b) processed.   *(Source: George Acquaah)*

27.11 ELEMENTS OF MARKETING

Marketing is a very complex and involved operation. To be successful in marketing agricultural products, the following should be considered:

1. *Packaging.* Many horticultural products are delicate and bruise easily and thus should be packaged or assembled in appropriate containers whenever they are moved or transported. Because some items do not tolerate being piled one upon the other or touching and rubbing against each other, they may be wrapped individually. A variety of packaging materials are available for use (Figure 27–5). Agricultural products for processing may be delivered without packaging; for example, tomatoes may be delivered by the truckload directly to processing plants.

2. *Storage.* Proper storage is required at various stages in the marketing process. Anytime the product will not be sold immediately, storage is necessary to preserve quality at least until it is sold. When fresh products have to be moved over long distances, special provisions should be made for storage in transit. In terms of storage conditions, some products simply need adequate ventilation so that heat does not build up in the package. Processed products (e.g., canned foods) often do not require refrigeration but should be stored in a cool, dry place.

3. *Transportation.* Mechanically refrigerated vehicles, containers, and the like are used to transport fresh products over long distances by road, rail, water, and air.

4. *Distribution.* An effective and efficient distribution network is critical to marketing success. Marketing thrives on supply and demand principles. Products should be moved in a timely fashion to where they are needed when they are needed. Retail chains aid in the distribution of products. To keep products fresh, suppliers are first sought in an area close to the customers.

5. *Financing.* Financing is required not only for marketing but also for the entire production operation. Horticultural crop production is a high-risk operation since products are perishable and cannot be stored for long periods of time. Prices are also unstable in this industry.

SUMMARY

Many horticultural products such as vegetables are perishable and should be used soon after harvesting or as appropriate. Products that are destined for the market may be washed, especially underground parts or tree fruits that were sprayed with pesticides before harvesting. Since crop products do not usually have identical features, the grower often has to sort and grade them into quality classes. During transportation or holding (warehousing) before sale, horticultural products often are stored under cold temperature conditions using mechanical refrigerators or air coolers, for example. Some products may be processed by solar dehydration or freeze-drying, pickling or canning, or other methods of preservation. Those who grow crops with the intention of selling have several options in terms of marketing strategies, including U-pick or self-harvest enterprises, truck or roadside marketing, farmers' markets, or wholesale operations. Marketing is complex, involving packaging, storage, transportation, and distribution.

REFERENCES AND SUGGESTED READING

Davis, D. C. 1980. *Moisture control and storage systems for vegetable crops.* In Drying and storage of agricultural crops, edited by C. W. Hall. Westport, Conn.: AVI Publishing.

Finney, E. E., Jr., ed. 1981. *CRC handbook of transportation and marketing in agriculture,* Vol. I. *Food commodities.* Boca Raton, Fla.: CRC Press.

O'Brien, M., B. F. Cargill, and R. B. Friedley. 1983. *Principles and practices for harvesting and handling of fruits and nuts.* Westport, Conn.: AVI Publishing.

Peleg, K. 1985. *Produce handling, packaging, and distribution.* Westport, Conn.: AVI Publishing.

Penson, J., R. Pope, and M. Cook. 1986. *Introduction to agricultural economics.* Englewood Cliffs, N.J.: Prentice Hall.

OUTCOMES ASSESSMENT

1. Explain why horticultural products like spinach and lettuce require higher relative humidity that dry onion and garlic while in storage.
2. Describe how high temperature in storage affects the quality of freshly harvested sweet corn.
3. Describe how deterioration of freshly harvested produce, due to respiration, can be reduced.
4. Explain why quick freezing is not recommended for produce such as fresh tomato.
5. Describe the operation of sorting and grading in horticultural crop production.

APPENDIX A

Temperature: Converting between Celsius and Fahrenheit Scales

°C	Known Temperature (°C or °F)	°F	°C	Known Temperature (°C or °F)	°F
−73.33	−100	−148.0	5.00	41	105.8
−70.56	−95	−139.0	5.56	42	107.6
−67.78	−90	−130.0	6.11	43	109.4
−65.00	−85	−121.0	6.67	44	111.2
−62.22	−80	−112.0	7.22	45	113.0
−59.45	−75	−103.0	7.78	46	114.8
−56.67	−70	−94.0	8.33	47	116.6
−53.89	−65	−85.0	8.89	48	118.4
−51.11	−60	−76.0	9.44	49	120.2
−48.34	−55	−67.0	10.0	50	122.0
−45.56	−50	−58.0	10.6	51	123.8
−42.78	−45	−49.0	11.1	52	125.6
−40.0	−40	−40.0	11.7	53	127.4
−37.23	−35	−31.0	12.2	54	129.2
−34.44	−30	−22.0	12.8	55	131.0
−31.67	−25	−13.0	13.3	56	132.8
−28.89	−20	−4.0	13.9	57	134.6
−26.12	−15	5.0	14.4	58	136.4
−23.33	−10	14.0	15.0	59	138.2
−20.56	−5	23.0	15.6	60	140.0
−17.8	0	32.0	16.1	61	141.8
−17.2	1	33.8	16.7	62	143.6
−16.7	2	35.6	17.2	63	145.4
−16.1	3	37.4	17.8	64	147.2
−15.6	4	39.2	18.3	65	149.0
−15.0	5	41.0	18.9	66	150.8
−14.4	6	42.8	19.4	67	152.6
−13.9	7	44.6	20.0	68	154.4
−13.3	8	46.4	20.6	69	156.2
−12.8	9	48.2	21.1	70	158.0
−12.2	10	50.0	21.7	71	159.8
−11.7	11	51.8	22.2	72	161.6
−11.1	12	53.6	22.8	73	163.4
−10.6	13	55.4	23.3	74	165.2
−10.0	14	57.2	23.9	75	167.0
−9.44	15	59.0	24.4	76	168.8
−8.89	16	60.8	25.0	77	170.6
−8.33	17	62.6	25.6	78	172.4

(continued)

Temperature: Converting between Celsius and Fahrenheit Scales (continued)

°C	Known Temperature (°C or °F)	°F	°C	Known Temperature (°C or °F)	°F
−7.78	18	64.4	26.1	79	174.2
−7.22	19	66.2	26.7	80	176.0
−6.67	20	68.0	27.2	81	177.8
−6.11	21	69.8	27.8	82	179.6
−5.56	22	71.6	28.3	83	181.4
−5.00	23	73.4	28.9	84	183.2
−4.44	24	75.2	29.4	85	185.0
−3.89	25	77.0	30.0	86	186.8
−3.33	26	78.8	30.6	87	188.6
−2.78	27	80.6	31.1	88	190.4
−2.22	28	82.4	31.7	89	192.2
−1.67	29	84.2	32.2	90	194.0
−1.11	30	86.0	32.8	91	195.8
−0.56	31	87.8	33.3	92	197.6
0	32	89.6	33.9	93	199.4
0.56	33	91.4	34.4	94	201.2
1.11	34	93.2	35.0	95	203.0
1.67	35	95.0	35.6	96	204.8
2.22	36	96.8	36.1	97	206.6
2.78	37	98.6	36.7	98	208.4
3.33	38	100.4	37.2	99	210.2
3.89	39	102.2	37.8	100	212.0
4.44	40	104.0			

To make conversions not included in the table use the following formulas:
1. °F = (9/5 × °C) + 32
2. °C = 5/9(°F − 32)

APPENDIX B

Metric Conversion Chart

Known	Multiplier	Desired
Length		
inches	2.54	centimeters
feet	30	centimeters
feet	0.303	meters
yards	0.91	meters
miles	1.6	kilometers
Area		
square inches	6.5	square centimeters
square feet	0.09	square meters
square yards	0.8	square meters
square miles	2.6	square kilometers
acres	0.4	hectares
Mass (Weight)		
ounces	28	grams
pounds	0.45	kilograms
short tons	0.9	metric tons
Volume		
teaspoons	5	milliliters
tablespoons	15	milliliters
fluid ounces	30	milliliters
cups	0.24	liters
pints	0.47	liters
quarts	0.95	liters
gallons	3.8	liters
cubic feet	0.03	cubic meters
cubic yards	0.76	cubic meters
Pressure		
pounds per square inch	0.069	bars
atmospheres	1.013	bars
atmospheres	1.033	kilograms per square centimeter
pounds per square inch	0.07	kilograms per square centimeter
Rates		
pounds per acre	1.12	kilograms per hectare
tons per acre	2.24	metric tons per hectare

English Units Conversion Chart

Known	Multiplier	Desired
Length		
millimeters	0.04	inches
centimeters	0.4	inches
meters	3.3	feet
kilometers	0.62	miles
Area		
square centimeters	0.16	square inches
square meters	1.2	square yards
square kilometers	0.4	square miles
hectares	2.47	acres
Mass (Weight)		
grams	0.035	ounces
kilograms	2.2	pounds
metric tons	1.1	short tons
Volume		
milliliters	0.03	fluid ounces
liters	2.1	pints
liters	1.06	quarts
liters	0.26	gallons
cubic meters	35	cubic feet
cubic meters	1.3	cubic yards
Pressure		
bars	14.5	pounds per square inch
bars	0.987	atmospheres
kilograms per square centimeter	0.968	atmospheres
kilograms per square centimeter	14.22	pounds per square inch
Rates		
kilograms per hectare	0.892	pounds per acre
metric tons per hectare	0.445	tons per acre

Common and Scientific Names of Selected Plants

Agave (*Agave* spp.)

Ageratum (*Ageratum houstonianum*)

Aglaonema (*Aglaonema simplex*)

Air plant (*Kalanchoe* spp.)

Almond (*Prunus amygdalus*)

Amaryllis (*Hippeastrum* spp.)

Apple (*Pyrus malus*)

Apricot (*Prunus armeniaca*)

Artichoke, Jerusalem (*Helianthus tuberosus*)

Ash (*Fraximus* spp.)

Aspen (*Populus tremuloides*)

Aster (*Callistephus chinensis*)

Avocado (*Persea americana*)

Azalea (*Rhododendron* spp.)

Baby's breath (*Gypsophila paniculata*)

Bamboo (*Bambusa* spp.)

Banana (*Musa paradisiaca*)

Basil (*Ocimum basilicum*)

Bay, sweet (*Laurus nobilis*)

Bean, broad (*Vicia faba*)

Bean, garden (*Phaseolus vulgaris*)

Bean, lima (*Phaseolus lunatus*)

Beech (*Fagus sylvatica, B. grandifolia*)

Beet, sugar (*Beta vulgaris*)

Begonia (*Begonia socotrana*)

Bentgrass, colonial (*Agrostis tenuis*)

Bentgrass, creeping (*Agrostis palustris*)

Birch (*Betula papyrifera*)

Bird-of-paradise (*Strelitzia reginae*)

Blackberry (*Rubus* spp.)

Bleeding heart (*Dicentra* spp.)

Blueberry (*Vaccinium* spp.)

Bluegrass, Kentucky (*Poa pratensis*)

Bougainvillea (*Bougainvillea spectablis*)

Boxwood, common (*Buxus semperivirens*)

Broccoli (*Brassica oleracea* var. *botrytis*)

Browallia (*Browallia* spp.)

Brussels sprouts (*Brassica oleracea* var. *gemmifera*)

Buffalo grass (*Buchloe dactyloides*)

Buttercup (*Ranunculus* spp.)

Cabbage (*Brassica oleracea*)

Camellia (*Camellia japonica*)

Canna lily (*Canna indica*)

Canterbury bells (*Campanula medium*)

Carnation (*Dianthus caryophyllus*)

Carpetgrass (*Axonopus affinis*)

Catnip (*Nepeta cataria*)

Cauliflower (*Brassica oleracea* var. *botrytis*)

Celery (*Apium graveolens*)

Century plant (*Agave* spp.)

Cherry (*Prunus avium*)

Chestnut (*Castanea* spp.)

Christmas cactus (*Zygocactus truncatus*; *Schlumbergera* hybrids)

Christmas flower (*Euphorbia pulcherrima*)

Chrysanthemum (*Chrysanthemum* spp.)

Cinnamon (*Cinnamomum zeylanicum*)

Citrus (*Citrus* spp.)

Clematis (*Clematis hybrida*)

Coleus (*Coleus blumei*)

Columbine (*Aquilegia* spp.)

Compass plant (*Lactuca serriola*)

Corn (*Zea mays*)
Corn plant (*Dracaena fragrans* 'Massangeana')
Cosmos (*Cosmos* spp.)
Cotoneaster (*Cotoneaster congesta*)
Cottonwood (*Populus deltoides*)
Crab apple (*Crataegus* spp.)
Cranberry (*Vaccinium macrocarpus*)
Crocus, autumn (*Cochicum autumnale*)
Croton (*Codiaeium variegatum*)
Cucumber (*Cucumis sativus*)
Cyclamen (*Cyclamen* spp.)
Cypress, bald (*Taxodium distichum*)
Daffodil (*Narcissus* spp.)
Dahlia (*Dahlia variabilis*)
Daisy (*Dimorphotheca* spp.)
Dandelion (*Taraxacum officinale*)
Daphne (*Daphne odora*)
Daylily (*Hermerocallis* spp.)
Dill (*Anethum graveolens*)
Dogwood (*Cornus* spp.)
Dumbcane (*Dieffenbachia exotica*)
Echeveria (*Echeveria secunda*)
Eggplant (*Solanum melongena*)
Elephant ears (*Colocasia* spp.)
Elm (*Ulmus* spp.)
Fatshedera (*Fatshedera lizei*)
Fern, asparagus (*Asparagus densiflorus* 'Sprengeri')
Fern, Boston (*Nephrolepis exaltata*)
Fig, common (*Ficus carica*)
Fir, Douglas (*Pseudotsuga menziesii*)
Foxglove (*Digitalis purpurea*)
Gardenia (*Gardenia jasminoides*)
Geranium (*Geranium* spp.; *Pelargonium* spp.)
Ginger (*Zingiber officinale*)
Gladiolia (*Gladiolus* spp.)
Globe amaranth (*Gomphrena globosa*)
Gloxinia (*Sinningia speciosa*)
Gooseberry (*Ribes* spp.)
Grape (*Vitis* spp.)
Grapefruit (*Citrus paradisi*)
Hazelnut (*Corylus* spp.)
Holly, American (*Ilex opaca*)
Horseradish (*Rorippa armoracia*)
Hosta (*Hosta undulata*)

Hyacinth (*Hyacinthus* spp.)
Impatiens (*Impatiens walleriana*)
Iris (*Iris* spp.)
Ivy, English (*Hedera helix*)
Jade plant (*Crassula argentea*)
Juniper (*Juniperus* spp.)
Kohlrabi (*Brassica oleracea* var. *caulorapa*)
Lantana (*Lantana camara*)
Larkspur (*Delphinium* spp.)
Lavender (*Lavandula officinalis*)
Lemon (*Citrus limon*)
Lettuce (*Lactuca sativa*)
Lily (*Lilium* spp.)
Lily of the valley (*Convallaria majalis*)
Lime (*Citrus aurantifolia*)
Lombardy poplar (*Poplus nigra*)
Magnolia (*Magnolia* spp.)
Maple (*Acer* spp.)
Marigold (*Tagetes* spp.)
Marjoram (*Majorana hortensis*)
Medicine plant (*Aloe vera*)
Melon (*Cucumis melo*)
Mistletoe (*Phoradendron* spp.)
Morning glory (*Ipomoea* spp.)
Moss, peat (*Sphagnum* spp.)
Moss rose (*Portulaca grandiflora*)
Mustard (*Brassica campestris*)
Nasturtium (*Tropaeolum* spp.)
Norfolk Island pine (*Araucaria excelsa*)
Oak (*Quercus* spp.)
Olive (*Olea europaea*)
Onion (*Allium cepa*)
Orange (*Citrus sinensis*)
Orchid (*Cattleya* spp.)
Oregano (*Origanum vulgare*)
Palm, coconut (*Cocos nucifera*)
Palm, date (*Phoenix dactylifera*)
Pansy (*Viola tricolor*)
Papaya (*Carica papaya*)
Parsley (*Petroselinum sativum*)
Pea (*Pisum sativum*)
Peach (*Prunus persica*)
Peanut (*Arachis hypogaea*)
Pear (*Pyrus communis*)

Pecan (*Carya illinoensis*)
Peony (*Paeonia* spp.)
Peperomia (*Peperomia* spp.)
Pepper (*Capsicum annuum; C. frutescens*)
Peppermint (*Mentha piperita*)
Periwinkle (*Vinca minor*)
Petunia (*Petunia* spp.)
Phlox (*Phlox* spp.)
Pine (*Pinus* spp.)
Pineapple (*Ananas comosus*)
Pistachio (*Pistacia vera*)
Pitcher plant (*Sarracenia* spp.)
Plum (*Prunus domestica*)
Poinsettia (*Euphorbia pulcherrima*)
Ponytail palm (*Beaucarnea recurvata*)
Potato, Irish (*Solanum tuberosum*)
Potato, sweet (*Ipomea batatas*)
Pothos (*Scindapsus aureus*)
Prayer plant (*Maranta* spp.)
Primrose (*Primula* spp.)
Quince (*Cydonia oblonga*)
Radish (*Raphanus sativus*)
Raspberry (*Rubus* spp.)
Redbud (*Cercis* spp.)
Redwood, coastal (*Sequoia sempervirens*)
Redwood, giant (*Sequoiadendron giganteum*)
Rhododendron (*Rhododendron* spp.)
Rhubarb (*Rheum rhaponticum*)
Rose (*Rosa* spp.)
Rose of Sharon (*Hibiscus syriacus*)
Rosemary (*Rosmarinus officinalis*)
Rubber plant (*Ficus elastica*)
Rutabaga (*Rutabaga campestris* var. *napobrassica*)
Sage (*Salvia officinalis*)

Sedge (*Carex* spp.)
Shasta daisy (*Chrysanthemum maximum*)
Snake plant (*Sansevieria trifasciata*)
Snapdragon (*Antirrhinum majus*)
Snowplant (*Sarcodes sanguinea*)
Spiderflower (*Cleome* spp.)
Spider plant (*Chlorophytum comosum*)
Spinach (*Spinacia oleracea*)
Spruce (*Picea* spp.)
Squash (*Cucurbita mixta; C. pepo*)
Saint Augustine grass (*Stenotaphtum secundatum*)
Statice (*Limonium* spp.)
Sugarcane (*Saccharum officinarum*)
Sunflower (*Helianthus annuus*)
Sweet alyssum (*Lobularia* spp.)
Sycamore (*Platanus* spp.)
Thyme (*Thymus vulgaris*)
Tomato (*Lycopersicon esculentum*)
Tulip (*Tulipa* spp.)
Turnip (*Brassica rapa*)
Velvet plant (*Gynura sarmentosa*)
Verbena (*Verbena hortensis*)
Violet, African (*Saintpaulia* spp.)
Walnut (*Juglans* spp.)
Wandering Jew (*Zebrina pendula*)
Watermelon (*Citrullus vulgaris*)
Willow (*Salix* spp.)
Wisteria (*Wisteria sinensis*)
Yam (*Dioscorea* spp.)
Yew (*Taxus* spp.)
Zebra plant (*Aphelandra squarrosa; Equus zebra*)
Zinnia (*Zinnia elegans*)
Zoysiagrass (*Zoysia japonica*)

Selected Botanical Gardens and Arboreta

Arnold Arboretum

Stephen F. Austin State University Arboretum

Bartram's Garden

The Botanical Research Institute of Texas

Brooklyn Botanical Garden

Harlow Carr Botanical Gardens, Harrogate, UK

Chanticleer Garden

Dallas Arboretum

University of California Davis Arboretum

The Dawes Arboretum

University of Delaware Botanic Garden

Fairchild Tropical Garden

Filoli House

Garfield Park Conservatory

Gray Herbarium, Harvard University

Holden Arboretum

Botanical Gardens of Leiden, Netherlands

Harry P. Leu Gardens, Orlando

Longwood Gardens

McLaughlin Garden

Memphis Botanical Garden

Moody Gardens

Missouri Botanical Garden

Myriad Botanical Garden

U.S. National Arboretum

University of Nebraska Botanic Garden and Arboretum

J.C. Raulston Arboretum, North Carolina
State University

Royal Botanic Gardens at Kew

Rhode Island Agricultural Experimental Station Virtual
Gardens

Royal Botanical Gardens, Canada

Smith College Botanic Garden

South Carolina Botanical Garden, Clemson University

Daniel Stowe Botanical Garden

Boyce Thompson Southwestern Arboretum

Tracy Herbarium

Tuscon Botanical Gardens

The Wichita Gardens

Zilker Botanical Garden

Source: Extracted from http://aggie-horticulture.tamu.edu/introhtml/botgard.html

GLOSSARY

A

Abaxial Turned away from the base or away from the axis (also dorsal).

Abscisic acid Plant hormone that induces abscission and dormancy and inhibits seed germination, among other plant responses.

Abscission The dropping of leaves, fruits, flowers, or other plant parts.

Absorption The uptake of materials by a plant or seed, such as water or nutrients by the roots or pesticide and fertilizer through the leaves.

Accent plant A plant used to create interest in a landscape by calling attention to a particular feature of an area.

Acid loving Plants that grow best in acidic potting media or soil.

Active growth A phase of the plant life cycle characterized by rapid stem lengthening and leaf production and sometimes flowering or fruiting.

Active ingredient The ingredient in a pesticide that determines its effectiveness.

Adaptation The process of change in structure or function of an individual or population due to environmental changes.

Adaxial Turned toward the apex or the axis (also ventral).

Adhesion The molecular attraction of liquids to solids, such as the attraction of water to soil particles.

Adventitious bud A bud produced on a part of a plant where it is not expected, such as on a leaf vein or root.

Adventitious root A root produced by a part of the plant other than seminal tissues, such as from the stem.

Aeration As pertaining to the soil, it is the movement of air from the atmosphere into and through the soil.

Aggregation The clinging together of soil particles to form larger units such as clods and clumps.

Agronomy The art and science of producing crops and managing the soil.

Air layering The rooting of a branch or top of a plant while it is still attached to the parent.

Algae A single-cell plant that often grows in colonies.

Allele An alternative form of a gene; one of a pair of genetic factors that occur at the same locus on homologous chromosomes.

Allelopathy The injury of one plant of one species by another through excretion of toxic chemicals by the roots.

Amendment A substance added to soil to alter its properties to make it more suitable for plant growth.

Amino acids The building blocks of proteins, each having the basic formula NH_2-CHR-COOH.

Anaerobic An environment deficient in oxygen.

Anatomy The internal structure of an organism.

Angiosperm A flowering plant or a plant that produces its seeds in ovaries.

Annual A plant that completes its life cycle in one year (grows, flowers, produces seed, and dies in one cropping season).

Antagonism The opposing action of different chemicals such that the action of one is impaired or the total effect is less than that of one acting separately.

Anther A saclike, pollen-producing portion of the stamen, usually found on top of the filament.

Anthocyanin Found in vacuoles of the cell, this water-soluble pigment is responsible for a variety of red to blue colors found in plant parts (fruits, leaves, and flowers).

Apical dominance Growth regulation in plants where auxins secreted by the terminal bud inhibit the growth of lateral buds on the same shoot.

Apomixis The asexual production of seed without fertilization.

Arboretum A place where trees are grown for educational and research purposes.

745

Arboriculture The science of growing and caring for ornamental trees.

Asexual reproduction The reproduction of a new plant without the union of male and female sex cells.

Assimilation The transformation of organic and inorganic materials into protoplasm.

Autogamy The pollination of a flower by its own pollen.

Auxin A plant hormone that accelerates growth and is also involved in dormancy, abscission, rooting, tuber formation, and other activities.

Available water The portion of water in the soil that can be readily absorbed by plant roots.

Axil The angle formed on the upper side of a leaf where a petiole joins a stem.

Axillary bud A bud located in a leaf axil.

B

Backcross breeding A cross of a hybrid with one of its parents.

Bactericide A chemical used to control bacterial disease.

Balled and burlapped A tree grown and sold with a ball of soil around its roots and wrapped in burlap.

Band application Applying fertilizer in shallow trenches on each side of a row of plants.

Bare root A tree (deciduous) sold dormant and without soil around its roots.

Basal plate The base of a bulb.

Bed A piece of land or area of soil prepared for planting.

Bench A raised platform for growing plants.

Berm A ridge of soil created around a newly planted tree to retain water.

Berry A simple fleshy fruit derived from a single ovary in which the ovary wall is fleshy.

Biennial A plant that completes its life cycle in two cropping seasons, the first season involving vegetative growth and the second flowering and death.

Binomial nomenclature The system of naming plants developed by Carolus Linnaeus whereby a plant is given a two-part name representing the genus and species.

Biological control The use of a natural enemy to control a pest.

Blanch The practice of improving the quality of a vegetable by excluding light.

Blight A bacterial or fungal disease of plants.

Bolting Rapid production of flower stalks in some herbaceous plants after sufficient chilling or a favorable photoperiod.

Borer An insect that burrows into the stems, roots, leaves, or fruits of a plant.

Bract A modified leaf from whose axil a flower or inflorescence may arise.

Brambles Collectively, the fruits in the genus *Rubus*.

Breeder seed Seed quantity increased by the plant breeder.

Broadcast Scattering of seed or fertilizer uniformly over a given area.

Bud A rudimentary structure consisting of meristematic tissue and a potential to develop into vegetative, reproductive, or a mixture of structures.

Budding The grafting of a bud of one plant onto another plant so that the inserted bud develops into the new shoot.

Bud scales Leaflike structures that cover the outside of a bud.

Bulb An underground storage organ consisting of highly compressed leaves.

Bulblet An immature bulb that develops at the base of a bulb.

C

Callus A mass of parenchyma cells that forms around the wounded area of a plant to start the healing process. It can be artificially induced under tissue culture conditions.

Candle The succulent new growth produced by a needle evergreen plant.

Cane Long shoots or weeping stems such as those produced by grapes and brambles.

Canker A disease that destroys the cambium and vascular tissue of a generally localized area of a plant.

Capillary action The movement of water through micropores of a growing medium owing to the adhesion of water molecules to the medium.

Capillary water The soil water held against gravitational force.

C_3 cycle The Calvin-Benson cycle of photosynthesis, in which the first products after carbon dioxide fixation are three-carbon molecules.

C_4 cycle The Hatch-Slack cycle of photosynthesis, in which the first products after carbon dioxide fixation are four-carbon molecules.

Carbon dioxide fixation The addition of H^1 to CO_2 to yield a chemically stable carbohydrate.

Carotene A yellow plant pigment that is a precursor of vitamin A and gives color to plant parts such as orange fruits.

Carpel Female reproductive organ of flowering plants; one or more carpels may unite to form the pistil.

Caryopsis A one-seeded dry fruit produced by grasses.

Cation exchange capacity (CEC) A measure of the total amount of the ability of a soil to attract and hold nutrients or exchange cations.

Cell pack A plastic container of seedlings in which each seedling has its own root packet.

Cellulose A complex carbohydrate that forms a major part of plant cell walls and provides strength to stems and other parts.

Central leader A training method for trees in which a central axis is maintained.

Certified seed An increase in quantity of foundation seed certified by an approved certifying agency.

Chilling injury Direct and or indirect injury to plants or plant part from exposure to low, but above-freezing temperatures.

Chlorosis A mineral deficiency symptom in which affected plants show yellowish or greenish-yellow coloration in their leaves.

Clay One of the three primary soil particles; it has extremely small particles with colloidal properties.

Climacteric The period in the development of some plant parts involving a series of biochemical changes associated with the natural respiratory rise and autocatalytic ethylene production.

Clod A hard, artificially produced (e.g., by tillage) lump of soil that is difficult to break.

Clone A plant that is asexually propagated from another; both plants are genetically identical.

Cold frame An enclosed, unheated structure covered on top with glass or plastic used to harden off plants or protect tender plants during the early spring.

Cold-hardiness The minimum temperature at which a plant can survive (tolerance).

Cole crop Vegetables of the genus *Brassica*.

Colloid Very fine organic or inorganic particles that are interspersed.

Common name The English name of a plant that may differ in various localities (e.g., maize and corn).

Compaction Excessive packing or settling of a growing medium.

Companion crop A crop planted along with another but harvested separately. The two crops positively impact each other.

Compatibility Ability of different species to be sexually or physically united and grow together as one.

Compensation point (light) The light intensity at which the rates of photosynthesis and respiration are equal.

Complete fertilizer A compound fertilizer containing a mixture of nitrogen, phosphorus, and potassium.

Complete flower A flower with both male and female parts; sexually complete.

Compost A soil amendment consisting primarily of decomposed organic matter.

Compound leaf A leaf composed of more than one distinct leaflet.

Container growing Growing plants to mature size in a container; also called pot gardening.

Cool-season plant A plant species that is frost tolerant and prefers daytime temperatures ranging from 15 to 18°C (60 to 65°F).

Cork cambium The layer of meristematic cells that produces bark on woody plants.

Corm A short, swollen, and vertically growing underground stem that stores food.

Cormel A young offshoot produced by a larger corm.

Corolla The collective term for all petals on a flower.

Cotyledons Leaflike structures at the first node of the seedling stem.

Cover crop A fast-growing crop grown primarily for the purpose of covering a bare soil.

Crop rotation Planting different species of crops in an area in a planned sequence, year after year, to prevent buildup of diseases or insects associated with particular crops.

Cross-pollination The transfer of pollen from the stamen of one flower to the stigma of a flower on another plant.

Crown The root-stem junction of woody plants; also the region at the base of the stem of herbaceous species from which branches or tillers arise.

Cultivar Derived from the words *cultivated* and *variety,* often designating a product of plant breeding.

Cultural control A method of pest control involving manipulation of the growing conditions of the plant.

Cut flower A flower grown for the sole purpose of cutting and displaying in a vase or other arrangement.

Cuticle An impermeable surface layer on the epidermis of plant organs.

Cutting A vegetative plant part used for propagation.

Cytochrome A class of several electron-transport proteins serving as carriers in mitochondrial oxidation and in photosynthesis electron transport.

Cytokinesis The division of the cytoplasmic constituents during cell division.

Cytokinin A naturally occurring plant hormone involved in activities such as cell division, organ initiation, breaking dormancy, and other activities.

Cytoplasm The living material of the cell, exclusive of the nucleus, consisting of a complex protein matrix or gel.

D

Damping-off A disease in which a soilborne fungus attacks seedlings soon after germination at the soil line and kills the plants.

Day-neutral plant A species that flowers regardless of the dark to light ratio.

Deciduous A plant that sheds its leaves in fall.

Decomposition The breakdown or rotting of plants or animals.

Defoliation The dropping of most or all leaves from a plant.

Dehiscence The splitting open of mature pods.

Desuckering The removal of suckers from a plant.

Determinate The growth pattern in which plants remain short (bush) and flower and ripen uniformly within a limited period.

Dethatching Removal of thatch from a turf or lawn.

Dicot A plant having two cotyledons (dicotyledons).

Differentiation The development of one cell to many cells, together with a modification of the new cells for the performance of particular functions.

Dihybrid cross A cross between organisms differing in two specific traits.

Dioecious A species in which the male and female organs of reproduction are produced on separate plants.

Diploid Refers to the two sets of chromosomes in the nucleus of a cell.

Direct seeding Sowing seeds in a permanent growing site.

Disease Any change from the state of metabolism necessary for the normal development and functioning of any organism.

Diurnal Recurring or repeated every day.

Division A method of asexual propagation requiring the cutting and dividing of plants.

Dominant Referring to the gene that, when present in a hybrid with a contrasting gene, completely dominates in the development of the character.

Dormancy A general term denoting a lack of growth of seeds, buds, bulbs, or tubers, due to unfavorable environmental or internal factors.

Drip irrigation A method of watering plants so that only soil in the plant's immediate vicinity is moistened.

Drupe A simple, fleshy fruit derived from one carpel, with a thin exocarp, fleshy mesocarp, and hard endocarp.

Dwarfing rootstock A special rootstock that has the capacity to slow and limit the growth of the scion grafted onto it.

E

Ecology The study of life in relation to its environment.

Emasculate To remove the anthers from a bud or flower before pollen is shed.

Embryo The immature plant in a seed.

Endosperm The part of a seed that serves as a food supply for the young, developing seedling.

Enzyme A chemical that regulates an internal chemical reaction in an organism.

Epicotyl The upper portion of the embryo axis or seedling above the cotyledons and below the first true leaves.

Epidermis The outer layer of plant parts.

Epigeous germination A type of seed germination, characteristic of dicots, in which cotyledons emerge above the soil surface.

Erosion The wearing away of soil caused by agents such as water and wind.

Espalier A method of training trees or shrubs to grow flat against a wall or trellis, sometimes in fancy patterns.

Essential elements The micro- and macronutrients required for plant growth.

Etiolation Tall, spindly growth induced by insufficient light conditions.

Evapotranspiration The total loss of water by evaporation from the soil surface and by transpiration from plants from a given area, and during a specified period of time.

Everbearing Strawberry and raspberry varieties that bear two crops annually.

Evergreen Trees or shrubs that are never entirely leafless.

Exocarp The outermost layer of the fruit wall.

Exogenous Produced outside of, originating from, or because of external causes.

Explant A piece of tissue obtained from part of the plant of interest to be used in tissue culture.

F

Fallow Cropland left idle for one or more seasons for a specific purpose.

Fermentation An anaerobic chemical reaction in foods, such as the production of alcohol from sugar by yeast.

Fertilizer Any substance, organic or inorganic, natural or synthetic in origin, that is added to the soil to supply elements essential to the growth of the plant.

Fertilizer analysis The proportions of essential plant elements (usually nitrogen, phosphorus, and potassium) contained in a fertilizer.

Fibrous roots A highly branched root system without a single dominant axis.

Field capacity Moisture retained by a soil after free drainage under gravity has ceased.

Filament The stalklike part of the stamen or male part of the flower that supports the anther.

Filler flowers Flowers used to fill in the gaps to tie together a floral arrangement to give a complete appearance.

Filler material An inert material added to a fertilizer to increase its volume.

Flat A shallow, oblong-shaped wooden or plastic container used to start seedlings.

Fleshy fruit Any fruit formed from an ovary that has fleshy or pulpy walls at maturity.

Fleshy roots Modified plant roots that store carbohydrates or water.

Floral foam A piece of dense, foamlike material with high water retention used to hold cut flowers in an arrangement.

Floriculture The science and practice of cultivating and arranging ornamental flowering plants.

Flower stalk The stem of the plant that supports the flower.

Foliar application A method of supplying nutrients to plants by spraying the leaves with liquid fertilizer.

Forcing A cultural practice of manipulating plants to flower at times other than their normal growing season.

Form The overall shape of a plant.

Form flower A type of flower with a unique shape such as bird-of-paradise, potea, or orchid.

Formal flower bed A symmetrically designed bed for annual and perennial flowers.

Foundation planting Planting shrubs or ground covers at the base of a house.

Foundation seed Seed stocks increased from breeder seed.

Freestanding bed A bed designed to be accessible from all sides.

Frost hardy Plants that are able to withstand frost.

Frost pocket A low-lying area more susceptible to frost than the surrounding vicinity.

Frost tender Plants that are killed at temperatures below freezing.

Fruit A mature, swollen ovary.

Fumigation Control of insects, disease-causing organisms, weeds or nematodes by gases applied in an enclosed area such as a greenhouse.

Fungicide A chemical used to control a fungus.

Furrow irrigation A method of irrigation by which the water is applied to row crops in ditches.

G

Gall An abnormal swelling on a plant part.

Genetic engineering The manipulation of the genome of an organism by incorporating genes from an alien source.

Genotype The genetic makeup of an individual.

Germination (seed) Sequence of events in a viable seed starting with imbibition of water that leads to growth of the embryo and development of a seedling.

Germination rate The percentage of seeds that will germinate under favorable conditions.

Germplasm The protoplasm of the sexual reproductive cells containing the units of heredity.

Gibberellin A plant hormone that stimulates growth in stem and leaf by cell elongation and also influences vernalization.

Glazing The clear or translucent material used to cover a greenhouse or related plant growing structure.

Grafting The method of asexual propagation in which a branch or bud from one plant is implanted on another.

Grain (caryopsis) A simple, dry, indehiscent fruit with ovary walls fused to the seed.

Gravitational water The water that the soil is unable to hold against the force of gravity.

Green manure crop A fast-growing plant grown for the purpose of turning under the soil before it reaches maturity to provide organic matter in the soil.

Greenhouse effect The heating of the air in an enclosed translucent or transparent structure due to trapped energy from the sun.

Ground cover Low-growing and spreading plants that form matlike growth over an area.

Growing medium A material used for rooting and growing plants.

Growth An irreversible increase in cell size and/or cell number.

Growth regulator A synthetic or natural compound that in low concentrations controls growth responses in plants.

Guard cells Specialized epidermal cells that contain chloroplasts and surround a stoma.

Guttation Exudation of water in liquid form from plants.

Gymnosperm A seed plant with seeds not enclosed by a megasporophyll or pistil.

Gynoceium The female part of a flower or pistil formed by one or more carpels and composed of the stigma, style, and ovary.

H

Haploid Having only one complete set of chromosomes.

Hardening off The cultural practice preceding transplanting whereby plants are acclimatized to field growing conditions by gradually subjecting them to decreasing temperature, moisture, and nutrition.

Hardpan A layer of compacted soil that slows or stops the movement of water.

Hardwood cutting A cutting made from the mature growth of a woody plant, usually taken in late fall or early spring.

Hardy plant A plant adapted to adverse climatic conditions, such as cold temperature, prevailing in the growing area.

Heading back A pruning strategy used to control the size and shape of shrubs by cutting back shoots to the parent branch to encourage new growth.

Heaving The partial lifting of plants out of the ground, frequently breaking their roots, as a result of freezing and thawing of the surface soil during the winter.

Heeling in A method of temporary storage of bare-rooted trees and shrub seedlings before transplanting by covering the roots with soil or some organic matter in a shallow trench.

Herbaceous A plant that does not normally produce woody growth.

Herbaceous cutting A cutting derived from nonwoody plant parts.

Herbicide A chemical used to control weeds.

Heterosis The phenomenon whereby the hybrid of a cross exhibits greater vigor and growth than either parent (hybrid vigor).

Heterozygous Having different genes of a Mendelian pair present in the same cell or organism.

Hill A group of seeds planted close together.

Horizon (soil) A layer of soil, approximately parallel to the soil surface, with distinct characteristics produced by soil forming processes.

Hormone (soil) A chemical substance that is produced in one part of a plant and used in minute amounts to induce a growth response in another part.

Horticulture The science and practice of growing, processing, and marketing fruits, nuts, vegetables, and ornamental plants.

Hot cap A paper or plastic dome set over warm-season vegetables in early spring to protect them against frost and wind and to increase the daytime growing temperature.

Hotbed A bed of soil enclosed in a low glass or transparent plastic frame and heated with electric cables, steam pipes, or other heat sources.

Humidity The amount of moisture in the atmosphere.

Hybrid An offspring of two different varieties of one plant that possesses certain characteristics of either parent.

Hybridization The crossing of genetically dissimilar individuals.

Hydroponics A method of growing plants using water fortified with nutrients as the medium.

Hypogeous germination A type of seed germination in which the cotyledon remains below the soil surface.

I

Imbibition The absorption of liquids or vapors into the ultramicroscopic spaces in materials.

Immune The state of being free from a given pathogen, or not subject to the disease.

Incompatibility The condition in which two plants will not cross-pollinate or a graft union is not successful in spite of appropriate conditions.

Incomplete flower A flower that is missing one or more of the following parts: sepals, petals, stamens, or pistils.

Indehiscent fruit A fruit that does not split open naturally at maturity.

Indeterminate A plant whose central stem or axis grows indefinitely while flowers are continually produced on lateral branches.

Inflorescence An axis bearing flowers, or a flower cluster.

Insecticide Any chemical compound that kills insects.

Integrated pest management (IPM) A system of pest control based on a good understanding of the life cycle of the pest as well as cultural and biological controls.

Internode The region of a stem between two successive nodes.

Irrigation The deliberate application of water to the soil.

J

Juvenility The first phase of plant development in which growth is vegetative.

L

Lamina The blade or expanded part of a leaf.

Latewood (summer wood) The denser part of the growth ring produced late in the season.

Layering A method of asexual propagation in which roots are developed on the stem of a plant while it is attached to the parent plant.

LD$_{50}$ The dose of a chemical at which 50 percent of the exposed test population dies.

Leaching The washing out of the soil or medium of soluble material with water.

Leaf apex The tip of a leaf.

Leaf base The section where the leaf blade joins the petiole.

Leaf blade The flattened portion of a leaf that extends from either side of the leaf stalk; also called lamina.

Leaf cutting A cutting made from a leaf and its attached petiole used for propagation.

Leaf margin The edge of a leaf blade.

Leaflet One of the expanded, small leaflike parts of a compound leaf.

Lean-to greenhouse A greenhouse that shares one wall in common with a house or other building.

Light intensity The brightness of light.

Light reactions The reactions of photosynthesis in which light energy is required.

Lignin An organic substance found in secondary cell walls that gives stems strength and hardness.

Limbing up The removal of the lower branches of a tree.

Limestone A natural rock used to reduce soil acidity or raise pH.

Loam A soil with approximately equal amounts of sand, silt, and clay.

Lodging A condition in which plants are caused to bend for various reasons at or near the soil surface and fall more or less flat on the ground.

Long-day plant A species that flowers under conditions of long duration of light and short daily dark period.

M

Macronutrient An essential element required in relatively large amounts for plant growth; also called major nutrient.

Macropore A large space found between large particles or aggregations of particles.

Male sterility A condition in which afflicted plants produce either no pollen or no viable pollen.

Medium A material in which plants grow.

Meiosis A nuclear cell division that occurs in reproductive organs resulting in the production of gametes with half the somatic chromosome number.

Meristem A region of the plant consisting of undifferentiated and rapidly growing and dividing cells.

Mesocarp Middle layer of the fruit wall (pericarp).

Mesophyll Parenchyma tissue in leaves found between the two epidermal layers.

Metabolism The overall physiological activities of an organism.

Microclimate A small area with a climate differing from that of the surrounding area because of factors such as exposure, elevation, and sheltering structures.

Micronutrient An essential element required in minute quantities for plant growth.

Micropore A tiny space found between fine soil particles or aggregations (capillary pore).

Mineral soil A soil consisting mainly of weathered rock particles such as sand or clay.

Miticide A chemical used to control mites.

Mitosis A nuclear cell division in which the products are genetically identical to the parent cell.

Modified central leader A pruning method in which the tip of the central leader is cut back to the nearest scaffold branch.

Monocarp A plant that grows vegetatively for more than one year but flowers only once and then dies.

Monocot Dimunitive for monocotyledon; a plant having one cotyledon or seed leaf.

Muck (soil) Highly decomposed organic material in which the original plant parts are not recognizable.

Mulch A material used to cover the soil for purposes such as moisture conservation or weed control.

Multiple fruit A cluster of matured fused ovaries produced by separate flower.

Mutation A sudden, heritable change appearing in an individual as the result of a change in genes or chromosomes.

Mycoplasma A microscopic organism intermediate between a virus and a bacterium that causes several plant diseases.

Mycorrhiza Soil fungi that live in association with plant roots to the benefit of both roots and fungi.

N

Necrosis Death associated with discoloration and dehydration of all or some parts of plant organs.

Nematicide A chemical used to control nematodes.

Nitrification The conversion of ammonium ions into nitrates through the activities of certain bacteria.

Node The joint of a stem where leaves and buds are attached.

Nonselective herbicide An herbicide that indiscriminately controls all kinds of plants.

No-till Also known as stubble culture. A cultural system most often used with annual crops in which the new crop is seeded or planted directly in a field on which the preceding crop plants were cut down or destroyed by a nonselective herbicide rather than being removed or incorporated into the soil as is common in preparing a seed bed.

Nucleic acid An acid found in all nuclei; all known nucleic acids fall into two classes: DNA and RNA.

Nut A dry, indehiscent, single-seeded fruit with a hard, woody pericarp (shell), such as the walnut and pecan.

O

Obligate parasite An organism that must live as a parasite and cannot otherwise survive.

Offset A young plant produced at the base of a parent plant.

Olericulture The science and practice of growing vegetables.

Opposite An arrangement of leaves or buds on a stem. They occur in pairs on opposite sides of a single node.

Organic matter The decomposing bodies of dead plants and animals.

Organic soil A soil that contains a high percentage (greater than 20 percent) of organic matter.

Ornamental horticulture The branch of horticulture that deals with the cultivation of plants for their aesthetic value.

Ovary The lower part of the pistil in which the eggs are fertilized and develop.

Ovule A rudimentary seed, containing before fertilization, the embryo sac, including an egg cell, all being enclosed in the nucleus and one or two integuments.

P

Palmate Arrangement of leaflets of a compound leaf or of the veins in a leaf. Characterized by subunits arising from a common point much as fingers arising from the palm of the hand.

Parenchyma A tissue composed of thin-walled, loosely packed, unspecialized cells.

Parent stock The plant from which material is obtained for propagation.

Parthenocarpy The development of a fruit without sexual fertilization.

Pathogen A disease-causing organism.

Peat Any unconsolidated soil mass of semicarbonized vegetable tissue formed by partial decomposition in water. An example is sphagnum peat moss.

Pedicel Individual flower stalk of an inflorescence.

Pedigree A record of ancestry.

Perennial A plant that grows year after year without replanting.

Pericarp The fruit wall, which develops from the ovary wall.

Perlite A coarse material made from expanded volcanic rock.

Pesticide A chemical used to control undesirable organisms (pests).

Petiole The stalk that attaches the lamina or leaf blade to the stem.

pH A measure of the acidity or alkalinity of a medium or liquid.

Phloem The portion of the vascular system in which photosynthates are transported throughout the plant.

Photoperiod The length of day.

Photoperiodism The response of plants to the relative length of light and darkness.

Photosynthesis The chemical process by which green plants manufacture food using carbon dioxide and water in the presence of light.

Phototropism The hormone-induced bending of a plant toward light.

Physiological disease A diseaselike symptom produced by plants due to an improper or inadequate supply of essential nutrients.

Phytochrome The chemical involved in plant response to photoperiod.

Pinch pruning The removal of the terminal bud of a plant to stimulate branching.

Pistil The female reproductive part of the flower, consisting of the stigma, style, and ovary.

Plant breeding The science of controlled pollination of plants to develop new cultivars.

Plastids The cellular organelles in which carbohydrate metabolism is localized.

Plugging A method of lawn establishment whereby small cores of sod are transplanted.

Pollarding A training method for deciduous trees whereby branches are severely pruned to leave stubs from which new shoots grow.

Pollen The male sex cells borne in the anthers of flowering plants.

Pollination The deposition of pollen on the flower stigma.

Polyploidy A condition in which a plant has somatic (non-sexual) cells with more than $2n$ chromosomes per nucleus.

Pome A simple fleshy fruit, the outer portion of which is formed by floral parts that surround the ovary.

Pomology The science and practice of fruit culture.

Pore spaces The gaps between the particles of soil or other growing media.

Postemergence herbicide An herbicide designed to kill weeds after they become established.

Pot-bound A condition in which the roots of a plant growing in a restrictive container environment grow around the walls.

Potting mixture (soil mix) Combination of various ingredients such as soil, peat, sand, perlite, or vermiculite designed for starting seeds or growing plants in containers.

Preemergence herbicide An herbicide designed to kill weeds as they germinate.

Profile The vertical section of the soil showing horizons or layers.

Propagation The reproduction or increase in the number of plants by sexual or vegetative methods.

Pruning The removal of parts to control a plant's growth, size, or appearance.

Public area The part of a landscape in front of a house and viewable from the street.

Pure line A population of plants descended from a single homozygous individual.

R

Raphe Ridge on seeds, formed by the stalk of the ovule, in those seeds in which the funiculus is sharply bent at the base of the ovule.

Recessive The condition of a gene such that it does not express itself in the presence of the contrasting (dominant) gene.

Recombination The mixing of genotypes that results from sexual reproduction.

Registered seed The progeny of foundation or registered seed produced and handled so as to maintain satisfactory genetic identity and purity, and approved and certified by an official certifying agency. Registered seed is normally grown for the production of certified seed.

Relative humidity The amount of water vapor present in the air compared to the total amount the air could hold at its present temperature.

Resistance The capacity of a plant to resist disease or insect attack.

Respiration The breakdown of carbohydrates to yield energy for use by the cell.

Rhizome The underground stem that grows horizontally and produces roots on the lower surface while producing shoots above the ground.

Root cap A mass of hard cells covering the tip of a root and protecting it from mechanical injury.

Rooting hormone A chemical used in promoting rooting of cuttings.

Rooting media Materials such as peat, sand, perlite, or vermiculite in which the basal ends of cuttings are placed vertically during the development of roots.

Rootstock The plant that functions as the root system in a grafted plant.

Runner An aboveground stem that grows horizontally on the soil surface.

S

Samara A dry, indehiscent, simple fruit that has winglike appendages on both sides of the ovary. These appendages help carry the wind-borne fruit.

Scaffold branch A main branch growing from the trunk of a tree.

Scarification The mechanical scraping of a seed coat to facilitate germination.

Scientific name The Latin name of a plant.

Scion A piece of shoot or bud grafted onto the rootstock.

Seed The mature ovule of a flowering plant containing an embryo, an endosperm (sometimes), and a seed coat.

Seedbed Soil that has been prepared for planting seeds or transplants.

Seed coat (testa) The outer covering of the seed.

Seed leaves The first leaves (cotyledons) produced by a seedling.

Selective herbicide A herbicide designed to control certain species of plants but not others.

Self-incompatibility The inability of pollen to fertilize eggs of the same plant.

Self-pollination The transfer of pollen from the stamen to the stigma of the same flower or to the flowers of genetically alike plants.

Semihardwood cutting A cutting made from the partially mature new growth of a woody plant.

Senescence The process of physiological aging of the tissue of a plant or any of its parts.

Sepal The usually green, leaflike, outermost part of a flower that encloses and protects the unopened flower bud.

Separation A type of propagation based upon natural breaking apart of plant segments, such as in bulbs or corms.

Service area The area of a home landscape designed for storage, garbage cans, and other such uses.

Sessile Used in reference to flowers, florets, leaves, leaflets, or fruits that are attached directly to a shoot and not borne on any type of a stalk.

Sexual reproduction Development of new plants by the processes of meiosis and fertilization in the flower to produce a viable embryo in a seed.

Short-day plant A species that flowers under conditions of short duration of light and prolonged darkness.

Sidedressing A method of fertilizer application in which fertilizer is placed in a narrow band along the sides of rows near plants.

Silt A soil textural class consisting of particles between 0.05 and 0.002 mm in diameter.

Simple leaf A leaf with a single blade or lamina.

Slow-release fertilizer A fertilizer chemically formulated to release its nutrients over a long period of time.

Small fruits The general terminology for plants that bear edible fruits of a relatively small size.

Sod Top 3 to 7 cm (1 to 3 in.) of soil permeated by and held together with grass roots or grass-legume roots.

Softwood cutting A cutting made from the new growth of a woody plant.

Soil sterilization Treating soil by gaseous fumigation, chemicals, heat (usually steam) at 100°C (212°F) to destroy all living organisms.

Soil structure The arrangement of primary soil particles into secondary particles, units, or peds that act as primary particles. The secondary units are characterized and classified on the basis of size, shape, and degree of distinctness.

Soil texture The relative percentages of sand, silt, and clay in a soil.

Soilless medium A plant growing medium that contains no natural mineral soil.

Somaclonal variation Existing genetic variation, which may not be seen until after plant cells have been through aseptic culture, or the culture may force the change.

Specimen plant A showy ornamental plant grown solely for its unique beauty.

Spreader board A piece of wood inserted between the trunk and branch of a tree to widen the crotch.

Sprigging Vegetative propagation by planting stolons or rhizomes (sprigs).

Stamen The male reproductive part of the flower consisting of the anther and filament.

Starter solution A liquid fertilizer high in phosphorus content applied to seedlings to hasten growth.

Stigma The top of the pistil that receives pollen.

Stolon A slender, prostrate aboveground stem.

Stool (horticultural) Sprouts that arise from the base of the plant below ground and become rooted. They are used for vegetative propagation.

Straight fertilizer A single-element fertilizer that is formulated to supply only one of the elements essential for plant growth.

Stratification The practice of exposing seeds to a low temperature to break dormancy.

Sucker A vertically growing shoot arising from the base of an established plant.

Systemic pesticide A pesticide absorbed into a plant, killing the organisms that prey on it.

T

Tap root A single root that grows vertically into the soil.

Taxonomy The science of identifying, naming, and classifying plants.

Terminal bud A bud located at the tip of a stem.

Terrarium A transparent glass or plastic container that retains high humidity; used for displaying and growing plants indoors.

Tetraploid Having four sets of chromosomes per nucleus.

Texture (plant) The visual impact of a plant due to the size of its leaves.

Thatch A layer of grass clippings, stems, and roots that accumulates between the surface of a turf and the soil.

Thinning The pruning technique for shrubs in which the oldest stems are removed to stimulate new growth; the selective removal of the excess fruits on a fruit tree to improve the size and quality of the remaining fruits. The term is also applied to the removal of excess seedlings from a row of dense planting for optimum growth.

Topdressing A method of fertilizer application that involves the sprinkling of fertilizer over the soil surface.

Topiary The formal training and pruning of a plant to grow in a controlled shape.

Topsoil The upper layer of soil moved in cultivation.

Topworking (top-grafting) To change the cultivar of a tree by grafting the main scaffold branches.

Trace element A micronutrient.

Translocation The movement of carbohydrates, water, minerals, and other materials within the vascular system of a plant.

Transpiration The loss of water from a plant, usually through leaves, in vapor form.

Tuber A thickened underground stem in which carbohydrates are stored.

Tunicate bulb A bulb that has a dry membranous outer scale.

Turgor pressure The pressure within the cell resulting from the absorption of water into the vacuole and the imbibition of water by the protoplasm.

V

Variegation The genetic patterning of leaves with white or yellow markings.

Variety (botanical) A subdivision of a species with distinct morphological characters and given a Latin name according to the rules of the International Code of Botanical Nomenclature. A taxonomic variety is known by the first validly published name applied to it so that nomenclature tends to be stable.

Vascular cambium A meristem that produces secondary xylem and secondary phloem cells. Vascular cambium is found in biennials and perennials.

Vector A carrier; for example, an insect that carries pathogenic organisms from plant to plant.

Vegetative Referring to asexual (stem, leaf, root) development in plants in contrast to sexual (flower, seed) development.

Vernalization The practice of subjecting a plant to cool temperatures for the promotion or enhancement of growth or flowering.

W

Water table The upper surface of groundwater or that level below which the soil is saturated with water.

Wavelength The distance between two corresponding points on any two consecutive waves.

Weathering All physical and chemical changes produced in rocks, at or near the earth's surface, by atmospheric agents.

Wilting point (permanent wilting point) The moisture content of soil at which plants wilt and fail to recover even when placed in a humid atmosphere.

Windbreak A planting of trees or shrubs, usually perpendicular or nearly so to the principal wind direction, to protect soil, crops, homesteads, roads, and so on, against the effects of winds.

Wood Secondary nonfunctioning xylem in a perennial shrub or tree.

X

Xanthophyll Yellow carotenoid pigment found along with chlorophyll in green plants.

Xylem The portion of a plant vascular system in which water and minerals, taken in by the roots, move throughout the plant.

Z

Zygote A protoplast resulting from the fusion of gametes (either isogametes or heterogametes).

INDEX